D0371979

THIS IS MY BEST

America's 93 Greatest Living Authors Present

This Is My Best

 OVER 150 SELF-CHOSEN AND
COMPLETE MASTERPIECES, TOGETHER WITH
THEIR REASONS FOR THEIR SELECTIONS

Edited by Whit Burnett

Burton C. Hoffman   THE DIAL PRESS   New York, 1943

Designed by Fred R. Siegle
Copyright, 1942, by Dial Press, Inc. Printed in the United
States of America

*The publishers and the editor
wish to acknowledge their indebtedness to*

JOHN PEN

*for his editorial assistance and for the
original idea of this anthology*

TABLE OF *Contents*

vii

IV
THE JUNGLE

V
THE DUST WHICH IS GOD

Foreword

IN THIS book ninety-three American authors have chosen the particular work of their own that is closest to their heart. Thus while THIS IS MY BEST is an anthology, it is more than the simple personal preference of any one man, which is the usual anthology —it is a book by the leading living authors in America, each one of whom has, in a sense, "edited" his entire lifetime output to select the one unit which in his own, uninfluenced opinion represents him at his best creative moment. It is a book without precedent in America: a book composed over many years, the focussing of many lifetime viewpoints, a public revelation of the private opinions of our best authors on how they look upon themselves, and what, in their writings, they most value.

For the choice of the authors, the editor gratefully acknowledges, at the very outset, the help of the public. The names of 169 representative authors were sent in ballot form to many readers of books and magazines. Polls were taken among subscribers of *The Atlantic Monthly, Harpers' Magazine,* and *The New Yorker,* and ballots were sent to librarians, literary critics and persons professionally connected with reading, writing, teaching or publishing. These individuals were asked to vote on those living American authors they deemed most fitted to be included in THIS IS MY BEST. The response was serious, intelligent, discriminating. And while the editor has not followed slavishly the results of the voting, he has been guided immeasurably by this response. It is interesting to note that on the first fifty authors receiving the most votes for inclusion, the editor, public and publishers were all in agreement.

In a book so essentially the work of many, any long comment by one editor must seem superfluous. It was the editor's job to get in touch with the authors—no mean task in wartime—and, once the authors were picked, to let them have free rein. And if the editor has had a rewarding time, with seemingly nothing to do but gather in the pieces, he seems to have had even less fun in the job than the authors themselves. An author is an author: he is familiar with his own work; why didn't someone think of asking him before? They were, in general, delighted. For this was the first time in their author-lives so many diverse, important American writers had ever been asked to say, without influence or qualification (there was a minor one of relative length): "This is myself in my very best manner."

The task was full of odd surprises—that Cabell was tired of being anthologized for his famous essays in *Beyond Life*; that when some-one dislikes a poem of Robert Frost's, it takes the poet a long time to regain his original affection for it; that Mr. Hemingway has been represented so many times for some of his things that now he can hardly bear to look at what every high-school student, through the usual anthologies, thinks is his only mood. It was interesting to learn that neither the publishers nor the author thinks the much anthol-ogized "Paul's Case" by Willa Cather is either her best or her most representative work—she is here represented by a more rounded work, "Neighbour Rosicky"; and one was to learn that some authors cannot read their old works, or that when they do, they do so with the utmost pain and difficulty; and that still some others think the work they did twenty years ago is as good or better than their present writing.

There are, of course, some omissions in the book. T. S. Eliot and Gertrude Stein were in Europe and unavailable. And there are many authors in America not included who are equal to the stature, no doubt, of many here included. One book cannot hold all the good writing in America; a limit had to be set somewhere. And the editor and his advisors can console themselves with the hope that if an author has been omitted, a reader will find that another and perhaps even more representative writer in the same field has been included. Choice is an anthologist's eternal dilemma, and anthologists notori-ously make more enemies than friends, since for twenty chosen, forty must needs be left out. For the sin of omission, we can only pray. Some of our best friends, heaven knows, are authors; and even some of those are not here with us. . . .

The editor has not in every case agreed on the author's own selection. But as this is a book of the authors', not the editor's, he has avoided influencing an author's choice. In shaping up the volume, he has likewise tried to avoid arbitrary groupings. He has meandered with the writers, following the main body of writing as the banks of a river follow the course of the stream. And even the divisions of the

book have taken their titles from the substance of the authors; there
are no artificial dams in the stream. The book is frankly not intended
as the best short stories, the best plays, the best essays, and the best
bits of humor. Here is rather a panorama of time and place, presented
to us by the best guides we have in America, the creative writers of
our time. And it is more than a passingly contemporary view. For
here are writers as long seasoned with us as Agnes Repplier, George
Ade, John Dewey and Theodore Dreiser. And others as young as
Clifford Odets, William Saroyan and Conrad Richter. What these
authors see and what they write is as various as they themselves are various. And if a great novelist chooses to like himself at his best in poetry,
that, indeed, is his prerogative. In this book we are privileged to return
with the "known" and public figure back to the quiet of his study where
he is with himself and writing was what it started out to be, his self-
communion with his deepest experience. And sometimes the picture an
author chooses as his favorite may not be the same the public has come
to recognize but, since this is so, that very choice of the author, uninfluenced, may sometimes tell us more about the author than a dozen
posed portraits.

And so, too, these selected writings, springing as they do from the
best moments of the best minds in our contemporary literature, should
tell us more than anything else about the environment of those
authors, the country we are living in.

In no small, single way, this book is America. America in its
many moods, its various colors, its many aspects. It is the New England of Frost and Coffin and Mary Ellen Chase; and the South of
Glasgow, Stuart, Rawlings and Faulkner; the Middle West of Tarkington and Ade; and the Far West of Steinbeck's old pioneer, stopped
and baffled forever at the Pacific Ocean and the end of the frontier,
in a later day. It is dinner with the Babbitts, a scared Negro washer-
woman in Mississippi, the stockyards of Chicago. It is a preface to a
Saroyan fantasy, an editor in Kansas writing an editorial on the death
of his daughter and projecting a wisp of a girl into a kind of immortality. . . . It is the goodly heritage of a more leisurely past, home in the
nineties, the old coal furnace in the Hergesheimer home in Pennsylvania, and back as far as Hawthorne in Salem and Jefferson in Virginia.
It is another side, less lovely, but exerting its power always throughout

the land, the America of the jungle, of wasted lives and lost illusion; it is America Was Promises, the American Dream, and contrastingly it is Studs and Bigger in the black slums of Chicago. It is the Old World and the old masters viewed here in contemporary essays distilling the values of the classics for our times and minds. It is poetry, drama, humor, history, biography, philosophy . . . and Europe at this moment in an upset world when all values have taken to hiding and a free survey of the life of the mind, by those who like these authors have spent their own lives distilling values, is more than a matter of superficial interest. The editor does not think it accidental that such a book, by such authors, appears at this particular time.

And so, the editor steps aside for those more qualified than he, the tellers of tales in The Man's Story . . . the broad viewers of America, and those who have particularized their love in a special place, or mood, or form, and the poet next the prose writer, the dramatist in the jungle. . . . Here is something serious, something light . . . Nobel prize and Pulitzer prize winners, and winners of all the other awards the country offers. And as these authors have their favorites, doubtless you have your favorite author. One way to read the book would be to start at the beginning and wind up at the end, for in such a way you would follow a kind of loose but interesting course, the way the editor followed it. But a simpler way is just to pick your favorite writer and find out what his favorite writing is. . . . And from there you go either to the rest of his books you missed till now . . . or on to the next author in the anthology.

Good reading!

WHIT BURNETT

New York, N. Y.
August 17, 1942.

I
THE MAN'S STORY

THEODORE DREISER

 Why he selected The HAND

The piece which I would like to be used is "The Hand" a short story of mine published some time ago in a volume entitled *Chains*. I look upon "The Hand" as illustrative as well as representative of the diversity of my subject matter and my psychological interests.

Hollywood, Cal.   THEODORE DREISER
June, 1942

I

DAVIDSON could distinctly remember that it was between two and three years after the grisly event in the Monte Orte range—the sickening and yet deserved end of Mersereau, his quondam partner and fellow adventurer—that anything to be identified with Mersereau's malice toward him, and with Mersereau's probable present existence in the spirit world, had appeared in his life.

He and Mersereau had worked long together as prospectors, investors, developers of property. It was only after they had struck it rich in the Klondike that Davidson had grown so much more apt and shrewd in all commercial and financial matters, whereas Mersereau had seemed to stand still—not to rise to the splendid opportunities which then opened to him. Why, in some of those later deals it had not been possible for Davidson even to introduce his old partner to some of the moneyed men he had to deal with. Yet Mersereau had insisted, as his right, if you please, on being "in on" everything—everything!

Take that wonderful Monte Orte property, the cause of all the subsequent horror. He, Davidson—not Mersereau—had discovered or heard of the mine, and had carried it along, with old Besmer as a tool or decoy—Besmer being the ostensible factor—until it was all ready for him to take over and sell or develop. Then it was that Mersereau, having been for so long his partner, demanded a full half—a third, at

3

least—on the ground that they had once agreed to work together in all these things.

Think of it! And Mersereau growing duller and less useful and more disagreeable day by day, and year by year! Indeed, toward the last he had threatened to expose the trick by which jointly, seven years before, they had possessed themselves of the Skyute Pass Mine; to drive Davidson out of public and financial life, to have him arrested and tried—along with himself, of course. Think of that!

But he had fixed him—yes, he had, damn him! He had trailed Mersereau that night to old Besmer's cabin on the Monte Orte, when Besmer was away. Mersereau had gone there with the intention of stealing the diagram of the new field, and had secured it, true enough. A thief he was, damn him. Yet, just as he was making safely away, as he thought, he, Davidson, had struck him cleanly over the ear with that heavy rail-bolt fastened to the end of a walnut stick, and the first blow had done for him.

Lord, how the bone above Mersereau's ear had sounded when it cracked! And how bloody one side of that bolt was! Mersereau hadn't had time to do anything before he was helpless. He hadn't died instantly, though, but had turned over and faced him, Davidson, with that savage, scowling face of his and those blazing, animal eyes.

Lying half propped up on his left elbow, Mersereau had reached out toward him with that big, rough, bony right hand of his—the right with which he always boasted of having done so much damage on this, that, and the other occasion—had glared at him as much as to say:

"Oh, if I could only reach you just for a moment before I go!"

Then it was that he, Davidson, had lifted the club again. Horrified as he was, and yet determined that he must save his own life, he had finished the task, dragging the body back to an old fissure behind the cabin and covering it with branches, a great pile of pine fronds, and as many as one hundred and fifty boulders, great and small, and had left his victim. It was a sickening job and a sickening sight, but it had to be.

Then, having finished, he had slipped dismally away, like a jackal, thinking of that hand in the moonlight, held up so savagely, and that look. Nothing might have come of that either, if he hadn't been inclined to brood on it so much, on the fierceness of it.

No, nothing had happened. A year had passed, and if anything had been going to turn up it surely would have by then. He, Davidson, had gone first to New York, later to Chicago, to dispose of the Monte Orte claim. Then, after two years, he had returned here to Mississippi, where he was enjoying comparative peace. He was looking after some sugar property which had once belonged to him, and which he was now able to reclaim and put in charge of his sister as a home against a rainy day. He had no other.

But that body back there! That hand uplifted in the moonlight—to clutch him if it could! Those eyes.

II—JUNE, 1905

Take that first year, for instance, when he had returned to Gatchard in Mississippi, whence both he and Mersereau had originally issued. After looking after his own property he had gone out to a tumble-down estate of his uncle's in Issaqueena County—a leaky old slope-roofed house where, in a bedroom on the top floor, he had had his first experience with the significance or reality of the hand.

Yes, that was where first he had really seen it pictured in that curious, unbelievable way; only who would believe that it was Mersereau's hand? They would say it was an accident, chance, rain dropping down. But the hand had appeared on the ceiling of that room just as sure as anything, after a heavy rain-storm—it was almost a cyclone—when every chink in the old roof had seemed to leak water.

During the night, after he had climbed to the room by way of those dismal stairs with their great landing and small glass oil-lamp he carried, and had sunk to rest, or tried to, in the heavy, wide, damp bed, thinking, as he always did those days, of the Monte Orte and Mersereau, the storm had come up. As he had listened to the wind moaning outside he had heard first the scratch, scratch, scratch, of some limb, no doubt, against the wall—sounding, or so it seemed in his feverish unrest, like some one penning an indictment against him with a worn, rusty pen.

And then, the storm growing worse, and in a fit of irritation and self-contempt at his own nervousness, he had gone to the window, but just as lightning struck a branch of the tree nearest the window and so very near him, too—as though some one, something, was seeking to strike him—(Mersereau?) and as though he had been lured by that scratching. God! He had retreated, feeling that it was meant for him.

But that big, knotted hand painted on the ceiling by the dripping water during the night! There it was, right over him when he awoke, outlined or painted as if with wet, gray whitewash against the wretched but normally pale-blue of the ceiling when dry. There it was—a big, open hand just like Mersereau's as he had held it up that night—huge, knotted, rough, the fingers extended as if tense and clutching. And, if you will believe it, near it was something that looked like a pen—an old, long-handled pen—to match that scratch, scratch, scratch!

"Huldah," he had inquired of the old Black mammy who entered in the morning to bring him fresh water and throw open the shutters, "what does that look like to you up there—that patch on the ceiling where the rain came through?"

He wanted to reassure himself as to the character of the thing he saw—that it might not be a creation of his own feverish imagination, accentuated by the dismal character of this place.

" 'Pears t' me mo' like a big han' 'an anythin' else, Marse Davi'son," commented Huldah, pausing and staring upward. "Mo' like a big fist, kinda. Dat air's a new drip come las' night, I reckon. Dis here ole place ain' gonna hang togethah much longah, less'n some repairin' be done mighty quick now. Yassir, dat air's a new drop, sho's yo' bo'n, en it come on'y las' night. I hain't never seed dat befo'."

And then he had inquired, thinking of the fierceness of the storm:

"Huldah, do you have many such storms up this way?"

"Good gracious, Marse Davi'son, we hain't seed no sech glow en—en come three years now. I hain't seed no sech lightnin' en I doan' know when."

Wasn't that strange, that it should all come on the night, of all nights, when he was there? And no such other storm in three years!

Huldah stared idly, always ready to go slow and rest, if possible, whereas he had turned irritably. To be annoyed by ideas such as this! To always be thinking of that Monte Orte affair! Why couldn't he forget it? Wasn't it Mersereau's own fault? He never would have killed the man if he hadn't been forced to it.

And to be haunted in this way, making mountains out of mole-hills, as he thought then! It must be his own miserable fancy—and yet Mersereau had looked so threateningly at him. That glance had boded something; it was too terrible not to.

Davidson might not want to think of it, but how could he stop? Mersereau might not be able to hurt him any more, at least not on this earth; but still, couldn't he? Didn't the appearance of this hand seem to indicate that he might? He was dead, of course. His body, his skeleton, was under that pile of rocks and stones, some of them as big as wash-tubs. Why worry over that, and after two years? And still——

That hand on the ceiling!

III—DECEMBER, 1905

Then, again, take that matter of meeting Pringle in Gatchard just at that time, within the same week. It was due to Davidson's sister. She had invited Mr. and Mrs. Pringle in to meet him one evening, without telling him that they were spiritualists and might discuss spiritualism.

Clairvoyance, Pringle called it, or seeing what can't be seen with material eyes, and clairaudience, or hearing what can't be heard with material ears, as well as materialization, or ghosts, and table-rapping, and the like. Table-rapping—that damned tap-tapping that he had been hearing ever since!

It was Pringle's fault, really. Pringle had persisted in talking. He, Davidson, wouldn't have listened, except that he somehow became fascinated by what Pringle said concerning what he had heard and seen in his time. Mersereau must have been at the bottom of that, too.

At any rate, after he had listened, he was sorry, for Pringle had had time to fill his mind full of those awful facts or ideas which had since harassed him so much—all that stuff about drunkards, degenerates, and weak people generally being followed about by vile, evil spirits and used to effect those spirits' purposes or desires in this world. Horrible!

Wasn't it terrible? Pringle—big, mushy, creature that he was, sickly and stagnant like a springless pool—insisted that he had even seen clouds of these spirits about drunkards, degenerates, and the like, in street-cars, on trains, and about vile corners at night. Once, he said, he had seen just one evil spirit—think of that!—following a certain man all the time, at his left elbow—a dark, evil, red-eyed thing, until finally the man had been killed in a quarrel.

Pringle described their shapes, these spirits, as varied. They were small, dark, irregular clouds, with red or green spots somewhere for eyes, changing in form and becoming longish or round like a jellyfish, or even like a misshapen cat or dog. They could take any form at will—even that of a man.

Once, Pringle declared, he had seen as many as fifty about a drunkard who was staggering down a street, all of them trying to urge him into the nearest saloon, so that they might re-experience in some vague way the sensation of drunkenness, which at some time or other they themselves, having been drunkards in life, had enjoyed!

It would be the same with a drug fiend, or indeed with any one of weak or evil habits. They gathered about such an one like flies, their red or green eyes glowing—attempting to get something from them, perhaps, if nothing more than a little sense of their old earth-life.

The whole thing was so terrible and disturbing at the time, particularly that idea of men being persuaded or influenced to murder, that he, Davidson, could stand it no longer, and got up and left. But in his room upstairs he meditated on it, standing before his mirror. Suddenly—would he ever forget it—as he was taking off his collar and tie, he had heard that queer tap, tap, tap, right on his dressing-table or under it, and for the first time, which Pringle said, ghosts made when table-rapping in answer to a call, or to give warning of their presence.

Then something said to him, almost as clearly as if he heard it:

"This is me, Mersereau, come back at last to get you! Pringle was just an excuse of mine to let you know I was coming, and so was that hand in that old house, in Issaqueena County. It was mine! I will be with you from now on. Don't think I will ever leave you!"

It had frightened and made him half sick, so wrought up was he. For the first time he felt cold chills run up and down his spine—the creeps. He felt as if some one were standing over him—Mersereau, of course—only he could not see or hear a thing, just that faint tap at first, growing louder a little later, and quite angry when he tried to ignore it.

People did live, then, after they were dead, especially evil people— people stronger than you, perhaps. They had the power to come back, to haunt, to annoy you if they didn't like anything you had done to them. No doubt Mersereau was following him in the hope of revenge, there in the spirit world, just outside this one, close at his heels, like that evil spirit attending the other man whom Pringle had described.

IV—FEBRUARY, 1906

Take that case of the hand impressed on the soft dough and plaster of Paris, described in an article that he had picked up in the dentist's office out there in Pasadena—Mersereau's very hand, so far as he could judge. How about that for a coincidence, picking up the magazine with that disturbing article about psychic materialization in Italy, and later in Berne, Switzerland, where the scientists were gathered to investigate that sort of thing? And just when he was trying to rid himself finally of the notion that any such thing could be!

According to that magazine article, some old crone over in Italy— spiritualist, or witch, or something—had got together a crowd of ex- perimentalists or professors in an abandoned house on an almost de- serted island off the coast of Sardinia. There they had conducted ex- periments with spirits, which they called materialization, getting the impression of the fingers of a hand, or of a whole hand and arm, or of a face, on a plate of glass covered with soot, the plate being locked in a small safe on the center of a table about which they sat!

He, Davidson, couldn't understand, of course, how it was done, but done it was. There in that magazine were half a dozen pictures, repro- ductions of photographs of a hand, an arm and a face—or a part of one, anyhow. And if they looked like anything, they looked exactly like Mersereau's! Hadn't Pringle, there in Gatchard, Miss., stated spirits could move anywhere, over long distances, with the speed of light. And would it be any trick for Mersereau to appear there at Sardinia, and then engineer this magazine into his presence, here in Los An- geles? Would it? It would not. Spirits were free and powerful *over there*, perhaps.

There was not the least doubt that these hands, these partial impressions of a face, were those of Mersereau. Those big knuckles! That long, heavy, humped nose and big jaw! Whose else could they be?—they were Mersereau's, intended, when they were made over there in Italy, for him, Davidson, to see later here in Los Angeles. Yes, they were! And looking at that sinister face reproduced in the magazine, it seemed to say, with Mersereau's old coarse sneer:

"You see? You can't escape me! I'm showing you how much alive I am over here, just as I was on earth. And I'll get you yet, even if I have to go farther than Italy to do it!"

It was amazing, the shock he took from that. It wasn't just that alone, but the persistence and repetition of this hand business. What could it mean? Was it really Mersereau's hand? As for the face, it wasn't all there—just the jaw, mouth, cheek, left temple, and a part of the nose and eye; but it was Mersereau's, all right. He had gone clear over there into Italy somewhere, in a lone house on an island, to get this message of his undying hate back to him. Or was it just spirits, evil spirits, bent on annoying him because he was nervous and sensitive now?

v—OCTOBER, 1906

Even new crowded hotels and new buildings weren't the protection he had at first hoped and thought they would be. Even there you weren't safe—not from a man like Mersereau. Take that incident there in Los Angeles, and again in Seattle, only two months ago now, when Mersereau was able to make that dreadful explosive or crashing sound, as if one had burst a huge paper bag full of air, or upset a china-closet full of glass and broken everything, when as a matter of fact nothing at all had happened. It had frightened him horribly the first two or three times, believing as he did that something fearful had happened. Finding that it was nothing—or Mersereau—he was becoming used to it now; but other people, unfortunately, were not.

He would be—as he had been that first time—sitting in his room perfectly still and trying to amuse himself, or not to think, when suddenly there would be that awful crash. It was astounding! Other people heard it, of course. They had in Los Angeles. A maid and a porter had come running the first time to inquire, and he had had to protest that he had heard nothing. They couldn't believe it at first, and had gone to other rooms to look. When it happened the second time, the management had protested, thinking it was a joke he was playing; and to avoid the risk of exposure he had left.

After that he could not keep a valet or nurse about him for long. Servants wouldn't stay, and managers of hotels wouldn't let him remain when such things went on. Yet he couldn't live in a house or apartment alone, for there the noises and atmospheric conditions would be worse than ever.

VI—JUNE, 1907

Take that last old house he had been in—but never would be in again!—at Anne Haven. There he actually visualized the hand—a thing as big as a washtub at first, something like smoke or shadow in a black room moving about over the bed and everywhere. Then, as he lay there, gazing at it spellbound, it condensed slowly, and he began to feel it. It was now a hand of normal size—there was no doubt of it in the world—going over him softly, without force, as a ghostly hand must, having no real physical strength, but all the time with a strange, electric, secretive something about it, as if it were not quite sure of itself, and not quite sure that he was really there.

The hand, or so it seemed—God!—moved right up to his neck and began to feel over that as he lay there. Then it was that he guessed just what it was that Mersereau was after.

It was just like a hand, the fingers and thumb made into a circle and pressed down over his throat, only it moved over him gently at first, because it really couldn't do anything yet, not having the material strength. But the intention! The sense of cruel, savage determination that went with it!

And yet, if one went to a nerve specialist or doctor about all this, as he did afterward, what did the doctor say? He had tried to describe how he was breaking down under the strain, how he could not eat or sleep on account of all these constant tappings and noises; but the

moment he even began to hint at his experiences, especially the hand
or the noises, the doctor exclaimed:

"Why, this is plain delusion! You're nervously run down, that's
all that ails you—on the verge of pernicious anemia, I should say. You'll
have to watch yourself as to this illusion about spirits. Get it out of your
mind. There's nothing to it!"

Wasn't that just like one of these nerve specialists, bound up in their
little ideas of what they knew or saw, or thought they saw?

VII—NOVEMBER, 1907

And now take this very latest development at Battle Creek recently
where he had gone trying to recuperate on the diet there. Hadn't Mersereau, implacable demon that he was, developed this latest trick of
making his food taste queer to him—unpalatable, or with an odd odor?

He, Davidson, knew it was Mersereau, for he felt him beside him
at the table whenever he sat down. Besides, he seemed to hear something—clairaudience was what they called it, he understood—he was
beginning to develop that, too, now! It was Mersereau, of course, saying
in a voice which was more like a memory of a voice than anything
real—the voice of some one you could remember as having spoken in
a certain way, say, ten years or more ago:

"I've fixed it so you can't eat any more, you——"

There followed a long list of vile expletives, enough in itself to
sicken one.

Thereafter, in spite of anything he could do to make himself think
to the contrary, knowing that the food was all right, really, Davidson
found it to have an odor or a taste which disgusted him, and which
he could not overcome, try as he would. The management assured
him that it was all right, as he knew it was—for others. He saw them
eating it. But he couldn't—had to get up and leave, and the little he
could get down he couldn't retain, or it wasn't enough for him to live
on. God, he would die, this way! Starve, as he surely was doing by
degrees now.

And Mersereau always seeming to be standing by. Why, if it weren't

for fresh fruit on the stands at times, and just plain, fresh-baked bread
in bakers' windows, which he could buy and eat quickly, he might
not be able to live at all. It was getting to that pass!

VIII—AUGUST, 1908

That wasn't the worst, either, bad as all that was. The worst was
the fact that under the strain of all this he was slowly but surely breaking down, and that in the end Mersereau might really succeed in driving him out of life here—to do what, if anything, to him there? What?
It was such an evil pack by which he was surrounded now, those who
lived just on the other side and hung about the earth, vile, debauched
creatures, as Pringle had described them, and as Davidson had come
to know for himself, fearing them and their ways so much, and really
seeing them at times.

Since he had come to be so weak and sensitive, he could see them
for himself—vile things that they were, swimming before his gaze in
the dark whenever he chanced to let himself be in the dark, which was
not often—friends of Mersereau, no doubt, and inclined to help him
just for the evil of it.

For this long time now Davidson had taken to sleeping with the
light on, wherever he was, only tying a handkerchief over his eyes
to keep out some of the glare. Even then he could see them—queer,
misshapen things, for all the world like wavy, stringy jellyfish or coils
of thick, yellowish-black smoke, moving about, changing in form at
times, yet always looking dirty or vile, somehow, and with those queer,
dim, reddish or greenish glows for eyes. It was sickening!

IX—OCTOBER, 1908

Having accomplished so much, Mersereau would by no means be
content to let him go. Davidson knew that! He could talk to him
occasionally now, or at least could hear him and answer back, if he
chose when he was alone and quite certain that no one was listening.

Mersereau was always saying, when Davidson would listen to him
at all—which he wouldn't often—that he would get him yet, that he
would make him pay, or charging him with fraud and murder.

"I'll choke you yet!" The words seemed to float in from some-where, as if he were remembering that at some time Mersereau had said just that in his angry, savage tone—not as if he heard it; and yet he was hearing it of course.

"I'll choke you yet! You can't escape! You may think you'll die a natural death, but you won't, and that's why I'm poisoning your food to weaken you. You can't escape! I'll get you, sick or well, when you can't help yourself, when you're sleeping. I'll choke you, just as you hit me with that club. That's why you're always seeing and feeling this hand of mine! I'm not alone. I've nearly had you many a time already, only you have managed to wriggle out so far, jumping up, but some day you won't be able to—see? Then——"

The voice seemed to die away at times, even in the middle of a sentence, but at the other times—often, often—he could hear it complet-ing the full thought. Sometimes he would turn on the thing and explain:

"Oh, go to the devil!" or, "Let me alone!" or, "Shut up!" Even in a closed room and all alone, such remarks seemed strange to him, ad-dressed to a ghost; but he couldn't resist at times, annoyed as he was. Only he took good care not to talk if any one was about.

It was getting so that there was no real place for him outside of an asylum, for often he would get up screaming at night—he had to, so sharp was the clutch on his throat—and then always, wherever he was, a servant would come in and want to know what was the matter. He would have to say that it was a nightmare—only the management always requested him to leave after the second or third time, say, or after an explosion or two. It was horrible!

He might as well apply to a private asylum or sanatorium now, having all the money he had, and explain that he had delusions—delu-sions! Imagine!—and ask to be taken care of. In a place like that they wouldn't be disturbed by his jumping up and screaming at night, feeling that he was being choked, as he was, or by his leaving the table because he couldn't eat the food, or by his talking back to Mer-sereau, should they chance to hear him, or by the noises when they occurred.

They could assign him a special nurse and a special room, if he wished—only he didn't wish to be too much alone. They could put him in charge of some one who would understand all these things, or to whom he could explain. He couldn't expect ordinary people, or hotels catering to ordinary people, to put up with him any more. Mersereau and his friends made too much trouble.

He must go and hunt up a good place somewhere where they understood such things, or at least tolerated them, and explain, and then it would all pass for the hallucinations of a crazy man—though, as a matter of fact, he wasn't crazy at all. It was all too real, only the average or so-called normal person couldn't see or hear as he could—hadn't experienced what he had.

X—DECEMBER, 1908

"The trouble is, doctor, that Mr. Davidson is suffering from the delusion that he is pursued by evil spirits. He was not committed here by any court, but came of his own accord about four months ago, and we let him wander about here at will. But he seems to be growing worse, as time goes on.

"One of his worst delusions, doctor, is that there is one spirit in particular who is trying to choke him to death. Dr. Major, our superintendent, says he has incipient tuberculosis of the throat, with occasional spasmodic contractions. There are small lumps or calluses here and there as though caused by outside pressure and yet our nurse assures us that there is no such outside irritation. He won't believe that; but whenever he tries to sleep, especially in the middle of the night, he will jump up and come running out into the hall, insisting that one of these spirits, which he insists are after him, is trying to choke him to death. He really seems to believe it, for he comes out coughing and choking and feeling at his neck as if some one has been trying to strangle him. He always explains the whole matter to me as being the work of evil spirits, and asks me to not pay any attention to him unless he calls for help or rings his call-bell; and so I never think anything more of it now unless he does.

"Another of his ideas is that these same spirits do something to his food—put poison in it, or give it a bad odor or taste, so that he can't eat it. When he does find anything he can eat, he grabs it and almost swallows it whole, before, as he says, the spirits have time to do anything to it. Once, he says, he weighed more than two hundred pounds, but now he only weighs one hundred and twenty. His case is exceedingly strange and pathetic, doctor!

"Dr. Major insists that it is purely a delusion, that so far as being choked is concerned, it is the incipient tuberculosis, and that his stomach trouble comes from the same thing; but by association of ideas, or delusions, he thinks some one is trying to choke him and poison his food, when it isn't so at all. Dr. Major says that he can't imagine what could have started it. He is always trying to talk to Mr. Davidson about it, but whenever he begins to ask him questions, Mr. Davidson refuses to talk, and gets up and leaves.

"One of the peculiar things about his idea of being choked, doctor, is that when he is merely dozing he always wakes up in time, and has the power to throw it off. He claims that the strength of these spirits is not equal to his own when he is awake, or even dozing, but when he's asleep their strength is greater and that then they may injure him. Sometimes, when he has had a fright like this, he will come out in the hall and down to my desk there at the lower end, and ask if he mayn't sit there by me. He says it calms him. I always tell him yes, but it won't be five minutes before he'll get up and leave again, saying that he's being annoyed, or that he won't be able to contain himself if he stays any longer, because of the remarks being made over his shoulders or in his ear.

"Often he'll say: 'Did you hear that, Miss Liggett? It's astonishing, the low, vile things that man can say at times!' When I say, 'No, I didn't hear,' he always says, 'I'm so glad!' "

"No one has ever tried to relieve him of this by hypnotism, I suppose?"

"Not that I know of, doctor. Dr. Major may have tried it. I have only been here three months."

"Tuberculosis is certainly the cause of the throat trouble, as Dr. Major says, and as for the stomach trouble, that comes from the same thing—natural enough under the circumstances. We may have to resort to hypnotism a little later. I'll see. In the meantime you'd better caution all who come in touch with him never to sympathize, or even to seem to believe in anything he imagines is being done to him. It will merely encourage him in his notions. And get him to take his medicine regularly; it won't cure, but it will help. Dr. Major has asked me to give especial attention to his case, and I want the conditions as near right as possible."

"Yes, sir."

XI—JANUARY, 1909

The trouble with these doctors was that they really knew nothing of anything save what was on the surface, the little they had learned at a medical college or in practise—chiefly how certain drugs, tried by their predecessors in certain cases, were known to act. They had no imagination whatever, even when you tried to tell them.

Take that latest young person who was coming here now in his good clothes and with his car, fairly bursting with his knowledge of what he called psychiatrics, looking into Davidson's eyes so hard and smoothing his temples and throat—massage, he called it—saying that he had incipient tuberculosis of the throat and stomach trouble, and utterly disregarding the things which he, Davidson, could personally see and hear! Imagine the fellow trying to persuade him, at this late date, that all that was wrong with him was tuberculosis, that he didn't see Mersereau standing right beside him at times, bending over him, holding up that hand and telling him how he intended to kill him yet—that it was all an illusion!

Imagine saying that Mersereau couldn't actually seize him by the throat when he was asleep, or nearly so, when Davidson himself, looking at his throat in the mirror, could see the actual finger prints,—Mersereau's,—for a moment or so afterward. At any rate, his throat was red and sore from being clutched, as Mersereau of late was able to clutch him! And that was the cause of these lumps. And to say, as they had said at first, that he himself was making them by rubbing and feeling his throat, and that it was tuberculosis!

Wasn't it enough to make one want to quit the place? If it weren't for Miss Liggett and Miss Koehler, his private nurse, and their devoted care, he would. That Miss Koehler was worth her weight in gold, learning his ways as she had, being so uniformly kind, and bearing with his difficulties so genially. He would leave her something in his will.

To leave this place and go elsewhere, though, unless he could take her along, would be folly. And anyway, where else would he go? Here at least were other people, patients like himself, who could understand and could sympathize with him,—people who weren't convinced as were these doctors that all he complained of was mere delusion. Imagine! Old Rankin, the lawyer, for instance, who had suffered untold persecution from one living person and another, mostly politicians, was convinced that his, Davidson's, troubles were genuine, and liked to hear about them, just as did Miss Koehler. These two did not insist, as the doctors did, that he had slow tuberculosis of the throat, and could live a long time and overcome his troubles if he would. They were merely companionable at such times as Mersereau would give him enough peace to be sociable.

The only real trouble, though, was that he was growing so weak from lack of sleep and food—his inability to eat the food which his enemy bewitched and to sleep at night on account of the choking— that he couldn't last much longer. This new physician whom Dr. Major had called into consultation in regard to his case was insisting that along with his throat trouble he was suffering from acute anemia, due to long undernourishment, and that only a solution of strychnin injected into the veins would help him. But as to Mersereau poisoning his food—not a word would he hear. Besides, now that he was practically bedridden, not able to jump up as freely as before, he was subject to a veritable storm of bedevilment at the hands of Mersereau. Not only could he see—especially toward evening, and in the very early hours of the morning—Mersereau hovering about him like a black shadow, a great, bulky shadow—yet like him in outline, but he could feel his enemy's hand moving over him. Worse, behind or about him he often saw a veritable cloud of evil creatures, companions or tools of Mersereau's, who were there to help him and who kept swimming about like fish in dark waters, and seemed to eye the procedure with satisfaction.

When food was brought to him, early or late, and in whatever form, Mersereau and they were there, close at hand, as thick as flies, passing over and through it in an evident attempt to spoil it before he could eat it. Just to see them doing it was enough to poison it for him. Besides, he could hear their voices urging Mersereau to do it.

"That's right—poison it!"

"He can't last much longer!"

"Soon he'll be weak enough so that when you grip him he will really die!"

It was thus that they actually talked—he could hear them.

He also heard vile phrases addressed to him by Mersereau, the iterated and reiterated words "murderer" and "swindler" and "cheat," there in the middle of the night. Often, although the light was still on, he saw as many as seven dark figures, very much like Mersereau's, although different, gathered close about him,—like men in consultation— evil men. Some of them sat upon his bed, and it seemed as if they were about to help Mersereau to finish him, adding their hands to his.

Behind them again was a complete circle of all those evil, swimming things with green and red eyes, always watching—helping, probably. He had actually felt the pressure of the hand to grow stronger of late, when they were all there. Only, just before he felt he was going to faint, and because he could not spring up any more, he invariably screamed or gasped a choking gasp and held his finger on the button which would bring Miss Koehler. Then she would come, lift him up, and fix his pillows. She also always assured him that it was only the inflammation of his throat, and rubbed it with alcohol, and gave him a few drops of something internally to ease it.

After all this time, and in spite of anything he could tell them, they still believed, or pretended to believe, that he was suffering from tuberculosis, and that all the rest of this was delusion, a phase of insanity!

And Mersereau's skeleton still out there on the Monte Orte!

And Mersereau's plan, with the help of others, of course, was to choke him to death, there was no doubt of that now; and yet they would believe after he was gone that he had died of tuberculosis of the throat. Think of that.

XII—MIDNIGHT OF FEBRUARY 10, 1909

THE GHOST OF MERSEREAU (*bending over Davidson*): "Softly! Softly! He's quite alseep! He didn't think we could get him—that I could! But this time,—yes. Miss Koehler is asleep at the end of the hall and Miss Liggett can't come, can't hear. He's too weak now. He can scarcely move or groan. Strengthen my hand, will you! I will grip him so tight this time that he won't get away! His cries won't help him this time! He can't cry as he once did! Now! Now!"

A CLOUD OF EVIL SPIRITS (*swimming about*): "Right! Right! Good! Good! Now! Ah!"

DAVIDSON (*waking, choking, screaming, and feebly striking out*): "Help! Help! H-e-l-p! Miss—Miss—H—e—l—p!"

MISS LIGGETT (*dozing heavily in her chair*): "Everything is still. No one restless. I can sleep." (Her head nods.)

THE CLOUD OF EVIL SPIRITS: "Good! Good! Good! His soul at last! Here it comes! He couldn't escape this time! Ah! Good! Good! Now!"

MERSEREAU (*to Davidson*): "You murderer! At last! At last!"

XIII—3 A.M. OF FEBRUARY 17, 1909

MISS KOEHLER (*at the bedside, distressed and pale*): "He must have died some time between one and two, doctor. I left him at one o'clock, comfortable as I could make him. He said he was feeling as well as could be expected. He's been very weak during the last few days, taking only a little gruel. Between half past one and two I thought I heard a noise, and came to see. He was lying just as you see here, except that his hands were up to his throat, as if it were hurting or choking him. I put them down for fear they would stiffen that way. In trying to call one of the other nurses just now, I found that the bell was out of order, although I know it was all right when I left, because he always made me try it. So he may have tried to ring."

DR. MAJOR (*turning the head and examining the throat*): "It looks as if he had clutched at his throat rather tightly this time, I must say. Here is the mark of his thumb on this side and of his four fingers on the other. Rather deep for the little strength he had. Odd that he should have imagined that someone else was trying to choke him, when he was always pressing at his own neck! Throat tubercuolsis is very painful at times. That would explain the desire to clutch at his throat."

Miss Liggett: "He was always believing that an evil spirit was trying to choke him, doctor."

Dr. Major: "Yes, I know—association of ideas. Dr. Scain and I agree as to that. He had a bad case of chronic tuberculosis of the throat, with accompanying malnutrition, due to the effect of the throat on the stomach; and his notion about evil spirits pursuing him and trying to choke him was simply due to an innate tendency on the part of the subconscious mind to join things together—any notion, say, with any pain. If he had had a diseased leg, he would have imagined that evil spirits were attempting to saw it off, or something like that. In the same way the condition of his throat affected his stomach, and he imagined that the spirits were doing something to his food. Make out a certificate showing acute tuberculosis of the esophagus as the cause, with delusions of persecution as his mental condition. While I am here we may as well look in on Mr. Baff."

ERNEST HEMINGWAY

Why he selected The SHORT HAPPY

LIFE of FRANCIS MACOMBER

Referring to the many kinds of stories in his collection, *The Fifth Column and the First 49 Stories,* Ernest Hemingway listed "The Short Happy Life of Francis Macomber" first in the seven stories of his own he liked the best. . . . A laconic man, Mr. Hemingway wrote on May 12 to the editor of this anthology:

"If you want to print a selection of my work, I would suggest your reprinting 'The Short Happy Life of Francis Macomber' and simply say that Mr. Hemingway thought that this was as reprintable as any other of his stories."

Cuba   ERNEST HEMINGWAY

June, 1942

IT WAS now lunch time and they were all sitting under the double green fly of the dining tent pretending that nothing had happened.

"Will you have lime juice or lemon squash?" Macomber asked.

"I'll have a gimlet," Robert Wilson told him.

"I'll have a gimlet too. I need something," Macomber's wife said.

"I suppose it's the thing to do," Macomber agreed. "Tell him to make three gimlets."

The mess boy had started them already, lifting the bottles out of the canvas cooling bags that sweated wet in the wind that blew through the trees that shaded the tents.

"What had I ought to give them?" Macomber asked.

"A quid would be plenty," Wilson told him. "You don't want to spoil them."

"Will the headman distribute it?"

"Absolutely."

Francis Macomber had, half an hour before, been carried to his tent from the edge of the camp in triumph on the arms and shoulders of the cook, the personal boys, the skinner and the porters. The gun-bearers had taken no part in the demonstration. When the native boys put him down at the door of his tent, he had shaken all their hands, received their congratulations, and then gone into the tent and sat on the bed until his wife came in. She did not speak to him when she came in and he left the tent at once to wash his face and hands in the portable wash basin outside and go over to the dining tent to sit in a comfortable canvas chair in the breeze and the shade.

"You've got your lion," Robert Wilson said to him, "and a damned fine one too."

Mrs. Macomber looked at Wilson quickly. She was an extremely handsome and well-kept woman of the beauty and social position which had, five years before, commanded five thousand dollars as the price of endorsing, with photographs, a beauty product which she had never used. She had been married to Francis Macomber for eleven years.

"He is a good lion, isn't he?" Macomber said. His wife looked at him now. She looked at both these men as though she had never seen them before.

One, Wilson, the white hunter, she knew she had never truly seen before. He was about middle height with sandy hair, a stubby mustache, a very red face and extremely cold blue eyes with faint white wrinkles at the corners that grooved merrily when he smiled. He smiled at her now and she looked away from his face at the way his shoulders sloped in the loose tunic he wore with the four big cartridges held in loops where the left breast pocket should have been, at his big brown hands, his old slacks, his very dirty boots and back to his red face again. She noticed where the baked red of his face stopped in a white line that marked the circle left by his Stetson hat that hung now from one of the pegs of the tent pole.

"Well, here's to the lion," Robert Wilson said. He smiled at her again and, not smiling, she looked curiously at her husband.

Francis Macomber was very tall, very well built if you did not mind that length of bone, dark, his hair cropped like an oarsman, rather thin-lipped, and was considered handsome. He was dressed in the same sort of safari clothes that Wilson wore except that his were new, he was thirty-five years old, kept himself very fit, was good at court games, had a number of big-game fishing records, and had just shown himself, very publicly, to be a coward.

"Here's to the lion," he said. "I can't ever thank you for what you did."

Margaret, his wife, looked away from him and back to Wilson.

"Let's not talk about the lion," she said.

Wilson looked over at her without smiling and now she smiled at him.

"It's been a very strange day," she said. "Hadn't you ought to put your hat on even under the canvas at noon? You told me that, you know."

"Might put it on," said Wilson.

"You know you have a very red face, Mr. Wilson," she told him and smiled again.

"Drink," said Wilson.

"I don't think so," she said. "Francis drinks a great deal, but his face is never red."

"It's red today," Macomber tried a joke.

"No," said Margaret. "It's mine that's red today. But Mr. Wilson's is always red."

"Must be racial," said Wilson. "I say, you wouldn't like to drop my beauty as a topic, would you?"

"I've just started on it."

"Let's chuck it," said Wilson.

"Conversation is going to be so difficult," Margaret said.

"Don't be silly, Margot," her husband said.

"No difficulty," Wilson said. "Got a damn fine lion."

Margot looked at them both and they both saw that she was going to cry. Wilson had seen it coming for a long time and he dreaded it. Macomber was past dreading it.

"I wish it hadn't happened. Oh, I wish it hadn't happened," she said and started for her tent. She made no noise of crying but they could see that her shoulders were shaking under the rose-colored, sun-proofed shirt she wore.

"Women upset," said Wilson to the tall man. "Amounts to nothing. Strain on the nerves and one thing'n another."

"No," said Macomber. "I suppose that I rate that for the rest of my life now."

"Nonsense. Let's have a spot of the giant killer," said Wilson. "Forget the whole thing. Nothing to it anyway."

"We might try," said Macomber. "I won't forget what you did for me though."

"Nothing," said Wilson. "All nonsense."

So they sat there in the shade where the camp was pitched under some wide-topped acacia trees with a boulder-strewn cliff behind them, and a stretch of grass that ran to the bank of a boulder-filled stream in front with forest beyond it, and drank their just-cool lime drinks and avoided one another's eyes while the boys set the table for lunch. Wilson could tell that the boys all knew about it now and when he saw Macomber's personal boy looking curiously at his master while he was putting dishes on the table he snapped at him in Swahili. The boy turned away with his face blank.

"What were you telling him?" Macomber asked.

"Nothing. Told him to look alive or I'd see he got about fifteen of the best."

"What's that? Lashes?"

"It's quite illegal," Wilson said. "You're supposed to fine them."

"Do you still have them whipped?"

"Oh, yes. They could raise a row if they chose to complain. But they don't. They prefer it to the fines."

"How strange!" said Macomber.

"Not strange, really," Wilson said. "Which would you rather do? Take a good birching or lose your pay?"

Then he felt embarrassed at asking it and before Macomber could answer he went on, "We all take a beating every day, you know, one way or another."

This was no better. "Good God," he thought. "I am a diplomat, aren't I?"

"Yes, we take a beating," said Macomber, still not looking at him. "I'm awfully sorry about that lion business. It doesn't have to go any further, does it? I mean no one will hear about it, will they?"

"You mean will I tell it at the Mathaiga Club?" Wilson looked at him now coldly. He had not expected this. So he's a bloody four-letter man as well as a bloody coward, he thought. I rather liked him too until today. But how is one to know about an American?

"No," said Wilson. "I'm a professional hunter. We never talk about our clients. You can be quite easy on that. It's supposed to be bad form to ask us not to talk though."

He had decided now that to break would be much easier. He would eat, then, by himself and could read a book with his meals. They would eat by themselves. He would see them through the safari on a very formal basis—what was it the French called it? Distinguished consideration—and it would be a damn sight easier than having to go through this emotional trash. He'd insult him and make a good clean break. Then he could read a book with his meals and he'd still be drinking their whisky. That was the phrase for it when a safari went bad. You ran into another white hunter and you asked, "How is everything going?" and he answered, "Oh, I'm still drinking their whisky," and you knew everything had gone to pot.

"I'm sorry," Macomber said and looked at him with his American face that would stay adolescent until it became middle-aged, and Wilson noted his crew-cropped hair, fine eyes only faintly shifty, good nose, thin lips and handsome jaw. "I'm sorry I didn't realize that. There are lots of things I don't know."

So what could he do, Wilson thought. He was all ready to break it off quickly and neatly and here the beggar was apologizing after he had just insulted him. He made one more attempt. "Don't worry about me talking," he said. "I have a living to make. You know in Africa no woman ever misses her lion and no white man ever bolts."

"I bolted like a rabbit," Macomber said.

Now what in hell were you going to do about a man who talked like that, Wilson wondered.

Wilson looked at Macomber with his flat, blue, machine-gunner's eyes and the other smiled back at him. He had a pleasant smile if you did not notice how his eyes showed when he was hurt.

"Maybe I can fix it up on buffalo," he said. "We're after them next, aren't we?"

"In the morning if you like," Wilson told him. Perhaps he had been wrong. This was certainly the way to take it. You most certainly could not tell a damned thing about an American. He was all for Macomber again. If you could forget the morning. But, of course, you couldn't. The morning had been about as bad as they come.

"Here comes the Memsahib," he said. She was walking over from her tent looking refreshed and cheerful and quite lovely. She had a very perfect oval face, so perfect that you expected her to be stupid. But she wasn't stupid, Wilson thought, no, not stupid.

"How is the beautiful red-faced Mr. Wilson? Are you feeling better, Francis, my pearl?"

"Oh, much," said Macomber.

"I've dropped the whole thing," she said, sitting down at the table. "What importance is there to whether Francis is any good at killing lions? That's not his trade. That's Mr. Wilson's trade. Mr. Wilson is really very impressive killing anything. You do kill anything, don't you?"

"Oh, anything," said Wilson. "Simply anything." They are, he thought, the hardest in the world; the hardest, the cruelest, the most predatory and the most attractive and their men have softened or gone to pieces nervously as they have hardened. Or is it that they pick men they can handle? They can't know that much at the age they marry, he thought. He was grateful that he had gone through his education on American women before now because this was a very attractive one.

"We're going after buff in the morning," he told her.

"I'm coming," she said.

"No, you're not."

"Oh, yes, I am. Mayn't I, Francis?"

"Why not stay in camp?"

"Not for anything," she said. "I wouldn't miss something like today for anything."

When she left, Wilson was thinking, when she went off to cry, she seemed a hell of a fine woman. She seemed to understand, to realize, to be hurt for him and for herself and to know how things really stood. She is away for twenty minutes and now she is back, simply enamelled in that American female cruelty. They are the damnedest women. Really the damnedest.

"We'll put on another show for you tomorrow," Francis Macomber said.

"You're not coming," Wilson said.

"You're very mistaken," she told him. "And I want *so* to see you perform again. You were lovely this morning. That is if blowing things' heads off is lovely."

"Here's the lunch," said Wilson. "You're very merry, aren't you?"

"Why not? I didn't come out here to be dull."

"Well, it hasn't been dull," Wilson said. He could see the boulders in the river and the high bank beyond with the trees and he remembered the morning.

"Oh, no," she said. "It's been charming. And tomorrow. You don't know how I look forward to tomorrow."

"That's eland he's offering you," Wilson said.

"They're the big cowy things that jump like hares, aren't they?"

"I suppose that describes them," Wilson said.

"It's very good meat," Macomber said.

"Did you shoot it, Francis?" she asked.

"Yes."

"They're not dangerous, are they?"

"Only if they fall on you," Wilson told her.

"I'm so glad."

"Why not let up on the bitchery just a little, Margot," Macomber said, cutting the eland steak and putting some mashed potato, gravy and carrot on the down-turned fork that tined through the piece of meat.

"I suppose I could," she said, "since you put it so prettily."

"Tonight we'll have champagne for the lion," Wilson said. "It's a bit too hot at noon."

"Oh the lion," Margot said. "I'd forgotten the lion!"

So, Robert Wilson thought to himself, she *is* giving him a ride, isn't she? Or do you suppose that's her idea of putting up a good show? How should a woman act when she discovers her husband is a bloody coward? She's damn cruel but they're all cruel. They govern, of course, and to govern one has to be cruel sometimes. Still, I've seen enough of their damn terrorism.

"Have some more eland," he said to her politely.

That afternoon, late, Wilson and Macomber went out in the motor car with the native driver and the two gun-bearers. Mrs. Macomber stayed in the camp. It was too hot to go out, she said, and she was going with them in the early morning. As they drove off Wilson saw her standing under the big tree, looking pretty rather than beautiful in her faintly rosy khaki, her dark hair drawn back off her forehead and gathered in a knot low on her neck, her face as fresh, he thought, as though she were in England. She waved to them as the car went off through the swale of high grass and curved around through the trees into the small hills of orchard bush.

In the orchard bush they found a herd of impala, and leaving the car they stalked one old ram with long, wide-spread horns and Macomber killed it with a very creditable shot that knocked the buck down at a good two hundred yards and sent the herd off bounding wildly and leaping over one another's backs in long, leg-drawn-up leaps as unbelievable and as floating as those one makes sometimes in dreams.

"That was a good shot," Wilson said. "They're a small target."

"Is it a worth-while head?" Macomber asked.

"It's excellent," Wilson told him. "You shoot like that and you'll have no trouble."

"Do you think we'll find buffalo tomorrow?"

"There's a good chance of it. They feed out early in the morning and with luck we may catch them in the open."

"I'd like to clear away that lion business," Macomber said. "It's not very pleasant to have your wife see you do something like that."

I should think it would be even more unpleasant to do it, Wilson thought, wife or no wife, or to talk about it having done it. But he said, "I wouldn't think about that any more. Any one could be upset by his first lion. That's all over."

But that night after dinner and a whisky and soda by the fire before going to bed, as Francis Macomber lay on his cot with the mosquito bar over him and listened to the night noises it was not all over. It was neither all over nor was it beginning. It was there exactly as it happened with some parts of it indelibly emphasized and he was miserably ashamed at it. But more than shame he felt cold, hollow fear in him The fear was still there like a cold slimy hollow in all the emptiness where once his confidence had been and it made him feel sick. It was still there with him now.

It had started the night before when he had wakened and heard the lion roaring somewhere up along the river. It was a deep sound and at the end there were sort of coughing grunts that made him seem just outside the tent, and when Francis Macomber woke in the night to hear it he was afraid. He could hear his wife breathing quietly, asleep. There was no one to tell he was afraid, nor to be afraid with him, and, lying alone, he did not know the Somali proverb that says a brave man is always frightened three times by a lion; when he first sees his track, when he first hears him roar and when he first confronts him. Then while they were eating breakfast by lantern light out in the dining tent, before the sun was up, the lion roared again and Francis thought he was just at the edge of camp.

"Sounds like an old-timer," Robert Wilson said, looking up from his kippers and coffee. "Listen to him cough."

"Is he very close?"

"A mile or so up the stream."

"Will we see him?"

"We'll have a look."

"Does his roaring carry that far? It sounds as though he were right in camp."

"Carries a hell of a long way," said Robert Wilson. "It's strange the way it carries. Hope he's a shootable cat. The boys said there was a very big one about here."

"If I get a shot, where should I hit him," Macomber asked, "to stop him?"

"In the shoulders," Wilson said. "In the neck if you can make it. Shoot for bone. Break him down."

"I hope I can place it properly," Macomber said.

"You shoot very well," Wilson told him. "Take your time. Make sure of him. The first one in is the one that counts."

"What range will it be?"

"Can't tell. Lion has something to say about that. Won't shoot unless it's close enough so you can make sure."

"At under a hundred yards?" Macomber asked.

Wilson looked at him quickly.

"Hundred's about right. Might have to take him a bit under. Shouldn't chance a shot at much over that. A hundred's a decent range. You can hit him wherever you want at that. Here comes the Memsahib."

"Good morning," she said. "Are we going after that lion?"

"As soon as you deal with your breakfast," Wilson said. "How are you feeling?"

"Marvellous," she said. "I'm very excited."

"I'll just go and see that everything is ready," Wilson went off. As he left the lion roared again.

"Noisy beggar," Wilson said. "We'll put a stop to that."

"What's the matter, Francis?" his wife asked him.

"Nothing," Macomber said.

"Yes, there is," she said. "What are you upset about?"

"Nothing," he said.

"Tell me," she looked at him. "Don't you feel well?"

"It's that damned roaring," he said. "It's been going on all night, you know."

"Why didn't you wake me," she said. "I'd love to have heard it."

"I've got to kill the damned thing," Macomber said, miserably.

"Well, that's what you're out here for, isn't it?"

"Yes. But I'm nervous. Hearing the thing roar gets on my nerves."

"Well then, as Wilson said, kill him and stop his roaring."

"Yes, darling," said Francis Macomber. "It sounds easy, doesn't it?"

"You're not afraid, are you?"

"Of course not. But I'm nervous from hearing him roar all night."

"You'll kill him marvellously," she said. "I know you will. I'm awfully anxious to see it."

"Finish your breakfast and we'll be starting."

"It's not light yet," she said. "This is a ridiculous hour."

Just then the lion roared in a deep-chested moaning, suddenly guttural, ascending vibration that seemed to shake the air and ended in a sigh and a heavy, deep-chested grunt.

"He sounds almost here," Macomber's wife said.

"My God," said Macomber. "I hate that damned noise."

"It's very impressive."

"Impressive. It's frightful."

Robert Wilson came up then carrying his short, ugly, shockingly big-bored .505 Gibbs and grinning.

"Come on," he said. "Your gun-bearer has your Springfield and the big gun. Everything's in the car. Have you solids?"

"Yes."

"I'm ready," Mrs. Macomber said.

"Must make him stop that racket," Wilson said. "You get in front. The Memsahib can sit back here with me."

They climbed into the motor car and, in the gray first daylight, moved off up the river through the trees. Macomber opened the breech of his rifle and saw he had metal-cased bullets, shut the bolt and put the rifle on safety. He saw his hand was trembling. He felt in his pocket for more cartridges and moved his fingers over the cartridges in the loops of his tunic front. He turned back to where Wilson sat in the rear seat of the doorless, box-bodied motor car beside his wife, them both grinning with excitement, and Wilson leaned forward and whispered,

"See the birds dropping. Means the old boy has left his kill."

On the far bank of the stream Macomber could see, above the trees, vultures circling and plummeting down.

"Chances are he'll come to drink along here," Wilson whispered. "Before he goes to lay up. Keep an eye out."

They were driving slowly along the high bank of the stream which here cut deeply to its boulder-filled bed, and they wound in and out through big trees as they drove. Macomber was watching the opposite bank when he felt Wilson take hold of his arm. The car stopped.

"There he is," he heard the whisper. "Ahead and to the right. Get out and take him. He's a marvellous lion."

Macomber saw the lion now. He was standing almost broadside, his great head up and turned toward them. The early morning breeze that blew toward them was just stirring his dark mane, and the lion looked huge, silhouetted on the rise of bank in the gray morning light, his shoulders heavy, his barrel of a body bulking smoothly.

"How far is he?" asked Macomber, raising his rifle.

"About seventy-five. Get out and take him."

"Why not shoot from where I am?"

"You don't shoot them from cars," he heard Wilson saying in his ear. "Get out. He's not going to stay there all day."

Macomber stepped out of the curved opening at the side of the front seat, onto the step and down onto the ground. The lion still stood looking majestically and coolly toward this object that his eyes only showed in silhouette, bulking like some super-rhino. There was no man smell carried toward him and he watched the object, moving his great head a little from side to side. Then watching the object, not afraid, but hesitating before going down the bank to drink with such a thing opposite him, he saw a man figure detach itself from it and he turned his heavy head and swung away toward the cover of the trees as he heard a cracking crash and felt the slam of a .30-06 220-grain solid bullet that bit his flank and ripped in sudden hot scalding nausea through his stomach. He trotted, heavy, big-footed, swinging wounded full-bellied, through the trees toward the tall grass and cover, and the crash came again to go past him ripping the air apart. Then it crashed again and he felt the blow as it hit his lower ribs and ripped on through, blood sudden hot and frothy in his mouth, and he galloped toward the high grass where he could crouch and not be seen and make them bring the crashing thing close enough so he could make a rush and get the man that held it.

Macomber had not thought how the lion felt as he got out of the car. He only knew his hands were shaking and as he walked away from the car it was almost impossible for him to make his legs move. They were stiff in the thighs, but he could feel the muscles fluttering. He raised the rifle, sighted on the junction of the lion's head and shoulders and pulled the trigger. Nothing happened though he pulled until he thought his finger would break. Then he knew he had the safety on and as he lowered the rifle to move the safety over he moved another frozen pace forward, and the lion seeing his silhouette now clear of the silhouette of the car, turned and started off at a trot, and, as Macomber fired, he heard a whunk that meant that the bullet was home; but the lion kept on going. Macomber shot again and every one saw the bullet throw a spout of dirt beyond the trotting lion. He shot again, remembering to lower his aim, and they all heard the bullet hit, and the lion went into a gallop and was in the tall grass before he had the bolt pushed forward.

Macomber stood there feeling sick at his stomach, his hands that held the Springfield still cocked, shaking, and his wife and Robert Wilson were standing by him. Beside him too were the two gun-bearers chattering in Wakamba.

"I hit him," Macomber said. "I hit him twice."

"You gut-shot him and you hit him somewhere forward," Wilson said without enthusiasm. The gun-bearers looked very grave. They were silent now.

"You may have killed him," Wilson went on. "We'll have to wait a while before we go in to find out."

"What do you mean?"

"Let him get sick before we follow him up."

"Oh," said Macomber.

"He's a hell of a fine lion," Wilson said cheerfully. "He's gotten into a bad place though."

"Why is it bad?"

"Can't see him until you're on him."

"Oh," said Macomber.

"Come on," said Wilson. "The Memsahib can stay here in the car. We'll go to have a look at the blood spoor."

"Stay here, Margot," Macomber said to his wife. His mouth was very dry and it was hard for him to talk.

"Why?" she asked.

"Wilson says to."

"We're going to have a look," Wilson said. "You stay here. You can see even better from here."

"All right."

Wilson spoke in Swahili to the driver. He nodded and said, "Yes, Bwana."

Then they went down the steep bank and across the stream, climbing over and around the boulders and up the other bank, pulling up by some projecting roots, and along it until they found where the lion had been trotting when Macomber first shot. There was dark blood on the short grass that the gun-bearers pointed out with grass stems, and that ran away behind the river bank trees.

"What do we do?" asked Macomber.

"Not much choice," said Wilson. "We can't bring the car over.

Bank's too steep. We'll let him stiffen up a bit and then you and I'll go in and have a look for him."

"Can't we set the grass on fire?" Macomber asked.

"Too green."

"Can't we send beaters?"

Wilson looked at him appraisingly. "Of course we can," he said. "But it's just a touch murderous. You see we know the lion's wounded. You can drive an unwounded lion—he'll move on ahead of a noise—but a wounded lion's going to charge. You can't see him until you're right on him. He'll make himself perfectly flat in cover you wouldn't think would hide a hare. You can't very well send boys in there to that sort of a show. Somebody bound to get mauled."

"What about the gun-bearers?"

"Oh, they'll go with us. It's their *shauri*. You see, they signed on for it. They don't look too happy though, do they?"

"I don't want to go in there," said Macomber. It was out before he knew he'd said it.

"Neither do I," said Wilson very cheerily. "Really no choice though." Then, as an afterthought, he glanced at Macomber and saw suddenly how he was trembling and the pitiful look on his face.

"You don't have to go in of course," he said. "That's what I'm hired for, you know. That's why I'm so expensive."

"You mean you'd go in by yourself? Why not leave him there?"

Robert Wilson, whose entire occupation had been with the lion and the problem he presented, and who had not been thinking about Macomber except to note that he was rather windy, suddenly felt as though he had opened the wrong door in a hotel and seen something shameful.

"What do you mean?"

"Why not just leave him?"

"You mean pretend to ourselves he hasn't been hit?"

"No. Just drop it."

"It isn't done."

"Why not?"

"For one thing, he's certain to be suffering. For another, some one else might run onto him."

"I see."

"But you don't have to have anything to do with it."

"I'd like to," Macomber said. "I'm just scared, you know."

"I'll go ahead when we go in," Wilson said, "with Kongoni tracking. You keep behind me and a little to one side. Chances are we'll
hear him growl. If we see him we'll both shoot. Don't worry about
anything. I'll keep you backed up. As a matter of fact, you know, perhaps you'd better not go. It might be much better. Why don't you go
over and join the Memsahib while I just get it over with?"

"No, I want to go."

"All right," said Wilson. "But don't go in if you don't want to. This
is my *shauri* now, you know."

"I want to go," said Macomber.

They sat under a tree and smoked.

"Want to go back and speak to the Memsahib while we're waiting?" Wilson asked.

"No."

"I'll just step back and tell her to be patient."

"Good," said Macomber. He sat there, sweating under his arms, his
mouth dry, his stomach hollow feeling, wanting to find courage to tell
Wilson to go on and finish off the lion without him. He could not
know that Wilson was furious because he had not noticed the state he
was in earlier and sent him back to his wife. While he sat there Wilson
came up. "I have your big gun," he said. "Take it. We've given him
time, I think. Come on."

Macomber took the big gun and Wilson said:

"Keep behind me and about five yards to the right and do exactly as
I tell you." Then he spoke in Swahili to the two gun-bearers who
looked the picture of gloom.

"Let's go," he said.

"Could I have a drink of water?" Macomber asked. Wilson spoke
to the older gun-bearer, who wore a canteen on his belt, and the man
unbuckled it, unscrewed the top and handed it to Macomber, who
took it noticing how heavy it seemed and how hairy and shoddy the
felt covering was in his hand. He raised it to drink and looked ahead
at the high grass with the flat-topped trees behind it. A breeze was
blowing toward them and the grass rippled gently in the wind. He

looked at the gun-bearer and he could see the gun-bearer was suffering too with fear.

Thirty-five yards into the grass the big lion lay flattened out along the ground. His ears were back and his only movement was a slight twitching up and down of his long, black-tufted tail. He had turned at bay as soon as he had reached this cover and he was sick with the wound through his full belly, and weakening with the wound through his lungs that brought a thin foamy red to his mouth each time he breathed. His flanks were wet and hot and flies were on the little openings the solid bullets had made in his tawny hide, and his big yellow eyes, narrowed with hate, looked straight ahead, only blinking when the pain came as he breathed, and his claws dug in the soft baked earth. All of him, pain, sickness, hatred and all of his remaining strength, was tightening into an absolute concentration for a rush. He could hear the men talking and he waited, gathering all of himself into this preparation for a charge as soon as the men would come into the grass. As he heard their voices his tail stiffened to twitch up and down, and, as they came into the edge of the grass, he made a coughing grunt and charged.

Kongoni, the old gun-bearer, in the lead watching the blood spoor, Wilson watching the grass for any movement, his big gun ready, the second gun-bearer looking ahead and listening, Macomber close to Wilson, his rifle cocked, they had just moved into the grass when Macomber heard the blood-choked coughing grunt, and saw the swishing rush in the grass. The next thing he knew he was running; running wildly, in panic in the open, running toward the stream.

He heard the *ca-ra-wong!* of Wilson's big rifle, and again in a second crashing *carawong!* and turning saw the lion, horrible-looking now with half his head seeming to be gone, crawling toward Wilson in the edge of the tall grass while the red-faced man worked the bolt on the short ugly rifle and aimed carefully as another blasting *carawong!* came from the muzzle, and the crawling, heavy, yellow bulk of the lion stiffened and the huge, mutilated head slid forward and Macomber, standing by himself in the clearing where he had run, holding a loaded rifle, while two black men and a white man looked back at him in contempt, knew the lion was dead. He came toward Wilson,

his tallness all seeming a naked reproach, and Wilson looked at him
and said:

"Want to take pictures?"

"No," he said.

That was all anyone had said until they reached the motor car.
Then Wilson had said:

"Hell of a fine lion. Boys will skin him out. We might as well stay
here in the shade."

Macomber's wife had not looked at him nor he at her and he had
sat by her in the back seat with Wilson sitting in the front seat. Once
he had reached over and taken his wife's hand without looking at her
and she had removed her hand from his. Looking across the stream to
where the gun-bearers were skinning out the lion he could see that
she had been able to see the whole thing. While they sat there his wife
had reached forward and put her hand on Wilson's shoulder. He
turned and she had leaned forward over the low seat and kissed him
on the mouth.

"Oh, I say," said Wilson, going redder than his natural baked
color.

"Mr. Robert Wilson," she said. "The beautiful red-faced Mr. Robert
Wilson."

Then she sat down beside Macomber again and looked away across
the stream to where the lion lay, with uplifted, white-muscled, tendon-
marked naked forearms, and white bloating belly, as the black men
fleshed away the skin. Finally the gun-bearers brought the skin over,
wet and heavy, and climbed in behind with it, rolling it up before they
got in, and the motor car started. No one had said anything more until
they were back in camp.

That was the story of the lion. Macomber did not know how the
lion had felt before he started his rush, nor during it when the unbelievable smash of the .505 with a muzzle velocity of two tons had hit
him in the mouth, nor what kept him coming after that, when the
second ripping crash had smashed his hind quarters and he had come
crawling on toward the crashing, blasting thing that had destroyed
him. Wilson knew something about it and only expressed it by saying,
"Damned fine lion," but Macomber did not know how Wilson felt

about things either. He did not know how his wife felt except that she was through with him.

His wife had been through with him before but it never lasted. He was very wealthy, and would be much wealthier, and he knew she would not leave him ever now. That was one of the few things that he really knew. He knew about that, about motor cycles—that was earliest—about motor cars, about duck-shooting, about fishing, trout, salmon and big-sea, about sex in books, many books, too many books, about all court games, about dogs, not much about horses, about hanging on to his money, about most of the other things his world dealt in, and about his wife not leaving him. His wife had been a great beauty and she was still a great beauty in Africa, but she was not a great enough beauty any more at home to be able to leave him and better herself and she knew it and he knew it. She had missed the chance to leave him and he knew it. If he had been better with women she would probably have started to worry about him getting another new, beautiful wife; but she knew too much about him to worry about him either. Also, he had always had a great tolerance which seemed the nicest thing about him if it were not the most sinister.

All in all they were known as a comparatively happily married couple, one of those whose disruption is often rumored but never occurs, and as the society columnist put it, they were adding more than a spice of *adventure* to their much envied and ever-enduring *Romance* by a *Safari* in what was known as *Darkest Africa* until the Martin Johnsons lighted it on so many silver screens where they were pursuing *Old Simba* the lion, the buffalo, *Tembo* the elephant and as well collecting specimens for the Museum of Natural History. This same columnist had reported them *on the verge* at least three times in the past and they had been. But they always made it up. They had a sound basis of union. Margot was too beautiful for Macomber to divorce her and Macomber had too much money for Margot ever to leave him.

It was now about three o'clock in the morning and Francis Macomber, who had been asleep a little while after he had stopped thinking about the lion, wakened and then slept again, woke suddenly, frightened in a dream of the bloody-headed lion standing over him, and listening while his heart pounded, he realized that his wife was not in the other cot in the tent. He lay awake with that knowledge for two hours.

At the end of that time his wife came into the tent, lifted her mosquito bar and crawled cozily into bed.

"Where have you been?" Macomber asked in the darkness.

"Hello," she said. "Are you awake?"

"Where have you been?"

"I just went out to get a breath of air."

"You did, like hell."

"What do you want me to say, darling?"

"Where have you been?"

"Out to get a breath of air."

"That's a new name for it. You *are* a bitch."

"Well, you're a coward."

"All right," he said. "What of it?"

"Nothing as far as I'm concerned. But please let's not talk, darling, because I'm very sleepy."

"You think that I'll take anything."

"I know you will, sweet."

"Well, I won't."

"Please, darling, let's not talk. I'm so very sleepy."

"There wasn't going to be any of that. You promised there wouldn't be."

"Well, there is now," she said sweetly.

"You said if we made this trip that there would be none of that. You promised."

"Yes, darling. That's the way I meant it to be. But the trip was spoiled yesterday. We don't have to talk about it, do we?"

"You don't wait long when you have an advantage, do you?"

"Please let's not talk. I'm so sleepy, darling."

"I'm going to talk."

"Don't mind me then, because I'm going to sleep." And she did.

At breakfast they were all three at the table before daylight and Francis Macomber found that, of all the many men that he had hated, he hated Robert Wilson the most.

"Sleep well?" Wilson asked in his throaty voice, filling a pipe.

"Did you?"

"Topping," the white hunter told him.

You bastard, thought Macomber, you insolent bastard.

So she woke him when she came in, Wilson thought, looking at them both with his flat, cold eyes. Well, why doesn't he keep his wife where she belongs? What does he think I am, a bloody plaster saint? Let him keep her where she belongs. It's his own fault.

"Do you think we'll find buffalo?" Margot asked, pushing away a dish of apricots.

"Chance of it," Wilson said and smiled at her. "Why don't you stay in camp?"

"Not for anything," she told him.

"Why not order her to stay in camp?" Wilson said to Macomber.

"You order her," said Macomber coldly.

"Let's not have any ordering, nor," turning to Macomber, "any silliness, Francis," Margot said quite pleasantly.

"Are you ready to start?" Macomber asked.

"Any time," Wilson told him. "Do you want the Memsahib to go?"

"Does it make any difference whether I do or not?"

The hell with it, thought Robert Wilson. The utter complete hell with it. So this is what it's going to be like. Well, this is what it's going to be like, then.

"Makes no difference," he said.

"You're sure you wouldn't like to stay in camp with her yourself and let me go out and hunt the buffalo?" Macomber asked.

"Can't do that," said Wilson. "Wouldn't talk rot if I were you."

"I'm not talking rot. I'm disgusted."

"Bad word, disgusted."

"Francis, will you please try to speak sensibly?" his wife said.

"I speak too damned sensibly," Macomber said. "Did you ever eat such filthy food?"

"Something wrong with the food?" asked Wilson quietly.

"No more than with everything else."

"I'd pull yourself together, laddybuck," Wilson said very quietly. "There's a boy waits at table that understands a little English."

"The hell with him."

Wilson stood up and puffing on his pipe strolled away, speaking a few words in Swahili to one of the gun-bearers who was standing waiting for him. Macomber and his wife sat on at the table. He was staring at his coffee cup.

"If you make a scene I'll leave you, darling," Margot said quietly.

"No, you won't."

"You can try it and see."

"You won't leave me."

"No," she said. "I won't leave you and you'll behave yourself."

"Behave myself? That's a way to talk. Behave myself."

"Yes. Behave yourself."

"Why don't *you* try behaving?"

"I've tried it so long. So very long."

"I hate that red-faced swine," Macomber said. "I loathe the sight of him."

"He's really *very* nice."

"Oh, *shut up,*" Macomber almost shouted. Just then the car came up and stopped in front of the dining tent and the driver and the two gun-bearers got out. Wilson walked over and looked at the husband and wife sitting there at the table.

"Going shooting?" he asked.

"Yes," said Macomber, standing up. "Yes."

"Better bring a woolly. It will be cool in the car," Wilson said.

"I'll get my leather jacket," Margot said.

"The boy has it," Wilson told her. He climbed into the front with the driver and Francis Macomber and his wife sat, not speaking, in the back seat.

Hope the silly beggar doesn't take a notion to blow the back of my head off, Wilson thought to himself. Women *are* a nuisance on safari.

The car was grinding down to cross the river at a pebbly ford in the gray daylight and then climbed, angling up the steep bank, where Wilson had ordered a way shovelled out the day before so they could reach the parklike wooded rolling country on the far side.

It was a good morning, Wilson thought. There was a heavy dew and as the wheels went through the grass and low bushes he could smell the odor of the crushed fronds. It was an odor like verbena and he liked this early morning smell of the dew, the crushed bracken and the look of the tree trunks showing black through the early morning mist, as the car made its way through the untracked, parklike country.

He had put the two in the back seat out of his mind now and was thinking about buffalo. The buffalo that he was after stayed in the daytime in a thick swamp where it was impossible to get a shot, but in the night they fed out into an open stretch of country and if he could come between them and their swamp with the car, Macomber would have a good chance at them in the open. He did not want to hunt buff with Macomber in thick cover. He did not want to hunt buff or anything else with Macomber at all, but he was a professional hunter and he had hunted with some rare ones in his time. If they got buff today there would only be rhino to come and the poor man would have gone through his dangerous game and things might pick up. He'd have nothing more to do with the woman and Macomber would get over that too. He must have gone through plenty of that before by the look of things. Poor beggar. He must have a way of getting over it. Well, it was the poor sod's own bloody fault.

He, Robert Wilson, carried a double size cot on safari to accommodate any windfalls he might receive. He had hunted for a certain clientele, the international, fast, sporting set, where the women did not feel they were getting their money's worth unless they had shared that cot with the white hunter. He despised them when he was away from them although he liked some of them well enough at the time, but he made his living by them; and their standards were his standards as long as they were hiring him.

They were his standards in all except the shooting. He had his own standards about the killing and they could live up to them or get some one else to hunt them. He knew, too, that they all respected him for this. This Macomber was an odd one though. Damned if he wasn't. Now the wife. Well, the wife. Yes, the wife. Hm, the wife. Well he'd dropped all that. He looked around at them. Macomber sat grim and furious. Margot smiled at him. She looked younger today, more innocent and fresher and not so professionally beautiful. What's in her heart God knows, Wilson thought. She hadn't talked much last night. At that it was a pleasure to see her.

The motor car climbed up a slight rise and went on through the trees and then out into a grassy prairie-like opening and kept in the shelter of the trees along the edge, the driver going slowly and Wilson looking carefully out across the prairie and all along its far side. He stopped the car and studied the opening with his field glasses. Then he motioned to the driver to go on and the car moved slowly along, the driver avoiding wart-hog holes and driving around the mud castles ants had built. Then, looking across the opening, Wilson suddenly turned and said,

"By God, there they are!"

And looking where he pointed, while the car jumped forward and Wilson spoke in rapid Swahili to the driver, Macomber saw three huge, black animals looking almost cylindrical in their long heaviness, like big black tank cars, moving at a gallop across the far edge of the open prairie. They moved at a stiff-necked, stiff-bodied gallop and he could see the up-swept wide black horns on their heads as they galloped heads out; the heads not moving.

"They're three old bulls," Wilson said. "We'll cut them off before they get to the swamp."

The car was going a wild forty-five miles an hour across the open and as Macomber watched, the buffalo got bigger and bigger until he could see the gray, hairless, scabby look of one huge bull and how his neck was a part of his shoulders and the shiny black of his horns as he galloped a little behind the others that were strung out in that steady plunging gait; and then, the car swaying as though it had just jumped a road, they drew up close and he could see the plunging hugeness of the bull, and the dust in his sparsely haired hide, the wide boss of horn and his outstretched, wide-nostrilled muzzle, and he was raising his rifle when Wilson shouted, "Not from the car, you fool!" and he had no fear, only hatred of Wilson, while the brakes clamped on and the car skidded, plowing sideways to an almost stop and Wilson was out on one side and he on the other, stumbling as his feet hit the still speeding-by of the earth, and then he was shooting at the bull as he moved away, hearing the bullets whunk into him, emptying his rifle at him as he moved steadily away, finally remembering to get his shots forward into the shoulder, and as he fumbled to re-load, he saw the bull was down. Down on his knees, his big head tossing, and seeing the other two still galloping he shot at the leader and hit him. He shot again and missed and he heard the *carawonging* roar as Wilson shot and saw the leading bull slide forward onto his nose.

"Get that other," Wilson said. "Now you're shooting!"

But the other bull was moving steadily at the same gallop and he missed, throwing a spout of dirt, and Wilson missed and the dust rose in a cloud and Wilson shouted. "Come on. He's too far!" and grabbed his arm and they were in the car again, Macomber and Wilson hanging on the sides and rocketing swayingly over the uneven ground, drawing up on the steady, plunging, heavy-necked, straight-moving gallop of the bull.

They were behind him, and Macomber was filling his rifle, dropping shells onto the ground, jamming it, clearing the jam, then they were almost up with the bull when Wilson yelled "Stop," and the car skidded so that it almost swung over and Macomber fell forward onto his feet, slammed his bolt forward and fired as far forward as he could aim into the galloping, rounded black back, aimed and shot again, then again, then again, and the bullets, all of them hitting, had no effect on the buffalo that he could see. Then Wilson shot, the roar deafening him, and he could see the bull stagger. Macomber shot again, aiming carefully, and down he came, onto his knees.

"All right," Wilson said. "Nice work. That's the three."

Macomber felt a drunken elation.

"How many times did you shoot?" he asked.

"Just three," Wilson said. "You killed the first bull. The biggest one. I helped you finish the other two. Afraid they might have got into cover. You had them killed. I was just mopping up a little. You shot damn well."

"Let's go to the car," said Macomber. "I want a drink."

"Got to finish off that buff first," Wilson told him. The buffalo was on his knees and he jerked his head furiously and bellowed in pig-eyed, roaring rage as they came toward him.

"Watch he doesn't get up," Wilson said. Then, "Get a little broadside and take him in the neck just behind the ear."

Macomber aimed carefully at the center of the huge, jerking, rage-driven neck and shot. At the shot the head dropped forward.

"That does it," said Wilson. "Got the spine. They're a hell of a looking thing, aren't they?"

"Let's get the drink," said Macomber. In his life he had never felt so good.

In the car Macomber's wife sat very white faced. "You were marvellous, darling," she said to Macomber. "What a ride."

"Was it rough?" Wilson asked.

"It was frightful. I've never been more frightened in my life."

"Let's all have a drink," Macomber said.

"By all means," said Wilson. "Give it to the Memsahib." She drank
the neat whisky from the flask and shuddered a little when she swallowed. She handed the flask to Macomber who handed it to Wilson.

"It was frightfully exciting," she said. "It's given me a dreadful
headache. I didn't know you were allowed to shoot them from cars
though."

"No one shot from cars," said Wilson coldly.

"I mean chase them from cars."

"Wouldn't ordinarily." Wilson said. "Seemed sporting enough to me
though while we were doing it. Taking more chance driving that way
across the plain full of holes and one thing and another than hunting
on foot. Buffalo could have charged us each time we shot if he liked.
Gave him every chance. Wouldn't mention it to any one though. It's
illegal if that's what you mean."

"It seemed very unfair to me," Margot said, "chasing those big helpless things in a motor car."

"Did it?" said Wilson.

"What would happen if they heard about it in Nairobi?"

"I'd lose my license for one thing. Other unpleasantnesses," Wilson
said, taking a drink from the flask. "I'd be out of business."

"Really?"

"Yes, really."

"Well," said Macomber, and he smiled for the first time all day.
"Now she has something on you."

"You have such a pretty way of putting things, Francis," Margot
Macomber said. Wilson looked at them both. If a four-letter man
marries a five-letter woman, he was thinking, what number of letters
would their children be? What he said was, "We lost a gun-bearer.
Did you notice it?"

"My God no," Macomber said.

"Here he comes," Wilson said. "He's all right. He must have fallen
off when we left the first bull."

Approaching them was the middle-aged gun-bearer, limping along in his knitted cap, khaki tunic, shorts and rubber sandals, gloomy-faced and disgusted looking. As he came up he called out to Wilson in Swahili and they all saw the change in the white hunter's face.

"What does he say?" asked Margot.

"He says the first bull got up and went into the bush," Wilson said with no expression in his voice.

"Oh," said Macomber blankly.

"Then it's going to be just like the lion," said Margot, full of anticipation.

"It's not going to be a damned bit like the lion," Wilson told her. "Did you want another drink, Macomber?"

"Thanks, yes." Macomber said. He expected the feeling he had had about the lion to come back but it did not. For the first time in his life he really felt wholly without fear. Instead of fear he had a feeling of definite elation.

"We'll go and have a look at the second bull," Wilson said. "I'll tell the driver to put the car in the shade."

"What are you going to do?" asked Margaret Macomber.

"Take a look at the buff," Wilson said.

"I'll come."

"Come along."

The three of them walked over to where the second buffalo bulked blackly in the open, head forward on the grass, the massive horns swung wide.

"He's a very good head," Wilson said. "That's close to a fifty-inch spread."

Macomber was looking at him with delight.

"He's hateful looking," said Margot. "Can't we go into the shade?"

"Of course," Wilson said. "Look," he said to Macomber, and pointed. "See that patch of bush?"

"Yes."

"That's where the first bull went in. The gun-bearer said when he fell off the bull was down. He was watching us helling along and the other two buff galloping. When he looked up there was the bull up and looking at him. Gun-bearer ran like hell and the bull went off slowly into that bush."

"Can we go in after him now?" asked Macomber eagerly.

Wilson looked at him appraisingly. Damned if this isn't a strange one, he thought. Yesterday he's scared sick and today he's a ruddy fire eater.

"No, we'll give him a while."

"Let's please go into the shade," Margot said. Her face was white and she looked ill.

They made their way to the car where it stood under a single, wide-spreading tree and all climbed in.

"Chances are he's dead in there," Wilson remarked. "After a little we'll have a look."

Macomber felt a wild unreasonable happiness that he had never known before.

"By God, that was a chase," he said. "I've never felt any such feeling. Wasn't it marvellous, Margot?"

"I hated it."

"Why?"

"I hated it," she said bitterly. "I loathed it."

"You know I don't think I'd ever be afraid of anything again," Macomber said to Wilson. "Something happened in me after we first saw the buff and started after him. Like a dam bursting. It was pure excitement."

"Cleans out your liver," said Wilson. "Damn funny things happen to people."

Macomber's face was shining. "You know something did happen to me," he said. "I feel absolutely different."

His wife said nothing and eyed him strangely. She was sitting far back in the seat and Macomber was sitting forward talking to Wilson who turned sideways talking over the back of the front seat.

"You know, I'd like to try another lion," Macomber said. "I'm really not afraid of them now. After all, what can they do to you?"

"That's it," said Wilson. "Worst one can do is kill you. How does it go? Shakespeare. Damned good. See if I can remember. Oh, damned good. Used to quote it to myself at one time. Let's see. 'By my troth, I care not; a man can die but once; we owe God a death and let it go which way it will he that dies this year is quit for the next.' Damned fine, eh?"

He was very embarrassed, having brought out this thing he had lived by, but he had seen men come of age before and it always moved him. It was not a matter of their twenty-first birthday.

It had taken a strange chance of hunting, a sudden precipitation into action without opportunity for worrying beforehand, to bring this about with Macomber, but regardless of how it had happened it had most certainly happened. Look at the beggar now, Wilson thought. It's that some of them stay little boys so long, Wilson thought. Sometimes all their lives. Their figures stay boyish when they're fifty. The great American boy-men. Damned strange people. But he liked this Macomber now. Damned strange fellow. Probably meant the end of cuckoldry too. Well, that would be a damned good thing. Damned good thing. Beggar had probably been afraid all his life. Don't know what started it. But over now. Hadn't had time to be afraid with the buff. That and being angry too. Motor car too. Motor cars made it familiar. Be a damn fire eater now. He'd seen it in the war work the same way. More of a change than any loss of virginity. Fear gone like an operation. Something else grew in its place. Main thing a man had. Made him into a man. Women knew it too. No bloody fear.

From the far corner of the seat Margaret Macomber looked at the two of them. There was no change in Wilson. She saw Wilson as she had seen him the day before when she had first realized what his great talent was. But she saw the change in Francis Macomber now.

"Do you have that feeling of happiness about what's going to happen?" Macomber asked, still exploring his new wealth.

"You're not supposed to mention it," Wilson said, looking in the other's face. "Much more fashionable to say you're scared. Mind you, you'll be scared too, plenty of times."

"But you *have* a feeling of happiness about action to come?"

"Yes," said Wilson. "There's that. Doesn't do to talk too much about all this. Talk the whole thing away. No pleasure in anything if you mouth it up too much."

"You're both talking rot," said Margot. "Just because you've chased some helpless animals in a motor car you talk like heroes."

"Sorry," said Wilson. "I have been gassing too much." She's worried about it already, he thought.

"If you don't know what we're talking about why not keep out of it?" Macomber asked his wife.

"You've gotten awfully brave, awfully suddenly," his wife said contemptuously, but her contempt was not secure. She was very afraid of something.

Macomber laughed, a very natural hearty laugh. "You know I *have*," he said. "I really have."

"Isn't it sort of late?" Margot said bitterly. Because she had done the best she could for many years back and the way they were together now was no one person's fault.

"Not for me," said Macomber.

Margot said nothing but sat back in the corner of the seat.

"Do you think we've given him time enough?" Macomber asked Wilson cheerfully.

"We might have a look," Wilson said. "Have you any solids left?"

"The gun-bearer has some."

Wilson called in Swahili and the older gun-bearer, who was skinning out one of the heads, straightened up, pulled a box of solids out of his pocket and brought them over to Macomber, who filled his magazine and put the remaining shells in his pocket.

"You might as well shoot the Springfield," Wilson said. "You're used to it. We'll leave the Mannlicher in the car with the Memsahib. Your gun-bearer can carry your heavy gun. I've this damned cannon. Now let me tell you about them." He had saved this until the last because he did not want to worry Macomber. "When a buff comes he comes with his head high and thrust straight out. The boss of the horns covers any sort of a brain shot. The only shot is straight into the nose. The only other shot is into his chest or, if you're to one side, into the neck or the shoulders. After they've been hit once they take a hell of a lot of killing. Don't try anything fancy. Take the easiest shot there is. They've finished skinning out that head now. Should we get started?"

He called to the gun-bearers, who came up wiping their hands, and the older one got into the back.

"I'll only take Kongoni," Wilson said. "The other can watch to keep the birds away."

As the car moved slowly across the open space toward the island of brushy trees that ran in a tongue of foliage along a dry water course that cut the open swale, Macomber felt his heart pounding and his mouth was dry again, but it was excitement, not fear.

"Here's where he went in," Wilson said. Then to the gun-bearer in Swahili, "Take the blood spoor."

The car was parallel to the patch of bush. Macomber, Wilson and the gun-bearer got down. Macomber, looking back, saw his wife, with the rifle by her side, looking at him. He waved to her, and she did not wave back.

The brush was very thick ahead and the ground was dry. The middle-aged gun-bearer was sweating heavily and Wilson had his hat down over his eyes and his red neck showed just ahead of Macomber. Suddenly the gun-bearer said something in Swahili to Wilson and ran forward.

"He's dead in there," Wilson said, "Good work," and he turned to grip Macomber's hand and as they shook hands, grinning at each other, the gun-bearer shouted wildly and they saw him coming out of the bush sideways, fast as a crab, and the bull coming, nose out, mouth tight closed, blood dripping, massive head straight out, coming in a charge, his little pig eyes bloodshot as he looked at them. Wilson, who was ahead, was kneeling shooting, and Macomber, as he fired, unhearing his shot in the roaring of Wilson's gun, saw fragments like slate burst from the huge boss of the horns, and the head jerked, he shot again at the wide nostrils and saw the horns jolt again and fragments fly, and he did not see Wilson now and, aiming carefully, shot again with the buffalo's huge bulk almost on him and his rifle almost level with the on-coming head, nose out, and he could see the little wicked eyes and the head started to lower and he felt a sudden white-hot, blinding flash explode inside his head and that was all he ever felt.

Wilson had ducked to one side to get in a shoulder shot. Macomber had stood solid and shot for the nose, shooting a touch high each time and hitting the heavy horns, splintering and chipping them like hitting a slate roof, and Mrs. Macomber, in the car, had shot at the buffalo with the 6.5 Mannlicher as it seemed about to gore Macomber and had hit her husband about two inches up and a little to one side of the base of his skull.

Francis Macomber lay now, face down, not two yards from where the buffalo lay on his side and his wife knelt over him with Wilson beside her.

"I wouldn't turn him over," Wilson said.

The woman was crying hysterically.

"I'd get back in the car," Wilson said. "Where's the rifle?"

She shook her head, her face contorted. The gun-bearer picked up the rifle.

"Leave it as it is," said Wilson. Then, "Go get Abdulla so that he may witness the manner of the accident."

He knelt down, took a handkerchief from his pocket, and spread it over Francis Macomber's crew-cropped head where it lay. The blood sank into the dry, loose earth.

Wilson stood up and saw the buffalo on his side, his legs out, his thinly-haired belly crawling with ticks. "Hell of a good bull," his brain registered automatically. "A good fifty inches, or better. Better." He called to the driver and told him to spread a blanket over the body and stay by it. Then he walked over to the motor car where the woman sat crying in the corner.

"That was a pretty thing to do," he said in a toneless voice. "He *would* have left you too."

"Stop it," she said.

"Of course it's an accident," he said. "I know that."

"Stop it," she said.

"Don't worry," he said. "There will be a certain amount of unpleasantness but I will have some photographs taken that will be very useful at the inquest. There's the testimony of the gun-bearers and the driver too. You're perfectly all right."

"Stop it," she said.

"There's a hell of a lot to be done," he said. "And I'll have to send a truck off to the lake to wireless for a plane to take the three of us into Nairobi. Why didn't you poison him? That's what they do in England."

"Stop it. Stop it. Stop it," the woman cried.

Wilson looked at her with his flat blue eyes.

"I'm through now," he said. "I was a little angry. I'd begun to like your husband."

"Oh, please stop it," she said. "Please, please stop it."

"That's better." Wilson said, "Please is much better. Now I'll stop."

JOHN STEINBECK

The LEADER of the PEOPLE

John Steinbeck, a reticent man and one who frankly says he is sorry to say he cannot make a choice of his favorite writing, and insists that he has no particular fondness for any special piece, is represented by a short story from his collection, *Long Valley*. Its selection was made by Pascal Covici, for many years Mr. Steinbeck's closest literary advisor and, from the beginning until the present, his editor and publisher.

From Mr. Covici has come the following comment:

The outstanding qualities that make John Steinbeck, at least as far as I am concerned, a significant writer are his command of the vernacular, his poetic rhythms, and his greatest intuitive social sympathies. I find these qualities in *Tortilla Flat*, *Of Mice and Men*, *The Moon Is Down* and, best of all, in *The Grapes of Wrath*. If I had to choose a single short passage to show Steinbeck at his best I would choose Chapter III from *The Grapes of Wrath*, "The Story of the Turtle." If it is a short story, I would recommend "The Leader of the People," the last story in *Long Valley*.

New York, N. Y.   PASCAL COVICI
April 23, 1942

ON SATURDAY afternoon Billy Buck, the ranch-hand, raked together the last of the old year's haystack and pitched small forkfuls over the wire fence to a few mildly interested cattle. High in the air small clouds like puffs of cannon smoke were driven eastward by the March wind. The wind could be heard whishing in the brush on the ridge crests, but no breath of it penetrated down into the ranch-cup.

The little boy, Jody, emerged from the house eating a thick piece of buttered bread. He saw Billy working on the last of the haystack. Jody tramped down scuffing his shoes in a way he had been told was destructive to good shoe-leather. A flock of white pigeons flew out of the black cypress tree as Jody passed, and circled the tree and landed again. A half-grown tortoise-shell cat leaped from the bunkhouse porch, galloped on stiff legs across the road, whirled and galloped back again. Jody picked up a stone to help the game along, but he was too late, for the cat was under the porch before the stone could be discharged. He threw the stone into the cypress tree and started the white pigeons on another whirling flight.

Arriving at the used-up haystack, the boy leaned against the barbed wire fence. "Will that be all of it, do you think?" he asked.

The middle-aged ranch-hand stopped his careful raking and stuck his fork into the ground. He took off his black hat and smoothed down his hair. "Nothing left of it that isn't soggy from ground moisture," he said. He replaced his hat and rubbed his dry leathery hands together.

"Ought to be plenty mice," Jody suggested.

"Lousy with them," said Billy. "Just crawling with mice."

"Well, maybe, when you get all through, I could call the dogs and hunt the mice."

"Sure, I guess you could," said Billy Buck. He lifted a forkful of the damp ground-hay and threw it into the air. Instantly three mice leaped out and burrowed frantically under the hay again.

Jody sighed with satisfaction. Those plump, sleepy, arrogant mice were doomed. For eight months they had lived and multiplied in the haystack. They had been immune from cats, from traps, from poison and from Jody. They had grown smug in their security, overbearing and fat. Now the time of disaster had come; they would not survive another day.

Billy looked up at the top of the hills that surrounded the ranch. "Maybe you better ask your father before you do it," he suggested.

"Well, where is he? I'll ask him now."

"He rode up to the ridge ranch after dinner. He'll be back pretty soon."

Jody slumped against the fence post. "I don't think he'd care."

As Billy went back to his work he said ominously, "You'd better ask him anyway. You know how he is."

Jody did know. His father, Carl Tiflin, insisted upon giving permission for anything that was done on the ranch, whether it was important or not. Jody sagged farther against the post until he was sitting on the ground. He looked up at the little puffs of wind-driven cloud. "Is it like to rain, Billy?"

"It might. The wind's good for it, but not strong enough."

"Well, I hope it don't rain until after I kill those damn mice." He looked over his shoulder to see whether Billy had noticed the mature profanity. Billy worked on without comment.

Jody turned back and looked at the side-hill where the road from the outside world came down. The hill was washed with lean March sunshine. Silver thistles, blue lupins and a few poppies bloomed among the sage bushes. Halfway up the hill Jody could see Doubletree Mutt, the black dog, digging in a squirrel hole. He paddled for a while and then paused to kick bursts of dirt out between his hind legs, and he dug with an earnestness which belied the knowledge he must have had that no dog had ever caught a squirrel by digging in a hole.

Suddenly, while Jody watched, the black dog stiffened, and backed out of the hole and looked up the hill toward the cleft in the ridge where the road came through. Jody looked up too. For a moment Carl Tiflin on horseback stood out against the pale sky and then he moved down the road toward the house. He carried something white in his hand.

The boy started to his feet. "He's got a letter," Jody cried. He trotted away toward the ranch house, for the letter would probably be read aloud and he wanted to be there. He reached the house before his father did, and ran in. He heard Carl dismount from his creaking saddle and slap the horse on the side to send it to the barn where Billy would unsaddle it and turn it out.

Jody ran into the kitchen. "We got a letter!" he cried.

His mother looked up from a pan of beans. "Who has?"

"Father has. I saw it in his hand."

Carl strode into the kitchen then, and Jody's mother asked, "Who's the letter from, Carl?"

He frowned quickly. "How did you know there was a letter?"

She nodded her head in the boy's direction. "Big-Britches Jody told me."

Jody was embarrassed.

His father looked down at him contemptuously. "He is getting to be a Big-Britches," Carl said. "He's minding everybody's business but his own. Got his big nose into everything."

Mrs. Tiflin relented a little. "Well, he hasn't enough to keep him busy. Who's the letter from?"

Carl still frowned on Jody. "I'll keep him busy if he isn't careful." He held out a sealed letter. "I guess it's from your father."

Mrs. Tiflin took a hairpin from her head and slit open the flap. Her lips pursed judiciously. Jody saw her eyes snap back and forth over the lines. "He says," she translated, "he says he's going to drive out Saturday to stay for a little while. Why, this is Saturday. The letter must have been delayed." She looked at the postmark. "This was mailed day before yesterday. It should have been here yesterday." She looked up questioningly at her husband, and then her face darkened angrily. "Now what have you got that look on you for? He doesn't come often."

Carl turned his eyes away from her anger. He could be stern with her most of the time, but when occasionally her temper arose, he could not combat it.

"What's the matter with you?" she demanded again.

In his explanation there was a tone of apology Jody himself might have used. "It's just that he talks," Carl said lamely. "Just talks."

"Well, what of it? You talk yourself."

"Sure I do. But your father only talks about one thing."

"Indians!" Jody broke in excitedly. "Indians and crossing the plains!"

Carl turned fiercely on him. "You get out, Mr. Big-Britches! Go on, now! Get out!"

Jody went miserably out the back door and closed the screen with elaborate quietness. Under the kitchen window his shamed, downcast eyes fell upon a curiously shaped stone, a stone of such fascination that he squatted down and picked it up and turned it over in his hands.

The voices came clearly to him through the open kitchen window. "Jody's damn well right," he heard his father say. "Just Indians and crossing the plains. I've heard that story about how the horses got driven off about a thousand times. He just goes on and on, and he never changes a word in the things he tells."

When Mrs. Tiflin answered her tone was so changed that Jody, outside the window, looked up from his study of the stone. Her voice had become soft and explanatory. Jody knew how her face would have changed to match the tone. She said quietly, "Look at it this way, Carl. That was the big thing in my father's life. He led a wagon train clear across the plains to the coast, and when it was finished, his life was done. It was a big thing to do, but it didn't last long enough. Look!" she continued, "it's as though he was born to do that, and after he finished it, there wasn't anything more for him to do but think about it and talk about it. If there'd been any farther west to go, he'd have gone. He's told me so himself. But at last there was the ocean. He lives right by the ocean where he had to stop."

She had caught Carl, caught him and entangled him in her soft tone.

"I've seen him," he agreed quietly. "He goes down and stares off west over the ocean." His voice sharpened a little. "And then he goes up to the Horseshoe Club in Pacific Grove, and he tells people how the Indians drove off the horses."

She tried to catch him again. "Well, it's everything to him. You might be patient with him and pretend to listen."

Carl turned impatiently away. "Well, if it gets too bad, I can always go down to the bunkhouse and sit with Billy," he said irritably. He walked through the house and slammed the front door after him.

Jody ran to his chores. He dumped the grain to the chickens without chasing any of them. He gathered the eggs from the nests. He trotted into the house with the wood and interlaced it so carefully in the woodbox that two armloads seemed to fill it to overflowing.

His mother had finished the beans by now. She stirred up the fire and brushed off the stove-top with a turkey wing. Jody peered cautiously at her to see whether any rancor toward him remained. "Is he coming today?" Jody asked.

"That's what his letter said."

"Maybe I better walk up the road to meet him."

Mrs. Tiflin clanged the stove-lid shut. "That would be nice," she said. "He'd probably like to be met."

"I guess I'll just do it then."

Outside, Jody whistled shrilly to the dogs. "Come on up the hill,"

he commanded. The two dogs waved their tails and ran ahead. Along
the roadside the sage had tender new tips. Jody tore off some pieces and
rubbed them on his hands until the air was filled with the sharp wild
smell. With a rush the dogs leaped from the road and yapped into the
brush after a rabbit. That was the last Jody saw of them, for when they
failed to catch the rabbit, they went back home.

Jody plodded on up the hill toward the ridge top. When he reached
the little cleft where the road came through, the afternoon wind struck
him and blew up his hair and ruffled his shirt. He looked down on the
little hills and ridges below and then out at the huge green Salinas
Valley. He could see the white town of Salinas far out in the flat and
the flash of its windows under the waning sun. Directly below him,
in an oak tree, a crow congress had convened. The tree was black with
crows all cawing at once.

Then Jody's eyes followed the wagon road down from the ridge
where he stood, and lost it behind a hill, and picked it up again on the
other side. On that distant stretch he saw a cart slowly pulled by a bay
horse. It disappeared behind the hill. Jody sat down on the ground and
watched the place where the cart would reappear again. The wind sang
on the hilltops and the puff-ball clouds hurried eastward.

Then the cart came into sight and stopped. A man dressed in black
dismounted from the seat and walked to the horse's head. Although
it was so far away, Jody knew he had unhooked the check-rein, for the
horse's head dropped forward. The horse moved on, and the man
walked slowly up the hill beside it. Jody gave a glad cry and ran
down the road toward them. The squirrels bumped along off the road,
and a road-runner flirted its tail and raced over the edge of the hill
and sailed out like a glider.

Jody tried to leap into the middle of his shadow at every step. A
stone rolled under his foot and he went down. Around a little bend
he raced, and there, a short distance ahead, were his grandfather and
the cart. The boy dropped from his unseemly running and approached
at a dignified walk.

The horse plodded stumble-footedly up the hill and the old man
walked beside it. In the lowering sun their giant shadows flickered
darkly behind them. The grandfather was dressed in a black broadcloth suit and he wore kid congress gaiters and a black tie on a short,

hard collar. He carried his black slouch hat in his hand. His white beard was cropped close and his white eyebrows overhung his eyes like moustaches. The blue eyes were sternly merry. About the whole face and figure there was a granite dignity, so that every motion seemed an impossible thing. Once at rest, it seemed the old man would be stone, would never move again. His steps were slow and certain. Once made, no step could ever be retraced; once headed in a direction, the path would never bend nor the pace increase nor slow.

When Jody appeared around the bend, Grandfather waved his hat slowly in welcome, and he called, "Why, Jody! Come down to meet me, have you?"

Jody sidled near and turned and matched his step to the old man's step and stiffened his body and dragged his heels a little. "Yes, sir," he said. "We got your letter only today."

"Should have been here yesterday," said Grandfather. "It certainly should. How are all the folks?"

"They're fine, sir." He hesitated and then suggested shyly, "Would you like to come on a mouse hunt tomorrow, sir?"

"Mouse hunt, Jody?" Grandfather chuckled. "Have the people of this generation come down to hunting mice? They aren't very strong, the new people, but I hardly thought mice would be game for them."

"No, sir. It's just play. The haystack's gone. I'm going to drive out the mice to the dogs. And you can watch, or even beat the hay a little."

The stern, merry eyes turned down on him. "I see. You don't eat them, then. You haven't come to that yet."

Jody explained, "The dogs eat them, sir. It wouldn't be much like hunting Indians, I guess."

"No, not much—but then later, when the troops were hunting Indians and shooting children and burning teepees, it wasn't much different from your mouse hunt."

They topped the rise and started down into the ranch-cup, and they lost the sun from their shoulders. "You've grown," Grandfather said. "Nearly an inch, I should say."

"More," Jody boasted. "Where they mark me on the door, I'm up more than an inch since Thanksgiving even."

Grandfather's rich throaty voice said, "Maybe you're getting too

much water and turning to pith and stalk. Wait until you head out,
and then we'll see."

Jody looked quickly into the old man's face to see whether his
feelings should be hurt, but there was no will to injure, no punishing
nor putting-in-your-place light in the keen blue eyes. "We might kill
a pig," Jody suggested.

"Oh, no! I couldn't let you do that. You're just humoring me. It
isn't the time and you know it."

"You know Riley, the big boar, sir?"

"Yes, I remember Riley well."

"Well, Riley ate a hole into that same haystack, and it fell down on
him and smothered him."

"Pigs do that when they can," said Grandfather.

"Riley was a nice pig, for a boar, sir. I rode him sometimes, and he
didn't mind."

A door slammed at the house below them, and they saw Jody's
mother standing on the porch waving her apron in welcome. And
they saw Carl Tiflin walking up from the barn to be at the house
for the arrival.

The sun had disappeared from the hills by now. The blue smoke
from the house chimney hung in flat layers in the purpling ranch-cup.
The puff-ball clouds, dropped by the falling wind, hung listlessly in
the sky.

Billy Buck came out of the bunkhouse and flung a wash basin of
soapy water on the ground. He had been shaving in mid-week, for
Billy held Grandfather in reverence, and Grandfather said that Billy
was one of the few men of the new generation who had not gone soft.
Although Billy was in middle age, Grandfather considered him a boy.
Now Billy was hurrying toward the house too.

When Jody and Grandfather arrived, the three were waiting for
them in front of the yard gate.

Carl said, "Hello, sir. We've been looking for you."

Mrs. Tiflin kissed Grandfather on the side of his beard, and stood
still while his big hand patted her shoulder. Billy shook hands solemnly
grinning under his straw mustache. "I'll put up your horse," said
Billy, and he led the rig away.

Grandfather watched him go, and then, turning back to the group, he said as he had said a hundred times before. "There's a good boy. I knew his father, old Mule-tail Buck. I never knew why they called him Mule-tail except he packed mules."

Mrs. Tiflin turned and led the way into the house. "How long are you going to stay, Father? Your letter didn't say."

"Well, I don't know. I thought I'd stay about two weeks. But I never stay as long as I think I'm going to."

In a short while they were sitting at the white oilcloth table eating their supper. The lamp with the tin reflector hung over the table. Outside the dining-room windows the big moths battered softly against the glass.

Grandfather cut his steak into tiny pieces and chewed slowly. "I'm hungry," he said. "Driving out here got my appetite up. It's like when we were crossing. We all got so hungry every night we could hardly wait to let the meat get done. I could eat about five pounds of buffalo meat every night."

"It's moving around does it," said Billy. "My father was a government packer. I helped him when I was a kid. Just the two of us could about clean up a deer's ham."

"I knew your father, Billy," said Grandfather. "A fine man he was. They called him Mule-tail Buck. I don't know why except he packed mules."

"That was it," Billy agreed. "He packed mules."

Grandfather put down his knife and fork and looked around the table. "I remember one time we ran out of meat—" His voice dropped to a curious low sing-song, dropped into a tonal groove the story had worn for itself. "There was no buffalo, no antelope, not even rabbits. The hunters couldn't even shoot a coyote. That was the time for the leader to be on the watch. I was the leader, and I kept my eyes open. Know why? Well, just the minute the people began to get hungry they'd start slaughtering the team oxen. Do you believe that? I've heard of parties that just ate up their draft cattle. Started from the middle and worked toward the ends. Finally they'd eat the lead pair, and then the wheelers. The leader of a party had to keep them from doing that."

In some manner a big moth got into the room and circled the hanging kerosene lamp. Billy got up and tried to clap it between his hands.

Carl struck with a cupped palm and caught the moth and broke it. He walked to the window and dropped it out.

"As I was saying," Grandfather began again, but Carl interrupted him. "You'd better eat some more meat. All the rest of us are ready for our pudding."

Jody saw a flash of anger in his mother's eyes. Grandfather picked up his knife and fork. "I'm pretty hungry, all right," he said. "I'll tell you about that later."

When supper was over, when the family and Billy Buck sat in front of the fireplace in the other room, Jody anxiously watched Grandfather. He saw the signs he knew. The bearded head leaned forward; the eyes lost their sternness and looked wonderingly into the fire; the big lean fingers laced themselves on the black knees. "I wonder," he began, "I just wonder whether I ever told you how those thieving Piutes drove off thirty-five of our horses."

"I think you did," Carl interrupted. "Wasn't it just before you went up into the Tahoe country?"

Grandfather turned quickly toward his son-in-law. "That's right. I guess I must have told you that story."

"Lots of times," Carl said cruelly, and he avoided his wife's eyes. But he felt the angry eyes on him, and he said, " 'Course I'd like to hear it again."

Grandfather looked back at the fire. His fingers unlaced and laced again. Jody knew how he felt, how his insides were collapsed and empty. Hadn't Jody been called a Big-Britches that very afternoon? He arose to heroism and opened himself to the term Big-Britches again. "Tell about Indians," he said softly.

Grandfather's eyes grew stern again. "Boys always want to hear about Indians. It was a job for men, but boys want to hear about it. Well, let's see. Did I ever tell you how I wanted each wagon to carry a long iron plate?"

Everyone but Jody remained silent. Jody said, "No. You didn't."

"Well, when the Indians attacked, we always put the wagons in a circle and fought from between the wheels. I thought that if every wagon carried a long plate with rifle holes, the men could stand the plates on the outside of the wheels when the wagons were in the circle and they would be protected. It would save lives and that would make up for the extra weight of the iron. But of course the party wouldn't do it. No party had done it before and they couldn't see why they should go to the expense. They lived to regret it, too."

Jody looked at his mother, and knew from her expression that she was not listening at all. Carl picked at a callus on his thumb and Billy Buck watched a spider crawling up the wall.

Grandfather's tone dropped into its narrative groove again. Jody knew in advance exactly what words would fall. The story droned on, speeded up for the attack, grew sad over the wounds, struck a dirge at the burials on the great plains. Jody sat quietly watching Grandfather. The stern blue eyes were detached. He looked as though he were not very interested in the story himself.

When it was finished, when the pause had been politely respected at the frontier of the story, Billy Buck stood up and stretched and hitched his trousers. "I guess I'll turn in," he said. Then he faced Grandfather. "I've got an old powder horn and a cap and ball pistol down to the bunkhouse. Did I ever show them to you?"

Grandfather nodded slowly. "Yes, I think you did, Billy. Reminds me of a pistol I had when I was leading the people across." Billy stood politely until the little story was done, and then he said, "Good night," and went out of the house.

Carl Tiflin tried to turn the conversation then. "How's the country between here and Monterey? I've heard it's pretty dry."

"It is dry," said Grandfather. "There's not a drop of water in the Laguna Seca. But it's a long pull from '87. The whole country was powder then, and in '61 I believe all the coyotes starved to death. We had fifteen inches of rain this year."

"Yes, but it all came too early. We could do with some now." Carl's eye fell on Jody. "Hadn't you better be getting to bed?"

Jody stood up obediently. "Can I kill the mice in the old haystack, sir?"

"Mice? Oh! Sure, kill them all off. Billy said there isn't any good hay left."

Jody exchanged a secret and satisfying look with Grandfather. "I'll kill every one tomorrow," he promised.

Jody lay in his bed and thought of the impossible world of Indians and buffaloes, a world that had ceased to be forever. He wished he could have been living in the heroic time, but he knew he was not of heroic timber. No one living now, save possibly Billy Buck, was worthy to do the things that had been done. A race of giants had lived then, fearless men, men of a staunchness unknown in this day. Jody thought of the wide plains and of the wagons moving across like centipedes. He thought of Grandfather on a huge white horse, marshaling the people. Across his mind marched the great phantoms, and they marched off the earth and they were gone.

He came back to the ranch for a moment, then. He heard the dull rushing sound that space and silence make. He heard one of the dogs, out in the doghouse, scratching a flea and bumping his elbow against the floor with every stroke. Then the wind arose again and the black cypress groaned and Jody went to sleep.

He was up half an hour before the triangle sounded for breakfast. His mother was rattling the stove to make the flames roar when Jody went through the kitchen. "You're up early," she said. "Where are you going?"

"Out to get a good stick. We're going to kill the mice today."

"Who is 'we'?"

"Why, Grandfather and I."

"So you've got him in it. You always like to have someone in with you in case there's blame to share."

"I'll be right back," said Jody. "I just wanted to have a good stick ready for after breakfast."

He closed the screen door after him and went out into the cool blue morning. The birds were noisy in the dawn and the ranch cats came down from the hill like blunt snakes. They had been hunting gophers in the dark, and although the four cats were full of gopher meat, they sat in a semi-circle at the back door and mewed piteously for milk. Doubletree Mutt and Smasher moved sniffing along the edge of the brush, performing the duty with rigid ceremony, but when Jody whistled, their heads jerked up and their tails waved. They plunged down to him, wriggling their skins and yawning. Jody patted their heads seriously, and moved on to the weathered scrap pile. He selected an old broom handle and a short piece of inch-square scrap wood. From his pocket he took a shoelace and tied the ends of the sticks loosely together to make a flail. He whistled his new weapon through the air and struck the ground experimentally, while the dogs leaped aside and whined with apprehension.

Jody turned and started down past the house toward the old hay-stack ground to look over the field of slaughter, but Billy Buck, sitting patiently on the back steps, called to him, "You better come back. It's only a couple of minutes till breakfast."

Jody changed his course and moved toward the house. He leaned his flail against the steps. "That's to drive the mice out," he said. "I'll bet they're fat. I'll bet they don't know what's going to happen to them today."

"No, nor you either," Billy remarked philosophically, "nor me, nor anyone."

Jody was staggered by this thought. He knew it was true. His imagination twitched away from the mouse hunt. Then his mother came out on the back porch and struck the triangle, and all thoughts fell in a heap.

Grandfather hadn't appeared at the table when they sat down. Billy nodded at his empty chair. "He's all right? He isn't sick?"

"He takes a long time to dress," said Mrs. Tiflin. "He combs his whiskers and rubs up his shoes and brushes his clothes."

Carl scattered sugar on his mush. "A man that's led a wagon train across the plains has got to be pretty careful how he dresses."

Mrs. Tiflin turned to him. "Don't do that, Carl! Please don't!" There was more of threat than of request in her tone. And the threat irritated Carl.

"Well, how many times do I have to listen to the story of the iron plates, and the thirty-five horses? That time's done. Why can't he forget it, now it's done?" He grew angrier while he talked, and his voice rose. "Why does he have to tell them over and over? He came across the plains. All right! Now it's finished. Nobody wants to hear about it over and over."

The door into the kitchen closed softly. The four at the table sat frozen. Carl laid his mush spoon on the table and touched his chin with his fingers.

Then the kitchen door opened and Grandfather walked in. His mouth smiled tightly and his eyes were squinted. "Good morning," he said, and he sat down and looked at his mush dish.

Carl could not leave it there. "Did—did you hear what I said?"

Grandfather jerked a little nod.

"I don't know what got into me, sir. I didn't mean it. I was just being funny."

Jody glanced in shame at his mother, and he saw that she was looking at Carl, and that she wasn't breathing. It was an awful thing that he was doing. He was tearing himself to pieces to talk like that. It was a terrible thing to him to retract a word, but to retract it in shame was infinitely worse.

Grandfather looked sidewise. "I'm trying to get right side up," he said gently. "I'm not being mad. I don't mind what you said, but it might be true, and I would mind that."

"It isn't true," said Carl. "I'm not feeling well this morning. I'm sorry I said it."

"Don't be sorry, Carl. An old man doesn't see things sometimes. Maybe you're right. The crossing is finished. Maybe it should be forgotten, now it's done."

Carl got up from the table. "I've had enough to eat. I'm going to work. Take your time, Billy!" He walked quickly out of the dining-room. Billy gulped the rest of his food and followed soon after. But Jody could not leave his chair.

"Won't you tell any more stories?" Jody asked.

"Why, sure I'll tell them, but only when—I'm sure people want to hear them."

"I like to hear them, sir."

"Oh! Of course you do, but you're a little boy. It was a job for men, but only little boys like to hear about it."

Jody got up from his place. "I'll wait outside for you, sir. I've got a good stick for those mice."

He waited by the gate until the old man came out on the porch. "Let's go down and kill the mice now," Jody called.

"I think I'll just sit in the sun, Jody. You go kill the mice."

"You can use my stick if you like."

"No, I'll just sit here a while."

Jody turned disconsolately away, and walked down toward the old haystack. He tried to whip up his enthusiasm with thoughts of the fat juicy mice. He beat the ground with his flail. The dogs coaxed and whined about him, but he could not go. Back at the house he could see Grandfather sitting on the porch, looking small and thin and black.

Jody gave up and went to sit on the steps at the old man's feet.

"Back already? Did you kill the mice?"

"No, sir. I'll kill them some other day."

The morning flies buzzed close to the ground and the ants dashed about in front of the steps. The heavy smell of sage slipped down the hill. The porch boards grew warm in the sunshine.

Jody hardly knew when Grandfather started to talk. "I shouldn't stay here, feeling the way I do." He examined his strong old hands. "I feel as though the crossing wasn't worth doing." His eyes moved up the side-hill and stopped on a motionless hawk perched on a dead limb. "I tell those old stories, but they're not what I want to tell. I only know how I want people to feel when I tell them.

"It wasn't Indians that were important, nor adventures, nor even getting out here. It was a whole bunch of people made into one big crawling beast. And I was the head. It was westering and westering. Every man wanted something for himself, but the big beast that was all of them wanted only westering. I was the leader, but if I hadn't been there, someone else would have been the head. The thing had to have a head.

"Under the little bushes the shadows were black at white noonday. When we saw the mountains at last, we cried—all of us. But it wasn't getting here that mattered, it was movement and westering.

"We carried life out here and set it down the way those ants carry eggs. And I was the leader. The westering was as big as God, and the slow steps that made the movement piled up and piled up until the continent was crossed.

"Then we came down to the sea, and it was done." He stopped and wiped his eyes until the rims were red. "That's what I should be telling instead of stories."

When Jody spoke, Grandfather started and looked down at him. "Maybe I could lead the people some day," Jody said.

The old man smiled. "There's no place to go. There's the ocean to stop you. There's a line of old men along the shore hating the ocean because it stopped them."

"In boats I might, sir."

"No place to go, Jody. Every place is taken. But that's not the worst —no, not the worst. Westering has died out of the people. Westering isn't a hunger any more. It's all done. Your father is right. It is finished." He laced his fingers on his knee and looked at them.

Jody felt very sad. "If you'd like a glass of lemonade I could make it for you."

Grandfather was about to refuse, and then he saw Jody's face. "That would be nice," he said. "Yes, it would be nice to drink a lemonade."

Jody ran into the kitchen where his mother was wiping the last of the breakfast dishes. "Can I have a lemon to make a lemonade for Grandfather?"

His mother mimicked— "And another lemon to make a lemonade for you."

"No, ma'am. I don't want one."

"Jody! You're sick!" Then she stopped suddenly. "Take a lemon out of the cooler," she said softly. "Here, I'll reach the squeezer down to you."

HENRY L. MENCKEN Why he

selected The DAYS of the GIANTS

After earnest prayer, I come to the conclusion that it would spoil "The Days of the Giants" if I attempted to do a foreword to it, however small. The thing is self-contained as it stands. It tells its story as well as I'll ever be able to tell it.

Baltimore, Md.   H. L. MENCKEN

June 26, 1942

NOT infrequently I am asked by young college folk, sometimes male and sometimes female, whether there has been any significant change, in my time, in the bacchanalian virtuosity of the American people. They always expect me, of course, to say that boozing is now at an all-time high, for they are a proud generation, and have been brought up to believe that Prohibition brought in refinements unparalleled on earth since the fall of Babylon. But when I speak for that thesis it is only to please them, for I know very well that the facts run the other way. My actual belief is that Americans reached the peak of their alcoholic puissance in the closing years of the last century. Along about 1903 there was a sudden and marked letting up—partly due, I suppose, to the accelerating pace and hazard of life in a civilization growing more and more mechanized, but also partly to be blamed on the lugubrious warning of the medical men, who were then first learning how to reinforce their hocus-pocus with the alarms of the uplift.

In my early days as a reporter they had no more sense of civic responsibility than so many stockbrokers or policemen. A doctor of any standing not only had nothing to say against the use of stimulants; he was himself, nine times out of ten, a steady patron of them, and argued openly that they sustained him in his arduous and irregular life. Dr. Z. K. Wiley, our family practitioner, always took a snifter with my father when he dropped in to dose my brother Charlie and me with castor oil, and whenever, by some unusual accident of his heavy practise, he had any free time afterward, he and my father gave it over to quiet wrestling with the decanters. His favorite prescription for a cold was rock-and-rye, and he believed and taught that a shot of Maryland whiskey was the best preventive of pneumonia in the R months. If you object here that Dr. Wiley was a Southerner, then I answer at once that Dr. Oliver Wendell Holmes was a Yankee of the Yankees, and yet held exactly the same views. Every schoolboy, I suppose, has heard by this time of Dr. Holmes's famous address before the Massachusetts Medical Society on May 30, 1860, in which he argued that "if the whole materia medica, as now used, could be sunk to the bottom of the sea, it would be all the better for mankind—and all the worse for the fishes"; but what the pedagogues always fail to tell their poor dupes is that he made a categorical exception of wine, which he ranked with opium, quinine, anesthetics and mercury among the sovereign and invaluable boons to humanity.

I was thus greatly surprised when I first heard a medical man talk to the contrary. This was in the Winter of 1899-1900, and the place was a saloon near a messy downtown fire. I was helping my betters to cover the fire, and followed them into the saloon for a prophylactic drink. The doctor, who was a fire department surgeon, thereupon made a speech arguing that alcohol was not a stimulant but a depressant, and advising us to keep off it until the fire was out and we were relaxing in preparation for bed. "You think it warms you," he said, sipping a hot milk, "but it really cools you, and you are seventeen point eight per cent more likely to catch pneumonia at the present minute than you were when you came into this doggery." This heresy naturally outraged the older reporters, and they became so prejudiced against the doctor that they induced the Fire Board, shortly afterward, to can him—as I recall it, by reporting that he was always drunk on duty. But his words made a deep impression on my innocence, and continue to lurk in my mind to this day. In consequence, I am what may be called a somewhat cagey drinker. That is to say, I never touch the stuff by daylight if I can help it, and I employ it of an evening, not to hooch up my faculties, but to let them down after work. Not in years have I ever written anything with so much as a glass of beer in my system. My compositions, I gather, sometimes seem boozy to the nobility and gentry, but they are actually done as soberly as those of William Dean Howells.

But this craven policy is not general among the literati, nor was it to be noted among the journalists of my apprentice days. Between 1899 and 1904 there was only one reporter south of the Mason & Dixon Line who did not drink at all, and he was considered insane. In New York, so far as I could make out, there was not even one. On my first Christmas Eve on the *Herald* but two sober persons were to be found in the office—one of them a Seventh Day Adventist office-boy in the editorial rooms, and the other a superannuated stereotyper who sold lunches to the printers in the composing-room. There was a printer on the payroll who was reputed to be a teetotaler—indeed his singularity gave him the nickname of the Moral Element—but Christmas Eve happened to be his night off. All the rest were full of what they called hand-set whiskey. This powerful drug was sold in a saloon next door to the *Herald* office, and was reputed to be made in the cellar by the proprietor in person—of wood alcohol, snuff, tabasco sauce, and coffin varnish. The printers liked it, and got down a great many shots of it. On the Christmas Eve I speak of its effects were such that more than half the linotype machines in the composing-room broke down, and one of the apprentices ran his shirt-tail through the proof-press. Down in the press-room four or five pressmen got hurt, and the city edition was nearly an hour late.

Nobody cared, for the head of the whole establishment, the revered managing editor, Colonel Cunningham, was locked up in his office with a case of Bourbon. At irregular intervals he would throw a wad of copy-paper over the partition which separated him from the editorial writers, and when this wad was smoothed out it always turned out to be part of an interminable editorial against General Felix Agnus, editor of the *American*. The General was a hero of the Civil War, with so much lead in his system that he was said to rattle as he walked, but Colonel Cunningham always hooted at his war record, and was fond of alleging—without any ground whatsoever—that he had come to America from his native France in the pussy-like character of a barber. The editorial that he was writing that Christmas Eve was headed, in fact, "The Barber of Seville." It never got into the paper, for it was running beyond three columns by press-time, and the night editor, Isidor Goodman, killed it for fear that its point was still to come. When the Colonel inquired about it two or three days afterward he was told that a truck had upset in the composing-room, and pied it.

The hero of the *Herald* composing-room in those days was a fat printer named Bill, who was reputed to be the champion beer-drinker of the Western Hemisphere. Bill was a first-rate linotype operator, and never resorted to his avocation in working-hours, but the instant his time was up he would hustle on his coat and go to a beer-house in the neighborhood, and there give what he called a setting. He made no charge for admission, but the spectators, of course, were supposed to pay for the beer. One night in 1902 I saw him get down thirty-two bottles in a row. Perhaps, in your wanderings, you have seen the same—but have you ever heard of a champion who could do it *without once retiring from his place at the bar*? Well, that is what Bill did, and on another occasion, when I was not present, he reached forty. Physiologists tell me that these prodigies must have been optical delusions, for there is not room enough in the coils and recesses of man for so much liquid, but I can only reply *Pfui* to that, for a record is a record. Bill avoided the door marked "Gents" as diligently as if he had been a débutante of the era, or the sign on it had been "For Ladies Only." He would have been humiliated beyond endurance if anyone had ever seen him sling through it.

In the year 1904, when the *Herald* office was destroyed in the great Baltimore fire, and we had to print the paper, for five weeks, in Philadelphia, I was told off to find accommodation for the printers. I found it in one of those old-fashioned $1-a-day hotels that were all bar on the first floor. The proprietor, a German with goat whiskers, was somewhat reluctant to come to terms, for he had heard that printers were wild fellows who might be expected to break up his furniture and work their wicked will upon his chambermaids, but when I told him that a beer-champion was among them he showed a more friendly interest, and when I began to brag about Bill's extraordinary talents his doubts disappeared and he proposed amiably that some Philadelphia foam-jumpers be invited in to make it a race. The first heat was run the very next night, and Bill won hands down. In fact, he won so easily that he offered grandly to go until he had drunk *twice* as much as the next best entry. We restrained him and got him to bed, for there had been some ominous whispering among the other starters, and it was plain that they were planning to call in help. The next night it appeared in the shape of a tall, knotty man from Allentown, Pa., who was introduced as the champion of the Lehigh Valley. He claimed to be not only a beer-drinker of high gifts, but also a member of the Bach Choir at Bethlehem; and when he got down his first dozen mugs—the boys were drinking from the wood—he cut loose with an exultant yodel that he said was one of Bach's forgotten minor works. But he might very well have saved his wind, for Bill soon had him, and at the end of the setting he was four or five mugs behind, and in a state resembling suffocation. The next afternoon I saw his disconsolate fans taking him home, a sadder and much less melodious man.

On the first two nights there had been only slim galleries, but on the third the bar was jammed, and anyone could see that something desperate was afoot. It turned out to be the introduction of two superchampions, the one a short, saturnine Welshman from Wilkes-Barré, and the other a hearty blond young fellow from one of the Philadelphia suburbs, who said that he was half German and half Irish. The Welshman was introduced as the man who had twice drunk Otto the Brewery Horse under the table, and we were supposed to know who Otto was, though we didn't. The mongrel had a committee with him, and the chairman thereof offered to lay $25 on him at even money. The printers in Bill's corner made up the money at once, and their stake had grown to $50 in forty minutes by the clock, for the hybrid took only that long to blow up. The Welshman lasted much better, and there were some uneasy moments when he seemed destined to make history again by adding Bill to Otto, but in the end he succumbed so suddenly that it seemed like a bang, and his friends laid him out on the floor and began fanning him with bar-towels.

Bill was very cocky after that, and talked grandiosely of taking on two champions at a time, in marathon series. There were no takers for several nights, but after that they began to filter in from the remoter wilds of the Pennsylvania Dutch country, and the whole *Herald* staff was kept busy guarding Bill by day, to make sure that he did not waste any of his libido for malt liquor in the afternoons. He knocked off twenty or thirty challengers during the ensuing weeks, including two more Welshmen from the hard-coal country, a Scotsman with an ear missing, and a bearded Dunkard from Lancaster county. They were mainly pushovers, but now and then there was a tough one. Bill did not let this heavy going interfere with the practise of his profession. He set type every night from 6 p.m. to midnight in the office of the *Evening Telegraph*, where we were printing the *Herald*, and never began his combats until 12.30. By two o'clock he was commonly in bed, with another wreath of laurels hanging on the gas-jet.

To ease your suspense I'll tell you at once that he was never beaten. Germans, Irishmen, Welshmen and Scotsmen went down before him like so many Sunday-school superintendents, and he bowled over everyday Americans with such facility that only two of them ever lasted more than half an hour. But I should add in candor that he was out of service during the last week of our stay in Philadelphia. What fetched him is still a subject of debate among the pathologists at the Johns Hopkins Medical School, to whom the facts were presented officially on our return to Baltimore. The only visible symptom was a complete loss of speech. Bill showed up one night talking hoarsely, the next night he could manage only whispers, and the third night he was as mute as a shad-fish. There was absolutely no other sign of distress. He was all for going on with his derisive harrying of the Pennsylvania lushers, but a young doctor who hung about the saloon and served as surgeon at the bouts forbade it on unstated medical grounds. The Johns Hopkins experts in morbid anatomy have never been able to agree about the case. Some argue that Bill's potations must have dissolved the gummy coating of his pharyngeal plexus, and thus paralyzed his vocal cords; the rest laugh at this as nonsense savoring of quackery, and lay the whole thing to an intercurrent laryngitis, induced by insufficient bedclothes on very cold nights. I suppose that no one will ever know the truth. Bill recovered his voice in a couple of months, and soon afterward left Baltimore. Of the prodigies, if any, that marked his later career I can't tell you.

He was but one of a notable series of giants who flourished in Baltimore at the turn of the century, bringing the city a friendly publicity and causing the theory to get about that life there must be delightful. They appeared in all the ranks of society. The Maryland Club had its champions, and the cops had theirs. Some were drinkers pure and

simple; others specialized in eating. One of the latter was an old
man of easy means who lived at the Rennert Hotel, then the undisputed
capital of gastronomy in the terrapin and oyster country. But for some
reason that I can't tell you he never did his eating there; instead, he
always took dinner at Tommy McPherson's eating-house, six or eight
blocks away. He would leave the hotel every evening at seven o'clock,
elegantly arrayed in a long-tailed black coat and a white waistcoat, and
carrying a gold-headed cane, and would walk the whole way. Tommy's
place was arranged in two layers, with tables for men only alongside
the bar downstairs, and a series of small rooms upstairs to which ladies
might be invited. The cops, goaded by vice crusaders, had forced him
to take the doors off these rooms, but he had substituted heavy por-
tières, and his colored waiters were instructed to make a noise as they
shuffled down the hall, and to enter every room backward. The old
fellow I speak of, though there were tales about his wild youth, had by
now got beyond thought of sin, and all his eating was done downstairs.
It consisted of the same dishes precisely every night of the week, year
in and year out. First he would throw in three straight whiskeys, and
then he would sit down to *two* double porterhouse steaks, with *two*
large plates of peas, *two* of French fried potatoes, *two* of cole-slaw, and
a mountain of rye-bread. This vast meal he could eat to the last speck,
and not infrequently he called for more potatoes or bread. He washed
it down with two quarts of Burgundy, and at its end threw in three
more straight whiskeys. Then he would light a cigar, and amble back
to the Rennert, to spend the rest of the evening conversing with the
politicoes who made their headquarters in its lobby.

One day a report reached the *Herald* office that he was beginning
to break up, and Max Ways sent me to take a look. He had, by then,
been on his diet for no less than twelve years. When I opened the subject delicately he hooted at the notion that he was not up to par. He
was, he told me, in magnificent health, and expected to live at least
twenty years longer. His excellent condition, he went on to say, was
due to his lifelong abstemiousness. He ate only a sparing breakfast,
and no lunch at all, and he had not been drunk for fifteen years—that
is, in the sense of losing all control of himself. He told me that people
who ate pork dug their graves with their teeth, and praised the Jews
for avoiding it. He also said that he regarded all sea-food as poisonous,
on the ground that it contained too much phosphorus, and that fowl

was almost as bad. There was, in his view, only one perfectly safe and wholesome victual, and that was beef. It had everything. It was nourishing, palatable and salubrious. The last bite tasted as good as the first. Even the bones had a pleasant flavor. He ate peas and potatoes with it, he said, mainly to give it some company: if he were ever cast on a desert island he could do without them. The cole-slaw went along as a sort of gesture of politeness to the grass that had produced the beef, and he ate rye-bread instead of wheat because rye was the bone and sinew of Maryland whiskey, the most healthful appetizer yet discovered by man. He would not affront me by presuming to discuss the virtues of Burgundy: they were mentioned in the Bible, and all humanity knew them.

The old boy never made his twenty years, but neither did he ever change his regimen. As the uplift gradually penetrated medicine various doctors of his acquaintance began to warn him that he was headed for a bad end, but he laughed at them in his quiet way, and went on going to Tommy's place every night, and devouring his two double porterhouses. What took him off at last was not his eating, but a trifling accident. He was knocked down by a bicycle in front of the Rennert, developed pneumonia, and was dead in three days. The resurrection men at both the Johns Hopkins and the University of Maryland tried to get his body for autopsy, and were all set to dig out of it a whole series of pathological monstrosities of a moral tendency, but his lawyer forbade any knifeplay until his only heir, a niece, could be consulted, and when she roared in from Eufaula, Ala., it turned out that she was a Christian Scientist, with a hate against anatomy. So he was buried without yielding any lessons for science. If he had any real rival, in those declining years of Baltimore gastronomy, it must have been John Wilson, a cop: I have always regretted that they were never brought together in a match. Once, at a cop party, I saw John eat thirty fried hard crabs at a sitting—no mean feat, I assure you, for though the claws are pulled off a crab before it is fried, all the body-meat remains. More, he not only ate the crabs, but sucked the shells. On another occasion, on a bet, he ate a ham and a cabbage in half an hour by the clock, but I was not present at that performance. When, a little later, he dropped dead in the old Central station-house, the police surgeons laid it to a pulmonary embolus, then a recent novelty in pathology.

STEPHEN LEACOCK

Why he selected **MY REMARKABLE**

UNCLE

I have suggested the selection of this example of my writing because, with all becoming modesty, I am proud of it. It is only after long practice and much interest in the work that one can set down plain truth, without over-embellishment or wandering from the point. When this is done the writing takes on an inevitable aspect, as if there were no other way to say what is said. In other words it looks as easy as Shakespeare. When this is done even the truth itself sounds a little better than true, which is the basis of what is called literature. Any depiction of life as it is, is depressing reading.

Orillia, Canada   STEPHEN LEACOCK

July, 1942

A PERSONAL DOCUMENT

THE most remarkable man I have ever known in my life was my uncle Edward Philip Leacock—known to ever so many people in Winnipeg fifty or sixty years ago as E. P. His character was so exceptional that it needs nothing but plain narration. It was so exaggerated already that you couldn't exaggerate it.

When I was a boy of six, my father brought us, a family flock, to settle on an Ontario farm. We lived in an isolation unknown, in these days of radio, anywhere in the world. We were thirty-five miles from a railway. There were no newspapers. Nobody came and went. There was nowhere to come and go. In the solitude of the dark winter nights the stillness was that of eternity.

. . . .

Into this isolation there broke, two years later, my dynamic Uncle

77

Edward, my father's younger brother. He had just come from a year's travel around the Mediterranean. He must have been about twenty-eight, but seemed a more than adult man, bronzed and self-confident, with a square beard like a Plantagenet King. His talk was of Algiers, of the African slave market; of the Golden Horn and the Pyramids. To us it sounded like the *Arabian Nights*. When we asked, "Uncle Edward, do you know the Prince of Wales?" he answered, "Quite intimately"—with no further explanation. It was an impressive trick he had.

In that year, 1878, there was a general election in Canada. E. P. was in it up to the neck in less than no time. He picked up the history and politics of Upper Canada in a day, and in a week knew everybody in the countryside. He spoke at every meeting, but his strong point was the personal contact of electioneering, of barroom treats. This gave full scope for his marvellous talent for flattery and make-believe.

"Why, let me see"—he would say to some tattered country specimen beside him glass in hand—"surely, if your name is Framley, you must be a relation of my dear old friend General Sir Charles Framley of the Horse Artillery?" "Mebbe," the flattered specimen would answer. "I guess, mebbe; I ain't kept track very good of my folks in the old country." "Dear me! I must tell Sir Charles that I've seen you. He'll be so pleased." . . . In this way in a fortnight E. P. had conferred honours and distinctions on half the township of Georgina. They lived in a re-captured atmosphere of generals, admirals and earls. Vote? How else could they vote than conservative, men of family like them?

It goes without saying that in politics, then and always, E. P. was on the conservative, the *aristocratic* side, but along with that was hail-fellow-well-met with the humblest. This was instinct. A democrat can't condescend. He's down already. But when a conservative stoops, he conquers.

The election, of course, was a walk-over. E. P. might have stayed to reap the fruits. But he knew better. Ontario at that day was too small a horizon. For these were the days of the hard times of Ontario farming, when mortgages fell like snowflakes, and farmers were sold up, or sold out, or went "to the States," or faded humbly underground.

But all the talk was of Manitoba now opening up. Nothing would do E. P. but that he and my father must go west. So we had a sale of our farm, with refreshments, old-time fashion, for the buyers. The poor, lean cattle and the broken machines fetched less than the price of the whisky. But E. P. laughed it all off, quoted that the star of the Empire glittered in the west, and off to the West they went, leaving us children behind at school.

They hit Winnipeg just on the rise of the boom, and E. P. came at once into his own and rode on the crest of the wave. There is something of magic appeal in the rush and movement of a "boom" town— a Winnipeg of the 80's, a Carson City of the 60's. . . . Life comes to a focus; it is all here and now, all *present*, no past and no outside—just a clatter of hammers and saws, rounds of drinks and rolls of money. In such an atmosphere every man seems a remarkable fellow, a man of exception; individuality separates out and character blossoms like a rose.

E. P. came into his own. In less than no time he was in everything and knew everybody, conferring titles and honours up and down Portage Avenue. In six months he had a great fortune, on paper; took a trip east and brought back a charming wife from Toronto; built a large house beside the river; filled it with pictures that he said were his ancestors, and carried on in it a roaring hospitality that never stopped.

His activities were wide. He was president of a bank (that never opened), head of a brewery (for brewing the Red River) and, above all, secretary-treasurer of the Winnipeg Hudson Bay and Arctic Ocean Railway that had a charter authorizing it to build a road to the Arctic Ocean, when it got ready. They had no track, but they printed stationery and passes, and in return E. P. received passes over all North America.

But naturally his main hold was politics. He was elected right away into the Manitoba Legislature. They would have made him Prime Minister but for the existence of the grand old man of the province, John Norquay. But even at that in a very short time Norquay ate out of E. P.'s hand, and E. P. led him on a string. I remember how they came down to Toronto, when I was a schoolboy, with an adherent group of "Westerners," all in heavy buffalo coats and bearded like Assyrians. E. P. paraded them on King Street like a returned explorer with savages.

Naturally E. P.'s politics remained conservative. But he pitched the note higher. Even the ancestors weren't good enough. He invented a Portuguese Dukedom (some one of our family once worked in Portugal)—and he conferred it, by some kind of reversion, on my elder brother Jim who had gone to Winnipeg to work in E. P.'s office. This enabled him to say to visitors in his big house, after looking at the ancestors—to say in a half-whisper behind his hand, "Strange to think that two deaths would make that boy a Portuguese Duke." But Jim never knew which two Portuguese to kill.

To aristocracy E. P. also added a touch of peculiar prestige by always being apparently just about to be called away—imperially. If some one said, "Will you be in Winnipeg all winter, Mr. Leacock?" he answered, "It will depend a good deal on what happens in West Africa." Just that; West Africa beat them.

.   .   .   .

Then came the crash of the Manitoba boom. Simple people, like my father, were wiped out in a day. Not so E. P. The crash just gave him a lift as the smash of a big wave lifts a strong swimmer. He just went right on. I believe that in reality he was left utterly bankrupt. But it made no difference. He used credit instead of cash. He still had his imaginary bank, and his railway to the Arctic Ocean. Hospitality still roared and the tradesmen still paid for it. Any one who called about a bill was told that E. P.'s movements were uncertain and would depend a good deal on what happened in Johannesburg. That held them another six months.

.   .   .   .

It was during this period that I used to see him when he made his periodic trips "east," to impress his creditors in the West. He floated, at first very easily, on hotel credit, borrowed loans and unpaid bills. A banker, especially a country town banker, was his natural mark and victim. He would tremble as E. P. came in, like a stock dove that sees a hawk. E. P.'s method was so simple; it was like showing a farmer peas under thimbles. As he entered the banker's side-office he would say: "I say. Do you fish? Surely that's a greenhart casting-rod on the wall?" (E. P. knew the names of everything.) In a few minutes the banker, flushed and pleased, was exhibiting the rod, and showing flies in a box out of a drawer. When E. P. went out he carried a hundred dollars with him. There was no security. The transaction was all over.

He dealt similarly with credit, with hotels, livery stables and bills in shops. They all fell for his method. He bought with lavish generosity, never asking a price. He never suggested pay till just as an afterthought, just as he was going out. And then: "By the way, please let me have the account promptly. I may be going away," and, in an aside to me, as if not meant for the shop, "Sir Henry Loch has cabled again from West Africa." And so out; they had never seen him before; nor since.

. . . .

The proceeding with a hotel was different. A country hotel was, of course, easy, in fact too easy. E. P. would sometimes pay such a bill in cash, just as a sportsman won't shoot a sitting partridge. But a large hotel was another thing. E. P., on leaving—that is, when all ready to leave, coat, bag, and all—would call for his bill at the desk. At the sight of it he would break out into enthusiasm at the reasonableness of it. "Just think!" he would say in his "aside" to me, "compare that with the Hotel Crillon in Paris!" The hotel proprietor had no way of doing this; he just felt that he ran a cheap hotel. Then another "aside," "Do remind me to mention to Sir John how admirably we've been treated; he's coming here next week." "Sir John" was our Prime Minister and the hotel keeper hadn't known he was coming—and he wasn't. . . . Then came the final touch—"Now, let me see . . . seventy-six dollars . . . seventy-six. . . . You give me"—and E. P. fixed his eye firmly on the hotel man—"give me twenty-four dollars, and then I can remember to send an even hundred." The man's hand trembled. But he gave it.

.   .   .   .   .

This does not mean that E. P. was in any sense a crook, in any degree dishonest. His bills to him were just "deferred pay," like the British debts to the United States. He never did, never contemplated, a crooked deal in his life. All his grand schemes were as open as sunlight—and as empty.

.   .   .   .   .

In all his interviews E. P. could fashion his talk to his audience. On one of his appearances I introduced him to a group of college friends, young men near to degrees, to whom degrees mean everything. In casual conversation E. P. turned to me and said, "Oh, by the way you'll be glad to know that I've just received my honorary degree from the Vatican—at last!" The "at last" was a knock-out—a degree from the Pope, and overdue at that!

.   .   .   .

Of course it could not last. Gradually credit crumbles. Faith weakens. Creditors grow hard, and friends turn their faces away. Gradually E. P. sank down. The death of his wife had left him a widower, a shuffling, half-shabby figure, familiar on the street, that would have been pathetic but for his indomitable self-belief, the illumination of his mind. Even at that, times grew hard with him. At length even the simple credit of the barrooms broke under him. I have been told by my brother Jim—the Portuguese Duke—of E. P. being put out of a Winnipeg bar, by an angry bar-tender who at last broke the mesmerism. E. P. had brought in a little group, spread up the fingers of one hand and said, "Mr. Leacock, five!" . . . The bar-tender broke into oaths. E. P. hooked a friend by the arm. "Come away," he said. "I'm afraid the poor fellow's crazy! But I hate to report him."

.   .   .   .   .

Presently even his power to travel came to an end. The railways found out at last that there wasn't any Arctic Ocean, and anyway the printer wouldn't print.

.   .   .   .

Just once again he managed to "come east." It was in June of 1891. I met him forging along King Street in Toronto—a trifle shabby but with a plug hat with a big band of crape around it. "Poor Sir John," he said. "I felt I simply must come down for his funeral." Then I remembered that the Prime Minister was dead, and realized that kindly sentiment had meant free transportation.

.   .   .   .

That was the last I ever saw of E. P. A little after that some one paid his fare back to England. He received, from some family trust, a little income of perhaps two pounds a week. On that he lived, with such dignity as might be, in a lost village in Worcestershire. He told the people of the village—so I learned later—that his stay was uncertain; it would depend a good deal on what happened in China. But nothing happened in China; there he stayed, years and years. There he might have finished out, but for a strange chance of fortune, a sort of poetic justice, that gave to E. P. an evening in the sunset.

.   .   .   .

It happened that in the part of England where our family belonged there was an ancient religious brotherhood, with a monastery and dilapidated estates that went back for centuries. E. P. descended on them, the brothers seeming to him an easy mark, as brothers indeed are. In the course of his pious "retreat," E. P. took a look into the brothers' finances, and his quick intelligence discovered an old claim against the British Government, large in amount and valid beyond a doubt.

In less than no time E. P. was at Westminster, representing the brothers. He knew exactly how to handle British officials; they were easier even than Ontario hotel keepers. All that is needed is hints of marvellous investment overseas. They never go there but they remember how they just missed Johannesburg or were just late on Persian oil. All E. P. needed was his Arctic Railway. "When you come out, I must take you over our railway. I really think that as soon as we reach the Coppermine River we must put the shares on here; it's too big for New York. . . ."

So E. P. got what he wanted. The British Government are so used to old claims that it would as soon pay as not. There are plenty left.

The brothers got a whole lot of money. In gratitude they invited E. P. to be their permanent manager; so there he was, lifted into ease and affluence. The years went easily by, among gardens, orchards and fishponds old as the Crusades.

When I was lecturing in London in 1921 he wrote to me: "Do come down; I am too old now to travel; but any day you like I will send a chauffeur with a car and two lay-brothers to bring you down." I thought the "lay-brothers" a fine touch—just like E. P.

I couldn't go. I never saw him again. He ended out his days at the monastery, no cable calling him to West Africa. Years ago I used to think of E. P. as a sort of humbug, a source of humour. Looking back now I realize better the unbeatable quality of his spirit, the mark, we like to think just now, of the British race.

If there is a paradise, I am sure he will get in. He will say at the gate—"Peter? Then surely you must be a relation of Lord Peter of Tichfield?"

But if he fails, then, as the Spaniards say so fittingly, "May the earth lie light upon him."

CONRAD AIKEN Why he selected

STRANGE MOONLIGHT

This little story is largely autobiographical, as will be at once obvious to anyone, and that may be one reason why the author has always been fond of it. But there is another reason as well. For I think when a writer makes over, or partly makes over, his experience into a poem or story, he will then tend to forget the experience itself. Somehow, in the act of thus formalizing and externalizing a memory, he has also lost his power to evoke it—it's as if he had put it into cold storage. Thereafter, when he wants to revisit that particular glimpse of the moon, he will find it more accessible, and far vivider, in the artifact than in his own recollection. "Strange Moonlight," thus, for me, constitutes the best memory I can command of a moment in childhood which had for me a very special magic.

Brewster, Mass.   CONRAD AIKEN
June, 1942

I

IT HAD been a tremendous week—colossal. Its reverberations around him hardly yet slept—his slightest motion or thought made a vast symphony of them, like a breeze in a forest of bells. In the first place, he had filched a volume of Poe's tales from his mother's bookcase, and had had in consequence a delirious night in inferno. Down, down he had gone with heavy clangs about him, coiling spouts of fire licking dryly at an iron sky, and a strange companion, of protean shape and size, walking and talking beside him. For the most part, this companion seemed to be nothing but a voice and a wing—an enormous jagged black wing, soft and drooping like a bat's; he had noticed veins in it. As for the voice, it had been singularly gentle. If it was mysterious, that was no doubt because he himself was stupid. Certainly it had sounded placid and reasonable, exactly, in fact, like his father's, ex-

85

plaining a problem in mathematics; but, though he had noticed the orderly and logical structure, and felt the inevitable approach towards a vast and beautiful or terrible conclusion, the nature and meaning of the conclusion itself always escaped him. It was as if, always, he had come just too late. When, for example, he had come at last to the black wall that enclosed the infernal city, and seen the arched gate, the voice had certainly said that if he hurried he would see, through the arch, a far low landscape of extraordinary wonder. He had hurried, but it had been in vain. He had reached the gate, and for the tiniest fraction of an instant he had even glimpsed the wide green of fields and trees, a winding blue ribbon of water, and a gleam of intense light touching to brilliance some far object. But then, before he had time to notice more than that every detail in this fairy landscape seemed to lead towards a single shining solution, a dazzling significance, suddenly the infernal rain, streaked fire and rolling smoke, had swept it away. Then the voice had seemed to become ironic. He had failed, and he felt like crying.

He had still, the next morning, felt that he might, if the opportunity offered, see that vision. It was always just round the corner, just at the head of the stairs, just over the next page. But other adventures had intervened. Prize-day, at school, had come upon him as suddenly as a thunderstorm—the ominous hushed gathering of the entire school into one large room, the tense air of expectancy, the solemn speeches, all had reduced him to a state of acute terror. There was something unintelligible and sinister about it. He had, from first to last, a peculiar physical sensation that something threatened him; and here and there, in the interminable vague speeches, a word seemed to have eyes and to stare at him. His prescience had been correct—abruptly his name had been called, he had walked unsteadily amid applause to the teacher's desk, had received a small black pasteboard box; and then had cowered in his chair again, with the blood in his temples beating like gongs. When it was over, he had literally run away—he didn't stop till he reached the park. There, among the tombstones (the park had once been a graveyard) and trumpet-vines, he sat on the grass and opened the box. He was dazzled. The medal was of gold, and rested on a tiny blue satin cushion. His name was engraved on it—yes, actually cut into the gold; he felt the incisions with his fingernail. It was an experience not wholly to be comprehended. He put the box down in the grass and detached himself from it, lay full length, resting his chin on his wrist, and stared first at a tombstone and then at the small gold object, as if to discover the relation between them. Humming-birds, tomb-stones, trumpet-vines, and a gold medal. Amazing! He unpinned the medal from its cushion, put the box in his pocket, and walked slowly homeward, carrying the small live gleaming thing between fingers and thumb as if it were a bee. This was an experience to be carefully concealed from mother and father. Possibly he would tell Mary and John. . . . Unfortunately, he met his father as he was going in at the door, and was thereafter drowned, for a day, in a glory without sig-nificance. He felt ashamed, and put the medal away in a drawer, sternly forbidding Mary and John to look at it. Even so, he was horribly conscious of it—its presence there burned him unceasingly. Nothing afforded escape from it, not even sitting under the peach-tree and whittling a boat.

II

The oddest thing was the way these and other adventures of the week all seemed to unite, as if they were merely aspects of the same thing. Everywhere lurked that extraordinary hint of the enigma and its shining solution. On Tuesday morning when it was pouring with rain, and he and Mary and John were conducting gigantic military operations in the back hall, with hundreds of paper soldiers, tents, cannon, battleships and forts, suddenly through the tall open window, a goldfinch flew in from the rain, beat wildly against a pane of glass, darted several times to and fro above their heads, and finally, finding the open window, flashed out. It flew to the peach-tree, rested there for a moment, and then over the outhouse and away. He saw it rising and falling in the rain. This was beautiful—it was like the vision in the infernal city, like the medal in the grass. He found it impossible to go on with the Battle of Gettysburg and abandoned it to Mary and John, who instantly started to quarrel. Escape was necessary, and he went into his own room, shut the door, lay on his bed and began thinking about Caroline Lee.

John Lee had taken him there to see his new air-gun and a bag of

BB shot. The strange house was dim and exciting. A long winding dark staircase went up from near the front door, a clock was striking in a far room, a small beautiful statue of a lady, slightly pinkish, and looking as if it had been dug out of the earth, stood on a table. The wall-paper beside the staircase was rough and hairy. Upstairs, in the play-room, they found Caroline sitting on the floor with a picture-book. She was learning to read, pointing at the words with her finger. He was struck by the fact that, although she was extraordinarily strange and beautiful, John Lee did not seem to be aware of it and treated her as if she were quite an ordinary sort of person. This gave him courage, and after the air-gun had been examined, and the bag of BB shot emptied of its gleaming heavy contents and then luxuriously refilled, he told her some of the words she couldn't make out. "And what's this?" she had said—he could still hear her say it, quite clearly. She was thin, smaller than himself, with dark hair and large pale eyes, and her forehead and hands looked curiously transparent. He particularly noticed her hands when she brought her five-dollar gold-piece to show him, opening a little jewel-box which had in it also a necklace of yellow beads from Egypt and a pink shell from Tybee Beach. She gave him the gold-piece to look at, and while he was looking at it, put the beads round her neck. "Now I'm an Egyptian!" she said, and laughed shyly, running her fingers to and fro over the smooth beads. A fearful temptation came upon him. He coveted the gold-piece, and thought that it would be easy to steal it. He shut his hand over it and it was gone. If it had beeen John's, he might have done so but, as it was, he opened his hand again and put the gold-piece back in the box. Afterwards, he stayed for a long while, talking with John and Caroline. The house was mysterious and rich, and he hadn't at all wanted to go out of it, or back to his own humdrum existence. Besides, he liked to hear Caroline talking.

But although he had afterwards for many days wanted to go back to that house, to explore further its dim rich mysteriousness, and had thought about it a great deal, John hadn't again suggested a visit, and he himself had felt a curious reluctance about raising the subject. It had been, apparently, a vision that was not to be repeated, an incursion into a world that was so beautiful and strange that one was permitted of it only the briefest of glimpses. He had almost to reassure himself that the house was really there; and for that reason he made rather a point of walking home from school with John Lee. Yes, the house was there—he saw John climb the stone steps and open the huge green door. There was never a sign of Caroline, however, nor any mention of her: until one day he heard from another boy that she was ill with scarlet fever, and observed that John had stayed away from school. The news didn't startle or frighten him. On the contrary, it seemed just the sort of romantic privilege in which such fortunate people would indulge. He felt a certain delicacy about approaching the house, however, to see if the red quarantine sign had been affixed by the door, and carefully avoided Gordon Square on his way home from school. Should he write her a letter? or send her a present of marbles? For neither action did there seem to be sufficient warrant. But he found it impossible to do nothing, and later in the afternoon, by a very circuitous route which took him past the county jail—where he was thrilled by actually seeing a prisoner looking out between the grey iron bars—he slowly made his way to Gordon Square and from a safe distance, more or less hiding himself behind a palmetto tree, looked for a long while at the wonderful house and saw, sure enough, the red sign.

Three days later he heard that Caroline Lee was dead. The news stunned him. Surely it could not be possible? He felt stifled, frightened and incredulous. In a way, it was just what one would expect of Caroline; but none the less he felt outraged. How was it possible for anyone, whom one actually *knew*, to *die*? Particularly anyone so vividly and beautifully remembered! The indignity, the horror of death, obsessed him. *Had* she actually died? He went again to Gordon Square, not knowing precisely what it was that he expected to find, and saw something white hanging by the green door. But if, as it appeared, it was true that Caroline Lee, somewhere inside the house, lay dead, lay motionless, how did it happen that he, who was so profoundly concerned, had not at all been consulted, had not been invited to come and talk with her, and now found himself so utterly and hopelessly and for ever excluded—from the house, as from her? This was a thing which he could not understand. As he walked home, pondering it, he thought of the five-dollar gold-piece. What would become of it? Probably John would get it and, if so, he would steal it from him. . . . All the same, he was glad he hadn't taken it.

To this reflection he came back many times, as now once more with
the Battle of Gettysburg raging in the next room. If he had actually
taken it, what a horror it would have been! As it was, the fact that he
had resisted the temptation, restored the gold-piece to the box, seemed
to have been a tribute to Caroline's beauty and strangeness. Yes, for
nobody else would he have made the refusal—nobody on earth. But,
for her, it had been quite simple, a momentary pang quickly lost in the
pleasure of hearing her voice, watching her pale hands twisting the
yellow beads, and helping her with her reading. "And what's this?"
she had said, and "Now I'm an Egyptian!" . . . What was death that
could put an end to a clear voice saying such things? . . . Mystery
was once more about him, the same mystery that had shone in the
vision of the infernal city. There was something beautiful which he
could not understand. He had felt it while he was lying in the grass
among the tombstones, looking at the medal; he had felt it when the
goldfinch darted in from the rain and then out again. All these things
seemed in some curious way to fit together.

III

The same night, after he had gone to bed, this feeling of enormous
and complicated mystery came upon him again with oppressive weight.
He lay still, looking from his pillow through the tall window at the
moonlight on the white out-house wall, and again it seemed to him
that the explanation for everything was extraordinarily near at hand if
he only could find it. The mystery was like the finest of films, like the
moonlight on the white wall. Surely, beneath it, there was something
solid and simple? He heard someone walk across the yard, with steps
that seemed astoundingly far apart and slow. The steps ceased, a door
creaked. Then there was a cough. It was old Selena, the negro cook,
going out for wood. He heard the sticks being piled up, then the creak
of the door again, and again the slow steps on the hard-baked ground
of the yard, æons apart. How did the peach tree look in the moonlight?
Would its leaves be dark, or shiny? And the chinaberry tree? He
thought of the two trees standing there motionless in the moonlight,
and at last felt that he must get out of bed and look at them. But when
ne had reached the hall, he heard his mother's voice from downstairs,

and he went and lay on the old sofa in the hall, listening. Could he have heard aright? His mother had just called his father "boy!"

"But two parties in a week, Tom—surely that's not excessive?"

"It's two parties *every* week, and sometimes three or four, that's excessive. You know it is."

"Darling, I *must* have *some* recreation!"

His father laughed in a peculiar angry way that he had never heard before—as strange, indeed, as his mother's tone had been.

"Recreation's all right," he said, "but you're neglecting your family. If it goes on, I'll have another child—that's all."

He got off the sofa and went softly down the stairs to the turn of the railing. He peered over the banisters with infinite caution, and what he saw filled him with horror. His mother was sitting on his father's knee, with her arms about his neck. She was kissing him. How awful! . . . He couldn't look at it. What on earth, he wondered as he climbed back into bed, was it all about? There was something curious in the way they were talking, something not at all like fathers and mothers, but more like children, though he couldn't in the least under-stand it. At the same time, it was offensive.

He began to make up a conversation with Caroline Lee. She was sitting under the peach-tree with him, reading her book. What beauti-ful hands she had! They were transparent, somehow, like her forehead, and her dark hair and large pale eyes delighted him. Perhaps she *was* an Egyptian!

"It must be nice to live in your house," he said.

"Yes, it's very nice. And you haven't seen half of it, either."

"No, I haven't. I'd like to see it all. I liked the hairy wall-paper and the pink statue of the lady on the table. Are there any others like it?"

"Oh, yes, lots and lots! In the secret room downstairs, where you heard the silver clock striking, there are fifty other statues, all more beautiful than that one, and a collection of clocks of every kind."

"Is your father very rich?"

"Yes, he's richer than anybody. He has a special carved ivory box to keep his collars in."

"What does it feel like to die—were you sorry?"

"Very sorry! But it's really quite easy—you just hold your breath and shut your eyes."

"Oh!"

"And when you're lying there, after you've died, you're really just pretending. You keep very still, and you have your eyes *almost* shut, but really you know everything! You watch the people and listen to them."

"But don't you want to talk to them, or get out of bed, or out of your coffin?"

"Well, yes, at first you do—but it's nicer than being alive."

"Why?"

"Oh, I don't know! You understand everything so easily!"

"How nice that must be!"

"It is."

"But after they've shut you up in a coffin and sung songs over you and carried you to Bonaventure and buried you in the ground, and you're down there in the dark with all that earth above you—isn't that horrible?"

"Oh, no! . . . As soon as nobody is looking, when they've all gone home to tea, you just get up and walk away. You climb out of the earth just as easily as you'd climb out of bed."

"That's how you're here now, I suppose."

"Of course!"

"Well, it's very nice."

"It's lovely. . . . Don't I look just as well as ever?"

"Yes, you do."

There was a pause, and then Caroline said:

"I knew you wanted to steal my gold-piece—I was awfully glad when you put it back. If you had asked me for it, I'd have given it to you."

"I like you very much, Caroline. Can I come to Bonaventure and play with you?"

"I'm afraid not. You'd have to come in the dark."

"But I could bring a lantern!"

"Yes, you could do that."

. . . It seemed to him that they were no longer sitting under the peach tree, but walking along the white shell road to Bonaventure. He held the lantern up beside a chinquapin tree, and Caroline reached up with her pale small hands and picked two chinquapins. Then they crossed the little bridge, walking carefully between the rails on the sleepers. Mossy trees were all about them; the moss, in long festoons, hung lower and lower, and thicker and thicker, and the wind made a soft seething sound as it sought a way through the grey ancient forest.

IV

It had been his intention to explore, the next morning, the vault under the mulberry tree in the park—his friend Harry had mentioned that it was open, and that one could go down very dusty steps and see, on the dark floor, a few rotted boards and a bone or two. At breakfast he enlisted Mary and John for the expedition: but then there were unexpected developments. His father and mother had abruptly decided that the whole family would spend the day at Tybee Beach. This was festive and magnificent beyond belief. The kitchen became a turmoil. Selena ran to and fro with sugar-sandwiches, pots of devilled ham, cookies, hard-boiled eggs and a hundred other things; piles of beautiful sandwiches were exquisitely folded up in shining clean napkins; and the wicker basket was elaborately packed. John and Mary decided to take their pails with them, and stamped up and down stairs, banging the pails with tin shovels. He himself was a little uncertain what to take. He stood by his desk, wondering. He would like to take Poe's tales, but that was out of the question, for he wasn't supposed to have the book at all. Marbles, also, were dismissed as unsuitable. He finally took his gold medal out of its drawer and put it in his pocket. He would keep it a secret, of course.

All the way to the station he was conscious of the medal burning in his pocket. He closed his fingers over it, and again felt it to be a live thing, as if it were buzzing, beating invisible wings. Would his fingers have a waxy smell, as they did after they'd been holding a June-bug, or tying a thread to one of its legs? . . . Father carried the basket, Mary and John clanked their pails, everybody was talking and laughing. They climbed into the funny, undignified little train, which almost immediately was lurching over the wide green marshes, rattling over red iron bridges enormously complicated with girders and trusses. Great excitement when they passed the grey stone fort. Fort Pulaski. They'd seen it once from the river, when they were on the steamer

going to the cotton islands. His father leaned down beside Mary to tell
her about Fort Pulaski, just as a cloud-shadow, crossing it, made it
sombre. How nice his father's smile was! He had never noticed it
before. It made him feel warm and shy. He looked out at the interminable green marshes, the flying clouds of rice-birds, the channels of
red water lined with red mud, and listened intently to the strange
complex rhythm of the wheels on the rails and the prolonged melancholy wail of the whistle. How curious it all was! His mother was
sitting opposite him, very quiet, her grey eyes turned absently toward
the window. She wasn't looking at things—she was thinking. If she
had been looking at things her eyes would have moved to and fro, as
Mary's were doing.

"Mother," he said, "did you bring our bathing-suits?"

"Yes, dear."

The train was rounding a curve and slowing down. They had
suddenly left the marshes and were among low sand-dunes covered
with tall grass. He saw a man, very red-faced, just staggering over the
top of one of the dunes and waving a stick. . . . It was hot. They filed
slowly off the train and one by one jumped down into the burning
sand. How strange it was to walk in! They laughed and shrieked,
feeling themselves helpless, ran and jumped, straddled up the steep
root-laced sides of dunes and slid down again in slow warm avalanches
of lazy sand. Mother and father, picking their way between the dunes,
walked slowly ahead, carrying the basket between them—his father
pointed at something. The sunlight came down heavily like sheets
of solid brass and they could feel the heat of the sand on their cheeks.
Then at last they came out on to the enormous white dazzling beach
with its millions of shells, its black and white striped lighthouse, and
the long, long sea, indolently blue, spreading out slow soft lines of
foam, and making an interminable rushing murmur like trees in a
wind.

He felt instantly a desire, in all this space and light, to run for
miles and miles. His mother and father sat under a striped parasol.
Mary and John, now barefooted, had begun laborious and intense
operations in the sand at the water's edge, making occasional sallies
into the sliding water. He began walking away along the beach close
to the waves, keeping his eye out for any particularly beautiful shell,

and taking great care not to step on jelly-fish. Suppose a school of flying-fish, such as he had seen from the ship, should swim in close to the beach and then, by mistake, fly straight up onto the sand! How delightful that would be! It would be almost as exciting as finding buried treasure, a rotten chest full of gold-pieces and seaweed and sand. He had often dreamt of thrusting his hand into such a sea-chest and feeling the small hard beautiful coins mixed with sand and weed. Some said that Captain Kidd had buried treasure on Tybee Beach. Perhaps he'd better walk a little closer to the dunes, where it was certainly more likely that treasure would have been hidden. . . . He climbed a hot dune, taking hold of the feathery grass, scraping his bare legs on the coarse leaves, and filling his shoes with warm sand. The dune was scooped at the top like a volcano, the hollow all ringed with tall whistling grass, a natural hiding-place, snug and secret. He lay down, made exquisitely smooth a hand's breadth of sand, then took the medal out of his pocket and placed it there. It blazed beautifully. Was it as nice as the five-dollar gold-piece would have been? He liked especially the tiny links of the little gold chains by which the shield hung from the pin-bar. If only Caroline could see it! Perhaps if he stayed here, hidden from the family, and waited till they had gone back home, Caroline would somehow know where he was and come to him as soon as it was dark. He wasn't quite sure what would be the shortest way from Bonaventure, but Caroline would know—certainly. Then they would spend the night here, talking. He would exchange his medal for the five-dollar gold-piece, and perhaps she would bring, folded in a square of silk, the little pink statue. . . . Thus equipped, their house would be perfect. . . . He would tell her about the goldfinch interrupting the Battle of Gettysburg.

v

The chief event of the afternoon was the burial of his father, who had on his bathing-suit. He and Mary and John all excitedly laboured at this. When they had got one leg covered, the other would suddenly burst hairily out, or an arm would shatter its mould, and his father would laugh uproariously. Finally they had him wholly buried, all except his head, in a beautiful smooth mound. On top of this they put the two pails, a lot of pink shells in a row, like the buttons of a coat, and a collection of seaweed. Mother, lying under her parasol, laughed lazily, deliciously. For the first time during the day she seemed to be really happy. She began pelting small shells at father, laughing in an odd delightful teasing way, as if she were a girl; and father pretended to be furious. How exactly like a new grave he looked! It was singularly as Caroline had described it, for there he was all alive in it, and talking, and able to get up whenever he liked. Mary and John, seeing mother throw shells, and hearing her teasing laughter, and father's comic rage, became suddenly excited. They began throwing things wildly—shells, handfuls of seaweed, and at last sand. At this, father suddenly leapt out of his tomb, terrifying them, scattered his grave-clothes in every direction, and galloped gloriously down the beach into the sea. The upturned brown soles of his feet followed him casually into a long curling green wave, and then his head came up shaking like a dog's and blowing water, and his strong white arms flashed slowly over and over in the sunlight as he swam far out. How magnificent! . . . He would like to be able to do that, to swim out and out and out, with a sea-gull flying close beside him, talking.

Later, when they had changed into their clothes again in the salty-smelling wooden bath-house, they had supper on the verandah of the huge hotel. A band played, the coloured waiters bowed and grinned. The sky turned pink, and began to dim; the sea darkened, making a far sorrowful sound; and twilight deepened slowly, slowly into night. The moon, which had looked like a white thin shell in the afternoon, turned now to the brightest silver, and he thought, as they walked silently towards the train, of which they could see the long row of yellow windows, that the beach and dunes looked more beautiful by moonlight than by sunlight. . . . How mysterious the flooded marshes looked, too, with the cold moon above them! They reminded him of something, he couldn't remember what. . . . Mary and John fell asleep in the train, his father and mother were silent. Someone in the car ahead was playing a concertina, and the plaintive sound mingled curiously with the clacking of the rails, the rattle of bridges, the long lugubrious cry of the whistle. *Hoo-o! Hoo-oo!* Where was it they were going—was it to anything so simple as home, the familiar house, the two familiar trees, or were they, rather, speeding like a fiery comet toward the world's edge, to plunge out into the unknown and fall down and down for ever?

No, certainly it was not to the familiar. . . . Everything was changed and ghostly. The long street, in the moonlight, was like a deep river, at the bottom of which they walked, making scattered thin sounds on the stones, and listening intently to the whisperings of elms and palmettoes. And their house, when at last they stopped before it, how strange it was! The moonlight falling through the two tall swaying live-oaks, cast a moving pattern of shadow and light all over its face. Slow swirls and spirals of black and silver, dizzy gallops, quiet pools of light abruptly shattered, all silently followed the swishing of leaves against the moon. It was like a vine of moonlight, which suddenly grew all over the house, smothering everything with its multitudinous swift leaves and tendrils of pale silver, and then as suddenly fading out. He stared up at this while his father fitted the key into the lock, feeling the ghostly vine grow strangely over his face and hands. Was it in this, at last, that he would find the explanation of all that bewildered him? Caroline, no doubt, would understand it, she was a sort of moonlight herself. He went slowly up the stairs. But as he took the medal and a small pink shell out of his pocket, and put them on his desk, he realized, at last, that Caroline was dead.

MORLEY CALLAGHAN

Why he selected   TWO FISHERMEN

When I wrote this story, I found I was liking the material because there was a certain grim contrast between the nice human and warm relationship of the young fellow and the hangman and the actual vocation of the hangman. Also I liked the hangman's rather wistful attachment to his despised job and his realization that it gave him an opportunity to get around the country and enjoy himself as a human being and a fisherman. And then after I had written it I saw that it had a certain social implication that I liked. The hangman, a necessary figure in society, a man definitely serving the public and the ends of justice, was entitled to a little human dignity. In fact he saw himself as a dignified human being. But of course as an instrument of justice he became a despised person, and even his young friend, who understood his wistful humanity, betrayed that humanity when the chips were down. If I had started out to write the story with that in mind it might have become very involved but I wrote it very easily and naturally and without any trouble at all. At the time I wrote it, I let the editor of *Esquire*, who published it, know that I thought it was one of my best stories. He was very dubious about it. I find looking back on it that the story seems to stand up well and I was right in my judgment of it.

Toronto, Canada   MORLEY CALLAGHAN
August 9, 1942

T HE only reporter on the town paper, the *Examiner*, was Michael
    Foster, a tall, long-legged, eager young fellow, who wanted to
go to the city some day and work on an important newspaper.

The morning he went into Bagley's hotel, he wasn't at all sure of himself. He went over to the desk and whispered to the proprietor, Ted Bagley, "Did he come here, Mr. Bagley?"

Bagley said slowly, "Two men came here from this morning's train. They registered." He put his spatulate forefinger on the open book and said, "Two men. One of them's a drummer. This one here, T. Woodley. I know because he was through this way last year and just a minute ago he walked across the road to Molson's hardware store. The other one . . . here's his name, K. Smith."

"Who's K. Smith?" Michael asked.

"I don't know. A mild, harmless looking little guy."

"Did he look like the hangman, Mr. Bagley?"

"I couldn't say that, seeing as I never saw one. He was awfully polite and asked where he could get a boat so he could go fishing on the lake this evening, so I said likely down at Smollet's place by the power house."

"Well, thanks. I guess if he was the hangman, he'd go over to the jail first," Michael said.

He went along the street, past the Baptist church to the old jail with the high brick fence around it. Two tall maple trees, with branches drooping low over the sidewalk, shaded one of the walls from the morning sunlight. Last night, behind those walls, three carpenters, working by lamplight, had nailed the timbers for the scaffold. In the morning, young Thomas Delaney, who had grown up in the town, was being hanged: he had killed old Mathew Rhinehart whom he had caught molesting his wife when she had been berrypicking in the hills behind the town. There had been a struggle and Thomas Delaney had taken a bad beating before he had killed Rhinehart. Last night a crowd had gathered on the sidewalk by the lamp post, and while moths and smaller insects swarmed around the high blue carbon light, the crowd had thrown sticks and bottles and small stones at the out of town workmen in the jail yard. Billy Hilton, the town constable, had stood under the light with his head down, pretending not to notice anything. Thomas Delaney was only three years older than Michael Foster.

Michael went straight to the jail office, where Henry Steadman, the sheriff, a squat, heavy man, was sitting on the desk idly wetting his long black mustaches with his tongue. "Hello, Michael, what do you want?" he asked.

"Hello, Mr. Steadman, the *Examiner* would like to know if the hangman arrived yet."

"Why ask me?"

"I thought he'd come here to test the gallows. Won't he?"

"My, you're a smart young fellow, Michael, thinking of that."

"Is he in there now, Mr. Steadman?"

"Don't ask me. I'm saying nothing. Say, Michael, do you think there's going to be trouble? You ought to know. Does anybody seem sore at me? I can't do nothing. You can see that."

"I don't think anybody blames you, Mr. Steadman. Look here, can't I see the hangman? Is his name K. Smith?"

"What does it matter to you, Michael? Be a sport, go on away and don't bother us any more."

"All right, Mr. Steadman," Michael said very competently, "just leave it to me."

Early that evening, when the sun was setting, Michael Foster walked south of the town on the dusty road leading to the power house and Smollet's fishing pier. He knew that if Mr. K. Smith wanted to get a boat he would go down to the pier. Fine powdered road dust whitened Michael's shoes. Ahead of him he saw the power plant, square and low, and the smooth lake water. Behind him the sun was hanging over the blue hills beyond the town and shining brilliantly on square patches of farm land. The air around the power house smelt of steam.

Out on the jutting, tumbledown pier of rock and logs, Michael saw a little fellow without a hat, sitting down with his knees hunched up to his chin, a very small man with little gray baby curls on the back of his neck, who stared steadily far out over the water. In his hand he was holding a stick with a heavy fishing line twined around it and a gleaming copper spoon bait, the hooks brightened with bits of feathers such as they used in the neighborhood when trolling for lake trout. Apprehensively Michael walked out over the rocks toward the stranger and called, "Were you thinking of going fishing, mister?" Standing up, the man smiled. He had a large head, tapering down to a small chin, a birdlike neck and a very wistful smile. Puckering his mouth up, he said shyly to Michael, "Did you intend to go fishing?"

"That's what I came down here for. I was going to get a boat back at the boat house there. How would you like if we went together?"

"I'd like it first rate," the shy little man said eagerly. "We could take turns rowing. Does that appeal to you?"

"Fine. Fine. You wait here and I'll go back to Smollet's place and ask for a row boat and I'll row around here and get you."

"Thanks. Thanks very much," the mild little man said as he began to untie his line. He seemed very enthusiastic.

When Michael brought the boat around to the end of the old pier and invited the stranger to make himself comfortable so he could handle the line, the stranger protested comically that he ought to be allowed to row.

Pulling strongly at the oars, Michael was soon out in the deep water and the little man was letting his line out slowly. In one furtive glance, he had noticed that the man's hair, gray at the temples, was inclined to curl to his ears. The line was out full length. It was twisted around the little man's forefinger, which he let drag in the water. And then Michael looked full at him and smiled because he thought he seemed so meek and quizzical. "He's a nice little guy," Michael assured himself and he said, "I work on the town paper, the *Examiner*."

"It is a good paper. Do you like the work?"

"Yes. But it's nothing like a first class city paper and I don't expect to be working on it long. I want to get a reporter's job on a city paper. My name's Michael Foster."

"Mine's Smith. Just call me Smitty."

"I was wondering if you'd been over to the jail yet."

Up to this time the little man had been smiling with the charming ease of a small boy who finds himself free, but now he became furtive and disappointed. Hesitating, he said, "Yes, I was over at the jail. I didn't think you knew. I tested the trap. I went there first thing this morning."

"Oh, 1 just knew you'd go there," Michael said. They were a bit afraid of each other. By this time they were far out on the water which had a millpond smoothness. The town seemed to get smaller, with white houses in rows and streets forming geometric patterns, just as the blue hills behind the town seemed to get larger at sundown.

Finally Michael said, "Do you know this Thomas Delaney that's dying in the morning?" He knew his voice was slow and resentful.

"No. I don't know anything about him. I never read about them. Aren't there any fish at all in this old lake? I'd like to catch some fish," he said rapidly. "I told my wife I'd bring her home some fish." Glancing at Michael, he was appealing, without speaking, that they should do nothing to spoil an evening's fishing.

The little man began to talk eagerly about fishing as he pulled out a small flask from his hip pocket. "Scotch," he said, chuckling with delight. "Here, take a swig." Michael drank from the flask and passed it back. Tilting his head back and saying "Here's to you, Michael," the little man took a long pull at the flask. "The only time I take a drink," he said still chuckling, "is when I go on a fishing trip by myself. I usually go by myself," he added apologetically as if he wanted the young fellow to see how much he appreciated his company.

They had gone far out on the water but they had caught nothing. It began to get dark. "No fish tonight, I guess, Smitty," Michael said.

"It's a crying shame," Smitty said. "I looked forward to coming up here when I found out the place was on the lake. I wanted to get some fishing in. I promised my wife I'd bring her back some fish. She'd often like to go fishing with me, but of course, she can't because she can't travel around from place to place like I do. Whenever I get a call to go some place, I always look at the map to see if it's by a lake or on a river, then I take my lines and hooks along."

"If you took another job, you and your wife could probably go fishing together," Michael suggested.

"I don't know about that. We sometimes go fishing together anyway." He looked away, waiting for Michael to be repelled and insist that he ought to give up the job. And he wasn't ashamed as he looked down at the water, but he knew that Michael thought he ought to be ashamed. "Somebody's got to do my job. There's got to be a hangman," he said.

"I just meant that if it was such disagreeable work, Smitty."

The little man did not answer for a long time. Michael rowed steadily with sweeping, tireless strokes. Huddled at the end of the boat,

Smitty suddenly looked up with a kind of melancholy hopelessness and said mildly, "The job hasn't been so disagreeable."

"Good God, man, you don't mean you like it?"

"Oh, no," he said, to be obliging, as if he knew what Michael expected him to say. "I mean you get used to it, that's all." But he looked down again at the water, knowing he ought to be ashamed of himself.

"Have you got any children?"

"I sure have. Five. The oldest boy is fourteen. It's funny, but they're all a lot bigger and taller than I am. Isn't that funny?"

They started a conversation about fishing rivers that ran into the lake farther north. They felt friendly again. The little man, who had an extraordinary gift for story telling, made many quaint faces, puckered up his lips, screwed up his eyes and moved around restlessly as if he wanted to get up in the boat and stride around for the sake of more expression. Again he brought out the whiskey flask and Michael stopped rowing. Grinning, they toasted each other and said together, "Happy days." The boat remained motionless on the placid water. Far out, the sun's last rays gleamed on the water line. And then it got dark and they could only see the town lights. It was time to turn around and pull for the shore. The little man tried to take the oars from Michael, who shook his head resolutely and insisted that he would prefer to have his friend catch a fish on the way back to the shore.

"It's too late now, and we may have scared all the fish away," Smitty laughed happily. "But we're having a grand time, aren't we?"

When they reached the old pier by the power house, it was full night and they hadn't caught a single fish. As the boat bumped against the rocks Michael said, "You can get out here. I'll take the boat around to Smollet's."

"Won't you be coming my way?"

"Not just now. I'll probably talk with Smollet a while."

The little man got out of the boat and stood on the pier looking down at Michael. "I was thinking dawn would be the best time to catch some fish," he said. "At about five o'clock. I'll have an hour and a half to spare anyway. How would you like that?" He was speaking with so much eagerness that Michael found himself saying, "I could try. But if I'm not here at dawn, you go on without me."

"All right. I'll walk back to the hotel now."

"Good night, Smitty."

"Good night, Michael. We had a fine neighborly time, didn't we?"

As Michael rowed the boat around to the boat house, he hoped that Smitty wouldn't realize he didn't want to be seen walking back to town with him. And later, when he was going slowly along the dusty road in the dark and hearing all the crickets chirping in the ditches, he couldn't figure out why he felt so ashamed of himself.

At seven o'clock next morning Thomas Delaney was hanged in the town jail yard. There was hardly a breeze on that leaden gray morning and there were no small whitecaps out over the lake. It would have been a fine morning for fishing. Michael went down to the jail, for he thought it his duty as a newspaperman to have all the facts, but he was afraid he might get sick. He hardly spoke to all the men and women who were crowded under the maple trees by the jail wall. Everybody he knew was staring at the wall and muttering angrily. Two of Thomas Delaney's brothers, big, strapping fellows with bearded faces, were there on the sidewalk. Three automobiles were at the front of the jail.

Michael, the town newspaperman, was admitted into the courtyard by old Willie Mathews, one of the guards, who said that two newspapermen from the city were at the gallows on the other side of the building. "I guess you can go around there, too, if you want to," Mathews said, as he sat down slowly on the step. White-faced, and afraid, Michael sat down on the step with Mathews and they waited and said nothing.

At last the old fellow said, "Those people outside there are pretty sore, ain't they?"

"They're pretty sullen, all right. I saw two of Delaney's brothers there."

"I wish they'd go," Mathews said. "I don't want to see anything. I didn't even look at Delaney. I don't want to hear anything. I'm sick." He put his head back against the wall and closed his eyes.

The old fellow and Michael sat close together till a small procession came around the corner from the other side of the yard. First came Mr. Steadman, the sheriff, with his head down as though he were crying, then Dr. Parker, the physician, then two hard-looking young newspapermen from the city, walking with their hats on the backs of their heads, and behind them came the little hangman, erect, stepping out with military precision and carrying himself with a strange cocky dignity. He was dressed in a long black cutaway coat with gray striped trousers, a gates ajar collar and a narrow red tie, as if he alone felt the formal importance of the occasion. He walked with brusque precision till he saw Michael, who was standing up, staring at him with his mouth open.

The little hangman grinned and as soon as the procession reached the door step, he shook hands with Michael. They were all looking at Michael. As though his work were over now, the hangman said eagerly to Michael, "I thought I'd see you here. You didn't get down to the pier at dawn?"

"No. I couldn't make it."

"That was tough, Michael. I looked for you," he said. "But never mind. I've got something for you." As they all went into the jail, Dr. Parker glanced angrily at Michael, then turned his back on him. In the office, where the doctor prepared to sign a certificate, Smitty was bending down over his fishing basket which was in the corner. Then he pulled out two good-sized salmon-bellied lake trout, folded in a newspaper, and said, "I was saving these for you, Michael. I got four in an hour's fishing." Then he said, "I'll talk about that later, if you'll wait. We'll be busy here, and I've got to change my clothes."

Michael went out to the street with Dr. Parker and the two city newspapermen. Under his arm he was carrying the fish, folded in the newspaper. Outside, at the jail door, Michael thought that the doctor and the two newspapermen were standing a little apart from him. Then the small crowd, with their clothes all dust-soiled from the road, surged forward, and the doctor said to them, "You might as well go home, boys. It's all over."

"Where's old Steadman?" somebody called.

"We'll wait for the hangman," somebody else shouted.

The doctor walked away by himself. For a while Michael stood beside the two city newspapermen, and tried to look as nonchalant as they were looking, but he lost confidence in them when he smelled whiskey. They only talked to each other. Then they mingled with the crowd, and Michael stood alone. At last he could stand there no longer

looking at all those people he knew so well, so he, too, moved out
and joined the crowd.

When the sheriff came out with the hangman and two of the
guards, they got half way down to one of the automobiles before someone threw an old boot. Steadman ducked into one of the cars, as the
boot hit him on the shoulder, and the two guards followed him. The
hangman, dismayed, stood alone on the sidewalk. Those in the car
must have thought at first that the hangman was with them for the
car suddenly shot forward, leaving him alone on the sidewalk. The
crowd threw small rocks and sticks, hooting at him as the automobile
backed up slowly towards him. One small stone hit him on the head.
Blood trickled from the side of his head as he looked around helplessly at all the angry people. He had the same expression on his face,
Michael thought, as he had had last night when he had seemed
ashamed and had looked down steadily at the water. Once now, he
looked around wildly, looking for someone to help him as the crowd
kept pelting him. Farther and farther Michael backed into the crowd
and all the time he felt dreadfully ashamed as though he were betraying Smitty, who last night had had such a good neighborly time with
him. "It's different now, it's different," he kept thinking, as he held
the fish in the newspaper tight under his arm. Smitty started to run
toward the automobile, but James Mortimer, a big fisherman, shot out
his foot and tripped him and sent him sprawling on his face.

Mortimer, the big fisherman, looking for something to throw, said
to Michael, "Sock him, sock him."

Michael shook his head and felt sick.

"What's the matter with you, Michael?"

"Nothing. I got nothing against him."

The big fisherman started pounding his fists up and down in the
air. "He just doesn't mean anything to me at all," Michael said quickly.
The fisherman, bending down, kicked a small rock loose from the
road bed and heaved it at the hangman. Then he said, "What are you
holding there, Michael, what's under your arm? Fish. Pitch them at
him. Here, give them to me." Still in a fury, he snatched the fish, and
threw them one at a time at the little man just as he was getting up
from the road. The fish fell in the thick dust in front of him, sending
up a little cloud. Smitty seemed to stare at the fish with his mouth

hanging open, then he didn't even look at the crowd. That expression on Smitty's face as he saw the fish on the road made Michael hot with shame and he tried to get out of the crowd.

Smitty had his hands over his head, to shield his face as the crowd pelted him, yelling "Sock the little rat. Throw the runt in the lake." The sheriff pulled him into the automobile. The car shot forward in a cloud of dust.

GEORGE ADE

Why he selected The JOY of SINGLE

 BLESSEDNESS

I selected "The Joy of Single Blessedness" to appear in your anthology because I thought it was rather entertaining and also because it told the truth about bachelors and married men. I tried to avoid sparing either one of them. I tried to be absolutely neutral. I read the article to a Woman's Club in Miami last year and most of it was received in grim silence. I certainly laid an egg. They could not take what I said about the married people or about the women who are captivated by bachelors. I find that bachelors who read the article resent some of the things I say about them. It is often dangerous to tell the truth. However, I still stand by my guns. You may print the article in the anthology and I am sure that many people of both sexes and in all stations of life will be pleased with what I have written.
Brook, Ind.   GEORGE ADE
June 16, 1942

THE bachelor is held up to contempt because he has evaded the draft. He is a slacker. He has side-stepped a plain duty. If he lives in a small town he is fifty per cent joke and fifty per cent object of pity. If he lives in a city, he can hide away with others of his kind, and find courage in numbers; but even in the crowded metropolis he has the hunted look of one who knows that the world knows something about him. He is led to believe that babies mistrust him. Young wives begin to warn their husbands when his name is mentioned. He is a chicken hawk in a world that was intended for turtle doves. It is always taken for granted that the bachelor *could* have married. Of course, he might not have netted the one he wanted first off. It is possible that, later on, circumstances denied him the privileges of

108

selection. *But* it is always assumed by critics of the selfish tribe, that any bachelor who has enough money in the bank to furnish a home, can, if he is persistent, hound some woman into taking a chance.

Undoubtedly the critics are right. When we review the vast army of variegated males who have achieved matrimony, it seems useless to deny that the trick can be turned by any man who is physically capable of standing up in front of a preacher or whose mental equipment enables him to decide that he should go into the house when it rains.

If Brigham Young, wearing throat whiskers, could assemble between thirty-five and forty at one time, how pitiful becomes the alibi of the modern maverick that he has never managed to arrive at any sort of arrangement with a solitary one!

We know that women will accept men who wear arctic overshoes. Statistics prove that ninety-eight per cent of all those you see on station platforms, wearing "elastics" on their shirt-sleeves, have wives at home.

The whole defense of bachelorhood falls to the ground when confronted by the evidence which any one may accumulate while walking through a residence district. He will see dozens of porch-broken husbands who never would have progressed to the married state if all the necessary processes had not been elementary to begin with, and further simplified by custom.

Even after he is convinced, he will stubbornly contend as follows: "Possibly I am a coward, but I refuse to admit that all these other birds are heroes."

At least, he will be ready to confess that any one can get married at any time, provided the party of the second part is no more fastidious and choosey than he is.

These facts being generally accepted, the presumption of guilt attaches to every single man beyond the age of thirty. And if, as the years ripen, he garners many dollars, and keeps them in a hiding place which is woman-proof, he slowly slumps in public opinion until he becomes classified with those granite-faced criminals who loot orphan asylums or steal candlesticks from an altar.

Finally he arrives at a state of ostracized isolation. He has every inducement to be utterly miserable, and probably would be so, except for frequent conversations with married men.

At this point we get very near to the weakest point in the general indictment against bachelors: Is it generally known that bachelors privately receive encouragement and approbation from married men?

Not from all married men, it is true. Not, for instance, from the husband of a woman who happens to read these lines. But they *do* receive assurances from married men, of the more undeserving varieties, that matrimony is not always a long promenade through a rose bower drenched with sunshine. The word "lucky" is frequently applied to them by the associate poker players who are happily married.

The difficulty in rescuing the hardened cases of bachelorhood is that the unregenerate are all the time receiving private signals from those supposed to be saved, to lay off and beat it, and escape while the escaping is good. Many of them would have fallen long ago except for these warnings.

There are times when the most confirmed, cynical, and self-centred celibate, influenced by untoward circumstances and unfavourable atmospheric conditions, believes that he could be rapturously content as a married man, and that he is cheating some good woman out of her destiny. Conversely, the Darby who wants the world to know that his Joan is a jewel and his children are intellectual prodigies and perfect physical specimens—even this paragon, who would shudder at mention of a divorce court, tells his most masonic friends that it must be great to have your freedom and to do as you darn please.

No matter which fork of the road you take, you will wonder, later on, if the scenery on the other route isn't more attractive.

The bachelor, being merely a representative unit of weak mankind, isn't essentially different from the Benedict. Probably at some time or other he wanted to get married and couldn't. Whereas, the married one didn't want to get married and was mesmerized into it by a combination of full moon, guitar music, and roly-boly eyes.

A poor wretch who had lived under the stigma of bachelorhood for years once confided to several of us that he was ready to be married at Columbus, Ohio, in 1892, and then learned that it would cost at least eight dollars to put the thing over.

Bachelors are willing to be segregated or even separately taxed, but they don't wish to be branded with too hot an iron. They come to regard themselves as potential married men who never received notice of their inheritances. Married men are merely bachelors who weakened under the strain. Every time a bachelor sees a man with an alpaca coat pushing a perambulator, he says, "There, but for the grace of God, goes me!"

Whatever excuses the bachelor may secrete in his own mind, the following definite counts have been drawn against him:

1st. It is the duty of every good man to become the founder of a home, because the home (and not the stag boarding-house) is the cornerstone of an orderly civilization.

2d. It is the duty of every high-minded citizen to approve publicly the sacrament of marriage, because legalized matrimony is the harbour of safety. When the bachelor ignores the sacrament, his example becomes an endorsement of the advantages offered to travellers by that famous old highway known as "The Primrose Path."

3d. It is the duty of every student of history and economics to help perpetuate the species and protect the birth rate.

These are the damning accusations. Any representative woman's club, anywhere, would bring in a verdict of "guilty" against a notorious bachelor, in two minutes, without listening to witnesses.

The moment a man marries, the indictment is quashed. For the time being, he is snow white. A little later, after the divorce proceedings, he may become speckled, but he never sinks quite back to the degraded estate of bachelorhood.

He tried to be a good citizen.

Having an altruistic and almost Chautauquan regard for home and the marriage sacrament, and feeling that *someone* had to step forward and save the birth rate, he put aside all considerations of personal convenience and, like a sun-kissed hero, stepped to the edge and jumped over the precipice.

Yes, he did! You know he did!

Here is what happened:

The dear old goof found himself in immediate juxtaposition to The Most Wonderful Woman in All the World. When she smiled at him, his blood pressure went up twenty points. When she appeared to forget that he was among those present, he wanted to rush into the street and lie down in front of a taxicab. He hovered near her, every night, until ordered out. Then he reeled back to his den, stepping from one cloud to another. He sat up in the still hours of the morning to write notes which elected him even if, later on, he had wanted to welch. He arrived at his office without remembering what had happened since he left home. He tried to dictate letters, and nothing came from him except gurgles. He wondered what was happening to Her. In the telephone booth—only about eight cubic feet of air—partial asphyxiation after twenty minutes. But who wouldn't be willing to die, with the sound of that Voice strumming in the ears, like an Æolian harp hanging in the gateway of Paradise?

Now, when Waldo finally got married, does any one really insist that he did it because he was prompted by a sense of his duty to provide food and lodging for a member of the opposite sex?

Did he calmly decide to give his endorsement to the sacrament of marriage and to help protect the birth rate?

Did he?

Lay the bride's curse on the bachelor, if you will, and let his name become a byword and hissing at every bridge party, but don't hang any medals on Waldo until you have all the facts in his case—which will prove to be a carbon copy of a million other cases.

Waldo got married because he needed sleep. It was a toss-up between Sweeties and a sanitarium, and he selected the easier way.

He could not picture an existence which did not include the radio-magnetic presence of Honey. He was governed by sex impulse and not by what he had read in books on sociology.

Not until weeks later, emerging from the honeymoon trance, did he discover that he had honorably discharged his obligations to Society and had become a member of the Matrimonial Legion of Honour.

What happened to Waldo might have happened to any petrified hermit now hiding at a club. And if Waldo, on a certain occasion, had happened to meet merely Another Flapper, instead of The Most Wonderful Woman in the World, he might now be camped at a hotel instead of being assistant manager of a nursery.

We are all wisps, and the winds of chance blow in many directions.

Just because a man gets married is no sign that he has a high and holy and abiding regard for womanhood. Visit any court room and hear the sufferer go into details: He threw a meat platter at her—squeezed her arm until it was black and blue—tore the feathers off her new hat—kicked the Pomeranian into the fireplace—made her sleep on the lounge, etc., etc., etc.

It isn't usually a lack of intense regard and reverence for womanhood that keeps the bachelor single. Often enough, it is a lack of regard for himself as a fit companion for the goddess up there above him on the pedestal.

One of the most highly despised bachelors I ever knew once said that if he ever asked a woman to marry him and she said, "Yes," he'd begin to have his suspicions of her. And yet he was supposed to be a woman-hater!

The rooming-houses are packed with mature single men, each of whom looks up to Class A women with such worshipful adoration that he never has felt worthy of possessing one of the angelic creatures.

Charley Fresh—who regards himself as the irresistible captivator—googles his way among the girls for six nights a week and is known as a "lady's man." The marooned and isolated males who watch his performance refuse to enter into any contest which features Charley Fresh as a formidable rival. If he is what the women want, they cannot qualify. They accept the inevitable, and decide that by habit and circumstances they are debarred from the matrimonial raffle, and they might as well make the best of it. They know that they lack the peacock qualities of the heartbreaker, as they have studied him in Robert W. Chambers and the movies. They never could live up to the specifications. Not one of them wants to compromise by grabbing a third-rater. They want a topnotcher, or nothing; and they haven't the financial rating, the parlour training, the glib vocabulary, the baby-blue eyes, the curly hair and the athletic shoulders to make them real mates for the distant Dianas of their day dreams.

Some are restrained by caution, some by diffidence, and some are put out of the running by Fate.

Is it not true that the bachelor uncle is always a hot favourite with the children? And doesn't he often tell Minnie, his brother's wife, that he would give a thousand shares of Steel Common if he could have one of his own? Of course, if he had one he wouldn't know what to do with it; but it just shows that the parental instinct can often be aroused by a good home-cooked dinner.

This defense of bachelors is getting to be pretty wobbly; but it still has a few guns in reserve. For instance, if the birth rate languishes, shall no part of the blame be put on the modernized young woman who is ring-shy until he can show her a five-thousand-dollar automobile?

How about the great armies of salaried women who have come into financial independence in the office buildings and don't wish to exchange it for the secluded dependency of the flat buildings?

There are oodles of reasons why the bachelors have not married. Let there be general rejoicing that many of them have remained single. Special congratulations to the might-have-been children! They will never know what they have escaped.

Who knows but your old friend Bill was made a bachelor by Divine decree, so that some poor, frail woman wouldn't have to sit up until two or three o'clock every morning?

And now for some pointed advice and inside information: If you believe that grown-up males who refuse to marry are, in the aggregate, a menace to society, don't base your propaganda on the assumption that bachelors live in a care-free Paradise, which they are loath to exchange for the harrowing responsibilities of the family circle. Try to convince the bridegroom that he is winning a prize instead of surrendering a birthright.

If you want to keep a line waiting at the marriage license window, preach to the wandering sheep that they should come in from the bleak hills, and gambol in the clover pastures of connubial felicity.

Arrange with the editors to suppress all detailed reports of divorce trials; also to blue-pencil the shoddy jokes which deal with mothers-in-law and rolling pins.

Fix it with theatrical producers so that the stage bachelor will not be a picturesque hero, just a trifle gray about the temples, who carries a packet of dried rose leaves next to his heart, while the husband is a pale crumpet who is always trembling and saying, "Yes, my dear."

Try to induce department stores to remove those terrifying price tags from things worn by women. Many a wavering bachelor has looked in a show window and found, by an easy mental calculation, that his full salary for one month would supply My Lady with sufficient wardrobe to take her past the morning tub, but not enough to carry her into the street.

The two lone items of hats and shoes would spell bankruptcy to a fellow of ordinary means, and he knows that there must be countless other intermediate items connecting up the $60 hats with the $22 shoes.

At least, give him credit for always picturing *his* phantom wife as being extremely well dressed. Married men may be tight with the checkbook and moan over the bills; but the intangible, make-believe wife of the secluded bachelor always wears the most *chic* and alluring confections shown by the shops.

He has no intention of giving up the two-room snuggery which has been his home for eight years, but if he *should* become adventurous at any time and go sailing the uncharted seas, he knows that his travelling companion will be a queen in royal garb. She will sit in the rear of the boat, bedecked with pearls and wearing a coronet. He never meets her, but his intentions are generous, up to the last.

"I wouldn't get hooked up unless I could give my wife the best of everything." How often have we heard those words, spoken by some brave outlaw. The inference being that he has passed up a sacred privilege for fear that he could not supply Her with all of the costly luxuries she deserved.

Whereas, his associates know that he has become encased with a hard crust of habits and could never adapt himself to the give-and-take conditions of married life.

They can't be taught new tricks after they begin to moult.

But they continue to explain, and even in the deepest recesses of the most funereal reading-room of the most masculine club, you cannot find one so fussy and crabbed but that he will insist that he is "fond of children."

The lexicon of the unyoked is full of Old Stuff. The most hopeless misogynist (see dictionary) can always hang the blame on someone else and give himself a clean bill.

The point now being made is that the information agencies, by which the credulous public is influenced, seem to aid and abet the bachelors. Newspapers, magazines, picture plays, novels, current

anecdotes—all have fallen into the easy habit of making it appear that
the bachelor is a devil of a fellow; that the spirit of youth abides with
him after it has deserted the stoop-shouldered slaves commonly depicted
as mowing lawns or feeding furnaces.

The bachelor, as an individual, may sell very low in his immediate
precinct; but the bachelor, as a type, has become fictionalized into a
fascinating combination of Romeo and Mephistopheles.

You never saw a bachelor apartment on the stage that was not
luxurious and inviting. Always there is a man servant: It is midnight in Gerald Heathcote's princely lodgings. Gerald returns from
the club. Evening clothes? Absolutely!

He sends Wilkins away and lights a cigarette. There is a brief
pause, with Gerald sitting so that the fireplace has a chance to spot-
light him. It is a bachelor's apartment and midnight. Which means
that the dirty work is about to begin.

If, at any time, you are sitting so far back in a theater that you
cannot distinguish the words, and you see a distinguished figure of
a man come on R. U. E., self-possessed, debonair, patronizing—no
need to look at the bill. He is a bachelor, and the most beautiful lady
in the cast is all snarled up in an "affair" with him. If she ever crosses
the threshold of his voluptuous "lodgings," unaccompanied by a private detective or a chaperon, her reputation won't be worth a rusty
nickel.

That's the kind of a reputation to have! Never too old to be
wicked! Lock up the debutantes—here come the bachelors.

Now, if you persistently represent single blessedness as seated in
a huge leather chair, with Wilkins bringing whisky and soda, and a
married woman of incredible attractiveness waiting to call him on the
'phone, you need not be surprised if, in time, the whole social organization is permeated with a grotesque misconception of the true status
of the bachelor.

For years I have been compelled to observe large flocks at close
range. Only about one half of one per cent have lodgings which
could be used effectively for a Belasco setting. Only a very few,
mostly east of Buffalo, employ English manservants to "do" for them.
Those who like to refer to "my man" are compelled to get new ones
every few weeks. Probably the lonesomest job in the world, next to

taking care of a lighthouse, is to valet an unmarried man who has gone in for dancing.

Bachelors do not habitually wear evening clothes. To get one of them into the extreme regalia may involve the use of chloroform. Nearly every bachelor knows a few married women; but these women are not pursuing him—that is, not all of the time. Once in a while they pursue him in order to find out what has become of their husbands.

If one of these charming matrons visited a bachelor apartment, it would be to throw a bomb. She has him down on her list as poison ivy.

The bachelor is a polite outcast, and he knows it. The married folks tell stories about him, and it is all for the best that he never hears them. For instance: "I helped him off with his overcoat when he came in. We wondered why he didn't follow us into the living-room. I went back and found him standing in the hallway. Yes, indeed, waiting for his check! When the children came in to meet him, he trembled like a leaf—thought they were going to kiss him. When he sat down for dinner he inspected the knife and then wiped the plate with his napkin. After dinner the maid found a quarter on the table-cloth."

The idealized bachelor of fiction may be a super-gallant, but the real article is a scared fish the moment he swims out of his own puddle.

Possibly you expected from me a wordy attempt to prove that a man may acquire happiness by avoiding matrimony. Well, you cannot secure contentment by a mere avoidance of anything. The only worth-while days are those on which you sell a part of yourself to the brotherhood of man and go to the mattress at night knowing that you have rendered service to some of the fellow travellers. The more you camp by yourself the more you shrivel. The curse and the risk of bachelorhood is the tendency to build all plans around the mere comforts and indulgences of the first person singular.

Sometimes a bachelor gets to taking such good care of himself that he forgets that some day or other he will need six friends to act as pallbearers.

Next to solitaire, probably the most interesting single-handed pastime is trying to visualize one's own funeral. The bachelor often wonders if it will be an impressive function.

No use talking, when a transient undertakes the journey alone, he is compelled to be in doubt as to terminal facilities. His friendships are insecure and all the arrangements unstable. He has a lot of liberty, but he doesn't know what to do with it.

No man can cheat the game by merely hiding in a hotel and having his meals served in his room.

He can run in the opposite direction from matrimony until he is all out of breath, but he will never travel far enough to get away from himself. When he flees from the responsibility of family life he is incidentally leaving behind him many of the experiences which belong to a normal career. He cannot get away from the double-entry system of accounts revealed in Doctor Emerson's essays on Compensation. The books must balance.

No man can take twelve months' vacation each year. A vacation is no fun except when it comes as a release from the regular routine. Each July the married man is supposed to sing:

"My wife's gone to the country. Hurrah! Hurrah!"

Thereby he gets an edge on the bachelor. He has a chance to throw his hat in the air at least once a year. When does the bachelor pull his "Hurrahs"? Think it over.

If the locked-up hubbies believe that the boys still at large are raising Cain seven nights a week and fifty-two weeks in the year, let them cease to be envious. It can't be done. The most fatiguing activity in the world is that of roystering. It is terrible to be fed up on roystering. Almost any group of case-hardened bachelors would rather row a boat than sit around a table and sing.

Bachelors do not regard their respective caves and caverns as modified cabarets. Their so-called home life is merely a recognition of the physical fact that no one can entirely dispense with slumber.

The "jolly bachelor" in his own retreat is often just as jolly as a festoon of crape. He is not discontented. He is calmly reconciled. But not celebrating.

He has been saved from the shipwreck by miraculous intervention, but he finds himself on a lonely island and not a sail in sight.

The bachelor doesn't have to watch the clock, and no one is waiting to ask him where he has been; but how about that rapidly approaching day when he will not find—in all the world—ham and eggs that are cooked just right or coffee fit to drink?

As the autumn days grow shorter, and each milestone begins to look more like a tombstone, the bachelor becomes less and less declamatory regarding the joys of single blessedness.

He doesn't weaken, mind you. He can explain why it would have been manifestly impossible for him, at any time, to undertake such a crazy experiment. His training, his temperament, the conditions enforced by his employment, the uncertainty of his financial outlook—these and thirty other good reasons made it utterly impossible for him even to think of playing such a ghastly joke on a nice woman.

He is there with a defense; but when you ask him to add up the net blessings and benefits which accrue to the bachelor, his discourse becomes diffuse and unconvincing. If he is past forty, he doesn't brag at all. If he is past fifty, he begins to talk about the weather.

And now, having received all of this secret information from the camp of the enemy, you know as much as we do regarding the joys of single blessedness.

II
THE AMERICAN
DREAM

ARCHIBALD MACLEISH Why he

selected AMERICA Was PROMISES

The meaning of the title of the poem is this: that America from the very beginning—from the first knowledge men had of it—was promises. It was a promise of wealth, of well-being, of escape, of freedom, of new beginnings. It was such a promise to all men who heard of it, whether by signs at sea or by discovery along its coasts, or by water and grass as they went west across it. And like all promises, it was a promise which men believed would come true of itself. Like the promises in the fairy tales. This is the meaning of the title of the poem. And the meaning of the poem itself is that the promises do not come true of themselves—that they must be made to come true—that they must be made to come true by men.

To say this, the poem tells of those to whom the promises were made. There was Columbus first who saw the promise made by the floating branch upon the sea-water, the birds, the rain. There were the Spaniards of Cortes, landing on the coast, moving westward toward Mexico, toward Colua, toward the promise of the silver moon and the golden sun, sent them from beyond those mountains. There was Thomas Jefferson who saw the spiritual promises of a new world of the human spirit, and thought they were promises made to the idea, the ideal of MAN. There was John Adams who saw the fat farms, the busy trade, of the new Republic, and thought their promises were made to the well-to-do and the intelligent—the Aristocracy of Wealth and Talents. There was Tom Paine who saw the wild American shore and the vast American forests and thought the promises of those high American horizons were promises made to all men everywhere.

The poem tells of these men and how the promise did not come true of itself for any of them.

And it tells of us and of what we have learned about the promises in our time—what we have learned in Austria and Czechoslovakia

and Poland and Spain and Norway and Holland and France—that
unless the people of a country, the whole people of a country, make
the promises come true for the sake of the people, others will make
them come true. And not for the sake of the people. For the sake of
others.

It is a poem about America. But more about ourselves.

Washington, D. C.   ARCHIBALD MacLEISH
June 25, 1942

WHO is the voyager in these leaves?
     Who is the traveler in this journey
Deciphers the revolving night: receives
The signal from the light returning?

America was promises to whom?

                                        East were the
Dead kings and the remembered sepulchres:
West was the grass.
            The groves of the oaks were at evening.

Eastward are the nights where we have slept.

And we move on: we move down:
With the first light we push forward:
We descend from the past as a wandering people from mountains.
We cross into the day to be discovered.
The dead are left where they fall—at dark
At night late under the coverlets.
We mark the place with the shape of our teeth on our fingers.
The room is left as it was: the love
Who is the traveler in these leaves these
Annual waters and beside the doors
Jonquils: then the rose: the eaves

Heaping the thunder up: the mornings
Opening on like great valleys
Never till now approached: the familiar trees
Far off: distant with the future:
The hollyhocks beyond the afternoons:
The butterflies over the ripening fruit on the balconies:
And all beautiful
All before us

America was always promises.
From the first voyage and the first ship there were promises—
'the tropic bird which does not sleep at sea'
'the great mass of dark heavy clouds which is a sign'
'the drizzle of rain without wind which is a sure sign'
'the whale which is an indication'
'the stick appearing to be carved with iron'
'the stalk loaded with roseberries'
'and all these signs were from the west'
'and all night heard birds passing.'

Who is the voyager on these coasts?
Who is the traveler in these waters
Expects the future as a shore: foresees
Like Indies to the west the ending—he
The rumor of the surf intends?

America was promises—to whom?

Jefferson knew:
Declared it before God and before history:
Declares it still in the remembering tomb.
The promises were Man's: the land was his—
Man endowed by his Creator:
Earnest in love: perfectible by reason:

Just and perceiving justice: his natural nature
Clear and sweet at the source as springs in trees are.
It was Man the promise contemplated.
The times had chosen Man: no other:
Bloom on his face of every future:
Brother of stars and of all travelers:
Brother of time and of all mysteries:
Brother of grass also: of fruit trees.
It was Man who had been promised: who should have.
Man was to ride from the Tidewater: over the Gap:
West and South with the water: taking the book with him:
Taking the wheat seed: corn seed: pip of apple:
Building liberty a farmyard wide:
Breeding for useful labor: for good looks:
For husbandry: humanity: for pride—
Practising self-respect and common decency.

And Man turned into men in Philadelphia
Practising prudence on a long-term lease:
Building liberty to fit the parlor:
Bred for crystal on the frontroom shelves:
Just and perceiving justice by the dollar:
Patriotic with the bonds at par
(And their children's children brag of their deeds for the Colonies).
Man rode up from the Tidewater: over the Gap:
Turned into men: turned into two-day settlers:
Lawyers with the land-grants in their caps:
Coon-skin voters wanting theirs and getting it.

Turned the promises to capital: invested it.

America was always promises:
'the wheel like a sun as big as a cart wheel
     with many sorts of pictures on it
     the whole of fine gold'

'twenty golden ducks
    beautifully worked and very natural looking
    and some like dogs of the kind they keep'

And they waved us west from the dunes: they cried out
Colua! Colua!
Mexico! Mexico! . . . Colua!

America was promises to whom?

Old Man Adams knew. He told us—
An aristocracy of compound interest
Hereditary through the common stock!
We'd have one sure before the mare was older.
"The first want of every man was his dinner:
The second his girl." Kings were by the pocket.
Wealth made blood made wealth made blood made wealthy.
Enlightened selfishness gave lasting light.
Winners bred grandsons: losers only bred!

And the Aristocracy of politic selfishness
Bought the land up: bought the towns: the sites:
The goods: the government: the people. Bled them.
Sold them. Kept the profit. Lost itself.

The Aristocracy of Wealth and Talents
Turned its talents into wealth and lost them.
Turned enlightened selfishness to wealth.
Turned self-interest into bankbooks: balanced them.
Bred out: bred to fools: to hostlers:
Card sharps: well dressed women: dancefloor doublers.
The Aristocracy of Wealth and Talents
Sold its talents: bought the public notice:
Drank in public: went to bed in public:
Patronized the arts in public: pall'd with
Public authors public beauties: posed in

Public postures for the public page.
The Aristocracy of Wealth and Talents
Withered of talent and ashamed of wealth
Bred to consinlaw: insane relations:
Girls with open secrets: sailors' Galahads:
Prurient virgins with the tales to tell:
Women with dead wombs and living wishes.

The Aristocracy of Wealth and Talents
Moved out: settled on the Continent:
Sat beside the water at Rapallo:
Died in a rented house: unwept: unhonored.

And the child says I see the lightning on you.

The weed between the railroad tracks
Tasting of sweat: tasting of poverty:
The bitter and pure taste where the hawk hovers:
Native as the deer bone in the sand

O my America for whom?

For whom the promises? For whom the river
"It flows west! Look at the ripple of it!"
The grass "So that it was wonderful to see
And endless without end with wind wonderful!"
The Great Lakes: landless as oceans: their beaches
Coarse sand: clean gravel: pebbles:
Their bluffs smelling of sunflowers: smelling of surf:
Of fresh water: of wild sunflowers . . . wilderness.
For whom the evening mountains on the sky:
The night wind from the west: the moon descending?

Tom Paine knew.
Tom Paine knew the People.
The promises were spoken to the People.

History was voyages toward the People.
Americas were landfalls of the People.
Stars and expectations were the signals of the People.

Whatever was truly built the People had built it.
Whatever was taken down they had taken down.
Whatever was worn they had worn—ax-handles: fiddle-bows:
Sills of doorways: names for children: for mountains.
Whatever was long forgotten they had forgotten—
Fame of the great: names of the rich and their mottos.
The People had the promises: they'd keep them.
They waited their time in the world: they had wise sayings.
They counted out their time by day to day.
They counted it out day after day into history.
They had time and to spare in the spill of their big fists.
They had all the time there was like a handful of wheat seed.
When the time came they would speak and the rest would listen.

And the time came and the People did not speak.

The time came: the time comes: the speakers
Come and these who speak are not the People.

These who speak with gunstocks at the doors:
These the coarse ambitious priest
Leads by the bloody fingers forward:
These who reach with stiffened arm to touch
What none who took dared touch before:
These who touch the truth are not the People.

These the savage fables of the time
Lick at the fingers as a bitch will waked at morning:
These who teach the lie are not the People.

The time came: the time comes

Comes and to whom? To these? Was it for these
The surf was secret on the new-found shore?
Was it for these the branch was on the water?—
These whom all the years were toward
The golden images the clouds the mountains?

Never before: never in any summer:
Never were days so generous: stars so mild:
Even in old men's talk or in books or remembering
Far back in a gone childhood
Or farther still to the light where Homer wanders—
The air all lucid with the solemn blue
That hills take at the distance beyond change. . . .
That time takes also at the distances.

Never were there promises as now:
Never was green deeper: earth warmer:
Light more beautiful to see: the sound of
Water lovelier: the many forms of
Leaves: stones: clouds: beasts: shadows
Clearer more admirable or the faces
More like answering faces or the hands
Quicker: more brotherly:

                              the aching taste of
Time more salt upon the tongue: more human
Never in any summer: and to whom?

At dusk: by street lights: in the rooms we ask this.

We do not ask for Truth now from John Adams.
We do not ask for Tongues from Thomas Jefferson.

We do not ask for Justice from Tom Paine.
We ask for answers.

And there is an answer.

There is Spain Austria Poland China Bohemia.
There are dead men in the pits in all those countries.
Their mouths are silent but they speak. They say
"The promises are theirs who take them."

Listen! Brothers! Generation!
Listen! You have heard these words. Believe it!
Believe the promises are theirs who take them!

Believe unless we take them for ourselves
Others will take them for the use of others!

Believe unless we take them for ourselves
All of us: one here; another there:
Men not Man: people not the People:
Hands: mouths: arms: eyes: not syllables—
Believe unless we take them for ourselves
Others will take them not for us: for others!

Believe unless we take them for ourselves
Now: soon: by the clock: before tomorrow:
Others will take them: not for now: for longer!

Listen! Brothers! Generation!
Companions of leaves: of the sun: of the slow evenings:

Companions of the many days: of all of them:
Listen! Believe the speaking dead! Believe
The journey is our journey. O believe
The signals were to us: the signs: the birds by
Night: the breaking surf.

                            Believe
America is promises to
Take!

America is promises to
Us
To take them
Brutally
With love but
Take them.

O believe this!

WILLA CATHER

NEIGHBOUR ROSICKY

Willa Cather, one of the most distinguished American writers of fiction, has at no time been a commentator on her own work. Even in a book such as *This Is My Best* Miss Cather preferred to continue her custom of allowing her work to speak for itself. Accordingly, "Neighbour Rosicky" is presented without benefit of any interpretation by her. It is a long story, first published in 1932.

I

WHEN Doctor Burleigh told neighbour Rosicky he had a bad heart, Rosicky protested.

"So? No, I guess my heart was always pretty good. I got a little asthma, maybe. Just a awful short breath when I was pitchin' hay last summer, dat's all."

"Well now, Rosicky, if you know more about it than I do, what did you come to me for? It's your heart that makes you short of breath, I tell you. You're sixty-five years old, and you've always worked hard, and your heart's tired. You've got to be careful from now on, and you can't do heavy work any more. You've got five boys at home to do it for you."

The old farmer looked up at the Doctor with a gleam of amusement in his queer triangular-shaped eyes. His eyes were large and lively, but the lids were caught up in the middle in a curious way, so that they formed a triangle. He did not look like a sick man. His brown face was creased but not wrinkled, he had a ruddy colour in his smooth-shaven cheeks and in his lips, under his long brown moustache. His hair was thin and ragged around his ears, but very little grey. His forehead, naturally high and crossed by deep parallel lines, now ran all the way up to his pointed crown. Rosicky's face had the habit of looking interested—suggested a contented disposition and a reflective

133

quality that was gay rather than grave. This gave him a certain detachment, the easy manner of an onlooker and observer.

"Well, I guess you ain't got no pills fur a bad heart, Doctor Ed. I guess the only thing is fur me to git me a new one."

Doctor Burleigh swung round in his desk-chair and frowned at the old farmer. "I think if I were you I'd take a little care of the old one, Rosicky."

Rosicky shrugged. "Maybe I don't know how. I expect you mean fur me not to drink my coffee no more."

"I wouldn't, in your place. But you'll do as you choose about that. I've never yet been able to separate a Bohemian from his coffee or his pipe. I've quit trying. But the sure thing is you've got to cut out farm work. You can feed the stock and do chores about the barn, but you can't do anything in the fields that makes you short of breath."

"How about shelling corn?"

"Of course not!"

Rosicky considered with puckered brows.

"I can't make my heart go no longer'n it wants to, can I, Doctor Ed?"

"I think it's good for five or six years yet, maybe more, if you'll take the strain off it. Sit around the house and help Mary. If I had a good wife like yours, I'd want to stay around the house."

His patient chuckled. "It ain't no place fur a man. I don't like no old man hanging round the kitchen too much. An' my wife, she's a awful hard worker her own self."

"That's it; you can help her a little. My Lord, Rosicky, you are one of the few men I know who has a family he can get some comfort out of; happy dispositions, never quarrel among themselves, and they treat you right. I want to see you live a few years and enjoy them."

"Oh, they're good kids, all right," Rosicky assented.

The Doctor wrote him a prescription and asked him how his oldest son, Rudolph, who had married in the spring, was getting on. Rudolph had struck out for himself, on rented land. "And how's Polly? I was afraid Mary mightn't like an American daughter-in-law, but it seems to be working out all right."

"Yes, she's a fine girl. Dat widder woman bring her daughters up very nice. Polly got lots of spunk, an' she got some style, too. Da's nice, for young folks to have some style." Rosicky inclined his head gallantly. His voice and his twinkly smile were an affectionate compliment to his daughter-in-law.

"It looks like a storm, and you'd better be getting home before it comes. In town in the car?" Doctor Burleigh rose.

"No, I'm in de wagon. When you got five boys, you ain't got much chance to ride round in de Ford. I ain't much for cars, noway."

"Well, it's a good road out to your place; but I don't want you bumping around in a wagon much. And never again on a hay-rake, remember!"

Rosicky placed the Doctor's fee delicately behind the desk-telephone, looking the other way, as if this were an absent-minded gesture. He put on his plush cap and his corduroy jacket with a sheepskin collar, and went out.

The Doctor picked up his stethoscope and frowned at it as if he were seriously annoyed with the instrument. He wished it had been telling tales about some other man's heart, some old man who didn't look the Doctor in the eye so knowingly, or hold out such a warm brown hand when he said good-bye. Doctor Burleigh had been a poor boy in the country before he went away to medical school; he had known Rosicky almost ever since he could remember, and he had a deep affection for Mrs. Rosicky.

Only last winter he had had such a good breakfast at Rosicky's, and that when he needed it. He had been out all night on a long, hard confinement case at Tom Marshall's—a big rich farm where there was plenty of stock and plenty of feed and a great deal of expensive farm machinery of the newest model, and no comfort whatever. The woman had too many children and too much work, and she was no manager. When the baby was born at last, and handed over to the assisting neighbour woman, and the mother was properly attended to, Burleigh refused any breakfast in that slovenly house, and drove his buggy—the snow was too deep for a car—eight miles to Anton Rosicky's place. He didn't know another farm-house where a man could get such a warm welcome, and such good strong coffee with rich cream. No wonder the old chap didn't want to give up his coffee!

He had driven in just when the boys had come back from the barn and were washing up for breakfast. The long table, covered with a bright oilcloth, was set out with dishes waiting for them, and the warm kitchen was full of the smell of coffee and hot biscuit and sausage. Five big handsome boys, running from twenty to twelve, all with what Burleigh called natural good manners—they hadn't a bit of the painful self-consciousness he himself had to struggle with when he was a lad. One ran to put his horse away, another helped him off with his fur coat and hung it up, and Josephine, the youngest child and the only daughter, quickly set another place under her mother's direction.

With Mary, to feed creatures was the natural expression of affection —her chickens, the calves, her big hungry boys. It was a rare pleasure to feed a young man whom she seldom saw and of whom she was as proud as if he belonged to her. Some country housekeepers would have stopped to spread a white cloth over the oilcloth, to change the thick cups and plates for their best china, and the wooden-handled knives for plated ones. But not Mary.

"You must take us as you find us, Doctor Ed. I'd be glad to put out my good things for you if you was expected, but I'm glad to get you any way at all."

He knew she was glad—she threw back her head and spoke out as if she were announcing him to the whole prairie. Rosicky hadn't said anything at all; he merely smiled his twinkling smile, put some more coal on the fire, and went into his own room to pour the Doctor a little drink in a medicine glass. When they were all seated, he watched his wife's face from his end of the table and spoke to her in Czech. Then, with the instinct of politeness which seldom failed him, he turned to the Doctor and said slyly: "I was just tellin' her not to ask you no questions about Mrs. Marshall till you eat some breakfast. My wife, she's terrible fur to ask questions."

The boys laughed, and so did Mary. She watched the Doctor devour her biscuit and sausage, too much excited to eat anything herself. She drank her coffee and sat taking in everything about her visitor. She had known him when he was a poor country boy, and was boastfully proud of his success, always saying: "What do people go to Omaha for, to see a doctor, when we got the best one in the State right here?" If Mary liked people at all, she felt physical pleasure in the sight of them, personal exultation in any good fortune that came to them. Burleigh didn't know many women like that, but he knew she was like that.

When his hunger was satisfied, he did, of course, have to tell them about Mrs. Marshall, and he noticed what a friendly interest the boys took in the matter.

Rudolph, the oldest one (he was still living at home then), said: "The last time I was over there, she was lifting them big heavy milk-cans, and I knew she oughtn't to be doing it."

"Yes, Rudolph told me about that when he come home, and I said it wasn't right," Mary put in warmly. "It was all right for me to do them things up to the last, for I was terrible strong, but that woman's weakly. And do you think she'll be able to nurse it, Ed?" She sometimes forgot to give him the title she was so proud of. "And to think of your being up all night and then not able to get a decent breakfast! I don't know what's the matter with such people."

"Why, Mother," said one of the boys, "if Doctor Ed had got breakfast there, we wouldn't have him here. So you ought to be glad."

"He knows I'm glad to have him, John, any time. But I'm sorry for that poor woman, how bad she'll feel the Doctor had to go away in the cold without his breakfast."

"I wish I'd been in practice when these were getting born." The doctor looked down the row of close-clipped heads. "I missed some good breakfasts by not being."

The boys began to laugh at their mother because she flushed so red, but she stood her ground and threw up her head. "I don't care, you wouldn't have got away from this house without breakfast. No doctor ever did. I'd have had something ready fixed that Anton could warm up for you."

The boys laughed harder than ever, and exclaimed at her: "I'll bet you would!" "She would, that!"

"Father, did you get breakfast for the doctor when we were born?"

"Yes, and he used to bring me my breakfast, too, mighty nice. I was always awful hungry!" Mary admitted with a guilty laugh.

While the boys were getting the Doctor's horse, he went to the window to examine the house plants. "What do you do to your geraniums to keep them blooming all winter, Mary? I never pass this house that from the road I don't see your windows full of flowers."

She snapped off a dark red one, and a ruffled new green leaf, and put them in his button hole. "There, that looks better. You look too solemn for a young man, Ed. Why don't you git married? I'm worried about you. Settin' at breakfast, I looked at you real hard, and I seen you've got some grey hairs already."

"Oh, yes! They're coming. Maybe they'd come faster if I married."

"Don't talk so. You'll ruin your health eating at the hotel. I could send your wife a nice loaf of nut bread, if you only had one. I don't like to see a young man getting grey. I'll tell you something, Ed; you make some strong black tea and keep it handy in a bowl, and every morning just brush it into your hair, an' it'll keep the grey from showin' much. That's the way I do!"

Sometimes the Doctor heard the gossipers in the drug-store wondering why Rosicky didn't get on faster. He was industrious, and so were his boys, but they were rather free and easy, weren't pushers, and they didn't always show good judgment. They were comfortable, they were out of debt, but they didn't get much ahead. Maybe, Doctor Burleigh reflected, people as generous and warm-hearted and affectionate as the Rosickys never got ahead much; maybe you couldn't enjoy your life and put it into the bank, too.

II

When Rosicky left Doctor Burleigh's office he went into the farm-implement store to light his pipe and put on his glasses and read over the list Mary had given him. Then he went into the general merchandise place next door and stood about until the pretty girl with the plucked eyebrows, who always waited on him, was free. Those eyebrows, two thin India-ink strokes, amused him, because he remembered how they used to be. Rosicky always prolonged his shopping by a little joking; the girl knew the old fellow admired her, and she liked to chaff with him.

"Seems to me about every other week you buy ticking, Mr. Rosicky, and always the best quality," she remarked as she measured off the heavy bolt with red stripes.

"You see, my wife is always makin' goose-fedder pillows, an' de thin stuff don't hold in dem little down-fedders."

"You must have lots of pillows at your house."

"Sure. She makes quilts of dem, too. We sleeps easy. Now she's makin' a fedder quilt for my son's wife. You know Polly, that married my Rudolph. How much my bill, Miss Pearl?"

"Eight eighty-five."

"Chust make it nine, and put in some candy fur de women."

"As usual. I never did see a man buy so much candy for his wife. First thing you know, she'll be getting too fat."

"I'd like dat. I ain't much fur all dem slim women like what de style is now."

"That's one for me, I suppose, Mr. Bohunk!" Pearl sniffed and elevated her India-ink strokes.

When Rosicky went out to his wagon, it was beginning to snow,— the first snow of the season, and he was glad to see it. He rattled out of town and along the highway through a wonderfully rich stretch of country, the finest farms in the county. He admired this High Prairie, as it was called, and always liked to drive through it. His own place lay in a rougher territory, where there was some clay in the soil and it was not so productive. When he bought his land, he hadn't the money to buy on High Prairie; so he told his boys, when they grumbled, that if their land hadn't some clay in it, they wouldn't own it at all. All the same, he enjoyed looking at these fine farms, as he enjoyed looking at a prize bull.

After he had gone eight miles, he came to the graveyard, which lay just at the edge of his own hay-land. There he stopped his horses and sat still on his wagon seat, looking about at the snowfall. Over yonder on the hill he could see his own house, crouching low, with the clump of orchard behind and the windmill before, and all down the gentle hill-slope the rows of pale gold cornstalks stood out against the white field. The snow was falling over the cornfield and the pasture and the hay-land, steadily, with very little wind,—a nice dry snow. The graveyard had only a light wire fence about it and was all overgrown with long red grass. The fine snow, settling into this red grass and upon the few little evergreens and the headstones, looked very pretty.

It was a nice graveyard, Rosicky reflected, sort of snug and home-like, not cramped or mournful,—a big sweep all round it. A man could lie down in the long grass and see the complete arch of the sky over him, hear the wagons go by; in summer the mowing-machine rattled right up to the wire fence. And it was so near home. Over there across the cornstalks his own roof and windmill looked so good to him that he promised himself to mind the Doctor and take care of himself. He was awful fond of his place, he admitted. He wasn't anxious to leave it. And it was a comfort to think that he would never have to go farther than the edge of his own hayfield. The snow, falling over his barnyard and the graveyard, seemed to draw things together like. And they were all old neighbours in the graveyard, most of them friends; there was nothing to feel awkward or embarrassed about. Embarrassment was the most disagreeable feeling Rosicky knew. He didn't often have it,—only with certain people whom he didn't understand at all.

Well, it was a nice snowstorm; a fine sight to see the snow falling so quietly and graciously over so much open country. On his cap and shoulders, on the horses' backs and manes, light, delicate, mysterious it fell; and with it a dry cool fragrance was released into the air. It meant rest for vegetation and men and beasts, for the ground itself; a season of long nights for sleep, leisurely breakfasts, peace by the fire. This and much more went through Rosicky's mind, but he merely told himself that winter was coming, clucked to his horses, and drove on.

When he reached home, John, the youngest boy, ran out to put away his team for him, and he met Mary coming up from the outside cellar with her apron full of carrots. They went into the house together. On the table, covered with oilcloth figured with clusters of blue grapes, a place was set, and he smelled hot coffee-cake of some kind. Anton never lunched in town; he thought that extravagant, and anyhow he didn't like the food. So Mary always had something ready for him when he got home.

After he was settled in his chair, stirring his coffee in a big cup, Mary took out of the oven a pan of *kolache* stuffed with apricots, examined them anxiously to see whether they had got too dry, put them beside his plate, and then sat down opposite him.

Rosicky asked her in Czech if she wasn't going to have any coffee.

She replied in English, as being somehow the right language for transacting business: "Now what did Doctor Ed say, Anton? You tell me just what."

"He said I was to tell you some compliments, but I forgot 'em." Rosicky's eyes twinkled.

"About you, I mean. What did he say about your asthma?"

"He says I ain't got no asthma." Rosicky took one of the little rolls in his broad brown fingers. The thickened nail of his right thumb told the story of his past.

"Well, what is the matter? And don't try to put me off."

"He don't say nothing much, only I'm a little older, and my heart ain't so good like it used to be."

Mary started and brushed her hair back from her temples with both hands as if she were a little out of her mind. From the way she glared, she might have been in a rage with him.

"He says there's something the matter with your heart? Doctor Ed says so?"

"Now don't yell at me like I was a hog in de garden, Mary. You know I always did like to hear a woman talk soft. He didn't say anything de matter wid my heart, only it ain't so young like it used to be, an' he tell me not to pitch hay or run de corn-sheller."

Mary wanted to jump up, but she sat still. She admired the way he never under any circumstances raised his voice or spoke roughly. He was city-bred, and she was country-bred; she often said she wanted her boys to have their papa's nice ways.

"You never have no pain there, do you? It's your breathing and your stomach that's been wrong. I wouldn't believe nobody but Doctor Ed about it. I guess I'll go see him myself. Didn't he give you no advice?"

"Chust to take it easy like, an' stay round de house dis winter. I guess you got some carpenter work for me to do. I kin make some new shelves for you, and I want dis long time to build a closet in de boys room and make dem two little fellers keep dere clo'es hung up."

Rosicky drank his coffee from time to time, while he considered. His moustache was of the soft long variety and came down over his mouth like the teeth of a buggy-rake over a bundle of hay. Each time he put down his cup, he ran his blue handkerchief over his lips. When he took a drink of water, he managed very neatly with the back of his hand.

Mary sat watching him intently, trying to find any change in his face. It is hard to see anyone who has become like your own body to you. Yes, his hair had got thin, and his high forehead had deep lines running from left to right. But his neck, always clean shaved except in the busiest seasons, was not loose or baggy. It was burned a dark reddish brown, and there were deep creases in it, but it looked firm and full of blood. His cheeks had a good colour. On either side of his mouth there was a half-moon down the length of his cheek, not wrinkles, but two lines that had come there from his habitual expression. He was shorter and broader than when she married him; his back had grown broad and curved, a good deal like the shell of an old turtle, and his arms and legs were short.

He was fifteen years older than Mary, but she had hardly ever thought about it before. He was her man, and the kind of man she liked. She was rough, and he was gentle,—city-bred, as she always said. They had been shipmates on a rough voyage and had stood by each other in trying times. Life had gone well with them because, at bottom, they had the same ideas about life. They agreed, without discussion, as to what was most important and what was secondary. They didn't often exchange opinions, even in Czech,—it was as if they had thought the same thought together. A good deal had to be sacrificed and thrown overboard in a hard life like theirs, and they had never disagreed as to the things that could go. It had been a hard life, and a soft life, too. There wasn't anything brutal in the short, broad-backed man with the three-cornered eyes and the forehead that went on to the top of his skull. He was a city man, a gentle man, and though he had married a rough farm girl, he had never touched her without gentleness.

They had been at one accord not to hurry through life, not to be always skimping and saving. They saw their neighbours buy more land and feed more stock than they did, without discontent. Once when the creamery agent came to the Rosickys to persuade them to sell him their cream, he told them how much money the Fasslers, their nearest neighbours, had made on their cream last year.

"Yes," said Mary, "and look at them Fassler children! Pale, pinched little things, they look like skimmed milk. I'd rather put some colour into my children's faces than put money into the bank."

The agent shrugged and turned to Anton.

"I guess we'll do like she says," said Rosicky.

III

Mary very soon got into town to see Doctor Ed, and then she had a talk with her boys and set a guard over Rosicky. Even John, the youngest, had his father on his mind. If Rosicky went to throw hay down from the loft, one of the boys ran up the ladder and took the fork from him. He sometimes complained that though he was getting to be an old man, he wasn't an old woman yet.

That winter he stayed in the house in the afternoons and carpentered, or sat in the chair between the window full of plants and the wooden bench where the two pails of drinking-water stood. This spot was called "Father's corner," though it was not a corner at all. He had a shelf there, where he kept his Bohemian papers and his pipes and tobacco, and his shears and needles and thread and tailor's thimble. Having been a tailor in his youth, he couldn't bear to see a woman patching at his clothes, or at the boys'. He liked tailoring, and always patched all the overalls and jackets and work shirts. Occasionally he made over a pair of pants one of the older boys had outgrown, for the little fellow.

While he sewed, he let his mind run back over his life. He had a good deal to remember, really; life in three countries. The only part of his youth he didn't like to remember was the two years he had spent in London, in Cheapside, working for a German tailor who was wretchedly poor. Those days, when he was nearly always hungry, when his clothes were dropping off him for dirt, and the sound of a strange language kept him in continual bewilderment, had left a sore spot in his mind that wouldn't bear touching.

He was twenty when he landed at Castle Garden in New York, and he had a protector who got him work in a tailor shop in Vesey Street, down near the Washington Market. He looked upon that part of his life as very happy. He became a good workman, he was indus-

trious, and his wages were increased from time to time. He minded
his own business and envied nobody's good fortune. He went to night
school and learned to read English. He often did overtime work and
was well paid for it, but somehow he never saved anything. He
couldn't refuse a loan to a friend, and he was self-indulgent. He liked
a good dinner, and a little went for beer, a little for tobacco; a good
deal went to the girls. He often stood through an opera on Saturday
nights; he could get standing-room for a dollar. Those were the great
days of opera in New York, and it gave a fellow something to think
about for the rest of the week. Rosicky had a quick ear, and a childish
love of all the stage splendour; the scenery, the costumes, the ballet.
He usually went with a chum, and after the performance they had
beer and maybe some oysters somewhere. It was a fine life; for the
first five years or so it satisfied him completely. He was never hungry
or cold or dirty, and everything amused him: a fire, a dog fight, a
parade, a storm, a ferry ride. He thought New York the finest, richest,
friendliest city in the world.

Moreover, he had what he called a happy home life. Very near the
tailor shop was a small furniture-factory, where an old Austrian,
Loeffler, employed a few skilled men and made unusual furniture,
most of it to order, for the rich German housewives up-town. The top
floor of Loeffler's five-storey factory was a loft, where he kept his
choice lumber and stored the odd pieces of furniture left on his hands.
One of the young workmen he employed was a Czech, and he and
Rosicky became fast friends. They persuaded Loeffler to let them have
a sleeping-room in one corner of the loft. They bought good beds and
bedding and had their pick of the furniture kept up there. The loft
was low-pitched, but light and airy, full of windows, and good-smelling
by reason of the fine lumber put up there to season. Old Loeffler used
to go down to the docks and buy wood from South America and the
East from the sea captains. The young men were as foolish about
their house as a bridal pair. Zichec, the young cabinet-maker, devised
every sort of convenience, and Rosicky kept their clothes in order. At
night and on Sundays, when the quiver of machinery underneath was
still, it was the quietest place in the world, and on summer nights all
the sea winds blew in. Zichec often practised on his flute in the eve-

ning. They were both fond of music and went to the opera together. Rosicky thought he wanted to live like that for ever.

But as the years passed, all alike, he began to get a little restless. When spring came round, he would begin to feel fretted, and he got to drinking. He was likely to drink too much of a Saturday night. On Sunday he was languid and heavy, getting over his spree. On Monday he plunged into work again. So he never had time to figure out what ailed him, though he knew something did. When the grass turned green in Park Place, and the lilac hedge at the back of Trinity church-yard put out its blossoms, he was tormented by a longing to run away. That was why he drank too much; to get a temporary illusion of free-dom and wide horizons.

Rosicky, the old Rosicky, could remember as if it were yesterday the day when the young Rosicky found out what was the matter with him. It was on a Fourth of July afternoon, and he was sitting in Park Place in the sun. The lower part of New York was empty. Wall Street, Liberty Street, Broadway, all empty. So much stone and asphalt with nothing going on, so many empty windows. The emptiness was intense, like the stillness in a great factory when the machinery stops and the belts and bands cease running. It was too great a change, it took all the strength out of one. Those blank buildings, without the stream of life pouring through them, were like empty jails. It struck young Rosicky that this was the trouble with big cities; they built you in from the earth itself, cemented you away from any contact with the ground. You lived in an unnatural world, like the fish in an aquarium, who were probably much more comfortable than they ever were in the sea.

On that very day he began to think seriously about the articles he had read in the Bohemian papers, describing prosperous Czech farm-ing communities in the West. He believed he would like to go out there as a farm hand; it was hardly possible that he could ever have land of his own. His people had always been workmen; his father and grandfather had worked in shops. His mother's parents had lived in the country, but they rented their farm and had a hard time to get along. Nobody in his family had ever owned any land,—that belonged to a different station of life altogether. Anton's mother died when he was little, and he was sent into the country to her parents. He stayed

with them until he was twelve, and formed those ties with the earth
and the farm animals and growing things which are never made at all
unless they are made early. After his grandfather died, he went back
to live with his father and stepmother, but she was very hard on him,
and his father helped him to get passage to London.

After that Fourth of July day in Park Place, the desire to return
to the country never left him. To work on another man's farm would
be all he asked; to see the sun rise and set and to plant things and
watch them grow. He was a very simple man. He was like a tree that
has not many roots, but one tap-root that goes down deep. He subscribed for a Bohemian paper printed in Chicago, then for one printed
in Omaha. His mind got farther and farther west. He began to save a
little money to buy his liberty. When he was thirty-five, there was a
great meeting in New York of Bohemian athletic societies, and Rosicky
left the tailor shop and went home with the Omaha delegates to try
his fortune in another part of the world.

IV

Perhaps the fact that his own youth was well over before he began
to have a family was one reason why Rosicky was so fond of his boys.
He had almost a grandfather's indulgence for them. He had never
had to worry about any of them—except, just now, a little about
Rudolph.

On Saturday night the boys always piled into the Ford, took little
Josephine, and went to town to the moving-picture show. One Saturday morning they were talking at the breakfast table about starting
early that evening, so that they would have an hour or so to see the
Christmas things in the stores before the show began. Rosicky looked
down the table.

"I hope you boys ain't disappointed, but I want you to let me have
de car tonight. Maybe some of you can go in with de neighbours."

Their faces fell. They worked hard all week, and they were still
like children. A new jackknife or a box of candy pleased the older
ones as much as the little fellow.

"If you and Mother are going to town," Frank said, "maybe you
could take a couple of us along with you, anyway."

"No, I want to take de car down to Rudolph's, and let him an' Polly go in to de show. She don't git into town enough, an' I'm afraid she's gettin' lonesome, an' he can't afford no car yet."

That settled it. The boys were a good deal dashed. Their father took another piece of apple-cake and went on: "Maybe next Saturday night de two little fellers can go along wid dem."

"Oh, is Rudolph going to have the car every Saturday night?"

Rosicky did not reply at once; then he began to speak seriously: "Listen, boys; Polly ain't lookin' so good. I don't like to see nobody lookin' sad. It comes hard fur a town girl to be a farmer's wife. I don't want no trouble to start in Rudolph's family. When it starts, it ain't so easy to stop. An American girl don't git used to our ways all at once. I like to tell Polly she and Rudolph can have the car every Saturday night till after New Year's, if it's all right with you boys."

"Sure it's all right, Papa," Mary cut in. "And it's good you thought about that. Town girls is used to more than country girls. I lay awake nights, scared she'll make Rudolph discontented with the farm."

The boys put as good a face on it as they could. They surely looked forward to their Saturday nights in town. That evening Rosicky drove the car the half-mile down to Rudolph's new, bare little house.

Polly was in a short-sleeved gingham dress, clearing away the supper dishes. She was a trim, slim little thing, with blue eyes and shingled yellow hair, and her eyebrows were reduced to a mere brush-stroke, like Miss Pearl's.

"Good evening, Mr. Rosicky. Rudolph's at the barn, I guess." She never called him father, or Mary mother. She was sensitive about having married a foreigner. She never in the world would have done it if Rudolph hadn't been such a handsome, persuasive fellow and such a gallant lover. He had graduated in her class in the high school in town, and their friendship began in the ninth grade.

Rosicky went in, though he wasn't exactly asked. "My boys ain't goin' to town tonight, an' I brought de car over fur you two to go in to de picture show."

Polly, carrying dishes to the sink, looked over her shoulder at him. "Thank you. But I'm late with my work tonight, and pretty tired. Maybe Rudolph would like to go in with you."

"Oh, I don't go to de shows! I'm too old-fashioned. You won't feel so tired after you ride in de air a ways. It's a nice clear night, an' it ain't cold. You go an' fix yourself up, Polly, an' I'll wash de dishes an' leave everything nice fur you."

Polly blushed and tossed her bob. "I couldn't let you do that, Mr. Rosicky. I wouldn't think of it."

Rosicky said nothing. He found a bib apron on a nail behind the kitchen door. He slipped it over his head and then took Polly by her two elbows and pushed her gently toward the door of her own room. "I washed up de kitchen many times for my wife, when de babies was sick or somethin'. You go an' make yourself look nice. I like you to look prettier'n any of dem town girls when you go in. De young folks must have some fun, an' I'm goin' to look out fur you, Polly."

That kind, reassuring grip on her elbows, the old man's funny bright eyes, made Polly want to drop her head on his shoulder for a second. She restrained herself, but she lingered in his grasp at the door of her room, murmuring tearfully: "You always lived in the city when you were young, didn't you? Don't you ever get lonesome out here?"

As she turned round to him, her hand fell naturally into his, and he stood holding it and smiling into her face with his peculiar, knowing, indulgent smile without a shadow of reproach in it. "Dem big cities is all right fur de rich, but dey is terrible hard fur de poor."

"I don't know. Sometimes I think I'd like to take a chance. You lived in New York, didn't you?"

"An' London. Da's bigger still. I learned my trade dere. Here's Rudolph comin', you better hurry."

"Will you tell me about London some time?"

"Maybe. Only I ain't no talker, Polly. Run an' dress yourself up."

The bedroom door closed behind her, and Rudolph came in from the outside, looking anxious. He had seen the car and was sorry any of his family should come just then. Supper hadn't been a very pleasant occasion. Halting in the doorway, he saw his father in a kitchen apron, carrying dishes to the sink. He flushed crimson and something flashed in his eye. Rosicky held up a warning finger.

"I brought de car over fur you an' Polly to go to de picture show, an' I made her let me finish here so you won't be late. You go put on a clean shirt, quick!"

"But don't the boys want the car, Father?"

"Not tonight dey don't." Rosicky fumbled under his apron and found his pants pocket. He took out a silver dollar and said in a hurried whisper: "You go an' buy dat girl some ice cream an' candy tonight, like you was courtin'. She's awful good friends wid me."

Rudolph was very short of cash, but he took the money as if it hurt him. There had been a crop failure all over the county. He had more than once been sorry he'd married this year.

In a few minutes the young people came out, looking clean and a little stiff. Rosicky hurried them off, and then he took his own time with the dishes. He scoured the pots and pans and put away the milk and swept the kitchen. He put some coal in the stove and shut off the draughts, so the place would be warm for them when they got home late at night. Then he sat down and had a pipe and listened to the clock tick.

Generally speaking, marrying an American girl was certainly a risk. A Czech should marry a Czech. It was lucky that Polly was the daughter of a poor widow woman; Rudolph was proud, and if she had a prosperous family to throw up at him, they could never make it go. Polly was one of four sisters, and they all worked; one was bookkeeper in the bank, one taught music, and Polly and her younger sister had been clerks, like Miss Pearl. All four of them were musical, had pretty voices, and sang in the Methodist choir, which the eldest sister directed.

Polly missed the sociability of a store position. She missed the choir, and the company of her sisters. She didn't dislike housework, but she disliked so much of it. Rosicky was a little anxious about this pair. He was afraid Polly would grow so discontented that Rudy would quit the farm and take a factory job in Omaha. He had worked for a winter up there, two years ago, to get money to marry on. He had done very well, and they would always take him back at the stockyards. But to Rosicky that meant the end of everything for his son. To be a landless man was to be a wage-earner, a slave, all your life; to have nothing, to be nothing.

Rosicky thought he would come over and do a little carpentering for Polly after the New Year. He guessed she needed jollying. Rudolph was a serious sort of chap, serious in love and serious about his work.

Rosicky shook out his pipe and walked home across the fields. Ahead of him the lamplight shone from his kitchen windows. Suppose he were still in a tailor shop on Vesey Street, with a bunch of pale, narrow-chested sons working on machines, all coming home tired and sullen to eat supper in a kitchen that was a parlour also; with another crowded, angry family quarrelling just across the dumbwaiter shaft, and squeaking pulleys at the windows where dirty washings hung on dirty lines above a court full of old brooms and mops and ash-cans. . . .

He stopped by the windmill to look up at the frosty winter stars and draw a long breath before he went inside. That kitchen with the shining windows was dear to him; but the sleeping fields and bright stars and the noble darkness were dearer still.

V

On the day before Christmas the weather set in very cold; no snow, but a bitter, biting wind that whistled and sang over the flat land and lashed one's face like fine wires. There was baking going on in the Rosicky kitchen all day, and Rosicky sat inside, making over a coat that Albert had outgrown into an overcoat for John. Mary had a big red geranium in bloom for Christmas, and a row of Jerusalem cherry trees, full of berries. It was the first year she had ever grown these; Doctor Ed brought her the seeds from Omaha when he went to some medical convention. They reminded Rosicky of plants he had seen in England; and all afternoon, as he stitched, he sat thinking about those two years in London, which his mind usually shrank from even after all this while.

He was a lad of eighteen when he dropped down into London, with no money and no connexions except the address of a cousin who was supposed to be working at a confectioner's. When he went to the pastry shop, however, he found that the cousin had gone to America. Anton tramped the streets for several days, sleeping in doorways and on the Embankment, until he was in utter despair. He knew no English, and the sound of the strange language all about him confused him. By chance he met a poor German tailor who had learned his trade in Vienna, and could speak a little Czech. This tailor, Lifschnitz, kept a repair shop in a Cheapside basement, underneath a cobbler. He didn't much need an apprentice, but he was sorry for the boy and took him in for no wages but his keep and what he could pick up. The pickings were supposed to be coppers given you when you took work home to a customer. But most of the customers called for their clothes themselves, and the coppers that came Anton's way were very few. He had, however, a place to sleep. The tailor's family lived upstairs in three rooms; a kitchen, a bedroom, where Lifschnitz and his wife and five children slept, and a living-room. Two corners of this living-room were curtained off for lodgers; in one Rosicky slept on an old horsehair sofa, with a feather quilt to wrap himself in. The other corner was rented to a wretched, dirty boy, who was studying the violin. He actually practised there. Rosicky was dirty, too. There was no way to be anything else. Mrs. Lifschnitz got the water she cooked and washed with from a pump in a brick court, four flights down. There were bugs in the place, and multitudes of fleas, though the poor woman did the best she could. Rosicky knew she often went empty to give another potato or a spoonful of dripping to the two hungry, sad-eyed boys who lodged with her. He used to think he would never get out of there, never get a clean shirt to his back again. What would he do, he wondered, when his clothes actually dropped to pieces and the worn cloth wouldn't hold patches any longer?

It was still early when the old farmer put aside his sewing and his recollections. The sky had been a dark grey all day, with not a gleam of sun, and the light failed at four o'clock. He went to shave and change his shirt while the turkey was roasting. Rudolph and Polly were coming over for supper.

After supper they sat round in the kitchen, and the younger boys were saying how sorry they were it hadn't snowed. Everybody was sorry. They wanted a deep snow that would lie long and keep the wheat warm, and leave the ground soaked when it melted.

"Yes, sir!" Rudolph broke out fiercely; "if we have another dry year like last year, there's going to be hard times in this country."

Rosicky filled his pipe. "You boys don't know what hard times is. You don't owe nobody, you got plenty to eat an' keep warm, an' plenty of water to keep clean. When you got them, you can't have it very hard."

Rudolph frowned, opened and shut his big right hand, and dropped it clenched upon his knee. "I've got to have a good deal more than that, Father, or I'll quit this farming gamble. I can always make good wages railroading, or at the packing house, and be sure of my money."

"Maybe so," his father answered dryly.

Mary, who had just come in from the pantry and was wiping her hands on the roller towel, thought Rudy and his father were getting too serious. She brought her darning-basket and sat down in the middle of the group.

"I ain't much afraid of hard times, Rudy," she said heartily. "We've had a plenty, but we've always come through. Your father wouldn't never take nothing very hard, not even hard times. I got a mind to tell you a story on him. Maybe you boys can't hardly remember the year we had that terrible hot wind, that burned everything upon the Fourth of July? All the corn an' the gardens. An' that was in the days when we didn't have alfalfa yet,—I guess it wasn't invented.

"Well, that very day your father was out cultivatin' corn, and I was here in the kitchen makin' plum preserves. We had bushels of plums that year. I noticed it was terrible hot, but it's always hot in the kitchen when you're preservin', an' I was too busy with my plums to mind. Anton come in from the field about three o'clock, an' I asked him what was the matter.

"'Nothin',' he says, 'but it's pretty hot, an' I think I won't work no more today.' He stood round for a few minutes, an' then he says: 'Ain't you near through? I want you should git up a nice supper for us tonight. It's Fourth of July.'

"I told him to git along, that I was right in the middle of preservin', but the plums would taste good on hot biscuit. 'I'm goin' to have fried chicken, too,' he says, and he went off an' killed a couple. You three oldest boys was little fellers, playin' round outside, real hot an' sweaty, an' your father took you to the horse tank down by the windmill an' took off your clothes an' put you in. Them two box-elder trees was little then, but they made shade over the tank. Then he took off all his own clothes, an' got in with you. While he was playin' in the water with you, the Methodist preacher drove into our place to say how all the neighbours was goin' to meet at the schoolhouse that night, to pray for rain. He drove right to the windmill, of course, and there was your father and you three with no clothes on. I was in the kitchen door, an' I had to laugh, for the preacher acted like he ain't never seen a naked man before. He surely was embarrassed, an' your father couldn't git to his clothes; they was all hangin' up on the windmill to let the sweat dry out of 'em. So he laid in the tank where he was, an' put one of you boys on top of him to cover him up a little, an' talked to the preacher.

"When you got through playin' in the water, he put clean clothes on you and a clean shirt on himself, an' by that time I'd begun to get supper. He says: 'It's too hot in here to eat comfortable. Let's have a picnic in the orchard. We'll eat our supper behind the mulberry hedge, under them linden trees.'

"So he carried our supper down, an' a bottle of my wild-grape wine, an' everything tasted good, I can tell you. The wind got cooler as the sun was goin' down, and it turned out pleasant, only I noticed how the leaves was curled up on the linden trees. That made me think, an' I asked your father if that hot wind all day hadn't been terrible hard on the gardens an' the corn.

" 'Corn,' he says, 'there ain't no corn.'

" 'What you talkin' about?' I said. 'Ain't we got forty acres?'

" 'We ain't got an ear,' he says, 'nor nobody else ain't got none. All the corn in this country was cooked by three o'clock today, like you'd roasted it in an oven.'

" 'You mean you won't get no crop at all?' I asked him. I couldn't believe it, after he'd worked so hard.

" 'No crop this year,' he says. 'That's why we're havin' a picnic. We might as well enjoy what we got.'

"An' that's how your father behaved, when all the neighbours was so discouraged they couldn't look you in the face. An' we enjoyed ourselves that year, poor as we was, an' our neighbours wasn't a bit better off for bein' miserable. Some of 'em grieved till they got poor digestions and couldn't relish what they did have."

The younger boys said they thought their father had the best of it. But Rudolph was thinking that, all the same, the neighbours had managed to get ahead more, in the fifteen years since that time. There must be something wrong about his father's way of doing things. He wished he knew what was going on in the back of Polly's mind. He knew she liked his father, but he knew, too, that she was afraid of something. When his mother sent over coffee-cake or prune tarts or a loaf of fresh bread, Polly seemed to regard them with a certain suspicion. When she observed to him that his brothers had nice manners, her tone implied that it was remarkable they should have. With his mother she was stiff and on her guard. Mary's hearty frankness and gusts of good humour irritated her. Polly was afraid of being unusual or conspicuous in any way, of being "ordinary," as she said!

When Mary had finished her story, Rosicky laid aside his pipe.

"You boys like me to tell you about some of dem hard times I been through in London?" Warmly encouraged, he sat rubbing his forehead along the deep creases. It was bothersome to tell a long story in English (he nearly always talked to the boys in Czech), but he wanted Polly to hear this one.

"Well, you know about dat tailor shop I worked in in London? I had one Chirstmas dere I ain't never forgot. Times was awful bad before Christmas; de boss ain't got much work, an' have it awful hard to pay his rent. It ain't so much fun, bein' poor in a big city like London, I'll say! All de windows is full of good t'ings to eat, an' all de pushcarts in de streets is full, an' you smell 'em all de time, an' you ain't got no money,—not a damn bit. I didn't mind de cold so much, though I didn't have no overcoat, chust a short jacket I'd outgrowed so it wouldn't meet on me, an' my hands was chapped raw. But I always had a good appetite, like you all know, an' de sight of dem pork pies in de windows was awful fur me!

"Day before Christmas was terrible foggy dat year, an' dat fog gits into your bones and makes you all damp like. Mrs. Lifschnitz didn't give us nothin' but a little bread an' drippin' for supper, because she was savin' to try for to give us a good dinner on Christmas Day. After supper de boss say I can go an' enjoy myself, so I went into de streets to listen to de Christmas singers. Dey sing old songs an' make very nice music, an' I run round after dem a good ways, till I got awful hungry. I t'ink maybe if I go home, I can sleep till morning an' forget my belly.

"I went into my corner real quiet, and roll up in my fedder quilt,

But I ain't got my head down, till I smell somet'ing good. Seem like it git stronger an' stronger, an' I can't git to sleep noway. I can't understand dat smell. Dere was a gas light in a hall across de court, dat always shine in at my window a little. I got up an' look around. I got a little wooden box in my corner fur a stool, 'cause I ain't got no chair. I picks up dat box, and under it dere is a roast goose on a platter! I can't believe my eyes. I carry it to de window where de light comes in, an' touch it and smell it to find out, an' den I taste it to be sure. I say, I will eat chust one little bite of dat goose, so I can go to sleep, and tomorrow I won't eat none at all. But I tell you, boys, when I stop, one half of dat goose was gone!"

The narrator bowed his head, and the boys shouted. But little Josephine slipped behind his chair and kissed him on the neck beneath his ear.

"Poor little Papa, I don't want him to be hungry!"

"Da's long ago, child. I ain't never been hungry since I had your mudder to cook fur me."

"Go on and tell us the rest, please," said Polly.

"Well, when I come to realize what I done, of course, I felt terrible. I felt better in de stomach, but very bad in de heart. I set on my bed wid dat platter on my knees, an' it all come to me; how hard dat poor woman save to buy dat goose, and how she get some neighbour to cook it dat got more fire, an' how she put it in my corner to keep it away from dem hungry children. Dey was a old carpet hung up to shut my corner off, an' de children wasn't allowed to go in dere. An' I know she put it in my corner because she trust me more'n she did de violin boy. I can't stand it to face her after I spoil de Christmas. So I put on my shoes and go out into de city. I tell myself I better throw myself in de river; but I guess I ain't dat kind of a boy.

"It was after twelve o'clock, an' terrible cold, an' I start out to walk about London all night. I walk along de river awhile, but dey was lots of drunks all along; men, and women too. I chust move along to keep away from de police. I git onto de Strand, an' den over to New Oxford Street, where dere was a big German restaurant on de ground floor, wid big windows all fixed up fine, an' I could see de people havin' parties inside. While I was lookin' in, two men and two ladies come out, laughin' and talkin' and feelin' happy about all dey been eatin' an' drinkin', and dey was speakin' Czech,—not like de Austrians, but like de home folks talk it.

"I guess I went crazy, an' I done what I ain't never done before nor since. I went right up to dem gay people an' begun to beg dem: 'Fellow-countrymen, for God's sake give me money enough to buy a goose!'

"Dey laugh, of course, but de ladies speak awful kind to me, an' dey take me back into de restaurant and give me hot coffee and cakes, an' make me tell all about how I happened to come to London, an' what I was doin' dere. Dey take my name and where I work down on paper, an' both of dem ladies give me ten shillings.

"De big market at Covent Garden ain't very far away, an' by dat time it was open. I go dere an' buy a big goose an' some pork pies, an' potatoes and onions, an' cakes an' oranges fur de children,—all I could carry! When I git home, everybody is still asleep. I pile all I bought on de kitchen table, an' go in an' lay down on my bed, an' I ain't waken up till I hear dat woman scream when she comes out into her kitchen. My goodness, but she was surprise! She laugh an' cry at de same time, an' hug me and waken all de children. She ain't stop fur no breakfast; she git de Christmas dinner ready dat morning, and we all sit down an' eat all we can hold. I ain't never seen dat violin boy have all he can hold before.

"Two three days after dat, de two men come to hunt me up, an' dey ask my boss, and he give me a good report an' tell dem I was a steady boy all right. One of dem Bohemians was very smart an' run a Bohemian newspaper in New York, an' de odder was a rich man, in de importing business, an' dey been travelling togedder. Dey told me how t'ings was easier in New York, an' offered to pay my passage when dey was goin' home soon on a boat. My boss say to me: 'You go. You ain't got no chance here, an' I like to see you git ahead, fur you always been a good boy to my woman, and fur dat fine Christmas dinner you give us all.' An' da's how I got to New York."

That night when Rudolph and Polly, arm in arm, were running home across the fields with the bitter wind at their backs, his heart leaped for joy when she said she thought they might have his family come over for supper on New Year's Eve. "Let's get up a nice supper, and not let your mother help at all; make her be company for once."

"That would be lovely of you, Polly," he said humbly. He was a very simple, modest boy, and he, too, felt vaguely that Polly and her sisters were more experienced and worldly than his people.

VI

The winter turned out badly for farmers. It was bitterly cold, and after the first light snows before Christmas there was no snow at all,— and no rain. March was as bitter as February. On those days when the wind fairly punished the country, Rosicky sat by his window. In the fall he and the boys had put in a big wheat planting, and now the seed had frozen in the ground. All that land would have to be ploughed up and planted over again, planted in corn. It had happened before, but he was younger then, and he never worried about what had to be. He was sure of himself and of Mary; he knew they could bear what they had to bear, that they would always pull through some-how. But he was not so sure about the young ones, and he felt trou-bled because Rudolph and Polly were having such a hard start.

Sitting beside his flowering window while the panes rattled and the wind blew in under the door, Rosicky gave himself to reflection as he had not done since those Sundays in the loft of the furniture-factory in New York, long ago. Then he was trying to find what he wanted in life for himself; now he was trying to find what he wanted for his boys, and why it was he so hungered to feel sure they would be here, working this very land, after he was gone.

They would have to work hard on the farm, and probably they would never do much more than make a living. But if he could think of them as staying here on the land, he wouldn't have to fear any great unkindness for them. Hardships, certainly; it was a hardship to have the wheat freeze in the ground when seed was so high; and to have to sell your stock because you had no feed. But there would be other years when everything came along right, and you caught up. And what you had was your own. You didn't have to choose between bosses and strikers, and go wrong either way. You didn't have to do with dishonest and cruel people. They were the only things in his ex-perience he had found terrifying and horrible; the look in the eyes of a dishonest and crafty man, of a scheming and rapacious woman.

In the country, if you had a mean neighbour, you could keep off his land and make him keep off yours. But in the city, all the foulness and misery and brutality of your neighbours was part of your life. The worst things he had come upon in his journey through the world were human,—depraved and poisonous specimens of man. To this day he could recall certain terrible faces in the London streets. There were mean people everywhere, to be sure, even in their own country town here. But they weren't tempered, hardened, sharpened, like the treacherous people in cities who live by grinding or cheating or poisoning their fellow-men. He had helped to bury two of his fellow-workmen in the tailoring trade, and he was distrustful of the organized industries that see one out of the world in big cities. Here, if you were sick, you had Doctor Ed to look after you; and if you died, fat Mr. Haycock, the kindest man in the world, buried you.

It seemed to Rosicky that for good, honest boys like his, the worst they could do on the farm was better than the best they would be likely to do in the city. If he'd had a mean boy, now, one who was crooked and sharp and tried to put anything over on his brothers, then town would be the place for him. But he had no such boy. As for Rudolph, the discontented one, he would give the shirt off his back to anyone who touched his heart. What Rosicky really hoped for his boys was that they could get through the world without ever knowing much about the cruelty of human beings. "Their mother and me ain't prepared them for that," he sometimes said to himself.

These thoughts brought him back to a grateful consideration of his own case. What an escape he had had, to be sure! He, too, in his time, had had to take money for repair work from the hand of a hungry child who let it go so wistfully; because it was money due his boss. And now, in all these years, he had never had to take a cent from anyone in bitter need,—never had to look at the face of a woman become like a wolf's from struggle and famine. When he thought of these things, Rosicky would put on his cap and jacket and slip down to the barn and give his work-horses a little extra oats, letting them eat it out of his hand in their slobbery fashion. It was his way of expressing what he felt, and made him chuckle with pleasure.

The spring came warm, with blue skies,—but dry, dry as a bone. The boys began ploughing up the wheat-fields to plant them over in corn. Rosicky would stand at the fence corner and watch them, and the earth was so dry it blew up in clouds of brown dust that hid the horses and the sulky plough and the driver. It was a bad outlook.

The big alfalfa field that lay between the home place and Rudolph's came up green, but Rosicky was worried because during that open windy winter a great many Russian thistle plants had blown in there and lodged. He kept asking the boys to rake them out; he was afraid their seed would root and "take the alfalfa." Rudolph said that was nonsense. The boys were working so hard planting corn, their father felt he couldn't insist about the thistles, but he set great store by that big alfalfa field. It was a feed you could depend on,—and there was some deeper reason, vague, but strong. The peculiar green of that clover woke early memories in old Rosicky, went back to something in his childhood in the old world. When he was a little boy, he had played in fields of that strong blue-green colour.

One morning, when Rudolph had gone to town in the car, leaving a work-team idle in his barn, Rosicky went over to his son's place, put the horses to the buggy-rake, and set about quietly raking up those thistles. He behaved with guilty caution, and rather enjoyed stealing a march on Doctor Ed, who was just then taking his first vacation in seven years of practice and was attending a clinic in Chicago. Rosicky got the thistles raked up, but did not stop to burn them. That would take some time, and his breath was pretty short, so he thought he had better get the horses back to the barn.

He got them into the barn and to their stalls, but the pain had come on so sharp in his chest that he didn't try to take the harness off. He started for the house, bending lower with every step. The cramp in his chest was shutting him up like a jack-knife. When he reached the windmill, he swayed and caught at the ladder. He saw Polly coming down the hill, running with the swiftness of a slim greyhound. In a flash she had her shoulder under his armpit.

"Lean on me, Father, hard! Don't be afraid. We can get to the house all right."

Somehow they did, though Rosicky became blind with pain; he could keep on his legs, but he couldn't steer his course. The next thing he was conscious of was lying on Polly's bed, and Polly bending over him wringing out bath towels in hot water and putting them on his chest. She stopped only to throw coal into the stove, and she kept the tea-kettle and the black pot going. She put these hot applications on him for nearly an hour, she told him afterwards, and all that time he was drawn up stiff and blue, with the sweat pouring off him.

As the pain gradually loosed its grip, the stiffness went out of his jaws, the black circles round his eyes disappeared, and a little of his natural colour came back. When his daughter-in-law buttoned his shirt over his chest at last, he sighed.

"Da's fine, de way I feel now, Polly. It was a awful bad spell, an' I was so sorry it all come on you like it did."

Polly was flushed and excited. "Is the pain really gone? Can I leave you long enough to telephone over to your place?"

Rosicky's eyelids fluttered. "Don't telephone, Polly. It ain't no use to scare my wife. It's nice and quiet here, an' if I ain't too much trouble to you, just let me lay still till I feel like myself. I ain't got no pain now. It's nice here."

Polly bent over him and wiped the moisture from his face. "Oh, I'm so glad it's over!" she broke out impulsively. "It just broke my heart to see you suffer so, Father."

Rosicky motioned her to sit down on the chair where the tea-kettle had been, and looked up at her with that lively affectionate gleam in his eyes. "You was awful good to me, I won't never forgit dat. I hate it to be sick on you like dis. Down at de barn I say to myself, dat young girl ain't had much experience in sickness, I don't want to scare her, an' maybe she's got a baby comin' or somet'ing."

Polly took his hand. He was looking at her so intently and affectionately and confidingly; his eyes seemed to caress her face, to regard it with pleasure. She frowned with her funny streaks of eyebrows, and then smiled back at him.

"I guess maybe there is something of that kind going to happen. But I haven't told anyone yet, not my mother or Rudolph. You'll be the first to know."

His hand pressed hers. She noticed that it was warm again. The twinkle in his yellow-brown eyes seemed to come nearer.

"I like mighty well to see dat little child, Polly," was all he said. Then he closed his eyes and lay half-smiling. But Polly sat still, thinking hard. She had a sudden feeling that nobody in the world, not her mother, not Rudolph, or anyone, really loved her as much as old Rosicky did. It perplexed her. She sat frowning and trying to puzzle it out. It was as if Rosicky had a special gift for loving people, something that was like an ear for music or an eye for colour. It was quiet, unobtrusive; it was merely there. You saw it in his eyes,—perhaps that was why they were merry. You felt it in his hands, too. After he dropped off to sleep, she sat holding his warm, broad, flexible brown hand. She had never seen another in the least like it. She wondered if it wasn't a kind of gypsy hand, it was so alive and quick and light in its communications,—very strange in a farmer. Nearly all the farmers she knew had huge lumps of fists, like mauls, or they were knotty and bony and uncomfortable-looking, with stiff fingers. But Rosicky's was like quicksilver, flexible, muscular, about the colour of a pale cigar, with deep, deep creases across the palm. It wasn't nervous, it wasn't a stupid lump; it was a warm brown human hand, with some cleverness in it, a great deal of generosity, and something else which Polly could only call "gypsy-like,"—something nimble and lively and sure, in the way that animals are.

Polly remembered that hour long afterwards; it had been like an awakening to her. It seemed to her that she had never learned so much about life from anything as from old Rosicky's hand. It brought her to herself; it communicated some direct and untranslatable message.

When she heard Rudolph coming in the car, she ran out to meet him.

"Oh, Rudy, your father's been awful sick! He raked up those thistles he's been worrying about, and afterwards he could hardly get to the house. He suffered so I was afraid he was going to die."

Rudolph jumped to the ground. "Where is he now?"

"On the bed. He's asleep. I was terribly scared, because, you know, I'm so fond of your father." She slipped her arm through his and they went into the house. That afternoon they took Rosicky home and put him to bed, though he protested that he was quite well again.

The next morning he got up and dressed and sat down to breakfast with his family. He told Mary that his coffee tasted better than usual to him, and he warned the boys not to bear any tales to Doctor Ed when he got home. After breakfast he sat down by his window to do some patching and asked Mary to thread several needles for him before she went to feed her chickens,—her eyes were better than his, and her hands steadier. He lit his pipe and took up John's overalls. Mary had been watching him anxiously all morning, and as she went out of the door with her bucket of scraps, she saw that he was smiling. He was thinking, indeed, about Polly, and how he might never have known what a tender heart she had if he hadn't got sick over there. Girls nowadays didn't wear their heart on their sleeve. But now he knew Polly would make a fine woman after the foolishness wore off. Either a woman had that sweetness at her heart or she hadn't. You couldn't always tell by the look of them; but if they had that, everything came out right in the end.

After he had taken a few stitches, the cramp began in his chest, like yesterday. He put his pipe cautiously down on the window-sill and bent over to ease the pull. No use,—he had better try to get to his bed if he could. He rose and groped his way across the familiar floor, which was rising and falling like the deck of a ship. At the door he fell. When Mary came in, she found him lying there, and the moment she touched him she knew that he was gone.

Doctor Ed was away when Rosicky died, and for the first few weeks after he got home he was hard driven. Every day he said to himself that he must get out to see that family that had lost their father. One soft, warm moonlight night in early summer he started for the farm. His mind was on other things, and not until his road ran by the graveyard did he realize that Rosicky wasn't over there on the hill where the red lamplight shone, but here, in the moonlight. He stopped his car, shut off the engine, and sat there for a while.

A sudden hush had fallen on his soul. Everything here seemed strangely moving and significant, though signifying what, he did not know. Close by the wire fence stood Rosicky's mowing-machine, where one of the boys had been cutting hay that afternoon; his own work-horses had been going up and down there. The new-cut hay perfumed all the night air. The moonlight silvered the long, billowy grass that grew over the graves and hid the fence; the few little evergreens stood out black in it, like shadows in a pool. The sky was very blue and soft, the stars rather faint because the moon was full.

For the first time it struck Doctor Ed that this was really a beautiful graveyard. He thought of city cemeteries; acres of shrubbery and heavy stone, so arranged and lonely and unlike anything in the living world. Cities of the dead, indeed; cities of the forgotten, of the "put away." But this was open and free, this little square of long grass which the wind for ever stirred. Nothing but the sky overhead, and the many-coloured fields running on until they met that sky. The horses worked here in summer; the neighbours passed on their way to town; and over yonder, in the cornfield, Rosicky's own cattle would be eating fodder as winter came on. Nothing could be more undeath-like than this place; nothing could be more right for a man who had helped to do the work of great cities and had always longed for the open country and had got to it at last. Rosicky's life seemed to him complete and beautiful.

SINCLAIR LEWIS

DINNER with the BABBITTS

Sinclair Lewis wished he could choose something "that I particularly favor in my own writing . . . I'd have to pass such a job over," he wrote the editor, "to Carl Van Doren, Harrison Smith or possibly Professor Joseph Warren Beach of the University of Minnesota. . . ."

The following letters are self-explanatory:

Dear Mr. Burnett:

It seems to me that Sinclair Lewis should be represented in your anthology not by one of his short stories but by an extract from a novel. His novels, of course, are pretty close-knit and depend a good deal on cumulative effect, so that few extracts do him justice. But there is one chapter in *Babbitt* that I have always liked very much. It is Chapter XV, which contains the brilliant account of a class reunion and the ironic, sensitive record of the two dinners the Babbitts give in consequence. Along with plenty of satiric force, here is also a fine example of the humane insight that is one of Lewis's strongest qualities. This chapter would not suffer by being excerpted, and Lewis could easily furnish you a title for it.

New York, N. Y.
April 15, 1942   CARL VAN DOREN

Dear Mr. Burnett:

I am glad that Carl Van Doren made that choice. I approve of it, and of the title "Dinner with the Babbitts."

All I can add for my own introduction—for I hope that you will use Carl's comment, the one you sent me, and the fact that he did the choosing for me—is:

For myself, I have no favorite passages among my books because I never re-read them, never open them after the pleasant first five minutes when they come new from the publisher. By the time I have finished one of them, I have put so much toil and fury—and probably self-adulation—into it that I don't want to be reminded of that labor. I am reserving my perusal of the

opera of Mr. Sinclair Lewis for my old age, just after I shall have finished
Dante and Sir Hall Caine and a manual of the wild flowers.

Excelsior, Minnesota
April 19, 1942   SINCLAIR LEWIS

I

HIS march to greatness was not without disastrous stumbling. Fame did not bring the social advancement which the Babbitts deserved. They were not asked to join the Tonawanda Country Club nor invited to the dances at the Union. Himself, Babbitt fretted, he didn't "care a fat hoot for all these highrollers, but the wife would kind of like to be Among Those Present." He nervously awaited his university class-dinner and an evening of furious intimacy with such social leaders as Charles McKelvey the millionaire contractor, Max Kruger the banker, Irving Tate the tool-manufacturer, and Adelbert Dobson the fashionable interior decorator. Theoretically he was their friend, as he had been in college, and when he encountered them they still called him "Georgie," but he didn't seem to encounter them often, and they never invited him to dinner (with champagne and a butler) at their houses on Royal Ridge.

All the week before the class-dinner he thought of them. "No reason why we shouldn't become real chummy now!"

II

Like all true American diversions and spiritual outpourings, the dinner of the men of the Class of 1896 was thoroughly organized. The dinner-committee hammered like a sales-corporation. Once a week they sent out reminders:

TICKLER NO. 3

Old man, are you going to be with us at the livest Friendship Feed the alumni of the good old U have ever known? The alumnæ of '08 turned out 60% strong. Are we boys going to be beaten by a bunch of skirts? Come on, fellows, let's work up some real genuine enthusiasm and all boost together for the snappiest dinner yet! Elegant eats, short ginger-talks, and memories shared together of the brightest, gladdest days of life.

The dinner was held in a private room at the Union Club. The club was a dingy building, three pretentious old dwellings knocked together, and the entrance-hall resembled a potato cellar, yet the Babbitt who was free of the magnificence of the Athletic Club entered with embarrassment. He nodded to the doorman, an ancient proud negro with brass buttons and a blue tail-coat, and paraded through the hall, trying to look like a member.

Sixty men had come to the dinner. They made islands and eddies in the hall; they packed the elevator and the corners of the private dining-room. They tried to be intimate and enthusiastic. They appeared to one another exactly as they had in college—as raw youngsters whose present mustaches, baldnesses, paunches, and wrinkles were but jovial disguises put on for the evening. "You haven't changed a particle!" they marveled. The men whom they could not recall they addressed, "Well, well, great to see you again, old man. What are you— Still doing the same thing?"

Some one was always starting a cheer or a college song, and it was always thinning into silence. Despite their resolution to be democratic they divided into two sets: the men with dress-clothes and the men without. Babbitt (extremely in dress-clothes) went from one group to the other. Though he was, almost frankly, out for social conquest, he sought Paul Riesling first. He found him alone, neat and silent.

Paul sighed, "I'm no good at this handshaking and 'well, look who's here' bunk."

"Rats now, Paulibus, loosen up and be a mixer! Finest bunch of boys on earth! Say, you seem kind of glum. What's matter?"

"Oh, the usual. Run-in with Zilla."

"Come on! Let's wade in and forget our troubles."

He kept Paul beside him, but worked toward the spot where Charles McKelvey stood warming his admirers like a furnace.

McKelvey had been the hero of the Class of '96; not only football captain and hammer-thrower but debater, and passable in what the State University considered scholarship. He had gone on, had captured the construction-company once owned by the Dodsworths, best-known pioneer family of Zenith. He built state capitols, skyscrapers, railway terminals. He was a heavy-shouldered, big-chested man, but not sluggish. There was a quiet humor in his eyes, a syrup-smooth quickness in his speech, which intimidated politicians and warned reporters; and in his presence the most intelligent scientist or the most sensitive artist felt thin-blooded, unworldly, and a little shabby. He was, particularly when he was influencing legislatures or hiring labor-spies, very easy and lovable and gorgeous. He was baronial; he was a peer in the rapidly crystallizing American aristocracy, inferior only to the haughty Old Families. (In Zenith, an Old Family is one which came to town before 1840.) His power was the greater because he was not hindered by scruples, by either the vice or the virtue of the older Puritan tradition.

McKelvey was being placidly merry now with the great, the manufacturers and bankers, the land-owners and lawyers and surgeons who had chauffeurs and went to Europe. Babbitt squeezed among them. He liked McKelvey's smile as much as the social advancement to be had from his favor. If in Paul's company he felt ponderous and protective, with McKelvey he felt slight and adoring.

He heard McKelvey say to Max Kruger, the banker, "Yes, we'll put up Sir Gerald Doak." Babbitt's democratic love for titles became a rich relish. "You know, he's one of the biggest iron-men in England, Max. Horribly well-off. . . . Why, hello, old Georgie! Say, Max, George Babbitt is getting fatter than I am!"

The chairman shouted, "Take your seats, fellows!"

"Shall we make a move, Charley?" Babbitt said casually to McKelvey.

"Right. Hello, Paul! How's the old fiddler? Planning to sit anywhere special, George? Come on, let's grab some seats. Come on, Max. Georgie, I read about your speeches in the campaign. Bully work!"

After that, Babbitt would have followed him through fire. He was enormously busy during the dinner, now bumblingly cheering Paul, now approaching McKelvey with "Hear you're going to build some piers in Brooklyn," now noting how enviously the failures of the class, sitting by themselves in a weedy group, looked up to him in his association with the nobility, now warming himself in the Society

Talk of McKelvey and Max Kruger. They spoke of a "jungle dance" for which Mona Dodsworth had decorated her house with thousands of orchids. They spoke, with an excellent imitation of casualness, of a dinner in Washington at which McKelvey had met a Senator, a Balkan princess, and an English major-general. McKelvey called the princess "Jenny," and let it be known that he had danced with her.

Babbitt was thrilled, but not so weighted with awe as to be silent. If he was not invited by them to dinner, he was yet accustomed to talking with bank-presidents, congressmen, and clubwomen who entertained poets. He was bright and referential with McKelvey:

"Say, Charley, juh remember in Junior year how we chartered a sea-going hack and chased down to Riverdale, to the big show Madame Brown used to put on? Remember how you beat up that hick constabule that tried to run us in, and we pinched the pants-pressing sign and took and hung it on Prof. Morrison's door? Oh, gosh, those were the days!"

Those, McKelvey agreed, were the days.

Babbitt had reached "It isn't the books you study in college but the friendships you make that counts" when the men at head of the table broke into song. He attacked McKelvey:

"It's a shame, uh, shame to drift apart because our, uh, business activities lie in different fields. I've enjoyed talking over the good old days. You and Mrs. McKelvey must come to dinner some night."

Vaguely, "Yes, indeed——"

"Like to talk to you about the growth of real estate out beyond your Grantsville warehouse. I might be able to tip you off to a thing or two, possibly."

"Splendid! We must have dinner together, Georgie. Just let me know. And it will be a great pleasure to have your wife and you at the house," said McKelvey, much less vaguely.

Then the chairman's voice, that prodigious voice which once had roused them to cheer defiance at rooters from Ohio or Michigan or Indiana, whooped, "Come on, you wombats! All together in the long yell!" Babbitt felt that life would never be sweeter than now, when he joined with Paul Riesling and the newly recovered hero, McKelvey, in:

Baaaaaattle-ax
Get an ax,
Bal-ax,
Get-nax,
Who, who? The U.!
Hooroo!

III

The Babbitts invited the McKelveys to dinner, in early December, and the McKelveys not only accepted but, after changing the date once or twice, actually came.

The Babbitts somewhat thoroughly discussed the details of the dinner, from the purchase of a bottle of champagne to the number of salted almonds to be placed before each person. Especially did they mention the matter of the other guests. To the last Babbitt held out for giving Paul Riesling the benefit of being with the McKelveys. "Good old Charley would like Paul and Verg Gunch better than some highfalutin' Willy boy," he insisted, but Mrs. Babbitt interrupted his observations with, "Yes—perhaps— I think I'll try to get some Lynn-haven oysters," and when she was quite ready she invited Dr. J. T. Angus, the oculist, and a dismally respectable lawyer named Maxwell, with their glittering wives.

Neither Angus nor Maxwell belonged to the Elks or to the Athletic Club; neither of them had ever called Babbitt "brother" or asked his opinions on carburetors. The only "human people" whom she invited, Babbitt raged, were the Littlefields; and Howard Littlefield at times became so statistical that Babbitt longed for the refreshment of Gunch's, "Well, old lemon-pie-face, what's the good word?"

Immediately after lunch Mrs. Babbitt began to set the table for the seven-thirty dinner to the McKelveys, and Babbitt was, by order, home at four. But they didn't find anything for him to do, and three times Mrs. Babbitt scolded, "Do please try to keep out of the way!" He stood in the door of the garage, his lips drooping, and wished that Littlefield or Sam Doppelbrau or somebody would come along and talk to him. He saw Ted sneaking about the corner of the house.

"What's the matter, old man?" said Babbitt.

"Is that you, thin, owld one? Gee, Ma certainly is on the warpath!

I told her Rone and I would jus' soon not be let in on the fiesta to-night, and she bit me. She says I got to take a bath, too. But, say, the Babbitt men will be some lookers to-night! Little Theodore in a dress-suit!"

"The Babbitt men!" Babbitt liked the sound of it. He put his arm about the boy's shoulder. He wished that Paul Riesling had a daughter, so that Ted might marry her. "Yes, your mother is kind of rouncing round, all right," he said, and they laughed together, and sighed together, and dutifully went in to dress.

The McKelveys were less than fifteen minutes late.

Babbitt hoped that the Dopplebraus would see the McKelveys' limousine, and their uniformed chauffeur, waiting in front.

The dinner was well cooked and incredibly plentiful, and Mrs. Babbitt had brought out her grandmother's silver candlesticks. Babbitt worked hard. He was good. He told none of the jokes he wanted to tell. He listened to the others. He started Maxwell off with a resounding, "Let's hear about your trip to the Yellowstone." He was laudatory, extremely laudatory. He found opportunities to remark that Dr. Angus was a benefactor to humanity, Maxwell and Howard Littlefield profound scholars, Charles McKelvey an inspiration to ambitious youth, and Mrs. McKelvey an adornment to the social circles of Zenith, Washington, New York, Paris, and numbers of other places.

But he could not stir them. It was a dinner without a soul. For no reason that was clear to Babbitt, heaviness was over them and they spoke laboriously and unwillingly.

He concentrated on Lucille McKelvey, carefully not looking at her blanched lovely shoulder and the tawney silken band which supported her frock.

"I suppose you'll be going to Europe pretty soon again, won't you?" he invited.

"I'd like awfully to run over to Rome for a few weeks."

"I suppose you see a lot of pictures and music and curios and everything there."

"No, what I really go for is: there's a little *trattoria* on the Via della Scrofa where you get the best *fettuccine* in the world."

"Oh, I— Yes. That must be nice to try that. Yes."

At a quarter to ten McKelvey discovered with profound regret that his wife had a headache. He said blithely, as Babbitt helped him with his coat, "We must lunch together some time, and talk over the old days."

When the others had labored out, at half-past ten, Babbitt turned to his wife pleading, "Charley said he had a corking time and we must lunch—said they wanted to have us up to the house for dinner before long."

She achieved, "Oh, it's just been one of those quiet evenings that are often so much more enjoyable than noisy parties where everybody talks at once and doesn't really settle down to—nice quiet enjoyment."

But from his cot on the sleeping-porch he heard her weeping, slowly, without hope.

IV

For a month they watched the social columns, and waited for a return dinner-invitation.

As the hosts of Sir Gerald Doak, the McKelveys were headlined all the week after the Babbitts' dinner. Zenith ardently received Sir Gerald (who had come to America to buy coal). The newspapers interviewed him on prohibition, Ireland, unemployment, naval aviation, the rate of exchange, tea-drinking *versus* whisky-drinking, the psychology of American women, and daily life as lived by English county families. Sir Gerald seemed to have heard of all those topics. The McKelveys gave him a Singhalese dinner, and Miss Elnora Pearl Bates, society editor of the *Advocate-Times*, rose to her highest lark-note. Babbitt read aloud at breakfast-table:

'Twixt the original and Oriental decorations, the strange and delicious food, and the personalities both of the distinguished guests, the charming hostess and the noted host, never has Zenith seen a more recherche affair than the Ceylon dinner-dance given last evening by Mr. and Mrs. Charles McKelvey to Sir Gerald Doak. Methought as we—fortunate one!—were privileged to view that fairy and foreign scene, nothing at Monte Carlo or the choicest ambassadorial sets of foreign capitals could be more lovely. It is not for nothing that Zenith is in matters social rapidly becoming known as the choosiest inland city in the country.

Though he is too modest to admit it, Lord Doak gives a cachet to our smart quartier such as it has not received since the ever-memorable visit of the Earl of Sittingbourne. Not only is he of the British peerage, but he is also, on dit, a leader of the British metal industries. As he comes from Nottingham, a favorite haunt of Robin Hood, though now, we are informed by Lord Doak, a live modern city of 275,573 inhabitants, and important lace as well as other industries, we like to think that perhaps through his veins runs some of the blood, both virile red and bonny blue, of that earlier lord o' the good greenwood, the roguish Robin.

The lovely Mrs. McKelvey never was more fascinating than last evening in her black net gown relieved by dainty bands of silver and at her exquisite waist a glowing cluster of Aaron Ward roses.

Babbitt said bravely, "I hope they don't invite us to meet this Lord Doak guy. Darn sight rather just have a nice quiet little dinner with Charley and the Missus."

At the Zenith Athletic Club they discussed it amply. "I s'pose we'll have to call McKelvey 'Lord Chaz' from now on," said Sidney Finkelstein.

"It beats all get-out," meditated that man of data, Howard Littlefield, "how hard it is for some people to get things straight. Here they call this fellow 'Lord Doak' when it ought to be 'Sir Gerald.' "

Babbitt marvelled, 'Is that a fact! Well, well! 'Sir Gerald,' eh? That's what you call um, eh? Well, sir, I'm glad to know that."

Later he informed his salesmen, 'It's funnier 'n a goat the way some folks that, just because they happen to lay upa big wad, go entertaining famous foreigners, don't have any more idea 'n a rabbit how to address 'em so's to make 'em feel at home!"

That evening, as he was driving home, he passed McKelvey's limousine and saw Sir Gerald, a large, ruddy, pop-eyed, Teutonic Englishman whose dribble of yellow mustache gave him an aspect sad and doubtful. Babbitt drove on slowly, oppressed by futility. He had a sudden, unexplained, and horrible conviction that the McKelveys were laughing at him.

He betrayed his depression by the violence with which he informed his wife, "Folks that really tend to business haven't got the time to waste on a bunch like the McKelveys. This society stuff is like any other hobby; if you devote yourself to it, you get on. But I like to have a chance to visit with you and the children instead of all this idiotic chasing round."

They did not speak of the McKelveys again.

v

It was a shame, at this worried time, to have to think about the Overbrooks.

Ed Overbrook was a classmate of Babbitt who had been a failure. He had a large family and a feeble insurance business out in the suburb of Dorchester. He was gray and thin and unimportant. He had always been gray and thin and unimportant. He was the person whom, in any group, you forgot to introduce, then introduced with extra enthusiasm. He had admired Babbitt's good-fellowship in college, had admired ever since his power in real estate, his beautiful house and wonderful clothes. It pleased Babbitt, though it bothered him with a sense of responsibility. At the class-dinner he had seen poor Overbrook, in a shiny blue serge business-suit, being diffident in a corner with three other failures. He had gone over and been cordial: "Why, hello, young Ed! I hear you're writing all the insurance in Dorchester now. Bully work!"

They recalled the good old days when Overbrook used to write poetry. Overbrook embarrassed him by blurting, "Say, Georgie, I hate to think of how we been drifting apart. I wish you and Mrs. Babbitt would come to dinner some night."

Babbitt boomed, "Fine! Sure! Just let me know. And the wife and I want to have you at the house." He forgot it, but unfortunately Ed Overbrook did not. Repeatedly he telephoned to Babbitt, inviting him to dinner. "Might as well go and get it over," Babbitt groaned to his wife. "But don't it simply amaze you the way the poor fish doesn't know the first thing about social etiquette? Think of him 'phoning me, instead of his wife sitting down and writing us a regular bid! Well, I guess we're stuck for it. That's the trouble with all this class-brother hooptedoodle."

He accepted Overbrook's next plaintive invitation, for an evening two weeks off. A dinner two weeks off, even a family dinner, never seems so appalling, till the two weeks have astoundingly disappeared and one comes dismayed to the ambushed hour. They had to change the date, because of their own dinner to the McKelveys, but at last they gloomily drove out to the Overbrooks' house in Dorchester.

It was miserable from the beginning. The Overbrooks had dinner at six-thirty, while the Babbitts never dined before seven. Babbitt permitted himself to be ten minutes late. "Let's make it as short as possible. I think we'll duck out quick. I'll say I have to be at the office extra early to-morrow," he planned.

The Overbrook house was depressing. It was the second story of a wooden two-family dwelling; a place of baby-carriages, old hats hung in the hall, cabbage-smell, and a Family Bible on the parlor table. Ed Overbrook and his wife were as awkward and threadbare as usual, and the other guests were two dreadful families whose names Babbitt never caught and never desired to catch. But he was touched, and disconcerted, by the tactless way in which Overbrook praised him: "We're mighty proud to have old George here to-night! Of course you've all read about his speeches and oratory in the papers—and the boy's good-looking, too, eh?—but what I always think of is back in college, and what a great old mixer he was, and one of the best swimmers in the class."

Babbitt tried to be jovial; he worked at it; but he could find nothing to interest him in Overbrook's timorousness, the blankness of the other guests, or the drained stupidity of Mrs. Overbrook, with her spectacles, drab skin, and tight-drawn hair. He told his best Irish story, but it sank like soggy cake. Most bleary moment of all was when Mrs. Overbrook, peering out of her fog of nursing eight children and cooking and scrubbing, tried to be conversational.

"I suppose you go to Chicago and New York right along, Mr. Babbitt," she prodded.

"Well, I get to Chicago fairly often."

"It must be awfully interesting. I suppose you take in all the theaters."

"Well, to tell the truth, Mrs. Overbrook, thing that hits me best is a great big beefsteak at a Dutch restaurant in the Loop!"

They had nothing more to say. Babbitt was sorry, but there was no hope; the dinner was a failure. At ten, rousing out of the stupor of meaningless talk, he said as cheerily as he could, "'Fraid we got to be starting, Ed. I've got a fellow coming to see me early to-morrow." As Overbrook helped him with his coat, Babbitt said, "Nice to rub up on the old days! We must have lunch together, P.D.Q."

Mrs. Babbitt sighed, on their drive home, "It was pretty terrible. But how Mr. Overbrook does admire you!"

"Yep. Poor cuss! Seems to think I'm a little tin archangel, and the best-looking man in Zenith."

"Well, you're certainly not that but— Oh, Georgie, you don't suppose we have to invite them to dinner at our house now, do we?"

"Ouch! Gaw, I hope not!"

"See here, now, George! You didn't say anything about it to Mr. Overbrook, did you?"

"No! Gee! No! Honest, I didn't! Just made a bluff about having him to lunch some time."

"Well. . . . Oh, dear. . . . I don't want to hurt their feelings. But I don't see how I could stand another evening like this one. And suppose somebody like Dr. and Mrs. Angus came in when we had the Overbrooks there, and thought they were friends of ours!"

For a week they worried, "We really ought to invite Ed and his wife, poor devils!" But as they never saw the Overbrooks, they forgot them, and after a month or two they said, "That really was the best way, just to let it slide. It wouldn't be kind to *them* to have them here. They'd feel so out of place and hard-up in our home."

They did not speak of the Overbrooks again.

JAMES TRUSLOW ADAMS Why he

selected The AMERICAN DREAM

An author is not always the best judge of his own work, and I was somewhat puzzled when asked to suggest some article or passage of about five thousand words from the twenty volumes or so of history, biography, and collected essays of which I have been guilty in the past twenty-five years. On the whole I decided upon the Epilogue to my *Epic of America*, here titled "The American Dream." For one reason, this book is best known of my works, still selling widely in America after more than ten years, used in schools in England, and translated into eight foreign languages in Europe and South America. But, another reason, I have a special affection for it. When I wrote it I had for some years had in mind trying to tell the wonderful story of America as the saga of the common man, and I was so full of my theme that, when I finally set myself before the little portable typewriter which I bought when in the army in 1918 and on which I have done all my work since, I spilled the whole book out in three months. It is primarily the story of "the American Dream" (a phrase since very current), and of how all sorts of men and women were lured by that dream from all lands and helped to make it a reality. It was a great dream and, in spite of bits of nightmare, is today a great reality. It was the biggest and finest subject I ever had to write about, and I let myself go. I still believe in it.

Southport, Conn.   JAMES TRUSLOW ADAMS

June 17, 1942

WE HAVE ... traced ... the course of our story from that dateless period when savages roamed over our continent, coming from we know not where. We reached time and dates with the records of the rich but cruel civilization of Mexico and Central America. We have seen the surprise with which the first white men were greeted when they landed on our islands and coasts, coming thereafter with increasing frequency and in larger numbers. We have seen the strivings and conflicts of French and English and Spanish. We have seen the rise of our own nation from a handful of starving Englishmen in Virginia to a people of 120,000,000* made up of all the races of the world. Beginning with a guard scarce sufficient to defend the stockade at Jamestown against a few naked Indians, we grew until we were able to select from nearly 25,000,000 men of military age such millions as we would to hurl back at our enemies across the sea, only nine generations later. A continent which scarce sufficed to maintain a half million savages now supports nearly two hundred and fifty times that number of as active and industrious people as there are in the world. The huge and empty land has been filled with homes, roads, railways, schools, colleges, hospitals, and all the comforts of the most advanced material civilization. The mere physical tasks have been stupendous and unparalleled. Supplied at each important stage of advance with new implements of science which quickened our pace; lured by such rewards for haste and industry as were never offered to man before; keyed to activity by a climate that makes expenditure of nervous energy almost a bodily necessity, we threw ourselves into the task of physical domination of our environment with an abandonment that perforce led us to discard much that we had started to build up in our earliest days.

Even so, the frontier was always retreating before us, and sending its influence back among us in refluent waves until almost yesterday. In the eighteenth century we had an established civilization, with stability of material and spiritual values. Then we began our scramble for the untold wealth which lay at the foot of the rainbow. As we have gone ever westward, stability gave place to the constant flux in which we have lived since. Recently a distinguished English man of letters complained to me at dinner that we made too much of the frontier as an excuse for everything. It is not an excuse, but it is assuredly an explanation. We let ourselves be too much deflected by it from the building of the civilization of which our forefathers laid the foundations, and the frontier has stretched from our doors until my own childhood. When my great-grandmother, an old lady with whom I

* Census of 193-.

frequently talked as a young man, was born, the United States extended only to the Mississippi, without including even Florida and the Gulf Coast. Both my grandfathers were children when Thomas Jefferson, who carried our bounds out to the Rockies, died. When my father was a baby, the entire country south of Oklahoma and from the Rockies westward was still Spanish territory. When I was born, the Sioux and the Nez Percés were still on the warpath. I was five when the Southwest was first spanned by the Southern Pacific, and twelve when the frontier was officially declared closed.

While thus occupied with material conquest and upbuilding, we did not wholly lose the vision of something nobler. If we hastened after the pot of gold, we also saw the rainbow itself, and felt that it promised, as of old, a hope for mankind. In the realm of thought we have been practical and adaptive rather than original and theoretical, although it may be noted that to-day we stand preëminent in astronomy. In medicine we have conferred discoveries of inestimable value on the world, which we have also led along the road of many humanitarian reforms, such as the treatment of debtors and the insane. Until the reaction after the World War, we had struggled for a juster law of nations and for the extension of arbitration as a substitute for war in international disputes. If in arts and letters we have produced no men who may be claimed to rank with the masters of all time, we have produced a body of work without which the world would be poorer and which ranks high by contemporary world standards. In literature and the drama, to-day, there is no work being done better anywhere than in the United States. In the intangible realm of character, there is no other country that can show in the past century or more two men of greater nobility than Washington and Lincoln.

But, after all, many of these things are not new, and if they were all the contribution which America had had to make, she would have meant only a place for more people, a spawning ground for more millions of the human species. In many respects, as I have not hesitated to say elsewhere, there are other lands in which life is easier, more stimulating, more charming than in raw America, for America *is* still raw, and unnecessarily so. The barbarian carelessness of the motoring millions, the littered roadsides, the use of our most beautiful scenery for the advertising of products which should be boycotted for that very reason, are but symptoms of our slipping down from civilized standards of life, as are also our lawlessness and corruption, with the cynical disregard of them by the public. Many of these matters I have discussed elsewhere, and may again. Some are also European problems as well as American. Some are urban, without regard to international boundaries. The mob mentality of the city crowd everywhere is coming to be one of the menaces to modern civilization. The ideal of democracy and the reality of the crowd are the two sides of the shield of modern government. "I think our governments will remain virtuous . . . as long as they are chiefly agricultural; and this will be as long as there shall be vacant lands in any part of America. When they get piled upon one another in large cities, as in Europe, they will become corrupt as in Europe," wrote Jefferson in the days of the Bourbons.

If, as I have said, the things already listed were all we had had to contribute, America would have made no distinctive and unique gift to mankind. But there has been also the *American dream*, that dream of a land in which life should be better and richer and fuller for every man, with opportunity for each according to his ability or achievement. It is a difficult dream for the European upper classes to interpret adequately, and too many of us ourselves have grown weary and mistrustful of it. It is not a dream of motor cars and high wages merely, but a dream of a social order in which each man and each woman shall be able to attain to the fullest stature of which they are innately capable, and be recognized by others for what they are, regardless of the fortuitous circumstances of birth or position. I once had an intelligent young Frenchman as guest in New York, and after a few days I asked him what struck him most among his new impressions. Without hesitation he replied, "The way that everyone of every sort looks you right in the eye, without a thought of inequality." Some time ago a foreigner who used to do some work for me, and who had picked up a very fair education, used occasionally to sit and chat with me in my study after he had finished his work. One day he said that such a relationship was the great difference between America and his homeland. There, he said, "I would do my work and might get a pleasant word, but I could never sit and talk like this. There is a difference there between social grades which cannot be got over. I would not talk to you there as man to man, but as my employer."

No, the American dream that has lured tens of millions of all nations to our shores in the past century has not been a dream of merely material plenty, though that has doubtless counted heavily. It has been much more than that. It has been a dream of being able to grow to fullest development as man and woman, unhampered by the barriers which had slowly been erected in older civilizations, unrepressed by social orders which had developed for the benefit of classes rather than for the simple human being of any and every class. And that dream has been realized more fully in actual life here than anywhere else, though very imperfectly even among ourselves.

It has been a great epic and a great dream. What, now, of the future?

From the material standpoint, it is probable that the extreme depression will pass in a year or two, barring social and political overturn in some countries, which might delay recovery. I am not here concerned with the longer economic problems raised by the relations of world distribution and consumption under mass production. The problems, fundamental and of extreme seriousness, have been amply discussed elsewhere and by those more competent. But whether, in the next decade, we shall have again to face a furious economic pace or whether we shall be confronted by a marked slowing down of our economic machine, the chief factor in how we shall meet either situation is that of the American mind. One of the interesting questions with regard to that is whether our long subjection to the frontier and other American influences has produced a new type or merely a transient change. Can we hold to the good and escape from the bad? Are the dream and the indealism of the frontier and the New Land inextricably involved with the ugly scars which have also been left on us by our three centuries of exploitation and conquest of the continent?

We have already tried to show how some of the scars were obtained; how it was that we came to insist upon business and money-making and material improvement as good in themselves; how they took on the aspects of moral virtues; how we came to consider an unthinking optimism essential; how we refused to look on the seamy and sordid realities of any situation in which we found ourselves; how we regarded criticism as obstructive and dangerous for our new communities; how we came to think manners undemocratic, and a cultivated mind a hindrance to success, a sign of inefficient effeminacy; how size and statistics of material development came to be more important in our eyes than quality and spiritual values; how in the ever-shifting advance of the frontier we came to lose sight of the past in hopes for the future; how we forgot to *live*, in the struggle to "make a living"; how our education tended to become utilitarian or aimless; and how other unfortunate traits only too notable to-day were developed.

While we have been absorbed in our tasks, the world has also been changing. We Americans are not alone in having to search for a new scale and basis for values, but for several reasons the task is more essential for us. On the one hand, our transplantation to the New World and our constant advance over its empty expanse unsettled the old values for us to a far greater extent than in Europe; and, on the other, the mere fact that there were no old things to be swept away here made us feel the full impact of the Industrial Revolution and the effect of machinery, when we turned to industrial life, to a far greater extent than in Europe, where the revolution originated.

It would seem as though the time had come when this question of values was of prime and pressing importance for us. For long we have been tempted and able to ignore it. Engaged in the work of building cities and developing the continent, values for many tended to be materialized and simplified. When a man staked out a clearing, and saw his wife and children without shelter, there was no need to discuss what were the real values in a humane and satisfying life. The trees had to be chopped, the log hut built, the stumps burned, and the corn planted. Simplification became a habit of mind and was carried into our lives long after the clearing had become a prosperous city. But such a habit of mind does not ignore values. It merely accepts certain ones implicitly, as does our most characteristic philosophy, the Pragmatism of William James. It will not do to say that we shall have no *a priori* standards and that the proof of the value of a thing or idea shall be whether it will "work." What do we mean by its "working"? Must we not mean that it will produce or conduce to some result that strikes us as desirable—that is, something that we have already set up in our minds as something worth while? In other words, a standard or value?

We no longer have the frontier to divert us or to absorb our energies. We shall steadily become a more densely populated country in which our social ideals will have to be such as to give us civilized contentment. To clear the muddle in which our education is at present, we shall obviously have to define our values. Unless we can agree on what the values in life are, we clearly can have no goal in education, and if we have no goal, the discussion of methods is merely futile. Once the frontier stage is passed—the acquisition of a bare living, and the setting up of a fair economic base—the American dream itself opens all sorts of questions as to values. It is easy to say a better and richer life for all men, but what *is* better and what *is* richer?

In this respect, as in many others, the great business leaders are likely to lead us astray rather than to guide us. For example, as promulgated by them, there is danger in the present popular theory of the high-wage scale. The danger lies in the fact that the theory is advanced not for the purpose of creating a better type of man by increasing his leisure and the opportunity for making a wise use of it, but for the sole and avowed purpose of increasing his powers as a "consumer." He is, therefore, goaded by every possible method of pressure or cajolery to spend his wages in consuming goods. He is warned that if he does not consume to the limit, instead of indulging in pleasures which do not cost money, he may be deprived not only of his high wages but of any at all. He, like the rest of us, thus appears to be getting into a treadmill in which he earns, not that he may enjoy, but that he may spend, in order that the owners of the factories may grow richer.

For example, Ford's fortune is often referred to as one of the "honestly" obtained ones. He pretends to despise money, and boasts of the high wages he pays and the cheapness of his cars, yet, either because his wages are still too low or the cars too high, he has accumulated $1,000,000,000 for himself from his plant. This would seem to be a high price for society to pay even him for his services to it, while the economic lives of some hundreds of thousands of men and women are made dependent on his whim and word.

Just as in education we have got to have some aims based on values before we can reform our system intelligently or learn in what direction to go, so with business and the American dream. Our democracy cannot attempt to curb, guide, or control the great business interests and powers unless we have clear notions as to the purpose in mind when we try to do so. If we are to regard man merely as a producer and consumer, then the more ruthlessly efficient big business is, the better. Many of the goods consumed doubtless make man healthier, happier, and better even on the basis of a high scale of human values. But if we think of him as a human being primarily, and only incidentally as a consumer, then we have to consider what values are best or most satisfying for him as a human being. We can attempt to regulate business for him not as a consumer but as a man, with many needs and desires with which he has nothing to do as a consumer. Our point of view will shift from efficiency and statistics to human nature. We shall not create a high-wage scale in order that the receiver will consume more, but that he may, in one way or another, live more abundantly, whether by enjoying those things which are factory-produced or those which are not. The points of view are entirely different, socially and economically.

In one important respect America has changed fundamentally from the time of the frontier. The old life was lonely and hard, but it bred a strong individualism. The farmer of Jefferson's day was independent and could hold opinions equally so. Steadily we are tending toward becoming a nation of employees—whether a man gets five dollars a day or a hundred thousand a year. The "yes-men" are as new to our national life as to our vocabulary, but they are real. It is no longer merely the laborer or factory hand who is dependent on the whim of his employer, but men all the way up the economic and social scales. In the ante-bellum South the black slave knew better than to express his views as to the rights of man. To-day the appalling growth of uniformity and timorousness of views as to the perfection of the present economic system held by most men "comfortably off" as corporation clerks or officials is not unrelated to the possible loss of a job.

Another problem is acute for us in the present extreme maladjustment of the intellectual worker to the present economic order. Just as the wage earner is told he must adjust his leisure pursuits to the advantage of business in his rôle of consumer, so there is almost irresistible economic pressure brought to bear on the intellectual worker to adjust his work to the needs of business or mass consumption. If wages are to go indefinitely higher, owing to mass-production possibilities for raising them, then the intellectual worker or artist will have to pay the price in the higher wages he himself pays for all services and in all the items of his expenses, such as rent, in which wages form a substantial element. His own costs thus rising, owing to the rising wage scale, he finds that a limited market for his intellectual wares no longer allows him to exist in a world otherwise founded on mass-production profits. He cannot forever pay rising mass-production costs without deriving for himself some form of mass-production profit. This would not be so bad if mass consumption did not mean for the most part a distinct lowering in the quality of his thought and expression. If the artist or intellectual worker could count on a wide audience instead of a class or group, the effect on his own work would be vastly stimulating, but for that the wide audience must be capable of appreciating work at its highest. The theory of mass production breaks down as yet when applied to the things of the spirit. Merging of companies in huge corporations, and the production of low-priced products for markets of tens of millions of consumers for one standard brand of beans or cars, may be possible in the sphere of our material needs. It cannot be possible, however, in the realm of the mind, yet the whole tendency at present is in that direction. Newspapers are merging as if they were factories, and daily, weekly, and monthly journals are all becoming as dependent on mass sales as a toothpaste.

The result is to lower the quality of thought as represented in them to that of the least common denominator of the minds of the millions of consumers.

If the American dream is to come true and to abide with us, it will, at bottom, depend on the people themselves. If we are to achieve a richer and fuller life for all, they have got to know what such an achievement implies. In a modern industrial State, an economic base is essential for all. We point with pride to our "national income," but the nation is only an aggregate of individual men and women, and when we turn from the single figure of total income to the incomes of individuals, we find a very marked injustice in its distribution. There is no reason why wealth, which is a social product, should not be more equitably controlled and distributed in the interests of society. But, unless we settle on the values of life, we are likely to attack in a wrong direction and burn the barn to find our penny in the hay.

Above and beyond the mere economic base. the need for a scale of values becomes yet greater. If we are entering on a period in which, not only in industry but in other departments of life, the mass is going to count for more and the individual less, and if each and all are to enjoy a richer and fuller life, the level of the mass has got to rise appreciably above what it is at present. It must either rise to a higher level of communal life or drag that life down to its own, in political leadership, and in the arts and letters. There is no use in accusing America of being a "Babbitt Warren." The top and bottom are spiritually and intellectually nearer together in America than in most countries, but there are plenty of Babbitts everywhere. "Main Street" is the longest in the world, for it encircles the globe. It is an American name, but not an American thoroughfare. One can suffocate in an English cathedral town or a French provincial city as well as in Zenith. That is not the point.

The point is that if we are to have a rich and full life in which all are to share and play their parts, if the American dream is to be a reality, our communal spiritual and intellectual life must be distinctly higher than elsewhere, where classes and groups have their separate interests, habits, markets, arts, and lives. If the dream is not to prove possible of fulfillment, we might as well become stark realists, become once more class-conscious, and struggle as individuals or classes against one another. If it is to come true, those on top, financially, intellectually, or otherwise, have got to devote themselves to the "Great Society," and those who are below in the scale have got to strive to rise, not merely economically, but culturally. We cannot become a great democracy by giving ourselves up as individuals to selfishness, physical comfort, and cheap amusements. The very foundation of the American dream of a better and richer life for all is that all, in varying degrees, shall be capable of wanting to share in it. It can never be wrought into a reality by cheap people or by "keeping up with the Joneses." There is nothing whatever in a fortune merely in itself or in a man merely in himself. It all depends on what is made of each. Lincoln was not great because he was born in a log cabin, but because he got out of it—that is, because he rose above the poverty, ignorance, lack of ambition, shiftlessness of character, contentment with mean things and low aims which kept so many thousands in the huts where they were born.

If we are to make the dream come true we must all work together, no longer to build bigger, but to build better. There is a time for quantity and a time for quality. There is a time when quantity may become a menace and the law of diminishing returns begins to operate, but not so with quality. By working together I do not mean another organization, of which the land is as full as was Kansas of grasshoppers. I mean a genuine individual search and striving for the abiding values of life. In a country as big as America it is as impossible to prophesy as it is to generalize, without being tripped up, but it seems to me that there is room for hope as well as mistrust. The epic loses all its glory without the dream. The statistics of size, population, and wealth would mean nothing to me unless I could still believe in the dream.

America is yet "The Land of Contrasts," as it was called in one of the best books written about us, years ago. One day a man from Oklahoma depresses us by yawping about it in such a way as to give the impression that there is nothing in that young State but oil wells and millionaires, and the next day one gets from the University there its excellent quarterly critical list of all the most recent books published in France, Spain, Germany, and Italy, with every indication of the beginning of an active intellectual life and an intelligent play of thought over the ideas of the other side of the world.

There is no better omen of hope than the sane and sober criticism of those tendencies in our civilization which call for rigorous examination. In that respect we are distinctly passing out of the frontier phase. Our life calls for such examination, as does that of every nation to-day, but because we are concerned with the evil symptoms it would be absurd to forget the good. It would be as uncritical to write the history of our past in terms of Morton of Merrymount, Benedict Arnold, "Billy the Kid," Thaddeus Stevens, Jay Gould, P. T. Barnum, Brigham Young, Tom Lawson, and others who could be gathered together to make an extraordinary jumble of an incomprehensible national story, as it would be to write the past wholly in terms of John Winthrop, Washington, John Quincy Adams, Jefferson, Lincoln, Emerson, Edison, General Gorgas, and others to afford an equally untrue picture.

The nation to-day is no more all made up of Babbitts (though there are enough of them) than it is of young poets. There is a healthy stirring of the deeps, particularly among the younger men and women, who are growing determined that they are not to function solely as consumers for the benefit of business, but intend to lead sane and civilized lives. When one thinks of the prostitution of the moving-picture industry, which might have developed a great art, one can turn from that to the movements everywhere through the country for the small theatre and the creation of folk drama, the collecting of our folk poetry, which was almost unknown to exist a generation ago, and other hopeful signs of an awakening culture deriving straight and naturally from our own soil and past. How far the conflicting good can win against the evil is our problem. It is not a cheering thought to figure the number of people who are thrilled nightly by a close-up kiss on ten thousand screens compared with the number who see a play of O'Neill's. But, on the other hand, we need not forget that a country that produced last year 1,500,000 Fords, which after their short day will in considerable numbers add to the litter along our country lanes as abandoned chassis, could also produce perhaps the finest example of sculpture in the last half century. We can contrast the spirit manifested in the accumulation of the Rockefeller fortune with the spirit now displayed in its distribution.

Like the country roads, our whole national life is yet cluttered up with the disorderly remnants of our frontier experience, and all help should be given to those who are honestly trying to clean up either the one or the other. But the frontier also left us our American dream, which is being wrought out in many hearts and many institutions.

Among the latter I often think that the one which best exemplifies the dream is the greatest library in this land of libraries, the Library of Congress. I take, for the most part, but little interest in the great gifts and Foundations of men who have incomes they cannot possibly spend, and investments that roll like avalanches. They merely return, not seldom unwisely, a part of their wealth to that society without which they could not have made it, and which too often they have plundered in the making. That is chiefly evidence of maladjustment in our economic system. A system that steadily increases the gulf between the ordinary man and the super-rich, that permits the resources of society to be gathered into personal fortunes that afford their owners millions of income a year, with only the chance that here and there a few may be moved to confer some of their surplus upon the public in ways chosen wholly by themselves, is assuredly a wasteful and unjust system.

It is, perhaps, as inimical as anything could be to the American dream. I do not belittle the generosity or public spirit of certain men. It is the system that as yet is at fault. Nor is it likely to be voluntarily altered by those who benefit most by it. No ruling class has ever willingly abdicated. Democracy can never be saved, and would not be worth saving, unless it can save itself.

The Library of Congress, however, has come straight from the heart of democracy, as it has been taken to it, and I here use it as a symbol of what democracy can accomplish on its own behalf. Many have made gifts to it, but it was created by ourselves through Congress, which has steadily and increasingly shown itself generous and understanding toward it. Founded and built by the people, it is for the people. Anyone who has used the great collections of Europe, with their restrictions and red tape and difficulty of access, praises God for American democracy when he enters the stacks of the Library of Congress.

But there is more to the Library of Congress for the American dream than merely the wise appropriation of public money. There is the public itself, in two of its aspects. The Library of Congress could not have become what it is to-day, with all the generous aid of Congress, without such a citizen as Dr. Herbert Putnam* at the directing head of it. He and his staff have devoted their lives to making the four million and more of books and pamphlets serve the public to a degree that cannot be approached by any similar great institution in the Old World. Then there is the public that uses these facilities. As one looks down on the general reading room, which alone contains ten thousand volumes which may be read without even the asking, one sees the seats filled with silent readers, old and young, rich and poor, black and white, the executive and the laborer, the general and the private, the noted scholar and the schoolboy, all reading in their own library provided by their own democracy. It has always seemed to me to be a

---

* In 1939 Dr. Putnam retired after more than forty years' service, becoming Librarian Emeritus. He left as his monument a complex, highly co-ordinated and unique institution, far different from the ordinary idea of a library as a depository for books, manuscripts, maps, etc. The appointment by the President of his successor came as a surprise. Mr. Archibald MacLeish had had no library experience, and was known only as a minor poet of high distinction, a writer for *Fortune* and other magazines, and as a lecturer. He continues his writing and public speaking, and has also been made head of one of the war bureaus—the Office of Facts and Figures. It is too early as yet to judge of his work as Librarian, but all who know and understand what the Library of Congress had become under Dr. Putnam assuredly wish him all success.

perfect working out in a concrete example of the American dream—
the means provided by the accumulated resources of the people themselves, a public intelligent enough to use them, and men of high distinction, themselves a part of the great democracy, devoting themselves to
the good of the whole, uncloistered.

It seems to me that it can be only in some such way, carried out in
all departments of our national life, that the American dream can be
wrought into an abiding reality. I have little trust in the wise pater-
nalism of politicians or the infinite wisdom of business leaders. We can
look neither to the government nor to the heads of the great corporations to guide us into the paths of a satisfying and humane existence
as a great nation unless we, as multitudinous individuals, develop some
greatness in our own individual souls. Until countless men and women
have decided in their own hearts, through experience and perhaps
disillusion, what is a genuinely satisfying life, a "good life" in the old
Greek sense, we need look to neither political nor business leaders.
Under our political system it is useless, save by the rarest of happy
accidents, to expect a politician to rise higher than the source of his
power. So long also as we are ourselves content with a mere extension
of the material basis of existence, with the multiplying of our material
possessions, it is absurd to think that the men who can utilize that
public attitude for the gaining of infinite wealth and power for themselves will abandon both to become spiritual leaders of a democracy
that despises spiritual things. Just so long as wealth and power are our
sole badges of success, so long will ambitious men strive to attain them.

The prospect is discouraging, to-day, but not hopeless. As we compare America to-day with the America of 1912 it seems as though we
had slipped a long way backwards. But that period is short, after all,
and the whole world has been going through the fires of Hell. There
are not a few signs of promise now in the sky, signs that the peoples
themselves are beginning once again to crave something more than is
vouchsafed to them in the toils and toys of the mass-production age.
They are beginning to realize that, because a man is born with a particular knack for gathering in vast aggregates of money and power for
himself, he may not on that account be the wisest leader to follow nor
the best fitted to propound a sane philosophy of life. We have a long
and arduous road to travel if we are to realize our American dream in

the life of our nation, but if we fail, there is nothing left but the old eternal round. The alternative is the failure of self-government, the failure of the common man to rise to full stature, the failure of all that the American dream has held of hope and promise for mankind.*

That dream was not the product of a solitary thinker. It evolved from the hearts and burdened souls of many millions, who have come to us from all nations. If some of them appear to us to have too great faith, we know not yet to what faith may attain, and may hearken to the words of one of them, Mary Antin, a young immigrant girl who came to us from Russia, a child out of "the Middle Ages," as she says, into our twentieth century. Sitting on the steps of the Boston Public Library, where the treasures of the whole of human thought had been opened to her, she wrote, "This is my latest home, and it invites me to a glad new life. The endless ages have indeed throbbed through my blood, but a new rhythm dances in my veins. My spirit is not tied to the monumental past, any more than my feet were bound to my grandfather's house below the hill. The past was only my cradle, and now it cannot hold me, because I am grown too big; just as the little house in Polotzk, once my home, has now become a toy of memory, as I move about at will in the wide spaces of this splendid palace, whose shadow covers acres. No! It is not I that belong to the past, but the past that belongs to me. America is the youngest of the nations, and inherits all that went before in history. And I am the youngest of America's children, and into my hands is given all her priceless heritage, to the last white star espied through the telescope, to the last great thought of the philosopher. Mine is the whole majestic past, and mine is the shining future."

* This was written in 1931. Americans have been through much since then—the Depression, the New Deal, and now World War II. It is a very different America in many ways from that which I was then writing about and trying to forecast. Our type of civilization, the American way of life, the American Dream are all at stake. I cannot go into details of prophecy here, and the entire world will be different when the war is over. Life will be altered in countless ways, but I believe that the cause of free men will prevail, and that the American Dream is so deeply rooted in the American heart that it, too, will survive, translated into perhaps a greater reality than ever. It can be lost only by us Americans ourselves, and I do not believe we want to forget it or cease striving to make it real.

MARK VAN DOREN Why he

selected AMERICA'S MYTHOLOGY

I choose these poems because they have a single theme, and because this theme—the beliefs of a people—seems important to me at present.

New York, N. Y.   MARK VAN DOREN
July, 1942

AMERICA'S MYTHOLOGY

AMERICA'S great gods live down the lane;
Or up the next block blend their bulk with stone;
Or stand upon the ploughed hills in the rain;
Or watch a mountain cabin left alone.

Gigantic on the path, they never speak.
Unwitnessed, they are walked through every hour.
They have an older errand; or they seek
New sweets beyond the bound of mortal sour;

Or love the living instant, and so minded,
Bestride the lesser lookers—who can say?
There is no man has seen them but was blinded;
And none has ever found them far away.

America's tall gods are veteran here:
Too close for view, like eagles in the eye:
Like day itself, impalpable and clear;
Like absolute noon's air, unflowing by.

They are the first of all. Before the grey,
Before the copper-colored, they were moving
Green-brown among the deep trees: deep as they,
As curious of the wind, as tempest-loving;

As shaggy dressed, as head-proud; and in summer,
As lazy. So they lived. And so they still
Live everywhere, unknown to the newcomer,
Whom genially they watch. And so they will

To earth's end, feeding on their ancient grain,
Wild wheat tips, and barbed rice tops, and the meat
Of mast whereover richest leaves have lain;
Although they pick the tame fields too, and eat

With fathers at the heads of merry tables;
And sleep on beds for change, and sit with talkers.
Whence all their lore; for man's least deeds are fables
To these old-natured gods, these ancient walkers.

STRANGE TOWN GOD

HE IS the one that meets us where the first
      Small houses, dark and poor, lead into light;
And tells us how the features, best and worst,
Make something like a face in country night.

He is the only townsman who would know.
For the lean rest it is familiar chaos.
His love is older; is a breath to blow
Strict lines from curb to roof till patterns stay us:

Till pausing by the dusk hotel, we count
Street lamps, store fronts, red jail; and farther on,
The first white house again, where the maples mount
That high east hill our road goes up—has gone

Each night like this since who knows when? Who'll say?
The sprawled god never answers in his pride.
The question is enough. And shows the way
To hot hamburgers, coffee, and thin fried.

CHERRY LEAF GOD

A DARK sky, the wind waiting;
   Ladders motionless, and heels
Of pickers vanishing, house-high, among the leaves;

Pails dangled, cherries dropping;
Twigs snapped; and there a limb
Bent low to breaking as a boy, too bold, forgets.

So seems it from the ground; so goes it
Here in the long grass whither he,
Never descending, peers between the green, the red:

The hanging leaves, the dripping hearts
He flutters while he swings beyond—
Huge picker, yet he lies, more light than robin's leg;

Lies; leans over Johnny there;
Swings over Nell; and topmost now,
Swings up and out, heigh ho, as seven pickers climb.

COMPASS GOD

WHICH way this forest faces;
   How sharp we angled there;
When the wind struck us, came it
Slantwise or square?

At home now is it certain—
The hay door—perfect west?

Our cousin in the spare room:
Will he rest?

He said he had it backwards:
Due south for simple north:
Turned full around, no matter
How he went forth.

There is a tall one watches
And pities our poor eyes:
Except that some are knowing;
Are needle-wise;

Were eastward set when Phosphor
Whitened the oldest dawn;
And are the eyes he blesses,
In babe or fawn.

BERNARD DEVOTO Why he selected

MARK TWAIN: The ARTIST

as AMERICAN

Dear Mr. Burnett:

If I have been slow in answering you it is because I lack practice at taking myself as seriously as your letter encourages me to. I sympathize with the purpose of your book and am glad to contribute to it, but I have never spent much time wondering what my best work is or what it stands for. I think of myself as a professional writer, a journalist if you will, and have never thought of myself as an artist. I suppose it follows that my pride is a professional's. I know my limitations better than anyone else has yet pointed them out. I attempt only such jobs as I know to be within my compass. I do them as intelligently as I can and with such craftsmanship as I possess. I observe my private code of professional ethics, I avoid literary behavior and literary ideas both from taste and from conviction—and the rest I leave to editors and the reading public.

The result of unfamiliar introspection is a conclusion that you had better take the chapter of *Mark Twain's America*. The book is ten years old, it would be a different book if I were to write it now, and it certainly is not my best work. But I don't know what my best work is. The only person who, so far as I know, ever undertook to say is Garret Mattingly. He chose two pieces, "The Life of Jonathan Dyer," in *Forays and Rebuttals*, and "Passage to India," in *Minority Report*. I don't agree with him but at least he gets the emphasis away from my ventures into literary criticism, which I do not feel to be the center of my work, if it has any center. The book of mine which I enjoy most is a novel and I see no way in which part of a novel can be satisfactory carved out for reprinting. The biggest and most completely achieved job I have ever done is a book now in page proof, called *The Year of Decision*, but it is disqualified

195

since it will not be out till after your book. So you had better use
"The Artist as American." When I read it over last week a certain
lushness in the writing vaguely offended me but I'm willing to stand
on it.

I don't think that I can usefully say much about it that it does not
say for itself. The book was frankly polemic. It was intended to repair what I felt was an injustice done to Mark Twain by the popular
literary criticism of the time. It was also intended to attack a basic
idea of that criticism which I held to be idiotic, the idea that American life and culture were hostile to art. Probably more people would
agree with me now in thinking that idea idiotic than agreed with me
when the book was published; perhaps the book is one reason why
there are more of them now. Since I wrote it I have had a better opportunity to study the facts of Mark Twain's life and works than
anyone before me ever had. I have found a number of places in which
my book did not go far enough, but none in which its assertions or
interpretations were wrong. I take a certain satisfaction in that fact.
Cambridge, Mass.   BERNARD DeVOTO
July 30, 1942

THE 1920's chose to think of Mark Twain not as a writer of
books but as a man who either betrayed something sacred or was
betrayed by something vile. During that decade, it appears, some facts
were, for the literary, too plain to see and some roads too plain to take.
If the opinions of the literary during that time truly stand for the
opinions of others instead of for their own wish fulfillments, a proposition which might be agreeably debated, then it is possible that countless thousands have mourned because the author of "The Celebrated
Jumping Frog of Calaveras County" did not write "The Revolt of
Islam," "Das Kapital," and "Men Like Gods." Literary opinion during the 1920's preferred to take that road rather than consider a fact
so plain that even the steerages of westward-bound liners are aware
of it. The fact that the author of "The Celebrated Jumping Frog of
Calaveras County" gave to American literature its two immortal
characters. Since Tom Sawyer was first seen hiding in a closet and

since Huckleberry Finn came down a lane in St. Petersburg with the intention of curing a wart, they have exercised the conviction of belief over more kinds and conditions of intelligence than any other persons who have been imagined in American books.

What is creation? What is art? The second question may profitably be ignored if anything realistic can be said about the first. It would seem that to bring to the material of literature in America new areas of life and experience is creation. To inform these areas with character so vivid that it produces the illusion of experience is creation. To erect where there was nothing a world at once unique and universal, to give that world an organic structure, and to people it with inhabitants who live as themselves and as an embodiment of the American race is creation. To stamp upon that world an impression of oneself so vivid and so inimitable that it can never possibly be mistaken for the seal of any one else is creation. To fructify a waste place so that dozens of writers who come after may thoughtfully reap the excess of one's sowing is creation. And finally, to add to the slender number of imagined people who are forever themselves in the minds of readers, two more so true, so inevitable, so universal that they join the world's legends—if this is not creation, then nothing is. In the presence of such facts as these, questions of form become a mere catechism from the classroom and definitions of art mere conversation in a salon.

For it is the final authority of these two boys that they have become the possession of every one. So simple a clue as a moment's honesty suggests their importance: any one may ask himself who, of all the characters in American literature, has the greatest vitality in his mind. . . . Barrett Wendell, writing about what passes as the importance of Harvard College in what passes as literature, had a curious instant of recognition. After devoting 450 pages to the obligations of Doctor Holmes, he asked leave to treat America in fifty pages. In those fifty pages, Mark Twain had, of natural right, three sentences. Mr. Wendell alluded to "a book which in certain moods one is disposed for all its eccentricity to call the most admirable work of literary art as yet produced on this continent . . . that Odyssean story of the Mississippi to which Mark Twain gave the grotesque name of 'Huckle-

berry Finn'."[1] He has suffered some deprecation ever since for imply-
ing that an American Odyssey was possibly unsanctified by a Harvard
degree. Yet the adjective Odyssean does convey the plain truth about
the two boys, not in the obvious sense that Huck Finn made a journey
by water but in the fundamental sense that his life is something which
the whole world shares. He and Tom have enriched the experience
of those who read books everywhere. They are universal in that they
have become legends, not as the expression of something fanciful or
fantastic, but as the embodiment of something forever true. In them
America has made incomparably its greatest communication to world
literature.

One of the finest passages of "Huckleberry Finn" appears not in
that book but in "Life on the Mississippi." In the same way, some of
the truest presentation of Tom, Huck, and Jim is to be encountered in
"Tom Sawyer Abroad" and "Tom Sawyer, Detective." The latter is a
trivial story psychologically related to the burlesques of detective fiction
that amused Mark at the time, but as if by accident it expresses a
native quality of the frontier. In this casual improvisation, Tom
Sawyer is utilizing the shrewdness which proceeds from the woods-
craft that the frontier found necessary for survival. It is a shrewdness
peculiarly and indigenously American. It was created by wilderness
life, derived from the chief skill of the Indians, and imposed as a
condition of success by the westward exploration. It attained its highest phase among the trail makers of the far West, so that Samuel
Parker, adventuring with Jim Bridger, Fitzpatrick, and Kit Carson,
encountered the foremost practitioners of a great craft. But it was a
craft essential to every one who participated in frontier life, and

[1] In Barrett Wendell's time the aristocratic tradition had not yet been debauched.
A Professor Paul Shorey, who writes in the house organ of Phi Beta Kappa, exhibits the
invective by means of which Humanism has become, by 1932, mere logorrhoea: "The
question I submit to you [the American Scholar] is whether those who think so shall
have the courage to unite in saying that the high culture, the sobriety, the common sense,
the patriotism, the decency, the sober optimism of Longfellow, Emerson, Holmes, and
Lowell and their immediate disciples, while we are waiting for something greater, more
nearly represent the true American tradition and ideal than do the wilfulness, the
incoherence, the inconsequences, and the fitful flashes of genius of Thoreau, Melville,
Whitman, Mark Twain, or the trivial vocabulary, the pseudo-science, the Freudism, the
anti-patriotic bias, the affected cosmopolitanism, the thumb-sucking *Weltschmerz*, the sex
obsession, the un-American tragedies, of the spokesmen of the generation at the second
remove from the older culture." Such an aspect as this of the thinking that calls itself
decorum is just vulgar.

belongs to the very center of the American experience. It must be recognized as native to the frontier mind.[2] Most of Mark Twain's characters exhibit it as instinctively and unconsciously as they assume the presence of slavery. In this anecdote of Tom Sawyer it becomes explicit. Elsewhere Tom casually identifies a dog by the individuality of its baying or knows where to find embers protected from a cloudburst; here he concentrates this sharp and cunning sagacity on the analysis of a situation. The decorations of the story and its set piece at the end are trivial inventions or mere repetitions of effects Mark had previously proved reliable, but the process of identification and proof is forged from something basic in America. When Tom observes a flaw in Jake Dunlap's sickness, interprets the shadows at the foot of sycamores, and identifies the pattern a finger makes on a cheek, many thousand inhabitants of our history nod assent, for they have found a voice. Cornstalks have moved when all breeze is dead, marauding hoofs have chipped a stone by night, and, in the month when the willows redden, the color of dusk above a mountain creek has shown a wisp of smoke where no smoke should be.

The Dunlaps are squatters and they with all the other personages of the anecdote share the careless fecundity of Mark Twain, so that not even the absurdity of the ghosts diminishes them. That fecundity is freely expended in the much more ambitious companion piece. If "Pudd'nhead Wilson" had not been selected to typify the paradox of Mark Twain's invention, "Tom Sawyer Abroad" could stand symbol for it. The fictional framework, the balloon and its inventor, is not only fantastic, it is anachronistic in the troubled sense that threatens much else of Tom's biography. Yet the statement of the backwoods mind is here elaborated on an equality with anything that the two principal books contain. It cannot be spared from the whole of which

[2] The interpretation of observed circumstance—what Poe called ratiocination—is an interest of American literature that seems to be inseparably bound up with frontier life. Leatherstocking and "Nick o' the Woods" may be instanced. The realistic humor of the southwestern frontier has many tales devoted to this theme. The best of them has never, so far as I know, been alluded to in print. I therefore take pleasure in calling to the attention of anthologists a remarkable short story, one which of right would be an American classic, the tale Uncle Billy tells of the murder of Charley Birkham and the identification of his murderer in Philip Paxton's "A Stray Yankee in Texas." (See Appendix A.)

the others are larger parts. It has, even, superiorities to them, since its
serene, almost loving exploration of ignorant thought is more detailed,
and since Nigger Jim is given more to do that reveals him. The sketch
is, in fact, an elaborate exposition of St. Petersburg trying to grapple
with an enlargement of its thinking, and in this exposition Jim is the
pivot. There can be no doubt that Mark's deliberate effort was to
explore the mentality of the common man.

Metaphor breaks across Jim's skull quite in vain. It is not the
welkin they are in but a balloon, and an explanation fails because
when Tom asserts that birds of a feather flock together, Jim falls back
on the unassailable logic of experience, inquiring whether Tom has
ever observed a bluebird in the company of a jaybird. Jim cannot
applaud the method of Zadig, because the tale neglects to reveal what
became of the camel. His theory of the Sahara as deity's waste heap
after creation, triumphs over its competitors by instancing the Milky
Way as the scraps of stars, and to that argument no answer is possible.
When the lake proves to be a mirage, clearly it is a ghost, for Jim had
seen it with his own eyes—and "forty thousand million people seen
the sun move from one side of the sky to the other every day." An
exquisite gradation carries the slave's thinking into the larger intelligence of Huck Finn. Huck takes pride in Tom's wide information
but is obliged to correct it steadily by reference to common sense. He
admires the reasoning that enables Tom to go direct to the dervish's
enchanted hill and infallibly recognize the ruin of Joseph's granary.
Nevertheless he must agree with Jim that two days cannot exist at the
same time, for there would then be no day of judgment in England,
and he enjoys the elation of proving by the map that no two States
have the same color. Tom's tribute to fleas convinces him and he manages to form the idea of longitude, but is scandalized by the story of a
bronze horse that flies. In an analysis that catches backwoods America
in the very act of vindicating its intelligence, he demonstrates that a
pyramid can't burn and a horse can't fly.

Such contexts give life to provinciality and ignorance. The thing
itself is in them. The pattern, the very rhythm of thought is communicated in a realism that extends to the basis and conditions of
the mind. The crossroads forum, the groggery and the steamboat

wharf, swallowed in the isolation of a continent, have spoken in the way instinctive to them. A society is made articulate.

Inquiry has sometimes concerned itself with the origin of "The Adventures of Tom Sawyer." Aldrich's "Story of a Bad Boy" has been suggested and one inquirer has wondered if "Sut Lovingood" may not have been an influence. The latter idea may now be given a further persuasion for classrooms, beyond the partial coincidence of themes, by mentioning Sut's acquaintance with a doctor who desires cadavers for dissection. Either inquiry seems idle, for when he came to write "Tom Sawyer," Mark Twain at last arrived at the theme that was most harmonious with his interest, his experience, and his talents. If anything may be confidently said about the processes of creation, one may confidently say that this book, with its companion, was inevitable. Foreordination is probably a fact: if it is, Mark Twain was predestined to this work. That is one source of its finality.

The sun shines on Tom's St. Petersburg. The simplest description of his book is this: the supreme American idyll. It is also an idyll of boyhood; such incidents as the whitewashing of the fence are, like a familiar landscape, so intimate to our experience that their importance is easily forgotten. Yet, even in the century that brought childhood to the attention of literature, it had no other expression quite so true. Tom Sawyer's morality, his religion, his black avengers, his rituals and tabus, his expeditions for glory or adventure, his trafficking with buried treasure, his exaltation, his very terror—are, for childhood, immortal. That fact carries its own weight: whatever achievement resides in writing a book eternally true about children, a book so expressive of them that they accept it as themselves, is Mark Twain's achievement. Yet these are American boys and the book they live in has a validity beyond their presence for the nation to which they are native.

For in "The Adventures of Tom Sawyer" exists, as nowhere else, the since polluted loveliness of a continent. That it is now defiled, that successive generations have seen the assault on natural beauty made more effective, gives this embodiment of it a greater evocation, a greater nostalgia, for the inheritors of wasteland. Americans would not have kept its innumerable editions streaming from the press[3] unless it expressed some emotion and satisfied some need at the very taproot of American life. One need not venture very far into mysti- cism, or into history or literature, to find that fundamental reality. In whatever mood of poetry or psychological curiosity one examines the passage upland from the Atlantic, with whatever instrument of pre- cision one tries to test its nature, one at once perceives that the sym- bolism of the Westward journey is tremendous. It has given the com- monplace word "frontier" a meaning for the Americans that it has had for no other people. Inseparable from that meaning and immediate in the symbolism, is the beauty of the land across which the journey passed. Whatever else the word means, it has also meant water flowing in clear rivers, a countryside under clean sun or snow, woods, prairies and mountains of simple loveliness. It is not necessary to think the literature of America a very noble literature in order to recognize the fact that one of its principal occupations has been the celebration of that beauty. Layer after layer of experience or frustration may come between but at the very base of the American mind an undespoiled country lies open to the sun.

St. Petersburg stands between the untouched forest and the end- lessly flowing river—symbols in which every American will find what import he may but all of us will find some import. That still, blue shadow and that movement underlie passion, desire, and fantasy: they are the landscape as truly of our sleep, as, now that they are mostly vanished, of our reverie. So much, hesitantly, for what happens below the threshold when Tom Sawyer goes down the far slope of Cardiff Hill into forest, or at midnight shoves a raft into the Mississippi bound for Jackson's Island. Above the threshold, there is a drowsy town in a season that is always summer. Time, with the westward journey, has halted. For this moment, between forest and river, Amer- ica is gracious and kind. Between those immensities the village is untroubled. It gossips around the pump or lounges a Sunday morning away at church, exalted only by temperance parades or the fantastic

---

[3] It is a safe assertion, even if one impossible of verification, that more copies of Mark Twain's books are bought annually than of those by any other American. That is, quite simply, what is wrong with them to some aspiring minds. "The Adventures of Tom Sawyer" stands second in the list of sales. The leader is, appropriately, "The Adventures of Huckleberry Finn."

Benton's oration on the Fourth of July, vivified only by the steamboats that tie up to its wharves. Nothing touches this serenity. The
steamboats bring pageantry, not pressure from the world outside. The
village is ignorant of that world—which is hardly a rumor, hardly a
dream. Life is unhurried, amidst this simple plenty of the folk.

If detachment can be tender, then Mark's is when he deals with
these folk. He was as aware of Aunt Polly as any one who has come
after him. The sum of pettiness is in the notabilities of St. Petersburg
or in the concerns of the Sunday school—and yet they are affirmed to
be a part of this enduring peace. They are disarming. They compose
the living town through which the boy's enchantment makes its way,
over which the cloud shadows drift toward Cardiff Hill. They are
recognized as a necessary condition of the idyll that is Tom Sawyer's
summer.

The pastoral landscape, however, is a part not of cloudland but of
America. It is capable of violence and terror. The episodes at the core
revolve around body-snatching, murder, robbery, and revenge. The
term melodrama must be here used with caution. The lore of buried
treasure, specifically the loot of John A. Murrell's clan, was a daily
possession of the villagers. Half-breeds were common to their experience and, being of the dispossessed, were charged with crime as a matter of course—and some accuracy. Revenge, a motive of infrequent
validity for most people, was axiomatic in the Indian nature. When
Injun Joe addresses Doctor Robinson across the blanketed corpse and
alludes to an affront put upon him, his language comes close to the
thrillers of the itinerant stage, but his emotions are genuine. Nor, to
boys whom slaves had instructed in darkness, was there anything unreasonable in the powers exerted in graveyards by ghosts or witches.
The idyll is fulfilled in terms that belong uniquely to itself: its native
horror is part of its ecstasy.

These belong to the multitudes that Mark Twain contains—that
find expression through him. It is wise to remember that they are
multitudes. Behind these white men and Negroes is the history of a
race. Whether Muff Potter remembers the good fishin' places he has
shown to boys or Mr. Dobbins studies anatomy with the vision of
practicing medicine, something speaks from the native soul. In the
terrors that afflict the boys, quite as much as in the beauty that solaces

them, are recorded generations who traveled darkness in the fear of the unseen. Engraftments from Africa, England, and the Apocalypse, sufficiently noticed earlier in this book, are part of the American experience here, as nowhere else, given existence in literature. Tom and Huck, shuddering in the moonlight when a dog's howl is the presage of death, are carriers of a truth struck from a whole population. The dark world of the slaves has made this gift. Yet Tom and Huck are merely actors in the foreground, behind whom the frontier community lives. There is no fumbling. The community is true.

There is that particular kind of truth. Sometimes literature forms out of the flux something realized to be a whole truth about a time or a people. Whether this literature shall or shall not be called art must depend on the caprice of its assayer: whatever else it is, it is finality. The St. Petersburg of Tom Sawyer is a final embodiment of an American experience many layers deep, from the surface to whatever depths one may care to examine, each layer true. What finds expression here is an America which every one knows to be thus finally transmuted into literature, which every one knows has never since Mark Twain had existence in type and never will again. In the presence of such a finality, technical defects, here freely acknowledged, are trivialities. It does not matter much that some of the artist's inventions are weak, that some of the situations and dialogue fail rather dismally, or that, by some canon of abstract form, the book lacks a perfect adjustment of part to part. It does matter that here something formed from America lives as it lives nowhere else.

It matters, too, that the boys and villagers of this landscape not only contain an age in which the nation shared but also record and evoke emotions unattached to that age. It is injudicious to examine the idea of universality in literature, for that also is a phrase which means merely what any critic uses it to mean. Still, Tom and Huck have been universal in this: that for half a century their adventures have fed the hunger of millions. Whether cowering in the shadows by an open grave or swimming at daybreak off Jackson's Island or digging for treasure near the haunted house, they have had authority over the belief of readers—over an audience probably more varied and widespread than any other American has addressed. On the authority of a poet whom Washoe told to hold his yawp it is asserted that a boy's will is the wind's will and the thoughts of youth are long, long thoughts—where else have they had a tongue? Whitewashing a fence, prodding a tick with a pin or dying in the greenwood to rhythms from the border balladry, Tom speaks as competently for his millions as in passages that go deeper into the untranslatable. Into that obscurity it is not necessary to follow him. He accompanies Huck Finn to the graveyard; he is not quite sane at night, remembering that horror; he swims the Mississippi on an errand; he wanders through a cave from which he can find no way into the light. During more than fifty years his summer has had, over the world, a necessity that belongs only to what is great in literature. It seems something more than unlikely that he will lose, hereafter, any of that necessity.

DOROTHY PARKER Why she selected

The STANDARD of LIVING

Now what is a writer to say about a sample of his own work? If he takes one course, he's simpering. If he goes the opposite way, he's Saroyan. There seems to be left open for him only that most ignoble route, the middle of the road.

I think that this story of mine is the nicest bit of writing, the most careful, that I have ever done. The story, of course, is not half what I meant it to be; it never is. It was supposed to tear your heart out, and it does not. But as to workmanship, it is my best.

That is why I chose "The Standard of Living" for this anthology. At least, I think that is why I chose it. It may be that I felt a certain maternal obligation to say a few words in its favor. Nobody else did.

Pipersville, Pa.   DOROTHY PARKER

July 20, 1942

ANNABEL and Midge came out of the tearoom with the arrogant slow gait of the leisured, for their Saturday afternoon stretched ahead of them. They had lunched, as was their wont, on sugar, starches, oils, and butterfats. Usually they ate sandwiches of spongy new white bread greased with butter and mayonnaise; they ate thick wedges of cake lying wet beneath ice cream and whipped cream and melted chocolate gritty with nuts. As alternates, they ate patties, sweating beads of inferior oil, containing bits of bland meat bogged in pale, stiffening sauce; they ate pastries, limber under rigid icing, filled with an indeterminate yellow sweet stuff, not still solid, not yet liquid, like salve that has been left in the sun. They chose no other sort of food, nor did they consider it. And their skin was like the petals of wood

anemones, and their bellies were as flat and their flanks as lean as those
of young Indian braves.

Annabel and Midge had been best friends almost from the day that
Midge had found a job as stenographer with the firm that employed
Annabel. By now, Annabel, two years longer in the stenographic department, had worked up to the wages of eighteen dollars and fifty
cents a week; Midge was still at sixteen dollars. Each girl lived at home
with her family and paid half her salary to its support.

The girls sat side by side at their desks, they lunched together every
noon, together they set out for home at the end of the day's work.
Many of their evenings and most of their Sundays were passed in each
other's company. Often they were joined by two young men, but there
was no steadiness to any such quartet; the two young men would give
place, unlamented, to two other young men, and lament would have
been inappropriate, really, since the newcomers were scarcely distinguishable from their predecessors. Invariably the girls spent the fine
idle hours of their hot-weather Saturday afternoons together. Constant
use had not worn ragged the fabric of their friendship.

They looked alike, though the resemblance did not lie in their features. It was in the shape of their bodies, their movements, their style,
and their adornments. Annabel and Midge did, and completely, all
that young office workers are besought not to do. They painted their
lips and their nails, they darkened their lashes and lightened their hair,
and scent seemed to shimmer from them. They wore thin, bright
dresses, tight over their breasts and high on their legs, and tilted slippers, fancifully strapped. They looked proud and cheap and charming.

Now, as they walked across to Fifth Avenue with their skirts
swirled by the hot wind, they received audible admiration. Young men
grouped lethargically about newsstands awarded them murmurs, exclamations, even—the ultimate tribute—whistles. Annabel and Midge
passed without the condescension of hurrying their pace; they held
their heads higher and set their feet with exquisite precision, as if they
stepped over the necks of peasants.

Always the girls went to walk on Fifth Avenue on their free afternoons, for it was the ideal ground for their favorite game. The game
could be played anywhere, and, indeed, was, but the great shop windows stimulated the two players to their best form.

Annabel had invented the game; or rather she had evolved it from an old one. Basically, it was no more than the ancient sport of what-would-you-do-if-you-had-a-million-dollars. But Annabel had drawn a new set of rules for it, had narrowed it, pointed it, made it stricter. Like all games, it was the more absorbing for being more difficult.

Annabel's version went like this: You must suppose that somebody dies and leaves you a million dollars, cool. But there is a condition to the bequest. It is stated in the will that you must spend every nickel of the money on yourself.

There lay the hazard of the game. If, when playing it, you forgot, and listed among your expenditures the rental of a new apartment for your family, for example, you lost your turn to the other player. It was astonishing how many—and some of them among the experts, too— would forfeit all their innings by such slips.

It was essential, of course, that it be played in passionate seriousness. Each purchase must be carefully considered and, if necessary, supported by argument. There was no zest to playing wildly. Once Annabel had introduced the game to Sylvia, another girl who worked in the office. She explained the rules to Sylvia and then offered her the gambit "What would be the first thing you'd do?" Sylvia had not shown the decency of even a second of hesitation. "Well," she had said, "the first thing I'd do, I'd go out and hire somebody to shoot Mrs. Gary Cooper, and then . . ." So it is to be seen that she was no fun.

But Annabel and Midge were surely born to be comrades, for Midge played the game like a master from the moment she learned it. It was she who added the touches that made the whole thing cozier. According to Midge's innovations, the eccentric who died and left you the money was not anybody you loved, or, for the matter of that, anybody you even knew. It was somebody who had seen you somewhere and had thought, "That girl ought to have lots of nice things. I'm going to leave her a million dollars when I die." And the death was to be neither untimely nor painful. Your benefactor, full of years and comfortably ready to depart, was to slip softly away during sleep and go right to heaven. These embroideries permitted Annabel and Midge to play their game in the luxury of peaceful consciences.

Midge played with a seriousness that was not only proper but extreme. The single strain on the girls' friendship had followed an announcement once made by Annabel that the first thing she would buy with her million dollars would be a silver-fox coat. It was as if she had struck Midge across the mouth. When Midge recovered her breath, she cried that she couldn't imagine how Annabel could do such a thing—silver-fox coats were common! Annabel defended her taste with the retort that they were not common, either. Midge then said that they were so. She added that everybody had a silver-fox coat. She went on, with perhaps a slight loss of head, to declare that she herself wouldn't be caught dead in silver fox.

For the next few days, though the girls saw each other as constantly, their conversation was careful and infrequent, and they did not once play their game. Then one morning, as soon as Annabel entered the office, she came to Midge and said that she had changed her mind. She would not buy a silver-fox coat with any part of her million dollars. Immediately on receiving the legacy she would select a coat of mink.

Midge smiled and her eyes shone. "I think," she said, "you're absolutely right."

Now, as they walked along Fifth Avenue, they played the game anew. It was one of those days with which September is repeatedly cursed; hot and glaring, with slivers of dust in the wind. People drooped and shambled, but the girls carried themselves tall and walked a straight line, as befitted young heiresses on their afternoon promenade. There was no longer need for them to start the game at its formal opening. Annabel went direct to the heart of it.

"All right," she said. "So you've got this million dollars. So what would be the first thing you'd do?"

"Well, the first thing I'd do," Midge said, "I'd get a mink coat." But she said it mechanically, as if she were giving the memorized answer to an expected question.

"Yes," Annabel said, "I think you ought to. The terribly dark kind of mink." But she, too, spoke as if by rote. It was too hot; fur, no matter how dark and sleek and supple, was horrid to the thoughts.

They stepped along in silence for a while. Then Midge's eye was caught by a shop window. Cool, lovely gleamings were there set off by chaste and elegant darkness.

"No," Midge said, "I take it back. I wouldn't get a mink coat the first thing. Know what I'd do? I'd get a string of pearls. Real pearls."

Annabel's eyes turned to follow Midge's.

"Yes," she said, slowly. "I think that's a kind of a good idea. And it would make sense, too. Because you can wear pearls with anything."

Together they went over to the shop window and stood pressed against it. It contained but one object—a double row of great, even pearls clasped by a deep emerald around a little pink velvet throat.

"What do you suppose they cost?" Annabel said.

"Gee, I don't know," Midge said. "Plenty, I guess."

"Like a thousand dollars?" Annabel said.

"Oh, I guess like more," Midge said. "On account of the emerald."

"Well, like ten thousand dollars?" Annabel said.

"Gee, I wouldn't even know," Midge said.

The devil nudged Annabel in the ribs. "Dare you to go in and price them," she said.

"Like fun!" Midge said.

"Dare you," Annabel said.

"Why, a store like this wouldn't even be open this afternoon," Midge said.

"Yes, it is so, too," Annabel said. "People just came out. And there's a doorman on. Dare you."

"Well," Midge said. "But you've got to come too."

They tendered thanks, icily, to the doorman for ushering them into the shop. It was cool and quiet, a broad, gracious room with panelled walls and soft carpet. But the girls wore expressions of bitter disdain, as if they stood in a sty.

A slim, immaculate clerk came to them and bowed. His neat face showed no astonishment at their appearance.

"Good afternoon," he said. He implied that he would never forget it if they would grant him the favor of accepting his soft-spoken greeting.

"Good afternoon," Annabel and Midge said together, and in like freezing accents.

"Is there something—" the clerk said.

"Oh, we're just looking," Annabel said. It was as if she flung the words down from a dais.

The clerk bowed.

"My friend and myself merely happened to be passing," Midge said, and stopped, seeming to listen to the phrase. "My friend here and myself," she went on, "merely happened to be wondering how much are those pearls you've got in your window."

"Ah, yes," the clerk said. "The double rope. That is two hundred and fifty thousand dollars, Madam."

"I see," Midge said.

The clerk bowed. "An exceptionally beautiful necklace," he said. "Would you care to look at it?"

"No, thank you," Annabel said.

"My friend and myself merely happened to be passing," Midge said.

They turned to go; to go, from their manner, where the tumbrel awaited them. The clerk sprang ahead and opened the door. He bowed as they swept by him.

The girls went on along the Avenue, and disdain was still on their faces.

"Honestly!" Annabel said. "Can you imagine a thing like that?"

"Two hundred and fifty thousand dollars!" Midge said. "Why, that's a quarter of a million dollars!"

"He's got his nerve!" Annabel said.

They walked on. Slowly the disdain went, slowly and completely as if drained from them, and with it went the regal carriage and tread. Their shoulders dropped and they dragged their feet; they bumped against each other, without notice or apology, and caromed away again. They were silent and their eyes were cloudy.

Suddenly Midge straightened her back, flung her head high, and spoke, clear and strong.

"Listen, Annabel," she said. "Look. Suppose there was this terribly rich person, see? You don't know this person, but this person has seen you somewhere and wants to do something for you. Well, it's a terribly old person, see? And so this person dies, just like going to sleep, and leaves you ten million dollars. Now, what would be the first thing you'd do?"

WOLCOTT GIBBS Why he selected

The CUSTOMER Is always

WRONG

Of all the illegitimate children of the arts, the theatrical press-agent is generally held in the lowest esteem. He is paid to exploit producers, trained seals, and actors; he is a parasite on a parasite. The interesting thing (to me) about Richard Maney is that he represents a distinct reversal in the normal order of things. In life, it is not usual for the hired publicist to maintain an ironical attitude about the thing publicized, any more than it is usual for the average flea to be superior and detached about a dog. Mr. Maney is also unique in his odd calling in that he tells the truth as often as not.

New York, N. Y.   WOLCOTT GIBBS
July, 1942

(A PROFILE)

JUST as the advance agent for a circus is not likely to be disturbed by even the largest elephant, so his metropolitan equivalent, the Broadway press agent, can look on the most succulent actor and still remain composed. This is a natural condition, since both actors and elephants, observed for any length of time at close range, are apt to seem no better than anybody else. It is remarkable only when the publicity man, who after all is paid to exploit these phenomena, makes no attempt to hide his good-natured derision.

There are a good many press agents in New York who operate on a sort of man-to-man basis with their clients; Richard Sylvester Maney, the most prosperous gnome of the lot, is the only one who persistently treats them with the genial condescension of an Irish cop addressing a Fifth Avenue doorman. This comparison isn't altogether arbitrary.

Most doormen are more ornamental than cops, and practically all actors are more beautiful than Maney, but fundamentally, like the cop, he is a more impressive figure and they know it. A few conspicuously high-class performers, such as Maurice Evans and Noel Coward, have reached a state of precarious equality with their employee, but the rest are kept strictly in their places.

Mr. Maney's manner toward his inferiors is firm, though not unkind. Playing with them in one of those interminable games of chance that serve to keep him from being even richer than he is, he seldom bothers with their actual names.

"All right, actor, it's your turn," he will shout impatiently when some Thespian appears to him to be dawdling, and "actor" in his mouth is an Elizabethan word, with low and foolish connotations. Being a gentleman, he is more restrained on the whole with the ladies of the profession and even greets them from time to time with what he probably imagines are terms of endearment. "Thanks for the baubles, my peculiar witch," he once said politely to Miss Grace Moore, for whom he was working at the time and who had given him some pretty cuff links in a timid effort to melt his spectacular indifference. Miss Moore was enchanted.

He has a little more respect for producers, perhaps on the ground that they are occasionally men of some slight substance, though even here his admiration can hardly be called slavish. His notorious love affair with Billy Rose, who once recklessly employed him to exploit his vast and quite incomprehensible enterprises, has been discussed in print far too often to be repeated now, but many other producers have paid handsomely to be insulted both in the newspapers and privately.

"Mr. Harris has finally combed the last Cossack out of his curls," Mr. Maney remarked genially in the *Tribune* by way of announcing that Jed Harris, after a series of noble but discouraging experiments with the Russian drama, was again prepared to grapple with our native product. He was also impolite to his sombre young master during office hours. Like many another man of large affairs, Mr. Harris lived with the dream of eventually getting a little order into things, and for this purpose he introduced an elaborate system of interoffice memoranda for the use of his staff. These were supposed to constitute a dignified and permanent record of what went on in the Harris organization, but for some reason Mr. Maney found this idea irksome. Memoranda began to appear bearing such messages as "To: Mr. Harris. From: Mr. Maney. Re: What time is it?" and presently the whole system collapsed from sheer overproduction. A sign also turned up one day on the door behind which Mr. Harris dreamed his majestic and turbulent dreams. "Where the grapes of wrath are stored," Maney had printed neatly. Insofar as he was capable of admiring anything except a mirror, however, Mr. Harris cherished his queer employee.

Once, during one of Maney's several operations with Herman Shumlin, he watched with disgust while his usually sensible colleague labored with the production of a spectacle called "Sweet Mystery of Life," in which the actors fumbled about in the bloom, dwarfed by acres of scenery. It flew closed like a door, as Maney sometimes describes this occupational mishap, and Mr. Shumlin turned to his press agent for consolation. He made a mistake. " 'Sweet Mystery of Life,' indeed!" retorted that rough diamond. "It was the triumph of lumber over art."

Another producer to suffer from Maney's basic inability to disguise his feelings was Courtney Burr, who once asked him whether a simple dinner coat or tails would be more appropriate for one of the Burr openings.

"You better wear your track suit," said Maney, and this, it turned out, was a prophecy.

Even Gilbert Miller, a famous cosmopolite, failed to awe Maney or shake his lofty integrity. One day, in a proud but misguided moment, Mr. Miller offered his hired man a shapely little announcement for the press which he had framed with his own cultivated hand. Maney read it through impassively and gave it back. "It isn't English," he said. Meekly, Mr. Miller made it English.

The problem of why so many sensitive and arrogant people continue to employ a man who is almost certain to hurt their feelings sooner or later is an interesting one. It would be easy to say that Maney is the best press agent in town and let it go at that, but somehow it seems too simple. He isn't indispensable. There are other boys in the business capable of handling publicity with about the same competence and doing it much more politely and quietly, without nearly so much wear and tear on delicate egos. The secret lies somewhere in the complex and difficult riddle of personality. It is profitable to be associated with Maney, but it is also quite an experience in its peculiar way—perhaps not unlike drinking a very dry Martini, which is rather shocking at first but develops its own special glow as you go along. Almost all producers who have worked with Maney find it hard to put on a show without the curious extra flavor he adds to their lives.

This is by no means a triumph of sheer physical charm. Maney is not a handsome man. His wide face is pure Celt. He looks like a tough Irish altar boy who has grown up to be a popular Second Avenue bartender. He has no eyebrows worth mentioning and forgotten fights —invariably lost—have blurred the classic detail of his nose. Usually, as the evening wears on, he has a tendency to settle inside his clothes, like a turtle in its shell, and his eyelids come down to hood his eyes. A habit of having his dusty hair cut very short makes his head seem even rounder than it is. His body has the solid, humorous rotundity of a Teddy bear's. Last year *Time*, in a rare spasm of felicity, called him a "roustabout George M. Cohan."

Maney's social behavior ranges from a wild truculence, when he lowers his head and bellows like a bull, to an equally furious gaiety, when community singing seems to charm him most. He particularly admires a noisy anthem called "My Dream of the U.S.A.," which involves banging glasses on the table, usually breaking them. At the match game, the standard entertainment at a restaurant called Bleeck's Artists' and Writers' Club and mathematically the most absurd form of gambling ever invented, Maney's vehement offer to play anybody for twenty fish can easily be heard in the *Herald Tribune* editorial rooms next door. There is seldom a dull moment and, in spite of all the tumult, almost never one when people feel like getting up and moving to another table.

By contrast, it is always a little startling to meet Maney in polite evening dress, supervising one of his own openings. Courtesy sits on him like a shroud, and for some reason he seems a good deal smaller than usual. Even on these grim occasions, however, the basic Maney isn't totally absent. He gets as many terrible shows as the next man and, while he doesn't enjoy them economically, he takes a certain sardonic interest in their effect on the public.

"How do you like it?" he asked a tactful but honest young woman during the first-act intermission at one such night not long ago.

"Well, that act seemed a little slow, Dick," she answered reluctantly, "but I'm sure the others are much better."

"That was supposed to be the good one, my deluded squaw," said Mr. Maney, and chuckled like a ghoul.

Meeting one of the authors of this same sad misadventure after the final curtain, Maney offered his fatherly comfort and advice. "Take to the hills," he muttered hoarsely.

The most fascinating thing about Maney, however, lies in something rich and strange he has done to the English language. This curious form of speech is one of the small miracles of the town and was once even imbedded in a play when Ben Hecht and Charles MacArthur transplanted its author intact to the stage in "Twentieth Century." The probabilities are that it was born in the first place as a form of compensation. Maney was properly brought up by a devout mother to whom blasphemy was as shocking as second-story work. To spare her pain, the child throttled his vocabulary, but as he grew older, the natural fury and exasperation in him mounted and, although his speech remained as pure as a radio announcer's, his fundamental outlook on life got to be as blasphemous as hell. An outlet was necessary before the little boy blew up and so there gradually came into existence a system of invective that *sounded* like swearing but was in fact as innocent as Mother Goose. Robert Louis Stevenson was operating on the same principle when he created the most satisfactory gang of pirates in literature and never permitted one of them to say anything that couldn't safely be read to an eight-year-old boy.

This theory is probably as good as any, but however it happened, Maney today is the world's greatest master of disinfected epithet. While other and lesser men monotonously employ such clichés of displeasure as "son of a bitch" and "bastard," his range is practically infinite. His clients and acquaintances escape the stigma of illegitimacy, but few other qualities or conditions are spared them. He is surrounded by Comic Spaniards. Unfortunate Aztecs, Foul Turtledoves, Penthouse

Cagliostros, and even more fascinating compounds. He seldom repeats himself. The well is deep and undefiled.

People who really know Maney submit to these caresses without resentment and usually with a certain amount of pleasure and admiration, although now and then a touch of bewilderment creeps into things, too. A young man who had been wanting to meet him for some time finally got his wish, but his report of his experience was a little plaintive.

"I can't seem to understand anything Mr. Maney says," he confessed. "Is this usual?"

It is only when Maney gets outside his own circle, however, that the real fuss is likely to begin. One night, in the company of an actor and some other negligible character, he set out on a tour of the drinking places in a strange and forbidding section of the town. Time passed agreeably, but at last, although nobody was prepared to go home, it began to look as if everything else was closed up. Maney approached a native of the district, a colored citizen, conceivably on his way to work.

"Where can we get a drink around here, my vile Corsican?" he asked amiably. The dark stranger, though appearing more baffled than annoyed, swung nervously and Mr. Maney bounced on the pavement. This was clearly an occasion when simple blasphemy would have been less provocative, and there have been several others, so that for the most part Maney confines his night life to places where he is known and understood. With the enthusiastic co-operation of their proprietors, he has banned himself for varying lengths of time from many resorts, including the Stork Club and Twenty-One, where he feels that the average customer doesn't appreciate fancy rhetoric even when it comes up and spits in his eye.

In one case, the coolness between Maney and a certain fashionable pump room arose because he referred to its proprietor as an inflated busboy; in another, he approached an unknown but stylish icicle in a white tie and advised him to stop tossing his money around like a drunken sailor, a remark generally felt to be in restraint of trade. He reached the depths, however, as the result of a sincere effort to be polite. Entering a restaurant one day at the cocktail hour, he stopped to speak to a rich and beautiful young matron seated near the door. What he said was merely jocular, but it was misunderstood, and when Maney got to the bar his companions urged him to go back and apologize. He agreed and started out on this courteous errand, but somewhere along the way Dr. Jekyll began to fade and the man who reached her table was unmistakably Mr. Hyde. "Listen, my painted Jezebel," he began. The late Percy Hammond sometimes said with awe that his friend Maney had a distinctly voodoo personality.

Maney's talent is by no means confined to calling peculiar names. His most casual pronouncement has an air about it, a quality of invention and balance and study. "Dames who put ginger ale in Scotch highballs should be submitted to the bastinado and reduced to moccasins," he remarked offhand one night on this important subject, and visitors to his untidy headquarters over the Empire Theatre are greeted with pleasant extravagance. "Ah," the proprietor will shout warmly, "a spent runner staggers into the blockade, a Blackfoot arrow protruding from his back!" In "Twentieth Century," Hecht and MacArthur put a pretty line into the mouth of the character representing Maney. There is some talk about a Mr. and Mrs. Lockwood, who are occupying Drawing Room A. "Mr. and Mrs., hell," says the pseudo-Maney. "It's Romeo and Juliet, hacking away at the Mann Act." While not genuine, this is an almost perfect example of Maney's verbal technique, being balanced in structure, florid in conception, and containing a useful classical reference. So fascinated was Billy Rose with some of his employee's remarks that gradually he came to appropriate them as his own. In a recent and rather unaccountable address to the Harvard Business School, Mr. Rose described his feelings at the opening of "Jumbo." "I stood on the Rubicon, rattling the dice," he told the enchanted students, who couldn't be expected to know that this comment had originally appeared in Maney's program notes some five years before. Mr. Rose has also quoted himself as having observed that "Jumbo" would either make Rose or break Whitney, another *mot* that was born elsewhere.

The literary bas-relief that ornaments Maney's speech, incidentally, is quite authentic. He is a formidable student, especially of Shakespeare and other antiquities. On an "Information Please" program last spring, he delivered a good part of the prologue to "The Canterbury Tales" and would have been delighted to furnish the rest if he hadn't been

restrained by the master of ceremonies. At his most typical, Maney
sounds a good deal like a circus barker with an LL.D.

The repository of all this charm and learning and fury was born
forty-nine years ago in Chinook, Montana, a whistle stop on the Great
Northern with a population in those days of some five hundred. Today
he describes it nostalgically as "a nest of mangy Crees," and adds that
it has the reputation of being the coldest damn place in the United
States. From saying so a good many times, Maney has almost come to
believe that he was the first white child born there and also that up to
the age of twelve he preferred to converse in the Indian tongues. These
things, however, seem rather unlikely. His father owned the local
hardware store, but his heart was really in politics and he ran doggedly
for everything, finally winding up as a trustee in the public-school
system. His other innocent ambition was to make a musician, specifically a cornet player, out of his smoldering offspring. Maney blew
the cornet from the time he was seven until he was twelve without developing much except a tendency to have a rather lopsided face. His
mother finally put a stop to that.

"I'll have no monster on this ranch," she said, and the musician laid
down his instrument without regret.

In 1906, Maney's father set out in a box car containing his family,
his furniture, and eight horses for Seattle, where he took up contracting
and his son went through high school and entered the state university.
In the summer, Maney drove a dump truck for his father and in
winter he studied, admiring the liberal arts and graciously tolerating
everything else. Nothing in particular has survived from this period.
Maney was not an athlete and his social life appears to have been
placid. From time to time he made fifty cents working as an usher at
the Moore Theatre, owned by John Cort, and after he was graduated
with a B.A. in 1913, he persuaded Mr. Cort to give him a job.

A mist obscures the next thirteen years, and our glimpses of the
principal actor are dim and intermittent. He was one of four advance
agents for Anna Held in her "All-Star Jubilee," though not the man
who thought up the celebrated milk bath. In fact, as he remembers it,
the tour progressed through such backward country that nobody got
any baths at all, including Miss Held. At one time he lived with, and

on, an enterprising associate who had collected $3,000 in damages for falling down an elevator shaft. At another he operated an electric baseball scoreboard in a saloon and at still another he was manager of a theatre on upper Broadway at which the leading attraction was a nervous performer who held a fork in his mouth and tried to catch potatoes thrown from the gallery. Both Maney and this unusual artist lasted exactly a week. Once, for a brooding moment, he found himself back under his father's roof in Seattle.

When everything else failed, he turned to a humiliating trade. "Whenever I couldn't eat any other way, I looked around for a door to guard," he says. There were a good many doors. He was visible to his fashionable friends taking tickets at various theatres, but particularly at the Morosco, where he wore a Cossack uniform weighing fourteen pounds. He was rescued from this public degradation by Bronco Billy Anderson, a star of the silent pictures, who, dreaming of better things, put on an opera called "The Frivolities of 1920" and employed Maney to publicize it for him. Accompanying this dubious charade to Boston, he fell in with a Shubert press agent fantastically christened A. Toxen Worm and through him at last entered the more or less respectable fringes of the profession. Sponsored by Mr. Worm, he was soon associated with the firm of Jones & Green, producers of "The Greenwich Village Follies," and finally, in 1927, he went to work for Jed Harris, succeeding S. N. Behrman and Arthur Kober, neither of whom found himself able to cope with that small, dark man about whose head the lightning played. In this fashion, by way of many strange back doors, Mr. Maney came to Broadway.

Before he did, however, he had been through one of the most singular experiences of his life. Back in 1919, when he was living an idle, carefree life with the man who fell down the shaft, Maney spent some of his abundant leisure contributing odds and ends to a sports column run by a friend. These compositions were informed as well as sprightly, for Maney knows almost as much about baseball as he does about Shakespeare, and at length the word got around that he was a weighty expert on all matters dealing with recreation. Almost before he knew it, and certainly without any particular volition on his own part, he found himself the forty-dollar-a-week editor and staff of a highly specialized publication known as the *American Angler*.

Up to then all the fish that Maney had known intimately had been cooked; he neither knew nor cared how they got from the stream to the kitchen, and his opinion of anglers was low. Nevertheless, he was a conscientious man and he did his best. "Keep your flies in the water—trout don't live in trees," he advised his readers in one early issue, and a little later he wrote thoughtfully, "It has always been my contention that in a piano tuner, to a greater degree than in any other artisan, is concealed—possibly congealed—that quality which marks the successful fly-fisherman. Did you ever watch a piano tuner plying his painstaking if promiscuous art? No? Then do so at your first opportunity." Maney went on for quite a while in this vein, to the confusion of the innocent fishermen.

The Great Trout-Fly Symposium, however, was a tremendous success. Looking for something to fill his yawning columns, Maney hit on a very nice problem for his single-minded readers. "If you were condemned to go through life with but three trout flies, regardless of weather, season, or locality, what three would you choose?" he asked them provocatively. The response was immediate and almost overwhelming. Dr. Henry Van Dyke wrote from Princeton, "If I were required to limit my trout-fly book to three flies (which upon the whole would not be an altogether bad thing) I should choose (1) Queen of the Water, (2) March Brown, and (3) Royal Coachman." The Doctor was remarkably brief. Most of Maney's readers spread themselves happily. "To limit myself to three flies is unthinkable," wrote one O. W. Smith, "though I might get along with five if allowed several sizes, for, in my judgment, size is a more determining factor than pattern. When the water is clear and low, as is often the case in August, a tiny 'Professor' will take the fish, whereas . . ." This rhapsody filled an entire page and was accompanied by a photograph of the author, his hat bristling defiantly with flies of every conceivable size and shape. Several of Mr. Maney's correspondents were appalled at the idea of trying to get through life so grotesquely handicapped, but with one exception they all agreed that it was a good, interesting question. The solitary dissenter was a Mr. Louis Rhead. "I think the question very foolish," he replied crossly.

After a while the atmosphere around the *American Angler*, with its strangely possessed visitors and the almost tangible memory of dead fish haunting the corridors, began to get on the editor's nerves, and the breaking point came one day when a meek but persistent contributor drifted in looking for an assignment. "Go interview a successful trout, you under-water Boswell!" roared Mr. Maney, the veins rather unpleasantly corded in his neck.

The writer vanished, but he was back again in a couple of days, and to Maney's amazement and horror he had done exactly what he was told. "An Interview with a Successful Trout," purporting to be a submarine conversation with a bright fish, appeared in the *American Angler* for April, 1919, and it is one of the most nerve-racking specimens of prose in the language. A brief sample of the hero's remarks is certainly enough:

"My friend Gorumpp, the bullfrog, keeps me pretty well informed about current events out of the water. He sits on a log and makes observations all day long, but at times he comes down here below for a visit. I love him as a companion although I would devour him were he conveniently smaller. You think it strange that I would like to dispose of a friend? As a matter of fact, I wonder how long I could be powerful and handsome unless I were to catch something a good many times a day. The minnows—a principal part of my diet—are engaged all day long in capturing ephemerids and cyclops, and various other kinds of things which in turn are catching something else.

"I suppose that right is might, and if it were not right for me to be here I might be lost altogether. I asked Rulee [the local fairy] about it, and she says that one thing catches another, clear down to the microbes, and that microbes catch each other. Your Molière or Shaw might have written about the sentimental features of the subject."

There was something about this educated talk that convinced Mr. Maney that he had had about enough, and when the anglers invited their lovable old editor to judge a fly-casting tournament in Chicago, he quietly turned in his resignation and returned to Broadway, where fish are sensibly kept in iceboxes and don't talk.

Once he was established as a New York press agent, Maney's progress was rapid. By the end of his third year he had represented such solid and memorable productions as "Broadway," "Coquette," "The Royal Family," "The Front Page," "Serena Blandish, and "Fifty Million Frenchmen." He had also perfected his attitude toward the theatre and the press. For the most part, Maney avoids the traditional milk-bath, tanbark, and stolen-jewelry approach to his trade, although he once abetted Ben Hecht and Gene Fowler when those two relentless elves announced that they were going to lie in separate coffins in a funeral parlor to celebrate the decease of an exhibit called "The Great Magoo," and he was responsible for an advertisement calling for one hundred genuine noblemen ("Bogus counts, masqueraders, and de-scendants of the Dauphin will get short shrift") to act as dancing part-ners at Billy Rose's Fort Worth Frontier Centennial. At the instigation of Mr. Rose, who never felt that he was quite sufficiently in the public eye, he even announced that an elephant would be shot out of a cannon as the first-act finale of "Jumbo." This was meant to be facetious, and it was taken that way by everybody except the editor of *Vanity Fair*, who sent a reporter around to get a blueprint explaining how this prodigy was to be accomplished.

Such elementary pranks as these, however, haven't had much to do with Maney's success. He manages to get practically everything he writes—about six thousand words a week—printed somewhere or other, partly because it is invariably accurate, partly because it is written a good deal better than most of the material an editor would be likely to get from members of his own staff, but mostly because it sounds so little like publicity. This isn't altogether intentional. Maney tries to turn out rich and beautiful prose about the work of the performers whom he genuinely admires—Helen Hayes, Maurice Evans, Ethel Barrymore, Tallulah Bankhead, and a few others—but there is a stub-born block between his enthusiasm and his typewriter, and what comes out is almost invariably tinged with derision and a suggestion that the theatre is a pretty comic business at best. Miss Hayes is his darling, but she is just as likely to find herself described as a scampering Columbine as the next girl. This frivolous tone, while a little dismaying to actors who dream of themselves as serious artists, is a relief to dramatic editors, who spend most of their days ploughing through thinly dis-guised advertising matter, and they print it gratefully.

The same flavor is evident in the capsule biographies which turn up in the programs of Maney attractions. Other press agents approach this routine task without much spirit, confining themselves to simple lists of the plays in which their subjects have previously appeared. Maney's notes, however, are a nice blend of the irrelevant, the scurrilous, and, with an air of reluctance, the foolish facts in the case. At one time or another he has written, "Brenda Forbes has a scar on her left wrist, weighs 120 pounds, and emerged from her cocoon to play the serving wench in 'The Taming of the Shrew.'" . . . "Frances Comstock was born during a blizzard in 1913, has sung in many of our toniest bistros, and over the air has given her lyric all for assorted toothpastes, lubricants, and juices." . . . "Alfred Drake sprouted as a baritone when the Steel Pier at Atlantic City was supporting a vagrant opera company. He was billed below the cinnamon bears." . . . "Donald Cameron got under way as a Roman rowdy, with spear, when Margaret Anglin came to grips with the Bard at the Hudson." . . . "Nadine Gay is a fugitive from a Fanchon and Marco unit." . . . "George Lloyd was last season understudy to a corpse."

Maney has also commented from time to time on the theatre in general. "Producing is the Mardi Gras of the professions," he once wrote sourly in the *Times*. "Anyone with a mask and enthusiasm can bounce into it." Somewhere else he paid his indignant respects to actresses. "All female stars have one thing in common: after you stand on your head to arrange an interview, they break the date because they have to go and get their hair washed." Of his own part in all these goings-on, he says, "The press agent is part beagle, part carrier pigeon, and part salmon (the salmon only goes home to die)." In fact, of all the people connected with the trade, the critics are about the only ones who have escaped his sinister attention. For obvious reasons, Maney treats these peevish but powerful men with mittens on, and if it remains a mystery to him how most of them got where they are, he keeps it politely to himself. He is an expert on all the curious feuds and phobias that afflict them and he is careful to seat them (fifty on first nights, seventy-five on second nights) where they will be as nearly happy as their twisted natures will permit. "It is not always possible for the first night press list to embrace the reviewer for *Racing Form* or the *Princeton Tiger*," he once remarked when pushed a little too far, but he is usually a model of discretion.

It is doubtful if this irascible behavior would work for everybody, but it has paid Maney handsome dividends. During the past five years he has handled the publicity for an average of eleven shows a season, out of which four could be described as hits. Considering that the total Broadway output during this period ran to something like eighty offerings a year, of which about fifteen were hits, and that some fifteen agents (there are fifty all told) were passionately competing for the business, it is evident that Maney has been doing all right.

For the information of posterity, his exact record has been as follows: In the season that opened in the fall of 1936, he had four hits out of six productions; in 1937, a discouraging year, only one out of eleven; in 1938, five out of thirteen; and in 1939, five out of fourteen; and, last year, out of the ten shows he handled, five were definitely successful, including "Arsenic and Old Lace," and the two winners of the Drama Critics' prizes, "Watch on the Rhine" and "The Corn Is Green," all three of which are still doing very well.

So far this season, Maney's average is exactly .500. A dismal vehicle called "The More the Merrier" came and went, causing no more than a slight local irritation, but "The Wookey," although not conspicuously admired by the critics, seems assured of a substantial run, largely for patriotic reasons. His further plans include a Maurice Evans production of "Macbeth," in which there are rumors that Maney himself will play the Third Witch; "Clash by Night," by Clifford Odets, with Tallulah Bankhead; and "Anne of England," with Flora Robson, which was due to arrive this week.

It isn't easy, even for Maney himself, to figure out exactly what income all this represents. Press agents are paid from $150 to $300 a week for each play, and Maney's salary is usually up near the top. Thus, at the peak of last season, with six shows running simultaneously, his office was taking in at least $1,200 a week, and throughout the season the average was probably around $800.

Maney doesn't get all this wealth himself, however. In 1937, after a period of bickering of no conceivable interest to anybody except another press agent, the less prosperous members of the trade, already weakly banded together in something known as T.M.A.T. (Theatre Managers, Agents, and Treasurers), affiliated themselves with the tough and powerful Teamsters' Union of the American Federation of Labor. While not openly directed against Maney or anybody else, this maneuver was designed to prevent any man from representing more than one show at a time without employing qualified assistants—men, that is, who had themselves been active press agents on Broadway within the preceding three years.

Maney, who up to then had been getting along handsomely without assistance, offered a certain amount of resistance to their demands. With a few almost equally fortunate colleagues, he retained Morris Ernst, an attorney not without his own grasp of publicity values, to preserve as much as possible of the status quo. Mr. Ernst went raging into battle.

"I shall never deliver this little group to the tender mercies of the teamsters," he promised his clients at a luncheon at the Algonquin, and they went away reassured. Some four weeks later, however, Maney and his friends were slightly dismayed to find themselves good and regular members of T.M.A.T. and very much at the mercy of the merry teamsters.

"I have a dim suspicion that somebody may have sold me out," said Maney upon being informed of this shotgun wedding, but on the whole he accepted his defeat philosophically. By the terms of the final agreement, he was obliged to hire one assistant at $75 a week as soon as he had two plays; to raise this salary to $100 when he got three; to employ a second man at $75 for his fourth, raising him to $100 for the fifth; and to hire still a third at $75 for the sixth. This was as far as it could go, since the union ruled arbitrarily that no agent should be allowed to represent more than six shows simultaneously. While Maney's payments to his staff have run up to the limit of $275 a week, they probably average $100, so that organized labor costs him about $5,000 a year. Nevertheless, the chances are that the season of 1940-1941 netted him at least $25,000, or approximately twice the amount made by his nearest competitor.

His remarkable preëminence in his field was demonstrated in a backhand sort of way once last year in the cooking column conducted by Lucius Beebe in the *Herald Tribune*. Mr. Beebe published a picture of Maney solely on the ground that all that week he hadn't phoned.

Maney hasn't any private life in particular. He is married and lives with his wife and stepson in a house in Westport, but he isn't there much. When he isn't on the road, engaged in preliminary tub-thumping, he gets to his office at ten in the morning, even on those occasional days when he feels as if he had eaten a bomb, and works grimly through until five or six. After that he has dinner somewhere and then, after calling professionally at a box office or two, he drops into Bleeck's or one of its equivalents, looking for a match game or perhaps just somebody to shout at. When he gets home, either to Westport or his room at the Parc Vendome in town, it is usually somewhere between two and six and he goes to bed. Sometimes it is even later than that. Coming in one morning from an especially merry gathering several years ago, he was astonished to find his stepson, Jock, neatly dressed and about to go out.

"Where do you think *you're* going at this ungodly hour?" asked Maney sternly.

"To school," said the child.

The weekends, in fact, are about the only time his wife really has much chance to observe him, and he spends them lying around in his pajamas, either reading about Napoleon, whom he admires even more than Helen Hayes, or else simply licking his wounds. In spite of the Westport homestead, he loathes the country and avoids it whenever he can. This is partly because he has hay fever and partly because people keep trying to include him in their futile and dangerous games.

This rather restricted program, not to mention the continual association with actors and other inferior and disreputable companions, might depress another man, but Maney has no wish to change his lot. He has had offers from Hollywood and at least one enterprising publisher has tried to extract a book of reminiscences from him, but he has turned them all down. Scornful, indignant, frequently beside himself with rage, he is at the same time in a state of almost perfect inward adjustment. Just as Joe Louis can go into cold transports of fury in the ring while still finding there the whole explanation and justification of his existence, life in the theatre irritates Maney to the border of insanity, but perversely he loves every minute of it and he couldn't conceivably exchange it for anything else. He is doing precisely what he wants to. In spite of all the thrashing around, he may well be the most contented man in New York. It is only fair to add that he denies this base charge even more passionately than he denounces fish.

III
A GOODLY HERITAGE

STEPHEN VINCENT BENÉT why

he selected The DEVIL and DANIEL

✎ WEBSTER

"The Devil and Daniel Webster" is the kind of story I had wanted to write for a good many years. We have our own folk-gods and giants and figures of earth in this country—I wanted to write something about them. But often you do not see your way clear as to how to deal with a subject. I wrote a series of American stories in 1927 and had an old man, called, I fear, the Oldest Inhabitant, telling the stories. I liked writing them, though they weren't as good as they should have been. *The Country Gentleman* published most of them and seemed to like them, too—at least the editors did. As far as I can remember the response from the readers of *The Country Gentleman* was absolute or mathematical zero. So the series died a natural death. But ten years later or so, after a good many other things had happened, I still wanted to write that sort of story. So I started all over again. Only this time I dropped the convention of the Oldest Inhabitant and made the story tell itself.

New York, N. Y.   STEPHEN VINCENT BENÉT
June, 1942

IT'S a story they tell in the border-country, where Massachusetts joins Vermont and New Hampshire.

Yes, Dan'l Webster's dead—or, at least, they buried him. But, every time there's a thunderstorm around Marshfield, they say you can hear his rolling voice in the hollows of the sky. And they say that if you go to his grave and speak loud and clear, "Dan'l Webster—Dan'l Webster!" the ground'll begin to shiver and the trees begin to shake. And, after a while, you'll hear a deep voice, saying, "Neighbour, how stands the Union?" Then you better answer the Union stands as she

231

stood, rock-bottomed and copper-sheathed, one and indivisible, or he's liable to rear right out of the ground. At least, that's what I was told, when I was a youngster.

You see, for a while he was the biggest man in the country. He never got to be President but he was the biggest man. There was thousands that trusted in him right next to God Almighty—and they told stories about him and all·the things that belonged to him that were like the stories of patriarchs and such. They said when he stood up to speak stars and stripes came right out in the sky—and once he spoke against a river and made it sink into the ground. They said when he walked the woods with his fishing-rod, Killall, the trout would jump out of the streams right into his pockets, for they knew it was no use putting up a fight against him—and, when he argued a case, he could turn on the harps of the blessed and the shaking of the earth underground. That was the kind of man he was, and his big farm up at Marshfield was suitable to him. The chickens he raised were all white meat down through the drumsticks, the cows were tended like children and the big ram he called Goliath had horns with a curl like a morning-glory vine and could butt through an iron door. But Dan'l wasn't one of your gentlemen-farmers—he knew all the ways of the land and he'd be up by candlelight to see that the chores got done. A man with a mouth like a mastiff, a brow like a mountain and eyes like burning anthracite—that was Dan'l Webster in his prime. And the biggest case he argued never got written down in the books, for he argued it against the Devil, nip and tuck and no holds barred. And this is the way I used to hear it told.

There was a man named Jabez Stone, lived at Cross Corners, New Hampshire. He wasn't a bad man to start with, but he was an unlucky man. If he planted corn, he got borers, if he planted potatoes, he got blight. He had good enough land but it didn't prosper him— he had a decent wife and children, but the more children he had, the less there was to feed them. If stones cropped up in his neighbour's field, boulders boiled up in his—if he had a horse with the spavins, he'd trade it for one with the staggers and give something extra. There's some folks bound to be like that, apparently. But, one day, Jabez Stone got sick of the whole business.

He'd been ploughing that morning and he'd just broke the plough-share on a rock that he could have sworn hadn't been there yesterday. And, as he stood looking at the ploughshare, the off horse began to cough—that ropy kind of cough that means sickness and horse-doctors. There were two children down with the measles, his wife was ailing, and he had a whitlow on his thumb. It was about the last straw for Jabez Stone.

"I vow," he said, and he looked around him kind of desperate, "I vow it's enough to make a man want to sell his soul to the Devil! And I would, too, for two cents!"

Then he felt a kind of queerness come over him, at having said what he'd said, though naturally, being New Hampshire, he wouldn't take it back. But, all the same, when it got to be evening and, as far as he could see no notice had been taken, he felt relieved in his mind, for he was a religious man. But notice is always taken, sooner or later, just like the Good Book says. And sure enough, next day, about supper-time, a soft-spoken, dark-dressed stranger drove up in a smart buggy and asked for Jabez Stone.

Well, Jabez told his family it was a lawyer, come to see him about a legacy. But *he* knew who it was. He didn't like the looks of the stranger, nor the way he smiled with his teeth. They were white teeth and plentiful—some say they were filed to a point, but I wouldn't vouch for that. And he didn't like it when the dog took one look at the stranger and ran away howling with his tail between his legs. But, having passed his word, more or less, he stuck to it, and they went out behind the barn and made their bargain. Jabez Stone had to prick his finger, to sign, and the stranger lent him a silver pin. The wound healed clean but it left a little white scar.

After that, all of a sudden, things began to pick up and prosper for Jabez Stone. His cows got fat and his horses sleek, his crops were the envy of the neighbourhood and lightning might strike all over the valley but it wouldn't strike his barn. Pretty soon he was one of the prosperous people of the county—they asked him to stand for select-man and he stood for it—there began to be talk of running him for State Senate. All in all, you might say the Stone family was as happy and contented as cats in a dairy. And so they were, except for Jabez Stone.

He'd been contented enough, the first few years. It's a great thing when bad luck turns—it drives most other things out of your head. True, every now and then, especially in rainy weather, the little white scar on his finger would give him a twinge. And once a year, punctual as clockwork, the stranger with the smart buggy would come driving by. But the sixth year the stranger lighted, and, after that, his peace was over for Jabez Stone.

The stranger came up through the lower field, switching his boots with a cane—they were handsome black boots, but Jabez Stone never liked the look of them, particularly the toes. And, after he'd passed the time of day, he said, "Well, Mr. Stone, you're a hummer! It's a very pretty property you've got here, Mr. Stone."

"Well, some might favour it and others might not," said Jabez Stone, for he was a New Hampshireman.

"Oh—no need to decry your industry!" said the stranger, very easy, showing his teeth in a smile. "After all, we know what's been done—and it's been, according to contract and specifications. So when—ahem—the mortgage falls due, next year, you shouldn't have any regrets."

"Speaking of that mortgage, Mister," said Jabez Stone, and he looked around for help to the earth and the sky, "I'm beginning to have one or two doubts about it."

"Doubts?" said the stranger, not quite so pleasantly.

"Why, yes," said Jabez Stone. "This being the U.S.A. and me always having been a religious man." He cleared his throat and got bolder. "Yes sir," he said, "I'm beginning to have considerable doubts as to that mortgage holding in court."

"There's courts *and* courts," said the stranger, clicking his teeth. "Still—we might as well have a look at the original document," and he hauled out a big black pocket-book, full of papers. "Sherwin—Slater—Stevens—Stone," he muttered. "I, Jabez Stone—for a term of seven years—oh, it's quite in order, I think ——"

But Jabez Stone wasn't listening, for he saw something else flutter out of the black pocket-book. It's something that looked like a moth but it wasn't a moth. And as Jabez Stone stared at it, it seemed to speak to him in a small sort of piping voice, terrible small and thin but terrible human. "Neighbour Stone!" it squeaked. "Neighbour Stone! Help me—for God's sake, help me!"

But, before Jabez Stone could stir hand or foot, the stranger whipped out a big bandanna handkerchief, caught the creature in it, just like a butterfly, and started tying up the ends of the bandanna.

"Sorry for the interruption," he said. "As I was saying——"

But Jabez Stone was shaking all over like a scared horse.

"That's Miser Stevens' voice!" he said, in a croak. "And you've got him in your handkerchief!"

The stranger looked a little embarrassed.

"Yes, I really should have transferred him to the collecting box," he said, with a simper, "but there were some rather unusual specimens there and I didn't want them crowded. Well, well, these little *contretemps* will occur——"

"I don't know what you mean by contertan," said Jabez Stone, "but that was Miser Stevens' voice! And he ain't dead! You can't tell me he is! He was just as spry and mean as a woodchuck, Tuesday!"

"In the midst of life," said the stranger, kind of pious. "Listen!" Then a bell begun to toll in the valley and Jabez Stone listened, with the sweat running down his face. For he knew it was tolled for Miser Stevens and that he was dead.

"These long-standing accounts," said the stranger, with a sigh. "One really hates to close them. But business is business."

He still had the bandanna in his hand and Jabez Stone felt sick as he saw the cloth struggle and flutter.

"Are they all as small as that?" he asked hoarsely.

"Small?" said the stranger. "Oh, I see what you mean. Why, they vary." He measured Jabez Stone with his eyes and his teeth showed. "Don't worry, Mr. Stone," he said. "You'll go with a very good grade. I wouldn't trust *you* outside the collecting box. Now, a man like Dan'l Webster of course—well, we'd have to build a special box for him, and even at that, I imagine the wing-spread would astonish you. He'd certainly be a prize—I wish we could see our way clear to him! But, in your case, as I was saying——"

"Put that handkerchief away!" said Jabez Stone, and he begun to beg and to pray. But the best he can get at the end is a three-years' extension, with conditions.

But till you make a bargain like that, you've got no idea of how fast four years can run. By the last months of those years, Jabez Stone's known all over the State and there's a talk of running him for Governor —and it's dust and ashes in his mouth. For every day, when he gets up, he thinks, "There's one more night gone," and every night when he lies down, he thinks of the black pocket-book and the soul of Miser Stevens and it makes him sick at heart. Till, finally, he can't bear it any longer, and, in the last days of the last year, he hitches up his horse and drives off to seek Dan'l Webster. For Dan'l was born in New Hampshire, only a few miles from Cross Corners, and it's well known that he has a particular soft spot for old neighbours.

It was early in the morning when he got to Marshfield, but Dan'l was up already, talking Latin to the farmhands and wrestling with the ram, Goliath, and trying out a new trotter and working up speeches to make against John C. Calhoun. But, when he heard a New Hampshireman had come to see him he dropped everything else he was doing, for that was Dan'l's way. He gave Jabez Stone a breakfast that five men couldn't eat, went into the living history of every man and woman in Cross Corners, and, finally, asked him how he could serve him.

Jabez Stone allowed that it was a mortgage-case.

"Well, I haven't pleaded a mortgage-case in a long time, and I don't generally plead now, except before the Supreme Court," said Dan'l. "But, if I can, I'll help you."

"Then I've got hope, for the first time in ten years," said Jabez Stone and told him the details.

Dan'l walked up and down as he listened, hands behind his back, now and then asking a question, now and then plunging his eyes at the floor, as if they'd bore through it like gimlets. When Jabez Stone had finished, he puffed out his cheeks and blew. Then he turned to Jabez Stone and a smile broke over his face, like the sunrise over Monadnock.

"You've certainly given yourself the Devil's own road to hoe, Neighbour Stone," he said. "But I'll take your case."

"You'll take it?" said Jabez Stone, hardly daring to believe.

"Yes," said Dan'l Webster. "I've got about seventy-five other things to do and the Missouri Compromise to straighten out—but I'll take your case. For if two New Hampshiremen ain't a match for the Devil, we might as well give the country back to the Indians."

Then he shook Jabez Stone by the hand and said, "Did you come down here in a hurry?"

"Well, I admit I made time," said Jabez Stone.

"You'll go back faster," said Dan'l Webster and he told 'em to hitch up Constitution and Constellation to the carriage. They were matched greys with one white forefoot, and they stepped like greased lightning.

Well, I won't describe how excited and pleased the whole Stone family was to have the great Dan'l Webster for a guest, when they finally got there. Jabez Stone had lost his hat on the way, blown off when they overtook a wind, but he didn't take much account of that. But, after supper, he sent the family off to bed, for he had most particular business with Mr. Webster. Mrs. Stone wanted them to sit in the front-parlour—but Dan'l Webster knew front-parlours and said he preferred the kitchen. So it was there they sat, waiting for the stranger, with a jug on the table between them and a bright fire on the hearth— the stranger being scheduled to show up on the stroke of midnight, according to specification and whereas and therefore.

Well, most men wouldn't have asked for better company than Dan'l Webster and a jug. But with every tick of the clock Jabez Stone got sadder and sadder. His eyes roved round the room, and, though he sampled the jug, you could see he couldn't taste it. Finally, on the stroke of eleven-thirty, he reached over and grabbed Dan'l Webster by the arm.

"Mr. Webster, Mr. Webster!" he said, and his voice was shaking with fear and a desperate courage. "For God's sake, Mr. Webster, harness your horses and get away from this place while you can!"

"You've brought me a long way, neighbour, to tell me you don't like my company," said Dan'l Webster, quite peaceable, pulling at the jug.

"Miserable wretch that I am!" groaned Jabez Stone. "I've brought you a devilish way—and now I see my folly. Let him take me if he wills—I don't hanker after it, I must say, but I can stand it. But you're the Union's stay and New Hampshire's pride! He mustn't get you, Mr. Webster! He mustn't get you!"

Dan'l Webster looked at the distracted man, all grey and shaking in the firelight, and laid a hand on his shoulder.

"I'm obliged to you, Neighbour Stone," he said gently. "It's kindly thought of. But there's a jug on the table and a case in hand. And I never left a jug or a case half-finished in my life."

And, just at that moment, there was a sharp rap on the door.

"Ah," said Dan'l Webster, very coolly, "I thought your clock was a trifle slow, Neighbour Stone." He stepped to the door and opened it. "Come in!" he said.

The stranger came in—very dark and tall he looked in the fire-light. He was carrying a box under his arm—a black, japanned box with little air-holes in the lid. At the sight of the box Jabez Stone gave a low cry and shrank into a corner of the room.

"Mr. Webster, I presume," said the stranger, very polite, but with his eyes glowing like a fox's deep in the woods.

"Attorney of record for Jabez Stone," said Dan'l Webster, but his eyes were glowing, too. "Might I ask your name?"

"I've gone by a good many," said the stranger, carelessly. "Perhaps Scratch will do for the evening. I'm often called that in these regions."

Then he sat down at the table and poured himself a drink from the jug. The liquor was cold in the jug, but it came steaming into the glass.

"And now," said the stranger, smiling and showing his teeth, "I shall call upon you, as a law-abiding citizen, to assist me in taking possession of my property."

Well, with that the argument began—and it went hot and heavy. At first Jabez Stone had a flicker of hope—but when he saw Dan'l Webster being forced back at point after point he just sat scrunched in his corner with his eyes on that japanned box. For there wasn't any doubt as to the deed or the signature—that was the worst of it. Dan'l Webster twisted and turned and thumped his fist on the table—but he couldn't get away from that. He offered to compromise the case—the stranger wouldn't hear of it. He pointed out the property had in-creased in value and State Senators ought to be worth more—the stranger stuck to the letter of the law. He was a great lawyer, Dan'l Webster—but we know who's the King of Lawyers, as the Good

Book tells us—and it seemed as if, for the first time, Dan'l Webster had met his match.

Finally, the stranger yawned a little. "Your spirited efforts on behalf of your client do you credit, Mr. Webster," he said. "But if you have no more arguments to adduce—I'm rather pressed for time," and Jabez Stone shuddered.

Dan'l Webster's brow looked dark as a thundercloud.

"Pressed or not, you shall not have this man!" he thundered. "Mr. Stone is an American citizen—and no American citizen may be forced into the service of a foreign prince! We fought England for that in '12 and we'll fight all Hell for it again!"

"Foreign?" said the stranger. "And who calls me a foreigner?"

"Well I never yet heard of the Dev—of your claiming American citizenship," said Dan'l Webster, with surprise.

"And who with better right?" said the stranger, with one of his terrible smiles. "When the first wrong was done to the first Indian—I was there. When the first slaver put out for the Congo—I stood on her deck. Am I not in your books and stories and beliefs, from the first settlements on? Am I not spoken of still, in every church in New England? 'Tis true the North claims me for a Southerner and the South for a Northerner—but I am neither. I am merely an honest American like yourself—and of the best descent—for, to tell the truth, Mr. Webster, though I don't like to boast of it, my name is older in this country than yours."

"Aha!" said Dan'l Webster, with the veins standing out in his forehead. "Then I stand on the Constitution! I demand a trial for my client!"

"The case is hardly one for an ordinary court," said the stranger, his eyes flickering, "and, indeed, the lateness of the hour ——"

"Let it be any court you choose, so it is an American judge and an American jury!" said Dan'l Webster in his pride. "Let it be the quick or the dead—I'll abide the issue!"

"You have said it," said the stranger and pointed his finger at the door. And with that, and all of a sudden, there was a rushing of wind outside and a noise of footsteps. They came clear and distinct, through the night. And yet, they were not like the footsteps of living men.

"In God's name, who comes by so late?" cried Jabez Stone, in an agony of fear.

"The jury Mr. Webster demands," said the stranger, sipping at his boiling glass. "You must pardon the rough appearance of one or two—they will have come a long way."

And, with that, the fire burned blue and the door blew open and twelve men entered, one by one.

If Jabez Stone had been sick with terror before, he was blind with terror now. For there was Walter Butler, the loyalist, who spread fire and horror through the Mohawk Valley in the times of the Revolution —and there was Simon Girty, the renegade, who saw white men burned at the stake and whooped with the Indians to see them. His eyes were green, like a catamount's, and the stains on his hunting-shirt did not come from the blood of the deer. King Philip was there, wild and proud as he had been in life, with the great gash in his head that gave him his death-wound, and cruel Governor Dale who broke men on the wheel. There was Morton of Merry Mount, who so vexed the Plymouth Colony, with his flushed, loose, handsome face and his hate of the godly—there was Teach, the bloody pirate, with his black beard curling on his breast. The Reverend John Smeet, with his strangler's hands and his Geneva gown, walked as daintily as he had to the gallows. The red print of the rope was still around his neck but he carried a perfumed handkerchief in one hand. One and all, they came into the room with the fires of hell still upon them, and the stranger named their names and their deeds as they came, till the tale of twelve was told. Yet the stranger had told the truth—they had all played a part in America.

"Are you satisfied with the jury, Mr. Webster?" said the stranger, mockingly, when they had taken their places.

The sweat stood upon Dan'l Webster's brow but his voice was clear.

"Quite satisfied," he said. "Though I miss General Arnold from the company."

"General Arnold is engaged upon other business," said the stranger, with a glower. "Ah, you asked for a justice, I believe."

He pointed his finger once more, and a tall man, soberly clad in

Puritan garb, with the burning gaze of the fanatic, stalked into the room and took his judge's place.

"Justice Hathorne is a jurist of experience," said the stranger. "He presided at certain witch-trials, once held in Salem. There were others who repented of the business later, but not he."

"Repent of such notable wonders and undertakings?" said the stern old justice. "Nay, hang them—hang them all!" and he muttered to himself in a way that struck ice into the soul of Jabez Stone.

Then the trial began, and, as you must expect, it didn't look anyways good for the defence. And Jabez Stone didn't make much of a witness in his own behalf. He took one look at Simon Girty and screeched, and they had to put him back in his corner, in a kind of swoon.

It didn't halt the trial, though—the trial went on, as trials do. Dan'l Webster had faced some hard juries and hanging judges in his time— but this was the hardest he'd ever faced, and he knew it. They sat there, with a kind of glitter in their eyes, and the stranger's smooth voice went on and on. Every time he'd raise an objection, it'd be, "Objection sustained," but whenever Dan'l objected, it'd be "Objection denied." Well, you couldn't expect fair play from a fellow like this Mr. Scratch.

It got to Dan'l in the end, and he began to heat, like iron in the forge. When he got up to speak, he was going to flay that stranger with every trick known to the law, and the judge and jury, too. He didn't care if it was contempt of court or what would happen to him for it. He didn't care any more what happened to Jabez Stone. He just got madder and madder, thinking of what he'd say. And yet, curiously enough, the more he thought about it, the less he was able to arrange his speech in his mind.

Till, finally, it was time for him to get up on his feet, and he did so—all ready to bust out with lightnings and denunciations. But before he started he looked over the judge and jury for a moment, such being his custom. And he noticed the glitter in their eyes was twice as strong as before, and they all leaned forward. Like hounds just before they get the fox, they looked—and the blue mist of evil in the room thickened as he watched them. Then he saw what he'd been about to do—

and he wiped his forehead, as a man might who's just escaped falling into a pit in the dark.

For it was him they'd come for—not only Jabez Stone. He read it in the glitter of their eyes and in the way the stranger hid his mouth with one hand. And, if he fought them with their own weapons, he'd fall into their power—he knew that, though he couldn't have told you how. It was his own anger and horror that burned in their eyes—and he'd have to wipe that out or the case was lost. He stood there for a moment, his black eyes burning like anthracite. And then he began to speak. He started off in a low voice, though you could hear every word. They say he could call on the harps of the blessed when he chose. And this was just as simple and easy as a man could talk. But he didn't start out by condemning or reviling. He was talking about the things that make a country a country, and a man a man.

And he begun with the simple things that everybody's known and felt—the freshness of a fine morning, when you're young and the taste of food when you're hungry and the new day that's every day when you're a child. He took them up and he turned them in his hands. They were good things for any man. But, without freedom, they sickened. And when he talked of those enslaved, and the sorrows of slavery, his voice got like a big bell. He talked of the early days of America and the men who had made those days. It wasn't a spread-eagle speech but he made you see it. He admitted all the wrong that had ever been done. But he showed how, out of the wrong and the right, the suffering and the starvations, something new had come. And everybody had played a part in it, even the traitors.

Then he turned to Jabez Stone and showed him as he was—an ordinary man who'd had hard luck and wanted to change it. And, because he'd wanted to change it, now he was going to be punished for all eternity. And yet there was good in Jabez Stone—and he showed that good. He was hard and mean, in some ways—but he was a man. There was sadness in being a man but it was a proud thing, too. And he showed what the pride of it was till you couldn't help feeling it. Yes, even in hell, if a man was a man, you'd know it. And he wasn't pleading for any one person any more—though his voice rang like an organ. He was telling the story and the failures and the endless journey of mankind. They got tricked and trapped and bamboozled, but it was a great journey. And no demon that was ever foaled could know the inwardness of it—it took a man to do that.

The fire began to die on the hearth and the wind before morning to blow. The light was getting grey in the room when Dan'l Webster finished. And his words come back at the end to New Hampshire ground—and the one spot of land that each man loves and clings to. He painted a picture of that—and, to each one of that jury he spoke of things long-forgotten. For his voice could search the heart, and that was his gift and his strength. And to one his voice was like the forest and its secrecy, and to another like the sea and the storms of the sea; and one heard the cry of his lost nation in it, and another saw a little harmless scene he hadn't remembered for years. But each saw something. And, when Dan'l Webster finished, he didn't know whether or not he'd saved Jabez Stone. But he knew he'd done a miracle. For the glitter was gone from the eyes of judge and jury, and, for the moment, they were men again, and knew they were men.

"The defence rests," said Dan'l Webster, and stood there like a mountain. His ears were still ringing with his speech and he didn't hear anything else till he heard Judge Hathorne say, "The jury will retire to consider its verdict."

Walter Butler rose in his place and his face had a dark gay pride on it.

"The jury has considered its verdict," he said, and looked the stranger full in the eye. "We find for the defendant, Jabez Stone."

With that the smile left the stranger's face, but Walter Butler did not flinch.

"Perhaps 'tis not strictly in accordance with the evidence," he said. "But even the damned may salute the eloquence of Mr. Webster."

With that, the long crow of a rooster split the grey morning sky, and judge and jury were gone from the room like a puff of smoke and as if they had never been there. The stranger turned to Dan'l Webster, smiling wryly.

"Major Butler was always a bold man," he said. "I had not thought him quite so bold. Nevertheless—my congratulations, as between two gentlemen."

"I'll have that paper first, if you please," said Dan'l Webster and he took it and tore it into four pieces. It was queerly warm to the touch.

"And now," he said, "I'll have you!" and his hand came down like a bear-trap on the stranger's arm. For he knew that once you bested anybody like Mr. Scratch in fair fight, his power on you was gone. And he could see that Mr. Scratch knew it, too.

The stranger twisted and wriggled but he couldn't get out of that grip. "Come, come, Mr. Webster," he said, smiling palely. "This sort of thing is ridic—ouch!—is ridiculous. If you're worried about the costs of the case—naturally, I'd be glad to pay——"

"And so you shall!" said Dan'l Webster, shaking him till his teeth rattled. "For you'll sit right down at that table and draw up a document, promising never to bother Jabez Stone nor his heirs or assigns nor any other Newhampshireman till Doomsday! For any Hades we want to raise in this State, we can raise ourselves, without assistance from strangers."

"Ouch!" said the stranger. "Ouch! Well, they never did run very big to the barrel but—ouch! I agree!"

So he sat down and drew up the document. But Dan'l Webster kept his hand on his coat-collar all the time.

"And now—may I go?" said the stranger, quite humble, when Dan'l's seen the document's in proper and legal form.

"Go?" said Dan'l, giving him another shake. "I'm still trying to figure out what I'll do with you. For you've settled the costs of the case, but you haven't settled with me. I think I'll take you back to Marshfield," he said, kind of reflective. "I've got a ram there named Goliath that can butt through an iron door. I'd kind of like to turn you loose in his field and see what he'd do."

Well, with that the stranger began to beg and to plead. And he begged and he pled so humble that finally Dan'l, who was naturally kind-hearted, agreed to let him go. The stranger seemed terrible grateful for that and said, just to show they were friends, he'd tell Dan'l's fortune, before leaving. So Dan'l agreed to that, though he didn't take much stock in fortune-tellers ordinarily. But, naturally, the stranger was a little different.

Well, he pried and peered at the lines in Dan'l's hands. And he told him one thing and another that was quite remarkable. But they were all in the past.

"Yes, all that's true, and it happened," said Dan'l Webster. "But what's to come in the future?"

The stranger grinned, kind of happily, and shook his head.

"The future's not as you think it," he said. "It's dark. You have a great ambition, Mr. Webster."

"I have," said Dan'l, firmly, for everybody knew he wanted to be President.

"It seems almost within your grasp," said the stranger. "But you will not attain it. Lesser men will be made President and you will be passed over."

"And, if I am, I'll still be Daniel Webster," said Dan'l. "Say on."

"You have two strong sons," said the stranger, shaking his head. "You look to found a line. But each will die in war and neither reach greatness."

"Live or die, they are still my sons," said Dan'l Webster. "Say on."

"You have made great speeches," said the stranger. "You will make more."

"Ah!" said Dan'l Webster.

"But the last great speech you make will turn many of your own against you," said the stranger. "They will call you Ichabod—they will call you by other names. Even in New England some will say you have turned your coat and sold your country, and their voices will be loud against you till you die."

"So it is an honest speech, it does not matter what men say," said Dan'l Webster. Then he looked at the stranger and their glances locked.

"One question," he said. "I have fought for the Union all my life. Will I see that fight won, against those who would tear it apart?"

"Not while you live," said the stranger, grimly. "But it will be won. And, after you are dead, there are thousands who will fight for your cause, because of words that you spoke."

"Why, then, you long-barrelled, slab-sided, lantern-jawed, fortune-telling note-shaver!" said Dan'l Webster with a great roar of laughter, "be off with you to your own place before I put my mark on you! For, by the Thirteen Original Colonies, I'd go to the Pit itself to save the Union!"

And with that he drew back his foot for a kick that would have stunned a horse. It was only the tip of his shoe that caught the stranger, but he went flying out of the door with his collecting-box under his arm.

"And now," said Dan'l Webster, seeing Jabez Stone beginning to rouse from his swoon, "let's see what's left in the jug, for it's dry work talking all night. I hope there's pie for breakfast, Neighbour Stone."

But they say that whenever the Devil comes near Marshfield, even now, he gives it a wide berth. And he hasn't been seen in the State of New Hampshire from that day to this. I'm not talking about Massachusetts or Vermont.

VAN WYCK BROOKS Why he selected

HAWTHORNE in SALEM

There was much in common—more than I thought when I wrote the chapters—between these two New Englanders of adjoining generations: Hawthorne and Emily Dickinson. Both remained aloof from the characteristic life of their time, but this life was, if not reflected, vividly present in their work. Both had long thoughts about it, though they watched it from the outside, as Hawthorne watched the Brook Farmers and Miss Dickinson watched from her Amherst window. As recluses or semi-recluses, they seem to me in line with many other American writers and artists, Eakins, Ryder, Henry Adams, Melville, and even Walt Whitman, who also withdrew from the foreground of the American scene. For three generations our dominant life, a life of instinctive and strenuous action, failed to afford a function for sensitive men. At least one may fairly say that it did not invite their cooperation. Many were forced into obscurity, or felt they were, such as Henry Adams, and proud men chose to be obscure. This was especially true in New England, which, with the growth of the West, lost in large measure its share of the control of the Union. New Englanders, always introspective, tended to grow more so, and numbers of them cultivated the "private life." This explains, in part at least, some traits these writers have in common. In our extroverted American world, I feel that this New England strain must have a very special importance and value.

Westport, Conn.
June, 1942

VAN WYCK BROOKS

WHILE Boston and little Concord were moving forward, Salem, like most of the other seaports, stricken by the War of 1812, had lapsed into quietude and decay. Beside its dilapidated wharves, where grew the fat weeds, the windlass chanty and the caulker's maul no longer broke the silence. The water-side streets were no longer thronged with sailors, "all right" for shore, with their blue jackets and checked shirts, their well-varnished hats and flowing ribbons, with bundles under their arms from the cannibal isles, or from India or China. One seldom heard the lively "Cheerily, men!" while all hands joined in the chorus. The grass choked the chinks of the cobblestones over which the drays had clattered. An occasional bark or brig discharged its hides. One saw some Nova Scotia schooner, drawn up at Derby's Wharf, unloading a cargo of firewood. A few idle seafaring men leaned against the posts, or sat on the planks, in the lee of some shabby warehouse, or lolled in the long-boats on the strand. But the great days of the port were a tale that was told, over and over, by the ancient skippers, who dozed away their mornings at the custom-house, with their chairs tilted against the wall.

Salem had an immemorial air, the air that gathers about a town which, having known a splendid hour, shrinks and settles back while its grandeurs fade. But Salem was old in spirit, aside from its faded grandeurs. The past that hovered there had much in common with that of the ancient ports of northern Europe, where the Gothic fancies of the Middle Ages have not been dispelled by modern trade. Salem was still Gothic, in a measure. In its moss-grown, many-gabled houses, panelled with worm-eaten wood and hung with half-obliterated portraits, dwelt at least the remnants of a race that retained the mental traits of a far-away past. In its isolation from the currents of world-thought and feeling, it seemed to be only a step removed from the age of the Dance of Death. In the mansions of Chestnut Street and Federal Street, one found the traces of a livelier culture, the books that were read in Boston, together with the Oriental spoils brought home by the Salem navigators. But over the quiet lanes and leafy side-streets, where the graveyards lay, brooded the hush of many generations. Queer old maids with turbaned heads peered from behind the curtains, quaint old simple-minded men hobbled along under the sweeping elms, "pixilated" creatures, many of them, as they said at Marblehead,—bewildered by the fairies,—half dead and buried in their houses, or buried in the morbid family pride that flourishes where life runs low.

There was vigour enough in Salem, there were plenty of stout merchants and politicians. One saw swarms of boys and little girls, in blue, yellow, green and crimson dresses, bursting from church and schoolhouse, like garden-beds of zinnias or water-colours of Maurice Prendergast. It was only in comparison with Lynn and Lowell, those near-by towns whose enterprising burghers, faced with the decline of shipping, had built their factories for internal trade, that Salem seemed somehow grey and sad. The Prescotts, Story, Pickering, Choate and Bowditch, the great circle of earlier days, had long since departed. At a stone's-throw from the Essex Institute, one almost heard the silence. One caught the tinkling of the bell at the door of some little cent-shop, even the quiver of the humming-birds darting about the syringa bushes. The rattling of the butcher's cart was the only event of the day for many a household, unless perhaps one of the family hens cackled and laid an egg. Spiders abounded in these houses, eluding the vigilant spinster's eye. Indeed, there were so many cobwebs that it might have occurred to a doctor,—some old Salem doctor, as odd as the rest,—to gather the webs together and distil an elixir of life from the dusty compound. In the burying-ground in Charter Street, where the Gothic emblems flourished,—death's-heads, cross-bones, scythes and hour-glasses, such as one found in Dürer's woodcuts,—the office of grave-digger passed from father to son. Just so passed the household legends, behind the bolted doors, grimmer with each generation. Beside the kitchen fires, old serving-women crouched as they turned the spit and darned the stockings, always ready to tell the children stories. Some of them seemed to remember the days of the witches. Their stories were as dusty as the cobwebs.

For Salem, like the whole New England sea-coast, bristled with old wives' tales and old men's legends. No need to invent stories there: one heard them in the taverns, from the sailors, from charcoal-burners who looked like wizards, from the good-for-nothings on the water-front. One heard of locked closets in haunted houses where skeletons had been found. One heard of walls that resounded with knocks where there had once been doorways, now bricked up. One heard of poisonous houses and blood-stained houses, old maids who lived in total darkness, misers who wallowed naked in heaps of pine-tree shillings. One even heard of Endicott's dreary times, when the stocks and the pillory were never empty. One heard of the magistrates who awoke each morning to the prospect of cropping an ear or slitting a nostril, stripping and whipping a woman at the tail of a cart, or giving her a stout hemp necklace or a brooch in the form of a scarlet letter. One heard of the grey champion who emerged from nowhere to rebuke the tyrannies of the British king, of children who had sprung from the loins of demons, of the wastrels of Merry Mount and the grizzled saints who had stamped out their light and idle mirth, clipping their curls and love-locks. Would they not have stamped out the sunshine and clipped all the flowers in the forest in order to clear a path for their psalms and sermons? In these quiet towns, where nothing happens—except an occasional murder—to agitate the surface of existence, history is ever-present, lying in visible depths under the unstirred waters; and who could have known in Salem what to believe or not? However it might have been on Chestnut Street, the fringes of Salem society were superstitious. If the ring that Queen Elizabeth gave to Essex had appeared in a collection-box on Sunday, it would not have seemed surprising to some of the people. There were plenty of old souls in the lanes and side-streets who never knew where to draw the line. They half believed the tales they told the children. Were there not hollows in the hills close by where the Devil and his subjects held communion? Were there not ill-famed men in the western mountains who were condemned to wander till the crack of doom? All these tales had their truth, and so did the Indian legends, which the farmers repeated. There was an element of fact behind them. Was there a carbuncle in the Crystal Hills that gleamed like the westering sun, as the Indians said? Or was it the sun itself? There were men still living down in Maine who had never settled the question. Carbuncle or not, they had certainly seen it. At least, they had caught its radiance, far up the valley of the Saco.

Salem was a centre for these legends. The mediæval mind had lingered there, in the absence of recent enterprise; and, while the town as a whole was sufficiently modern, there were odd corners and shadowy households where symbols and realities seemed much the same. The young men and women knew the difference, but sometimes it amused them to ignore it. They did not believe in ghosts, but mesmerism had become the fashion: they let their fancies play on the border-line. They sat up at night and told tales of ghosts, largely in default of mundane gossip. Occasionally, they even thought they saw one. The Hawthornes, who lived in Herbert Street, under the shadow of a family curse, were often troubled by an apparition that seemed to haunt their yard. The only son of the household, Nathaniel Hawthorne, who lived like a ghost himself, haunting a little chamber under the eaves, appearing only at nightfall, could not count the times he had raised his head, or turned towards the window, with a perception that somebody was passing through the gate. He could only perceive the presence with a sidelong glance, by a certain indirection; if he looked straight at the dim thing, behold, it was not there. As no one ever passed through the Hawthornes' gate, it may have been Elizabeth, his sister, who also appeared only when dusk had fallen. In fact, one could live for two years under the same roof with this spectral sister and see her only once. That was the way with the Hawthornes. The father, a Salem skipper, had died of yellow fever, years ago, in far-off Surinam; and no mortal eye had penetrated, or was to penetrate for forty years, the Castle Dismal on the second floor where the mother of the family had taken refuge on the day she heard the news. Her meals were brought up and left outside the door, as they were at Elizabeth's door, and Louisa's door,—at least, as often as not,—and, one flight further up, at Nathaniel's door. When twilight came, one heard the sound of footsteps echoing on the stairs, and a door that must have been opened was certainly shut. Elizabeth went out for a little walk. Then Nathaniel went for a walk, alone, in another direction.

All day long, every day, or almost every day, for twelve years, he had sat in his flag-bottomed chair in his little room, beside the pine table, with a sheet of foolscap spread out before him. He was writing stories that rose in his mind as mushrooms grow in a meadow, where the roots of some old tree are buried under the earth. He had no love of secrecy or darkness, uncanny as he seemed to the handful of neighbours who knew that he existed; he was merely following the household pattern. His family, prominent once, had been almost forgotten, even in Herbert Street. No one came to see him. He had few friends,

aside from the circle of his Bowdoin class-mates, with whom he had
almost ceased to correspond. As a boy, he had often said he was going
to sea and would never come back again; and he sometimes remarked
to an acquaintance that he thought of disappearing, changing his name,
escaping from the orbit of the postman, as if he had not sufficiently
disappeared merely by staying at home. He had lapsed into this solitary life, half through a kind of inertia, and half,—he had always
known he was going to write,—as if to protect a sensibility that was
not yet ready to yield its fruits. His nickname had been Oberon at college, a reference to his shy, elusive ways. He had a massive head; his
eyes were black and brilliant; he walked with the rolling gait of a
sailor; he had a somewhat truculent voice and presence. Standing, he
could leap shoulder-high. He liked to look at himself in the upright
mirror and make up stories about the image he found reflected there.
This image was dark and picturesque, tall and rather imposing. There
was something vaguely foreign in its aspect.

He felt like a man under a spell, who had somehow put himself
into a dungeon and could not find the key to let himself out. He had
seated himself by the wayside of life, and a dense growth of shrubbery
had sprung up about him, and the bushes had turned into saplings
and the saplings into trees. Through the entangling depths he could
find no exit. His style, his personality, his habits had been formed as
far back as he could remember. At six he had read the *Pilgrim's
Progress*. The first book he had bought was the *Faerie Queene*. To see
the world in terms of allegory, or in the light of symbols, was second
nature with him. At twelve, in a note-book his grandfather had given
him, urging him to write out his thoughts—a few every day—he had
described a child named Betty Tarbox as "flitting among the rose-
bushes, in and out of the arbour, like a tiny witch"—phrases that might
have occurred in the tales he was writing now. At sixteen, he had writ
ten a poem, precisely in the vein of some of these tales, about a young
man dying for love of a ghost. He had certainly not acquired from
Godwin's novels, however they intensified the taste, the feeling for
romantic mystery that had sprung, for him, out of the Salem air. The
novels of Scott had only excited further what seemed to be an inborn
predilection for the history and the scenery of New England. All he
knew was that these habits of mind, already formed in Salem, had been

fostered in Maine, where he had spent a year, during his boyhood, on
a lonely farm in a border hamlet. He had heard all sorts of stories from
the farmers, tales of the supernatural, tales of ghosts, legends of the old
colonial wars. He had heard the story of Father Moody of York, who
had worn a black veil over his face. In summer, he had seen the Indians, on the Penobscot River, in their birch canoes, building their wig-
wams by the mill-dams. Round about stood the pine forests, bordering
the northern lakes. He had skated all winter in the moonlight, alone
and silent. He loved the black shadows cast by the frozen hills.

He might well have been thought uncanny. He was certainly
"deep," as the country people said, deep as a night-scene by Albert
Ryder. His mind was bathed in a kind of *chiaroscuro* that seemed to
be a natural trait; and yet it was a trait that he cultivated, half by
instinct, half by deliberation. He had a painter's delight in tone. He
liked to throw a ghostly glimmer over scenes that he chose because they
were ghostly. It was a taste like Claude Lorrain's for varnish. He liked
to study chimneys in the rain, choked with their own smoke, or a
mountain with its base enveloped in fog while the summit floated aloft.
He liked to see a yellow field of rye veiled in a morning mist. He liked
to think of a woman in a silvery mantle, covering her face and figure.
A man's face, with a patched eye, turning its profile towards him; an
arm and hand extended from behind a screen; a smile that seemed to
be only a part of a smile seen through a covering hand; a sunbeam
passing through a cobweb, or lying in the corner of a dusty floor. Dis-
solving and vanishing objects. Trees reflected in a river, reversed and
strangely arrayed and as if transfigured. The effects wrought by
moonlight on a wall. Moonlight in a familiar sitting-room, investing
every object with an odd remoteness—one's walking-stick or a child's
shoe or doll—so that, instead of seeing these objects, one seemed to
remember them through a lapse of years. Hawthorne could never have
said why it was that, after spending an evening in some pleasant
room, lighted by a fire of coals, he liked to return and open the door
again, and close it and re-open it, peeping back into the ruddy dimness
that seemed so like a dream, as if he were enacting a conscious dream.
For the rest, he was well aware why he had withdrawn to this little
chamber, where there was nothing to measure time but the progress
of the shadow across the floor. Somewhere, as it were beneath his feet, a

hidden treasure lay, like Goldthwaite's chest, brimming over with
jewels and charms, goblets and golden salvers. It was the treasure of
his own genius, and it was to find this precious treasure that he had
sat at his desk through summer and winter. The snow-flakes pelted
against the window-panes, the casement rattled in the December gusts,
clouds of dust blew through the open window. Seasons and years
rolled by. He had his doubts. Was he tearing down the house of his
mind in order to find the treasure? In the end, when the house was
destroyed, for all he could say, there might be nothing in the chest
but rubbish.

Sometimes, in summer, on a Sunday morning, he stood by the hour
behind the curtain, watching the church across the way. The sunrise
stole down the steeple, touching the weather-cock and gilding the dial,
till the other steeples awoke and began to ring. His fancy played about
this conversation carried on by all the bells of Salem. At twilight, he
would still be standing there, watching the people on the steps after
the second sermon. Then, as dusk set in, with a feeling of unreality, as
if his heart and mind had turned to vapour, he ventured into the
street. Sometimes, he was out all day, for the sake of observation. He
would spend an hour at the museum, looking at the black old portraits
that brought back the days of Cotton Mather. These portraits explained the books that he was reading, histories of Maine and Massachusetts, the *History of Haverhill*, Felt's *Annals of Salem*. Or he
walked over to Marblehead and Swampscott, where the old salts
gathered in the store, in their red baize shirts and oilcloth trousers,
enthroned on mackerel barrels. He felt a natural bond with all these
Yankees, fishermen, cattle-drovers, sailors, pilots. Some of them could
steer with bandaged eyes into any port from Boston to Mount Desert,
guided by the sound of the surf on every beach, island or line of
rocks. He liked to sit with them in the bar-rooms, alive with curiosity,
over a steaming hot whiskey-punch. He studied the coloured prints on
the tavern walls. He noted the gateways in the crooked streets, the
whales' jaw-bones set like Gothic arches, the bulging windows in the
little shop-fronts, filled with needles, fishhooks, pins and thimbles,
gingerbread horses, picture-books and sweetmeats. He stood at the
toll-house on the Beverly bridge, watching the procession of carts and
sulkies that rolled over the timber ribbon under which the sea ebbed

and flowed; or he strolled on to Browne's Hill and traced out the grass-grown hollows, the cellars of Browne's Folly. Occasionally, he spent a day in Boston, haunting the public-houses in Washington Street. He penetrated behind the sober shop-front that masked the old Province House. Oftener, setting out at dawn, he rambled over Endicott's Orchard Farm, over the witchcraft ground and Gallows Hill, or perhaps Phillips's Beach, exploring the coast from Marblehead to Glouces-ter. He would bathe in a cove, overhung with maples and walnuts, pick up shells on the water's edge, skip pebbles on the water and trail the seaweed after him, draw names and faces in the sand. He would sit on the top of a cliff and watch his shadow, gesturing on the sand far below.

Occupations worthy of a poet who knew the value of reverie. These idle, whimsical movements absorbed his body while his mind pursued its secret operations. One had to be bored in order to think. Passivity was Hawthorne's element, when it was not curiosity. Usually, in the summer, dressed in his blue stuff frock, he undertook a longer expedi-tion, to Maine or the Berkshires, perhaps, or to Martha's Vineyard, or along the Erie canal, as far as Detroit, where the old Connecticut poet, John Trumbull, was spending his last years. Nothing escaped him then; he had resumed his habit of keeping a note-book. He would stop for commencement at some country college, at Williams, so like his own Bowdoin, and mingle with the sheepish-looking students, half scholar-like, half bumpkin, fidgeting in their black broadcloth coats. He would spend a day at a cattle-fair, among the ruddy, round-paunched country squires who, with their wonderful breadth of fundament, waddled about, whip in hand, discoursing on the points of the sheep and oxen. He fell in with big-bellied blacksmiths, essence-pedlars chattering about their trade, old men sitting at railway stations, selling nuts and gingerbread, oblivious of the rush and roar about them, wood-choppers with their jugs and axes who had lived so long in the forest that their legs seemed to be covered with moss, like tree-trunks, pedlars of tobacco, walking beside their carts—green carts with gaily painted panels—conjurors, tombstone-carvers, organ-grinders, travelling surgeon-dentists, the queer confraternity of the road. He would ex-change a word with a tavern-keeper, reading his Hebrew Bible, with the aid of a lexicon and an English version. If it was a rainy day, the toddy-stick was in active use and the faces gleamed about the bar-room fire. He would stop at a farm for a glass of milk or linger in the market-place at Pittsfield, among the buckboards and the farmers' wagons, while the stage-coach discharged its passengers. Opening his note-book in the evening, he jotted down his observations. Why these trivial details? He had seen a tame crow on the peak of a barn. A half-length figure had appeared at a window, with a light shining on the shrouded face. A little boy had passed him on the road, lugging a basket of custard-cups. An intrusive reader, looking over his shoulder, might have wondered why it was worth his while to record such trifling items. To Hawthorne they were anything but trifling. Every one of these notes possessed for him a golden aureole of associations. Traits of New England life, aspects of New England scenery: a stone wall covered with vines and shrubs and elm-trees that had thrust their roots beneath it, a valley like a vast bowl, filled with yellow sunlight as with wine, the effect of the morning sun on dewy grass, sunlight on a sloping, swelling landscape beyond a river in the middle distance, an afternoon light on a clump of trees, evening light falling on a lonely figure, perhaps a country doctor on his horse, with his black leather saddle-bags behind him. Dark trees, decaying stumps, a cave in the side of a hill, with the sunlight playing over it. How like the human heart, this cave, with the glancing sun and the flowers about its entrance! One stepped within and found oneself surrounded with a terrible gloom and monsters of divers kinds.

Once, before turning homeward, he pressed on to Crawford's Notch. This was the artery over the mountains through which the groaning wagons from the seaports carried the goods of Europe and the Indies to northern New Hampshire and Vermont. There stood the Great Stone Face. One dined on bear's meat in these northern woods, echoing with the notes of horn and bugle. Under some avalanche an ambitious guest, a young story-teller, for example, might have been crushed at Crawford's Notch. Who would ever have heard of him then, his history, his plans, his way of life? Or suppose this young writer had frozen to death on the summit of Mount Washington? The mountain would have been a pedestal, worthy of a story-teller's statue. Hawthorne roamed up and down the Connecticut Valley. He fell in with a group of vagabonds, on their way to the camp-meeting at Stamford, a book-pedlar with the usual stock—a handful of gilded picture-books and ballads, a Life of Franklin, Byron's Minor Poems, Webster's Spelling-book, the New England Primer—a degenerate Indian with his bow and arrows, willing to turn a penny by shooting at it, an Italian conjuror with a merry damsel attired in all the colours of the rainbow. A travelling puppet-show had joined the troupe. The grave old show-man, in his snuff-coloured coat, turned the crank of the organ, and all the little people on the miniature stage broke into lively movement. The blacksmith's hammer fell on the anvil, the tailor plied his needle, the dancers whirled about on their feathery tiptoes, the soldiers wheeled in platoons, the old toper lifted his bottle, the merry-andrew shook his head and capered. Prospero entertaining his island crew! It was a masque of shadows that seemed as real as any other world that Hawthorne lived in. Would it not have been a good idea for a young story-teller to join this group and become an itinerant novelist, like the Oriental story-tellers, reciting his extemporaneous fictions at camp-meetings and cattle-fairs, wherever two or three were gathered together?

Most of Hawthorne's journeys, to be sure, were journeys *autour de sa chambre*. He was never away from Salem long. His note-books, however, filled along the road with incidents and casual observations, were precious memorabilia. They gave his ideas a local habitation. One saw this in the stories he was writing, sketches of actual life, historical tales and allegories. He thought of these as "twice-told" tales because, in several cases, he had heard them first before he had worked them out himself. How did he feel about his work? It seemed to him easier to destroy it than to court an indifferent public. He had thrown into the fire the *Seven Tales of My Native Land*, for which he had failed to find a publisher, and he had burned every available copy of his little published novel, *Fanshawe*. There was a devil in his manuscripts! He saw it laughing at him as the sparks flew upward. As for his recent stories—the annual magazines had begun to accept them, the *Souvenir* and Peter Parley's *Token*—they seemed to him to have an effect of tameness. They had, he felt, the pale tint of flowers that have blossomed in too retired a shade. If they were read at all, they should be read in the twilight in which they were written. They had been concocted from thin air; but it was this that gave the tales their

magic. Some of them were really insubstantial, dim as ghosts basking
in the starlight; in others, the apparently insubstantial was a new and
original substance. In Tieck's and Hoffmann's Germany, where the
Gothic mind had reawakened, in harmony with this mood of spectral
Salem, even in Poe's New York, one found similar tales of the listening
dead, of graves and flitting shadows and lovers knocking at each
other's tombs. Processions of mourners passed with measured tread,
trailing their garments on the ground. One saw figures melting in mist.
Black veils, boys with bandaged eyes, bridegrooms dressed in shrouds.
Pools paved with marble and mosaic. Images shimmering in water.
One heard the cries of children lost in the woods. Young men slept
in the road-side shade, oblivious of the fates that might have been theirs
if they had been awake; for fortune, crime and love hovered about
them.

They were tales like evening moths or butterflies, light as clouds or
flowers of early May, blooming in a woodland solitude. Out of them
rose, when they were gathered together, an opalescent world that was
strangely old, yet fresh and unfamiliar; it was like Prospero's island,
half terrestrial, half an ethereal fabric. It was a new creation, this world
of Hawthorne, with a past in Merry Mount and the Province House, in
Howe's Masquerade and Esther Dudley, a present in pedlars and
Shakers, in vagabonds and white old maids, in sunny Connecticut
valleys and forest hollows, in snowstorms and ambiguous lime-burners,
a future in little puckish boys and girls at play in the flickering sunshine. All very simple, it appeared, simple as the brightly coloured leaves
that drift over a sedgy stream, only that too often, before one's eyes, the
stream sang its way out of the meadow and carried its bright burden
into the forest, where all grew dark and baleful.

Such was Hawthorne's world, as it rose in the minds of his readers.
No other American writer had revealed such a gift for finding his
proper subjects; no other had so consciously pursued his ends. Hawthorne had jotted down four rules of life: to break off customs, to medi-
tate on youth, to shake off spirits ill-disposed, to do nothing against
one's genius. He had shaped a poetic personality as valid and distinct
as Emerson's; but the "spirits ill-disposed" were not easily conquered.
He was drifting towards a cataract, he felt. "I'm a doomed man," he
wrote to a friend, "and over I must go." He was threatened with

melancholia, and he knew it. Out of this fear had sprung, or were to spring, the themes of many of his other stories, *Wakefield, The Man of Adamant, Ethan Brand,* tales of the unpardonable sin that consists in losing one's hold of the human chain. The Man of Adamant turns to stone, Ethan Brand forfeits, in his lonely bleakness, the key that unlocks human nature, Wakefield, who leaves his family and lives for twenty years in a neighboring street, makes himself an outcast from the world without being admitted among the dead. Hawthorne repeated this note in twenty stories, tales of minds and hearts like chilly caverns, hung with glittering icicles of fancy. Tales of hyper-sensitive recluses who find themselves in white-washed cells. Tales of diabolical intellects—*Rappaccini's Daughter* and *The Birthmark*—which, in the name of some insane abstraction, destroy the life that they have ceased to feel. Tales like that of Lady Eleanore who, wrapped in pride as in a mantle, courts the vengeance of nature. Tales of diseased self-contemplation, of egoists who swallow serpents and sleepers who have missed their destiny. What traits, or, rather, what predicament, what fears did these tales reveal in the mind that conceived them? Hawthorne had lived too long in this border-region, these polar solitudes where the spirit shivered, so that the substance of the world about him hung before his eyes like a thing of vapour. He felt as if he had not lived at all, as if he were an ineffectual shadow, as if, having stepped aside from the highway of human affairs, he had lost his place forever. One night he had a dream that told him this. He seemed to be walking in a crowded street. Three beautiful girls approached him and, seeing him, screamed and fled. An old friend gave him a look of horror. He was promenading in his shroud.

Luckily, Hawthorne had another self, a sensible double-ganger. This other Hawthorne, this prosaic Hawthorne, the son of a Salem skipper, was interested in his own self-preservation; and, while he would never have taken too much trouble to keep himself afloat, he was glad to listen to his friends in matters of worldly wisdom. Eleven years were enough in a haunted chamber, filled with thoughts of suicide and madness. In 1836, this other Hawthorne entered the publishing house of Peter Parley, wrote his *Universal History* for him and edited his *American Magazine.* Then, having broken the spell and gone to

Boston, this matter-of-fact, substantial, physical Hawthorne accepted a position at the custom-house.

To the end of Hawthorne's life, these separate personalities dominated his destiny in turn. When one of them came to the front, as fishes, in pursuit of oxygen, rise to the surface of the water, the other vanished or concealed himself behind the nearest curtain. The story-teller scarcely knew the practical man of business who worked on the steaming docks, amid the coal-dust. Was this resolute, forcible being really himself, or was it someone who assumed his aspect and performed these duties in his name? Which was the true Hawthorne, which the phantom? The story-teller lived in a trance as long as the automaton carried on. His writing was accomplished in the happy seasons when the automaton was packed away, in the box where he belonged, when custom-houses, ships and offices lay like dreams behind him.

2: EMILY DICKINSON

THE Dickinsons lived in the principal house in Amherst. A large, square, red-brick mansion that stood behind a hemlock hedge, with three gates accurately closed, it was a symbol of rural propriety and all the substantialities of western New England. Edward Dickinson, the lawyer, had always had his office in the village, and four times a day, in his broadcloth coat and beaver hat, with a gold-headed cane in his hand, he had passed through one of the gates, going or coming. A thin, severe, punctilious man who had once been a member of Congress, a friend of Daniel Webster in his youth, a Calvinist of the strictest persuasion, he was a pillar of Amherst College until his death in 1874. The college had been founded, largely by his father, to check the sort of errors that were spreading from Harvard, and he never abated his rigour in the interests of pleasure. He was said to have laughed on one occasion, but usually he was as cold and still as the white marble mantel in his parlour. The story was told in Amherst, however, that once he had rung the church-bell, as if to summon the people to a fire. The whole town came running, for he rang the bell excitedly. He wished to call attention to the sunset.

Next door, behind the hemlock hedge, another ample dwelling stood, suggesting in its style an Italian villa. Here lived the Squire's son Austin, once his partner, who kept open house for the college. While the Dickinson mansion was somewhat forbidding, with the stamp of the Squire's grim ways and his invalid wife, the villa was a centre of Hampshire hospitality that shared its rolling lawns and charming garden. Olmsted had visited there, when he was planning Central Park to examine the shrubs and trees, the plants and flowers, and distinguished guests at the college commencements and lecturers during the winter season were received and welcomed there as nowhere else. Emerson, Phillips, Beecher and Curtis had stayed in this house next door, and Samuel Bowles of the *Springfield Republican* was an intimate friend of all the Dickinsons. In an age when the newspaper was largely taking the place of the pulpit, Samuel Bowles was known all over the country as one who fought for honest politics. He had joined with Carl Schurz in the movement for reform that was also the cause of Henry Adams. The *Republican* was a school for journalists, known far and wide, and travellers—Dickens and Kingsley among them— constantly stopped at Springfield in order to have a chat with Samuel Bowles. His paper was a sovereign authority in Amherst, and he often drove over for a call at the villa or the mansion, sometimes bringing manuscripts by well-known authors to show the Dickinson daughters before they were published. His favourite was Emily, who was older than Lavinia, but Emily usually "elfed it" when visitors came. She was always in the act of disappearing. Through the blinds of her western windows, overlooking the garden, she observed the hospitalities of the villa, and snatches of whatever was current in the books and talk of a college town, in the politics and thought of the moment, reached her when the guests had gone away. But even her oldest friends seldom saw her. While sometimes, in the evening, she flitted across the garden, she never left the place by day or night. To have caught a fleeting glimpse of her was something to boast of, and a young girl across the way who watched at night for a light at her window was thrilled if Miss Emily's shadow appeared for a moment.

There were nurse-maids who thought she was a witch. They frightened the children by uttering her name, as if there were something malign in Miss Dickinson's queerness.

While her friends seldom saw her, and almost never face to face—for she spoke from the shadows of the hallway, as they sat in the parlour, or sometimes down the stairs—they were used to receiving little letters from her. These letters were also peculiar. Miss Dickinson rarely addressed the envelopes. Some other hand, perhaps her sister's, performed this office for her. More often the names of the person and town had been clipped from a printed paper and pasted together, as if it were a sort of violation to expose the strokes of her pen to the touch of the postman. The letters themselves were brief and cryptic, usually only a line or two: "Do you look out tonight?" for example. "The moon rides like a girl through a topaz town." Or "The frogs sing sweet today—they have such pretty, lazy times—how nice to be a frog." Or "Tonight the crimson children are playing in the West." Or "The lawn is full of south and the odours tangle, and I hear today for the first the river in the tree." Now and again, some fine phrase emerged from the silvery spray of words—"Not what the stars have done, but what they are to do, is what detains the sky." Sometimes her notes had a humorous touch: "Father steps like Cromwell when he gets the kindlings," or "Mrs. S. gets bigger, and rolls down the lane to church like a reverend marble." But her messages often contained no words at all. She would lower baskets of goodies out of the window to children waiting below. At times, instead of a letter, she sent a poem, an odd little fragment of three or four lines, with a box of chocolate caramels or frosted cakes and a flower or a sprig of pine on top, heliotrope, perhaps, or an oleander blossom or a dandelion tied with a scarlet ribbon. Her letters were rhythmical, they scanned like the poems, and they were congested with images—every phrase was an image; and the poems themselves suggested nursery-rhymes or Dr. Watts's hymns, broken up and filled with a strange new content. They might have struck unsympathetic readers as a sort of transcendental baby-talk. It was evident that Miss Dickinson had lost the art of communication, as the circle of her school-friends understood it. She vibrated towards them, she put forth shy, impalpable tentacles, she instantly signalized with a verse or a note every event in their lives. But she did not speak the language of the world outside her, and one gathered that she did not wish to touch it. She was rapt in a private world of sensations and thoughts. It was even observed that her hand-writing went through three distinct phases and that towards the end the letters never touched. Each character, separately formed, stood quite alone.

She had been a recluse since the early sixties, and her family surmised the reason. She had fallen in love with a married man, a Philadelphia clergyman, and had buried herself at home by way of refuge. When her supposed lover supposedly pursued her there, her sister dashed across to the house next door and exclaimed to their brother Austin's wife, "Sue, come! That man is here. Father and mother are away, and I am afraid Emily will go away with him." Such was the family legend, which may have been apocryphal. Undoubtedly, the clergyman came to see her, but probably only to call. Was he in love with Emily? Probably not. In any case, she did not go away. She withdrew from all activities outside the household, and her mind turned in upon itself. She had hitherto been eminently social, or as much so as her little world permitted. Born in 1830, in the red-brick mansion, she had grown up a lively girl who was always a centre of attention. She was a capital mimic. She travestied the young-lady pieces, the "Battle of Prague" and others, which she played on the mahogany piano, and her odd and funny stories enthralled her friends. Later they remembered that she placed bouquets of flowers in the pews of those she liked best, at church. Helen Hunt Jackson, now a well-known writer, had been her favourite playmate in early childhood. Dancing and card-playing were not allowed in Amherst, but Noah Webster's granddaughter, who lived there, evaded the prohibition on behalf of her circle. She held "P.O.M." meetings for the Poetry of Motion, and Emily Dickinson excelled in this branch of learning. She joined in picnics and walks over the Amherst hills with groups of boys and girls from the town and the college. They had "sugaring-off" parties and valentine parties, and they often climbed Mount Norwottuck where they found ferns and lady-slippers; and sometimes they met at a brookside in the woods, where the boys went fishing and the girls made chowder. Emily was an ardent botanist. She knew the haunts of all the wild flowers in the region, and sometimes she scrambled alone through the forest, perhaps with her big dog Carlo. She was an expert cook. At home she baked the bread and boiled her father's puddings, but her father was difficult to please. He read "lonely and rigorous books," she said, on Sunday afternoons, fearing that anything else might "joggle the mind"; and Shakespeare, the Bible and Dr. Watts's hymns were the reading that he chose for his daughter. He did not like her to work in the garden, or to make visits without him, and when she was too witty he left the table. At fifteen she could not tell the time; her father supposed he had taught her, but she had not understood him, and she did not dare to ask him again or ask anyone else who might have told him. Now and again, she rebelled. She smashed a plate or a tea-cup and her friends and her brother found ways to provide her with books, hiding them in the box-bush that stood beside the front door or on the parlour piano, under the cover. In one way or another, she contrived to read most of the current authors, especially the Brontës and the Brownings, with Hawthorne, Coleridge, Irving, Keats and Ruskin. One of her special favourites was Sir Thomas Browne, and she loved the drollery of Dickens. For the rest, she read Heine in German and Emerson's poems, and Frank B. Sanborn's letters in the *Springfield Republican* kept her in the literary current. She was by no means passive in this house of duty. Once, at a funeral in Hadley, whither she had gone with her father in the family barouche, she ran away for several hours with a young cousin from Worcester and drove back to Amherst in his buggy. At school, she declared her independence. She had been sent as a boarding-pupil to Mary Lyon's seminary, where she had written her themes on the nature of sin. She had listened to lectures on total depravity as if, like most of the other girls, she had meant to be a missionary's wife; but when, one day, Miss Lyon asked all the girls to rise, all who wished to be Christians, Emily alone refused to do so. She had found that she could not share the orthodox faith. Otherwise her life went on, with a few journeys here and there, like that of any country lawyer's daughter. As a young girl, she had visited Boston. She remembered the concerts and Bunker Hill, the Chinese Museum and Mount Auburn; and later, on two occasions, she stayed in Cambridge, to receive some treatment for her eyes. When her father was serving his term in Congress in 1854, she spent seven weeks in Washington with him. Her father's friends were struck by her charm and her wit. It was on her way home that she stopped at Philadelphia and received the sudden shock that had changed her life.

This was the whole of Miss Dickinson's story, so far as outward events were concerned, when Thomas Wentworth Higginson entered the picture. Higginson had written an appeal in *The Atlantic*, addressed to the rising generation. Remembering the days of *The Dial*, when the hazel wand, waved over New England, had indicated hidden springs of talent in many a country town, he said that to find a "new genius" was an editor's greatest privilege. If any such existed who read *The Atlantic*, let him court the editor—"draw near him with soft approaches and mild persuasions." Higginson added a number of admonitions: "Charge your style with life . . . Tolerate no superfluities . . . There may be years of crowded passion in a word, and half a life in a sentence." This appeal was anonymous, but many of the Amherst people knew who wrote the articles in *The Atlantic*, for Sanborn's literary gossip kept them posted; and presently Colonel Higginson, who was living in Worcester, received an odd little letter. The letter was unsigned, but the writer sent four poems, and she placed in a separate envelope the signature "Emily Dickinson." She begged this distant friend to be her "master." The poems puzzled Higginson. While he felt a curious power in them, he was not prepared for a "new genius" who broke so many rules as this lady in Amherst, who punctuated with dashes only and seemed to have small use for rhyme and merely wished to know if she was "clear." She did not ask him to publish the poems, and he did not pass them on to the editor, but he wrote her a sympathetic letter that was followed by a long correspondence. She continued to send him poems at intervals, signing her notes "your gnome" and "your scholar," but, although she asked him again if he would be her "preceptor," and he offered her a number of suggestions, she never changed a line or a word to please him. In one note she said, "If I read a book and it makes my whole body so cold no fire can ever warm me, I know that is poetry. If I feel physically as if the top of my head were taken off, I know that is poetry. These are the only ways I know it. Is there any other way?" And once she replied, when he asked her for a photograph, "I have no portrait now, but am small, like the wren; and my hair is bold, like the chestnut burr; and my eyes like the sherry in the glass that the guest leaves." This feminine mystification piqued the colonel. He wrote, "You enshroud yourself in this fiery mist and I cannot reach you, but only rejoice in the rare sparkles of light." When she told him that her companions were the hills and the sundown, he replied that she ought to come to Boston; she would find herself at home at Mrs. Sargent's. At last, in 1870, he went to Amherst. After a brief delay, while he waited in the parlour, he heard a faint footstep in the hallway and a shy, little childlike creature glided in. She carried two day-lilies, which she placed in his hand, saying, in a soft, breathless voice, "These are my introduction," adding in a whisper, "Forgive me if I am frightened. I never see strangers and hardly know what to say." She spoke of her household occupations and said that "people must have puddings," and she added a few detached, enigmatic remarks. She seemed to the amiable Higginson as unique and remote as Undine or Mignon or Thekla. But he was disturbed by the tension in the air and was glad he did not live too near this lady. There was something abnormal about her, he felt. He had never met anyone before who drained his nerve-power so much.

At that time, Miss Dickinson was forty years old and had long since withdrawn from the world; and the friends who came to see her sister were used to the "hurrying whiteness" that was always just going through a door. She sometimes swept into the parlour, bowed and touched a hand or two, poised over the flowered Brussels carpet, and vanished like a ghost or an exhalation; but even these appearances had grown rarer and rarer. Only the neighbours' children really saw her. She had given up wearing colours and was always dressed in diaphanous white, with a cameo pin that held the ruching together. She was decisive in manner, anything but frail. Her complexion was velvety white, her lips were red. Her hair was bound with a chestnut-coloured snood, and when it was chilly she wore a little shoulder-cape crocheted of soft white worsted run through with a ribbon. She often had a flower in her hand. She moved about in a sort of revery, flitting "as quick as a trout" when she was disturbed. This was one of her sister Lavinia's phrases. The children knew her "high, surprised voice." They knew her dramatic way of throwing up her hands as she ended one of the stories she liked to tell them. She made them her fellow-conspirators. They followed her upstairs and heard her comments on the guests she had left in the parlour. She would say, with finger on lip, as feminine callers left, "Listen! Hear them kiss, the traitors!" Or, peeping down the stairs, she would say of some man, "Look, dear, his face is as pretty as a cloth pink," or "His face is as handsome and meaningless as the full moon." She remarked, apropos of some scholarly person, "He has the facts, but not the phosphorescence of learning." She said that her own ideal caller was always just going out of sight, and that it made her shiver to hear people talk as if they were "taking all the clothes off their souls." She called herself the "cow-lily," because of the orange lights in her hair and her eyes, and she observed that the housemaid moved about "in a calico sarcophagus." Once she said to her little niece, who was puzzled by her shy ways, "No one could ever punish a Dickinson by shutting her up alone." Meanwhile, her life went on with her flowers and her sister. She had a small conservatory, opening out of the dining-room, a diminutive glass chamber with shelves around it; and there she grouped the ferns and the jasmine, the lilies and the heliotrope and the oxalis plants in their hanging baskets. She had a little watering-pot, with a long, slender spout that was like the antenna of an insect, and she sat up all night at times in winter to keep her flowers from freezing. The garden was her special care, and occasionally one saw her at dusk through the gate fluttering about the porch like a moth in the moonlight. When it was damp, she knelt on an old red army blanket that she had thrown on the ground, to reach the flowers. Usually, on summer evenings, she sat for a while with Lavinia on the side piazza, overlooking the flagged path that led to the villa. There stood the giant daphne odora, moved out from the conservatory, and the two small oleanders in their tubs.

Meanwhile, since 1862, Miss Dickinson had been writing poems, although there were very few of her friends who knew it. They all knew the little rhymes she sent them with arbutus buds, but they did not know how seriously she pursued her writing, at night, beside the Franklin stove, in the upstairs corner bedroom, in the light that often glimmered over the snow. From her window she had caught suggestions that gave her a picture, a fancy, an image. Perhaps a boy passed whistling, or a neighbour on her way to church, or a dog with feet "like intermittent plush"; or perhaps she knew that a travelling circus was going to pass in the early morning, and she sat up to watch the

"Algerian procession." A dead fly on the window-pane stirred her imagination, and once in the glare of a fire at night she saw a caterpillar measuring a leaf far down in the orchard. She saw the bluebirds darting round "with little dodging feet,"

> The motions of the dipping birds,
> The lightning's jointed road;

and all these observations went into her verses. She wrote on sheets of note-paper, which she sewed together, rolling and tying the bundles with a thread or a ribbon and tucking them away in the drawers of her bureau; although sometimes the back of an envelope served her as well, or a scrap of the *Springfield Republican*. But, casual in this, she was anything but casual—she was a cunning workman—in her composition. Poetry was her solitaire and, so to speak, her journal, for, like Thoreau in Concord, she watched the motions of her mind, recording its ebbs and flows and the gleams that shot through it; and she laboured over her phrases to make them right. Were they all her own? Were there echoes in them, or anything of the conventional, the rhetorical, the fat? Were they clear, were they exact, were they compact? She liked the common hymn-metres, and the metres of nursery-jingles, which had been deeply ingrained in her mind as a child, and she seemed to take a rebellious joy in violating all their rules, fulfilling the traditional patterns while she also broke them. She was always experimenting with her rhymes and her rhythms, sometimes adding extra syllables to break up their monotony, sometimes deliberately twisting a rhyme, as Emerson did, for the sake of harshness, to escape the mellifluous effect of conventional poems. Many of her pieces were like parodies of hymns, whose gentle glow in her mind had become heat-lightning. For Emily Dickinson's light was quick. It was sudden, sharp and evanescent; and this light was the dry light that is closest to fire.*

The visible setting of these poems was the New England countryside, the village, the garden, the household that she knew so well, a

---

* Why did not Miss Dickinson publish her poems? This question is insoluble and idle. One can only say that, if she had published them, the poems would have been quite different in their total effect. If she had seen her work in proof, she would have arranged the poems in some reasonable order, she would have rectified the punctuation, etc. Her work would have seemed less arbitrary and less eccentric. The poems as they stand abound in misprints; and Miss Dickinson's collected work consists of serious poems, fragments and trivialities confusedly shuffled together.

scene, the only scene she knew, that she invested with magic, so that the familiar objects became portents and symbols. Here were the hills, the changing seasons, the winter light, the light of spring, the bee, the mouse, the humming-bird, the cricket, the lonely houses off the road, the village inn, the lamp-post that became, in the play of her fancy, sublime or droll; and with what gifts of observation she caught the traits of her birds and insects, of everything that crept or ran or flew— the snake "unbraiding in the sun," the robin's eyes, "like frightened beads," the umbrella of the bat that was "quaintly halved." She often seemed a little girl, amusing herself with childish whimsies, and, in fact, as the ward of her father, she remained in some ways adolescent; and, as she dressed to the end in the fashion of her early youth, so she retained the imagery of the child in the household. But her whim-sies sometimes turned into bold ideas that expressed an all but fathom-less insight or wisdom. She saw the mountain, like her father, sitting "in his eternal chair"; her ocean had a "basement," like the house in Amherst, and her wind and snow swept the road like the brooms that she had been taught to use—the brooms of the breeze swept vale and tree and hill. A journey to the Day of Judgment struck her as a "buggy-ride," and she saw a "schoolroom" in the sky. She domesticated the universe and read her own experience into the motions of nature and the world she observed. The sun rose in the East for her "a ribbon at a time," and the "housewife in the evening West" came back to "dust the pond." Clouds for her were "millinery," mountains wore bonnets, shawls and sandals, eternity "rambled" with her, like her dog Carlo; the wind had fingers and combed the sky, and March walked boldly up and knocked like a neighbour. Volcanoes purred for her like cats, and she saw the planets "frisking about," and her Providence kept a store on the village street, and she thought of death as coming with a broom and a dustpan. The moon slid down the stairs for her "to see who's there," and the grave for her was a little cottage where she could "lay the marble tea." One could not "fold a flood," she said, and "put it in a drawer," but she rolled up the months in moth-balls and laid them away, as she had swept up the heart and put away love; and she saw hope, fear, time, future and past as persons to rally, tease, flee, welcome, mock or play with.

The turns of fancy that marked these poems were sharp and unpredictable, and yet they were singularly natural—nothing was forced. Miss Dickinson lived in a world of paradox, for, while her eye was microscopic, her imagination dwelt with mysteries and grandeurs. Ribbons and immortality were mingled in her mind, which passed from one to the other with the speed of lightning, though she sometimes took a mischievous pleasure in extravagant combinations of thought, uniting the droll, and the sublime, the trivial and the grand. There was in this an element of the characteristic American humour that liked to play with incongruities, and Miss Dickinson maintained in the poems of her later years the fun-loving spirit she had shown as a schoolgirl. To juxtapose the great and the small, in unexpected ways, had been one of her prime amusements as the wit of her circle, and this, like the laconic speech that also marked the Yankee, had remained an essential note of her style as a poet. "Shorter than a snake's delay," her poems were packed with meaning; and, swiftly as her images changed, they were scarcely able to keep the pace with which her mind veered from mood to mood, from faith to mockery, from mysticism to rationalism, through ecstasy, disillusion, anguish, joy. These poems were fairylike in their shimmer and lightness, they moved like bees upon a raft of air; and yet one felt behind them an energy of mind and spirit that only the rarest poets ever possessed. Was not Emily Dickinson's idiom the final proof that she possessed it? Her style, her stamp, her form were completely her own.

MARY ELLEN CHASE

Why she selected The LORD'S DAY in the NINETIES

I have selected portion of a chapter from *A Goodly Heritage* partly because I like it as well as I like any portion of my books, largely because it is characteristic of what through many years I have tried to do for my native state of Maine: to put into words as accurately as possible those attributes and qualities which made life in rural Maine of the "nineties" unique and interesting. The memory of those Sundays, now so changed even in Maine, still supplies me with humorous gratitude; and I hope the description of them may give pleasure to my readers.

Millbridge, Me.   MARY ELLEN CHASE
July 8, 1942

TO ALL Protestant communities in rural New England during the nineties (and in the State of Maine there was almost no distinctly rural community which was not wholly Protestant) Sunday was unmistakably the Lord's Day. That we were glad and rejoiced therein cannot be claimed with the same degree of certainty. Foretaste, perhaps even foreboding, of Sunday began with our Saturday dinner, which was invariable. It consisted of salt fish boiled in a cloth bag and in a pot well filled with potatoes. This sustenance, commonly known in New England as "Cape Cod turkey," was served with a generous supply of hot pork scraps floating in a bowl of equally hot grease. Strangers to Maine ways who came to our table often had to be shown how to shred the fish on their plates, how to mash their potatoes, how to pour upon the mixture the pork gravy. Under my mother's cooking the result was not only palatable but delicious. This meal had originated many years before because it made possible the Sunday dinner with-

271

out undue labour on that day. In the afternoon the large remainder was made into fish-balls and set in a cool place to await the morrow.

Another foretaste of Sunday came, in our large family, immediately after dinner was cleared away. By two o'clock the weekly bathing began. Before the turn of the century no house in Blue Hill possessed a bath-room. Ours, the first in town, was installed when I was seventeen, and its exciting installation followed a law-suit of several years' standing in which we became involved because of our inordinate desire for a water supply of our own. There was no town water supply; indeed, there is not to this day; and one paid dearly both financially and emotionally for any rebellion against wells, cisterns, or pasture springs.

The weekly bath, therefore, was fraught with inconvenience and difficulty; nevertheless, in all well-regulated families, the omission of it was inconceivable. Although in warmest weather the sea proved helpful, a salt water bath by tacit consent of all the "best people" was looked upon with suspicion as not fulfilling the requirements either of cleanliness or of moral and religious duty. Custom and time alike had prescribed a washtub by the kitchen stove; and time and custom in the nineties were not lightly set aside.

One by one we scrubbed ourselves or were scrubbed, the odour of the warm soap-suds mingling with the smell of the beans in the oven. One by one we arrayed ourselves or were arrayed in clean underwear and fresh, well-mended stockings. If we finished early, we were encouraged to play at temperate games, to spend an hour at a neighbour's house, or to read quietly in our corners of the library. Riotousness on late Saturday afternoons was frowned upon; it was too much like jocularity after the performance of a sacred rite. On Saturday evenings it was with a sense of corporate decency and order that we gathered around the supper table—a sense which modern plumbing with all its comforts cannot produce.

Sundays in all seasons dawned soberly. Toys of all kinds had been put away in closed drawers or in the corners of the stable. To allow a sled or a cart in the driveway was unthinkable. After a somewhat later breakfast of warmed-over beans and brown bread, we prepared for church and Sunday school, warned of such necessity by the nine o'clock bells which pealed alternately from the two white steeples on opposite hills. In our earlier years my mother, for the sake of family integrity, forsook her Baptist heritage and accompanied her husband, mother-in-law, and children to the Congregational church.

Our family left the house shortly after 10:15 as we must be ascending the church steps by the time the sombre tolling of the last bell began just before the half hour. My father always walked a bit ahead of the rest of us. In all seasonable weather he wore a top hat and a black frock coat, and he carried a gold-headed cane. My mother, often flurried a bit by her morning's undertaking, always had very pink cheeks as she brought up the rear. The appearance of us children varied only with the change from fall and winter to late spring and summer. We each had one best costume and we wore it. My father having a passion for blue serge, which he bought by the bolt, our winter dresses were often fashioned from this material, my mother cleverly disguising one frock from another by bands, braids, pipings, and divergence in pattern. In the summer we wore white or sprigged muslins and wide leghorn hats. The blue serge of my brothers did not change with any season although occasionally it was alleviated by trousers of white duck. We went silently down the country road, skirting a wide field on the right filled with violets, or daisies, or goldenrod, and climbed the hill to the church. At the door we met my grandmother, whose sedate and solitary progress had been accomplished earlier since she liked to confer with her friend, the sexton, over the morning lesson assigned to the minister's Bible class.

Our pew was taxed to its capacity to hold us in the nineties, and as years elapsed we spilled over into another. We had certain rules which we followed in regard to occupation and behaviour during the long morning service. Children up to the age of six were encouraged to sit on crickets throughout the sermon and draw or look at pictures; from six to ten years they might read their Sunday-school books; from ten on they must sit quietly and at least pretend attention. During the hymns, the responsive reading, and the long prayer all of whatever age must listen and participate in so far as each was able. My father not infrequently annoyed my mother after the sermon had gone on for three-quarters of an hour by turning in his corner seat at the outside of our pew to look at the great circular clock which hung below the choir gallery; but if we perchance followed his bad example, we were admonished by a shake of her head or, for that matter, of his own.

Although church provided in the nineties no such dramatic possibilities as it had promised in the days of the Reverend Jonathan Fisher, it was not entirely bereft of excitement. Once my brother Edward, deep in his Sunday-school book, and forgetful of his surroundings, laughed aloud in the midst of the sermon. This act, however, which my father singularly enough allowed to go unreproved, was as nothing compared to the consternation and embarrassment which he caused us all on one memorable day. Seized by a spirit of defiance and of rebellion unknown among us, he had on the morning in question purposely hitched himself in his white duck trousers around on the grass of the lawn until their seat was a sight to behold. Our hearts stood still as my father, issuing from the house, beheld this proof of insurrection. But instead of the swift retribution which we expected, my brother was forced to walk to church and to stand, during the Doxology and the hymns, on the highest cricket, his pants in full view of the congregation. The mortification which we as a family experienced on that devastating occasion can never be minimized or forgotten! Surely one cannot pay singly for his own transgressions!

My grandmother also afforded drama, now amusing to recollect but then embarrassing to undergo. As she grew older and the deafness which crept early upon her became more acute, a certain practice of hers was a source of no little confusion. Since she contributed fifty dollars yearly to the support of the minister, an amount almost unheard of in those days and equalled only by a certain well-to-do parishioner, Mrs. Harriet Morton by name, she made it an unchangeable rule to place no offering at all in the contribution plate. Her generosity and her habit alike being well and favourably known to the entire community, she was upheld by public sentiment. Imagine then her distress when her rival in good works developed suddenly and without fair warning the custom of giving also some coin as the plate was passed. Not to be outdone, my grandmother prepared with reluctance but with commendable spirit to do the same; her refusal, however, to give one jot or tittle more than her neighbour was destined sorely to test the ingenuity and the peace of mind of the grandchild who sat next her.

Mrs. Morton sat across the aisle and one pew ahead of our own. The task of the child next my grandmother was to ascertain the amount of the coin which she drew from her black reticule and placed upon the plate and to communicate its size to my grandmother before the arrival of the deacon who collected the alms on our side of the church. This information was not so difficult to procure as it might have been in view of the fact that our respective pews were at the extreme front; but the conveying of it required no little ingenuity. It was usually given by signs, one finger signifying a nickel, two a dime, the full hand (a gesture very rarely displayed!) a quarter. But as my grandmother grew older and more hard of hearing, the nervousness engendered by this trying situation increased until, forgetting her deafness, she would say in a voice perfectly audible to the entire congregation, though unheard by herself, "How much did Hattie Morton give *this* morning?" I regret to say, moreover, that neither her voice nor her intonation was strictly in keeping with the ideal atmosphere of a Christian edifice.

After all, the most unalloyed, if less exciting, drama occurred every Sunday morning when my father made his contribution. This was a never failing source of pride to us; for as coins were drawn from pockets and from purses, my father invariably procured from one small pocket at the bottom of his waistcoat a new one-dollar bill and laid it upon the plate. The amount and the occasion alike were too momentous to allow comment at any time. We should have liked to know how he obtained always a new note, how he managed to afford such a prodigious offering. But we never asked, only remained secure in social and financial distinction which his weekly act conferred upon us.

I do not know that the church service itself engendered much religion within us. The sermons were long and abstruse, and, even as I grew older, I do not recall any which meant much to me. But the solemnity of the occasion, the observance together of a custom, the sense of well-being and of well-doing—memories of these I would not be without. Details, too, impressed themselves on my mind and in my imagination to bring later their longer, richer consequences: the black shadows of birds passing and repassing behind the coloured glass of a memorial window; the sunlight lying in bright, precise figures across the pulpit steps; the order and beauty of the white panelled pews with their polished, mahogany railings; the words and the imagery of old hymns. Most of all I remember verses of the Bible as they were read by the singularly beautiful voice of the old pastor whom I knew throughout my childhood. Sometimes the sonorous quality of the words themselves quite apart from their sense stayed long with me:

"Wherefore, seeing we also are encompassed about by so great a cloud of witnesses . . ."

"The former treatise have I made, O Theophilus. . . ."

"Now faith is the substance of things hoped for, the evidence of things not seen."

Once when I was hardly ten I was startled, aroused from my wandering thoughts, by the awful discovery, the stupendous announcement, that someone had actually *seen* the Lord. This was the prophet Isaiah in the year that King Uzziah died; but for the moment, so convincing was his voice, I felt sure it was our minister himself—that in his black coat and white linen necktie he, the Reverend Ebenezer Bean, had been before that great throne, high and lifted up, in that train which filled the temple. As he read, I felt a tingling sensation down my back, the tiny hairs rising in my excitement. In one of those inexplicable feats of memory, the words were stamped henceforth indelibly upon my mind.

"Above it stood the seraphim; each had six wings; with twain he covered his face, and with twain he covered his feet; and with twain he did fly.

"And one cried to another saying, 'Holy, Holy, Holy, is the Lord of hosts. The whole earth is full of His glory.'"

ROBERT FROST

Why he selected SIXTEEN POEMS

It would be hard to gather biography from poems of mine except as they were all written by the same person, out of the same general region north of Boston, and out of the same books, a few Greek and Latin, practically no others in any other tongue than our own. This was as it happened. To show that there was no rule about place laid down, I may point to two or three poems reminiscent of my ten years as a child in San Francisco and a few others actually written in California at the time of the Olympic games. More than a few were written in Beaconsfield and in Ryton, England, where I farmed, or rather gardened in a very small way from 1912 to 1915. My first two books were published in England by the Scotch and English, to whom I am under obligations for life for my start in life. This too was as it happened. I had on hand when I visited England the material of those two books and more than half of another. I had had poems in American magazines, but not many, and my relative unsuccess with magazines had kept the idea of a book from ever entering my head. It was perhaps the boldness of my adventure among entire strangers that stirred me up to try appealing from the editors of magazines to the publishers of books.

I have made this selection much as I made the one from my first book, *A Boy's Will*, and my second book, *North of Boston,* looking backward over the accumulation of years to see how many poems I could find towards some one meaning it might seem absurd to have had in advance, but it would be all right to accept from fate after the fact. The interest, the pastime, was to learn if there had been any divinity shaping my ends and I had been building better than I knew. In other words could anything of larger design, even the roughest, any broken or dotted continuity, or any fragment of a figure be discerned among the apparently random lesser designs of the several

poems? I had given up convictions when young from despair of learning how they were had. Nevertheless I might not have been without
them. They might be turned up out of the heap by assortment. And
if not convictions, then perhaps native prejudices and inclinations. I
took thirty poems for *A Boy's Will* to plot a curved line of flight away
from people and so back to people. For *North of Boston* I took group
enough to show the people and to show that I had forgiven them for
being people. The group here given brings out my inclination to country occupations. It began with a farm in the back yard in San Francisco. This is no prejudice against the city. I am fond of several great
cities. It is merely an inclination to country things. My favorite implements (after the pen) are the axe and the scythe, both of which besides
being tools of peace have also been weapons of war. The Hungarian
peasantry under Kossuth carried the scythe into battle in their attempt
at independence from Austria, and the axle of an ancient war chariot
was prolonged into a scythe at either end. In three of the poems I celebrate the axe, in one the scythe.

Ripton, Vt.   ROBERT FROST
July 26, 1942

THE NEED OF BEING VERSED IN COUNTRY THINGS

THE house had gone to bring again
  To the midnight sky a sunset glow.
Now the chimney was all of the house that stood,
Like a pistil after the petals go.

The barn opposed across the way,
That would have joined the house in flame
Had it been the will of the wind, was left
To bear forsaken the place's name.

No more it opened with all one end
For teams that came by the stony road

To drum on the floor with scurrying hoofs
And brush the mow with the summer load.

The birds that came to it through the air
At broken windows flew out and in,
Their murmur more like the sigh we sigh
From too much dwelling on what has been.

Yet for them the lilac renewed its leaf,
And the aged elm, though touched with fire;
And the dry pump flung up an awkward arm;
And the fence post carried a strand of wire.

For them there was really nothing sad.
But though they rejoiced in the nest they kept,
One had to be versed in country things
Not to believe the phoebes wept.

COME IN

AS I came to the edge of the woods,
Thrush music—hark!
Now if it was dusk outside,
Inside it was dark.

Too dark in the woods for a bird
By sleight of wing
To better its perch for the night,
Though it still could sing.

The last of the light of the sun
That had died in the west
Still lived for one song more
In a thrush's breast.

Far in the pillared dark
Thrush music went—
Almost like a call to come in
To the dark and lament.

But no, I was out for stars:
I would not come in.
I meant not even if asked;
And I hadn't been.

THE ONSET

ALWAYS the same, when on a fated night
At last the gathered snow lets down as white
As may be in dark woods, and with a song
It shall not make again all winter long
Of hissing on the yet uncovered ground,
I almost stumble looking up and round,
As one who overtaken by the end
Gives up his errand, and lets death descend
Upon him where he is, with nothing done
To evil, no important triumph won,
More than if life had never been begun.

Yet all the precedent is on my side:
I know that winter death has never tried
The earth but it has failed: the snow may heap
In long storms an undrifted four feet deep
As measured against maple, birch and oak,
It cannot check the peeper's silver croak;
And I shall see the snow all go down hill
In water of a slender April rill
That flashes tail through last year's withered brake
And dead weeds, like a disappearing snake.
Nothing will be left white but here a birch,
And there a clump of houses with a church.

STOPPING BY WOODS ON A SNOWY EVENING

WHOSE woods these are I think I know.
His house is in the village though;
He will not see me stopping here
To watch his woods fill up with snow.

My little horse must think it queer
To stop without a farmhouse near
Between the woods and frozen lake
The darkest evening of the year.

He gives his harness bells a shake
To ask if there is some mistake.
The only other sound's the sweep
Of easy wind and downy flake.

The woods are lovely, dark and deep.
But I have promises to keep,
And miles to go before I sleep,
And miles to go before I sleep.

ON A TREE FALLEN ACROSS THE ROAD
(To Hear Us Talk)

THE tree the tempest with a crash of wood
Throws down in front of us is not to bar
Our passage to our journey's end for good,
But just to ask us who we think we are

Insisting always on our own way so.
She likes to halt us in our runner tracks,
And make us get down in a foot of snow
Debating what to do without an axe.

And yet she knows obstruction is in vain:
We will not be put off the final goal
We have it hidden in us to attain,
Not though we have to seize earth by the pole

And, tired of aimless circling in one place,
Steer straight off after something into space.

THE WOOD-PILE

OUT walking in the frozen swamp one grey day,
    I paused and said, 'I will turn back from here.
No, I will go on farther—and we shall see.'
The hard snow held me, save where now and then
One foot went through. The view was all in lines
Straight up and down of tall slim trees
Too much alike to mark or name a place by
So as to say for certain I was here
Or somewhere else: I was just far from home.
A small bird flew before me. He was careful
To put a tree between us when he lighted,
And say no word to tell me who he was
Who was so foolish as to think what *he* thought.
He thought that I was after him for a feather—
The white one in his tail; like one who takes
Everything said as personal to himself.
One flight out sideways would have undeceived him.
And then there was a pile of wood for which
I forgot him and let his little fear
Carry him off the way I might have gone,
Without so much as wishing him good-night.
He went behind it to make his last stand.
It was a cord of maple, cut and split
And piled—and measured, four by four by eight.
And not another like it could I see.
No runner tracks in this year's snow looped near it.

And it was older sure than this year's cutting,
Or even last year's or the year's before.
The wood was grey and the bark warping off it
And the pile somewhat sunken. Clematis
Had wound strings round and round it like a bundle.
What held it though on one side was a tree
Still growing, and on one a stake and prop,
These latter about to fall. I thought that only
Someone who lived in turning to fresh tasks
Could so forget his handiwork on which
He spent himself, the labour of his axe,
And leave it there far from a useful fireplace
To warm the frozen swamp as best it could
With the slow smokeless burning of decay.

WILFUL HOMING

IT IS growing late and time he drew to a house,
  But the blizzard blinds him to any house ahead.
The snow gets down his neck in a chilly souse,
That sucks his breath like a wicked cat in bed.

The snow blows on him and off him, exerting force
Downward to make him sit astride a drift,
Imprint a saddle, and calmly consider his course.
He peers out shrewdly into the thick and swift.

Since he means to come to a door he will come to a door,
Although so compromised of aim and rate;
He may stumble wide of a latch a yard or more,
And to those concerned he may seem a little late.

A BLUE RIBBON AT AMESBURY

SUCH a fine pullet ought to go
   All coiffured to a winter show,
And be exhibited, and win.
The answer is this one has been—

And come with all her honors home.
Her golden leg, her coral comb,
Her fluff of plumage, white as chalk,
Her style, were all the fancy's talk.

It seems as if you must have heard.
She scored an almost perfect bird.
In her we make ourselves acquainted
With one a Sewell might have painted.

Here common with the flock again,
At home in her abiding pen,
She lingers feeding at the trough,
The last to let night drive her off.

The one who gave her ankle-band,
Her keeper, empty pail in hand,
He lingers too, averse to slight
His chores for all the wintry night.

He leans against the dusty wall,
Immured almost beyond recall,
A depth past many swinging doors
And many litter-muffled floors.

He meditates the breeder's art.
He has a half a mind to start,
With her for Mother Eve, a race
That shall all living things displace.

'Tis ritual with her to lay
The full six days, then rest a day;
At which rate barring broodiness
She well may score an egg-success.

The gatherer can always tell
Her well-turned egg's brown sturdy shell,
As safe a vehicle of seed
As is vouchsafed to feathered breed.

No human spectre at the feast
Can scant or hurry her the least.
She takes her time to take her fill.
She whets a sleepy sated bill.

She gropes across the pen alone
To peck herself a precious stone.
She waters at the patent fount,
And so to roost, the last to mount.

The roost is her extent of flight.
Yet once she rises to the height,
She shoulders with a wing so strong
She makes the whole flock move along.

The night is setting in to blow.
It scours the windowpane with snow,
But barely gets from them or her
For comment a complacent chirr.

The lowly pen is yet a hold
Against the dark and wind and cold
To give a prospect to a plan
And warrant prudence in a man.

TWO TRAMPS IN MUD TIME

OUT of the mud two strangers came
　　And caught me splitting wood in the yard.
And one of them put me off my aim
By hailing cheerily 'Hit them hard!'
I knew pretty well why he dropped behind
And let the other go on a way.
I knew pretty well what he had in mind:
He wanted to take my job for pay.

Good blocks of beech it was I split,
As large around as the chopping block;
And every piece I squarely hit
Fell splinterless as a cloven rock.
The blows that a life of self-control
Spares to strike for the common good
That day, giving a loose to my soul,
I spent on the unimportant wood.

The sun was warm but the wind was chill.
You know how it is with an April day
When the sun is out and the wind is still,
You're one month on in the middle of May.
But if you so much as dare to speak,
A cloud comes over the sunlit arch,
A wind comes off a frozen peak,
And you're two months back in the middle of March.

A bluebird comes tenderly up to alight
And fronts the wind to unruffle a plume
His song so pitched as not to excite
A single flower as yet to bloom.
It is snowing a flake: and he half knew
Winter was only playing possum.

Except in color he isn't blue,
But he wouldn't advise a thing to blossom.

The water for which we may have to look
In summertime with a witching-wand,
In every wheelrut's now a brook,
In every print of a hoof a pond.
Be glad of water, but don't forget
The lurking frost in the earth beneath
That will steal forth after the sun is set
And show on the water its crystal teeth.

The time when most I loved my task
These two must make me love it more
By coming with what they came to ask.
You'd think I never had felt before
The weight of an ax-head poised aloft,
The grip on earth of outspread feet.
The life of muscles rocking soft
And smooth and moist in vernal heat.

Out of the woods two hulking tramps
(From sleeping God knows where last night,
But not long since in the lumber camps).
They thought all chopping was theirs of right.
Men of the woods and lumberjacks,
They judged me by their appropriate tool.
Except as a fellow handled an ax,
They had no way of knowing a fool.

Nothing on either side was said.
They knew they had but to stay their stay
And all their logic would fill my head:
As that I had no right to play
With what was another man's work for gain.
My right might be love but theirs was need.

And where the two exist in twain
Theirs was the better right—agreed.

But yield who will to their separation,
My object in living is to unite
My avocation and my vocation
As my two eyes make one in sight.
Only where love and need are one,
And the work is play for mortal stakes,
Is the deed ever really done
For Heaven and the future's sakes.

A PRAYER IN SPRING

OH, GIVE us pleasure in the flowers today;
    And give us not to think so far away
As the uncertain harvest; keep us here
All simply in the springing of the year.

Oh, give us pleasure in the orchard white,
Like nothing else by day, like ghosts by night;
And make us happy in the happy bees,
The swarm dilating round the perfect trees.

And make us happy in the darting bird
That suddenly above the bees is heard,
The meteor that thrusts in with needle bill,
And off a blossom in mid air stands still.*

MOWING

THERE was never a sound beside the wood but one,
    And that was my long scythe whispering to the ground.
What was it it whispered? I knew not well myself;
Perhaps it was something about the heat of the sun,
Something, perhaps, about the lack of sound—

* The last (fourth) stanza has here been omitted at the request of the author. W. B.

And that was why it whispered and did not speak.
It was no dream of the gift of idle hours,
Or easy gold at the hand of fay or elf:
Anything more than the truth would have seemed too weak
To the earnest love that laid the swale in rows,
Not without feeble-pointed spikes of flowers
(Pale orchises), and scared a bright green snake.
The fact is the sweetest dream that labor knows.
My long scythe whispered and left the hay to make.

A DRUMLIN WOODCHUCK

ONE thing has a shelving bank,
   Another a rotting plank,
To give it cozier skies
And make up for its lack of size.

My own strategic retreat
Is where two rocks almost meet,
And still more secure and snug,
A two-door burrow I dug.

With those in mind at my back
I can sit forth exposed to attack
As one who shrewdly pretends
That he and the world are friends.

All we who prefer to live
Have a little whistle we give,
And flash, at the least alarm
We dive down under the farm.

We allow some time for guile
And don't come out for a while
Either to eat or drink.
We take occasion to think.

And if after the hunt goes past
And the double-barrelled blast
(Like war and pestilence
And the loss of common sense),

If I can with confidence say
That still for another day,
Or even another year,
I will be there for you, my dear,

It will be because, though small
As measured against the All,
I have been so instinctively thorough
About my crevice and burrow.

SITTING BY A BUSH IN BROAD SUNLIGHT

WHEN I spread out my hand here today,
I catch no more than a ray
To feel of between thumb and fingers;
No lasting effect of it lingers.

There was one time and only the one
When dust really took in the sun;
And from that one intake of fire
All creatures still warmly suspire.

And if men have watched a long time
And never seen sun-smitten slime
Again come to life and crawl off,
We must not be too ready to scoff.

God once declared he was true
And then took the veil and withdrew,
And remember how final a hush
Then descended of old on the bush.

God once spoke to people by name.
The sun once imparted its flame.
One impulse persists as our breath;
The other persists as our faith.

SAND DUNES

SEA waves are green and wet,
But up from where they die,
Rise others vaster yet,
And those are brown and dry.

They are the sea made land
To come at the fisher town,
And bury in solid sand
The men she could not drown.

She may know cove and cape,
But she does not know mankind
If by any change of shape,
She hopes to cut off mind.

Men left her a ship to sink:
They can leave her a hut as well;
And be but more free to think
For the one more cast off shell.

A SOLDIER

HE IS that fallen lance that lies as hurled,
That lies unlifted now, come dew, come rust,
But still lies pointed as it plowed the dust.
If we who sight along it round the world,
See nothing worthy to have been its mark,
It is because like men we look too near,
Forgetting that as fitted to the sphere,

Our missiles always make too short an arc.
They fall, they rip the grass, they intersect
The curve of earth, and striking, break their own;
They make us cringe for metal-point on stone.
But this we know, the obstacle that checked
And tripped the body, shot the spirit on
Further than target ever showed or shone.

THE GIFT OUTRIGHT

THE land was ours before we were the land's.
   She was our land more than a hundred years
Before we were her people. She was ours
In Massachusetts, in Virginia,
But we were England's, still colonials,
Possessing what we were still unpossessed by,
Possessed by what we now no more possessed.
Something we were withholding made us weak
Until we found out that it was ourselves
We were withholding from our land of living,
And forthwith found salvation in surrender.
Such as we were we gave ourselves outright
(The deed of gift was many deeds of war)
To the land vaguely realizing westward,
But still unstoried, artless, unenhanced,
Such as she was, such as she would become.

ROBERT NATHAN Why he selected

CENTRAL PARK

The artist works either through the macrocosm, or the microcosm; which is to say that he either sees the whole world and its oceans, its vast landscapes, down to the smallest drop of dew—or he sees the dew, and the world inside it. The first is a method of definition, the other of suggestion; in one the full chord is struck, in the other, only a few notes. But to work within the smaller limits does not necessarily imply an indifference to what lies outside. In this landscape, I have tried to picture one small corner of the earth, and to suggest rather than to define the world beyond. To catch the feel and flavor of the city, I chose to recreate its park rather than its multiplicity of streets, because the park is whole, and the streets are many. And so, too, in *One More Spring*, I tried to suggest slantwise, the spirit of the early 'thirties, the depression years. Where—or if—I have in any sense succeeded, it is in striking a note, not too big nor too loud, whose overtones, heard within the ear of the listener, produce the authentic hum of life.

New York, N. Y.   ROBERT NATHAN
May, 1942

T HAT was the year business failed, and many families, investors, and business houses were ruined. In the country, farmers plowed their fields under, rather than harvest the wheat or cotton they were unable to sell; and in the cities, people starved, or sold apples on the streets. Everywhere was misery and apathy, for no one could see any hope for the future.

As a result, a tragic calm, induced by surprise, by despair, and aided by the weather, filled everyone's heart. It was autumn, a season of skies as blue as cornflowers, of yellow sunlight, of warm, unmoving air. The poor stood in lines, waiting for their cup of soup and piece of bread; they sat on the park benches and, warming themselves in the last sun of summer, or breathing the cool, kind air of autumn, turned their faces with a certain trust to the sky, in which were the sun and the stars, just as always.

Their fate was of interest to no one but themselves. Even the poets did not write about them, because the poets also were poor, and their nature made them indignant. They no longer wished to write poetry; on the contrary, they wished to fight; they threw themselves into the coal wars in the south, and were sent home with broken heads, like the heroes of antiquity.

Their foes wasted no time in calling them atheists, hypocrites, and communists. And they replied by silence, or in prose which did not cause anyone's heart to beat any faster.

In the larger cities, there was not a street without its auction, or clearance sale in some little shop which was obliged to go out of business. As a result, each day there were more poor people than before, and each day the bread-lines grew longer.

Among the failures was the shop of Jared Otkar, Antiques. Nothing that Mr. Otkar had been able to do could stave off his ruin. The chairs and tables bought for high prices a few years before, had remained on his hands, while their values steadily declined. To pay the rent of his business, to save the few old pieces which he loved, and also because he hoped for better times, Mr. Otkar had sold his own few belongings and gone to live in his shop. It was all in vain; in the end his debts caught up with him, and he lost everything.

Now, as he stood in the doorway, gazing mildly out at the street which he felt he was seeing for the last time, an auctioneer's red flag, inscribed with the words "Sale Today," obscured the window on which was painted the sign: "Otkar, Antiques."

The little storeroom behind him was already empty, for the auction had been held the day before. Of all his cherished possessions, only an old bed remained; scrolled with the flowers and cupids of the eighteenth century, and too large for comfort, it did not seem like the sort of bed anyone would wish to buy. When Mr. Otkar realized that the bed was to be left to him, he was delighted. If one has a bed, he thought, then at least one knows where one will sleep at night.

And wishing to feel grateful on that account, he turned back into the shop again.

The bare interior smelt of dust, of glue, and broken wood. Mr.

Otkar went to a closet in the rear, and drew forth a small bottle of milk, an egg, half a loaf of bread, and a little stove made of aluminum and heated by alcohol. Then, while he waited for the water to boil, he sat himself down on the bed, to think things over.

He had been willing, honest, and industrious all his life. But, like everybody else, he had expected too much of those virtues. And he was too old now to change his ways. Perhaps, if he had his life to live over again, he might do better for himself. His youth, for instance; what strange ideas he had had when he was young. Had he really expected to find love and joy in the world? And justice? Love and joy were for the young; and wisdom and justice for the old. Well, there were many old men in the world; what had they done for themselves?

He had to admit they had done themselves no good, for no one believed any longer in justice and wisdom.

And as for joy and love, no one believed in those any more, either.

When he arrived at this point in his reflections, he decided to take stock of himself, to make a statement of his position, like any business man. With this intention, he took a sheet of paper and wrote down first of all the word "Liabilities."

Next to that he put a zero.

Then came his assets. These consisted of his bed, with its mattress; the stove; a few books; a clean shirt; an extra handkerchief or two; and a few pieces of silver in his pocket.

Under plans and expectations, he was obliged to write: "None."
And under faith: "None."

It was this last item which troubled him most of all.

For the old faiths were gone; and he had nothing to put in their places. That innocence of mind with which, in the past, men had clung to their beliefs, no longer existed in the world. In the midst of the most dreadful disasters, they had perished happily for the sake of God, for the East India Company, science, the divine right of kings, or the dawn of democracy. Now they were obliged to die for no other reason than starvation.

Mr. Otkar was not a very religious man; at the same time he was neither a scientist nor a democrat. He saw God divided up year after year like a meatball among the pious; and he had learned that among the pigs there is also a democracy. As for science, it must be remembered that Mr. Otkar was only a small dealer in antiques, whose business had been ruined. It made no difference to him that the physicists had decided that space was curved, and that the universe was exploding, like a balloon.

What he wanted was something to believe in. At the same time he was obliged to consider where and how he was to live.

The water in the little aluminum pot was boiling by now, and Mr. Otkar put in his egg. A moment later a shadow darkened the shop, and he looked up to see a young man standing in the doorway. "The shop is closed," said Mr. Otkar shortly, because he was still vexed by what he had been thinking.

The young man paid no attention to him. Instead, he advanced through the litter left over from the auction. He was pale and thin; in one hand he carried a coat with a fur collar, and in the other a shabby violin-case.

"There is nothing for sale here," repeated Mr. Otkar, without looking up.

"I did not come to buy anything," replied the young man.

Mr. Otkar shrugged his shoulders. "I have nothing to **give** you, either," he said.

There was no reply to this. Mr. Otkar, who had been watching his egg dancing about in the pot of hot water, let his glance travel upward as far as the stranger's knees, which he saw were trembling. He was surprised and for a moment did not say anything. But after a while he remarked in more kindly tones: "Sit down, young man. I do not know why you are here, or what you want; but you can rest a few minutes, before you go further."

Still holding his coat and his violin, the young man sat down on the bed and gave a deep sigh. "The weather, anyhow, is perfect," he said wearily.

"It is indeed," agreed Mr. Otkar. "It is very good weather to be out of doors." And he added gently: "Have you been walking far?"

The other replied with a loud sigh; after which he sat back and gazed around him in silence. "So," he said at last; "it is quite empty here. Then you also are poor, and will not be able to help me."

He did not seem to doubt that Mr. Otkar would help him if he could. Already, in advance, and for no reason, his pale thin face took on a look of gratitude. "I do not want anything in the way of money," he said proudly, "because I am not a beggar. What I would like is to give some concerts. If people could hear me play, they would go crazy over me.

"You understand, also, with me," he continued, "it is not like a beginner or an amateur. I have already had a great success in Europe, and in Pittsburgh, Pennsylvania."

And taking from his pocket a much creased circular, he presented it to Mr. Otkar.

MORRIS ROSENBERG. CONCERT VIOLINIST.

LESSONS. MASTER CLASSES. CONCERTS.

FIRST PRIZE PARIS CONSERVATORY.

SOLOIST WITH THE PITTSBURGH

SYMPHONY ORCHESTRA, PITTSBURGH, PA.

"Mr. Rosenberg is a genius on the violin."
Oswego *Press.*
"Morris Rosenberg was the violinist of the evening."
Galesburg *Democrat.*
"Mr. Rosenberg was adequate."
Pittsburgh *Times.*

MANAGEMENT, ROSE MORRIS, 1467 MARKET STREET,
PITTSBURGH, PA.

"That was myself," he said, leaning over and pointing to the management. "Because, naturally, I had no money to hire a manager. That was a good idea, I think."

And, sitting back again, he favored Mr. Otkar with an anxious smile.

"Very good indeed," said Mr. Otkar. "But why, in that event, did you decide to leave Pittsburgh, which seems in your case to have been the land of opportunity?"

Mr. Rosenberg sighed. "There was no money any more in Pittsburgh," he said. "There was nothing to do there at all, no lessons, nothing. It is not a musical city. So I thought, if I go to a big city like New York, perhaps I can get some work to do. But the truth is, I do not seem able to begin. Perhaps here, also, they do not want concerts?"

And he looked at Mr. Otkar as though to say: I cannot believe such a thing.

Mr. Otkar looked back at him; he saw how hungry and tired he was. "Be sensible," he said; "stop talking about concerts. When did you eat last?"

Mr. Rosenberg looked away. "Oh well," he said; "as long as you ask; two days ago I had something."

Mr. Otkar took a deep breath. Then he pushed the egg and the milk over to Mr. Rosenberg. "Eat it slowly," he said, "or it will give you indigestion."

"Well, perhaps—if you say so—just a bite—" said Mr. Rosenberg, in a voice which trembled with eagerness, with despair, and with the desire not to express either of these emotions.

While the concert violinist devoured the egg, Mr. Otkar thought to himself: when farmers and bankers cannot get along any more, what is the good of music? This young man is starving; but all he thinks about is playing on a fiddle. One must admire such singleness of mind, in view of the fact that nobody wants to hear him.

"Besides," he went on, continuing his thoughts aloud, "what is there left to make music about? The artist cannot forget that he is starving, and that the entire world is probably coming to an end. Should he try to overlook such things? That is not very good for the artist. Or should he try, on the contrary, to express in art his anxiety and his indignation? That is not very good for art. You can see that there is no peace for him, either way."

The young man, who had paid no attention to this discourse and whose mouth was full of bread, attempted to make a slight sound of assent.

"For that reason," concluded Mr. Otkar, "what I say is: sell your violin, and start up at some corner in the apple business."

Mr. Rosenberg swallowed hastily. "The man is crazy," he exclaimed, staring at Mr. Otkar. "How could I give a concert without my violin? All that I have left in the world is what you see here; my violin to play on, and my coat with the fur collar, so that nobody can think I have not made a success.

"Everything else is gone—my watch, my hat, everything. What you see is all there is. I have no longer even a bed to sleep on; last night I slept on a bench in the park. Early in the morning the birds woke me, singing out of tune."

He added simply: "I hadn't eaten for two days. So the birds were out of tune. It was my ears, not the birds."

His eyes suddenly filled with tears. "What is the matter with everybody," he cried, "that a man cannot find work to do any more? Is that a way to run the world? Did I study all my life in order to walk up and down the streets like a beggar? I tell you, there is something wrong, there is something rotten in all this. I am grateful to you for feeding me."

Mr. Otkar sat still, thinking. The shop was silent, and smelt of dust; it seemed to fall gently and without a sound from the ceiling, and to dance a little in the air. How quiet it was, and empty—just like himself, he thought, waiting as he was waiting, for whatever was to come.

And what, after all, was to come? He, too, was homeless and penniless; and he did not believe that a knowledge of antiques would help him very much in the new life. What he needed was to believe in something. And he envied Mr. Rosenberg, who believed in his art and in the hearts of men and women, before whom he hoped to play. It was a beginning, it was something; it left out a great deal, but it was better than nothing. And Mr. Otkar had nothing.

"As you see," he said to Mr. Rosenberg, "I have nothing to offer you. The egg you have already eaten; what more there is you can see for yourself; a bed, for which there are slats and a mattress; a few books; a little stove; and my own company. After today I am as homeless as yourself. And so it occurs to me that we might, perhaps, be homeless together. At all events, we have neither of us much to lose by such an arrangement. What do you say?" And he held out his hand, which the young man took in his strong fiddler's fingers.

"Why not?" said Mr. Rosenberg, who had nothing more to lose in the world.

With these words they became partners. Mr. Rosenberg helped Mr. Otkar to take the bed apart; then Mr. Otkar went next door to see if he could borrow some sort of wagon on which to carry it. In a short time he returned with a little pushcart, which they loaded with the bed, the coat, the fiddle, and the alcohol stove; then shutting behind them the door of the shop, which now looked dark and empty, the two men started down the street together. "Where are we going?" asked Mr. Rosenberg, not unreasonably.

"For a long while," replied Mr. Otkar, "I have had a longing to be in the country. There is still grass in the park; let us go there and find a place to put our bed. After the uncertainties of the last few weeks it will seem like heaven to me, or at least until the cold sets in."

And, with a serene expression, he headed the pushcart toward the park.

It was already cold in the park when the sun went down, which Mr. Otkar had not expected. They chose a hollow among some trees and within sight of the dark waters of a pond; it was impossible not to see at the same time the road with its motors going by, but Mr. Otkar determined to ignore it.

There, upon grass turned dry and brown and under trees from whose branches the leaves had already fallen, Mr. Otkar and Mr. Rosenberg put up their bed garlanded with cupids. Above them was the empty sky; and they could smell faintly through the vapors of the city the meager earth under their feet. Around them stretched in miniature the landscape for which Mr. Otkar had longed, already in the shadow of evening. All was quiet; no frogs or crickets sang with a sound of country in the air, in which only the far-off hum of the city made a murmur like wind or water.

No dew fell, yet the breeze turned colder. Lamps were lighted along the avenues and in the park; but in the little hollow where they had placed their bed the blue of evening deepened. Mr. Otkar gazed about him with an air of satisfaction; he was hungry, and he wished to hide it even from himself. "What we need," he said, "is a fire. It would keep us warm and help us to feel that this hollow of ground belongs to us."

"It doesn't belong to us," objected Mr. Rosenberg.

"That is true," replied Mr. Otkar, "but only because the police will put us out of it; which is all the more reason to enjoy it while we can. So let us have a fire by all means; and afterwards you can play on your fiddle in the firelight."

But Mr. Rosenberg shook his head. "What do you think I am," he asked; "a gypsy? My fiddle would catch a cold in the night air. And if a string goes, I have no money to buy another."

Nevertheless Mr. Otkar had set his heart on having a fire and began to gather a few twigs and sticks. "We'll be arrested," said Mr. Rosenberg, helping him.

Mr. Otkar hoped not. He was cold and hungry, but he was enjoying a feeling of freedom. "The jails are already full," he said; "perhaps they will leave us alone. After all, we are not doing very much harm."

"We are breaking the law," said Mr. Rosenberg, in hollow tones. But Mr. Otkar, whose conscience was clear, was convinced that they would be forgiven. "You are a sentimentalist," said Mr. Rosenberg, with regret.

"Perhaps I am," agreed Mr. Otkar. "But I am surprised to learn that you are not."

"A musician has as much chance to be a sentimentalist," replied Mr. Rosenberg, "as a lion or a tiger." Returning to the bed, he placed his violin on the ground under the mattress, in order to protect it. Then he sat down and gave a yawn. "To be a musician," he remarked, "is to fight, every day, for your life."

Mr. Otkar agreed that a musician's life was full of pain and difficulty. "It is also," he added, "filled with the choicest consolations, and with the most glorious rewards. It is true that the rewards do not as a rule occur until some time after death."

"It is a life," said Mr. Rosenberg gloomily, "of toil. The work of a musician is never finished; every day he must start all over again, from the beginning. And in the end what has he got? A few notices which say: 'Mr. Rosenberg was adequate.'"

"Give it up," urged Mr. Otkar, stooping to add a twig to the fire; "go into the apple business."

"Listen to him," cried Mr. Rosenberg bitterly; "there it is again— the apple business. I have a great career in music ahead of me. . . . But, as I was saying, it is only because I am not a sentimentalist; and because I know every moment what I am doing.

"Now I am going to bed."

The evening was growing darker. Already in the east, night rolled like thunder in the sky. Mr. Otkar's little fire winked yellow in the hollow; he bent over and warmed his hands above it. The fiddler is right, he thought; one must not be too tender if one is to get along in

the world. Perhaps the trouble with me is that I am too fond of everything. What weakness it is to be fond!

Mr. Rosenberg went to bed, as he said he would; he wrapped his
coat around him and soon fell asleep. Lying beside him, his face turned
to the remains of the little fire, Mr. Otkar thought sadly about himself.
It is true, he mused, that I am no eagle. I do not struggle like a hawk
to live. Well, that is a serious fault, after all. For I am not a vegetable
either, and I cannot live on dampness alone.

And remembering the egg and the milk he had given away, he
gave a dry swallow in his throat.

"What will become of me?" he said aloud.

Mr. Rosenberg stirred at his side. "Go to sleep," he murmured drowsily; "tomorrow there is work to do." And he hummed a scale under
his breath: do re me fa sol.

But in the restless chill of the city night, Mr. Otkar found it hard to
sleep. What is the good of talk? he asked himself. As it is, there are
too many opinions in the world. Everybody has his own idea, and
wants to profit by it. Some want money and others want a seat in
heaven, or some other comfort. The wise man lives like an eagle, or
Mr. Rosenberg; he wraps himself up in his own coat and says nothing
of any importance. Then, when the time comes, he can act without
having to give any reasons; he can hurl himself down from the sky
upon his dinner and make away with it while the others are still talking
about what they intend to do.

In the midst of these reflections Mr. Otkar fell asleep. And as the
night deepened about him, he dreamed that he was a child again, in the
little mid-west town in which he had been born. It was a warm summer's day, and he had gone down to the mill-pond, to sit in the cool
grass and watch the dragon-flies darting over the water or listen to the
frogs croaking among the reeds. . . .

He opened his eyes with a start; for he thought that he had really
heard a frog croaking near by. Was he at home again, in the sun, by
the mill-pond? For a moment his heart beat with joy. But no—it was
still night; he had been asleep in the park without a cover; and what
he had thought to be a frog was only a pigeon, ruffling her feathers,
and cooing to herself.

The embers of the fire still glowed before him. In their faint light he lay still and watched the bird. What a plump pigeon she was. And not at all wild—fed by the children upon popcorn and peanuts. A ward of the city, innocent and free. . . . Under those gray feathers beat a very small heart, but the meat above it was firm and tender. Roasted, it would give off an appetizing fragrance. . . .

"I am not an eagle," said Mr. Otkar to himself. Nevertheless, the very next moment, without meaning to, but with a muffled cry, he threw himself upon the bird.

After that it was necessary to gather more wood for the fire.

When the fire was bright again, he set himself to prepare his dinner. He took off as many feathers as he could; after which he placed the pigeon on a spit made of wood, and held it out over the flames. At once an odor of roasting flesh and burning feathers filled the air, very acrid and disagreeable.

His eyes smarting from smoke, Mr. Otkar held on to the pigeon and tried to turn the spit above the fire. In the meanwhile he could see, out of the corner of one eye, that Mr. Rosenberg had awakened and was sitting up, staring at him in surprise. "What have you got?" asked Mr. Rosenberg at last; "a chicken?"

"A pigeon," said Mr. Otkar shortly.

Mr. Rosenberg sniffed the air. "What are you doing to it?" he asked.

Mr. Otkar replied that he was cooking it.

"With all its feathers on?" asked Mr. Rosenberg.

There was no reply to this remark; for Mr. Otkar felt that he was doing the best he could.

The fiddler leaned over to look. "Yes," he said in wondering tones; "it is a pigeon. Well . . . who gave it to you?"

Mr. Otkar replied with dignity: "While you were asleep, I went hunting. Like an Indian, or an explorer, I found this bird and threw myself upon it."

"What," cried Mr. Rosenberg, "you killed it?"

"I did," said Mr. Otkar.

Mr. Rosenberg uttered a groan. "Then," he declared, "we shall all be arrested."

But Mr. Otkar, whose knees hurt from being pressed to the hard ground, and whose face was too hot from the fire, waved him away.

"Go back to sleep again," he said. "You know nothing about all this. You are guiltless; and I will eat the pigeon all by myself."

At these words Mr. Rosenberg became more unhappy than ever. "Do you mean to say you wouldn't give me any?" he exclaimed.

"As you like," replied Mr. Otkar. "But," he added, rising to his feet, "then we must both be ready to go to jail—because we are both guilty."

Mr. Rosenberg hesitated; he was afraid, but he was hungry. "Very well," he said at last; "I am with you."

And his hand closed over the bird.

As it turned out, the pigeon was almost too tough to be eaten at all. But it was better than nothing. "Save the bones," said Mr. Otkar; "We will make a stew out of them." Then he lay down again, next to Mr. Rosenberg. "One must not be too tender in this world," he said. And he took part of the fiddler's coat, to cover himself.

He felt warm and at peace; and he fell asleep before dawn. But Mr. Rosenberg did not sleep any more that night. He was cold; and he was waiting for the police to find him. He lay awake, thinking of what he would say to them when they came to arrest him.

ROBERT P. TRISTRAM COFFIN

Why he selected MAINE Is a

PERPETUAL POEM

I HAVE favorites among my poems, of course.
There are some poems that came to me sudden, out of the blue.
I did not have to do anything about them. They were alive and came.
One was a humming-bird that called on my morning-glories. Another
was a hawk who was my friend and flew two feet over my head and
let me see the translucent amber stones set each side of his head.

HUMMING-BIRD

It would take an angel's eye
   To see the humming-bird's hot wings,
He stands raptly on thin air
   At his banquetings.

He flies so fast he is at rest,
   His vibrant body poises still,
His wings into the crystal light
   Melt invisible.

A bobbin winding off the threads
   Of sunlight from the spools of flowers,
His hunger is a weightless thing
   And holier than ours.

Saints and lovers bathed in flame
  Know far less of flame than he
As he hovers pinionless,
  A minute ecstasy.

GOLDEN FALCON

He sees the circle of the world
  Alive with wings that he
Was born to rend; his eyes are stars
  Of amber cruelty.

God lit the fires in his eyes
  And bound swords on his feet,
God fanned the furnace of his heart
  To everlasting heat.

His two eyes take in all the sky,
  East, west, north, and south,
Opposite as poles they burn;
  And death is in his mouth.

Death because his Maker knew
  That death is last and best,
Because he gives to those he loves
  The benison of rest.

Golden, cruel word of God
  Written on the sky!
Living things are lovely things,
  And lovely things must die.

One poem that came to me fierce and alive was a buck deer pursued
by hounds across a bay. They swam right past my boat, near enough
for me to reach out and touch them with an oar. But I did no such
foolish thing, for though I was young then, I knew a poem when I
saw one going by that close.

CRYSTAL MOMENT

Once or twice this side of death
Things can make one hold his breath.

From my boyhood I remember
A crystal moment of September.

A wooded island rang with sounds
Of church bells in the throats of hounds.

A buck leaped out and took the tide
With jewels flowing past each side.

With his high head like a tree
He swam within a yard of me.

I saw the golden drop of light
In his eyes turned dark with fright.

I saw the forest's holiness
On him like a fierce caress.

Fear made him lovely past belief,
My heart was trembling like a leaf.

He leaned towards the land and life
With need upon him like a knife.

In his wake the hot hounds churned,
They stretched their muzzles out and yearned.

They bayed no more, but swam and throbbed,
Hunger drove them till they sobbed.

Pursued, pursuers reached the shore
And vanished. I saw nothing more.

So they passed, a pageant such
As only gods could witness much,

Life and death upon one tether
And running beautiful together.

But the best sudden poem that ever came to me came to me as a light
in my father's big hands. I was nine, and I was desperately ill, in a
high fever, and lying on my bed in the dead of the night, half awake,
half asleep. My father came in to see how I was, and he struck a match
and stood at the foot of my bed, looking down. His face, lit up by the
sudden fire in his hands, was one of the most beautiful sights I ever
saw. My father did not know I was looking at him from under my
eyelids, or he would never have looked at me that way. Again, though
I was a boy, I knew a poem when I saw one at the foot of my bed. I
thought I would always remember that poem. But I didn't. The
memory faded from my mind. I should never have recalled that poem
if it hadn't been that a few years ago I found myself in that same situation, when my own small son lay ill in his room, in the dead of the
night, in a fever, too, and I went in to see how he did. I went in the
gloom and struck a match. In the spurt of the flame the old poem of
my father's face came back to me, and all I had to do was write it
down:

THE SECRET HEART

Across the years he could recall
His father one way best of all.

In the stillest hour of night
The boy awakened to a light.

Half in dreams he saw his sire
With his great hands full of fire.

The man had struck a match to see
If his son slept peacefully.

He held his palms each side the spark
His love had kindled in the dark.

His two hands were curved apart
In the semblance of a heart.

He wore, it seemed to his small son,
A bare heart on his hidden one.

A heart that gave out such a glow
No son awake could bear to know.

It showed a look upon a face
Too tender for the day to trace.

One instant, it lit all about,
And then the secret heart went out.

But it shone long enough for one
To know that hands held up the sun.

DOROTHY CANFIELD FISHER

Why she selected The NIGHT on the

COBBLE

This chapter is the turning-point of the novel *Seasoned Timber*. Timothy Hulme, middle-aged Principal of an old Vermont Academy, has fallen whole-heartedly in love with Susan, a teacher young enough to be his daughter. She feels for him a warm, admiring affection, which, in her ignorance of life and herself, she is beginning to think may be love.

While she is way from town on a short vacation, a younger-generation member of Timothy Hulme's family connection, Canby Hunter, in his twenties, comes breezing back to the little Vermont town where, a decade before, he was prepared for college under Timothy's care. He is restlessly footloose, on the rebound from an unsatisfactory engagement, emotionally electric.

From his long experience, Timothy recognizes in the younger man the qualities which, because of his maturity, he himself lacks, and which make an irresistible appeal to other youth—reckless, exuberant power and dashing physical magnetism. He is also a decent and likable, although undistinguished fellow. When he arrived, Canby had intended to make a visit of but a day or two. But he casually decides to stay on for a time in Clifford. Timothy is instantly and instinctively impelled to send him packing before Susan returns. He knows that it would be easy for him to do this because of the authority and personal prestige which his years and success as an educator have brought him. Canby has always from his boyhood looked up to his old teacher, and has no special reason for staying on in a sleepy country town. With a few cold, wounding words, Timothy could sting the young man into resentful departure. And this would leave Timothy's ripe, kind, self-controlled, protective, selfless love for young

310

Susan safe from any comparison with the younger man's capacity to sweep a girl off her feet with sheer youthful vitality.

But has he the right to do this? Would it be fair play to Susan thus to allow her no chance to make her own choice, even to know that a choice is possible? Scrupulous, brought up in a strict family tradition of honorable conduct, with fastidiously civilized standards, he hesitates in an anguish of uncertainty for a few days, making first one decision and then its opposite, hour after hour. Finally, in an anguish of effort to live up to the ideal of personal honor which has been the basis of his inner life, he decides to do nothing to send Canby away; and at once becomes more than ever aware, by a premonitory dread, of the power of Canby's hot young masculine vitality. But he cannot go counter to his life-long loyalty to the principle of not taking advantage of others for his own profit.

The meeting between Canby and Susan, so much feared by the older man, takes place in a storm, in the midst of an alarming accident which throws them together for some hours on a lonely road. The circumstances, their common youth, their readiness for love, make a dramatic effect on both the young people. Canby falls violently and openly in love with Susan and she soon knows what, in her ignorance of life she did not before divine—the difference between affection and love.

The half-god goes, the god arrives. Timothy is carelessly pushed to one side. The young man, the girl in love, see no one but themselves. They do not even glance at the older man, to whom they are both sincerely attached, long enough to perceive that he is suffering.

But he is suffering. Intolerably. What he cannot endure is the thought that except for what now seems like a hair-splitting scruple, he might have saved himself from this pain, almost beyond his power to endure. His every waking moment is poisoned by a corroding doubt of the standards of honorable action, by which he has charted his life. He feels that he has simply made a fool of himself.

At this point the following chapter begins. Following an old local custom, Timothy has gone up with the boys of the Academy on a moonlit night in June, to sleep on a rocky ledge, (called The Cobble) on the side of the mountain, from which there is a fine view of sunrise. With the group goes the very old chairman of the Board of Trustees of the Academy, an ancient Vermonter, Mr. Dewey, whose presence on this annual mountain expedition is part of the school tradition.

One of the students is Jules, a Jewish, French, half-orphan from New York, musical, high-strung, more sensitive and impressionable than his Yankee school-mates. Timothy has admitted him to the student body against the angry protests of a rich New York Trustee, who is a bitter anti-Semite and who is—although Timothy and Mr. Dewey have no idea of this—to die in the city, by apoplexy, that very night, leaving a will in which he bequeaths a million dollars to the Academy, now desperately poor, on condition that they exclude all Jewish students.

During the night on The Cobble, Timothy Hulme has no faintest idea that a second ordeal, another searching test of his honor, looms before him in the days and weeks immediately to follow. Will he use his great influence in the Academy and town to have this bequest accepted? This decision will put him at the head of a prosperous, well-endowed school, suitable for his personal distinction and providing him with an ample income and an easy life. Or, confronted by this temptation not to play perfectly fair, not to act in a perfectly honorable way, not to exploit others for his own profit, will he stick by that principle of delicately accurate honor which has always given his life moral elevation, but which is now costing him so tragic a price in unhappiness?

His whole conscious attention focussed on his own misery, his subconscious spirit, painfully tearing at his heart, struggles to free itself from the personal, and to lift itself into the spacious serenity of the universal. An exalting conviction of healing oneness comes to him, after the bodily exhaustion of his sleepless vigil, frees his spirit for a mystic flight beyond what words can express, what the senses or the mind can grasp.

This chapter is thus not only a solvent of the sorrow and pain just

behind him in his individual personal life. It is a spiritual preparation
for what is just before him—a fiery test of his character in his rôle as
a member of civilized human society.

Arlington, Vt.   DOROTHY CANFIELD FISHER
June, 1942

H E HAD known at that moment all that was to be, and he might
as well—he thought, leaning forward to drop a dry stick on the
sober little June watch-fire—he might as well have yielded at once to
the first intimation, as to resist for these last three months of misery.

The white-hot core of the fire, tiny but ardently alive, throbbed as
it seized with passion on the new food for flames. A column of murky
smoke rose into the still night air, and then, as the blaze burned clear,
thinned to an airy plume. Timothy sat back on his granite ledge, his
eyes fixed on the bowing of the little plume of smoke towards the west,
where, long hours ago, the sun had gone down. Often enough he had
noticed that smoke-drift in other Junes, up here at night on the Cobble. In those other years, rational years, he and Mr. Dewey and the
boys sitting around the fire had sometimes speculated about the reason
for this, wondering whether on still nights the warmed lightness of
the air around the setting sun created everywhere on the globe this
soft almost imperceptible steady breathing towards the west of the
night wind.

At the other end of the Cobble, a shower of sparks, rising in the
darkness, showed that old Mr. Dewey too had put fresh wood on his
watch-fire. Between the two, stretched rows of dark forms, rolled in
blankets. They lay motionless in the trancelike sleep of youth, still as
the great rock that was their bed; but just below, where the granite
crest of the Cobble softened into upland pasture, the sheep, uneasy at
the invasion of their solitude, moved restlessly. Sometimes a bell
tinkled. Sometimes a ewe called with a low bleating and was answered by a thudding of little hoofs on sod and stones.

Timothy held his watch to the glow of the fire. Past midnight. In
an hour the moon would be up. By the traditional routine of this
yearly expedition on the mountain with the Senior boys, he was to

waken the sleepers to see the moon rise over The Wall. He knew what would happen when he did: yawns, grunts, momentary openings of an eye, the blankets re-rolled more tightly around motionless forms. The teacher's life, he had often thought—continually waking sleepers to see beauties or meanings they cared nothing about, and watching them sink back to apathy.

Enough light fell from the sky, thick sown with stars, to show him that Mr. Dewey now stood up from his fire, and followed by his old dog, picked his way among the sleepers, along the Cobble. When he reached Timothy, "Do you feel like sleeping, T. C.?" he asked in a low voice. "If you do, turn in for an hour or so. I'll keep watch."

"Thank you, Mr. Dewey, I don't believe I will," said Timothy in the carefully natural voice he had been using for three months. "How about you?"

Mr. Dewey smiled, looked around him from the dusky stretch of the Crandall Pitch pasture to the mountains brooding under the glittering black sky, looked back at Timothy and shook his head. "No, I'm not sleepy," he said in a peaceful voice, and went back to his own small fire.

Timothy was not sleepy either, although he was very tired.

He gave a rough animal-like shudder, as if to shake off a gadfly, and dropped his head between his hands. The night breeze, so mild as almost to be stillness, blew gently on one cheek, tilting the immaterial column of the smoke ever so little towards where the sun had last shed its warmth.

Later Mr. Dewey stood up again and picked his way along the rock to the other fire. "Moon's due to rise in three four minutes," he said. Wrenching himself away from his hypnotized glare back on the past, Timothy remembered where he was, got to his feet and stepped with the old man from one to another of the sleeping boys, giving each shoulder a shake, saying clearly in their ears, "The moon will soon be up. If you want to see the moon rise, now's the time." They grunted, nodded, and sat up, or propped themselves unsteadily on one elbow and looked around sleepily. All but Eli Kemp. He said clearly, although his eyes continued tightly closed, "What of it!" and pulled

his blanket over his head to shut out the light. But Eli had been conditioned by his poverty never to think of anything but how to make
another penny and keep from spending it, thought Professor Hulme,
going back to his fire.

By the time he had sat down again beside it, he had forgotten Eli
and the other adolescents, his eyes fixed in anguish on the slow thinning of the black velvet back of The Wall. Just so—how many times
had he thought it—love had brought light to his darkness. Just so,
instant by instant, his loneliness and apathy had been suffused with
tenderness and hope. He began to tremble with the violence of sorrow
repressed, clenching his hands hard in his pockets as he had clenched
them before when shaken by the first gusts of passion.

"Fine, isn't it?" said Mr. Dewey dreamily, watching with heart
unwrung.

After a pause, "Yes, it's very fine," said Timothy, correctly.

The dark globe spun fast and smoothly under the feet of the watch-
ers. The eastern mountains sank. The great disk, white with its heatless
fire, swam up to its triumph. The twilight dimness of the pasture
below the rock turned to silver. The sheep, as if the light had been a
sound, stood up, drifted aimlessly about, talking to each other in
sleepy, secret voices. Every weather-worn knob and ridge of the Cobble's granite wave emerged from darkness to visible strength, transfigured from strength to beauty.

Mr. Dewey mused, "Doesn't seem possible—up here—now—tomorrow's newspapers will tell about the same old hellish goings-on of
humans, does it?"

Timothy knew what he meant. He had been for months increasingly horrified by the statements of Nazi ideals in the news, and the
evening before as they talked around the fire, he had asked the boys,
"Don't it kind of make you wonder what General George Washington would ha' said? The history books tell us he swore his head off at
the battle of Monmouth. What cuss-words could he ha' found for
Hitler!"

Timothy thought drearily, "Oh, he's trying to start that up again!"
Wanting only one thing, to have the old man leave him alone in his
pain, he made no rejoinder.

Mr. Dewey waited a moment, and then went back to his own fire, his dog stepping gravely at his heels.

Timothy sat rigid, horribly impervious to the night's apotheosis of peace. His mind tiptoed up timidly to remind him to look at the beauty around him, and shrank back, appalled by his suffering.

But presently his professional conscience, reaching him on a reflex of habit, bade him make sure that all was well with those entrusted to his protection. He turned his head to look and saw that, as he had thought, the boys had collapsed again into stone-sound sleep. No, one of them was stirring. Bending his eyes more intently, Timothy saw that the blanketed form nearest him was stirring. He rose to his feet, he took the two or three steps that brought him to the boy, stooped, put his hand on his shoulder.

It was Jules. Wide awake, he lay looking out over the silvered upland pasture and across the valley brimming with white.

Timothy asked, "Something the matter, Jules?"

The boy clutched at Timothy's arm and sat up. "Oh, Professor Hulme, I can't *stand* it!" He pulled the teacher down to sit beside him. "It's like that swell place in the Kreutzer—w-where the octaves . . ." He choked and rubbed his sleeve back and forth over his nose. Timothy pulled out his handkerchief and passed it to the boy, who blew his nose, handed back the handkerchief and pointing to a scraggly small bush near him said, his voice cracking grotesquely from treble to bass and back again, "Professor Hulme, maybe I'm crazy, but when that bush—when the light came—when that bush came out of the darkness, it c-came *singing*! Honest! Do *you* think I'm crazy? Oh, gosh, I wish my darn voice would get through changing."

"You probably weren't quite waked up, Jules," suggested the teacher calmingly. "Sounds to me as though you were dreaming. Rather a nice dream!"

The boy leaned against Timothy's shoulder, turning his head back and forth to look from the luminous bulk of the mountain above them to the valley where a river of white mist marked the course of the Necronsett.

. . . He whispered dreamily, "D'you suppose that mist hangs over the river like that every night, when we're asleep?" And dropping his voice to an even lower murmur, "D'you hear those sheep, Mr. Hulme? They don't sound like that in the daytime. They sound as though they'd put their mutes on to go with the moonshine, they're—Oh, *why* did papa have to die!"

The insensitive sleepers had the best of it, thought Timothy, those with open eyes found only sorrow in their waking, the old man to see his ideals down under the hobnailed boots of Storm Troopers, the boy in the memory of his irreparable loss, he himself—"Well, Jules, I think you'd better lie down again," he said. "Perhaps you can get to sleep now. Here, I'll leave my handkerchief with you, in case you get the sniffles again."

He tucked the blanket around the thin shoulders and stood for a moment watching with envy how the enormous peacefulness of the night flowed over the child, emptied now of his wonder and his sorrow; looking around him with envy at the other sleepers, not one of whom had wakened.

The fire burned low. He crossed two sticks over the coals and sat down, his eyes on the delicate column of smoke, bowing slightly in the faint breath of the night-breeze which so faithfully followed the setting sun, all around the world.

Well, it was over again—for this time. To live through it exhausted him, each time, to blessed apathy. He looked around at the lyric poem of the night and could not have told where he was. The moon was high now, straight over his head. It had blotted out all the stars which earlier filled the darkness with the pride of their glittering. Every twig, every bush, every commonplace pebble, every tree and blade of grass had put off the shifting many-coloured mortality of daylight and stood transfigured in white peace. All but the man keeping his dark watch. From his anger and stubborn misery the light fell away, bathing the weather-beaten granite of the rock in glory.

There was no glory in the world where Timothy sat, holding hard to all he had left—for he had something left, he had found that out. He had the ability to make Susan unhappy with a blighting look, to undermine her confidence with well-chosen insinuation wrapped in a pleasant phrase she associated with good will. He could still tarnish with doubt the brightness of her response to the torch held up by Canby. He could whirl over her head like a club that ignorant unsuspecting young trust of hers in his wisdom and good faith, and bring it down with all its shattering impact on her unawareness. He could do it! He hardened his heart, blacking out all its light, he trod resolutely down the path from one circle of his inferno to a lower, to a lower, to the lowest, and planned how he could do it. It had not been honourableness but middle-age that had betrayed him into the mawkishness of that dark hour of indecision in his office when like an idiot gentleman bowing and scraping and holding open the door to a caveman intruder—would Canby in his place have invited disaster with that bloodless elderly weighing of civilized standards against the timeless savage hunger of the heart? Never! Never! Never! Canby was no such fool! And he was young. Canby would have struck out with those great fists of his, heedless if they battered down honour, rejoicing in the letting of blood.

Well, it was not too late for him to batter down scruples. It was not too late to do something! He had piled up, had he not—he knew he had—an enormous influence with Susan. He weighed in his memory like unexploded bombs, one after another, the hours with her that made him sure of this. She might not be in love with him—the breath went out of his chest as though he had been struck a blow—and came in again hot and swollen with the certainty that she loved and trusted him. Well, he could wield the power given him by that love and trust, he could stamp out as he would stamp out a treason, that damnable radiance in her face of which she was not yet conscious.

He shaded his eyes with his hands from another radiance, hating the moonlight, detesting the stillness and peace around him, and took out from its dark hole his dearest, surest grievance, pressing its thorn deep into his outraged sense of justice—there was no sense, no meaning in all this. It did not come from the nature of things, but from blank idiot chance. It need not have happened. There was no inner logic or rightness in it, nothing but bad luck. He ran through his fingers the familiar rosary of chance sequence of chance events—if Susan had not happened to be away that week, if she had not chanced to come back earlier from her vacation—if Canby had not taken up

ski-running, if he had not chanced to remember there on the Schenec-
tady viaduct, or wherever it was, that Clifford existed—why, if Downer
as a boy had not chanced to go to work in that office where he met the
girl who was Canby's aunt, Canby never would have been sent to the
Academy, never would——

"'What's on your mind, T. C.?" Mr. Dewey was saying. "I been
asking you for the last five minutes what time your watch says. Mine's
stopped."

"Oh, I beg your pardon. It's"—he looked—"half-past one."

Mr. Dewey set his watch, but did not at once turn away. He poked
meditatively at the coals with the toe of his thick, lumberjack boot.
"What were you thinking about so hard?" he asked again.

Timothy said bitterly, "I was thinking about luck—about chance,
hazard—whatever you want to call it. I was thinking how imbecile
we are to try to plan life, or make any sense of it, when everything in
it is decided by mere brute chance. Something happens—or it doesn't
happen. And that's all there is to it!"

Mr. Dewey sat down on the ledge to consider this. Don came
around in front of him and with a sigh of happiness laid a grizzled
head on his knee. Caressing it absently, Mr. Dewey remarked after a
time, "Wa-al, that's only the way it looks to young folks. When you're
my age, you'll have found out that there's no such thing as luck.
Nothing ever just happens to anybody."

Timothy looked sidelong at him with a hostile eye, resentful of the
dreamy quiet of his voice, as a man in great bodily pain is resentful
of the cheap cheerfulness of good health. The old man lifted off his
battered felt hat, laid it on his knee, and looked around him gravely.
The moonlight, which took the warring chaos of colour out of the
world, replacing it by a patterned harmony of silver and delicate
black, took the grey out of his thick hair and turned it to a line of
shining white around his head. "What I mean is, I guess," he advanced, "that nothing can really happen to a person till he *lets* it
happen. That's been my experience."

"I don't know what you mean, Mr. Dewey," said Timothy coldly.

"Wa-al," said the old countryman meditatively, "I'm not exactly
sure what I mean, myself." He put his hat back on, stood up, and said

very earnestly, "But I mean *some*thing!" and turned to walk towards his end of the rock. He had not taken three steps before he came back to say, "Now you try to get some sleep, T. C. You look to me as though you needed it! Unroll your blanket and lie down anyhow. I took my nap earlier."

"I must think about what to do. I must come to some decision about what I am to *do*!" Timothy told himself desperately. He could not have told what the old man had said. He thought he had not heard it. He thought he had forgotten it. But from his body, battered by the chaotic swirling of its deepest instincts, hurled back from rocky barriers it could not recognize, came now a muffled warning that it was about at the limit of its power to endure. The echo in his outer ear of the old man's compassionate counsel, although it did not reach his brain, stretched out his arm to unroll his blanket. The instant he lay down on it, his fatigue-poisoned muscles, the watchful weary nerve-centres which had kept those muscles taut, his very bones, abandoned themselves to that unheard, unremembered suggestion to rest. His sinews loosened, let his flesh sink down to the support of the granite; even his proud pulse that was to know no truce with effort till the grave, slackened speed, beat low and murmured mildly as in a dream along the avenues still echoing to the roll of its loud insistent drumming. His eyelids, their lining inflamed with the long vigil, drooped over his eyes.

Yet he did not sleep. Or did he?

His vesture of decay lay heavy on the stone, gathering strength from old mysterious reservoirs of bodily renewal for the next bout with living. It lay so still, so rapt in unconsciousness, that his spirit, at the summons of the old man's other unheard, unremembered suggestion, floated free from the body—for the first time, the only time in his life—and, in careless effortless victory over time and space and death and mystery, went searching for its own old reservoirs of renewal, went looking for the meaning of meaningless chance.

It was in the past, the future, among the living, the dead, the forgotten, the remembered—it was everywhere at once in all that Timothy had ever known, as when the moon rose the light had been everywhere at once. His mother, his father, lived again before the man's eyes as they had lived before the little boy's—a year of their life no longer than one beat of his heart; and the man, living all those years at once, saw what the child had taken for granted, the great tree of honour spreading its shelter over their heads, its roots struck deep into a tradition ancient beyond the memory of man, the old honourable human tradition of protection due to the weak from the strong, due to youth from maturity. *Noblesse oblige*—how could he have taken the old motto as a silly expression of caste-vanity! Like all things that survive, it was the expression of a law of nature, the unbreakable law which enjoins upon those whom experience has taught, upon those who know what they do, who know where a step will take them and what a gesture will cost them, not to exploit but to stand guard over helplessness and ignorance—like that of youth, holding out its hands heaped with gold of which it does not dream the value. From every corner of his child-world—from all the hours of all his life, incidents, sayings, expressions, voices, happenings of which he had never spoken and others he had forgotten, came singingly together in a rhythmic whole.

It was the significance of things he saw in that hour, the weary, inflamed, flesh-and-blood of his closed eyelids transparent as crystal. All that he had ever known, seen, felt or been, emerged from the darkness of mere fact into the ineffable clarity of its true meaning. Yes, yes, he saw how nothing ever just happens, to anyone.

He pushed open again the door to the dirty, disordered hall bedroom, he was the adolescent beaten down by more than he could endure, and he was the man of forty-five staggering under more than was bearable—and there was Aunt Lavinia again, beautiful and vital as an angel in tweeds; but now the man saw her in the glory of universal light that gave meaning to her individual sacrifice: Timothy's poor father had not lived up to the debt of honour of the strong to the weak, of the experienced and mature to the unprotected defencelessness of youth. Well, that was a debt that must be paid. Lavinia would throw her heart away and pay it, since someone must.

All its turbulence stilled in exhaustion, all its demands silenced in sleep, Timothy's body unloosed its troubled hold on the spirit, ranging far and weightless in its search for strength and understanding. His eyes were open, were they not—or was it only by glimpses that he watched the frail column of smoke rising from his fire and bowing itself towards where the sun had set, that he saw Mr. Dewey coming and going, noiselessly feeding the little flames? The old man was no more real than Susan, who came and went and stood there, silently begging him not to stamp out that radiance on her face of which she yet knew nothing. Or was that Canby, saying humbly, proudly, with his brown eyes clear as peat-water, that moneyless, futureless, nobody in particular though he was, he must be allowed to give Susan and take from her, what youth alone can give and take, what youth has a right to demand that maturity protect, since it is the core of life?

You are of no mean race—the proud challenge to which he had been brought up rang in his ears—what race? Humanity. From where his spirit soared, high above the body annihilated by fatigue, it had the one vision of wholeness without which no mortal should go down to death, saw the oneness of all and his part in that oneness—and burst into song, as a bird does when night ends and day begins.

It was a bird's song. From a stunted oak tree, clutching its roots into a crack of the granite, a white-throated sparrow was singing in his very ear.

For a moment he lay listening with his spiritual and with his fleshly ear to the two songs blending, before he thought that if a bird were singing, dawn must be at hand. He sat up and looked to the east. Yes, back of The Wall the sky was grey.

The bird, in a tranquil ecstasy for life renewed, swelled its tiny feathered breast and sang again. In the west, the moon hung low where the sun had gone down.

But it gave off no light. The earth had spun its great bulk all around its axis since light had come from the west. Not from there, from the east brightness sprang to the zenith with one bound, paling the moon to silver.

Timothy looked at his fire. Night was no more. The night wind held its breath. The grey column of smoke, released from the night-long pressure, stood straight in the still of the dawn.

Over the mountain wall the sky brightened from grey to mauve to pink to scarlet. Timothy kept his eyes on the omen of the faery column of smoke. He did not breathe. The sun thrust one fiery shoulder over the mountain, and all the world gave a shout of colour. Oh, what was peace with its pallor compared to the many-coloured confusion of light!

The new day began. The day wind woke. The column of smoke slowly, gently, bowed itself to the rising sun.

"So be it," said Timothy Hulme, and got stiffly up to go on with the teacher's work of arousing those who sleep.

EDMUND WILSON Why he selected

The OLD STONE HOUSE

"The Old Stone House" simply means to me one of those of my shorter pieces that came out best.

Wellfleet, Mass.   EDMUND WILSON

June, 1942

A S I go north for the first time in years in the slow, the constantly stopping, milk train, which carries passengers only in the back part of the hind car and has an old stove to heat it in winter, I look out through the dirt-yellowed double pane and remember how once, as a child, I had felt thwarted till I had gotten the windows up so that there should be nothing between me and the widening pastures, the great boulders, the black and white cattle, the rivers, stony and thin, the lone elms like feather dusters, the high air which sharpens all outlines, makes all colors so breath-takingly vivid, in the clear light of late afternoon.

The little stations again: Barneveld, Stittville, Steuben—a tribute to the Prussian soldier who helped drill our troops for the Revolution. The woman behind me in the train talks to the conductor with a German accent. They came over here for land and freedom.

Boonville: that pale boxlike building, smooth gray, with three floors of slots that look in on darkness and a roof like a flat overlapping lid— cold, dark, clear air, fresh water. Like nothing else but upstate New York. Rivers running easily among stones, or deeper, stained dark with dead leaves. I used to love to follow them—should still. A fresh breath of water off the Black River, where the blue closed gentians grow. What forests, what hillsides, what distant falls!

There was never any train to Talcottville. Our house was the center

of the town. It is strange to get back now: it seems not quite like anything else I have ever known. But is this merely the apparent unique-
ness of places associated with childhood?

The settlers of this part of New York were a first westward migra-
tion from New England. At the end of the eighteenth century they
drove ox-teams from Connecticut and Massachusetts over into the
wild northern country below Lake Ontario and the St. Lawrence, and
they established here an extension of New England.

Yet an extension that was already something new. I happened last
week to be in Ipswich, Massachusetts, the town from which my grandfather's family emigrated; and, for all the pride of white houses with
green blinds, I was oppressed by the crampedness of Boston. Even the
House of the Seven Gables, which stimulated the imagination of Hawthorne, though it is grim perhaps, is not romantic. It, too, has the tight-
ness and self-sufficiency of that little provincial merchant society, which
at its best produced an intense little culture, English in its concrete-
ness and practicality—as the block letters of the signs along the docks
make Boston look like Liverpool. But life must have hit its head on
those close and low-ceilinged coops. That narrowness, that meagerness,
that stinginess, still grips New England today: the drab summer cottages along the shore seem almost as slit-windowed and pinched as the
gray twin houses of a milltown like Lawrence or Fall River. I can
feel the relief myself of coming away from Boston to these first uplands of the Adirondack wilderness, where, sustained by the New
England religion, still speaking the language of New England, the
settlers found limitless space. They were a part of the new America,
now forever for a century on the move.

They moved on before they had been able to build here anything
comparable to the civilization of New England. The country, magnificent and vast, has never really been humanized as New England
has: the landscape still overwhelms the people. But this house, the
only one of its kind among farms and wooden towns of later periods,
was an attempt to found a civilization. And it blends in a peculiar
fashion the amenities of the eastern seaboard with the rudeness and
toughness of the frontier.

It was built at the end of the eighteenth century: the first event
recorded in connection with it is a memorial service for General Wash-

ington. And it took four years in the building. The stone had to be quarried out of the river. The walls of the house were a foot and a half thick, and the plaster was applied to the stone without any intervening lattice. The beams were secured by enormous nails, made by hand and some of them eighteen inches long. Solid and simple as a fortress, the place has also the charm of something which has been made to order. There is a front porch with white wooden columns which support a white wooden balcony, running along the second floor. The roof comes down close over the balcony, and the balcony and the porch are draped with vines. Large ferns grow along the porch, and there are stone hitching posts and curious stone ornaments, cut out of the quarry like the house: on one side, a round-bottomed bowl in which red geraniums bloom, and on the other, an unnamable object, crudely sculptured and vaguely pagodalike. The front door has real beauty: the door is dark green with a brass knocker, and the woodwork which frames it is white: it is crowned by a wide fanlight and flanked by two narrow panes of glass in which a white filigree of wood makes a webbing like ice on winter ponds. On one of the broad sides of the house, where the mortar has come off the stone, there is a dappling of dark gray under pale gray like the dapping of light in shallow water, and the feathers of the elms make dapplings of sun among their shadows of large lace on the grass.

The lawn is ungraded and uneven like the pastures, and it merges eventually with the fields. Behind, there are great clotted masses of myrtle beds, lilac bushes, pink phlox, and other things I can't identify; pink and white hollyhocks, some of them leaning, fine blue and purple dye of larkspur; a considerable vegetable garden with long rows of ripe gooseberries and currants, a patch of yellow pumpkin flowers, and bushes of raspberries, both white and red—among which are sprinkled like confetti the little flimsy California poppies, pink, orange, white and red. In an old dark red barn where the hayloft is almost collapsing, I find spinning wheels, a carder, candle molds, a patent bootjack, obsolete implements of carpentry, little clusters of baskets for berry-picking, and a gigantic pair of scales, such as is nowadays seen only in the hands of allegorical figures.

The house was built by the Talcotts, after whom the town is

named. They owned the large farm in front of the house, which stretches down to the river and beyond. They also built a grist-mill, but were thought—I learn from the county history—to have "adopted a policy adverse to the building up of the village at the point where natural advantages greatly favored," for they "refused to sell village lots to mechanics, and retained the water power on Sugar River, although parties offered to invest liberally in manufactures." In time, there was only one Talcott left, an old maid. My great-grandfather Baker, who lived across the street and had been left by the death of his first wife with a son and eight daughters, came over and married Miss Talcott. She was kind to the children, and they remembered her with affection. Great-grandfather Baker owned the quarry on the river just a little way from the house.

Most of the daughters, of whom my grandmother was one—"six of them beauties," I am told—got married and went away. There was only one left in the house when I first remember Talcottville, my great-aunt Rosalind, the spinster daughter who was invariably included in the big old-fashioned families and whose rôle was to stay home and take care of her parents. Aunt "Lin" had devoted her life to her father. When I knew her, she was very old. It was impressive and rather frightening to call on her—you did it only by special arrangement, as she had to prepare herself to be seen. She would be beautifully dressed in a lace cap, a lavender dress and a white crocheted shawl, but she had become so bloodless and shrunken as dreadfully to resemble a mummy and reminded you uncomfortably of Miss Haversham in Dickens's "Great Expectations." She had a certain high and formal coquetry and was the only person I ever really knew who talked like the characters in old novels. When she had been able to get about, I am told, she had habitually treated the townspeople with a condescension almost baronial. According to the family legend, the great-grandmother of great-grandmother Baker had been a daughter of one of the Earls of Essex, who had eloped with a gardener to America.

Another of my Baker great-aunts, whom I found one of the most interesting members of the family, had married and lived in the town and known tragic disappointments. Only intellectual interests and a mind capable of philosophic pessimism had maintained her through the wreck of her domestic life. She used to tell me how, as a young married woman, she had taught herself French by the dictionary and grammar, sitting up at night alone by the stove through one of their cold and dark winters. She had read a great deal of French, subscribed to French magazines, without being able to pronounce a word. She had rejected revealed religion and did not believe in immortality; and when she considered that she had been relieved of the last of her family obligations, though her hair was now beginning to turn gray, she came on to New York City and lived there for years alone, occupying herself with the theater, books, visits to her nephews and nieces, and all the spectacle and reading of the great world which she had always loved so much and from which she had spent her life removed.

When she died, only the youngest of the family was left, the only son, my great-uncle Tom. His mother must have been worn out with child-bearing—she died after the birth of this ninth child—and he had not turned out so well as the others. He had been born with no roof to his mouth and had to wear a gold palate, and it was difficult to understand him. He was not precisely simple-minded—he held a small political job under Cleveland and he usually beat you at checkers—but he was childlike and ill-equipped to deal with life in any very effective way. He sold the farm to a German and the quarry to the town. Then he died, and the house was empty, except when my mother and father would come here to open it up for a month or two in the summer.

I have not been back here in years, and I have never before examined the place carefully. It has become for me something like a dream —unreal with the powerful impressions of childhood. Even now that I am here again, I have to shake off the dream. I keep walking from room to room, inside and out, upstairs and down, with uneasy sensations of complacency which are always falling through into depression.

These rooms are admirably proportioned; the white mantelpieces are elegant and chaste, and each is ornamented with a different design of carving. The big living-room seems a little bare because the various members of the family have claimed and taken away so many things; and there are some disagreeable curtains and carpets, for which my great-uncle Tom is to blame. But here are all the things they have in

the antique stores: "How like an antique store!" I keep thinking. Red
Bohemian glass decanters; a rusty silver snuff-box; a mirror with the
American eagle painted at the top of the glass. Little mahogany tables
with slim legs; a set of curly-maple furniture, deep seasoned yellow
like satin; a yellow comb-backed rocker, with a design of green conch-
shells like snails. A small bust of Dante with the nose chipped; a little
old-fashioned organ stored here years ago by the church and never
afterwards reclaimed. Large engravings of the family of Washington
and of the Reformers Presenting their Famous Protest before the Diet
of Spires; a later engraving of Charles Dickens. Old tongs and poker,
impossibly heavy. A brown mahogany desk inlaid with yellow bird-
wood, with a pair of old steel-rimmed spectacles and a thing to shake
sand on wet ink. Daguerreotypes in fancy cases: they seem to last
much better than photographs—my grandmother looks fresh and cun
ning—I remember hearing that when my grandfather first saw her,
she was riding on a load of hay—he came back up here to marry her
as soon as he had gotten his medical degree. An old wooden flute—
originally brought over from New England, I remember my great-
uncle's telling me, in one of the ox-team loads—he used to get a lonely
piping out of it—I try it, but cannot make a sound. Two big oval
paintings in gold frames, of landscapes mountainous and romantic:
they came from the Utica house of great-grandfather Baker's brother
—he married a rich wife and invented excelsior and was presented
with a solid silver table service by the grateful city of Utica.

Wall-paper molded by the damp from the stone; uninviting old
black haircloth furniture. A bowl of those enormous upcountry sweet-
peas, incredibly fragrant and bright—they used to awe and trouble
me—why?

In the dining-room, a mahogany china-closet, which, in the days
when letters were few and great-grandfather Baker was postmaster,
used to be the village post-office. My grandmother's pewter tea-service
with its design of oak-leaves and acorns, which I remember from her
house in New Jersey. Black iron cranes, black pipkins and kettles, for
cooking over the hearth; a kind of flat iron pitchfork for lifting the
bread in and out when they baked at the back of the fireplace. On the
sideboard, a glass decanter with a gilt black-letter label: "J. Rum." If
there were only some rum in the decanter!—if the life of the house

were not all past!—The kitchens that trail out behind are almost too old-smelling and deserted—in spite of the wonderful big brown crocks with blue long-tailed birds painted on them, a different bird on each crock.

In the ample hall with its long staircase, two large colored pictures of trout, one rising to bait, one leaping. Upstairs, a wooden pestle and mortar; a perforated tin box for hot coals that people took to keep their feet warm on sleigh-rides or in church; a stuffed heron; a horrible bust of my cousin Dorothy which her mother had had done of her in Germany, larger than life and with the hair-ribbon and ruffles faithfully reproduced in marble—Cousin Dorothy, who got to detest it, took it out and threw it into the pond, but Uncle Tom worked hard to dredge it up and quietly replaced it on its pedestal. An ugly chair with a round rag back; an ugly bed with the head of Columbus sticking out above the pillows like a figurehead. Charming old bedquilts with patterns of rhomboids in softened brown, greens and pinks, or of blue polka-dotted hearts that ray out on stiff phallic stalks. A footstool innocently covered in white, which, however, when you step on a tab at the side, opens up into a spittoon. (There used to be a musical chair, brought back from Germany along with the bust, but it seems to have disappeared.) A jar of dried rose leaves, and a jar of little pebbles and shells that keep their bright colors in alcohol.

The old panes up here have wavy lines in the glass. There are cobweb-filthy books, which I examine: many religious works, the annals of the state legislature, a book called "The Young Wife, or Duties of Women in the Marriage Relation," published in Boston in 1838 and containing a warning against tea and coffee, which "loosen the tongue, fire the eye, produce mirth and wit, excite the animal passions, and lead to remarks about ourselves and others, that we should not have made in other circumstances, and which it were better for us and the world, never to have made." But there is also, I noticed downstairs, Grant Allan's "The Woman Who Did," from 1893.

I come upon the History of Lewis County and read it with a certain pride. I say to myself that it is an excellent piece of work—admirably full in its information on flora and fauna, geology and politics; diversified with anecdotes and biographies never over-flattering

and often pungent; and written in a sound English style. Could anyone in the county today, I wonder, command such a sound English
style? I note with gratification that the bone of a prehistoric cuttlefish,
discovered in one of the limestone caves of the river, is the largest of
its kind on record, and that a flock of wild swans was seen here in
1821. In the eighties, there were still wolves and panthers. There are
still bears and deer today.

I also look into the proceedings of the New York State Assembly.
My great-grandfather Baker was primarily a politician and at that
time a member of the Assembly. I have heard that he was a Jacksonian
Democrat and that he made a furious scene when my grandmother
came back from New Jersey and announced that she had become a
Republican: it spoiled her whole visit. There is a photograph of him
in an oval gilt frame, with his hair sticking out in three great spikes
and a wide and declamatory mouth. I look into the record of the
Assembly to see what rôle great-grandfather Baker played. It is the
forties; the Democrats are still savage about the United States Bank.
But when I look up great-grandfather Baker in the index, it turns out
that he figured solely, though repeatedly, as either not being present or
as requesting leaves of absence. They tell me he used to go West to
buy cattle.

That sealed-up space on the second floor which my father had
knocked out—who did they tell me was hidden in it?—a soldier? I
see by one of the new historical road-signs that there are caves somewhere here where slaves were hidden. Maybe it was part of the underground route for smuggling Negroes over the border.—Is the attic, the
"kitchen chamber," which is always so suffocating in summer, still
full of carpetbags and crinolines and bonnets and beaver-hats in the
old cowhide-covered trunks? We used to dress up in them for charades.

It was the custom for the married Baker daughters to bring their
children back in the summer; and their children in time brought their
children. In those days, how I loved coming up here! It was a reunion
with cousins fom Boston and New York, Ohio and Wisconsin; we
fished and swam in the rivers, had all sorts of excursions and games.—
Later on, I got to dislike it: the older generation died, the younger
ceased to come back. I wanted to be elsewhere, too. The very fullness
with life of the past, the memory of those many families of cousins
and uncles and aunts, made the emptiness of the present more oppres-

sive.—Isn't it still?—didn't my gloom come from that, the night of
my first arrival?—Wasn't it the dread of it that kept me away?—I am
aware, as I walk through the rooms, of the amplitude and completeness of the place—the home of a large old-fashioned family, which had
to be a city in itself. And not merely did it house a clan: the whole
life of the community passed through it. Situated in the corner of the
crossroads, it has been post-office and town hall—at one time great-
grandfather Baker put up travelers on the Albany post-road. And now
for five-sixths of the year it is nothing but a shell full of antiques, with
no intimate relation to the community.

The community itself today is half the size of the community of
those days, and its condition is very much changed. It is now merely
one of the clusters of houses that people shoot through along the state
highway; and there will presently perhaps be little left but our house
confronting the hot-dog stand and the gas station.

ERSKINE CALDWELL

Why he selected COUNTRY FULL of

SWEDES

I like to write about people. I put them into the traditional form of the short story or novel merely because they happen to be ideal means of expression for me. However, I do not write short stories and novels and people them with characters. I fit people into fiction, not fiction around people. At least, these are the things I try to do; sometimes I succeed to some extent, sometimes fail.

There is nothing unusual about the fact that "Country Full of Swedes," for example, is a story of people in the State of Maine. I have written many stories about people in the South merely because it happened that I spent more time in Georgia than anywhere else. I have written a few stories about people in northern New England because I lived there for a short time. If I had lived in Montana, Wyoming, or Utah, I would have written about people I lived among there.

There is more than one way of skinning a rabbit. I found that out early in life when one rabbit skinner told me to do it in such-and-such a manner, and another one told me to do it differently. I tried both, but either the rabbit's legs slipped off the knob on the barn door, or I could not get the jacket down over the shoulders. After that I did it my own way, and I've been doing it that way ever since.

Darien, Conn.   ERSKINE CALDWELL
June, 1942

THERE I was, standing in the middle of the chamber, trembling like I was coming down with the flu, and still not knowing what god-awful something had happened. In all my days in the Back Kingdom, I never heard such noises so early in the forenoon.

It was about half an hour after sun-rise, and a gun went off like a coffer-dam breaking up under ice at twenty below, and I'd swear it sounded like it wasn't any farther away than my feet are from my head. That gun shot off, pitching me six-seven inches off the bed, and, before I could come down out of the air, there was another roar like somebody coughing through a megaphone, with a two weeks' cold, right in my ear. God-helping, I hope I never get waked up like that again until I can get myself home to the Back Kingdom where I rightfully belong to stay.

I must have stood there ten-fifteen minutes shivering in my night-shirt, my heart pounding inside of me like a ram-rod working on a plugged-up bore, and listening for that gun again, if it was going to shoot some more. A man never knows what's going to happen next in the State of Maine; that's why I wish sometimes I'd never left the Back Kingdom to begin with. I was making sixty a month, with the best of bed and board, back there in the intervale; but like a God damn fool I had to jerk loose and come down here near the Bay. I'm going back where I came from, God-helping; I've never had a purely calm and peaceful day since I got here three-four years ago. This is the damnedest country for the unexpected raising of all kinds of unlooked-for hell a man is apt to run across in a lifetime of traveling. If a man's born and raised in the Back Kingdom, he ought to stay there where he belongs; that's what I'd done if I'd had the sense to stay out of this down-country near the Bay, where you don't ever know, God-helping, what's going to happen next, where, or when.

But there I was, standing in the middle of the upstairs chamber, shaking like a rag weed in an August wind-storm, and not knowing what minute, maybe right at me, that gun was going to shoot off again, for all I knew. Just then, though, I heard Jim and Mrs. Frost trip-trapping around downstairs in their bare feet. Even if I didn't know what god-awful something had happened, I knew things around the place weren't calm and peaceful, like they generally were of a Sunday morning in May, because it took a stiff mixture of heaven and hell to get Jim and Mrs. Frost up and out of a warm bed before six of a forenoon, any of the days of the week.

I ran to the window and stuck my head out as far as I could get it, to hear what the trouble was. Everything out there was as quiet and peaceful as midnight on a backroad in middlemost winter. But I knew something was up, because Jim and Mrs. Frost didn't make a practice of getting up and out of a warm bed that time of forenoon in the chillish May-time.

There wasn't any sense in me standing there in the cold air shivering in my night-shirt, so I put on my clothes, whistling all the time through my teeth to drive away the chill, and trying to figure out what God damn fool was around so early shooting off a gun of a Sunday morning. Just then I heard the downstairs door open, and up the steps, two at a time, came Jim in his breeches and his shirt-tail flying out behind him.

He wasn't long in coming up the stairs, for a man sixty-seven, but before he reached the door to my room, that gun went off again: boom! Just like that; and the echo came rolling back through the open window from the hills: *Boom! Boom!* Like fireworks going off with your eyes shut. Jim had busted through the door already, but when he heard that *Boom!* sound he sort of spun around, like a cock-eyed weathervane, five-six times, and ran out the door again like he had been shot in the hind parts with a moose gun. That *Boom!* so early in the forenoon was enough to scare the day-lights out of any man, and Jim wasn't any different from me or anybody else in the town of East Joloppi. He just turned around and jumped through the door to the first tread on the stairway like his mind was made up to go somewhere else in a hurry, and no fooling around at the start.

I'd been hired to Jim and Mrs. Frost for all of three-four years, and I was near about as much of a Frost, excepting name, as Jim himself was. Jim and me got along first-rate together, doing chores and haying and farm work in general, because neither one of us was ever trying to make the other do more of the work. We were hitched to make a fine team, and I never had a kick coming, and Jim said he didn't either. Jim had the name of Frost, to be sure, but I wouldn't ever hold that against a man.

The echo of that gun-shot was still rolling around in the hills and coming in through the window, when all at once that god-awful cough-like whoop through a megaphone sounded again right there in the room and everywhere else, like it might have been, in the whole town of East Joloppi. The man or beast or whatever animal he was who

hollered like that ought to be locked up to keep him from scaring all
the women and children to death, and it wasn't any stomach-comfort-
ing sound for a grown man who's used to the peaceful calm of the
Back Kingdom all his life to hear so early of a Sunday forenoon, either.

I jumped to the door where Jim, just a minute before, leaped
through. He didn't stop till he got clear to the bottom of the stairs.
He stood there, looking up at me like a wild-eyed cow moose surprised
in the Sheriff's corn field.

"Who fired that god-awful shot, Jim?" I yelled at him, leaping down
the stairs quicker than a man of my years ought to let himself do.

"Good God!" Jim said, his voice hoarse, and falling all to pieces like
a stump of punk-wood. "The Swedes! The Swedes are shooting, Stan!"

"What Swedes, Jim—those Swedes who own the farm and buildings
across the road over there?" I said, trying to find the buttonholes in my
shirt. "Have they come back here to live on that farm?"

"Good God, yes!" he said, his voice croaking deep down in his
throat, like he had swallowed too much water. "The Swedes are all over
the place. They're everywhere you can see, there's that many of them."

"What's their name, Jim?" I asked him. "You and Mrs. Frost never
told me what their name is."

"Good God, I don't know. I never heard them called anything but
Swedes, and that's what it is, I guess. It ought to be that, if it ain't."

I ran across the hall to look out a window, but it was on the wrong
side of the house, and I couldn't see a thing. Mrs. Frost was stepping
around in the downstairs chamber, locking things up in the drawers
and closet and forgetting where she was hiding the keys. I could see
her through the open door, and she was more scared-looking than Jim
was. She was so scared of the Swedes she didn't know what she was
doing, none of the time.

"What made those Swedes come back for, Jim?" I said to him. "I
thought you said they were gone for good, this time."

"Good God, Stan," he said, "I don't know what they came back for.
I guess hard times are bringing everybody back to the land, and the
Swedes are always in the front rush of everything. I don't know what
brought them back, but they're all over the place, shooting and yelling
and raising hell. There are thirty-forty of them, looks like to me,
counting everything with heads."

COUNTRY FULL OF SWEDES

"What are they doing now, Jim, except yelling and shooting?"

"Good God," Jim said, looking behind him to see what Mrs. Frost was doing with his things in the downstairs chamber. "I don't know what they're not doing. But I can hear them, Stan! You hurry out right now and lock up all the tools in the barn and bring in the cows and tie them up in the stalls. I've got to hurry out now and bring in all of those new cedar fence posts across the front of the yard before they start pulling them up and carrying them off. Good God, Stan, the Swedes are everywhere you look out-doors! We've got to make haste, Stan!"

Jim ran to the side door and out the back of the house, but I took my time about going. I wasn't scared of the Swedes, like Jim and Mrs. Frost were, and I didn't aim to have Jim putting me to doing tasks and chores, or anything else, before breakfast and the proper time. I wasn't any more scared of the Swedes than I was of the Finns and Portuguese, anyway. It's a god-awful shame for Americans to let Swedes and Finns and the Portuguese scare the day-lights out of them. God-helping, they are no different than us, and you never see a Finn or a Swede scared of an American. But people like Jim and Mrs. Frost are scared to death of Swedes and other people from the old countries; Jim and Mrs. Frost and people like that never stop to think that all of us Americans came over from the old countries, one time or another, to begin with.

But there wasn't any sense in trying to argue with Jim and Mrs. Frost right then, when the Swedes, like a fired nest of yellow-headed bumble bees, were swarming all over the place as far as the eye could see, and when Mrs. Frost was scared to death that they were coming into the house and carry out all of her and Jim's furniture and house-hold goods. So while Mrs. Frost was tying her and Jim's shoes in pillow cases and putting them out of sight in closets and behind beds, I went to the kitchen window and looked out to see what was going on around that tall yellow house across the road.

Jim and Mrs. Frost both were right about there being Swedes all over the place. God-helping, there were Swedes all over the country, near about all over the whole town of East Joloppi, for what I could see out the window. They were as thick around the barn and pump and the woodpile as if they had been a nest of yellow-headed bumble bees strewn over the countryside. There were Swedes everywhere a man could see, and the ones that couldn't be seen, could be heard yelling their heads off inside the yellow clapboarded house across the road. There wasn't any mistake about their being Swedes there, either; because I've never seen a man who mistakes a Swede or a Finn for an American. Once you see a Finn or a Swede you know, God-helping, that he is a Swede or a Finn, and not a Portugee or an American.

There was a Swede everywhere a man could look. Some of them were little Swedes, and women Swedes, to be sure; but little Swedes, in the end, and women Swedes too, near about, grow up as big as any of them. When you come right down to it, there's no sense in counting out the little Swedes and the women Swedes.

Out in the road in front of their house were seven-eight autos and trucks loaded down with furniture and household goods. All around, everything was Swedes. The Swedes were yelling and shouting at one another, the little Swedes and the women Swedes just as loud as the big Swedes, and it looked like none of them knew what all the shouting and yelling was for, and when they found out, they didn't give a damn about it. That was because all of them were Swedes. It didn't make any difference what a Swede was yelling about; just as long as he had leave to open his mouth, he was tickled to death about it.

I have never seen the like of so much yelling and shouting anywhere else before; but down here in the State of Maine, in the down-country on the Bay, there's no sense in being taken-back at the sights to be seen, because anything on God's green earth is likely and liable to happen between day and night, and the other way around, too.

Now you take the Finns; there's any God's number of them around in the woods, where you least expect to see them, logging and such. When a Finn crew breaks a woods camp, it looks like there's a Finn for every tree in the whole State, but you don't see them going around making the noise that Swedes do, with all their yelling and shouting and shooting off guns. Finns are quiet about their hell-raising. The Portuguese are quiet, too; you see them tramping around, minding their own business, and working hard on a river dam or something, but you never hear them shouting and yelling and shooting off guns at five-six of a Sunday morning. There's no known likeness to the noise that a houseful of Swedes can make when they get to yelling and shouting at one another early in the forenoon.

I was standing there all that time, looking out the window at the Swedes across the road, when Jim came into the kitchen with an armful of wood and threw it into the woodbox behind the range.

"Good God, Stan," Jim said, "the Swedes are everywhere you can look out-doors. They're not going to get that armful of wood, anyway, though."

Mrs. Frost came to the door and stood looking like she didn't know it was her business to cook breakfast for Jim and me. I made a fire in the range and put on a pan of water to boil for the coffee. Jim kept running to the window to look out, and there wasn't much use in expecting Mrs. Frost to start cooking unless somebody set her to it, in the shape she was in, with all the Swedes around the place. She was so up-set, it was a downright pity to look at her. But Jim and me had to eat, and I went and took her by the arm and brought her to the range and left her standing there so close she would get burned if she didn't stir around and make breakfast.

"Good God, Stan," Jim said, "those Swedes are into everything. They're in the barn, and in the pasture running the cows, and I don't know what else they've been into since I looked last. They'll take the tools and the horses and cows, and the cedar posts, too, if we don't get out there and put everything under lock and key."

"Now, hold on, Jim," I said, looking out the window. "Them you see are little Swedes out there, and they're not going to make off with anything of yours and Mrs. Frost's. The big Swedes are busy carrying in furniture and household goods. Those Swedes aren't going to tamper with anything of yours and Mrs. Frost's. They're people just like us. They don't go around stealing everything in sight. Now, let's just sit here by the window and watch them while Mrs. Frost is getting breakfast ready."

"Good God, Stan, they're Swedes," Jim said, "and they're moving into the house across the road. I've got to put everything under lock and key before——"

"Hold on, Jim," I told him. "It's their house they're moving into. God-helping, they're not moving into your and Jim's house, are they, Mrs. Frost?"

"Jim," Mrs. Frost said, shaking her finger at him and looking at me wild-eyed and sort of flustered-like, "Jim, don't you sit there and let Stanley stop you from saving the stock and tools. Stanley doesn't know the Swedes like we do. Stanley came down here from the Back Kingdom, and he doesn't know anything about Swedes."

Mrs. Frost was partly right, because I've never seen the things in my whole life that I've seen down here near the Bay; but there wasn't any sense in Americans like Jim and Mrs. Frost being scared of Swedes. I've seen enough Finns and Portuguese in my time in the Back Kingdom, up in the intervale, to know that Americans are no different from the others.

"Now, you hold on a while, Jim," I said. "Swedes are no different than Finns. Finns don't go around stealing another man's stock and tools. Up in the Back Kingdom the Finns are the finest kind of neighbors."

"That may be so up in the Back Kingdom, Stan," Jim said, "but Swedes down here near the Bay are nothing like anything that's ever been before or since. Those Swedes over there across the road work in a pulp mill over to Waterville three-four years, and when they've got enough money saved up, or when they lose it all, as the case may be, they all move back here to East Joloppi on this farm of theirs for two-three years at a time. That's what they do. And they've been doing it for the past thirty-forty years, ever since I can remember, and they haven't changed none in all that time. I can recall the first time they came to East Joloppi; they built that house across the road then, and if you've ever seen a sight like Swedes building a house in a hurry, you haven't got much else to live for. Why! Stan, those Swedes built that house in four-five days—just like that! I've never seen the equal to it. Of course now, Stan, it's the damnedest-looking house a man ever saw, because it's not a farm house, and it's not a city house, and it's no kind of a house an American would erect. Why! those Swedes threw that house together in four-five days—just like that! But whoever saw a house like that before, with three storeys to it, and only six rooms in the whole building! And painted yellow, too; Good God, Stan, white is the only color to paint a house, and those Swedes went and painted it yellow. Then on top of that, they went and painted the barn red. And of all of the shouting and yelling, at all times of the day and night, a man never saw or heard before. Those Swedes acted like they were purely crazy for the whole of four-five days, and they were, and they still are. But what gets me is the painting of it yellow, and the making of it three storeys high, with only six rooms in the whole building. Nobody but Swedes would go and do a thing like that; an American would have built a farm house, here in the country, resting square on the ground, with one storey, maybe a storey and a half, and then painted it lead-white. But Good God, Stan, those fool Swedes had to put up three storeys, to hold six rooms, and then went and painted the building yellow."

"Swedes are a little queer, sometimes," I said. "But Finns and Portuguese are too, Jim. And Americans sometimes ——"

"A little queer!" Jim said. "Why! Good God, Stan, the Swedes are the queerest people on the earth, if that's the right word for them. You don't know Swedes, Stan. This is the first time you've ever seen those Swedes across the road, and that's why you don't know what they're like after being shut up in a pulpwood mill over to Waterville for four-five years. They're purely wild, I tell you, Stan. They don't stop for anything they set their heads on. If you was to walk out there now and tell them to move their autos and trucks off of the town road so the travelers could get past without having to drive around through the brush, they'd tear you apart, they're that wild, after being shut up in the pulp mill over to Waterville these three-four, maybe four-five, years."

"Finns get that way, too," I tried to tell Jim. "After Finns have been shut up in a woods camp all winter, they make a lot of noise when they get out. Everybody who has to stay close to the job for three-four years likes to act free when he gets out from under the job. Now, Jim, you take the Portuguese ——"

"Don't you sit there, Jim, and let Stanley keep you from putting the tools away," Mrs. Frost said. "Stanley doesn't know the Swedes like we do. He's lived up in the Back Kingdom most of his life, tucked away in the intervale, and he's never seen Swedes ——"

"Good God, Stan," Jim said, standing up, he was that nervous and up-set, "the Swedes are over-running the whole country. I'll bet there are more Swedes in the town of East Joloppi than there are in the rest of the country. Everybody knows there's more Swedes in the State of

Maine than there are in the old country. Why! Jim, they take to this
State like potato bugs take to——"

"Don't you sit there and let Stanley keep you back, Jim," Mrs.
Frost put in again. "Stanley doesn't know the Swedes like we do.
Stanley's lived up there in the Back Kingdom most of his life."

Just then one of the big Swedes started yelling at some of the little
Swedes and women Swedes. I'll swear, those big Swedes sounded like
a pastureful of hoarse bulls, near the end of May, mad about the black-
flies. God-helping, they yelled like they were fixing to kill all the little
Swedes and women Swedes they could get their hands on. It didn't
amount to anything, though; because the little Swedes and the women
Swedes yelled right back at them just like they had been big Swedes
too. The little Swedes and women Swedes couldn't yell hoarse bull
bass, but it was close enough to it to make a man who's lived most of
his life up in the Back Kingdom, in the intervale, think that the whole
town of East Joloppi was full of big Swedes.

Jim was all for getting out after the tools and stock right away, but
I pulled him back to the table. I wasn't going to let Jim and Mrs.
Frost set me to doing tasks and chores before breakfast and the regular
time. Forty dollars a month isn't much to pay a man for ten-eleven
hours' work a day, including Sundays, when the stock has to be attended to like any other day, and I set myself that I wasn't going to
work twelve-thirteen hours a day for them, even if I was practically
one of the Frosts myself, except in name, by that time.

"Now, hold on a while, Jim," I said. "Let's just sit here by the
window and watch them carry their furniture and household goods
inside while Mrs. Frost's getting the cooking ready to eat. If they start
taking off any of you and Mrs. Frost's things, we can see them just as
good from here by the window as we could out there in the yard and
road."

"Now, Jim, I'm telling you," Mrs. Frost said, shaking all over, and
not even trying to cook us a meal, "don't you sit there and let Stanley
keep you from saving the stock and tools. Stanley doesn't know the
Swedes like we do. He thinks they're like everybody else."

Jim wasn't for staying in the house when all of his tools were lying
around in the yard, and while his cows were in the pasture unprotected, but he saw how it would be better to wait where we could hurry

up Mrs. Frost with the cooking, if we were ever going to eat breakfast that forenoon. She was so excited and nervous about the Swedes moving back to East Joloppi from the pulp mill in Waterville that she hadn't got the beans and brown bread fully heated from the night before and we had to sit and eat them cold.

We were sitting there by the window eating the cold beans and brown bread, and watching the Swedes, when two of the little Swedes started running across Jim and Mrs. Frost's lawn. They were chasing one of their big yellow tom cats they had brought with them from Waterville. The yellow tom was as large as an eight-months collie puppy, and he ran like he was on fire and didn't know how to put it out. His great big bushy tail stuck straight up in the air behind him, like a flag, and he was leaping over the lawn like a devilish calf, newborn.

Jim and Mrs. Frost saw the little Swedes and the big yellow tom cat at the same time I did.

"Good God," Jim shouted, raising himself part out of the chair. "Here they come now!"

"Hold on now, Jim," I said, pulling him back to the table. "They're only chasing one of their tom cats. They're not after taking anything that belongs to you and Mrs. Frost. Let's just sit here and finish eating the beans, and watch them out the window."

"My crown in heaven!" Mrs. Frost cried out, running to the window and looking through. "Those Swedes are going to kill every plant on the place. They'll dig up all the bulbs and pull up all the vines in the flower bed."

"Now you just sit and calm yourself, Mrs. Frost," I told her. "Those little Swedes are just chasing a tom cat. They're not after doing hurt to your flowers."

The big Swedes were unloading the autos and trucks and carrying the furniture and household goods into their three storey, yellow clapboarded house. None of them was paying any attention to the little Swedes chasing the yellow tom over Jim and Mrs. Frost's lawn.

Just then the kitchen door burst open, and the two little Swedes stood there looking at us, panting and blowing their heads off.

Mrs. Frost took one look at them, and then she let out a yell, but the kids didn't notice her at all.

"Hey," one of them shouted, "come out here and help us get the cat. He climbed up in one of your trees."

By that time, Mrs. Frost was all for slamming the door in their faces, but I pushed in front of her and went out into the yard with them. Jim came right behind me, after he had finished calming Mrs. Frost, and telling her we wouldn't let the Swedes come and carry out her furniture and household goods.

The yellow tom was all the way up in one of Jim's young maple shade trees. The maple wasn't strong enough to support even the smallest of the little Swedes, if he should take it into his head to climb to the top after the cat, and neither Jim nor me was hurting ourselves trying to think of a way to get the feline down. We were all for letting the cat stay where he was, till he got ready to come down of his own free will, but the little Swedes couldn't wait for anything. They wanted the tom right away, then and there, and no wasting of time in getting him.

"You boys go home and wait for the cat to come down," Jim told them. "There's no way to make him come down now, till he gets ready to come down of his own mind."

But no, those two boys were little Swedes. They weren't thinking of going back home till they got the yellow tom down from the maple. One of them ran to the tree, before Jim or me could head him off, and started shinnying up it like a pop-eyed squirrel. In no time, it seemed to me like, he was up amongst the limbs, jumping around up there from one limb to another like he had been brought up in just such a tree.

"Good God, Stan," Jim said, "can't you keep them out of the trees?"

There was no answer for that, and Jim knew there wasn't. There's no way of stopping a Swede from doing what he has set his head on doing.

The boy got almost to the top branch, where the yellow tom was clinging and spitting, when the tree began to bend towards the house. I knew what was coming, if something wasn't done about it pretty quick, and so did Jim. Jim saw his young maple shade tree begin to bend, and he almost had a fit looking at it. He ran to the lumber stack and came back dragging two lengths of two-by-fours. He got them set up against the tree before it had time to do any splitting, and then we

stood there, like two damn fools, shoring up the tree and yelling at the
little Swede to come down out of there before we broke his neck for
being up in it.

The big Swedes across the road heard the fuss we were making, and
they came running out of that three-storey, six-room house like it had
been on fire inside.

"Good God, Stan," Jim shouted at me, "here comes the Swedes!"

"Don't turn and run off, Jim," I cautioned him, yanking him back
by his coat-tail. "They're not wild beasts; we're not scared of them.
Hold on where you are, Jim."

I could see Mrs. Frost's head almost breaking through the window-
glass in the kitchen. She was all for coming out and driving the Swedes
off her lawn and out of her flowers, but she was too scared to unlock
the kitchen door and open it.

Jim was getting ready to run again, when ne saw the Swedes
coming toward us like a nest of yellow-headed bumble bees, but I
wasn't scared of them, and I held on to Jim's coat-tail and told him I
wasn't. Jim and me were shoring up the young maple, and I knew if
one of us let go, the tree would bend to the ground right away and
split wide open right up the middle. There was no sense in ruining a
young maple shade tree like that, and I told Jim there wasn't.

"Hey," one of the big Swedes shouted at the little Swede up in the
top of the maple, "come down out of that tree and go home to your
mother."

"Aw, to hell with the old lady," the little Swede shouted down.
"I'm getting the cat by the tail."

The big Swede looked at Jim and me. Jim was almost ready to run
again by that time, but I wasn't, and I held him and told him I wasn't.
There was no sense in letting the Swedes scare the day-lights out of us.

"What in hell can you do with kids when they get that age?" he
asked Jim and me.

Jim was all for telling him to make the boy come down out of the
maple before it bent over and split wide open, but I knew there was no
sense in trying to make him come down out of there until he got good
and ready to come, or else got the yellow tom by the tail.

Just then another big Swede came running out of that three-storey,
six-room house across the road, holding a double-bladed ax out in

front of him, like it was a red-hot poker, and yelling for all he was worth at the other Swedes.

"Good God, Stan," Jim said, "don't let those Swedes cut down my young maple!"

I had lots better sense than to try to make the Swedes stop doing what they had set their heads on doing. A man would be purely a fool to try to stop it from raining from above when it got ready to, even if he was trying to get his corn crop planted.

I looked around again, and there was Mrs. Frost all but popping through the window-glass. I could see what she was thinking, but I couldn't hear a word she was saying. It was good and plenty though, whatever it was.

"Come down out of that tree!" the Swede yelled at the boy up in Jim's maple.

Instead of starting to climb down, the little Swede reached up for the big yellow tom cat's tail. The tom reached out a big fat paw and harried the boy five-six times, just like that, quicker than the eye could follow. The kid let out a yell and a shout that must have been heard all the way to the other side of town, sounding like a whole houseful of Swedes up in the maple.

The big Swede covered the distance to the tree in one stride, pushing everything behind him.

"Good God, Stan," Jim shouted at me, "we've got to do something!"

There wasn't anything a man could do, unless he was either a Swede himself, or a man of prayer. Americans like Jim and me had no business getting in a Swede's way, especially when he was swinging a big double-bladed ax, and he just out of a pulp mill after being shut up making paper four-five years.

The big Swede grabbed the ax and let go at the trunk of the maple with it. There was no stopping him then, because he had the ax going, and it was whipping around his shoulders like a cow's tail in a swarm of black-flies. The little maple shook all over every time the ax-blade struck it, like wind blowing a corn stalk, and then it began to bend on the other side from Jim and me where we were shoring it up with the two-by-fours. Chips as big as dinner plates were flying across the lawn and pelting the house like a gang of boys stoning telephone insulators. One of those big dinner-plate chips crashed through the window where Mrs. Frost was, about that time. Both Jim and me thought at first she had fallen through the window, but when we looked again, we could see that she was still on the inside, and madder than ever at the Swedes.

The two-by-fours weren't any good any longer, because it was too late to get to the other side of the maple in time to keep it from bending in that direction. The Swede with the double-bladed ax took one more swing, and the tree began to bend toward the ground.

The tree came down, the little Swede came down, and the big yellow tom came down on top of everything, holding for all he was worth to the top of the little Swede's head. Long before the tree and the boy struck the ground, the big yellow tom had sprung what looked like thirty feet, and landed in the middle of Mrs. Frost's flowers and bulbs. The little Swede let out a yell and a whoop when he hit the ground that brought out six-seven more Swedes from that three-storey, six-room house, piling out into the road like it was the first time they had ever heard a kid bawl. The women Swedes and the little Swedes and the big Swedes piled out on Jim and Mrs. Frost's front lawn like they had been dropped out of a dump-truck and didn't know which was straight up from straight down.

I thought Mrs. Frost was going to have a fit right then and there in the kitchen window. When she saw that swarm of Swedes coming across her lawn, and the big yellow tom cat in her flower bed among the tender plants and bulbs, digging up the things she had planted, and the Swedes with their No. 12 heels squashing the green shoots she had been nursing along—well, I guess she just sort of caved in, and fell out of sight for the time being. I didn't have time to run to see what was wrong with her, because Jim and me had to tear out behind the tom and the Swedes to try to save as much as we could.

"Good God, Stan," Jim shouted at me, "go run in the house and ring up all the neighbors on the line, and tell them to hurry over here and help us before the Swedes wreck my farm and buildings. There's no telling what they'll do next. They'll be setting fire to the house and barn the next thing, maybe. Hurry, Stan!"

I didn't have time to waste talking to the neighbors on the telephone line. I was right behind Jim and the Swedes to see what they were going to do next.

"I pay you good pay, Stan," Jim said, "and I want my money's worth. Now, you go ring up the neighbors and tell them to hurry."

The big yellow tom made one more spring when he hit the flower bed, and that leap landed him over the stonewall. He struck out for the deep woods with every Swede on the place behind him. When Jim and me got to the stonewall, I pulled up short and held Jim back.

"Well, Jim," I said, "if you want me to, I'll go down in the woods and raise hell with every Swede on the place for cutting down your young maple and tearing up Mrs. Frost's flower-bed."

We turned around and there was Mrs. Frost, right behind us. There was no knowing how she got there so quick after the Swedes had left for the woods.

"My crown in heaven," Mrs. Frost said, running up to Jim and holding on to him. "Jim, don't let Stanley make the Swedes mad. This is the only place we have got to live in, and they'll be here a year now this time, maybe two-three, if the hard times don't get better soon."

"That's right, Stan," he said. "You don't know the Swedes like we do. You would have to be a Swede yourself to know what to tell them. Don't go over there doing anything like that."

"God-helping, Jim," I said, "you and Mrs. Frost aren't scared of the Swedes, are you?"

"Good God, no," he said, his eyes popping out; "but don't go making them mad."

HENRY SEIDEL CANBY Why he

selected HOME in the NINETIES

When, in 1934, I wrote *The Age of Confidence* from which this chapter "Home in the Nineties" is reprinted, I stated in the introduction and the conclusion of the book what it was I had tried to do.

I prefer in short to contribute to history (for the most modest memoir is a contribution to history) rather than to write it. History, as I shall repeat later in this volume, deals with the present in terms of the future. The tendencies of a period, for a historian, may be more significant than the period, but that is not how those who lived then felt. For them, the present was naturally more important than posterity, and the present of one era (the late eighties, the nineties, the earliest nineteen hundreds) I have tried to recapture as a rather ill-educated, but sensitive, person saw and felt it. No era lives on its tendencies, though it has to live with them. It lives for itself, and can only be so rightly understood, and its own values estimated before the historian approves or discards them.

Memory—and I have trusted to memory entirely—is bound to be narrow, to be unduly selective, to be prejudiced by the accidents of experience, to be intensely personal, to be occasionally inaccurate. But documents also are equally certain to lend themselves to wrong interpretation, to get detached from the emotions or the ideas that made them significant, to be colored by the prejudices of the historian, and to become more fact than truth. And memory and documents make a bad mixture, in which both are falsified. I have therefore chosen to write of what I knew and saw,—a scene unimportant if it had not been a significant part of America; unaware, generally speaking, of me, who was only a youth in what was still the youth of America; a small city in the East, much loved, possessing perhaps more of the faults and more of the virtues of its era than others; an authentic part of the soil from which our troublous civilization of the nineteen thirties sprang.

But in writing this book I have been neither a *laudator tempores acti* nor a disillusioned critic of my native town—but, so far as possible, both. I believe that there were values in that period called the nineties, and scandalously misdescribed in current films and novels, which were as worthy (greatness aside) as any cultural period has ever developed, and which are now lost, perhaps irrevocably. I have tried to describe them, because nothing is really irrevocable except one's own youth. But I believe also that no one living in the distressed thirties and writing of this past Age of Confidence, can fail to see in looking back the seeds of dissolution, the shams, the animated corpses of belief, the diseases of culture, which were also coexistent with this pausing time in our American history, when there was such real content, and such a complacent yet enviable and sometimes splendid trust in the future; when, if I may quote from myself in a subsequent chapter, for the last time in living memory everyone knew exactly what it meant to be an American.

I had thought at one time of calling this book "Nostalgia," but realized before I had written a chapter that this title would be utterly false. If the opportunity were given to me to choose between youth then and youth in the era of my own sons I think I would probably choose the present. Choose it with an almost agonized memory of the struggles in the early nineteen hundreds to break away from that strong pattern of confident convention, to get through that friendly atmosphere into something that was a more vital reality, to escape from the dominance of a narrow code of morals and an inflexible impulsion toward a drab business life. This book is neither praise nor dispraise, unmixed and undefined, of the past. It is a study in values, and my own summary is a simple one. Our confidence was illusion, but like most illusions it had many of the benefits of a fact. Because of our confidence there were values in living in the nineties which are simply unpurchasable now. They are, in a true sense of the word, historical, and I have tried to describe them here because soon they will be discoverable only by research and then without the emotional margin which gave proportion and emphasis to the text. As experience, they are, I am sure, irrevocable, or at least not likely to occur again in our cycle; and youth of our day, whatever else it may enjoy and profit by, will not have them, and will live differently because of the loss. For I believe that while the age of mobility may be better or worse than the age of confidence, there have been these definite, describable losses to check against our gains. We can put our children on wheels to see the world, but we cannot give them the kind of home that any town provided in the nineties,—not at any price.

In 1942, with the United States in the midst of social and economic changes so rapid as to be dizzying, this study of values in a remembered American past seems to me more worthy of reprinting than other, and perhaps more pretentious, writings of my own. The edge of criticism rusts and blunts with time, but autobiography freely handled as a contribution to remembered history has at least this merit, that it is evidential and a part of the record of that American

tradition which is now our best guarantee that America will stay
what we call American.
New York, N. Y.   HENRY SEIDEL CANBY
April 14, 1942.

"GOD bless our home," which I can just remember in worsted
tapestry, framed in jig-saw walnut, and hung on a spare-room
wall, never meant "God make our home a happy one." The blessing
was asked upon virtues which were often more conducive to moral
conduct and material success than happiness. And indeed it was not a
superior quality of happiness that distinguished the pre-Ford, pre-
radio, pre-boarding school home from our perches between migrations.
Those who read their social history in fiction will remember how many
nineteenth century novels deal with unhappy homes—tyrannical or
stuffy homes, homes that were prisons or asylums for the suppressed
and inhibited. Toward the end of the century parents, like Jehovah as
the churches preached him, began to soften. Homes were happier then,
I believe, than in the previous generation, for the gradual democratizing
of life had worked itself indoors and was subtly changing the atmosphere of both sitting room and kitchen. There was more give and take
between parents and children, more liberty, and more cheerfulness.

It was confidence, however, not happiness, that made the great difference between then and now, a confidence that reached down below
comfort or pleasure into stability itself. My cousins, who tiptoed
around the chair of an old-fashioned, self-willed father, never knew
from day to day what his authority might require of them. Their manners and their careers were both whipped into them. Yet they had this
same confidence, and would be sure as I, with a memory of a happy
and easy-going home, that something solid and valuable has been lost
by our children.

In our town, and I think in the American nineties generally, home
was the most impressive experience in life. Our most sensitive and our
most relaxed hours were spent in it. We left home or its immediate
environment chiefly to work, and neither radio nor phonograph
brought the outer world into its precincts. Time moved more slowly

there, as it always does when there is a familiar routine with a deep background of memory. Evening seemed spacious then, with hour upon hour in which innumerable intimate details of picture, carpet, wall paper, or well-known pointing shadow were printed upon consciousness. When bicycles came in and flocks of young people wheeled through twilight streets past and past again the porches where the elders were sitting, it was the first breakaway from home, a warning of the new age, but then more like a flight of May flies round and round their hatching place.

The home came first in our consciousness and thus in our culture, clubs, civic life, business, schools, society being secondary, and success there, except in money making, a work of supererogatory virtue. The woman who could not make a home, like the man who could not support one, was condemned, and not tacitly. Not size, nor luxury, nor cheerfulness, nor hospitality made a home. The ideal was subtler. It must be a house where the family wished to live even when they disliked each other, it must take on a kind of corporate life and become a suitable environment for its diverse inhabitants. Hence a common tragedy in our town, often noted, though seldom traced to its causes, was the slow crushing of a family by its home. The sprawling house, such as they built in the early eighties, grew and grew until parents, aunts, grandparents, children all had their districts and retiring places in its wings and stories. Though the family might quarrel and nag the home held them all, protecting them against the outside world and each other. Deaths came, children migrated, taxes went up, repairs became numerous, yet still the shrinking remnant of the family held on from use and wont, or deep affection, until in a final scene of depleted capital or broken health, the hollow shell of the home collapsed on a ruined estate and fiercely quarreling heirs.

So often tragedy at the end, the home of the nineties was quite as often idyllic, if not ideal, in its best years. It had a quality which we have lost. We complain today of the routine of mechanical processes, yet routine in itself is very persuasive to the spirit, and has attributes of both a tonic and a drug. There was a rhythm in the pre-automobile home that is entirely broken now, and whose loss is perhaps the exactest index of the decline of confidence in our environment. Life seems to be sustained by rhythm, upset by its changes, weakened by its loss.

An apartment house with a car at the door, though comfort sum-
marized, has no rhythm, except for a broken, excited syncopation, or
the spondaic movement of boredom.

Our houses moved with felt rhythms, not set, nor identical, yet so
sensible that what one felt first in a strange home was the tempo of
life there. We were away for brief intervals only, at home long enough
to be harmonized, and even the heads of families, whose working
hours were incredible in their length, seemed never to lose their conditioning by the home. If business and the home lived by different ethical standards, as was commonly said, it may be because the worker was
a different man outside the rhythm of the house. And women lived
almost exclusively within.

It was this familiar movement, this routine with a certainty of repetition, that inspired a confidence in a patterned universe missing today.
(Our love of nature helped too—more of this in a later chapter.) The
European peasant got it from the cycles of the soil, and this also made
him a different creature from the artifacts of industrialism. There was
a slur upon boarders in our town and upon the strays who lived in
hotel suites or the transients who moved from rent to rent. They were
not quite like us, even though sometimes more cheerful; they had no
home. We could have said, with equal truth, that they lacked something of confidence in tomorrow and in circumstance, which, in spite
of the common incidence of misfortune or disaster, we held with a
tenacity not easily explained by religion or philosophy.

Most of us in the late eighties and the nineties still lived in squarish
houses of red or painted brick, heavily corniced with wood at the top,
or mansarded, with porches at front and back, and painted iron fences
between the lawns and the brick sidewalks with their rows of button-
woods or Norway maples. There were a few old houses of lovelier
lines, and many bizarrities of Italian, Greek, Queen Anne, and Egyptian inspiration, or of bastard Gothic pointed with gray slate. All,
except the very oldest, had spacious, high-ceilinged rooms, hung with
chandeliers recently converted to electricity, and trimmed with dark,
polished walnut which also spiralled down giant stairways, and were
upholstered wherever possible. Golden oak in the very latest houses
relieved the gloom by substituting the frivolous for the dignified.

It is possible to describe what that generation would have called, say about 1890, an ideal home. The hall was broad and deep, a waiting place hung with steel prints and furnished with benches, stiff chairs, and a hat rack. It was Main Street, meant for traffic. On the right the parlor, on the left the sitting room. The parlor was for decorum. It was the largest room in the house, and the least used, with the most massive tables, the biggest pictures, and the showiest chairs. Mirrors at each end gave it an illusion of still greater spaciousness, and between them the piano which, when used for practising, admitted the only disorder allowed in that room. On the center table were the more pretentious gift books, for show, not reading. Indeed there is a whole literature of gift books, all illustrated and bound in stamped leather, the only reason for whose existence was the parlor table. They came in and went out with it and many a childish knuckle has been rapped for opening them with smutty fingers. It was a sign of change in the times when in thousands of homes parlors were made over into "living rooms." The date, which was the late nineties, is more significant than many better remembered.

Across the hall was the sitting room, smaller, cosier, with easier chairs, bookcases, a tall brass lamp, a gas stove in the corner (fireplaces had not yet come back except as tiled ornaments for the hall where of course no one ever used them), and an air of comfort and usability. Here the family sat and friends were entertained (company went into the parlor). Here were the magazines, the books to be read, the cat, the dog, and the children studying after supper. This was the heart of the home.

The dining room, again, was formal, family portraits on the wall, a china cupboard out of which glinted what never was used even on the grandest occasion. Morning sun in the dining room was one of the specifications, as important as the sideboard and the serving table. The pantry was built up to the high ceilings in tiers of shelves and closets on and in which were kept that incredible clutter of household china and glass which every family seemed to accumulate. There was a drawer labelled "cake," another "bread," and a lead-lined sink with cockroach poison on the edges. The kitchens sprawled—coal stoves, laundry tubs, tables for baskets, tables for rolling dough, hooks and closets for a forest of tinware, and so on out into the shed with its tables and bins and closets. And in the cellar more bins, more shelves, a cold room, and a bricked in furnace as big as a funeral vault.

The main stairs followed a curving serpent of black walnut to a long upstairs hall off which opened vast bedrooms. The bath room was here (often the only one) with doors in at least two directions, accessible to all. The parents' room would be an upstairs sitting room also, with a desk somewhere spilling with small change and account books, and at the further end a vast walnut bed whose back rose to the ceiling, a cliff of polished veneer topped by a meaningless escutcheon. Other monumental pieces of black walnut flanked it at either side, and at the foot was a crib for the smallest child, or a green plush sofa for naps.

Across the hall would be the spare rooms, usually "blue" and "red," as in the White House, very bleak and usually shrouded in sheets. On their walls the outmoded pictures collected: "Old Swedes' Church," by Robert C., "Scene on the Brandywine," "Pauline" on glass. Guests in those days usually went home at night.

The stair banister to the third floor was scratched by children's slidings. This was where freedom began. There was the boy's room and the girl's room, indistinguishable in furnishing (cast-offs mostly) but differing in the kind of disorder, and an alcove at the end of the hall for doll houses, and mineral or birds' eggs collections. On the other side of the hall, last relic of the self-contained age of our grandparents, a "lumber room," with its bench, tools, oddments for repairs and plumbing, the rest of the floor space carrying a *massif* of family trunks piled up on each other in buttes and mesas. Last of all a cubicle where the visiting sempstress slept and some drawers for her scanty clothes. (She came of the *good* "plain people," and kept up her tiny remnant of gentry by gifts of big red apples to the children.) Here freedom ended, since the next door led to the servants' quarters (white only, the black slept outside) and no one, not even a parent, was supposed to trespass there except on monthly inspections of the sanitation.

Such was the house, which lived by a rhythm in which all these familiar backgrounds had their part. Morning was early, in the winter dark and cold, with faint gurglings from the radiators and faint breaths of warmth from the registers, too late for comfortable dressing. Earlier, in bed, one heard the slender rattle of chains on the heavy storm door,

the distant whisk-whisk as Isaac, the waiter, swept the front porch—
or, if it were an old-fashioned Quaker house, the soft slop-slush of wet
cloths over the marble steps which had to be polished each morning.
The faint joyous barks of the dog released, the first street cars banging
down the hill—then, through the open window, sunlight pale on the
far away river, then bright on the carpet—the double gong ringing
stridently—seven struck high and clear on the old clock far below—
and a rush downstairs for breakfast.

A meal that, no snack. No fruit then, until strawberries, canta-
loupes, or peaches were ripe, then in vast platters—but oatmeal and
milk that was still foamy from the milkman's crook-necked cans, hot
rolls or beaten biscuit, chops or scrapple or sausages with hashed potatoes, eggs as a side dish, waffles three times a week. A Quaker blessing
first, heads down but no word spoken. A full meal to all, then a scurry
of children for coats and hats, the buggy at the door for father, hard-
tired bicycles bumping down the pavement, green bags of school books
swung against the trees.

Quiet in the home when the mother left with her basket to join the
housewives of all the first families shopping down the long row of
wagon tilts backed against the curb of the street market, and spilling
with greens, vegetables, ducks, chickens, and bunches of wild flowers.
When she had gone the child left behind heard the faint moaning
spirituals of Isaac in the pantry polishing the silver, "O Lo—ad, O my
Lo—ad," more distant and fainter the creak of the cook's laughter. The
house was a personality, inscrutable, like God. It was the other half of
ego, without which the ego was only a sense of existence, it was external reality familiarly incarnate. It was something so embracing yet
so intimate that a word could name it only by indirection and overtones. It was home.

And while the slow synthetic beat of the house pulsed in a tempo
so well known that the senses responded subconsciously, knowing the
hours of the day or night, the dawn hours being different appreciably
from those near midnight or in the sleepiest afternoon, many subsidiary
rhythms joined or separated their quicker or slower motions. In the
yard at afternoon the children had their moments of idle wandering
or dreamy meditation, or sudden impulses to frenzied play, or hours
of quiet industry in the sand pile or on the bending branches of the

cherry trees. Sounds from within sank to the squeak of a cleaning cloth or the polite laugh of a guest in the parlor, then rose, crescendo, until by supper at six the whole house was again alive with activity. As night deepened the tempo gently slackened. Children's feet dragged upward to bed, the street noises sank to quiet, murmurs above stairs drowsed down until the clocks rang the hour through a silent house, and the head of the household, bolting the shutters, chaining the storm door, locking the front door, side door, back door, climbed the stairs, and set the silver basket on its shelf with the revolver and the watchman's rattle, a ritual act (since burglaries were most rare) celebrating the inviolability of the home.

I once rose at dawn and tiptoeing out into the silent street, saw those familiar houses relaxed and off their guard. There was no human life about, no dogs even were stirring; it was still dusky but clear. The slant light from the brightening East shone on the brick façades and overhanging cornices as upon faces, glinting with windows like eyes. And each one of those houses became the individual it was, an organism, hunched and humorous, or with open arms and serene forehead, a personality which recalled the family it sheltered and yet seemed to have its own life, dominating theirs. I was seeing, with that irrational and fleeting clairvoyance peculiar to youth, an environment incarnate in contorted brick and mortar, feeling in those crouching house people a grudging security offered to inmates who shaped their spirits accordingly. And in that moment the insipid smile of the Judge's mansard across the way, the reticent severity of the doctor's wooden mansion behind its trees, the brutal simplicity of the brick cube that housed the iron master and his brother, the coquettish insincerity of the minister's turrets of *fin de siècle*, and the toothy grin of the talkative widow's cornice, seemed more real than the sleeping inmates, so real that they mocked those that they sheltered, and were indeed grotesque symbols of the power of Things protecting and coercing the impressionable spirit of Life. Then the sun rose, looking up at our own house, bland, familiar, welcoming, surcharged with secret comforts. I shrugged away philosophy.

That feeling of a daily rhythm, in which each hour had its characteristic part, in a house where change came slowly and which was always home, nourished, if did not create, the expectancy of our generation that the norm of life was repetition and therefore security. Our house, with the tall two-hundred year old clock ticking at its heart, sank into the subconsciousness and became a sense of stability and permanence. It was a proof of a friendly universe, to which memory could always return. When a home was closed on our street, its shutters flapping, its blinds pulled awry to show empty floors and bare walls, we pitied the family that had lost their external self. The homeless, like the landless men of the Middle Ages, seemed to have no country.

The family made the home, yet the home, when it was made, had its own laws. Thus while the relaxing of family ties in the present era has had its powerful effect upon the home, the auto, the radio, commuting, boarding school, and apartment life have struck direct at the laws which made the laws of the home and on through to the family. It is the latter cause which seems more fundamental. Confidence is a habit which must be acquired young and from an environment that is constant and rhythmically continuous. The kaleidoscopic patterns of life today are more exciting and probably liberate the intelligence when there is an intelligence to be liberated; but the pattern they make is seldom realized by youth which turns and twists and darts in an environment which to its seeing never once makes a whole. Home life in the nineties could be very sweet, and often profoundly dull, and sometimes an oppressive weight of routine inescapable; security was often bought at a ruinous price; yet what conditioned reflexes it set up! The peace movement of the early nineteen hundreds, naively confident amidst a world in arms, was an attempt to make that world our home, our American home. Nor was heaven exempt from the home-making activities of the American family. We sang lustily in church—

> There we shall rest,
> There we shall rest,
> In Our Father's House,
> In Our Father's House.

The Age of Confidence got the habit of security in its homes.

JOHN P. MARQUAND

Why he selected LAST DAYS

of a BOSTONIAN

. A discovery has recently been made by certain highly successful
editors that nearly everything which has been written may readily be
condensed. The enthusiasm engendered by this discovery has even
caused certain of these gentlemen to say and perhaps honestly to believe that a condensed version of nearly anything which has been
written is clearer and better than the original. They have found that
any novel may be condensed and still be comprehensible, so that we
now see works of a hundred thousand or more words compressed into
the space of five, forming what is known in the editorial trade as a
"one shot" or "bookette." Needless to say, the energy and the pain
saved the reader by these methods is enormous. My only quarrel with
the whole system is that the impression produced by these abbreviated
efforts can never be the impression which the original author of the
original work intended to convey. Words at best are a difficult artistic
medium of expression for they present a different picture to every
mind which encounters them, and yet to make this medium at all
successful time and space must play an important part. The leisurely
approach and the opportunity for digression which are permitted in
the novel, have an importance in creating a final result since a reader's
impression of atmosphere and character is created almost entirely by
the cumulative effect of words. This is lost in condensation. It is lost
also in the selections for an anthology.

I only make this point so that a reader may understand that the
following chapters from a novel I once wrote were never intended to
stand alone. They are the end of a book in fact and before reading
them, the reader is supposed to have gained a definite idea of the character and the environment of the man about whom they are written.
Nevertheless, standing by themselves, these chapters give a picture
of an attitude of mind or a way of life—to use a current phrase—which

may have a certain value simply because it is so different from what
we usually observe today or may see in the future.

Newburyport, Mass.   JOHN P. MARQUAND
August 9, 1942

LAST PILGRIMAGE

*Rome Through the Eyes of an Enthusiast,
Although in Failing Health*

I N THE autumn of 1929 we find a pleasant interlude in Apley's
life, for at this time he took a much needed rest from his great
activities and we see him embarking from Boston upon a trip to
Europe and particularly for an extended visit to Rome, a city of his
dreams which he had never visited. There were two reasons for this
decision. The first largely concerned the important post which was
given that year to a distant cousin, Horatio Apley, in the United
States Embassy at Rome. Although George Apley had only met
Horatio Apley once, at a football game many years before, this lack of
acquaintance did not dim his interest in this relative's unexpected success. He speaks affectionately of Horatio Apley in a letter to his son.

Dear John:—
    You have doubtless heard the news about your Cousin Horatio and the
Embassy. This is one of the reasons why we are all going to Rome for some
months. I think we owe it to Horatio as well as to others to show him that
the family is squarely behind him in his spectacular success. Not since your
Cousin Applegate married Sir George, the baronet, has such a really worth-
while tribute been paid the family. We must do our part, even though I
have never approved of Horatio from what I have heard of him.
    Besides this, it will give Eleanor an opportunity to see something of the
gay cosmopolitan world where it is pleasant to know a place is always
reserved for us. I have sent Horatio a cable telling him that we are coming
and asking that we be included in some of the more exclusive social functions for the coming months. I have explained to him that I should prefer
not to meet His Holiness. As for that remarkable man, Mussolini, who

seems to have had the courage to stamp out radicalism, that is quite another matter. Of course, Horatio will be glad to attend to all of this. We do not wish to stay at his house, but in some near-by hotel.

Between you and me, I greatly hope that all this may turn Eleanor's mind in another direction. I have asked you before what you think of this man William Budd, and you were noncommittal. I for one am not. How my daughter, my own little girl, should be able to abide such a man is more than I can imagine. Though I may not have always shown it, Eleanor has always seemed to me one of the most delicate, sweet, and sensitive flowers in our family. That this blossom which has cheered me so often should be plucked by the fingers of a penniless journalist, none of whose work is even familiar to me, fills me with a very honest indignation. When Budd called to see me last week, I was frankly too ill to receive him. He is obviously an adventurer, utterly unfamiliar with the world which he is trying to enter. He is obviously marrying Eleanor for her money and position. I cannot for the life of me see why Eleanor should be delighted, nor can I see, speaking to you frankly, why you have not taken a more definite stand. Surely you must dislike this man, Budd, as intensely as I do, because Eleanor is, after all, your sister. . . .

This allusion will be almost sufficient for what was to Apley, and is still to nearly all the family, a sad example of infatuation.

It was thus that Apley was absent from America at the time of the stock market crash which has caused such deserved and undeserved misfortune, the end of which is not yet. His absence from home, however, did not remove his thoughts from home. He recognized that we were facing another real crisis.

Dear John:—

I am just back from a very interesting walk with Clara Goodrich on the Palatine Hill where there are so many interesting foundations of imperial palaces. Your mother and Eleanor and the Chickerings elected to go to an Embassy tea party as did Mr. Goodrich, so that Clara and I had the palaces quite to ourselves, except for a very loquacious guide who charged me ten lire more than was correct—I still do not know quite how. On my return, I found that the worst has happened; the market has collapsed. I am sending you a list of certain friends who I believe may be seriously involved through their own carelessness. Tell them I am standing ready to help them, but I wish nothing to be said about it. Good always comes out of these panics and this one should show our working people how necessary it is to save in good times instead of buying worthless odds and ends and becoming softened by a new mode of living. They must get back to basic principles; we all must.

Rome is really a delightful place, particularly when one brings one's own group with one. Having a group does away with a great deal of what I consider the danger of travel. The danger is that travel always gets one a little bit out of touch with home; the sight of new faces and the reception of new ideas is sometimes a little bit unsettling to the best of us, and makes for the restlessness which you felt when you returned from the War. I am too old to be restless now. To-day Rome only teaches me the beauties of the place I live in.

It seems to me that Mrs. Gardner has brought back to us all that is really best of Rome and Italy and has considerably left the rest behind. A visit to her Fenway Palace really suffices to show one everything. The head of Aphrodite in our Museum is superior to anything I have seen in the Vatican. I also think that we have by far the better half of the so-called Ludovici Throne. I wish the Coliseum was situated in a more open space as is our Harvard Stadium, so that one could view its proportions at a single glance. I have been, of course, to see the grave of Keats, but that burying ground does not seem to me as interesting as our own Granary burying ground which one can see so comfortably from the upper windows of our own Athenaeum. I know that you will laugh at me for all this, but I really mean it, in a way. Of course Rome is the Eternal City; its yellow bricks, its masses of old construction, its old tombs in the Campagna give a great sense of antiquity. Rome has been loved by everyone. That is why we have brought so much of it home. I suppose I am getting old. I suppose this is why so much of it makes me homesick. I see in it the ruins of so many hopes greater than any of mine. Personally, I long to get back, but I think that the change is doing Eleanor a great deal of good. Although Horatio is very busy, he is doing what he can for us, a luncheon and two teas where we have met nearly everyone who is worth while. Yet I still feel a little out of touch with things. Will you please, if you can spare the time, go up to Boston and see if the roof at Hillcrest, near the angle by the Terrace, is still leaking. I have been having great difficulty with the carpenter about this. I should also like to know what is being done about the family of squirrels which has invaded the attic. I do not want them killed, but I do want them put out of the attic. This worries me very much. Eleanor sends her love. As far as I know she has not written to Budd for the last three days. Your mother and I both think that she is getting over it, and that is reason enough for the sacrifice we make in being here. I picked up a flea yesterday, I think in one of the small churches. That is one thing which we have not got at home. . . .

Dear John:—

I have just been to the Villa at Frascati. As I looked at the numerous fountains, I could not for the life of me remember whether or not the

plumbing has been turned off at Hillcrest. Will you please wire about this?
Also the cypresses reminded me that the evergreen hedge in the family
lot has not been cut back at the cemetery. Will you please see about this,
too? I cannot go away without neglecting a great deal. Eleanor has met a
young man in the Guarda Nobile, and I do hope he will take her mind off
Budd. He seems to be making the effort. I have bought several pictures for
little John. Will you please get him the very best rocking horse that you
can find for his Christmas present? I am counting the days when I can get
home; so is Clara Goodrich. Your mother keeps wishing to remain.
Believe me, I am only here on account of Eleanor. If Rome is beautiful, the
food is not good. Will you please see that the locks are secure on the wine
cellar at Beacon Street? . . .

Dear John:—

I have been very ill for the last three weeks, one of the first times that I
have been ill in my life. It started with a cold I contracted from looking
too long at the sunset. It developed into influenza. I still am very weak.
The only good that has come out of all this trip is what it may do for
Eleanor. She and your mother have been with me constantly. The thing
which worries me, as your mother may have written, but you must not
believe too much of it, is something one of the doctors has said about my
heart. Please do not say anything about this to anyone. My heart has always
been all right, and after all I am not so old. At any rate these Italian doctors
have not improved since the days of Benvenuto Cellini, and they are all
unsanitary. I shall not be in the least worried until I get an overhauling at
home, and I don't want you to be. Clara Goodrich has been reading me
the "Marble Faun." I do think Hawthorne has hit off the spirit of this
place excellently. Again I caution you not to tell anyone about my heart
because it is all bosh. . . .

Thus we have the first intimation ever conveyed that Apley's health
was failing. That he faced this failing in health with the gallantry of
his kind is natural, and part of his tradition. Though he treated the
matter lightly this opinion was not shared by his wife or daughter, and
doubtless he himself secretly knew that there was reason to fear. This
may account for his activities in the last years of his life and for his
anxiety to set his mind and his house in order. Ever after this illness,
one receives the very definite impression that Apley is taking leave of
something, that he is balancing accounts with himself, that he is living
more and more in a world of memory. He was more and more the
spectator watching the world pass by. Even the marriage of his daughter Eleanor with William Budd, a New York journalist from Lan-

caster, Pennsylvania, did not disturb him as it might have in former years. Apley's only comment was that he had done his best.

I have done my best [he writes to his friend Walker]. And that is all anyone can do. It is now time for someone else to try. The doctors, who seem to me to be painfully ignorant men, are keeping me very still at Hillcrest this summer, but I have insisted on my Saturday bird walk with Clara Goodrich, and Catharine and the doctors can't stop that. As for Eleanor I am glad to say that I have never in any way tried to influence my children. She must lead her own life. I have led mine. The wedding, of course, was an important one, and I think at last my new son-in-law understands what he is getting into. He seemed quite shaken when I gave Eleanor away. At the reception, he appeared to do his best to pull himself together, but his manner was distrait. He and Eleanor are now somewhere on the West Coast. Of course, I am telling everyone that I am greatly pleased with Budd, and we shall let it go at that. This seems to me the definite end of a chapter. I am glad that my little grandson is here with me, now able to walk. I seem to have more in common with him than I have with most people. He has the Apley eyes and the same yellow hair. His nurse, both his grandmother and I feel, neglects him shamefully, but he seems to survive it.

My real reason for this letter is to ask you to come up to see me. I have not seen you for a long while, Mike. I really think you have been away from Boston long enough so that there would be no great flutter of gossip if you came back here on a little visit. I should see that only our own crowd met you, and we could have some good talks about the old days. I really do not think it would do any harm if you came up now on the grounds of seeing an old friend who is not well, although this talk of my not being well is largely bosh.

There are many reasons against the inclusion of the following letter, as it was written quite obviously at this time when Apley's health was failing. When one remembers the gallantry with which he faced as an active man the impairment of his physical faculties, for medical examination had proved only too clearly the existence of serious constitutional organic defects, the publication of this letter may seem unsportsmanlike; yet despite the depression of mood which it illustrates it contains an inherent soundness and is besides such an exposition of his philosophy that it cannot but be included.

Dear John:—

I have a good deal of time on my hands these days, more than I ever remember having. Except for two hours in the morning managing correspondence with Miss Fearing from the office I seem to spend most of my time on the porch watching John, Jr., playing in the sand pile we have built for him. I have been impressed to-day that he seems to do the same thing over and over again. He has definite limitations of activity and thought, but then that is true with most of us. We all do the same things over and over again.

I have been amusing myself to-day by reading Emerson's essay on Self-Reliance. There is a brave ring to the words. There is a courage about them which I like to think that Emerson and the rest of us, in a lesser measure, have drawn from the rocky soil and from this harsh climate. I like to think we are all self-reliant in a way, but sometimes Emerson leads one's thoughts along disturbing channels. Emerson disturbed me this afternoon.

He made me do something which I have never really done. He made me examine my life objectively, and I cannot say that I liked it very much; however, I could see myself as perhaps you and some others see me. It seems to me that, although I have tried, I have achieved surprisingly little compared with my own father and his father, for instance. I repeat that this negative result has not been for want of trying. The difficulty seems to have been that something has always stepped in the way to prevent me. I have always been faced from childhood by the obligation of convention, and all of these conventions have been made by others, formed from the fabric of the past. In some way these have stepped in between me and life. I had to realize that they were designed to do just that. They were designed to promote stability and inheritance. Perhaps they have gone a little bit too far.

When I stopped to think of it, I had the unpleasant conviction that everything I have done has amounted almost to nothing. I tried to think of the things which I have cared about most. In all conscience they have been simple things. They have been the relaxation after physical weariness—the feel of wind on the face, the feel of cold water on the body. I may say parenthetically that the doctors will no longer permit me to take my daily cold tub. Now and then something has come to me in unexpected moments when I have been near the woods or water at sundown. I have felt at such odd times a peace and happiness amounting to a belief that I was in tune with a sort of infinity. It has been like moments I have had with you and Eleanor when you were growing up. I have known the joys of companionship now and then, and I have known the deep satisfaction of friendship. I have known the satisfaction of accomplishing something on which I have centred all my energies and hopes. I have known the feeling of warm earth. I have heard the sleigh bells sound in winter. All this has been very good. Yet somehow I seem to have enjoyed very little of these pleasures, for I have never seemed to have had the time to enjoy them.

More than this, I will tell you frankly I have sometimes deliberately tried
not to enjoy them. I have turned away from them because I have believed
that most of these were pleasures of the senses rather than of the intellect.
I have been taught since boyhood not to give way to sensuality. I think this
afternoon, now that it is almost too late, that this viewpoint may be a little
wrong. There has been too much talk in my life. There has been too little
action.

These thoughts were still in my mind when I came in here to the library
to write this letter, and now that I am here, I feel very much better. The
family portraits are all around me. There is my grandfather painted on one
of his visits to Paris. There is my own father when he was a young man.
There are the Chippendale chairs and the tall clock and the gate-legged
table. All these objects are very consoling this afternoon. I can realize now
that these are the things which make people like you and me behave, the
exacting tyrants from which we cannot escape, but there is something bene-
ficial in their rule. Memory and tradition are the tyrants of our environment. You cannot be very radical or very wrong when you see Moses
Apley's face. He made me think of some other things on the favorable
ledger of my life. I have always told the truth. I have never shirked standing by my convictions. I have tried to realize that my position demanded
and still demands the giving of help to others. I have tried in my poor way
to behave toward all men in a manner which might not disgrace that position. Now I can feel a humble sense of pride that I have done so.

I have not had a very good time in doing it. There is a great deal of
talk in these days about happiness. An English woman named Mrs.
Bertrand Russell, whose life in many ways has not been the same as mine,
has written a strange book entitled "The Right To Be Happy" which has
disturbed even your mother's admirable sense of balance. It seems to me
to-day in all this unhappy country there is a loud, lonely cry for happiness.
Perhaps it would be better if people realized that happiness comes only by
indirection, that it can never exist by any conscious effort of the will. I
think this is a mistake that you and Eleanor and all the rest of you are
making. When the hour comes for you to balance your accounts I wonder
if you will have had any better time than I. I doubt it.

At any rate, I feel that I have been the means of continuing something
which is worth more than happiness. I have stood for many things which
I hope will not vanish from the earth. I am only one of many here who
have done so. The world I have lived in may be in a certain sense restricted
but it has been a good world and a just world. Much of it may have been
built on a sense of security which is now disappearing but it has also been
built on certain elements of the spirit which will always be secure: on
honour and on courage and on truth.

I have been engaged during the past two weeks in going over the details of my will. I am very anxious that certain small possessions go to the

right people and that you and Eleanor will not quarrel over my wishes. I have sent the bronzes to the Art Museum yesterday, where they will be exhibited on the Apley side of the large wing. I, for one, am very glad to have them out of the house. The silver is being carefully listed and so is the furniture. I want you to take particular care to look after Norman Rowe at Pequod Island. There is also a fund being set aside for the servants. Do you want your great-grandmother's locket with your great-grandfather's hair inside it? If you don't I shall give it to the Historical Society. I am very much puzzled about what to do with certain family letters. I do not think there is anything in them which will do much harm and I do not wish to burn them. They are in five tin boxes on the left-hand side of the attic stairs. As you know, most of the Apley letter books are on loan at the Essex Institute, where I imagine you will be willing to leave them. For the rest you must come up here to see me. Copies of my own letters, pamphlets, and papers I am having arranged in suitable boxes marked and documented. A great many people are coming to call on me every afternoon, all sorts of younger members of the family and many older friends. I had not realized that I was so popular. . . .

A HOUSE IN ORDER

The Final Arrangements
For a Pilgrim's Departure

DEAR John:—
    This letter may seem a gloomy one to you but it is not to me. It is prompted by a conversation I had with my doctor, Minot Wingate. I am convinced that he is an alarmist, as in many ways I have never felt better in my life or more appreciative of everything which is going on around me. Yet it is necessary at a certain time to make certain arrangements. These requests and suggestions I am making to you are in no sense urgent but will stand for a number of years.

    In the event of my death a good deal of pressure will be brought to bear on you to have an elaborate funeral. All the societies to which I belong and also the philanthropic organizations will in the nature of things send representatives, who will in all probability seek positions as honorary pallbearers. In this way the church aisle is apt to become very crowded and uncomfortable and this tendency seems to be growing, according to my observations of the funerals which I have attended recently. For myself I do not want anything of the sort. I simply want places reserved in the middle of the church for these representatives. The elaborate floral wreaths which they will present I want placed to one side as inconspicuously as is compatible with politeness. The order in which the family are to sit may be somewhat confusing to you. As you may not be as conversant with the various branches as I am, I am giving you a memorandum and a diagram. I am also giving a list of pallbearers and their order. You notice that I include Norman Rowe and our old coachman, if he is still alive, and also according to custom one representative to be chosen among the workers of the Apley Mills. This I think will give the necessary simplicity of tone. I need not tell you that these men must be treated with the same courtesy and respect which is accorded to the other pallbearers. After the funeral you will have special refreshments served to these three in the small servants' dining-room, either at Beacon Street or Hillcrest. My only reason for this is that I do not wish them to be embarrassed by the weight of the other company. I want you to spend at least fifteen minutes with them yourself and to take a personal interest in seeing that all their wants are satisfied. Also, you are to give each of them a twenty-dollar gold piece as coming directly from me, with my kindest regards.

I want you to be especially careful to see that the secretary and officers of my Harvard class are made comfortable and are treated cordially. There must be whisky and cigars for these and a few others in the library, including of course the executors. I want you to be particularly careful that any friends of mine who may attend the church and whose dress and appearance may cause them embarrassment are looked out for with every possible attention and are thanked by you or by some other representative of the family personally for their thoughtfulness in attending. You may add, in speaking to them, that this was my particular wish.

A word about the family will be enough. In my experience these occasions are apt to be the source of friction and ill feeling which may last over a period of years. There is apt to be a certain amount of jealousy displayed by those who wish to show themselves as having stood high in the regard of the deceased. Your mother and my sister Amelia will help you in estimating exactly the degree of attention which you must show to everyone. The Douglas Apleys will be apt as always to be somewhat officious and pushing. It may be as well to put them in one of the pews farther back. I shall hope that your Aunt Jane, if she is alive, may be able to attend but you must leave this decision to the doctors of the institution. In other words, I want everything to go as smoothly as though I were here myself to oversee it.

The arrangements about the stone have been already made. I do not want any verse or inscription added. These few words with the memoranda I am giving you will cover the whole matter, except for a few afterthoughts I may have from time to time that will relieve you of considerable responsibility. There is one task which I am leaving up to you and which I want you to oversee personally in such a way that no gossip may be connected with it. I have put together a few odd articles, including some books which I owned in college. These I want you to bring yourself to a Mrs. Monahan O'Reilly, whose address you will find in my address book. I want you to see her personally and to tell her that it was my wish that she should have these things and my wish also, which you will agree to fulfill, that she shall come to you for your assistance in any time that she may be in any difficulty. I shall not say anything more about this matter but shall rely on your tact and your good judgment.

If I do not get around to it myself I wish you to remember that the joists in the cellar beneath the old laundry at Hillcrest are in very bad condition. They all have dry-rotted and should be replaced. If you attend to this I want you to get a new carpenter. The one I have has taken advantage of me of late in his bills. You must learn to watch this sort of person very carefully. I do not need to recommend to your care the four dogs on the place and the horses, because you have always been very fond of animals. Jacob the groom has been drinking heavily lately. You must wink at this as much as you possibly can. Jacob in many ways has been a fine fellow and has taught you to ride, himself. Somehow horses and liquor have a way of going together. Perhaps it is not for either of us to reason why.

Things have been very gay and cheerful around here during the last few weeks. I have never had so many callers. A special dinner is being given for me at the Province Club and two old salts from the Apley Sailors' Home who remember your grandfather have come up especially to see me. Your great-uncle's gardener from Pachogue Neck has come up also and Norman Rowe has come down from Maine. Cousins of yours come in every day to see me. I think they are fine young people. Their ideas may be slightly different from mine but on the whole the family traits are about the same, and I am very proud to be related to them.

Preparations are on foot already for the customary Thanksgiving party which will be a large one this year as I wish every possible member of the family to be included. I shall want, if it can be arranged, you and Louise to come up a week in advance. Your ideas are needed for the pencil and paper games and I am composing a small family pageant. You, of course, are to take the part of the first John Apley. I have found some of his old clothes in the attic, which I hope will fit you. It is high time for you to enter into the spirit of this occasion rather more assiduously than you have in the past.

During the last week I have been working on several plans to rid the attic of those gray squirrels. I think now the only thing to do is to keep watch near the limb of the elm tree and to shoot them as they enter by that hole under the gutter. If the hole is stopped up they simply gnaw another. I should rather have you shoot them than one of the hired men. I really think it would look better. . . .

My dear boy:—

I cannot tell you how deeply your last letter, with its budget of good news, has moved me. You must give me credit for always knowing that

you had the "right stuff" in you. If the War put some odd notions in your
head, you cannot be blamed for that. In many ways it made me a little bit
eccentric myself. I have always known in the back of my mind that eventually you would settle down and that you would find that New York,
though it may be agreeable in a way, is not the right place to raise children. Your acquaintances there may be more sprightly and amusing but
they are not the same as old friends here. What makes me happier than
anything else is the knowledge that you have come to this decision without
my urging. I have told you more than once that there are certain things
you cannot get away from and now you know it. You have had your fling
and now you are coming back, as one of our flesh and blood inevitably
must, to take up your responsibilities. I cannot be thankful enough that I
have lived to see the time when all this "bosh" and nonsense is over with.

You will understand, of course, that your long absence from Boston
will be a considerable loss to you always. You and Louise will find difficulties and annoyances in taking up the position which was always waiting
for you here. As you say that Louise is really the person who is obliging
you to take this step, perhaps she will understand these difficulties better
than you. Your mother is already writing to her and is taking steps to have
her made a member of the Sewing Circle suitable to her age. By the time
she arrives she will also find herself a member of the Thursday Afternoon
Debating Club, which has given your mother and your Aunt Amelia such
pleasure always. If she comes up a month from now she will have the opportunity of discussing "Is True Happiness Derived from Work Rather
Than from Play?" The ladies all like these questions very much. Perhaps
you and I can think of something more amusing, in the library, over a good
cigar. The doctors still allow me one cigar a day. I shall take two on the
day you come. Be sure to bring up some of the latest stories with you.

It goes without saying that you will face many problems on your return
among us. I am planning to resign from several boards, nominating you in
my place. You will of necessity be the next president of the Apley Sailors'
Home but a membership on the Lending Library is a different matter. I
do not think you had better attempt this until your views on literature are
a little bit more sound.

Here, by the way, is something which I wish to advance to you confi-
dentially. I have heard from very good authority that there may be a
vacancy in the Harvard Corporation. Certain of us are looking for a
younger man and one of the right sort. There is altogether too much sentiment here lately for getting outsiders and so-called "new blood" into Harvard. The traditions of the place must not be spoiled. There is actually
some talk about a new president, about whom no one seems to have heard.
Needless to say, this is only one of the wild rumours which circulate at such
a time. Harvard will be Harvard, just as Harvard was old Harvard when
Yale was but a pup. Seriously, I think you might be fitted to take your

place on the corporation. It is true you have never been a scholar but now that you are actually going to live in Boston this does not really make much difference. I shall have some of the right people meet you and we shall see what can be done.

There will be a good deal of hard work ahead for you at both the Province and the Berkley Clubs. Though you have been a member of both for some years you have not really identified yourself with either. This will take a long time because there are certain cliques in each with which one must cope very carefully. I do think, however, given the requisite amount of patience, you may be able to do rather well. There is one thing you must remember. Although you must show yourself at both these places as often as possible, even at the expense of other social obligations, you must try on the whole to be silent and observing. Do not above anything else, until you have been in Boston for at least five years, become involved in discussions with any of the regular members. This sort of thing creates a very bad general impression. The Berkley Club, which is founded on a more informal spirit, you must never treat too lightly. Although you must unbend there as much as possible be sure to unbend in a friendly way. You will doubtless be called upon, on one of the regular evenings, to tell some sort of story or perhaps to sing a song. Be sure that you pick out a very good story indeed because you will be largely identified by this first venture and you will frequently be called upon to repeat the same story. I have noticed that you are interested in certain social questions. Be sure to deal with these very lightly, if at all—better not at all. You must understand that the Berkley Club and the Province Club are both havens of refuge where no one wishes to be emotionally disturbed.

But I am getting very far afield. I am speaking very prosily, out of sheer joy at having you come back. We can talk about all these matters together much more sensibly than I can ever put them down on paper. My mind and my heart are both too full for writing. I repeat I always knew that you had the right stuff in you and now we will have a chance to get to know each other. What I want particularly is to have a great many small men's dinners. There is so much to say. There is so much to talk about. God bless you. . . .

George Apley died in his own house on Beacon Street on the thirteenth of December, 1933, two weeks after John Apley returned to Boston.

The DEEP PAST

I select this chapter from *The Sheltered Life* because it deals, in a way I like, with my favorite theme, the reflections of a civilized mind in a world that is virtually, and perhaps essentially, barbarian.
Richmond, Va.   ELLEN GLASGOW
May 15, 1942

"YOU look tired, Father," Mrs. Archbald remarked, when she had studied the old general for a moment. "Hadn't you better lie down?"

"No, I like to feel the sun on me, and so does William. We'll sit in the park awhile and then walk up to the hospital."

"Jenny Blair will go with you. She can wait downstairs while you are in Eva's room. The child is so distressed. She has always adored Eva."

"Every one adores her."

"Well, try not to worry. Something tells me that she will come through. Doctor Bridges feels very hopeful."

"He would naturally—but maimed for life—" his voice trembled.

"We must try not to think of that. If only she comes through it well." Then after a moment's thought, she added cheerfully, "It isn't as if she were a younger woman and still hoped to have children. She is forty-two, and has been married almost twenty years. One would never suspect that to look at her."

After she finished, he lingered a moment, hoping and fearing that she might, if only by accident, become more explicit. Was she shielding Eva's modesty from him, an old man, who would have loved her had she been stripped bare not only of modesty but of every cardinal virtue? Or was such evasion merely an incurable habit of mind? Would George tell him the truth? Or was it conceivable that George did not know?

372

"Will Jenny Blair come in time?" he asked, pricked by sudden fear. "I should not like to be late."

"Why, you've at least two hours, Father, and if Jenny Blair isn't back in time, I'll go with you myself."

"But I don't need anybody. I am able to go alone." No man needed protection less; but because he had lived a solitary male among women, he could never escape it, and because these women depended upon him, old General Archbald had remained at their mercy. It was impossible to wound the feelings of women who owed him the bread they ate and the roof over their heads, and so long as he did not hurt their feelings, they would be stronger than he was. Always, from his earliest childhood, he mused, with a curious resentment against life, he had been the victim of pity. Of his own pity, not another's. Of that double-edged nerve of sympathy, like the aching nerve in a tooth, which throbbed alive at the sight of injustice or cruelty. One woman after another had enslaved his sympathy more than his passion, and never had she seemed to be the woman his passion demanded.

Well, it is over, he thought, and knew that it would never be over. Again this secret hostility swept through his nerves, surprising him by its vehemence. Was it possible that he was beginning to break in mind before the infirmities of the flesh had attacked a single physical organ? Only yesterday, Bridges had told him that a man of sixty might be proud of his arteries. Only yesterday! And today he was annoyed by this queer tingling in his limbs, by this hollow drumming which advanced along his nerves and then receded into the distance. "Let us sit down a bit, William," he murmured, walking very erect, with a proper pride in his straight back and thighs and his well-set-up figure for a man of his eighty-three years. "I suppose this bad news about Eva has disturbed me. I'd rather lose my right arm than have anything happen to her."

Dropping down on a green bench in the park, beneath a disfigured tulip tree, which was putting out into bud, he tried to imagine her ill, suffering, and waiting calmly for that dreaded hour under the knife. But no, she chose, as always capriciously, her own hour and mood to return to him. Never had he seen her cast aside her armour of gaiety. Never, among all the women he had known, had she asked him for sympathy. Never once had she tried to take care of him. For all her loveliness, she was, he found himself thinking aloud to William, curled up on the grass by the bench, a strong soul in affliction. A strong soul, still undefeated by life, she came to him now. She came to him out of the pale green distance, out of the flying clouds, out of the April bloom of the sky. Even to-day, he mused proudly, there wasn't a girl in Queenborough who was worthy to step into her shoes. Not one of them. Not Jenny Blair, a vivid little thing, but lacking in queenliness.

Resting there, with his tired old hands clasped on the crook of his stick, he told himself that Eva Birdsong in her prime, before misfortune had sapped her ardent vitality, would have to put to shame all the professional beauties of Paris or London. Why, he had seen Mrs. Langtry, and had considered her deficient in presence. "Eva would have had all London at her feet," he meditated, without jealousy, since his devotion, at eighty-three, was of the mind alone. Or was this deception? Did one go down into the grave with the senses still alive in the sterile flesh? Well, no matter. The thread had snapped, and the question had floated out of his thoughts. Airy and fragile as mist, he watched it blown away into the April world, into that windy vastness which contained the end of all loving and all living.

At least she had had, he pondered, sitting beside a triangular flower-bed, beneath the pale buds on the tulip tree, what she believed that she wanted. True, her life might have been easier if they hadn't been poor. Yet being poor, which kept her from parties where she once shone so brilliantly, had saved her also from brooding, from that fatal introspection which is the curse of women and poets. She had not had time to fall out of love. She had not had time to discover that George was unworthy.

Or was it conceivable, as Cora suspected, that Eva knew the truth, and was merely preserving appearances? No, he could not believe this, he mused, poking the end of his stick into a tuft of young dandelions. Yet, while he rejected Cora's suspicion, he admitted that life would be more agreeable if women could realize that man is not a monogamous animal, and that even a man in love does not necessarily wish to love all the time. Certainly, there would be less unhappiness abroad in the world if good women could either accept or reject the moral nature of man. Over and over, he had seen the faithful lover lose to the rake in an affair of the heart. Over and over, he had seen a miracle of love that failed to make a conversion. Yet he knew, having much experience to build on, that even loose-living men are not all of one quality. It was not a simple question of merit. The diversity went deeper, far down through the nature of man into nature itself. George had lived according to life; his very faults were the too lavish defects of generosity. He was generous with himself always, and with his money whenever he was affluent. Not without a pang, the General remembered that long ago, when he was caught on the verge of financial ruin, George alone among his sympathetic friends had offered him help. The year before George had inherited his father's modest estate, and he would have sacrificed this fortune to save a friend from disaster. Later on, to be sure, he had speculated unwisely and lost his inheritance—but it was not of this that the General was thinking while he poked at the dandelions.

He saw George, with his thick wind-blown hair, his smiling eyes, his look of virile hardness, of inexhaustible energy. Well-favoured enough if you judged by appearances, and did women, or men either for that matter, ever judge by anything else? But it was more than George's fine features, ruddy skin, and friendly grey eyes that made one reluctant to blame him. Yes, there was something more, some full-bodied virtue, some compensating humanity. "But I am human too," thought old General Archbald, "and what good has it done me?" . . .

As a child, at Stillwater, they had called him a milk-sop, because he saw visions in the night and wanted to be a poet. The sight of blood sickened him; yet his grandfather assured him, with truth, that hunting had given greater pleasure to a greater number of human beings than all the poetry since Homer. Pity, said the men who had none, is a woman's virtue; but he had known better than this. A poet's virtue, it may be. He was not sure. So much virtue passed into a poet when he was dead; when his immortal part was bound in English calf and put into a library. Little girls, however, were not pitiful. Little girls were as savage as boys, only weaker. They had never failed to torment him. They had laughed when he was made sick; they had mocked at his visions; they had stolen his poems and used them for curl-papers. Strange, the images that were dragged up like bits of shell, in a net of the memory! All his life curl-papers had remained, for him, the untidy symbol of an aversion. No, little girls were not gentle. And even his tender-hearted mother, who nursed her servants in illness, and had never used the word "slave" except in the historical sense— even his mother was incapable of the pity that becomes a torment to the nerves. She accepted meekly, as an act of God's inscrutable wisdom, all the ancient wrongs and savage punishments of civilization. . . .

Again General Archbald sighed and prodded the dandelions. Again the thread snapped and a flock of unrelated images darted into his mind. . . .

"Where did the boy get his tomfool ideas?" his robust grandfather inquired sternly. "Was he born lacking?"

"Not lacking, Father," his mother protested, "but different. Some very nice people," she added, with an encouraging glance at her peculiar child, "are born different. He may even turn out to be a poet."

"Do you think," his father asked in a troubled tone, "that we had better try changing his tutor? Is it possible that Mr. Davis has infected him with newfangled ideas?"

His mother shook her head in perplexity, for it distressed her that one of her sons should be deficient in manliness. "But the other boys are all manly. Even if Mr. Davis has talked of abolition, after giving us his word that he would treat the—the institution with respect, I have never heard that New Englanders disliked bloodshed. I thought, indeed, it was exactly the opposite. Don't you remember I opposed your engaging Mr. Davis because I had always heard the Puritans were a hard and cruel people? Perhaps," she confessed bravely, "he may inherit his eccentric notions from me. Though I try to be broad-minded, I can't help having a sentiment against cock-fights."

"Pooh! Pooh!" his grandfather blustered, for he belonged to the Georgian school of a gentleman. "Would you deprive the lower classes of their favourite sport? As for this young nincompoop, I'll take him deerhunting tomorrow. If he is too much of a mollycoddle to kill his buck, we'll try to scare up a fawn for him."

A famous hunter in his prime, the old gentleman still pursued with hounds any animal that was able to flee. Fortunately, game was plentiful and game laws unknown in the fields and forests of Stillwater. For nothing escaped his knife or his gun, not the mole in the earth, not the lark in the air. He could no more look at a wild creature without lusting to kill than he could look at a pretty girl without lusting to kiss. Well, it was a pity he had not lived to enjoy the war; for the killing nerve, as his grandson had once said of him, was the only nerve in his body. Yet he had fallen in love with a woman because of her fragile appearance; and when she had gone into a decline after the birth of her fifth child, and had lost her reason for a number of years, he had remained still devoted to her. Against the advice of his family and his physician, he had refused to send her away, and had kept her, behind barred windows, in the west wing of the house. To be sure, when she died, he had married again within seven months; but only his first wife, though he had buried two others, had given him children, and through her the strain of melancholy had passed into the Archbald blood. . . .

From his father, with filial patience, "For my part, I try not to kill a doe or a fawn."

"Fiddlesticks, sir! You talk like an abolitionist. Didn't the Lord provide negroes for our servants and animals for our sport? Haven't you been told this from the pulpit? I hope, sir, I shan't live to see the day when every sort of sport is no longer welcome at Stillwater." Even the field hands in the quarters, General Archbald remembered, had their "coon or possum dawgs," and went rabbit chasing on holidays when there were no cock-fights. High or low, good or bad, manners at Stillwater were a perpetual celebration of being alive. No other way of living had ever seemed to him so deeply rooted in the spirit of place, in an established feeling for life. Not for happiness alone, not for life at its best only, but for the whole fresh or salty range of experience. There was, too, a quality, apart from physical zest, that he had found nowhere else in the world, a mellow flavour he had never forgotten.

Naturally, as a child, he did not hunt or shoot with his grandfather; but several weeks later, on a brilliant November morning, he watched a buck at bay pulled down by the hounds in a rocky stream. He could not remember how it happened. By accident, probably, when he was out with his tutor. At first, watching the death, he had felt nothing. Then, in a spasm, the retch of physical nausea. For the eyes of the hunted had looked into his at the end; and that look was to return to him again and again, as a childish fear of the dark returns to the grown man when his nerves are unstrung. In how many faces of men, women, children, and animals, all over the world, had he seen that look of the hunted reflected? A look of bewilderment, of doubt, of agony, of wondering despair; but most of all a look that is seeking some God who might, but does not, show mercy. All over the world! North, South, East, West. On the heights, in the desert.

With blood on his hands and a savage joy inflaming his face, his grandfather strode over to smear stains on a milksop. "If you don't like the taste of blood better than milk, you'll have to be blooded. Hold still, sir, I say, and be blooded." Then, as the blood touched him, the boy retched with sickness, and vomited over the anointing hand and the outstretched arm. "Damn you, sir!" the old gentleman bellowed, while he wiped away the mess with his silk handkerchief. "Go back to the nursery where you belong!"

Still retching, furious and humiliated because he had been born a milksop, the boy rode home with his tutor. "I don't love people!" he sobbed passionately. "I don't love people!" Was it fair to blame him because he had been born different? Was anybody to blame for the way God had let him be born?

How close that day seemed to him now, that day and others at Stillwater. The more distant a scene, the clearer it appeared in his vision. Things near at hand he could barely remember. Even yesterday was smothered in fog. But when he looked far back in the past, at the end of seventy years or more, the fog lifted, and persons and objects started out in the sunken glow on the horizon. Instead of diminishing with time, events in the deep past grew larger, and the faces of persons long dead became more vivid and lifelike than life itself. "It is old age," he thought wearily. "It is a sign of old age to lack proper control." Or was the cause deeper still? he mused, while the shadow of a bird flitted over the grass and was gone. Was this second self of his mind, as variable as wind, as nebulous as mist, merely the forgotten consciousness of the poet who might have been? Sitting here in the spring sunshine, was he living again, was he thinking again, with that long buried part of his nature? For his very words, he realized, were the words of that second self, of the self he had always been in dreams and never been in reality. Again the bird flitted by. He did not know. He could not tell. No matter how hard he tried, it was impossible to keep his thoughts from rambling back into the past. It was impossible to trace a connection between the past and present. Was he growing in his old age, like poor Rodney, who had surrendered to shadows? Better let the past disappear and hold firmly to the bare structure of living.

For an instant his look wandered from the trees in the park to the few carriages and many motor cars in Washington Street. Yes, the world was changing rapidly, and he wondered what was waiting ahead. He could remember when Queenborough had the charm of a village; but now, wherever he looked, he found ugliness. Beauty, like every other variation from type, was treated more or less as a pathological symptom. Did Americans, especially Southerners, prefer ugliness? Did ugliness conform, he pondered fancifully, to some automatic æsthetic spring in the dynamo? But even if the scientific method destroyed beauty, there would be no more great wars, only little wars that no one remembered, said John Welch. What, indeed, would be left to fight about when people thought alike everywhere, and exact knowledge had spread in a vast cemetery for ideals all over the world?

So John Welch, being very advanced in opinion, would argue for hours; but when argument was ended, old General Archbald could not see that human nature was different from what it had been in his youth. To be sure, idealism, like patriotism, appeared to diminish with every material peace between conflicts; but he was near enough to the Spanish War, and indeed to the Civil War, to realize that the last battle has never been fought and the last empty word has never been spoken. Not that it mattered. All he knew now was that he was too old to bother about life. He was too old to bother about cruelty, which he had seen all over the world, in every system invented by man; which he had seen in a velvet mask, in rags, and naked except for its own skin. Yes, he was too old to suffer over the evils that could not be cured. Only, whenever he listened to John Welch assailing the present order, he was reminded of his own revolt against slavery in the eighteen fifties. The reformers of that age had believed that all the world needed was to have negro slavery abolished. Yet negro slavery was gone, and where it had been, John said, another system had ushered in the old evils with a clean, or at least a freshly wiped face. What the world needed now, cried the modern reformers, like John Welch, was the new realism of science. For one confirmed habit had not changed with the ages. Mankind was still calling human nature a system and trying vainly to put something else in its place.

But a world made, or even made over, by science was only a stark and colourless spectacle to old David Archbald. A thin-lipped world of facts without faith, of bones without flesh. Better the red waistcoats and the soulful vapouring of early Romanticism. Better even the excessive sensibility of mid-Victorian æsthetics. Since he belonged to the past, if he belonged anywhere, his mental processes, it seemed, were obliged to be disorderly. When he said, "I am more than myself," when he said, "Life is more than living," when he blundered about "the nature of reality," he was still, or so John Welch declared, harping on a discredited idealism. "Transcendental!" John would snap when he meant "Nonsense!"

Glancing from the street to the sky, while the thread broke again, General Archbald reflected that it was easy to be an idealist in this pleasant spring of the year 1914, and to look with hope, if not with confidence, to the future. It was true that the familiar signs of uneasiness were abroad in the world. There was trouble not only in China and Mexico, where one naturally expected trouble to be, but among a part at least of the population of Europe. Power everywhere was growing more arrogant, and unrest more unrestful. Socialism was springing up and taking root in soil that appeared sterile. In Great Britain, Ulster and the suffragettes were disturbing a peace that turned in its broken sleep and dreamed of civil war. Nearer home, pirates had deserted the seas and embarked afresh as captains of industry.

But in the realm of ideas, where hope reigned, the prospect was brighter. There the crust of civilization, so thin and brittle over the world outside, was beginning to thicken. Religion and science, those hoary antagonists, were reconciled and clasped in a fraternal embrace. Together, in spite of nationalism, in spite even of nature, they would build, or invent, the New Jerusalem for mankind. In that favoured province, smooth, smiling, well-travelled, there would be neither sin nor disease, and without wars all the ancient wrongs would be righted. Nobody, not even the old sunning themselves on green benches, would be allowed to ramble in mind.

Well, perhaps. . . . No harm could come, he supposed, of a san-
guine outlook. Only—only, did not that outlook approach a little too
close to a formula? Were material ends all the world needed to build
on? Was passion, even in the old, a simple problem of lowering your
blood pressure and abandoning salt? Could a man discard his thinking
self as lightly as he discarded the doctrine of an ultimate truth? When
John said, "A green bench is only a green bench," was he wiser than
old David Archbald, who replied, "A green bench is not the green
bench I touch"? True, men no longer wrangled in public halls over
the nature of reality. But he could not see that exact knowledge and
precision of language had improved the quality of mankind. Well, the
wonder in every age, he supposed, was not that most men were savage, but that a few men were civilized. Only a few in every age, and
these few were the clowns in the parade. . . .

Suddenly, while he meditated, it seemed to him that the shape
of the external world, this world of brick and asphalt, of men and
women and machines moving, broke apart and dissolved from blown
dust into thought. Until this moment he had remembered with the
skin of his mind, not with the arteries; but now, when the concrete
world disappeared, he plunged downward through a dim vista of
time, where scattered scenes from the past flickered and died and flickered again. At eighty-three, the past was always like this. Never the
whole of it. Fragments, and then more fragments. No single part, not
even an episode, complete as it had happened.

In each hour, when he had lived it, life had seemed important to
him; but now he saw that it was composed of things that were all
little things in themselves, of mere fractions of time, of activities so
insignificant that they had passed away with the moment in which
they had quivered and vanished. How could any one, he asked, resting
there alone at the end, find a meaning, a pattern? Yet, though his
mind rambled now, he had walked in beaten tracks in his maturity.
His soul, it is true, had been a rebel; but he had given lip-homage, like
other men all over the world, to creeds that were husks. Like other
men all over the world, he had sacrificed to gods as fragile as the
bloom of light on the tulip tree. And what was time itself but the
bloom, the sheath enfolding experience? Within time, and within

time alone, there was life—the gleam, the quiver, the heart-beat, the immeasurable joy and anguish of being. . . .

The trail plunged straight and deep into the November forest. There was the tang of woodsmoke far off in a clearing. Frost was spun over the ground. The trees were brilliant with the yellow of hickory, the scarlet of sweet gum, the wine-red of oaks.

Why was he here? How had he come? Was he awake or asleep? Ah, he knew the place now. A forest trail at Stillwater. But they had left Stillwater fifty years ago. Well, no matter. No matter that he was a boy and an old man together, or that the boy wanted to be a poet. It was all the same life. A solitary fragment, but the same fragment of time. Time was stranger than memory. Stranger than his roaming again through this old forest, with his snack and a thin volume of Byron tucked away in his pocket. Here was the place he had stopped to eat his snack, while his pointer puppies, Pat and Tom, started game in the underbrush.

Then, as he stood with his head up and his eyes on the westering sun through the trees, he knew that he was watched. He knew that there were eyes somewhere among the leaves, and that these eyes, the eyes of the hunted, were watching him. It was the look in the eyes of the dying buck, but now it was everywhere. In the trees, in the sky, in the leaf-strewn pool, in the underbrush, in the very rocks by the trail. All these things reflected and magnified to his quivering nerves the look of the hunted. Because of the fear in his nerves, he cried out, expecting no answer. But before his call ended, there was a stir in the woods; the leaves scattered; and through the thick branches, he met the eyes of a runaway slave. Ragged, starved, shuddering, a slave crouched on the forest mould, and stared at the bread and meat in the boy's hand. When the food was given to him, he gulped it down and sat watching. Haggard with terror and pain, a dirty rag wrapping his swollen jaw, his clothes as tattered as the shirt of a scarecrow, he had been driven by hunger and cold up from the swamps. His breath came with a wheezing sound, and his flesh shed the sour smell of a wild animal. (A sour smell and a filthy rag after nearly seventy years!)

For weeks—for months, even, he may have lain hidden; but the deep swamps were far away, and he was the first fugitive slave to come within the boundaries of Stillwater. Beyond speech, beyond prayer, nothing remained in his eyes but bewilderment. "Nobody will hurt you," the boy said, emptying his pockets of the cornbread he had brought for the puppies. "Nobody will hurt you," he repeated, as if the creature were deaf or inarticulate. While he gave the promise, a wave of courage, of daring, of high adventure, rushed over him. For the second time in his young life he was defying the established order, he was in conflict with the moral notions of men. Is it true, he asked himself now, that man's pity and man's morality are for ever in conflict? Is it true that pity is by nature an outlaw? Well, he liked to think that he had not hesitated; no, not for an instant.

Again that day he had returned to the hidden place in the forest. He had brought clothes taken from the old garments in his father's and his grandfather's closets, food that he had found put away in the pantry, and a little wine that had been left over in the glasses at lunch. From his own bed he had stolen a blanket, and from his grandfather's "body servant" he had borrowed, as if in jest, the "ticket" that permitted Abram Jonas to visit his wife in another county. "When it is over, they will have to know," the boy thought, as he trudged back into the forest with the help he had come to fetch. "When it is over."

And then what had happened? His memory faded, died down to ashes, and shot up more brightly. Two mornings later, he had set out in an old buggy, with a decently clothed servant on the seat at his side. Miles away, screened from the turnpike, he had put a knapsack of food and the money he was saving to buy a colt into the hands of the runaway. "Your name is Abram Jonas. This is a paper that says so. You belong to Gideon Archbald, and you are going to visit your wife in Spottsylvania. Do you remember that? What is your name? Say it once more." "Abram Jonas, marster." "You'd better repeat it as you go along. I am Abram Jonas. Here is the paper that says so." "I'se Abram Jonas, marster. Dis heah is de paper." The fugitive looked up at him, first with the fear of the hunted, then with a dawning intelligence. "Thanky, marster," and turning, he had limped away from the turnpike into a forest trail. What had become of him? Had he escaped? Was he caught? Did he drop down like an animal and die of the shuddering misery of life?

After all these years General Archbald was still curious. But no

word had come. Only silence. Only silence, and the feeling that he
had taken his stand against the forces men about him called civilization. He had defied not only the moral notions of his age and his
place, but the law and the Constitution and the highest court in the
land. The truth came out at last when the real Abram Jonas asked for
the return of his "ticket"; and, as a measure of discipline, David's
father sent his youngest son abroad to be educated. He was sixteen
then; and years afterwards, when he left Oxford, he had lived in Paris
and London. Ironically, he had begun to think of himself as a stranger
in his world and his age. Yet when the war came, he was drawn back
to his own. He was drawn back to fight for old loyalties. After the
war he had endured poverty and self-denial and, worst of all, darned
clothes for a number of years. Then, while he was still burdened by
defeat, he had compromised Erminia and proposed to her the next
morning. Well, the past was woven of contradictions. For eighty-three
years he had lived two lives, and between these two different lives,
which corresponded only in time, he could trace no connection. What
he had wanted, he had never had; what he had wished to do, he had
never done. . . .

A fog clouded his mind, and he heard a voice like his own remark
testily, "Rambling is a sign of age, but I can't keep hold of the present." He couldn't keep hold of yesterday, of last month, of last year,
of the faces he knew best, of the features even of his wife, which had
grown vague since her death. Now, at the end, all faces of women,
even the faces of women he had slept with, looked alike to him. All
faces of women, except, perhaps—he wasn't sure—the face of Eva
Birdsong. "No, I can't remember," he repeated, while this suppressed
irritation clotted his thoughts. "I'm too old to remember that anything, especially any woman, made a difference in life."

Then, softly, while he was thinking this, the fog in his mind dis-
persed, and the crowd of women's faces melted to air, and reassembled
in a solitary face he had not forgotten. Fifty years—nearer sixty years
now—since he had lost her. What was the use, he pondered resentfully, in dragging back that old memory, that old passion? Why
couldn't the dead stay dead when one had put them away? Half a
century of dust! Yet she came to him, unspoiled by time, out of the
drifting haze of the present. Was it because he had loved her alone?
Or did she shine there, lost, solitary, unforgotten, merely because she

was farther away than the others? Not that it mattered. The cause
was unimportant beside the vast significance of that remembrance.

But why, after all, had he loved her? Even when he had fallen in
love with her that April in England, he could not point to a single
perfection and say, "I love her because she is beautiful, or brilliant,
or gifted." There was nothing unusual about her, his friends had remarked wonderingly. Dozens of women he knew in London were
handsomer, or wittier, or more conspicuously good. Small, shy, pale,
she was utterly lacking in the presence so much admired by English
society in the eighteen fifties.

When he first met her, she was married to the wrong man, and
was the mother of two delicate children. Had he fallen in love with
a veiled emptiness, a shadow without substance? Yet her blue eyes, as
soft as hyacinths, had promised joy that was infinite. Or had he loved
her because he had seen in her face the old fear and bewilderment of
the hunted? Had her memory endured because it was rooted not in
desire but in pity? Happier loves, lighter women, he had forgotten.
No matter what people say, he thought moodily, it takes more than
going to bed with a woman to fix her face in one's mind. For this
woman alone he had loved and lost without wholly possessing. Yet
she was there when he turned back, clear, soft, vivid, with some
secret in her look that thrilled, beckoned, and for ever eluded him.
Her eyes were still eloquent with light; the promised joy was still infinite; the merest glimmer of a smile had outlasted the monuments of
experience.

Yet like everything else in his life, important or unimportant, his
passion seemed, when it occurred, to come at the wrong moment. He
had intended to leave London; his ticket to Paris was in his pocket;
his bags were packed. Then a tooth had begun to ache—a tooth he
had lost only last year—and he had decided to stay over a day or two
and consult an English dentist who had once treated him for an
abscess. Not an act of God, he told himself (unless a twinge of pain
were an act of God), but a toothache had decided his destiny. Had the
pain come a day later, just one sunrise and one sunset afterwards, he
might have escaped. But falling as it did in that infinitesimal pin point
of time, his fate had been imprisoned in a single luminous drop of
experience.

Looking back, he had often wondered why there had been no

suspicion of danger, no visible or invisible warning that he was approaching the crossroads. Even the voice of his old friend was not ruffled when she met him on his way to the dentist and asked him to dinner. Some one had dropped out at the last moment. Tony Bracken (he had not forgotten that it was Tony Bracken) had been summoned to the deathbed of his great-uncle, and since Tony was the heir, he was obliged, naturally, to go when he was summoned. So, in spite of an occasional twinge, young David had braced himself with whiskey, applied laudanum to his tooth, and set out on an adventure beside which all the other occasions of his life were as flat as balloons that are pricked.

Even then, if she had not stood alone in that particular spot, between a lamp and a window, he might never have noticed her. "I wonder who she is," he thought, observing her loneliness; and then, as she raised her lowered lashes and he met her gaze, "She looks frightened." Was he called or driven when he went straight to her through the crowded room? Was it pity or the compulsion of sex that awakened while he watched her hesitate, bite her lip with a nervous tremor, and try in vain to think of something to say? "What can have frightened her?" he thought, as his hand closed over hers. Her eyes held him, and he asked, "Are you alone?" She shook her head, "No, my husband is with me." Her husband! Well, most women had husbands, especially most women one met at dinner in London. It was too late after that first look to think of a husband. It was too late to think even of children. In the end her marriage had won, as dead sounds inevitably win over living voices; but while he stood there and looked into her upturned face, that sulky, well-set-up sportsman and his two vague children had no part in the moment. Nothing mattered to him but the swift, tumultuous, utterly blissful sense of recognition—of now, here, this is my hour. Not the indefinite perhaps, to-morrow, some day in the future. The world, so colourless an instant before, had become alive to the touch. People and objects, sights, sounds, scents even, were vibrating with light.

And now, after sixty years, he could see that moment as clearly and coldly as if it were embedded in crystal. What is memory, a voice asked on the surface of thought, that it should outlast emotion?

For he remembered, but he could feel nothing. Nothing of the old rapture, the wildness, the illusion of love's immortality. He still mused with remorseful sympathy of Erminia, whom he had never loved, whose death had brought him release; but the burning ecstasy of desire had left only emptiness. Only emptiness, and the gradual chill of decay. Why had it happened? What was the meaning of it all? he demanded, caught within the twisting vision of age. Why had passion strong enough to ruin his life forsaken him while he lived? Why had it left only two diminished shapes, performing conventional gestures in a medium that was not time—that was not eternity? Did they still exist, those diminished shapes, in a timeless reality? Were they blown off from time into some transparent substance superior to duration? Did he survive there and here also? Which was the real David Archbald, the lover in memory, or the old man warming his inelastic arteries in the April sunshine? Or were they both merely spirals of cosmic dust, used and discarded in some experimental design? . . .

For an hour, a single hour, of her love he would have given his life when he was young. Her death had left a jagged rent in the universe. Yet if she returned to him now, he knew that it would mean only an effort—only the embarrassment that comes to persons who have loved and separated when they were young, and then meet again, unexpectedly, after they have grown old apart. Strangely enough, if any woman were to return from the dead, he preferred that she should be Erminia. Were the dead like that to the old? Were the intenser desires obliterated by the duller sensations? Joy, longing, disappointment, personalities that impinged upon one another, and then, separating, left only a faint outline of dust. Life was not worth the trouble, he thought. Life was not worth the pang of being, if only that faint outline remained. For the passion of his youth had ended as swiftly as it had begun, and at first he had not even suspected that the vehement craving was love. Helpless, bewildered, he had struggled blindly in the grasp of a power he could not resist and could not understand. All he knew was that her presence brought the world into beauty, that his whole being was a palpitating ache for her when she was absent. Inarticulate, passive, without the compelling ardour of sex, she had exercised that ruthless tyranny over desire. Or was it true, as he had sometimes imagined, that he himself was a rare, or perhaps a solitary, variation from sex? Were his deeper instincts awakened only by pity? As the generations went on, would there be others and still others of his breed born into an aging world? Was he more civilized than the average race of males, or simply more white-livered, as his virile grandfather believed? Well, he was too old, he repeated stubbornly, and life was too long over, to bother about what couldn't be helped. All he asked now was to sit in the April sunshine and wait for death with William beside him.

But was it really long over? What if it were true that some fragment of his lost ecstasy still survived there, burning' with its own radiance, beyond that dim vista of time? What if it were true that such bliss, such agony, such unavailing passion, could never end? All that spring and a part of the summer they had met secretly and joyously; and their secret joy had overflowed into the visible world. The landscape in which they moved borrowed the intense, quivering brightness of a place seen beneath the first or the last sunbeams. Spring was as fair as it looks to a man about to be hanged. Never again were the fields so starry with flowers, the green so luminous on the trees, the blue of the April sky so unearthly.

Years afterwards (sometimes as a young man in a strange bed, or again in the long fidelity to a wife he had never desired) a flitting dream of that English spring would flood his heart with an extraordinary delight. For a moment, no longer, since he invariably awoke while the joy flickered and died. Always, except in dreams, the past had escaped him. The anguish alone had stayed by him in the beginning, closer than the flesh to his bones or the nerves to his brain. And even in sleep, his bliss, when it returned, was only the tremor of light before a dawn that never approached.

Would it have been different if she had lived? For she had not lived, and he could never know what his life might have been without that ugly twist in the centre. They had planned to go away together, he devoured by love and longing, she fearful, passive, yielding mutely to that implacable power. In July, they would go to Venice and begin life over in Italy. The tickets were bought; her few boxes were at the station; the compartment was reserved; and then the merest accident had detained them. In the middle of that last night, while she was destroying her letters, one of the children had awakened with a sore throat. The nurse had come for her; she had sat till dawn beside the crib in the nursery; and when morning came she had lost the courage for flight. Fear, the old fear of life, of the unknown, had triumphed over them both.

For an eternity, it seemed to him, he walked the station platform. The guard shut the doors fast; the train drew out slowly. Still he watched with an intolerable ache of desolation while the engine was sliding over the straight track to the gradual curve in the distance. Then, turning away, he wandered, distraught with misery, out into the street. Why? why? why? he demanded of a heaven that seemed as unstable as water. Overhead, low, flying clouds scudded like foam driven by wind. In the country, he walked for hours through rain vague as suspense, soft, fine, slow as mist falling. Afterwards, she wrote that the struggle was over; she could not give up her children —and in the early autumn he heard from a stranger that she had drowned herself in a lake. Lost, vanished, destroyed by the fear for which he had loved her in the beginning!

When he knew that she was dead, he went alone into the country, to the secret places where they had met and loved in the spring. In his memory, these places shone out suddenly, one after another, as scattered lights come out in a landscape at dusk. The woods, the fields, the stream where cowslips bloomed, the grey bench with its blurred marking, the flowers, the bright grass. Now it was spring, but in this flickering scene, he walked there in autumn. Everything returned to him; the falling leaves, the trail of autumn scents in the air, everything but the vital warmth in his agony. Yet he knew, while this light flashed out and moved on again, through the encompassing darkness, that the form, if not the essence, of his passion had lain hidden somewhere beneath the surface of life.

In his anguish, he had flung himself beyond time, beyond space, beyond the boundaries of ultimate pain. A panic stillness was in the air; the whole external world, the blue sky, the half-bared trees, the slow fall of the leaves, the grass sprinkled with bloom,—all this was as hollow as a bubble blown from a pipe. Nothing remained alive, nothing but his despair in a universe that was dead to the touch. Again and again, he had cried her name in this panic stillness. He had cried her name; but she was gone; she could never return. Not though he waited for ever in the place she had left, could she return to him. In the end, she had escaped the terror of life. She had escaped his love and his pity. She had escaped into hollowness. But while the light shone in that vacant place, every twig on the trees, every blade of grass stood out illuminated.

Then this also had passed. Anguish, he discovered, was scarcely less brief than joy. The light went out and moved on again. Days, weeks, months, years passed, and a thick deposit of time hardened into a crust of despair over his wound. "I do not wish to forget," he said, and in forming the thought had already begun to forget and to recover. Yet, though he enjoyed life again, he never lost entirely the feeling that he was crippled in spirit, that there was a twisted root, an ugly scar, at the source of his being. The poet had died in him, and with the poet had died the old living torment of pity. When he sailed home to fight with his people, he found that the hunted buck, the driven slave, the killing of men in battle, left him more annoyed than distressed. Nothing, not even death, not even dying, seemed important; yet it was amazing to discover how much pleasure could come after one had ceased to expect happiness. Little things began to matter supremely. A smile, a kiss, a drink, a chance encounter in love or war. Appetite, he told himself, with gay cynicism, had taken the place of desire; and it was well that it should be so. There was much to be said in favour of living if only one were careful not to probe deeply, not to touch life on the nerve. If only one were careful, too, not to shatter the hardened crust of despair.

Even so, there were moments, there were hours when he was visited by the old sensation of something missing, as if he were part of a circle that was bent and distorted and broken in pieces. Life, as well as himself, seemed to be crippled, to have lost irrevocably a part of the whole. Still, in the solitude of the night, he would awake from his dream of a bliss that hovered near but never approached, and think, with a start of surprise, "If I awoke and found her beside me, would all the broken pieces come together again? Should I find that life was simple and right and natural and whole once more?" Then the dream, the surprise, the pang of expectancy, would fade and mingle and dissolve into emptiness. Like a man hopelessly ill who realizes that his malady is incurable, he would distract his mind with those blessed little things of life that bear thinking about. Well, he was used to it now, he would repeat again and again; he was used to the ache, the blackness, even to the stab of delight which pierced him in sleep. He had accepted the sense of something missing as a man accepts bodily disfigurement. After the first years of his loss, he was prepared, he felt, for all the malicious pranks grief can play on the memory. He was prepared even for those mocking resemblances that beckoned him in the street, for those arrowy glimpses of her in the faces of strange women, for that sudden wonder, poignant as a flame, "What if the past were a delusion!" "What if she were within reach of my arms!" No, it had been many years, thirty, almost forty years, since life had so mocked him.

He had fought through the war. Strange, how insignificant, how futile, any war appeared to him now! He could never, not even when he took an active part in one, understand the fascination war exercised over the human mind. Then, when it was over, he had let life have its way with him. Though the poet in him was lost, he became in later years a prosperous attorney, and a member in good standing, so long as one did not inquire too closely, of the Episcopal Church. . . .

Sitting there in the pale sunshine, so carefully brushed and dressed by his man Robert, he told himself that, in spite of the ugly twist in the centre, he had had a fair life. Nothing that he wanted, but everything that was good for him. Few men at eighty-three were able to look back upon so firm and rich a past, upon so smooth and variegated a surface. A surface! Yes, that, he realized now, was the flaw in the structure. Except for that one defeated passion in his youth, he had lived entirely upon the shifting surface of facts. He had been a good citizen, a successful lawyer, a faithful husband, an indulgent father; he had been, indeed, everything but himself. Always he had fallen into the right pattern; but the centre of the pattern was missing. Once again, the old heartbreaking question returned. Why and what is human personality? An immortal essence? A light that is never blown out? Or a breath, a murmur, the rhythm of molecular changes, scarcely more than the roving whisper of wind in the tree-tops?

A multitude of women people the earth: fair women, dark women; tall women, short women; kind women, cruel women; warm women, cold women; tender women, sullen women—a multitude of women, and only one among them all had been able to appease the deep unrest in his nature. Only one unit of being, one cluster of living cells, one vital ray from the sun's warmth, only one ripple in the endless cycle of time or eternity, could restore the splintered roots of his life, could bring back to him the sense of fulfilment, completeness, perfection. A single personality out of the immense profusion, the infinite numbers! A reality that eluded analysis! And yet he had been happy as men use the word happiness. Rarely, since his youth, had he remembered that something was missing, that he had lost irrevocably a part from the whole, lost that sense of fulfilment not only in himself but in what men call Divine goodness. Irrevocably—but suppose, after all, the loss were not irrevocable!

Suddenly, without warning, a wave of joy rose from the unconscious depths. Suppose that somewhere beyond, in some central radiance of being, he should find again that ecstasy he had lost without ever possessing. For one heart-beat, while the wave broke and the dazzling spray flooded his thoughts, he told himself that he was immortal, that here on this green bench in the sun, he had found the confirmation of love, faith, truth, right, Divine goodness. Then, as swiftly as it had broken, the wave of joy spent itself. The glow, the surprise, the startled wonder, faded into the apathetic weariness of the end. He was only an old man warming his withered flesh in the April sunshine. "My life is nearly over," he thought, "but who knows what life is in the end?"

A cloud passed overhead; the changeable blue of the sky darkened and paled; a sudden wind rocked the buds on the tulip tree; and in the street, where life hurried by, a pillar of dust wavered into the air, held together an instant, and then sank down and whirled in broken eddies over the pavement.

Marjorie KINNAN RAWLINGS

Why she selected HYACINTH DRIFT

I believe that the chapter in my last book, *Cross Creek,* titled "Hyacinth Drift," expresses my feeling for a natural background, which to me must always stand like a back-drop behind any study of human relations.

Hawthorn, Fla.　　　　　　　MARJORIE KINNAN RAWLINGS
May 19, 1942

ONCE I lost touch with the Creek. I had had hardships that seemed to me more than one could bear alone. I loved the Creek, I loved the grove, I loved the shabby farmhouse. Suddenly they were nothing. The difficulties were greater than the compensations. I talked morosely with my friend Dessie. I do not think she understood my torment, for she is simple and direct and completely adjusted to all living. She knew only that a friend was in trouble.

She said, "We'll take one of those river trips we've talked about. We'll take that eighteen-foot boat of yours with a couple of outboard motors and put in at the head of the St. John's River. We'll go down the river for several hundred miles."

I agreed, for the Creek was torture.

Men protested.

"Two women alone? The river runs through some of the wildest country in Florida. You'll be lost in the false channels. No one ever goes as far as the head of the river." Then, passionately, betraying themselves, "It will be splendid. What if you do get lost? Don't let any one talk you out of it."

The river was a blue smear through the marsh. The marsh was tawny. It sprawled to the four points of the compass; flat; interminable; meaningless.

I thought, "This is fantastic. I am about to deliver myself over to a nightmare."

But life was a nightmare. The river was at least of my own choosing.

The St. John's River flows from south to north and empties into the Atlantic near the Florida-Georgia line. Its great mouth is salt and tidal, and ocean-going vessels steam into it as far as Jacksonville. It rises in a chain of small lakes near the Florida east coast, south of Melbourne. The lakes are linked together by stretches of marsh through which, in times of high water, the indecisive course of the young river is discernible. Two years of drought had shrunken the stream and dried the marshes. The southernmost sources were overgrown with marsh grass. Water hyacinths had filled the channels. The navigable head of the St. John's proved to be near Fort Christmas, where the highway crosses miles of wet prairie and cypress swamp between Orlando and Indian River City.

There is a long high fill across the marsh, with a bridge over the slight blue twisting that is the river. We drove car and trailer down an embankment and unloaded the small boat in the backwaters. The bank was of black muck, smelling of decay. It sucked at our feet as we loaded our supplies. We took our places in the boat and drifted slowly into midchannel.

Water hyacinths began to pass us, moving with a faint anxiety in their lifted leaves. The river was no more than a path through high grass. We swung under the bridge and the boy at the wheel of our car lifted his hand in parting and shot away. Something alive and potent gripped the flat bottom of the boat. The hyacinths moved more rapidly. The river widened to a few yards and rounded a bend, suddenly decisive. Dess started the outboard motor. I hunched myself together amidships and spread the U. S. Coast and Geodetic Survey river chart on my knees and clicked open my compass. I noticed disconsolately, "Lights, Beacons, Buoys and Dangers Corrected for Information Received to Date of Issue." There would be neither lights, beacons nor buoys for at least a hundred miles. Bridge and highway disappeared, and there was no longer any world but this incredible marsh, this unbelievable amount of sky.

Half a mile beyond the bridge a fisherman's shack leaned over the river. For sociability, we turned in by the low dock. The fisherman and his wife squatted on their haunches and gave us vague directions. We pointed to Bear Island on our chart.

He said, "You won't never see Bear Island. Where they got a channel marked on your map it's plumb full o' hyacinths. Down the river a ways you'll see a big ol' sugar-berry tree stickin' up in the marsh. That's your mark. You keep to the left. The next mark you'll get is a good ways down the river. You go left by a pertickler tall piece o' grass."

The woman said, "You just got to keep tryin' for the main channel. You'll get so you can tell."

The man said, "I ain't never been as far as you-all aim to go. From what I hear, if you oncet get through Puzzle Lake, you got right clare river."

The woman said, "You'll some kind of enjoy yourselves. The river life's the finest kind of life. You couldn't get you no better life than the river."

We pushed away from the dock.

The man said, "I'd be mighty well obliged if you'd send me a post-card when you get where you're goin'. That-a-way I won't have to keep on worryin' about you."

Dess cranked the motor and they waved after us. Dess began to whistle, shrilly and tunelessly. She is an astonishing young woman. She was born and raised in rural Florida and guns and campfires and fishing-rods and creeks are corpuscular in her blood. She lives a sophisticate's life among worldly people. At the slightest excuse she steps out of civilization, naked and relieved, as I should step out of a soiled chemise. She is ten years my junior, but she calls me, with much tenderness, pitying my incapabilities, "Young un."

"Young un," she called, "it's mighty fine to be travelling."

I was prepared for marsh. It was startling to discover that there was in sight literally nothing else. Far to the west, almost out of sight to the east, in a dark line like cloud banks was the distant swamp that edged this fluid prairie. We may have taken the wrong channel for a mile or so, for we never saw the sugar-berry tree; nothing but river grass, brittle and gold, interspersed, where the ground was highest, with butter-yellow flowers like tansy. By standing up in the boat I could see the rest of the universe. And the universe was yellow marsh, with a pitiless blue infinity over it, and we were lost at the bottom.

At five o'clock in the afternoon the river dissolved without warning into a two-mile spread of flat confusion. A mile of open water lay ahead of us, neither lake nor river nor slough. We advanced into the center. When we looked over our shoulders, the marsh had closed in over the channel by which we had come. We were in a labyrinth. The stretch of open water was merely the fluid heart of a maze. Channels extended out of it in a hundred directions—some shallow, obviously no outlets; others as broad as the stream we had left behind us, and tempting. We tried four. Each widened in a deceptive sweep. A cirling of the shore-line showed there was no channel. Each time we returned to the one spot we could again identify—a point of marsh thrust into the water like a swimming moccasin.

Dess said, "That map and compass don't amount to much."

That was my fault. I was totally unable to follow the chart. I found later, too late for comfort, that my stupidity was not entirely to blame, for, after the long drought, half the channels charted no longer existed. The sun had become a prodigious red disc dropping into a distant slough. Blue herons flew over us to their night's quarters. Somewhere the river must continue neatly out of this desolation. We came back once more to the point of land. It was a foot or two out of water and a few square yards of the black muck were comparatively dry. We beached the rowboat and made camp.

There was no dry wood. We carried a bag of fat pine splinters but it occurred to me desperately that I would save them. I laid out a cold supper while Dess set up our two camp cots side by side on the open ground. As the sun slid under the marsh to the west, the full moon surged out of it to the east. The marsh was silver and the water was steel, with ridges of rippled ebony where ducks swam in the twilight. Mosquitoes sifted against us like a drift of needles. We were exhausted. We propped our mosquito bar over the cots on crossed oars, for there was no bush, no tree, from which to hang it.

We did not undress, but climbed under the blankets. Three people had had a hand in loading our cots and the wooden end-pieces were missing. The canvas lay limp instead of taut, and our feet hung over one end and our heads over the other, so that we were disposed like corpses on inadequate stretchers. The crossed oars slid slowly to the muck, the mosquito bar fluttered down and mosquitoes were about us in a swarm. Dess reached under her cot for her light rifle, propped it between us, and balanced the mosquito bar accurately on the end of its barrel.

"You can get more good out of a .22 rifle than any other kind of gun," she informed me earnestly.

I lay on my back in a torment of weariness, but there was no rest. I had never lain in so naked a place, bared so flatly to the sky. The moon swung high over us and there was so sleeping for the brightness. Toward morning dewdrops collected over the netting as though the moonlight had crystallized. I fell asleep under a diamond curtain and wakened with warm full sunlight on my face. Cranes and herons were wading the shore near me and Dess was in the rowboat a few hundred yards away, casting for bass.

Marsh and water glittered iridescent in the sun. The tropical March air was fresh and wind-washed. I was suddenly excited. I made campfire with fatwood splinters and cooked bacon and toast and coffee. Their fragrance eddied across the water and I saw Dess lift her nose and put down her rod and reel. She too was excited.

"Young un," she called, "where's the channel?"

I pointed to the northeast and she nodded vehemently. It had come to both of us like a revelation that the water hyacinths were drifting faintly faster in that direction. From that instant we were never very long lost. Forever after, where the river sprawled in confusion, we might shut off the motor and study the floating hyacinths until we caught, in one direction, a swifter pulsing, as though we put our hands close and closer to the river's heart. It was very simple. Like all simple facts, it was necessary to discover it for oneself.

We had, in a moment, the feel of the river; a wisdom for its vagaries. When the current took us away that morning, we gave ourselves over to it. There was a tremendous exhilaration, an abandoning of fear. The new channel was the correct one, as we knew it should be. The river integrated itself again. The flat golden banks closed in on both sides of us, securing a snug safety. The strangeness of flowing water was gone, for it was all there was of living.

In midmorning, solid land made its way here and there toward us, and then in time withdrew. For a mile we had a low rolling hill for company, with traces of ancient habitation at its peak: a few yards of rotting fence, a crepe myrtle, an orange tree.

We passed a lone fisherman hauling his seine. His legs were planted cranelike in the water. His long arms looped up folds of the gray net with the rhythm of a man swinging a sickle. We told him our origin and our destination. Because we were now a part of the river he offered us a fish. His catch was meager and we refused it. We passed cattle, wild on the marsh. They loomed startlingly above us, their splotched black and brown and red and white luminous against the blue sky, like cattle in Bonheur pictures hung high above the eye-level.

The river dissolved into shallow pools and was interspersed with small islands, palm-crowded and lonely. It was good to see trees, lifting the eyes from so many miles of flatness. The pools gathered themselves together and there was under us again a river, confined between obvious banks. Sometimes the low-lying land was dry for a great distance, specked with soapberry bushes, and the wild cattle cropped a short grass that grew there.

We had Puzzle Lake and then Lake Harney, we knew, somewhere ahead of us. We came out from a canal-like stretch of river into a body of open water. Dess and I stiffened. She shut off the motor.

Far away across the marsh there was a long white rolling as though all the sheep in the world were being driven through prehistoric dust clouds. The mad thought came to me that we had embarked on the wrong river and had suddenly reached the ocean, that the vast billowing in the distance was surf. But something about the thing was familiar. That distant line was a fill, a forty-foot sand embankment across the marsh between the St. John's River and the east coast town of Mimms, and I had driven its one-rut grade two weeks before. The marsh had been even more desolate from the height of that untravelled, unfinished roadway. The fill ended, I remembered, in a forty-foot drop to a decrepit ferry that crossed the river. The billowing we now saw was loose white sand moving along the embankment ahead of a high wind. I ran my finger along the chart. There was no ferry mapped for the far side of Puzzle Lake. A ferry was indicated, however, on the far side of Lake Harney.

I said, "Dess, we've come through Puzzle Lake and didn't know it. We've reached Lake Harney."

She did not question my surety. She spun the motor.

"All right, young un. Which way across?"

I compared chart and compass. I pointed. She headed the boat as I directed. I split nautical points to keep our position exactly. I took her across water so shoal we had to pole through it; under overhanging banks and through dense stiff sedge, when often a plainly better channel swung a few feet away in another direction. The extreme low water, I called, had evidently dried Lake Harney to this confused alternating of open lake and maze. Dess whistled dubiously but asked no questions. We struck deep water at last and were at the ferry I had indeed remembered. The old ferryman peered from his hut and came down to meet us, shading his eyes. He seemed to find us very strange indeed. Where had we come from?

"We put in yesterday at Fort Christmas," I answered him, "and I'm glad to say we've just finished navigating Lake Harney."

He stared in earnest.

"Lady," he said, "you haven't even reached Lake Harney. You've just come through Puzzle Lake."

The ferry here simply was not charted, and the episode proves anything one may wish it to prove. I felt contentedly that it proved a harmony with the river so complete that not even the mistaking of whole lakes could lose us. Others of more childish faith were sure it proved the goodness of God in looking after imbeciles. I know only that we were congratulated by fishermen the entire length of the river on navigating Puzzle Lake successfully.

"I brought our boat through Puzzle Lake," I told them with simple dignity, "by the sternest use of chart and compass."

And it was only in Dess' more evil moments that she added, "—in the firm belief that she was crossing Lake Harney."

Lake Harney itself was four miles long, unmistakably broad and open. We crossed it in late afternoon with the westerly sun on our left cheeks and a pleasant March wind ruffling the blue water. Passing out of the lake we bought roe shad, fresh and glistening from the seine. The current quickened. The hyacinths plunged forward. The character of the river changed the instant the lake was left behind. It was deep and swift, the color of fine clear coffee that is poured with the sun against it. It was mature. All its young torture was forgotten, and its wanderings in the tawny marsh. The banks had changed. They were high. Tall palms crowded great live oaks and small trees grew humbly in their shadows. Toward sunset we swung under the western bank at one of those spots a traveller recognized instinctively as, for the moment, home.

If I could have, to hold forever, one brief place and time of beauty, I think I might choose the night on that high lonely bank about the St. John's River. We found there a deserted cabin, gray and smooth as only cypress weathers. There was no door for its doorway, no panes or shutters for its windows, but the roof was whole, with lichens thick across the shingles. Dess built me a fire of red cedar. She sat on the sagging steps and whittled endpieces for our cots, and I broiled shad and shad roe over fragrant coals, and French-fried potatoes, and found I had the ingredients for Tartar sauce.

Dess nailed a board between low rafters in the cabin from which to hang the mosquito bar over our cots, and said, "Young un, Christopher Columbus had nothing on us. He had a whole ocean to fool around in, and a what-do-you call it:—a continent, to come out on. Turn that boy loose in the St. John's marsh, and he'd have been lost as a hound puppy."

We had hot baths out of a bucket that night, and sat on the cabin steps in pajamas while the fire died down. Suddenly the soft night turned silver. The moon was rising. We lay on our cots a long time, wakeful because of beauty. The moon shone through the doorway and windows and the light was patterned with the shadows of Spanish moss waving from the live oaks. There was a deserted grove somewhere behind the cabin, and the incredible sweetness of orange bloom drifted across us.

A mocking-bird sang from a palm tree at sunrise. We found by daylight that the cabin sat among guava trees higher than the roof. The yard was pink and white with periwinkles. Dess shot a wild duck on the wing with the .22 and I roasted it in the Dutch oven for breakfast. We lay all morning on the bank in the strong sunlight, watching the mullet jumping in the river. At noon we went reluctantly to the water's edge to load the boat and move on. The boat was half filled with water and was resting with an air of permanence on the river bottom.

My first thought was of pure delight that it was no longer necessary to leave this place. But Dess was already stepping out of her sailor trousers. I too removed superfluous clothing. We bailed the boat and found two streams of water gushing in steadily under bow and stern seats. We managed to drag the boat on shore and turn it upside down. We found that the caulking had worked loose out of two seams. Dess donated a shirt, and for two hours with pocket knives we stuffed strips of cloth into treacherous cracks. When we put the boat in the river again, the caulking held.

I begged to stay another night, but Dess was restless. We pushed on for the few hours left of daylight. The shore line narrowed to thin strips of sand with tall twisted palms along them. The clear brown river was glassy in the windless evening. The palms were mirrored along both banks, so that when white ibises flew over in a rosy sunset, the river might have been the Nile.

We camped that night in comparative comfort under an upturned tree root. The spot was not tempting from the water, but once we were snugged down, it proved cavelike and cozy. A moccasin slithered from under my feet at the edge of camp and went harmlessly about his business. Dess cut down a young palmetto and we had swamp cabbage for dinner. I cooked it with a piece of white bacon and baked corn sticks in the Dutch oven to go with it.

In the morning we watched the hyacinth drift closely to be sure of taking the cut to Prairie Landing instead of wandering into Lake Jessup. A highway crossed the river here and folk waved down to us. In the cut a woman was running a catfish line. She was gaunt and sun-tanned, ragged and dirty. She pulled in the line, hand over hand, with a quick desperate accuracy. She lifted a shaggy head when we called "Howdy" and said "Hey," and bent again to her line with a terrifying absorption. Something about her shamed all soft, clean women.

We cut across the south end of Lake Monroe and found that it was Sunday in the city of Sanford. We had reached the outpost of large-vessel traffic on the St. John's, and we put-putted under the bow of an incoming freight steamer. We had meant to bathe and put on clean shirts and slacks that morning, but there had been no landing place among the marshes. Dess strapped around her waist the leather belt that held her bowie knife at one hip and her revolver at the other, and felt better prepared for Sanford than if we had been clean. She landed us neatly at the city dock, in the lee of an immaculate pleasure yacht from Long Island Sound. The owner, trim in double-breasted blue, came to the rail and looked down at us. We had also intended to do a better job of stowing. The bow end of our boat was piled untidily with our supplies, our folded cots, our extra outboard motor and our gasoline tins. Dess stood up in the stern and stretched and shifted her armored belt.

She called up to the yacht owner, "Safe to come into this town?"

"That depends on what you are coming for," he said, and smiled.

"Not a thing but gasoline. Where's the nearest place a fellow can fuel up?"

"All the filling stations near the docks are closed this morning. But I'm having my yacht refuelled, and a station is opening for me. How much do you need?"

Dess checked out tins with her eye.

"Five gallons is about right."

He smiled again.

"I'm sending my car to the station. If you will bring your tins up, I'll be very happy to have my man take you along and bring you back."

"Thanks, fellow," Dess said. "You're a white man."

There was a sound inside the yacht. There simmered up the companionway a woman, magnificent in pink spectator sports costume. The crew jumped almost to attention and escorted her down the yacht's gangplank.

The woman snapped over her shoulders, "I must have the car at once. I cannot be late to church for this nonsense."

Our white man turned rosy and made a comradely gesture to us.

He leaned over and whispered, "The car will be back in just a moment. If you don't mind waiting—. Please wait."

"O.K., fellow," Dess said.

The pink spectator sports swept into a limousine. In a few minutes the car had returned. We were driven in style to a filling station and our tins filled with gasoline. We bought the New York Sunday papers. The yacht crew brought the tins down to us and helped us re-stow our duffle. Dess outlined our trip briefly to the owner. She cranked up and we were off again.

"Good luck!" called the yacht owner. "The very best of good luck!"

He waved after us as far as we could see him, as though reluctant to break a mystic thread. His face was wistful.

"The poor b—," Dess said pityingly and indignantly. "I'll bet he'd give his silk shirt to go down the river with us instead of with Pink Petticoats."

We used the gasoline and forgot to read the papers.

Out of Lake Monroe we began to see fishermen pulling seines every few miles along the river. Here and there was a camp. Once a pal-metto thatching made a tip-tilted shelter and a startlingly pretty girl in overalls looked out with a placid face. We passed an old fisherman and a little girl in a boat. The child was rowing. We encountered a tall lumber steamer in mid-stream. The book of Pilot Rules on my lap provided that the boat in our position should swing to starboard, passing to port, and should give two short distinct blasts on the boat's whistle to signify its intention. Two lusty blasts on my dog whistle brought no answering blow from the steamer, but the cook, paring potatoes in the open stern, waved to us as we angled to cross their wake.

We had "right clare river" now, the river life was indeed the finest of lives, and there was no hurry left in the world. We put up a golden-brown deep creek and fished all afternoon. A white egret fished com-panionably with us a few yards away, and water turkeys flapped their wings lazily from high cypresses. A water moccasin arched his six feet of magnificent mottled hide between a spider lily and a swamp laurel. The laurel was in full bloom and the sunny creek was a wedge of fragrance. We found a white sand bar and had a swim in water clear as amber.

Camp that night was on a pine bluff, very high and dry and decent after the tree root and the moccasin. Storm threatened for the first time and we stretched a tarpaulin between slash pines to make a shelter. We were on the east bank. The moon and sun rose behind us. In the morning we found that small animals had dug holes all about us while we slept.

We pushed the motor that day. The river was deep and narrow. The banks were dense swamp, black with undergrowth. A landing would have been, for the most, impossible. We ate a cold lunch as we travelled. Beyond Deland Landing we called at a houseboat tethered to the bank. Its owner had been captain of the old Clyde River Line, and he received our request for advice on crossing Lake George with the old-school graciousness of large craft meeting small. He took my compass well forward of the houseboat, away from its metal stanchions, to chart our course across the fourteen-mile lake the more precisely. I made the mental note that perhaps I had better move the cast iron Dutch oven from under my seat. He gave us a set of distance cards and a choice of courses. The more sporting course was the main channel used by large steamers. In a boat as small as ours we should be out of sight of land for nearly an hour. The west channel never entirely lost the land, but if it came on to blow, we would do best by taking neither, and hugging the west shore. He bowed us courteously on our way.

We planned to camp as close as possible that night to the Volusia bar. We wanted to cross Lake George in the early morning before the wind rose. Beyond the village of Astor the scrub reared high against the west. Cypress swamp bordered the river. There was scarcely a patch of ground large enough to step out on. We pushed on to a cluster of fishing huts at the junction of lake and river. Hyacinths moved here in vast green flexible sheets. The huts were on stakes over the river and were not inviting.

Only one stood on enough ground to offer camping facilities. We poled through the hyacinths and called from the rickety small dock. A sullen-faced woman spoke curtly from the doorway. We could see the interior of the shack. There were pallets on the floor; a table; a chair or two. A dirty child peered from her skirts. We were not wanted here, it was plain, but she was a squatter, with no right to refuse us. Dess and I debated the matter in low voices. The woman, the place, seemed to me preferable to the dark swamp to which we must return. But the wind was freshening from the west. Even now, hyacinths were piling in behind us.

Dess said, "I'd rather sleep with a moccasin over each shoulder than get caught in a hyacinth block."

We swung about to turn back up the river. As we pushed away, the child dropped to the doorsill and began to pat his hands together. He chanted with shrill delight, "They're going away! They're going away!" I wondered what life had done to this woman and this child, that, among a friendly fisher-folk, they should know such fear and hate of strangers.

When the sun dropped behind the scrub, swamp and river were in darkness. At twilight we had retraced several miles. When we landed at the only promising opening, we found a comfortable square of high ground. As we were making camp three fishermen hailed us excitedly. Were we the women who had put in at Fort Christmas nearly a week before? If so, they must know. Word had been sent down the river from other fishermen to watch for us and to report our safety. The three were camped across the river from us. They had a trail cut into the swamp to a spot of sound dry earth. Their campfire flickered sociably all night.

The course for the main channel was, simply, north by east. But there was fog at daylight, and when the fog lifted a little the wind came freshly from its week-long westerly quarter. Boats twice our size had been in trouble on Lake George. Its squalls were notably dangerous. It seemed needlessly heroic to deny ourselves the comfort of the sight of land. We had no intention of hugging the safe shore, so we compromised on the west channel. We left the great channel markers behind and a gust of wind twisted our stern. There was a half hour when the haze threatened to obscure all visible shore lines. Then Drayton's Island lifted ahead.

Midway, the wind was blowing the whitecaps off the waves, but it was helpfully behind us. With both arms braced against the steering handle of the motor, Dess kept the boat headed when water that rolled like surf lifted our stern. The propeller churned high out of the water. When it dropped again the boat lunged and turned.

I called, "She's slueing badly!"

Dess shouted, "Young un, if you had this wind under your stern, you'd slue, too!"

The distant shore seemed stationary. We passed the north point of Drayton's Island, where the main channel joined the west, with the lake boiling after us. At the first sheltered dock we stopped to rest and an old Negro gave us fresh drinking water. We had been some two and a half hours in crossing the lake.

The river resumed its broad quiet way as though it had left no tumult behind it. It had the dignity of age, was not now in that dark hurry to reach the sea. At Welaka one afternoon we left the hyacinths swirling leisurely and turned up our home river, the Ocklawaha. I thought in a panic, I shall never be happy on land again. I was afraid once more of all the painful circumstances of living.

But when the dry ground was under us, the world no longer fluid, I found a forgotten loveliness in all the things that have nothing to do with men. Beauty is pervasive, and fills, like perfume, more than the object that contains it. Because I had known intimately a river, the earth pulsed under me. The Creek was home. Oleanders were sweet past bearing, and my own shabby fields, weed-tangled, were newly dear. I knew, for a moment, that the only nightmare is the masochistic human mind.

JESSE STUART Why he selected

ANOTHER APRIL

It is very strange how a man whose life has been filled with hard work and the associations of many human beings would in his declining days start talking to a terrapin. Maybe there is an understanding between an old man and an old terrapin when each knows his time to be alive is very limited. This sort of a thing haunts me when a ruthless dynamic sort of a human being, who has been as tough as the tough-butted white oaks on the rugged mountain slopes, is calmed enough by the passing of time to sit down and talk with a wrinkled-neck terrapin, who is and has been quite willing to live half-buried in the dry dirt under the smokehouse floor during the cold winter months and to eat tomatoes in the garden during the summer. Maybe it is because I am partial to this material—the reason I like this story— the reason why I am willing to put it forward as the representative of my best work. Furthermore there is something to man's associations with earth and the living creatures upon the earth and his fight with the elements—his cutting trees, plowing the rugged soil for a scanty livelihood—these are enduring things. There is not a tint of false propaganda in this type of thing; it is as solid and substantial as stone.

It took me less than two hours to write this short story; it happened to be one of two short stories I wrote the same day. The other story, too, sold to a reputable magazine. I knew every detail in this story, "Another April," before I sat down at the typewriter. Two days after I had written this story, I sat down and added another paragraph. Strange that the editor of *Harper's Magazine*, Frederick Allen, asked that this paragraph be removed. I wrote him to remove it—that made the story published just the way I wrote it. The story wrote itself. My mind was only a medium to put it on paper. This is one of Nature's own stories, that Nature and Life have worked out together, dealing with three generations of people and a terrapin. I cannot say this is a great story; I rather doubt that it is. I cannot say it is the best story I have written. It all depends on the judge's tastes for a short story and his standards for judgement.

Riverton, Ky.   JESSE STUART
August 9, 1942

"NOW, Pap, you won't get cold," Mom said as she put a heavy wool cap over his head.

"Huh, what did ye say?" Grandpa asked, holding his big hand cupped over his ear to catch the sound.

"Wait until I get your gloves," Mom said, hollering real loud in Grandpa's ear. Mom had forgotten about his gloves until he raised his big bare hand above his ear to catch the sound of Mom's voice.

"Don't get 'em," Grandpa said, "I won't ketch cold."

Mom didn't pay any attention to what Grandpa said. She went on to get the gloves anyway. Grandpa turned toward me. He saw that I was looking at him.

"Yer Ma's a-puttin' enough clothes on me to kill a man," Grandpa said, then he laughed a coarse laugh like March wind among the pine tops at his own words. I started laughing but not at Grandpa's words. He thought I was laughing at them and we both laughed together. It pleased Grandpa to think that I had laughed with him over something funny that he had said. But I was laughing at the way he was dressed. He looked like a picture of Santa Claus. But Grandpa's cheeks were not cherry-red like Santa Claus' cheeks. They were covered with white thin beard—and above his eyes were long white eyebrows almost as white as percoon petals and very much longer.

Grandpa was wearing a heavy wool suit that hung loosely about his big body but fitted him tightly round the waist where he was as big and as round as a flour barrel. His pant legs were as big round his pipe-stem legs as emptied meal sacks And his big shoes, with his heavy wool socks dropping down over their tops, looked like sled runners. Grandpa wore a heavy wool shirt and over his wool shirt he wore a heavy wool sweater and then his coat over the top of all this. Over his coat he wore a heavy overcoat and about his neck he wore a wool scarf.

The way Mom had dressed Grandpa you'd think there was a heavy snow on the ground but there wasn't. April was here instead and the sun was shining on the green hills where the wild plums and the wild crab apples were in bloom enough to make you think there were big snowdrifts sprinkled over the green hills. When I looked at Grandpa and then looked out at the window at the sunshine and the green grass I laughed more. Grandpa laughed with me.

"I'm a-goin' to see my old friend," Grandpa said just as Mom came down the stairs with his gloves.

"Who is he, Grandpa?" I asked, but Grandpa just looked at my mouth working. He didn't know what I was saying. And he hated to ask me the second time.

Mom put the big wool gloves on Grandpa's hands. He stood there just like I had to do years ago, and let Mom put his gloves on. If Mom didn't get his fingers back in the glove-fingers exactly right Grandpa quarreled at Mom. And when Mom fixed his fingers exactly right in his gloves the way he wanted them Grandpa was pleased.

"I'll be a-goin' to see 'im," Grandpa said to Mom. "I know he'll still be there."

Mom opened our front door for Grandpa and he stepped out slowly, supporting himself with his big cane in one hand. With the other hand he held to the door facing. Mom let him out of the house just like she used to let me out in the spring. And when Grandpa left the house I wanted to go with him, but Mom wouldn't let me go. I wondered if he would get away from the house—get out of Mom's sight—and pull off his shoes and go barefooted and wade the creeks like I used to do when Mom let me out. Since Mom wouldn't let me go with Grandpa, I watched him as he walked slowly down the path in front of our house. Mom stood there watching Grandpa too. I think she was afraid that he would fall. But Mom was fooled; Grandpa toddled along the path better than my baby brother could.

"He used to be a powerful man," Mom said more to herself than she did to me. "He was a timber cutter. No man could cut more timber than my father; no man in the timber woods could sink an ax deeper into a log than my father. And no man could lift the end of a bigger saw log than Pap could."

"Who is Grandpa goin' to see, Mom?" I asked.

"He's not goin' to see anybody," Mom said.

"I heard 'im say that he was goin' to see an old friend," I told her.

"Oh, he was just a-talkin'," Mom said.

I watched Grandpa stop under the pine tree in our front yard. He set his cane against the pine tree trunk, pulled off his gloves and put them in his pocket. Then Grandpa stooped over slowly, as slowly as the wind bends down a sapling, and picked up a pine cone in his big soft fingers. Grandpa stood fondling the pine cone in his hand. Then, one by one, he pulled the little chips from the pine cone—tearing it to pieces like he was hunting for something in it—and after he had torn it to pieces he threw the pine-cone stem on the ground. Then he pulled pine needles from a low hanging pine bough and he felt of each pine needle between his fingers. He played with them a long time before he started down the path.

"What's Grandpa doin'?" I asked Mom.

But Mom didn't answer me.

"How long has Grandpa been with us?" I asked Mom.

"Before you's born," she said. "Pap has been with us eleven years. He was eighty when he quit cuttin' timber and farmin'; now he's ninety-one."

I had heard her say that when she was a girl he'd walk out on the snow and ice barefooted and carry wood in the house and put it on the fire. He had shoes but he wouldn't bother to put them on. And I heard her say that he would cut timber on the coldest days without socks on his feet but with his feet stuck down in cold brogan shoes and he worked stripped above the waist so his arms would have freedom when he swung his double-bitted ax. I had heard her tell how he'd sweat and how the sweat in his beard would be icicles by the time he got home from work on the cold winter days. Now Mom wouldn't let him get out of the house for she wanted him to live a long time.

As I watched Grandpa go down the path toward the hog pen he stopped to examine every little thing along his path. Once he waved his cane at a butterfly as it zigzagged over his head, its polkadot wings fanning the blue April air. Grandpa would stand when a puff of wind came along, and hold his face against the wind and let the wind play with his white whiskers. I thought maybe his face was hot under his beard and he was letting the wind cool his face. When he reached the hog pen he called the hogs down to the fence. They came running and grunting to Grandpa just like they were talking to him. I knew that Grandpa couldn't hear them trying to talk to him but he could see their mouths working and he knew they were trying to say something. He leaned his cane against the hog pen, reached over the fence, and patted the hogs' heads. Grandpa didn't miss patting one of our seven hogs.

As he toddled up the little path alongside the hog pen he stopped under a blooming dogwood. He pulled a white blossom from a bough that swayed over the path above his head, and he leaned his big bundled body against the dogwood while he tore each petal from the blossom and examined it carefully. There wasn't anything his dim blue eyes missed. He stopped under a redbud tree before he reached the garden to break a tiny spray of redbud blossoms. He took each blossom from the spray and examined it carefully.

"Gee, it's funny to watch Grandpa," I said to Mom, then I laughed.

"Poor Pap," Mom said, "he's seen a lot of Aprils come and go. He's seen more Aprils than he will ever see again."

I don't think Grandpa missed a thing on the little circle he took before he reached the house. He played with a bumblebee that was bending a windflower blossom that grew near our corncrib beside a big bluff. But Grandpa didn't try to catch the bumblebee in his big bare hand. I wondered if he would and if the bumblebee would sting him, and if he would holler. Grandpa even pulled a butterfly cocoon from a blackberry briar that grew beside his path. I saw him try to tear it into shreds but he couldn't. There wasn't any butterfly in it, for I'd seen it before. I wondered if the butterfly with the polka-dot wings, that Grandpa waved his cane at when he first left the house, had come from this cocoon. I laughed when Grandpa couldn't tear the cocoon apart.

"I'll bet I can tear that cocoon apart for Grandpa if you'd let me go help him," I said to Mom.

"You leave your Grandpa alone," Mom said. "Let 'im enjoy April."

Then I knew that this was the first time Mom had let Grandpa out of the house all winter. I knew that Grandpa loved the sunshine and the fresh April air that blew from the redbud and dogwood blossoms. He loved the bumblebees, the hogs, the pine cones, and pine needles. Grandpa didn't miss a thing along his walk. And every day

from now on until just before frost Grandpa would take this little walk.
He'd stop along and look at everything as he had done summers before. But each year he didn't take as long a walk as he had taken the
year before. Now this spring he didn't go down to the lower end of
the hog pen as he had done last year. And when I could first remember
Grandpa going on his walks he used to go out of sight. He'd go all
over the farm. And he'd come to the house and take me on his knee
and tell me about all that he had seen. Now Grandpa wasn't getting
out of sight. I could see him from the window along all of his walk.

Grandpa didn't come back into the house at the front door. He
tottled around back of the house toward the smokehouse and I ran
through the living room to the dining room so I could look out at the
window and watch him.

"Where's Grandpa goin'?" I asked Mom.

"Now never mind," Mom said. "Leave your Grandpa alone. Don't
go out there and disturb him."

"I won't bother 'im, Mom," I said. "I just want to watch 'im."

"All right," Mom said.

But Mom wanted to be sure that I didn't bother him so she followed me into the dining room. Maybe she wanted to see what
Grandpa was going to do. She stood by the window and we watched
Grandpa as he walked down beside our smokehouse where a tall sassafras tree's thin leaves fluttered in the blue April wind. Above the
smokehouse and the tall sassafras was a blue April sky—so high you
couldn't see the sky-roof. It was just blue space and little white clouds
floated upon this blue.

When Grandpa reached the smokehouse he leaned his cane against
the sassafras tree. He let himself down slowly to his knees as he looked
carefully at the ground. Grandpa was looking at something and I
wondered what it was. I just didn't think or I would have known.

"There you are, my good old friend," Grandpa said.

"Who is his friend, Mom?" I asked.

Mom didn't say anything. Then I saw.

"He's playin' with that old terrapin, Mom," I said.

"I know he is," Mom said.

"The terrapin doesn't mind if Grandpa strokes his head with his
hand," I said.

"I know it," Mom said.

"But the old terrapin won't let me do it," I said. "Why does he let Grandpa?"

"The terrapin knows your Grandpa."

"He ought to know me," I said, "but when I try to stroke his head with my hand, he closes up in his shell."

Mom didn't say anything. She stood by the window watching Grandpa and listening to Grandpa talk to the terrapin.

"My old friend, how do you like the sunshine?" Grandpa asked the terrapin.

The terrapin turned his fleshless face to one side like a hen does when she looks at you in the sunlight. He was trying to talk to Grandpa; maybe the terrapin could understand what Grandpa was saying.

"Old fellow, it's been a hard winter," Grandpa said. "How have you fared under the smokehouse floor?"

"Does the terrapin know what Grandpa is sayin'?" I asked Mom.

"I don't know," she said.

"I'm awfully glad to see you, old fellow," Grandpa said.

He didn't offer to bite Grandpa's big soft hand as he stroked his head.

"Looks like the terrapin would bite Grandpa," I said.

"That terrapin has spent the winters under that smokehouse for fifteen years," Mom said. "Pap has been acquainted with him for eleven years. He's been talkin' to that terrapin every spring."

"How does Grandpa know the terrapin is old?" I asked Mom.

"It's got 1847 cut on its shell," Mom said. "We know he's ninety-five years old. He's older than that. We don't know how old he was when that date was cut on his back."

"Who cut 1847 on his back, Mom?"

"I don't know, child," she said, "but I'd say whoever cut that date on his back has long been under the ground."

Then I wondered how a terrapin could get that old and what kind of a looking person he was who cut the date on the terrapin's back. I wondered where it happened—if it happened near where our house stood. I wondered who lived here on this land then, what kind of a house they lived in, and if they had a sassafras with tiny thin April leaves on its top growing in their yard, and if the person that cut the date on the terrapin's back was buried at Plum Grove, if he had farmed these hills where we lived to-day and cut timber like Grandpa had—and if he had seen the Aprils pass like Grandpa had seen them and if he enjoyed them like Grandpa was enjoying this April. I wondered if he had looked at the dogwood blossoms, the redbud blossoms, and talked to this same terrapin.

"Are you well, old fellow?" Grandpa asked the terrapin.

The terrapin just looked at Grandpa.

"I'm well as common for a man of my age," Grandpa said.

"Did the terrapin ask Grandpa if he was well?" I asked Mom.

"I don't know," Mom said. "I can't talk to a terrapin."

"But Grandpa can."

"Yes."

"Wait until tomatoes get ripe and we'll go to the garden together," Grandpa said.

"Does a terrapin eat tomatoes?" I asked Mom.

"Yes, that terrapin has been eatin' tomatoes from our garden for fifteen years," Mom said. "When Mick was tossin' the terrapins out of the tomato patch, he picked up this one and found the date cut on his back. He put him back in the patch and told him to help himself. He lives from our garden every year. We don't bother him and don't allow anybody else to bother him. He spends his winters under our smokehouse floor buried in the dry ground."

"Gee, Grandpa looks like the terrapin," I said.

Mom didn't say anything; tears came to her eyes. She wiped them from her eyes with the corner of her apron.

"I'll be back to see you," Grandpa said. "I'm a-gettin' a little chilly; I'll be gettin' back to the house."

The terrapin twisted his wrinkled neck without moving his big body, poking his head deeper into the April wind as Grandpa pulled his bundled body up by holding to the sassafras tree trunk.

"Good-by, old friend!"

The terrapin poked his head deeper into the wind, holding one eye on Grandpa, for I could see his eye shining in the sinking sunlight.

Grandpa got his cane that was leaned against the sassafras tree trunk and hobbled slowly toward the house. The terrapin looked at him with first one eye and then the other.

CONRAD RICHTER Why he selected

LUTIE

This short fragment has been chosen for inclusion here because it gives, if faintly, the feeling the writer had for a place and person. As a rule, life and nature are so much more real and vivid than the reflection that finds its way on paper. Many times, in my case at least, the attempted transfer fails. Here, I hope, it has more nearly succeeded. This fragment is from *The Sea of Grass* and was written in Albuquerque in 1936.

Pine Grove, Pa.   CONRAD RICHTER
August 21, 1942

FOR a long time I lay awake that night in the bunk that had once been my uncle's, listening at intervals to the faint bawling of a calf for its mother in some dim, starlit *cañada*. And when I fell asleep I dreamed that something vaguely beautiful had gone out of this massive ranch house like the kernel of life out of a prairie seed, and all that remained was the brown shell of adobe walls staring from its empty sockets. And everywhere about the house in my dream, the sand was endlessly blowing, burying the print of the coyote and lizard, rattling in the vibora seed, drifting close to the ground like barren snow so that the whole earth seemed to be moving, a restless gray ghost of itself trying to find those full, lusty prairie breasts, fertile as a woman and flowing with milk and wild honey, that used to be.

At the first sound of morning I was up pulling on my clothes in the darkness and drinking coffee in the kitchen to escape the breakfast-table, and lending a hand in the starlight to the hitching of the teams. And when I came back to the long dark hall, I glimpsed in a candle-lighted room, framed like a picture by the heavy doorway, Lutie Brewton, suited, hatted, and one hand gloved, sitting with three sleepy youngsters in their nightgowns about her. And I heard her promising

415

in that clear, delightful, fun-loving voice she always used to children, that she would see them all sooner than soon and would have a double present for each one that Black Hetty should say had been a little lady or gentleman.

Old Jeff helped me to carry out her trunk to the sagging buck-board. And soon Lutie Brewton came, a slender, almost jaunty figure in the dim, blue-black light, answering the children's good-by before my uncle helped her up into the top buggy. Before the horses started, she answered again. And from somewhere down beyond the spring I heard her voice a last time, high and clear above the thud of hoofs and rattle of spokes, like some incredibly sweet and lingering bell.

Old Jeff had waited by one of the buckboard wheels, never saying a word, but I could hear him draw hard and furiously on his pipe until the sounds of the buggy grew faint on the night air. Still saying nothing, he moved grimly into the house while I climbed into the rig and my horses without urging followed those that had gone before.

To the newcomer in our Southwestern land it seems that the days are very much alike, the same blue sky and unchanging sunshine and endless heat waves rising from the plain. But after he is here a year he learns to distinguish nuances in the weather he would never have noticed under a more violent sky; that one day may be clear enough, and yet some time during the night, without benefit of rain or cloud, a mysterious desert influence sweeps the heavens. And the following morning there is air clearer by half than yesterday, as if freshly rinsed by storm and rain.

It was such a morning that I hauled Lutie Brewton's trunk through the crystal air to Salt Fork, with horses and buckboard moving at first under the swinging lamp of the morning planet, and then through a green, velvet twilight that was half-way between stars and sun, and finally in the early purple light that poured over the plain like wine, until it seemed that with every breath I could taste it, and even the stolid cattle feeding beside the trail seemed to lift their heads to stare at it. And when the sun shook the earth finally clear, I saw a wave of antelope flowing inquisitively toward the buggy far ahead, a wave rusty as with kelp, rising and falling over the grassy swells and eventu-ally turning in alarm, so that a thousand white rumps, whirled suddenly into view, were the breaking of that wide prairie wave on some unseen reef of this tossing upland sea.

Most of the way across the vegas I could have reached out my hand and touched the fragrant rows of bee balm starting to bloom on either side of the trail. But all I could smell was the perfume of violets rising from Lutie Brewton's trunk. And all I could see now was a faint, distant column of black smoke hanging in the sky, little more than a smudge in that illimitable air, yet already it threw a shadow over buckboard and trail.

The sun was a branding iron on the back of my neck when we came at last to the edge of the sand hills and I saw the cottonwoods standing already cool in shadow in the river valley below. My spent horses plowed the floury dust of the long street. And the red-faced station agent himself came bustling out to oversee the careful lifting of Lutie Brewton's trunk to the steel-protected baggage truck slatted like a buckboard and trundled like a barrow.

Not until then did I look up and see with relief that everything about the station was normal and everyday, the groups of passengers through the open door of the waiting-room, the loafers playing mumbletypeg on the plank platform, and out near the tracks a circle of friends surrounding Lutie Brewton, laughing and chattering as always, wishing her a pleasant visit to St. Louis and promising gay times when she returned. I could smell the calm unhurried redolence of ties lately simmering in the sun, could hear down in their white-washed shipping pens the monotonous baas of a flock of lambs. And nearer, the white dust floated from a car of flour being unloaded in sacks to a dusty wagon.

Then I glimpsed Lawyers Henry McCurtin and Archie Meade talking together in low, grave tones beyond the baggage barrow, and was slowly conscious that all was not quite what it seemed. And when I glanced around again, I was aware that the loafers kept peering up stealthily from under their brows, and a group of passengers whispered from the waiting-room doorway.

And now I was sure that all those happy friends were frantically playing a part and that they really had no more belief that Lutie Brewton was going to St. Louis than I had. And when I stumbled by as if I noticed nothing, I saw that for all her gay animation, her high lace collar was a pale branch whip-sawing in the pounding stream of blood at her throat and that the veins on one of my uncle's hands stood out like long-suppressed whipcords of blue lightning. . . .

The train was whistling now by the small river ranchos and finally through the cottonwood bosque where of a summer afternoon the town boys played Jesse James. Some of the silent crowd, I saw, tried not to look up the street, but it was plain that everyone was standing there in a kind of strained expectancy, waiting for Chamberlain's creamy Western hat and brown-checked Eastern suit to appear.

Only Lutie Brewton refused to be still, throwing herself into saying good-by to her friends with an animated gayety that was almost incoherence, laughing to this one and chattering to that, hugging Myra Netherwood and dabbing quick kisses on Cora Holderness's cheeks, while her hands fluttered and flew and drew back like a pair of white falcons on the leash.

Some of the ladies were crying, although when Lutie Brewton turned to say good-by to me, I stood deaf and stony to hide everything I felt.

"Thank you for bringing my trunk," she said brightly, but when I was kissed, with the scent of violets swimming about me, she whispered in my long hair: "Say nice things about me to my babies till I send for them, Hal!"

And now without a sign as yet of Brice Chamberlain, the train was in, with black smoke drifting from the bulging smokestack, and with woman passengers staring curiously at Lutie Brewton as their full skirts rustled to the train. My uncle himself carried her valises into the palace car, where I could see him standing by her seat as she gracefully chatted and laughed at her open window to her friends outside on the raised plank platform, her modulated voice clear and charming as if nothing had happened or could happen and she might be only taking a flying trip to Santa Fe.

Even after the conductor, who had waited respectfully for my uncle to alight, gave the signal for the train to start, and when she and everybody else knew that the man who was to be United States district attorney in Colorado had not appeared from that tangle of emigrant canvas to join her, Lutie Brewton sat there alone and gallant as I had ever seen her, leaning from the window to wave gayly and throw kisses to us all.

"Good-by! Good-by!" For a moment the air was filled with eager cries. Then she was gone. And suddenly the platform was silent and most curiously empty, and everyone stood there looking after the train that was already just a retreating door with a narrow window on either side and a streak of dark smoke drifting above it.

Only my uncle refused to look at it. With his head up and his dark eyes a warning to all he met, he walked toward the hotel, a lone, powerful figure to whom no one at the moment dared to speak. . . .

Long after, I watched him in the bright June moonlight that was almost like day, standing motionless on the gallery facing the big vega. And that night as I lay in my sleepless bunk staring into the white haze that entered my deep window, I fancied that in the milky mist I could see the prairie as I had seen it all my life and would never see it again, with the grass in summer sweeping my stirruped thighs and prairie chickens scuttling ahead of my pony; with the ponds in fall black and noisy with waterfowl, and my uncle's seventy thousand head of cattle rolling in fat; with the tracks of endless game in the winter snow and thousands of tons of wild hay cured and stored on the stem; and when the sloughs of the home range greened up in the spring, with the scent of warming wet earth and swag after swag catching the emerald fire, with horses shedding and snorting and grunting as they rolled, and everywhere the friendly indescribable solitude of that lost sea of grass.

WILLIAM ALLEN WHITE Why he

 selected MARY WHITE

If I have ever written anything charged with emotion, it is this short editorial on my daughter. It was written the day after her funeral. I tried to transfer to paper what I felt. It has been copied in thirty-four books to be read in high schools and colleges. It is often reprinted elsewhere. Probably nothing I ever have written has traveled so far and so wide. Mary thus has an immortality in the hearts of the young, where she would rather live than any other place on earth. I suppose that if I ever have any fame half a decade after my funeral I shall come into that fame with Mary leading me by the finger.

Emporia, Kan.   WILLIAM ALLEN WHITE
August, 1942

THE Associated Press reports carrying the news of Mary White's death declared that it came as the result of a fall from a horse. How she would have hooted at that! She never fell from a horse in her life. Horses have fallen on her and with her—"I'm always trying to hold 'em in my lap," she used to say. But she was proud of few things, and one was that she could ride anything that had four legs and hair. Her death resulted not from a fall, but from a blow on the head which fractured her skull, and the blow came from the limb of an overhanging tree on the parking.

The last hour of her life was typical of its happiness. She came home from a day's work at school, topped off by a hard grind with the copy on the High School Annual, and felt that a ride would refresh her. She climbed into her khakis, chattering to her mother about the work she was doing, and hurried to get her horse and be out on the dirt roads for the country air and the radiant green fields of the spring. As she rode through the town on an easy gallop she kept waving at passers-by. She knew everyone in town. For a decade the little figure with the long pigtail and the red hair ribbon has been

familiar on the streets of Emporia, and she got in the way of speaking
to those who nodded at her. She passed the Kerrs, walking the horse.
in front of the Normal Library, and waved at them; passed another
friend a few hundred feet further on, and waved at her. The horse
was walking and as she turned into North Merchant street she took
off her cowboy hat, and the horse swung into a lope. She passed the
Tripletts and waved her cowboy hat at them, still moving gaily north
on Merchant street. A Gazette carrier passed—a High School boy
friend—and she waved at him, but with her bridle hand; the horse
veered quickly, plunged into the parking where the low-hanging limb
faced her, and, while she still looked back waving, the blow came.
But she did not fall from the horse; she slipped off, dazed a bit, staggered and fell in a faint. She never quite recovered consciousness.

But she did not fall from the horse, neither was she riding fast. A
year or so ago she used to go like the wind. But that habit was broken,
and she used the horse to get into the open to get fresh, hard exercise,
and to work off a certain surplus energy that welled up in her and
needed a physical outlet. That need had been in her heart for years.
It was back of the impulse that kept the dauntless, little brown-clad
figure on the streets and country roads of this community and built
into a strong, muscular body what had been a frail and sickly frame
during the first years of her life. But the riding gave her more than
a body. It released a gay and hardy soul. She was the happiest thing
in the world. And she was happy because she was enlarging her horizon. She came to know all sorts and conditions of men; Charley
O'Brien, the traffic cop, was one of her best friends. W. L. Holtz, the
Latin teacher, was another. Tom O'Connor, farmer-politician, and
Rev. J. H. J. Rice, preacher and police judge, and Frank Beach, music
master, were her special friends, and all the girls, black and white,
above the track and below the track, in Pepville and Stringtown, were
among her acquaintances. And she brought home riotous stories of
her adventures. She loved to rollick; persiflage was her natural expression at home. Her humor was a continual bubble of joy. She seemed
to think in the hyperbole and metaphor. She was mischievous without
malice, as full of faults as an old shoe. No angel was Mary White,
but an easy girl to live with, for she never nursed a grouch five minutes in her life.

With all her eagerness for the out-of-doors, she loved books. On her table when she left her room were a book by Conrad, one by Galsworthy, "Creative Chemistry" by E. E. Slossen, and a Kipling book. She read Mark Twain, Dickens and Kipling before she was 10—all of their writings. Wells and Arnold Bennett particularly amused and diverted her. She was entered as a student in Wellesley in 1922; was assistant editor of the High School Annual this year, and in line for election to the editorship of the Annual next year. She was a member of the executive committee of the High School Y. W. C. A.

Within the last two years she had begun to be moved by an ambition to draw. She began as most children do by scribbling in her school books, funny pictures. She bought cartoon magazines and took a course—rather casually, naturally, for she was, after all, a child, with no strong purposes—and this year she tasted the first fruits of success by having her pictures accepted by the High School Annual. But the thrill of delight she got when Mr. Ecord, of the Normal Annual, asked her to do the cartooning for that book this spring, was too beautiful for words. She fell to her work with all her enthusiastic heart. Her drawings were accepted, and her pride—always repressed by a lively sense of the ridiculousness of the figure she was cutting—was a really gorgeous thing to see. No successful artist ever drank a deeper draught of satisfaction than she took from the little fame her work was getting among her schoolfellows. In her glory, she almost forgot her horse—but never her car.

For she used the car as a jitney bus. It was her social life. She never had a "party" in all her nearly seventeen years—wouldn't have one; but she never drove a block in the car in her life that she didn't begin to fill the car with pick-ups! Everybody rode with Mary White— white and black, old and young, rich and poor, men and women. She liked nothing better than to fill the car full of long-legged High School boys and an occasional girl, and parade the town. She never had a "date," nor went to a dance, except once with her brother, Bill, and the "boy proposition" didn't interest her—yet. But young people— great, spring-breaking, varnish-cracking, fender-bending, door-sagging carloads of "kids"—gave her great pleasure. Her zests were keen. But the most fun she ever had in her life was acting as chairman of the committee that got up the big turkey dinner for the poor folks at the county home; scores of pies, gallons of slaw; jam, cakes, preserves, oranges and a wilderness of turkey were loaded in the car and taken to the county home. And, being of a practical turn of mind, she risked her own Christmas dinner by staying to see that the poor folks actually got it all. Not that she was a cynic; she just disliked to tempt folks. While there she found a blind colored uncle, very old, who could do nothing but make rag rugs, and she rustled up from her school friends rags enough to keep him busy for a season. The last engagement she tried to make was to take the guests at the county home out for a car ride. And the last endeavor of her life was to try to get a rest room for colored girls in the High School. She found one girl reading in the toilet, because there was no better place for a colored girl to loaf, and it inflamed her sense of injustice and she became a nagging harpy to those who she thought could remedy the evil. The poor she had always with her, and was glad of it. She hungered and thirsted for righteousness; and was the most impious creature in the world. She joined the Congregational Church without consulting her parents; not particularly for her soul's good. She never had a thrill of piety in her life, and would have tooted at a "testimony." But even as a little child she felt the church was an agency for helping people to more of life's abundance, and she wanted to help. She never wanted help for herself. Clothes meant little to her. It was a fight to get a new rig on her; but eventually a harder fight to get it off. She never wore a jewel and had no ring but her High School class ring, and never asked for anything but a wrist watch. She refused to have her hair up; though she was nearly 17. "Mother," she protested, "you don't know how much I get by with, in my braided pigtails that I could not, with my hair up." Above every other passion of her life was her passion not to grow up, to be a child. The tom-boy in her, which was big, seemed to loathe to be put away forever in skirts. She was a Peter Pan, who refused to grow up.

Her funeral yesterday at the Congregational Church was as she would have wished it; no singing, no flowers save the big bunch of red roses from her Brother Bill's Harvard classmen—Heavens, how proud that would have made her—and the red roses from the Gazette force—in vases at her head and feet. A short prayer, Paul's beautiful essay on "Love" from the Thirteenth Chapter of First Corinthians, some remarks about her democratic spirit by her friend, John H. J. Rice, pastor and police judge, which she would have deprecated if she could, a prayer sent down for her by her friend, Carl Nau, and opening the service the slow, poignant movement from Beethoven's Moonlight Sonata, which she loved, and closing the service a cutting from the joyously melancholy first movement of Tschaikowski's Pathetic Symphony, which she liked to hear in certain moods on the phonograph; then the Lord's Prayer by her friends in the High School.

That was all.

For her pallbearers only her friends were chosen; her Latin teacher, W. L. Holtz; her High School principal, Rice Brown; her doctor, Frank Foncannon; her friend, W. W. Finney; her pal at the Gazette office, Walter Hughes; and her brother Bill. It would have made her smile to know that her friend, Charley O'Brien, the traffic cop, had been transferred from Sixth and Commercial to the corner near the church to direct her friends who came to bid her goodbye.

A rift in the clouds in a gray day threw a shaft of sunlight upon her coffin as her nervous, energetic little body sank to its last sleep. But the soul of her, the glowing, gorgeous, fervent soul of her, surely was flaming in eager joy upon some other dawn.

ONE WHO HAS LIVED

This week the graduating exercises are being held at Wellesley college, Wellesley, Mass., and Emporia people may have an interest in that graduation. Seven years ago, when Mary White was in the Emporia high school, she was entered by her parents as a student in Wellesley college, to go there in 1922 and graduate in 1926. She was preparing her work in high school to pass the Wellesley examination when she died in May, 1921. An editorial published in The Gazette the day after her funeral has been reprinted in many textbooks and collections of essays since that time. The textbooks are used in many colleges and high schools, and Mary has the immortality which would delight her—to live in the heart of youth. One of the textbooks in which the editorial was printed is used in Wellesley college. In reading the article, the girls in the Wellesley class of 1926 saw that Mary had been entered at Wellesley so they enrolled her as a member of the class of 1926 and have kept her with them through the four years. Mr. and Mrs. White do not know a member of the class and for years did not know that the girls of Wellesley were considering Mary among them. This spring they notified her parents in Emporia that the class annual, The Wellesley Legenda, had been dedicated to the memory of Mary White, and this week sent a number of copies of the annual to her parents. So her parents have paid Mary's class assessment and her name will be entered as a contributor to the memorial which the class will leave in Wellesley upon its graduation.

Thus the commencement has a local interest to her friends in Emporia. This is her graduating year, but she will remain for many years immortal among students in colleges and high schools where her story is read in the textbooks. So she will never grow up even after her graduation.

TWENTY YEARS AGO

Twenty years ago today, Mary White died. She had been registered in Wellesley college and was preparing to graduate from high school so that she could enter Wellesley in 1922 and join the class of 1926. By 1926, a short editorial about her having appeared in The Gazette, had been included in half a dozen books and college and high school textbooks, including Woolcott's Reader, Christopher Morley's Anthology and other similar collections of essays. On that basis, the Wellesley class of 1926 dedicated the annual at Wellesley to Mary White.

Since then all together 34 different high school and college class texts and other collections of school reader pieces have published the Mary White editorial between book covers and this year the class of '26 at Wellesley at its fifteenth reunion, which is accumulating a loan fund called the Daughters' fund of '26, changed the name of their fund to the Mary White Daughters' fund.

Twenty years is a long time for a girl to live in the immortality she would choose above all others—a bright, gay glow in the heart of youth.

IV
THE JUNGLE

UPTON SINCLAIR Why he selected

The Jungle: The SLAUGHTER

of the PIGS

Anyone who reads these five thousand words will have his imagination stimulated, his sympathies widened, and his understanding of the world he lives in increased. At least, that is why the book* (from which this excerpt was taken) was written, and if it doesn't happen there is something wrong with either you or with the author.

Pasadena, Cal.   UPTON SINCLAIR

June, 1942

THEY passed down the busy street that led to the yards. It was still early morning and everything was at its high tide of activity. A steady stream of employees was pouring through the gate—employees of the higher sort, at this hour, clerks and stenographers and such. For the women there were waiting big two-horse wagons, which set off at a gallop as fast as they were filled. In the distance there was heard again the lowing of the cattle, a sound as of a far-off ocean calling. They followed it, this time, as eager as children in sight of a circus menagerie—which, indeed, the scene a good deal resembled. They crossed the railroad tracks, and then on each side of the street were the pens full of cattle; they would have stopped to look, but Jokubas hurried them on, to where there was a stairway and a raised gallery, from which everything could be seen. Here they stood, staring, breathless with wonder.

There is over a square mile of space in the yards, and more than half of it is occupied by cattle-pens; north and south as far as the eye can reach there stretches a sea of pens. And they were all filled—so many cattle no one had ever dreamed existed in the world. Red cattle,

* From *The Jungle*, 1906.

black, white, and yellow cattle; old cattle and young cattle; great bellowing bulls and little calves not an hour born; meek-eyed milch cows and fierce, long-horned Texas steers. The sound of them here was as of all the barnyards of the universe; and as for counting them—it would have taken all day simply to count the pens. Here and there ran long alleys, blocked at intervals by gates; and Jokubas told them that the number of these gates was twenty-five thousand. Jokubas had recently been reading a newspaper article which was full of statistics such as that, and he was very proud as he repeated them and made his guests cry out with wonder. Jurgis too had a little of this sense of pride. Had he not just gotten a job, and become a sharer in all this activity, a cog in this marvellous machine?

Here and there about the alleys galloped men upon horseback, booted, and carrying long whips; they were very busy, calling to each other, and to those who were driving the cattle. They were drovers and stock-raisers, who had come from far states, and brokers and commission-merchants, and buyers for all the big packing-houses. Here and there they would stop to inspect a bunch of cattle, and there would be a parley, brief and business-like. The buyer would nod or drop his whip, and that would mean a bargain; and he would note it in his little book, along with hundreds of others he had made that morning. Then Jokubas pointed out the place where the cattle were driven to be weighed, upon a great scale that would weigh a hundred thousand pounds at once and record it automatically. It was near to the east entrance that they stood, and all along this east side of the yards ran the railroad tracks, into which the cars were run, loaded with cattle. All night long this had been going on, and now the pens were full; by to-night they would all be empty, and the same thing would be done again.

"And what will become of all these creatures?" cried Teta Elzbieta.

"By to-night," Jokubas answered, "they will all be killed and cut up; and over there on the other side of the packing-houses are more railroad tracks, where the cars come to take them away."

There were two hundred and fifty miles of track within the yards, their guide went on to tell them. They brought about ten thousand head of cattle every day, and as many hogs, and half as many sheep—which meant some eight or ten million live creatures turned into food every year. One stood and watched, and little by little caught the drift of the tide, as it set in the direction of the packing-houses. There were groups of cattle being driven to the chutes, which were roadways about fifteen feet wide, raised high above the pens. In these chutes the stream of animals was continuous; it was quite uncanny to watch them, pressing on to their fate, all unsuspicious—a very river of death. Our friends were not poetical, and the sight suggested to them no metaphors of human destiny; they thought only of the wonderful efficiency of it all. The chutes into which the hogs went climbed high up—to the very top of the distant buildings; and Jokubas explained that the hogs went up by the power of their own legs, and then their weight carried them back through all the processes necessary to make them into pork.

"They don't waste anything here," said the guide, and then he laughed and added a witticism, which he was pleased that his unsophisticated friends should take to be his own: "They use everything about the hog except the squeal." In front of Brown's General Office building there grows a tiny plot of grass, and this, you may learn, is the only bit of green thing in Packingtown; likewise this jest about the hog and his squeal, the stock in trade of all the guides, is the one gleam of humor that you will find there.

After they had seen enough of the pens, the party went up the street, to the mass of buildings which occupy the centre of the yards. These buildings, made of brick and stained with innumerable layers of Packingtown smoke, were painted all over with advertising signs, from which the visitor realized suddenly that he had come to the home of many of the torments of his life. It was here that they made those products with the wonders of which they pestered him so—by placards that defaced the landscape when he travelled, and by staring advertisements in the newspapers and magazines—by silly little jingles that he could not get out of his mind, and gaudy pictures that lurked for him around every street corner. Here was where they made Brown's Imperial Hams and Bacon, Brown's Dressed Beef, Brown's Excelsior Sausages! Here was the headquarters of Durham's Pure Leaf Lard, of Durham's Breakfast Bacon, Durham's Canned Beef, Potted Ham, Devilled Chicken, Peerless Fertilizer!

Entering one of the Durham buildings, they found a number of other visitors waiting; and before long there came a guide, to escort them through the place. They made a great feature of showing strangers through the packing-plants, for it is a good advertisement. But ponas Jokubas whispered maliciously that the visitors did not see any more than the packers wanted them to.

They climbed a long series of stairways outside of the building, to the top of its five or six stories. Here was the chute, with its river of hogs, all patiently toiling upward; there was a place for them to rest to cool off, and then through another passageway they went into a room for which there is no returning for hogs.

It was a long, narrow room, with a gallery along it for visitors. At the head there was a great iron wheel, about twenty feet in circumference, with rings here and there along its edge. Upon both sides of this wheel there was a narrow space, into which came the hogs at the end of their journey; in the midst of them stood a great burly negro, bare-armed and bare-chested. He was resting for the moment, for the wheel had stopped while men were cleaning up. In a minute or two, however, it began slowly to revolve, and then the men upon each side of it sprang to work. They had chains which they fastened about the leg of the nearest hog, and the other end of the chain they hooked into one of the rings upon the wheel. So, as the wheel turned, a hog was suddenly jerked off his feet and borne aloft.

At the same time the ear was assailed by a most terrifying shriek; the visitors started in alarm, the women turned pale and shrank back. The shriek was followed by another, louder and yet more agonizing— for once started upon that journey, the hog never came back; at the top of the wheel he was shunted off upon a trolley, and went sailing down the room. And meantime another was swung up, and then another, and another, until there was a double line of them, each dangling by a foot and kicking in frenzy—and squealing. The uproar was appalling, perilous to the ear-drums; one feared there was too much sound for the room to hold—that the walls must give way or the ceiling crack. There were high squeals and low squeals, grunts, and wails of agony; there would come a momentary lull, and then a fresh outburst, louder than ever, surging up to a deafening climax. It was too much for some of the visitors—the men would look at each other laughing nervously, and the women would stand with hands clenched, and the blood rushing to their faces, and the tears starting in their eyes.

Meantime, heedless of all these things, the men upon the floor were going about their work. Neither squeals of hogs nor tears of visitors made any difference to them; one by one they hooked up the hogs, and one by one with a swift stroke they slit their throats. There was a long line of hogs, with squeals and life-blood ebbing away together; until at last each started again, and vanished with a splash into a huge vat of boiling water.

It was all so very businesslike that one watched it fascinated. It was pork-making by machinery, pork-making by applied mathematics. And yet somehow the most matter-of-fact person could not help thinking of the hogs; they were so innocent, they came so very trustingly; and they were so very human in their protests—and so perfectly within their rights! They had done nothing to deserve it; and it was adding insult to injury, as the thing was done here, swinging them up in this cold-blooded, impersonal way, without a pretense of apology, without the homage of a tear. Now and then a visitor wept, to be sure; but this slaughtering-machine ran on, visitors or no visitors. It was like some horrible crime committed in a dungeon, all unseen and unheeded, buried out of sight and of memory.

One could not stand and watch very long without becoming philosophical, without beginning to deal in symbols and similes, and to hear the hog-squeal of the universe. Was it permitted to believe that there was nowhere upon the earth, or above the earth, a heaven for hogs, where they were requited for all this suffering? Each one of these hogs was a separate creature. Some were white hogs, some very black; some were brown, some were spotted; some were old, some were young; some were long and lean, some were monstrous. And each of them had an individuality of his own, a will of his own, a hope and a heart's desire; each was full of self-confidence, of self-importance, and a sense of dignity. And trusting and strong in faith he had gone about his business, the while a black shadow hung over him and a horrid Fate waited in his pathway. Now suddenly it had swooped upon him, and had seized him by the leg. Relentless, remorseless, it was; all his protests, his screams, were nothing to it—it did its cruel will with him, as if his wishes, his feelings, had simply no existence at all; it cut his throat and watched him gasp out his life. And now was one to believe that there was nowhere a god of hogs, to whom this hog-personality was precious, to whom these hog-squeals and agonies had a meaning? Who would take this hog into his arms and comfort him, reward him for his work well-done, and show him the meaning of his sacrifice? Perhaps some glimpse of all this was in the thoughts of our humble-minded Jurgis, as he turned to go on with the rest of the party, and muttered: "Dieve—but I'm glad I'm not a hog!"

The carcass hog was scooped out of the vat by machinery, and then it fell to the second floor, passing on the way through a wonderful machine with numerous scrapers, which adjusted themselves to the size and shape of the animal, and sent it out at the other end with nearly all of its bristles removed. It was then again strung up by machinery, and sent upon another trolley ride; this time passing between two lines of men, who sat upon a raised platform, each doing a certain single thing to the carcass as it came to him. One scraped the outside of a leg; another scraped the inside of the same leg. One with a swift stroke cut the throat; another with two swift strokes severed the head, which fell to the floor and vanished through a hole. Another made a slit down the body; a second opened the body wider; a third with a saw cut the breast-bone; a fourth loosened the entrails; a fifth pulled them out—and they also slid through a hole in the floor. There were men to scrape each side and men to scrape the back; there were men to clean the carcass inside, to trim it and wash it. Looking down this room, one saw, creeping slowly, a line of dangling hogs a hundred yards in length; and for every yard there was a man, working as if a demon were after him. At the end of this hog's progress every inch of the carcass had been gone over several times; and then it was rolled into the chilling-room, where it stayed for twenty-four hours, and where a stranger might lose himself in a forest of freezing hogs.

Before the carcass was admitted here, however, it had to pass a government inspector, who sat in the doorway and felt of the glands in the neck for tuberculosis. This government inspector did not have the manner of a man who was worked to death; he was apparently not haunted by a fear that the hog might get by him before he had finished his testing. If you were a sociable person, he was quite willing to enter into conversation with you, and to explain to you the deadly nature of the ptomaines which are to be found in tubercular pork; and while he was talking with you you could hardly be so ungrateful as to notice that a dozen carcasses were passing him untouched. This inspector wore an imposing silver badge, and he gave an atmosphere of authority to the scene, and, as it were, put the stamp of official approval upon the things which were done in Durham's.

Jurgis went down the line with the rest of the visitors, staring open-mouthed, lost in wonder. He had dressed hogs himself in the forest of Lithuania; but he had never expected to see one hog dressed by several hundred men. It was like a wonderful poem to him, and he took it all in guilelessly—even to the conspicuous signs demanding immaculate cleanliness of the employees. Jurgis was vexed when the cynical Jokubas translated these signs with sarcastic comments, offering to take them to the secret-rooms where the spoiled meats went to be doctored.

The party descended to the next floor, where the various waste materials were treated. Here came the entrails, to be scraped and washed clean for sausage-casings; men and women worked there in the midst of a sickening stench, which caused the visitors to hasten by, gasping. To another room came all the scraps to be "tanked," which meant boiling and pumping off the grease to make soap and lard; below they took out the refuse, and this, too, was a region in which the visitors did not linger. In still other places men were engaged in cutting up the carcasses that had been through the chilling-rooms. First there were the "splitters," the most expert workmen in the plant, who earned as high as fifty cents an hour, and did not a thing all day except chop hogs down the middle. Then there were "cleaver men," great giants with muscles of iron; each had two men to attend him—to slide the half carcass in front of him on the table; and hold it while he chopped it. and then turn each piece so that he might chop it once more. His cleaver had a blade about two feet long, and he never made but one cut; he made it so neatly, too, that his implement did not smite through and dull itself—there was just enough force for a perfect cut, and no more. So through various yawning holes there slipped to the floor below—to one room hams, to another forequarters, to another sides of pork. One might go down to this floor and see the pickling-rooms, where the hams were put into vats, and the great smoke-rooms, with their air-tight iron doors. In other rooms they prepared salt-pork—there were whole cellars full of it, built up in great towers to the ceiling. In yet other rooms they were putting up meat in boxes and barrels, and wrapping hams and bacon in oiled paper, sealing and labelling and sewing them. From the doors of these rooms went men with loaded trucks, to the platform where freight-cars were waiting to be filled; and one went out there and realized with a start that he had come at last to the ground floor of this enormous building.

Then the party went across the street to where they did the killing of the beef—where every hour they turned four or five hundred cattle into meat. Unlike the place they had left, all this work was done on one floor; and instead of there being one line of carcasses which moved to the workmen, there were fifteen or twenty lines, and the men moved from one to another of these. This made a scene of intense activity, a picture of human power wonderful to watch. It was all in one great room, like a circus amphitheatre, with a gallery for visitors running over the centre.

Along one side of the room ran a narrow gallery, a few feet from the floor; into which gallery the cattle were driven by men with goads which gave them electric shocks. Once crowded in here, the creatures were prisoned, each in a separate pen, by gates that shut, leaving them no room to turn around; and while they stood bellowing and plunging, over the top of the pen there leaned one of the "knockers," armed with a sledge-hammer, and watching for a chance to deal a blow. The room echoed with the thuds in quick succession, and the stamping and kicking of the steers. The instant the animal had fallen, the "knocker" passed on to another; while a second man raised a lever, and the side of the pen was raised, and the animal, still kicking and struggling, slid out to the "killing-bed." Here a man put shackles about one leg, and pressed another lever, and the body was jerked up into the air. There were fifteen or twenty such pens, and it was a matter of only a couple of minutes to knock fifteen or twenty cattle and roll them out. Then once more the gates were opened, and another lot rushed in; and so out of each pen there rolled a steady stream of carcasses, which the men upon the killing-beds had to get out of the way.

The manner in which they did this was something to be seen and never forgotten. They worked with furious intensity, literally upon the run—at a pace with which there is nothing to be compared except a football game. It was all highly specialized labor, each man having his task to do; generally this would consist of only two or three specific cuts, and he would pass down the line of fifteen or twenty carcasses, making these cuts upon each. First there came the "butcher," to bleed them; this meant one swift stroke, so swift that you could not see it—only the flash of the knife; and before you could realize it, the man had darted on to the next line, and a stream of bright red was pouring out upon the floor. This floor was half an inch deep with blood, in spite of the best efforts of men who kept shovelling it through holes; it must have made the floor slippery, but no one could have guessed this by watching the men at work.

The carcass hung for a few minutes to bleed; there was no time lost, however, for there were several hanging in each line, and one was always ready. It was let down to the ground, and there came the "headsmen," whose task it was to sever the head, with two or three swift strokes. Then came the "floorsman," to make the first cut in the skin; and then another to finish ripping the skin down the centre; and then half a dozen more in swift succession, to finish the skinning. After they were through, the carcass was again swung up; and while a man with a stick examined the skin, to make sure that it had not been cut, and another rolled it up and tumbled it through one of the inevitable holes in the floor, the beef proceeded on its journey. There were men to cut it, and men to split it, and men to gut it and scrape it clean inside. There were some with hose which threw jets of boiling water upon it, and others who removed the feet and added the final touches. In the end, as with the hogs, the finished beef was run into the chilling-room, to hang its appointed time.

The visitors were taken there and shown them, all neatly hung in rows, labelled conspicuously with the tags of the government inspectors—and some, which had been killed by a special process, marked with the sign of the "kosher" rabbi, certifying that it was fit for sale to the orthodox. And then the visitors were taken to the other parts of the building, to see what became of each particle of the waste material that had vanished through the floor; and to the pickling-rooms, and the salting-rooms, the canning-rooms, and the packing-rooms, where choice meat was prepared for shipping in refrigerator-cars, destined to be eaten in all the four corners of civilization. Afterward they went outside, wandering about among the mazes of buildings in which was done the work auxiliary to this great industry. There was scarcely a thing needed in the business that Durham and Company did not make for themselves. There was a great steam-power plant and an electricity plant. There was a barrel factory, and a boiler-repair shop. There was a building to which the grease was piped, and made into soap and lard; and then there was a factory for making lard cans, and another for making soap boxes. There was a building in which the bristles were cleaned and dried, for the making of hair cushions and such things; there was a building where the skins were dried and tanned, there was another where heads and feet were made into glue, and another where bones were made into fertilizer. No tiniest particle of organic matter was wasted in Durham's. Out of the horns of the cattle they made combs, buttons, hair-pins, and imitation ivory; out of the shin bones and other big bones they cut knife and tooth-brush handles, and mouth-pieces for pipes; out of the hoofs they cut hair-pins and buttons, before they had made the rest into glue. From such things as feet, knuckles, hide clippings, and sinews came such strange and unlikely products as gelatin, isinglass, and phosphorus, bone-black, shoe-blacking, and bone-oil. They had curled-hair works for the cattle-tails, and a "wool-pullery" for the sheep skins; they made pepsin from the stomachs of the pigs, and albumen from the blood, and violin strings from the ill-smelling entrails. When there was nothing else to be done with a thing, they first put it into a tank and got out of it all the tallow and grease, and then they made it into fertilizer. All these industries were gathered into buildings near by, connected by galleries and railroads with the main establishment; and it was estimated that they had handled nearly a quarter of a billion of animals since the founding of the plant by the elder Durham a generation or more ago. If you counted with it the other big plants—and they were now really all one—it was, so Jokubas informed them, the greatest aggregation of labor and capital ever gathered in one place. It employed thirty thousand men; it supported directly two hundred and fifty thousand people in its neighborhood, and indirectly it supported half a million. It sent its products to every country in the civilized world, and it furnished the food for no less than thirty million people!

To all of these things our friends would listen open mouthed—it seemed to them impossible of belief that anything so stupendous could have been devised by mortal man. That was why to Jurgis it seemed almost profanity to speak about the place as did Jokubas, sceptically; it was a thing as tremendous as the universe—the laws and ways of its working no more than the universe to be questioned or understood. All that a mere man could do, it seemed to Jurgis, was to take a thing like this as he found it, and do as he was told; to be given a place in it and a share in its wonderful activities was a blessing to be grateful for, as one was grateful for the sunshine and the rain. Jurgis was even glad that he had not seen the place before meeting with his triumph, for he felt that the size of it would have overwhelmed him. But now he had been admitted—he was a part of it all! He had the feeling that this whole huge establishment had taken him under his protection, and had become responsible for his welfare. So guileless was he, and ignorant of the nature of business, that he did not even realize that he had become an employee of Brown's, and that Brown and Durham were supposed by all the world to be deadly rivals—were even required to be deadly rivals by the law of the land, and ordered to try to ruin each other under penalty of fine and imprisonment!

JAMES T. FARRELL

Why he selected STUDS

I have not undertaken the task of selecting from my published work that story, or that fragment of a novel, which I consider, absolutely, to be "my best" piece of writing: rather, I have chosen a story which I consider to be highly representative of the content and character of my writing up to date. This story, "Studs," was originally written for a composition course conducted at the University of Chicago by the late Professor James Weber Linn in the spring of 1929. It was first published in the magazine *This Quarter* in the summer of 1930. I made minor changes in this story for its publication in my book, *Guillotine Party and Other Stories:* it is here reprinted with these changes. However, in all essential matters the story remains as it was originally written.

"Studs" describes the original experience which led me to write what eventually became my trilogy, *Studs Lonigan:* it is the germ of that work. As such, it became a prediction of what I was to write, what types of character and environment I was to be interested in, what direction I would take in my first years as a novelist and short story writer. It is one of my first stories in which I attempted to use the kind of dialogue that I have since relied upon so extensively. Furthermore, this story embodies my original approach to my material. In the course of writing *Studs Lonigan* this approach was altered, expanded, refined. A strong reaction to the patterns of experience with which I had been familiar since my boyhood was here a starting point: it was a guiding chart (so to speak) directing me into certain avenues of the American way of life as that life is lived concretely by a great number of Americans. From this beginning I was led forward in a search for what this particular way of life meant to those who have lived it. The results of such effort are embodied in *Studs Lonigan*, and in various of my other published works. But this story constitutes one of the beginnings of that effort. Thus, I include it in this anthology, rather than any later writing of mine.

New York, N. Y.   JAMES T. FARRELL
July 12, 1942

I T IS raining outside; rain pouring like bullets from countless machine guns; rain spat-spattering on the wet earth and paving in endless silver crystals. Studs' grave out at Mount Olivet will be soaked and soppy, and fresh with the wet, clean odors of watered earth and flowers. And the members of Studs' family will be looking out of the windows of their apartment on the South Side, thinking of the cold, damp grave and the gloomy, muddy cemetery, and of their Studs lying at rest in peaceful acceptance of that wormy conclusion which is the common fate.

At Studs' wake last Monday evening everybody was mournful, sad that such a fine young fellow of twenty-six should go off so suddenly with double pneumonia; blown out of this world like a ripped leaf in a hurricane. They sighed and the women and girls cried, and everybody said that it was too bad. But they were consoled because he'd had the priest and had received Extreme Unction before he died, instead of going off like Sport Murphy who was killed in a saloon brawl. Poor Sport! He was a good fellow, and tough as hell. Poor Studs!

The undertaker (it was probably old man O'Reedy who used to be usher in the old parish church) laid Studs out handsomely. He was outfitted in a sombre black suit and a white silk tie. His hands were folded over his stomach, clasping a pair of black rosary beads. At his head, pressed against the satin bedding, was a spiritual bouquet, set in line with Studs' large nose. He looked handsome, and there were no lines of suffering on his planed face. But the spiritual bouquet (further assurance that his soul would arrive safely in Heaven) was a dirty trick. So was the administration of the last sacraments. For Studs will be miserable in Heaven, more miserable than he was on those Sunday nights when he would hang around the old poolroom at Fifty-eighth and the elevated station, waiting for something to happen. He will find the land of perpetual happiness and goodness dull and boresome, and he'll be resentful. There will be nothing to do in Heaven but to wait in timeless eternity. There will be no can houses, speakeasies, whores (unless they are reformed) and gambling joints; and neither will there be a shortage of plasterers. He will loaf up and down gold-paved streets where there is not even the suggestion of a poolroom, thinking of Paulie Haggerty, Sport Murphy, Arnold Sheehan and Hink Weber, who are possibly in Hell together because there was no priest around to play a dirty trick on them.

I thought of these things when I stood by the coffin, waiting for Tommy Doyle, Red Kelly, Les, and Joe to finish offering a few perfunctory prayers in memory of Studs. When they had showered some Hail Marys and Our Fathers on his already prayer-drenched soul, we went out into the dining room.

Years ago when I was a kid in the fifth grade in the old parish school, Studs was in the graduating class. He was one of the school leaders, a light-faced, blond kid who was able to fight like sixty and who never took any sass from Tommy Doyle, Red Kelly, or any of those fellows from the Fifty-eighth Street gang. He was quarterback on the school's football team, and liked by the girls.

My first concrete memory of him is of a rainy fall afternoon. Dick Buckford and I were fooling around in front of Helen Shires' house bumping against each other with our arms folded. We never thought of fighting but kept pushing and shoving and bumping each other. Studs, Red O'Connell, Tubby Connell, the Donoghues, and Jim Clayburn came along. Studs urged us into fighting, and I gave Dick a bloody nose. Studs congratulated me, and said that I could come along with them and play tag in Red O'Connell's basement, where there were several trick passageways.

After that day, I used to go around with Studs and his bunch. They regarded me as a sort of mascot, and they kept training me to fight other kids. But any older fellows who tried to pick on me would have a fight on their hands. Every now and then he would start boxing with me.

"Gee, you never get hurt, do you?" he would say.

I would grin in answer, bearing the punishment because of the pride and the glory.

"You must be goofy. You can't be hurt."

"Well, I don't get hurt like other kids."

"You're too good for Morris and those kids. You could trim them with your eyes closed. You're good," he would say, and then he would go on training me.

I arranged for a party on one of my birthdays, and invited Studs and the fellows from his bunch. Red O'Connell, a tall, lanky, cowardly kid, went with my brother, and the two of them convinced my folks that Studs was not a fit person for me to invite. I told Studs what had happened, and he took such an insult decently. But none of the fellows he went with would accept my invitation, and most of the girls also refused. On the day of the party, with my family's permission, I again invited Studs but he never came.

I have no other concrete recollections of Studs while he was in grammar school. He went to Loyola for one year, loafed about for a similar period; and then he became a plasterer for his father. He commenced going round the poolroom. The usual commonplace story resulted. What there was of the boy disappeared in slobbish dissipation. His pleasures became compressed within a hexagonal of whores, movies, pool, alky, poker, and craps. By the time I commenced going into the poolroom (my third year in high school) this process had been completed.

Studs' attitude toward me had also changed to one of contempt. I was a goofy young punk. Often he made cracks about me. Once, when I retaliated by sarcasm, he threatened to bust me, and awed by his former reputation I shut up. We said little to each other, although Studs occasionally condescended to borrow fifty or seventy-five cents from me, or to discuss Curley, the corner imbecile.

Studs' companions were more or less small-time amateur hoodlums. He had drifted away from the Donoghues and George Gogarty, who remained bourgeois young men with such interests as formal dances and shows. Perhaps Slug Mason was his closest friend; a tall, heavy-handed, good-natured, child-minded slugger, who knew the address and telephone number of almost every prostitute on the South Side. Hink Weber, who should have been in the ring and who later committed suicide in an insane asylum, Red Kelly, who was a typical wise-cracking corner habitué, Tommy Doyle, a fattening, bull-dozing, half-good-natured moron, Stan Simonsky and Joe Thomas were his other companions.

I feel sure that Studs' family, particularly his sisters, were appalled by his actions. The two sisters, one of whom I loved in an adolescently romantic and completely unsuccessful manner, were the type of middle-class girls who go in for sororities and sensibilities. One Saturday evening, when Studs got drunk earlier than usual, his older sister (who the boys always said was keen) saw him staggering around under the Fifty-eighth Street elevated station. She was with a young man in an

automobile, and they stopped. Studs talked loudly to her, and finally
they left. Studs reeled after the car, cursing and shaking his fists.
Fellows like Johnny O'Brien (who went to the U. of C. to become a
fraternity man) talked sadly of how Studs could have been more
discriminating in his choice of buddies and liquor; and this, too, must
have reached the ears of his two sisters.

Physical decay slowly developed. Studs, always a square-planed, broad
person, began getting soft and slightly fat. He played one or two years
with the corner football team. He was still an efficient quarterback, but
slow. When the team finally disbanded, he gave up athletics. He fought
and brawled about until one New Year's Eve he talked out of turn to
Jim McGeoghan, who was a boxing champ down at Notre Dame. Jim
flattened Studs' nose, and gave him a wicked black eye. Studs gave
up fighting.

My associations with the corner gradually dwindled. I went to college, and became an atheist. This further convinced Studs that I wasn't
right, and he occasionally remarked about my insanity. I grew up contemptuous of him and the others; and some of this feeling crept into
my overt actions. I drifted into other groups and forgot the corner.
Then I went to New York, and stories of legendary activities became
fact on the corner. I had started a new religion, written poetry, and
done countless similar monstrous things. When I returned, I did not see
Studs for over a year. One evening, just before the Smith-Hoover
election day, I met him as he came out of the I. C. station at Randolph
Street with Pat Carrigan and Ike Dugan. I talked to Pat and Ike, but
not to Studs.

"Aren't you gonna say hello to me?" he asked in friendly fashion,
and he offered me his hand.

I was curious but friendly for several minutes. We talked of Al
Smith's chances in an uninformed, unintelligent fashion and I injected
one joke about free love. Studs laughed at it; and then they went on.

The next I heard of him, he was dead.

When I went out into the dining room, I found all the old gang
there, jabbering in the smoke-thick, crowded room. But I did not have
any desire or intention of giving the world for having seen them. They
were almost all fat and respectable. Cloddishly, they talked of the

tragedy of his death, and then went about remembering the good old days. I sat in the corner and listened.

The scene seemed tragi-comical to me. All these fellows had been the bad boys of my boyhood, and many of them I had admired as proper models. Now they were all of the same kidney. Jackie Cooney (who once stole fifteen bottles of grape juice in one haul from under the eyes of a Greek proprietor over at Sixty-fifth and Stony Island), Monk Mc-Carthy (who lived in a basement on his pool winnings and peanuts for over a year), Al Mumford (the good-natured, dumbly well-inten-tioned corner scapegoat), Pat Carrigan, the roly-poly fat boy from Saint Stanislaus high school—all as alike as so many cans of tomato soup.

Jim Nolan, now bald-headed, a public accountant, engaged to be married, and student in philosophy at Saint Vincent's evening school, was in one corner with Monk.

"Gee, Monk, remember the time we went to Plantation and I got drunk and went down the alley over-turning garbage cans?" he re-called.

"Yeh, that was some party," Monk said.

"Those were the days," Jim said.

Tubby Connell, whom I recalled as a moody, introspective kid, singled out the social Johnny O'Brien and listened to the latter talk with George Gogarty about Illinois U.

Al Mumford walked about making cracks, finally observing to me, "Jim, get a fiddle and you'll look like Paderwooski."

Red Kelly sat enthroned with Les, Doyle, Simonsky, Bryan, Young Floss Campbell (waiting to be like these older fellows), talking oracularly.

"Yes, sir, it's too bad. A young fellow in the prime of life going like that. It's too bad," he said.

"Poor Studs!" Les said.

"I was out with him a week ago," Bryan said.

"He was all right then," Kelly said.

"Life is a funny thing," Doyle said.

"It's a good thing he had the priest," Kelly said.

"Yeh," Les said.

"Sa-ay, last Saturday I pushed the swellest little baby at Rosy's," Doyle said.

"Was she a blonde?" Kelly said.

"Yeh," Doyle said.

"She's cute. I jazzed her, too," Kelly said.

"Yeh, that night at Plantation was a wow," Jim Nolan said.

"We ought to pull off a drunk some night," Monk said.

"Let's," Nolan said.

"Say, Curley, are you in love?" Mumford asked Curley across the room.

"Now, Duffy," Charley said with imbecile superiority.

"Remember the time Curley went to Burnham?" Carrigan asked. Curley blushed.

"What happened, Curley?" Duffy asked.

"Nothing, Al," Curley said, confused.

"Go on, tell him, Curley! Tell him! Don't be bashful now! Don't be bashful! Tell him about the little broad!" Carrigan said.

"Now, Pat, you know me better than that," Curley said.

"Come on, Curley, tell me," Al said.

"Some little girl sat on Curley's knee, and he shoved her off and called her a lousy whore and left the place," Carrigan said.

"Why, Curley, I'm ashamed of you," Al said.

Curley blushed.

"I got to get up at six every morning. But I don't mind it. This not workin' is the bunk. You ain't got any clothes or anything when you ain't got the sheets. I know. No, sir, this loafin' is all crap. You wait around all day for something to happen," Jackie Cooney said to Tommy Rourke.

"Gee, it was tough on Studs," Johnny O'Brien said to George Gogarty.

Gogarty said it was tough, too. Then they talked of some student from Illinois U. Phil Rolfe came in. Phil was professional major-domo of the wake; he was going with Studs' kid sister. Phil used to be a smart Jewboy, misplaced when he did not get into the furrier business. Now he was sorry with everybody, and thanking them for being sorry. He and Kelly talked importantly of pall-bearers. Then he went out. Some fellow I didn't know started telling one of Red Kelly's brothers what time he got up to go to work. Mickey Flannagan, the corner drunk, came in and he, too, said he was working.

They kept on talking, and I thought more and more that they were a bunch of slobs. All the adventurous boy that was in them years ago had been killed. Slobs, getting fat and middle-aged, bragging of their stupid brawls, reciting the commonplaces of their days.

As I left, I saw Studs' kid sister. She was crying so pitifully that she was unable to recognize me. I didn't see how she could ever have been affectionate toward Studs. He was so outside of her understanding. I knew she never mentioned him to me the few times I took her out. But she cried pitifully.

As I left, I thought that Studs had looked handsome. He would have gotten a good break, too, if only they hadn't given him Extreme Unction. For life would have grown into fatter and fatter decay for him, just as it was starting to do with Kelly, Doyle, Cooney and McCarthy. He, too, was a slob; but he died without having to live countless slobbish years. If only they had not sent him to Heaven where there are no whores and poolrooms.

I walked home with Joe, who isn't like the others. We couldn't feel sorry over Studs. It didn't make any difference.

"Joe, he was a slob," I said.

Joe did not care to use the same language, but he did not disagree.

And now the rain keeps falling on Studs' new grave, and his family mournfully watches the leaden sky, and his old buddies are at work wishing that it was Saturday night, and that they were just getting into bed with a naked voluptuous blonde.

RICHARD WRIGHT Why he selected

HOW "BIGGER" WAS BORN

The basic symbols and images that went into the writing of *Native Son* were born of my living as a Negro in the United States. "How 'Bigger' Was Born" states how those symbols and images, over a long period of time, came to exercise a certain meaningful fascination over my mind and feelings. Here are fear, hate, guilt, murder, rape, brutality, deception, misguided kindness, and fumbling helpfulness. I don't think I ever enjoyed writing anything more than this preface and it was my first attempt to account publicly for the genesis of my attitude toward life.

If I were asked what is the one, over-all symbol or image gained from my living that most nearly represents what I feel to be the essence of American life, I'd say that it was that of a man struggling mightily to free his personality from the daily and hourly encroachments of American life. Bigger represents that to me. Of course, *Native Son* is but one angle of what I feel to be the struggle of the individual in America for self-possession. If I am lucky, I hope to depict many more, from varied angles and other planes.

Brooklyn, N. Y.   RICHARD WRIGHT
July, 1942

I AM not so pretentious as to imagine that it is possible for me to account completely for my own book, *Native Son*. But I am going to try to account for as much of it as I can, the sources of it, the material that went into it, and my own years' long changing attitude toward that material.

Acknowledgment is made to *The Saturday Review of Literature* and Harper & Brothers, for permission to reproduce those parts of this article which appeared in the *Review* issue of June 1, 1940.

In a fundamental sense, an imaginative novel represents the merging of two extremes; it is an intensely intimate expression on the part of a consciousness couched in terms of the most objective and commonly known events. It is at once something private and public by its very nature and texture. Confounding the author who is trying to lay his cards on the table is the dogging knowledge that his imagination is a kind of community medium of exchange: what he has read, felt, thought, seen, and remembered is translated into extensions as impersonal as a worn dollar bill.

The more closely the author thinks of why he wrote, the more he comes to regard his imagination as a kind of self-generating cement which glued his facts together, and his emotions as a kind of dark and obscure designer of those facts. Always there is something that is just beyond the tip of the tongue that could explain it all. Usually, he ends up by discussing something far afield, an act which incites skepticism and suspicion in those anxious for a straight-out explanation.

Yet the author is eager to explain. But the moment he makes the attempt his words falter, for he is confronted and defied by the inexplicable array of his own emotions. Emotions are subjective and he can communicate them only when he clothes them in objective guise; and how can he ever be so arrogant as to know when he is dressing up the right emotion in the right Sunday suit? He is always left with the uneasy notion that maybe *any* objective drapery is as good as *any* other for any emotion.

And the moment he does dress up an emotion, his mind is confronted with the riddle of that "dressed up" emotion, and he is left peering with eager dismay back into the dim reaches of his own incommunicable life. Reluctantly, he comes to the conclusion that to account for his book is to account for his life, and he knows that that is impossible. Yet, some curious, wayward motive urges him to supply the answer, for there is the feeling that his dignity as a living being is challenged by something within him that is not understood.

So, at the outset, I say frankly that there are phases of *Native Son* which I shall make no attempt to account for. There are meanings in my book of which I was not aware until they literally spilled out upon the paper. I shall sketch the outline of how I *consciously* came into possession of the materials that went into *Native Son*, but there will be many things I shall omit, not because I want to, but simply because I don't know them.

The birth of Bigger Thomas goes back to my childhood, and there was not just one Bigger, but many of them, more than I could count and more than you suspect. But let me start with the first Bigger, whom I shall call Bigger No. 1.

When I was a bareheaded, barefoot kid in Jackson, Mississippi, there was a boy who terrorized me and all of the boys I played with. If we were playing games, he would saunter up and snatch from us our balls, bats, spinning tops, and marbles. We would stand around pouting, sniffling, trying to keep back our tears, begging for our playthings. But Bigger would refuse. We never demanded that he give them back; we were afraid, and Bigger was bad. We had seen him clout boys when he was angry and we did not want to run that risk. We never recovered our toys unless we flattered him and made him feel that he was superior to us. Then, perhaps, if he felt like it, he condescended, threw them at us and then gave each of us a swift kick in the bargain, just to make us feel his utter contempt.

That was the way Bigger No. 1 lived. His life was a continuous challenge to others. At all times he *took* his way, right or wrong, and those who contradicted him had him to fight. And never was he happier than when he had someone cornered and at his mercy; it seemed that the deepest meaning of his squalid life was in him at such times.

I don't know what the fate of Bigger No. 1 was. His swaggering personality is swallowed up somewhere in the amnesia of my childhood. But I suspect that his end was violent. Anyway, he left a marked impression upon me; maybe it was because I longed secretly to be like him and was afraid. I don't know.

If I had known only one Bigger I would not have written *Native Son*. Let me call the next one Bigger No. 2; he was about seventeen and tougher than the first Bigger. Since I, too, had grown older, I was a little less afraid of him. And the hardness of this Bigger No. 2 was not directed toward me or the other Negroes, but toward the whites who ruled the South. He bought clothes and food on credit and would not pay for them. He lived in the dingy shacks of the white landlords and refused to pay rent. Of course, he had no money, but neither did we. We did without the necessities of life and starved ourselves, but he never would. When we asked him why he acted as he did, he would tell us (as though we were little children in a kindergarten) that the white folks had everything and he had nothing. Further, he would tell us that we were fools not to get what we wanted while we were alive in this world. We would listen and silently agree. We longed to believe and act as he did, but we were afraid. We were Southern Negroes and we were hungry and we wanted to live, but we were more willing to tighten our belts than risk conflict. Bigger No. 2 wanted to live and he did; he was in prison the last time I heard from him.

There was Bigger No. 3, whom the white folks called a "bad nigger." He carried his life in his hands in a literal fashion. I once worked as a ticket-taker in a Negro movie house (all movie houses in Dixie are Jim Crow; there are movies for whites and movies for blacks), and many times Bigger No. 3 came to the door and gave my arm a hard pinch and walked into the theater. Resentfully and silently, I'd nurse my bruised arm. Presently, the proprietor would come over and ask how things were going. I'd point into the darkened theater and say: "Bigger's in there." "Did he pay?" the proprietor would ask. "No, sir," I'd answer. The proprietor would pull down the corners of his lips and speak through his teeth: "We'll kill that goddamn nigger one of these days." And the episode would end right there. But later on Bigger No. 3 was killed during the days of Prohibition: while delivering liquor to a customer he was shot through the back by a white cop.

And then there was Bigger No. 4, whose only law was death. The Jim Crow laws of the South were not for him. But as he laughed and cursed and broke them, he knew that some day he'd have to pay for his freedom. His rebellious spirit made him violate all the taboos and consequently he always oscillated between moods of intense elation and depression. He was never happier than when he had outwitted some foolish custom, and he was never more melancholy than when brooding over the impossibility of his ever being free. He had no job, for he regarded digging ditches for fifty cents a day as slavery. "I can't live on that," he would say. Ofttimes I'd find him reading a book; he would stop and in a joking, wistful, and cynical manner ape the antics of the white folks. Generally, he'd end his mimicry in a

depressed state and say: "The white folks won't let us do nothing."
Bigger No. 4 was sent to the asylum for the insane.

Then there was Bigger No. 5, who always rode the Jim Crow
streetcars without paying and sat wherever he pleased. I remember
one morning his getting into a streetcar (all streetcars in Dixie are
divided into two sections: one section is for whites and is labeled—
FOR WHITES; the other section is for Negroes and is labeled—FOR
COLORED) and sitting in the white section. The conductor went to
him and said: "Come on, nigger. Move over where you belong. Can't
you read?" Bigger answered: "Naw, I can't read." The conductor
flared up: "Get out of that seat!" Bigger took out his knife, opened it,
held it nonchalantly in his hand, and replied: "Make me." The conductor turned red, blinked, clenched his fists, and walked away, stammering: "The goddamn scum of the earth!" A small angry conference
of white men took place in the front of the car and the Negroes sitting
in the Jim Crow section overheard: "That's that Bigger Thomas
nigger and you'd better leave 'im alone." The Negroes experienced
an intense flash of pride and the streetcar moved on its journey without incident. I don't know what happened to Bigger No. 5. But I can
guess.

The Bigger Thomases were the only Negroes I know of who consistently violated the Jim Crow laws of the South and got away with
it, at least for a sweet brief spell. Eventually, the whites who restricted
their lives made them pay a terrible price. They were shot, hanged,
maimed, lynched, and generally hounded until they were either dead
or their spirits broken.

There were many variations to this behavioristic pattern. Later on
I encountered other Bigger Thomases who did not react to the locked-in
Black Belts with this same extremity and violence. But before I use
Bigger Thomas as a springboard for the examination of milder types,
I'd better indicate more precisely the nature of the environment that
produced these men, or the reader will be left with the impression
that they were essentially and organically bad.

In Dixie there are two worlds, the white world and the black world,
and they are physically separated. There are white schools and black
schools, white churches and black churches, white businesses and black

businesses, white graveyards and black graveyards, and, for all I know, a white God and a black God. . . .

This separation was accomplished after the Civil War by the terror of the Ku Klux Klan, which swept the newly freed Negro through arson, pillage, and death out of the United States Senate, the House of Representatives, the many state legislatures, and out of the public, social, and economic life of the South. The motive for this assault was simple and urgent. The imperialistic tug of history had torn the Negro from his African home and had placed him ironically upon the most fertile plantation areas of the South; and, when the Negro was freed, he outnumbered the whites in many of these fertile areas. Hence, a fierce and bitter struggle took place to keep the ballot from the Negro, for had he had a chance to vote, he would have automatically controlled the richest lands of the South and with them the social, political, and economic destiny of a third of the Republic. Though the South is politically a part of America, the problem that faced her was peculiar and the struggle between the whites and the blacks after the Civil War was in essence a struggle for power, ranging over thirteen states and involving the lives of tens of millions of people.

But keeping the ballot from the Negro was not enough to hold him in check; disfranchisement had to be supplemented by a whole panoply of rules, taboos, and penalties designed not only to insure peace (complete submission), but to guarantee that no real threat would ever arise. Had the Negro lived upon a common territory, separate from the bulk of the white population, this program of oppression might not have assumed such a brutal and violent form. But this war took place between people who were neighbors, whose homes adjoined, whose farms had common boundaries. Guns and disfranchisement, therefore, were not enough to make the black neighbor keep his distance. The white neighbor decided to limit the amount of education his black neighbor could receive; decided to keep him off the police force and out of the local national guards; to segregate him residentially; to Jim Crow him in public places; to restrict his participation in the professions and jobs; and to build up a vast, dense ideology of racial superiority that would justify any act of violence taken against him to defend white dominance; and further, to condition him to hope for little and to receive that little without rebelling.

But, because the blacks were so *close* to the very civilization which sought to keep them out, because they could not *help* but react in some way to its incentives and prizes, and because the very tissue of their consciousness received its tone and timbre from the strivings of that dominant civilization, oppression spawned among them a myriad variety of reactions, reaching from outright blind rebellion to a sweet, other-worldly submissiveness.

In the main, this delicately balanced state of affairs has not greatly altered since the Civil War, save in those parts of the South which have been industrialized or urbanized. So volatile and tense are these relations that if a Negro rebels against rule and taboo, he is lynched and the reason for the lynching is usually called "rape," that catchword which has garnered such vile connotations that it can raise a mob anywhere in the South pretty quickly, even today.

Now for the variations in the Bigger Thomas pattern. Some of the Negroes living under these conditions got religion, felt that Jesus would redeem the void of living, felt that the more bitter life was in the present the happier it would be in the hereafter. Others, clinging still to that brief glimpse of post-Civil War freedom, employed a thousand ruses and stratagems of struggle to win their rights. Still others projected their hurts and longings into more naïve and mundane forms—blues, jazz, swing—and, without intellectual guidance, tried to build up a compensatory nourishment for themselves. Many labored under hot suns and then killed the restless ache with alcohol. Then there were those who strove for an education, and when they got it, enjoyed the financial fruits of it in the style of their bourgeois oppressors. Usually they went hand in hand with the powerful whites and helped to keep their groaning brothers in line, for that was the safest course of action. Those who did this called themselves "leaders." To give you an idea of how completely these "leaders" worked with those who oppressed, I can tell you that I lived the first seventeen years of my life in the South without so much as hearing of or seeing one act of rebellion from *any* Negro, save the Bigger Thomases.

But why did Bigger revolt? No explanation based upon a hard and fast rule of conduct can be given. But there were always two factors psychologically dominant in his personality. First, through some quirk of circumstance, he had become estranged from the religion and the folk culture of his race. Second, he was trying to react to and answer the call of the dominant civilization whose glitter came to him through the newspapers, magazines, radios, movies, and the mere imposing sight and sound of daily American life. In many respects his emergence as a distinct type was inevitable.

As I grew older, I became familiar with the Bigger Thomas conditioning and its numerous shadings no matter where I saw it in Negro life. It was not, as I have already said, as blatant or extreme as in the originals; but it was there, nevertheless, like an undeveloped negative.

Sometimes, in areas far removed from Mississippi, I'd hear a Negro say: "I wish I didn't have to live this way. I feel like I want to burst." Then the anger would pass; he would go back to his job and try to eke out a few pennies to support his wife and children.

Sometimes I'd hear a Negro say: "God, I wish I had a flag and a country of my own." But that mood would soon vanish and he would go his way placidly enough.

Sometimes I'd hear a Negro ex-soldier say: "What in hell did I fight in the war for? They segregated me even when I was offering my life for my country." But he, too, like the others, would soon forget, would become caught up in the tense grind of struggling for bread.

I've even heard Negroes, in moments of anger and bitterness, praise what Japan is doing in China, not because they believed in oppression (being objects of oppression themselves), but because they would suddenly sense how empty their lives were when looking at the dark faces of Japanese generals in the rotogravure supplements of the Sunday newspapers. They would dream of what it would be like to live in a country where they could forget their color and play a responsible role in the vital processes of the nation's life.

I've even heard Negroes say that maybe Hitler and Mussolini are all right; that maybe Stalin is all right. They did not say this out of any intellectual comprehension of the forces at work in the world, but because they felt that these men "did things," a phrase which is charged with more meaning than the mere words imply. There was in the back of their minds, when they said this, a wild and intense longing (wild and intense because it was suppressed!) to belong, to be identified, to feel that they were alive as other people were, to be caught up forget fully and exultingly in the swing of events, to feel the clean, deep, organic satisfaction of doing a job in common with others.

It was not until I went to live in Chicago that I first thought seriously of writing of Bigger Thomas. Two items of my experience combined to make me aware of Bigger as a meaningful and prophetic symbol. First, being free of the daily pressure of the Dixie environment, I was able to come into possession of my own feelings. Second, my contact with the labor movement and its ideology made me see Bigger clearly and feel what he meant.

I made the discovery that Bigger Thomas was not black all the time; he was white, too, and there were literally millions of him, everywhere. The extension of my sense of the personality of Bigger was the pivot of my life; it altered the complexion of my existence. I became conscious, at first dimly, and then later on with increasing clarity and conviction, of a vast, muddied pool of human life in America. It was as though I had put on a pair of spectacles whose power was that of an x-ray enabling me to see deeper into the lives of men. Whenever I picked up a newspaper, I'd no longer feel that I was reading of the doings of whites alone (Negroes are rarely mentioned in the press unless they've committed some crime!), but of a complex struggle for life going on in my country, a struggle in which I was involved. I sensed, too, that the Southern scheme of oppression was but an appendage of a far vaster and in many respects more ruthless and impersonal commodity-profit machine.

Trade-union struggles and issues began to grow meaningful to me. The flow of goods across the seas, buoying and depressing the wages of men, held a fascination. The pronouncements of foreign governments, their policies, plans, and acts were calculated and weighed in relation to the lives of people about me. I was literally overwhelmed when, in reading the works of Russian revolutionists, I came across descriptions of the "holiday energies of the masses," "the locomotives of history," "the conditions prerequisite for revolution," and so forth. I approached all of these new revelations in the light of Bigger Thomas, his hopes, fears, and despairs; and I began to feel far-flung kinships, and sense, with fright and abashment, the possibilities of *alliances* between the American Negro and other people possessing a kindred consciousness.

As my mind extended in this general and abstract manner, it was fed with even more vivid and concrete examples of the lives of Bigger Thomas. The urban environment of Chicago, affording a more stimulating life, made the Negro Bigger Thomases react more violently than even in the South. More than ever I began to see and understand the environmental factors which made for this extreme conduct. It was not that Chicago segregated Negroes more than the South, but that Chicago had more to offer, that Chicago's physical aspect—noisy, crowded, filled with the sense of power and fulfillment—did so much more to dazzle the mind with a taunting sense of possible achievement that the segregation it did impose brought forth from Bigger a reaction more obstreperous than in the South.

So the concrete picture and the abstract linkages of relationships fed each other, each making the other more meaningful and affording my emotions an opportunity to react to them with success and understanding. The process was like a swinging pendulum, each to and fro motion throwing up its tiny bit of meaning and significance, each stroke helping to develop the dim negative which had been implanted in my mind in the South.

During this period the shadings and nuances which were filling in Bigger's picture came, not so much from Negro life, as from the lives of whites I met and grew to know. I began to sense that they had their own kind of Bigger Thomas behavioristic pattern which grew out of a more subtle and broader frustration. The waves of recurring crime, the silly fads and crazes, the quicksilver changes in public taste, the hysteria and fears—all of these had long been mysteries to me. But now I looked back of them and felt the pinch and pressure of the environment that gave them their pitch and peculiar kind of being. I began to feel with my mind the inner tensions of the people I met. I don't mean to say that I think that environment *makes* consciousness (I suppose God makes that, if there is a God), but I do say that I felt and still feel that the environment supplies the instrumentalities through which the organism expresses itself, and if that environment is warped or tranquil, the mode and manner of behavior will be affected toward deadlocking tensions or orderly fulfillment and satisfaction. . . .

I don't know if *Native Son* is a good book or a bad book. And I

don't know if the book I'm working on now will be a good book or a
bad book. And I really don't care. The mere writing of it will be more
fun and a deeper satisfaction than any praise or blame from anybody.

I feel that I'm lucky to be alive to write novels today, when the
whole world is caught in the pangs of war and change. Early American
writers, Henry James and Nathaniel Hawthorne, complained bitterly
about the bleakness and flatness of the American scene. But I think
that if they were alive, they'd feel at home in modern America. True,
we have no great church in America; our national traditions are still
of such a sort that we are not wont to brag of them; and we have no
army that's above the level of mercenary fighters; we have no group
acceptable to the whole of our country upholding certain humane
values; we have no rich symbols, no colorful rituals. We have only a
money-grubbing, industrial civilization. But we do have in the Negro
the embodiment of a past tragic enough to appease the spiritual
hunger of even a James; and we have in the oppression of the Negro
a shadow athwart our national life dense and heavy enough to satisfy
even the gloomy broodings of a Hawthorne. And if Poe were alive, he
would not have to invent horror; horror would invent him.

ELMER RICE Why he selected

The ADDING MACHINE

The Adding Machine has for me a peculiar interest because of the rather extraordinary circumstances in which it was written: quite unlike anything else in my life as an author. In the summer of 1922 I was sitting up late one night working on a play which in theme and in treatment was as unlike *The Adding Machine* as possible. Suddenly, without any premonition or any reason that I have been able to discover, *The Adding Machine* popped into my mind complete: title, characters, scenes, situations and even a lot of the dialogue. It was really a rather startling experience. After a while I went to bed but couldn't sleep and at daybreak got up again, went to my desk and started to write the play! I kept at it for seventeen days and then, as far as I was concerned, the play was finished.

Except for the omission of one entire scene, the play was produced practically as it was originally written. It was given an excellent presentation by the Theatre Guild in the spring of 1923 with an impressive cast which included Dudley Digges, Margaret Wycherly, Helen Westley, Edward G. Robinson and the late Louis Calvert. But it met with anything but a warm reception. It got two or three good notices but most of the critics pooh-poohed or ridiculed it and it just managed to eke out a run of nine weeks. Later it was produced with considerable success by Gaston Baty in Paris and Barry Jackson in London, and, in the twenty years that have elapsed since it was written, it has been produced by practically every art theatre or repertory theatre in the United States and the British Empire and in a considerable number of non-English-speaking countries.

People have often asked me what I was trying to do when I wrote *The Adding Machine*. The plain truth is that I was not trying to do anything. I know now what the place of the play is (and it is an important one) in the development of my own psychic life, but while I was writing it I had very little control over the material. As I have indicated, it sprang straight from my unconscious

and its composition was as close to automatic writing as I ever expect
to get.

Stamford, Conn.   ELMER RICE
July 31, 1942

SCENE ONE

[*SCENE: A bedroom.*

*A small room containing an "installment plan" bed, dresser, and
chairs. An ugly electric light fixture over the bed with a single glaring
naked lamp. One small window with the shade drawn. The walls are
papered with sheets of foolscap covered with columns of figures.*

MR. ZERO *is lying in the bed, facing the audience, his head and
shoulders visible. He is thin, sallow, under-sized, and partially bald.*
MRS. ZERO *is standing before the dresser arranging her hair for the
night. She is forty-five, sharp-featured, gray streaks in her hair. She
is shapeless in her long-sleeved cotton nightgown. She is wearing her
shoes, over which sag her ungartered stockings.*]

MRS. ZERO

[*As she takes down her hair*]: I'm gettin' sick o' them Westerns.
All them cowboys ridin' around an' foolin' with them ropes. I don't
care nothin' about that. I'm sick of 'em. I don't see why they don't
have more of them stories like "For Love's Sweet Sake." I like them
sweet little love stories. They're nice an' wholesome. Mrs. Twelve was
sayin' to me only yesterday, "Mrs. Zero," says she, "what I like is one
of them wholesome stories, with just a sweet, simple little love story."
"You're right, Mrs. Twelve," I says. "That's what I like, too." They're
showin' too many Westerns at the Rosebud. I'm gettin' sick of them.
I think we'll start goin' to the Peter Stuyvesant. They got a good bill
there Wednesday night. There's a Chubby Delano comedy called
"Sea-Sick." Mrs. Twelve was tellin' me about it. She says it's a scream.
They're havin' a picnic in the country and they sit Chubby next to
an old maid with a great big mouth. So he gets sore an' when she
ain't lookin' he goes and catches a frog and drops it in her clam

chowder. An' when she goes to eat the chowder the frog jumps out of it an' right into her mouth. Talk about laugh! Mrs. Twelve was tellin' me she laughed so she nearly passed out. He sure can pull some funny ones. An' they got that big Grace Darling feature, "A Mother's Tears." She's sweet. But I don't like her clothes. There's no style to them. Mrs. Nine was tellin' me she read in *Pictureland* that she ain't livin' with her husband. He's her second, too. I don't know whether they're divorced or just separated. You wouldn't think it to see her on the screen. She looks so sweet and innocent. Maybe it ain't true. You can't believe all you read. They say some Pittsburgh millionaire is crazy about her and that's why she ain't livin' with her husband. Mrs. Seven was tellin' me her brother-in-law has a friend that used to go to school with Grace Darling. He says her name ain't Grace Darling at all. Her right name is Elizabeth Dugan, he says, an' all them stories about her gettin' five thousand a week is the bunk, he says. She's sweet, though. Mrs. Eight was tellin' me that "A Mother's Tears" is the best picture she ever made. "Don't miss it, Mrs. Zero," she says. "It's sweet," she says. "Just sweet and wholesome. Cry!" she says, "I nearly cried my eyes out." There's one part in it where this big bum of an Englishman—he's a married man, too—an' she's this little simple country girl. An' she nearly falls for him, too. But she's sittin' out in the garden, one day, and she looks up and there's her mother lookin' at her, right out of the clouds. So that night she locks the door of her room. An' sure enough, when everybody's in bed, along comes this big bum of an Englishman an' when she won't let him in what does he do but go an' kick open the door. "Don't miss it, Mrs. Zero," Mrs. Eight was tellin' me. It's at the Peter Stuyvesant Wednesday night, so don't be tellin' me you want to go to the Rosebud. The Eights seen it downtown at the Strand. They go downtown all the time. Just like us—nit! I guess by the time it gets to the Peter Stuyvesant all that part about kickin' in the door will be cut out. Just like they cut out that big cabaret scene in "The Price of Virtue." They sure are pullin' some rough stuff in the pictures nowadays. "It's no place for a young girl," I was tellin' Mrs. Eleven, only the other day. An' by the time they get uptown half of it is cut out. But you wouldn't go downtown—not if wild horses was to drag you. You can wait till they come uptown! Well, I don't want to wait, see? I want to see 'em when everybody else is seein' them an' not a month later. Now don't go tellin' me you ain't got the price. You could dig up the price all right, all right, if you wanted to. I notice you always got the price to go to the ball game. But when it comes to me havin' a good time then it's always: "I ain't got the price, I gotta start savin'." A fat lot you'll ever save! I got all I can do now makin' both ends meet an' you talkin' about savin'. [*She seats herself on a chair and begins removing her shoes and stockings.*] An' don't go pullin' that stuff about bein' tired. "I been workin' hard all day. Twice a day in the subway's enough for me." Tired! Where do you get that tired stuff, anyhow? What about me? Where do I come in? Scrubbin' floors an' cookin' your meals an' washin' your dirty clothes. An' you sittin' on a chair all day, just addin' figgers an' waitin' for five-thirty. There's no five-thirty for me. I don't wait for no whistle. I don't get no vacations neither. And what's more I don't get no pay envelope every Saturday night neither. I'd like to know where you'd be without me. An' what have I got to show for it?—slavin' my life away to give you a home. What's in it for me, I'd like to know? But it's my own fault, I guess. I was a fool for marryin' you. If I'd 'a' had any sense, I'd 'a' known what you were from the start. I wish I had it to do over again, I hope to tell you. You was goin' to do wonders, you was! You wasn't goin' to be a bookkeeper long—oh, no, not you. Wait till you got started— you was goin' to show 'em. There wasn't no job in the store that was too big for you. Well, I've been waitin'—waitin' for you to get started —see? It's been a good long wait, too. Twenty-five years! An' I ain't seen nothin' happen. Twenty-five years in the same job. Twenty-five years tomorrow! You're proud of it, ain't you? Twenty-five years in the same job an' never missed a day! That's somethin' to be proud of, ain't it? Sittin' for twenty-five years on the same chair, addin' up figures. What about bein' store-manager? I guess you forgot about that, didn't you? An' me at home here lookin' at the same four walls an' workin' my fingers to the bone to make both ends meet. Seven years since you got a raise! An' if you don't get one to-morrow, I'll bet a nickel you won't have the guts to go an' ask for one. I didn't pick much when I picked you, I'll tell the world. You ain't much to be proud of. [*She rises, goes to the window, and raises the shade. A few lighted windows are visible on the other side of the closed court.*

Looking out for a moment]: She ain't walkin' around to-night, you can bet your sweet life on that. An' she won't be walkin' around any more nights, neither. Not in this house, anyhow. [*She turns away from the window*]: The dirty bum! The idea of her comin' to live in a house with respectable people. They should 'a' gave her six years, not six months. If I was the judge I'd of gave her life. A bum like that. [*She approaches the bed and stands there a moment*]: I guess you're sorry she's gone. I guess you'd like to sit home every night an' watch her goin's-on. You're somethin' to be proud of, you are! [*She stands on the bed and turns out the light . . . A thin stream of moonlight filters in from the court. The two figures are dimly visible.* Mrs. Zero *gets into bed*]:

You'd better not start nothin' with women, if you know what's good for you. I've put up with a lot, but I won't put up with that. I've been slavin' away for twenty-five years, makin' a home for you an' nothin' to show for it. If you was any kind of a man you'd have a decent job by now an' I'd be gettin' some comfort out of life—instead of bein' just a slave, washin' pots an' standin' over the hot stove. I've stood it for twenty-five years an' I guess I'll have to stand it twenty-five more. But don't you go startin' nothin' with women—— [*She goes on talking as the curtain falls.*]

Scene Two

[*SCENE: An office in a department store. Wood and glass partitions. In the middle of the room, two tall desks back to back. At one desk on a high stool is* Zero. *Opposite him at the other desk, also on a high stool, is* Daisy Diana Dorothea Devore, *a plain, middle-aged woman. Both wear green eye shades and paper sleeve protectors. A pendent electric lamp throws light upon both desks.* Daisy *reads aloud figures from a pile of slips which lie before her. As she reads the figures,* Zero *enters them upon a large square sheet of ruled paper which lies before him.*]

Daisy

[*Reading aloud*]: Three ninety-eight. Forty-two cents. A dollar fifty. A dollar fifty. A dollar twenty-five. Two dollars. Thirty-nine cents. Twenty-seven fifty.

ZERO

[*Petulantly*]: Speed it up a little, cancha?

DAISY

What's the rush? To-morrer's another day.

ZERO

Aw, you make me sick.

DAISY

An' you make me sicker.

ZERO

Go on. Go on. We're losin' time.

DAISY

Then quit bein' so bossy.
[*She reads*]: Three dollars. Two sixty-nine. Eighty-one fifty. Forty dollars. Eight seventy-five. Who do you think you are, anyhow?

ZERO

Never mind who I think I am. You tend to your work.

DAISY

Aw, don't be givin' me so many orders. Sixty cents. Twenty-four cents. Seventy-five cents. A dollar fifty. Two fifty. One fifty. One fifty. Two fifty. I don't have to take it from you and what's more I don't.

ZERO

Aw, quit talkin'.

DAISY

I'll talk all I want. Three dollars. Fifty cents. Fifty cents. Seven dollars. Fifty cents. Two fifty. Three fifty. Fifty cents. One fifty. Fifty cents.
[*She goes bending over the slips and transferring them from one pile to another. ZERO bends over his desk, busily entering the figures.*]

ZERO

[*Without looking up*]: You make me sick. Always shootin' off your face about somethin'. Talk, talk, talk. Just like all the other women. Women make me sick.

DAISY

[*Busily fingering the slips*]: Who do you think you are, anyhow? Bossin' me around. I don't have to take it from you, and what's more I won't.
[*They both attend closely to their work, neither looking up.*]

ZERO

Women make me sick. They're all alike. The judge gave her six months. I wonder what they do in the work-house. Peel potatoes. I'll bet she's sore at me. Maybe she'll try to kill me when she gets out. I better be careful. Hello, Girl Slays Betrayer. Jealous Wife Slays Rival. You can't tell what a woman's liable to do. I better be careful.

DAISY

I'm gettin' sick of it. Always pickin' on me about somethin'. Never a decent word out of you. Not even the time o' day.

ZERO

I guess she wouldn't have the nerve at that. Maybe she don't even know it's me. They didn't even put my name in the paper, the big bums. Maybe she's been in the work-house before. A bum like that. She didn't have nothin' on that one time—nothin' but a shirt. [*He glances up quickly, then bends over again*]: You make me sick. I'm sick of lookin' at your face.

DAISY

Gee, ain't that whistle ever goin' to blow? You didn't used to be like that. Not even good mornin' or good evenin'. I ain't done nothin to you. It's the young girls. Goin' around without corsets.

ZERO

Your face is gettin' all yeller. Why don't you put some paint on it? She was puttin' on paint that time. On her cheeks and on her lips. And that blue stuff on her eyes. Just sittin' there in a shimmy puttin' on the paint. An' walkin' around the room with her legs all bare.

DAISY

I wish I was dead.

ZERO

I was a goddam fool to let the wife get on to me. She oughta get six months at that. The dirty bum. Livin' in a house with respectable people. She'd be livin' there yet, if the wife hadn't o' got on to me. Damn her!

DAISY

I wish I was dead.

ZERO

Maybe another one'll move in. Gee, that would be great. But the wife's got her eye on me now.

DAISY

I'm scared to do it, though.

ZERO

You oughta move into that room. It's cheaper than where you're livin' now. I better tell you about it. I don't mean to be always pickin' on you.

DAISY

Gas. The smell of it makes me sick.
[ZERO *looks up and clears his throat.*]

DAISY

[*Looking up, startled*]: Whadja say?

ZERO

I didn't say nothin'.

DAISY

I thought you did.

ZERO

You thought wrong.
[*They bend over their work again.*]

DAISY

A dollar sixty. A dollar fifty. Two ninety. One sixty-two.

ZERO

Why the hell should I tell you? Fat chance of you forgettin' to
pull down the shade!

DAISY

If I asked for carbolic they might get on to me.

ZERO

Your hair's gettin' gray. You don't wear them shirt waists any
more with the low collars. When you'd bend down to pick somethin'
up——

DAISY

I wish I knew what to ask for. Girl Takes Mercury After All-
Night Party. Woman In Ten-Story Death Leap.

ZERO

I wonder where'll she go when she gets out. Gee, I'd like to make
a date with her. Why didn't I go over there the night my wife went
to Brooklyn? She never woulda found out.

DAISY

I seen Pauline Frederick do it once. Where could I get a pistol
though?

Zero

I guess I didn't have the nerve.

Daisy

I'll bet you'd be sorry then that you been so mean to me. How do I know, though? Maybe you wouldn't.

Zero

Nerve! I got as much nerve as anybody. I'm on the level, that's all. I'm a married man and I'm on the level.

Daisy

Anyhow, why ain't I got a right to live? I'm as good as anybody else. I'm too refined, I guess. That's the whole trouble.

Zero

The time the wife had pneumonia I thought she was goin' to pass out. But she didn't. The doctor's bill was eighty-seven dollars. [*Looking up*]: Hey, wait a minute! Didn't you say eighty-seven dollars?

Daisy

[*Looking up*]: What?

Zero

Was the last you said eighty-seven dollars?

Daisy

[*Consulting the slip*]: Forty-two fifty.

Zero

Well, I made a mistake. Wait a minute. [*He busies himself with an eraser*]: All right. Shoot.

Daisy

Six dollars. Three fifteen. Two twenty-five. Sixty-five cents. A dollar twenty. You talk to me as if I was dirt.

ZERO

I wonder if I could kill the wife without anybody findin' out. In bed some night. With a pillow.

DAISY

I used to think you was stuck on me.

ZERO

I'd get found out, though. They always have ways.

DAISY

We used to be so nice and friendly together when I first came here. You used to talk to me then.

ZERO

Maybe she'll die soon. I noticed she was coughin' this mornin'.

DAISY

You used to tell me all kinds o' things. You were goin' to show them all. Just the same, you're still sittin' here.

ZERO

Then I could do what I damn please. Oh, boy!

DAISY

Maybe it ain't all your fault neither. Maybe if you'd had the right kind o' wife—somebody with a lot of common-sense, somebody refined —me!

ZERO

At that, I guess I'd get tired of bummin' around. A feller wants some place to hang his hat.

DAISY

I wish she would die.

ZERO

And when you start goin' with women you're liable to get into trouble. And lose your job maybe.

DAISY

Maybe you'd marry me.

ZERO

Gee, I wish I'd gone over there that night.

DAISY

Then I could quit workin'.

ZERO

Lots o' women would be glad to get me.

DAISY

You could look a long time before you'd find a sensible, refined girl like me.

ZERO

Yes, sir, they could look a long time before they'd find a steady meal-ticket like me.

DAISY

I guess I'd be too old to have any kids. They say it ain't safe after thirty-five.

ZERO

Maybe I'd marry you. You might be all right, at that.

DAISY

I wonder—if you don't want kids—whether—if there's any way ——

ZERO

[*Looking up*]: Hey! Hey! Can't you slow up? What do you think
I am—a machine?

DAISY

[*Looking up*]: Say, what do you want, anyhow? First it's too slow
an' then it's too fast. I guess you don't know what you want.

ZERO

Well, never mind about that. Just you slow up.

DAISY

I'm gettin' sick o' this. I'm goin' to ask to be transferred.

ZERO

Go ahead. You can't make me mad.

DAISY

Aw, keep quiet. [*She reads*]: Two forty-five. A dollar twenty. A
dollar fifty. Ninety cents. Sixty-three cents.

ZERO

Marry you! I guess not! You'd be as bad as the one I got.

DAISY

You wouldn't care if I did ask. I got a good mind to ask.

ZERO

I was a fool to get married.

DAISY

Then I'd never see you at all.

ZERO

What chance has a guy got with a woman tied around his neck?

Daisy

That time at the store picnic—the year your wife couldn't come—you were nice to me then.

Zero

Twenty-five years holdin' down the same job!

Daisy

We were together all day—just sittin' around under the trees.

Zero

I wonder if the boss remembers about it bein' twenty-five years.

Daisy

And comin' home that night—you sat next to me in the big delivery wagon.

Zero

I got a hunch there's a big raise comin' to me.

Daisy

I wonder what it feels like to be really kissed. Men—dirty pigs! They want the bold ones.

Zero

If he don't come across I'm goin' right up to the front office and tell him where he gets off.

Daisy

I wish I was dead.

Zero

"Boss," I'll say, "I want to have a talk with you." "Sure," he'll say, "sit down. Have a Corona Corona." "No," I'll say, "I don't smoke." "How's that?" he'll say. "Well, boss," I'll say, "it's this way. Every time I feel like smokin' I just take a nickel and put it in the old

sock. A penny saved is a penny earned, that's the way I look at it."
"Damn sensible," he'll say. "You got a wise head on you, Zero."

DAISY

I can't stand the smell of gas. It makes me sick. You coulda kissed
me if you wanted to.

ZERO

"Boss," I'll say, "I ain't quite satisfied. I been on the job twenty-
five years now and if I'm gonna stay I gotta see a future ahead of
me." "Zero," he'll say, "I'm glad you came in. I've had my eye on you,
Zero. Nothin' gets by me." "Oh, I know that, boss," I'll say. That'll
hand him a good laugh, that will. "You're a valuable man, Zero," he'll
say, "and I want you right up here with me in the front office. You're
done addin' figgers. Monday mornin' you move up here."

DAISY

Them kisses in the movies—them long ones—right on the
mouth——

ZERO

I'll keep a-goin' right on up after that. I'll show some of them
birds where they get off.

DAISY

That one the other night—"The Devil's Alibi"—he put his arms
around her—and her head fell back and her eyes closed—like she was
in a daze.

ZERO

Just give me about two years and I'll show them birds where they
get off.

DAISY

I guess that's what it's like—a kinda daze—when I see them like
that, I just seem to forget everything.

Zero

Then me for a place in Jersey. And maybe a little Buick. No tin Lizzie for mine. Wait till I get started—I'll show 'em.

Daisy

I can see it now when I kinda half-close my eyes. The way her head fell back. And his mouth pressed right up against hers. Oh, Gawd! it must be grand! [*There is a sudden shrill blast from a steam whistle.*]

Daisy and Zero

[*Together*]: The whistle!
[*With great agility they get off their stools, remove their eye shades and sleeve protectors and put them on the desks. Then each produces from behind the desk a hat—*Zero, *a dusty derby,* Daisy, *a frowsy straw . . .* Daisy *puts on her hat and turns toward* Zero *as though she were about to speak to him. But he is busy cleaning his pen and pays no attention to her. She sighs and goes toward the door at the left.*]

Zero

[*Looking up*]: G'night, Miss Devore.
[*But she does not hear him and exits.* Zero *takes up his hat and goes left. The door at the right opens and the* Boss *enters—middle-aged, stoutish, bald, well-dressed.*]

The Boss

[*Calling*]: Oh—er—Mister—er——
[Zero *turns in surprise, sees who it is and trembles nervously.*]

Zero

[*Obsequiously*]: Yes, sir. Do you want me, sir?

Boss

Yes. Just come here a moment, will you?

ZERO

Yes, sir. Right away, sir. [*He fumbles his hat, picks it up, stumbles, recovers himself, and approaches the* Boss, *every fibre quivering.*]

BOSS

Mister—er—er ——

ZERO

Zero.

BOSS

Yes, Mr. Zero. I wanted to have a little talk with you.

ZERO

[*With a nervous grin*]: Yes sir, I been kinda expectin' it.

BOSS

[*Staring at him*]: Oh, have you?

ZERO

Yes, sir.

BOSS

How long have you been with us, Mister—er—Mister ——

ZERO

Zero.

BOSS

Yes, Mister Zero.

ZERO

Twenty-five years to-day.

BOSS

Twenty-five years! That's a long time.

ZERO

Never missed a day.

Boss

And you've been doing the same work all the time?

ZERO

Yes, sir. Right here at this desk.

Boss

Then, in that case, a change probably won't be unwelcome to you.

ZERO

No, sir, it won't. And that's the truth.

Boss

We've been planning a change in this department for some time.

ZERO

I kinda thought you had your eye on me.

Boss

You were right. The fact is that my efficiency experts have recommended the installation of adding machines.

ZERO

[*Staring at him*]: Addin' machines?

Boss

Yes, you've probably seen them. A mechanical device that adds automatically.

ZERO

Sure. I've seen them. Keys—and a handle that you pull. [*He goes through the motions in the air.*]

Boss

That's it. They do the work in half the time and a high-school girl can operate them. Now, of course, I'm sorry to lose an old and faithful employee ——

Zero

Excuse me, but would you mind sayin' that again?

Boss

I say I'm sorry to lose an employee who's been with me for so many years ——
[*Soft music is heard—the sound of the mechanical player of a distant merry-go-round. The part of the floor upon which the desk and stools are standing begins to revolve very slowly.*]

Boss

But, of course, in an organization like this, efficiency must be the first consideration ——
[*The music becomes gradually louder and the revolutions more rapid.*]

Boss

You will draw your salary for the full month. And I'll direct my secretary to give you a letter of recommendation ——

Zero

Wait a minute, boss. Let me get this right. You mean I'm canned?

Boss

[*Barely making himself heard above the increasing volume of sound*]: I'm sorry—no other alternative—greatly regret—old employee —efficiency—economy—business—*business*—BUSINESS ——
[*His voice is drowned by the music. The platform is revolving rapidly now. Zero and the Boss face each other. They are entirely motionless save for the Boss's jaws, which open and close incessantly. But the words are inaudible. The music swells and swells. To it is added every off-stage effect of the theatre: the wind, the waves,*]

the galloping horses, the locomotive whistle, the sleigh bells, the automobile siren, the glass-crash. New Year's Eve, Election Night, Armistice Day, and the Mardi-Gras. The noise is deafening, maddening, unendurable. Suddenly it culminates in a terrific peal of thunder. For an instant there is a flash of red and then everything is plunged into blackness.]

[*Curtain*]

E. B. WHITE Why he selected

QUO VADIMUS?

I don't remember when "Quo Vadimus?" was written, but it must have been about ten years ago. I used to work in the production detail department of an advertising agency, and I suppose this piece reminds me of the way I sometimes used to feel—like a reluctant conspirator in a plot I didn't understand.

North Brooklin, Me.   E. B. WHITE
April 18, 1942

A GLIMPSE INTO THE FUTURE—YOU KNOW, LIKE IN THE SUNDAY TIMES MAGAZINE

A MAN approaching me in East Thirty-fourth Street, in the thick of noon, had so queer a look in his eye, such a fudgy and fearful expression, I stopped him.

"Quo vadis?" I asked.

"You mean me?" he said, sheepishly.

"Yes, sure. Quo vadis?" I repeated. "Where the hell are you going?"

"I won't tell you, because you wouldn't understand," he replied.

"Well then," I said, "I'll put it this way: quo vadimus? Where are either of us going?"

He seemed stunned. A woman, shopping, bumped lightly against him. At length he spoke, in a clear, low, frightened voice.

"I'll tell you where I'm going. I'm on my way to the Crowbar Building, Forty-first and Park, in Pershing Square, named after General Pershing in the Grand Central zone, zone as in Zonite, because I forgot to tell Miss Cortwright to leave a note for Mr. Josefson when he comes in, telling him he should tell the engraver to vignette the halftone on page forty-three of the salesmen's instruction book that

479

Irwain, Weasey, Weasey & Button are getting out for the Fretherby-
Quigley Company, which is to go to all their salesmen on the road."

"What do the salesmen sell?" I said, quietly.

"They sell a new kind of shorthand course, called the Quigley
Method of Intensive Speedwriting."

"Very good," I said. "That's just the kind of errand I imagined
you to be on. As I understand it, recapitulating, you are on your way
to the Crowbar Building, Forty-first and Park, in Pershing Square
named after General Pershing, hero of the song, 'Many a cootie came
over from France in General Pershing's underpants,' in the Grand
Central zone, zone as in Zonite, because you forgot to tell Miss Cortwright to leave a note for Mr. Josefson when he comes in, telling him
he should tell the engraver to vignette the halftone on page forty-three
of a booklet that Irwain, Weasey, Weasey & Button are getting out for
the Fretherby-Quigley Company, instructing their salesmen how to
approach people to sell the Quigley Method of Intensive Speedwriting,
which in turn will enable girls like Miss Cortwright to take Mr.
Josefson's dictation when he has to send a memo to the engraver telling him not to forget to vignette a halftone in a booklet telling salesmen how to sell shorthand courses. Is that correct?"

"That's where I'm going," said the man.

"Well, aren't you ashamed of yourself!" I cried.

"I don't know whether I am or not," he said, with a slight touch
of indignation.

"Listen, my friend," I went on, fixing him with my eye, "all you
really want is a decent meal when it comes mealtime, isn't it?"

"And a warm place to sleep when it comes night," he added
quickly, almost eagerly.

"Exactly, and a warm place to sleep when it comes night. All right
then, don't you think that you, who just want a decent meal when it
comes mealtime, and a warm place to sleep when it comes night—
don't you think you are pretty far from the main issue if you're on
your way to tell a Miss Cortwright to leave a note for a Mr. Josefson
telling him to . . ."

He motioned me with his hand to stop. "You needn't go on. Yes,
I'm far from the issue, sir," he said. "But I do not know what to do.
It must be something about the age—what do they call it, the 'machine'

age? This Miss Cortwright . . . I don't know. This Josefson . . . I don't know. Nice people, I suppose. It is all so complex. I just drifted into it."

"Exactly," I said. "And it's getting worse, mind you. I predict a bright future for complexity in this country. Did it ever occur to you that there's no limit to how complicated things can get, on account of one thing always leading to another? Did you ever stop to consider how the Cortwrights lead to the Josefsons, and how the Josefsons lead to the engravers? Paths of glory, leading to the engravers, my man. Did you ever stop to think what might happen if people by accident forgot where the whole thing started?"

The man shook his head, very slightly. His eyes were bright but out of focus. I went on, sternly.

"Only the other evening," I said, "I stopped a man on Broadway who had in his face the same look that I detected in *your* face a moment ago. To him, too, I said: 'Quo vadis?' And he, too, told me a story much like yours. He told me, my friend, that he was on his way to see a Mr. Fitch in the Pari-Mutuel Building, who wanted to get permission to make a talking picture of an airplane towing a glider in which was seated a man listening to a radio which was receiving a colored dialogue between two men named Amos and Andy who were talking together in order to advertise a toothpaste and the name of the toothpaste was . . ."

"Pepsodent," put in my man.

"Yes, Pepsodent. And that man—all he really wanted, when you came right down to it, was a decent meal when it came mealtime."

"And a warm place to sleep when it came night," added my friend, hurriedly.

"Exactly."

There was a pause in our conversation at this point. Cars passed back and forth in the street. Women shoppers brushed lightly against us—women who were on their way to buy fringes for lampshades, women who were on their way to buy printed silk, women who were on their way to buy the hooks that hold the rods that hold the curtains. Suddenly my friend addressed me.

"Now *you* tell *me* where *you're* going!" he said, sharply.

"Ha, not on your life—you don't catch me that way," I cried. "I'm not telling you where I'm going."

"I suppose you're going fishing," said the man, smirking.

"Smirk again and I'll smack you," I said. "I always smack smirkers." He smirked. I smacked him.

"Now ask me where I'm going!" I said, holding him by the arm.

"I bet I can guess where you're going. I bet you're a writer, on his way to write something. I know your type. You're going to write a story about 'complexity'—about meeting a man in East Thirty-fourth Street who was on his way to the Crowbar Building in Pershing Square, named after General Pershing in the Grand Central zone, zone as in Zonite, because he forgot to tell Miss Cortwright to leave a note for Mr. Josefson to tell the engraver to vignette the halftone . . ."

"Don't repeat it," I said, breaking down. "That's exactly where I'm going."

". . . so a person like Miss Cortwright will have something to read, and not understand, when she isn't busy with dictation," he said, finishing up.

"That's it."

"And all you want is a decent meal when it comes mealtime, isn't it?" asked my friend.

"And a warm place to sleep when it comes night," I added quickly, almost eagerly.

"Sure, I know," he said. "Well, vale!"

"Vale, kid!" I replied. And we continued on our lonely and imponderable ways.

LOUIS ADAMIC Why he selected

GIRL ON THE ROAD

Based upon actual experience, "Girl on the Road" was written in two or three days late in 1937, and I put it in a book called *My America*, published by Harpers in May 1938. The story was rejected by nineteen magazine editors, by some perhaps because of its length; but my egoism inclines me to agree with the considerable number of people who have written me about it that it is a rather good piece.

It seems to me a very American tale. It sweeps over "the road" between the Arizona-California line to New York, and takes in a good deal of the agony and absurdity of America during the middle 1930s.

I still often wonder what finally happened to the actual girl I picked up outside of Cleveland and left in Harrisburg.

Milford, N. J.   LOUIS ADAMIC
May 1, 1942

I T WAS near seven o'clock on a mid-November morning, cold and windy under a bleak Ohio sky, and—New York-bound—I was driving out of Cleveland, where I had spent the previous evening with pleasant friends, dining at their home, and spending the rest of the night at a comfortable hotel. I had had my breakfast and was warm in the new overcoat and gloves I had bought in Detroit a few days before. There was a heater in the car, and when the wind occasionally lurched into me with great force and threatened to swerve me off the road, I almost enjoyed the sensation I experienced.

For two or three miles, approaching the village of Chagrin Falls, not far from Cleveland, I met or passed no car, and none passed me. Then, just ahead, as I swung around a turn, I noticed a little figure— woman or girl—moving across the top of a slight rise in the road. Stumbling and staggering under the wind's impact, she carried a suitcase; and, wondering what she was doing out so early on such a morning,

483

I assumed she must be going some place close by. I decided to offer her the lift she evidently sought, and I slowed down going up the incline.

She turned about and beckoned to me with a feeble, despairing gesture of her arm, then stumbled—seemingly over her own feet, as the wind pushed her—and fell on the suitcase, which hit the pavement simultaneously with her knees. This occurred when I was perhaps fifty feet from her, and I had to shift into second to enable the car to pull upgrade against the strong wind. By the time I had stopped she had scrambled up again, and was about to pick up the suitcase when, abruptly, it blew open, and the wind scooped out most of its contents and flung them against the fence and amid the cornstalks of the field along the highway.

I hurriedly stepped out of the automobile, ran to her, and was confronted at closest proximity by a girl who was but little more than a skin-enveloped skeleton. Her cheap clothing was threadbare, wrinkled, ripped in several places. Her thin, sharp face was blue from the cold and wind, except where it was black and yellow around two considerable scars, one on her left cheek and the other above her right eye. Her whole body, and every part of it separately, quaked and twitched in short, swift jerks.

The palms and the under sides of the fingers of her black cloth gloves were worn through from carrying the suitcase. Her shoes were broken. Her cheap silk stockings, with several holes and runs, afforded scarcely any covering. The wind whipped against her, and I knew that underneath her frayed garments she was also all blue and bruised and scratched, for, an instant before I reached her and put a hand on her shoulder lest the wind take her off, her light coat and skirt had billowed about her and, flying up, revealed her skinny legs midway above her knees.

She seemed small, the size of a girl of twelve or thirteen. Later she told me the last time she weighed herself, days before, she had tipped the scales at eighty-four, but now she probably was even less than eighty. Her normal weight was a hundred and six or seven. Her teeth chattered so it was a wonder they did not shatter one another. Her lower lip was covered with little cuts and congealed blood, as though the teeth had been hacking at it for a long time.

"Get in the car!" I yelled, feeling as though I myself would begin to tremble at any moment. The wind pushed the words back into my mouth. As she did not move, I pulled her toward the automobile. She was at once limp and rigid.

Just then a car rushed toward us and I yanked the girl out of the way. She dragged the open suitcase along with her.

Except for a small package tied with a faded red ribbon which evidently was too heavy to be blown out, the suitcase was empty. The girl clutched its handle frenziedly. But immediately the car whizzed by us, a sudden convulsion in her, which originated perhaps in the cold center of her bones, caused her to lose her grip on it, and the suitcase began to slither across the road. Unable to talk through her chattering teeth, she let out a shrill, pathetic whimper, and I quickly stepped on the suitcase, halting its progress ditchward.

I stooped over to close it, but the girl emitted another piercing whimper. An indescribable misery in her eyes, she pointed at her things snapping in the wind on the wire fence and the cornstalks on the other side of the road, which I had seen a moment before but since momentarily forgotten.

"All right," I shouted, "I'll get them. You go inside!"

But she was frantic about her things and the suitcase, and I felt compelled to seize her and carry her into the car: which gave me one of the worst sensations of my life. The whole horror of her wretched, cold-pierced being engulfed me. There was no strength left in it. A wisp of her stringy hair, which stuck out from under her tiny, battered summer hat, touched my face, and it was all I could do not to drop her. My sensation was a mixture of revulsion and pity and shame—shame at the revulsion that pulsed through me; but I could not help feeling as I did.

My car was a coupé, and I managed to get her in and at least into the semblance of a sitting position. She whimpered and made faint half-gestures while shaking as violently as she had shaken outside.

The motor and the heater were going, but I had left the car open, and now it was as cold inside as out; so, I wrapped the girl in my old autumn topcoat and the raincoat which I had with me on the ledge above the seat. Then I closed the car and proceeded to gather up her things. I was terribly awkward crawling through the wire fence . . . and for a moment I wondered if all this were not really a nightmare.

There was that girl in my car; here was I collecting her soiled, torn garments from the barbed-wire fence and the cornstalks. . . .

I spent probably five minutes in the field, making sure I did not leave anything. Besides the pitifully cheap, bedraggled, and torn underthings, I found also a frayed garter, a red belt, and a photograph of a rather handsome young fellow in the uniform of the United States Navy with a somewhat flashy young lady, who I guessed was identical with the girl in my car, though she no longer resembled her. I crawled back to the road and hastily jammed everything I had found into the suitcase. Then, closing it as well as I could, I put it on the ledge inside the coupé, and got in myself and shut the door.

Trying to get as close to the heater as possible, the girl had, meantime, slid from the seat, and, all tangled in my coats, she half sat and half squatted on the floor, her head between her knees. She looked up and wanted to say something, but was still unable to talk, though she appeared to shake less and her teeth no longer rat-tat-tatted so violently.

I said, "I picked up everything I saw."

She let out a weak sound I could not make out over the whir of the heater; it probably was "Thank you."

Now, of a sudden, I was deeply confused. What was I going to do with her? Where was she going? Of course, I might find that out eventually when, or if, she became able to speak, but——

Several *buts* occurred to me. My gasoline gauge indicated only two or three more gallons in the tank, and I would have to stop soon to have it refilled: but what would the gas-station attendant say when he saw the battered, wasted girl in my car? He might telephone the police; the thing might get into the newspapers, and who knew what reporters—say, in Warren or Youngstown, which were the next big towns on my route—would do with my explanation of how I had found her on the road.

And there was this: while she doubtless was cold and, to all appearances, in a dreadful condition, the whole thing might conceivably be a trap. I had heard of female racketeers on state lines exploiting the Mann Act by all manner of tricks to extort money from solitary male motorists. In a few hours, on the other side of Youngstown, I would be crossing the Ohio-Pennsylvania line; then she was apt to give me trouble.

But at the same time I felt a twinge of shame. In all probability, the girl was in actual distress. Those cuts and black and yellowing marks on her face were real. Were she a Mann Act racketeer, she very likely would be nearer the state line than this. And she would not be operating on so unpleasant a morning. Even now she might be in danger of pneumonia or some other equally serious illness. Certainly she was cold and near exhaustion; the thing to do was to act on the assumption she was in trouble.

"Shouldn't I take you to a hospital or a doctor?" I inquired.

She looked up, to stare at me. I repeated my question twice, whereupon she wagged her head desperately in the negative.

"You're probably ill," I said.

She shook her head again.

Huddling against the heater, she was also close to the gear-shift and emergency brake. I asked her to get back on the seat, and, with a faint " 'Scuse me," she complied as quickly as she could. I helped her to raise herself, then put my coats around her again, and I drove on. She scarcely shook any more and her teeth clicked only intermittently. Vaguely uneasy, I glanced at her every half-minute or so. I inquired how she was, but she could not talk yet.

She tried to place her feet upon the heater, but her leg muscles lacked strength to keep them there. They plunked down immediately she lifted them.

I said, "You'll have some breakfast at the first eating-place we come to."

She whimpered and struggled to say something, but I could not understand her. She got an arm out from under the topcoat and attempted some signs and gestures, but just then some cars came, and I was obliged to keep my eyes on the road and could not watch her. Presently, however, she managed to say, "Gotta cigarette?"

I had no cigarettes, said I was sorry, and asked her again how she was.

"Oh," she said, "this is . . . wunnerful." She spoke with difficulty.

"You needn't talk," I said; "take it easy. Besides, I can hardly hear you; the heater makes so much noise."

She closed her eyes and evidently fell asleep.

In Chagrin Falls I looked for an eating-place, but saw none except one, which, however, was not yet open. So I went on, assuming the girl's destination, if she had one, was some distance in the direction I was going. I doubtless would come to a restaurant or "diner" before long.

After about ten minutes' sleep, my passenger awoke with a start and a cry, and stared at me. The brief slumber had helped her to recover her speech and the partial control of her limbs. She moved and kicked her legs a little. The blueness of her face faded to pallor, and she looked slightly less a skeleton.

"Sure you ain't gotta cigarette?" she asked. Her faint voice rasped a trifle.

I said: "No. I'm sorry. I don't smoke."

"Gee! funny you don't smoke. Nearly all the guys smoke."

I came to a stretch of straight road with no other car in view, and I looked at her a long moment.

"I must be a sight!" she cried, self-consciously, half ashamed, half defiant. She reached for the mirror over the windshield and manipulated it so she could see herself. "I look awful, don't I? How old do you suppose I am?"

I said, "About twenty-two," though she could have been taken for a good deal older.

"That's right, twenty-two," she echoed, eagerly. "But, gee, I do look a mess! He oughta see me now, the son-of-a-bee! 'Scuse me; but I only said *bee*!"

"You needn't apologize. I don't care."

"You don't care if I say *bee* or—you know what?"

"No," I said.

"Say, I bet you think I'm bad."

"No, I don't think anything at all," I said, "except that—apparently —you've had a strong dose of hard luck."

"Oh boy! did I!" she cried. Her voice was getting stronger.

"Just take it easy," I repeated. "You'd probably better not talk. Try to get warm."

She seemed not to be listening. "I'd give a million for a Lucky, Camel, Bull Durham—anythin'! Out West I smoked lotsa Bull Durham. Truck-drivers roll 'eir own."

"We'll get some cigarettes, too, the first chance. There don't seem to be any towns on this stretch."

"Gotta needle?"

"No."

"Gee! you ain't got nothin', have you?"

"I'm sorry."

"You're 'scused. But don't mind me. I'm just talkin'; I don't mean nothin'. You ain't mad, are you? I was fresh."

"I don't care."

"You're funny; you don't care about nothin'. But you sure gotta swell car, no kiddin'. Chevvy, ain't it? How much you got on the speedometer?" She bent over to read the mileage figure, and bumped her head on the steering-wheel.

"Careful," I cautioned.

"One bump more or less don't matter. Say, you ain't even got four thousand. Gee! almos' a bran'-new car. Sure you ain't gotta needle 'n' thread? . . . Lotsa guys got needles 'n' thread with 'em—sewin'-kits— but, oh yeah, this ain't no truck. 'Scuse me." She made a stab at laughing. "Truck-drivers carry needles, all kinds, big 'n' small. They use the big ones to sew up canvas; the small ones to stitch rips in their pants or shirts. Las' few weeks I sewed up lotsa truck-drivers' shirts. Well, coupla, anyhow. Now I'd like to sew myself up a little. I'm all torn everywhere."

She would talk for a few minutes, then close her eyes and be perfectly still for five or ten minutes, sleeping; whereupon she would suddenly start and stare at me bug-eyed, then again resume talking as though there were in her an hysterical necessity to talk, almost as if to reassure herself that she could talk and there was someone to listen to her. "You know what?" she said, "I'm tough. You wouldn't think so, lookin' at me, but I am, and how! Tough's my middle name."

"I guess you *are* tough," I agreed.

"Oh boy, am I! Me 'n' Popeye the Sailor! You like Popeye? . . . My fav'rite movie star, only I don't like spinach. But say, where's my suitcase? . . . Oh yeah. 'Scuse me. I saw you put it there, but forgot. 'Scuse me. I'm all groggy yet, I guess, and don't know the half-a what's goin' on. I feel like I been on a long drunk. But what I really am is punch-drunk."

She went on, but I missed entire stretches of her talk. Then, raising her feeble voice: "You know, 'twas white of you to pick up all that stuffa mine all over that field. Did you find a pitcher, me with a guy?"

"Yes, it's in the suitcase—you and the sailor."

"That's who I mean when I say 'the son-of-a-bee,' and you know what I mean when I say *bee*. He was my husband—still is, matter of fack." She paused, as though waiting for me to say something; then, as I kept silent, "Say, don't you wanna hear my story?"

"I don't know if it's interesting," I said.

This remark seemed to worry her. "It's interestin', all right. Lotsa guys that pick me up want to know my story."

"All I want to know," I said, "is where you're going, if you want to tell me."

"You *are* polite, no kiddin'. Think it's a secret? I'm goin' to Baltimore. Where you goin'?"

"New York. But I can take you as far as Harrisburg. A route from there goes to Baltimore."

"Harrisburg—how far's that from here?"

"Well over two hundred miles. I'm planning to stop there overnight."

"Will you take me far's you go today?"

"Yes." By now I was certain she was no Mann Act racketeer, and also, I had lost my feeling of shame in relation to her.

She fell asleep again.

I took this opportunity to stop at a gasoline station, where I half covered her face with a sleeve of my topcoat, so the attendant, who came out hurriedly, could not see it. He barely noticed her. I told him to fill the tank; he sold cigarettes, and I bought a package and got a box of matches. He told me there were roadside eating-places ahead, but it was early, not quite eight, and they might not be open yet. Some, he said, were even closed altogether till spring.

I drove on.

When the girl awoke, I gave her the cigarettes and matches. She took them eagerly, but, her fingers numbed and weak, she had difficulty in opening the package. I offered to stop the car and open it for her, but she said, "Ne'r mind, I'll open it myself. I'm tough. I guess I slept some, didn't I? . . . Lookit, sun's comin' out!"

Finally she opened the package, lighted her cigarette, and smoked ravenously. "Ummm!" She inhaled deeply and held the smoke in her lungs, then exhaled slowly. "Believe it or not, my first cigarette in two days, and, boy! there was times in my life when I useta smoke two packs a day. It drives me nuts when I can't get a smoke. . . . I bet you think I'm bad."

"No," I said. "Why should I?"

"Because the way I talk and look. Matter of fack, I'm not bad; I'm just no good, if you know what I mean. But you saved my life with this pack, no kiddin'. Mind if I have 'nother right away?"

"Go ahead; they're yours. Smoke all you want."

But instead of lighting another cigarette she passed out again for another five or ten minutes. I took the smoking stub of her first cigarette out of her hand.

The sun broke through the mist and the wind had subsided considerably. I felt warm, and opened the window on my side about halfway down, leaving the heater on.

Suddenly she screamed and awakened, to stare at me. "Did I yell?" she asked then.

"Yes," I said.

"I guess I slept and musta been dreamin' or somethin'. Or I got the jitters. Say, I had a cigarette, didn't I? I smell it. Oh, yeah, I forgot. Where's the package?" She found it and smoked another cigarette. "You know, this country right 'round here is pretty, no kiddin'; a little like where I was born and raised. Know where I was born? . . . Near Carbondale, Pee-ay—little burg called Simpson, but no relation to Mrs. Simpson. Say, what do you think of 'er? I mean Mrs. Wally Simpson."

"I don't know what to think."

"I guess it'd be pretty swell for 'er if she married the king, don't you think?"

"I guess."

"She'd be the Queen of England then, wouldn't she?"

"I suppose so."

"*I* say it'd be swell . . . Anyhow, I was born in this town called Simpson, just a mining town—coal—all grimy 'n' black—you wouldna wanna live there—but the country 'round it is nice. There's a lake near

Simpson, Crystal Lake, where I used to go as a kid with my old man,
He's dead——"

Listening to her, I saw none too soon a car that came speeding
toward us in the middle of the road, and the girl screamed, seizing my
right arm. Luckily, I was not going very fast and had no trouble getting out of the roadhog's way. I rebuked her for grabbing my arm;
then I noticed she trembled all over, and for a minute she was unable
to talk.

At last she said: "I'm sorry . . . gee! I'm sorry, honest. Don't be
mad. Was a dumb thing to do, to grab your arm like I did when you
drive, but I got scared 'cause I was in a accident in Missouri, drivin'
with a guy that give me a lift. That's where I got these cuts on my
face. I ain't gonna do it again, honest; I ain't gonna grab your arm
again. You ain't gonna ditch me now somewhere, are you?"—panic
in her voice.

"No, no," I said, annoyed at myself for having rebuked her.

"Gonna take me all the way to Harrisburg like you said you
would?"

"Yes."

"Honest—cross your heart?"

"Yes. Forget the whole thing."

"And you'll treat me to breakfast?"

"Soon as we come to a town."

"You don't have to treat me, you know."

"I know."

"Are you rich?"

"No, but I can buy you a breakfast."

"O. K., it's up to you. I didn't ask you to buy me breakfast, did I?"

"No."

"Say I *didn't*."

"You didn't."

"No, I didn't, by God! I got my pride, too."

A pause; then, suddenly, irrelevantly, she broke into song—*I can't
give you anything but love, baby*—but her voice cracked on the high
note and she gave it up, taking another long pull at her cigarette.
"You're a life-saver, all right. I may be down, but I ain't out, am I?"

"Of course not."

"I'll get back on my feet. What's the next big town?"

"Warren, Ohio."

"Maybe we can get somethin' to eat there. How far's Warren?"

"Fifteen, twenty miles."

"You had breakfast yet?"

"Yes. When did you eat last?"

"Day before yesterday morning in Toledo. My stomach thinks my throat's cut."

She threw away the cigarette end, made another attempt at *I can't give you anything but love, baby*; and, failing, fell asleep once more, and slept all the way to Warren.

In Warren, I parked near the least pretentious of the restaurants—the sign over it was merely "EATS." I shook the girl, but she gave no sign of awakening.

It was half past nine, and it had taken me all that time to get here from Cleveland, while but for my passenger I could easily have been beyond Youngstown. I had wired my friend in Harrisburg to expect me shortly after one, and asked him to wait for lunch for me; but at this rate of speed, with this girl in my car, talking to me, I would be doing well if I got there for dinner.

I shook her again . . . several times . . . finally she stirred, then jumped and screamed, so that a frumpy middle-aged female passer-by stopped and peered into my car to see what was going on. Seeing the girl's scarred face, the woman motioned to a man, evidently her husband, and bid him interest himself in us.

"What's the trouble here?" he demanded.

"She screamed," said the woman, also coming closer.

"What'd she scream for?" asked the man, looking at me, then at the girl, who, drugged by sleep, stared at me.

"I don't know," I replied. "I picked her up this side of Cleveland. She's been in an accident; she was cold; then she fell asleep here; and now I woke her up to get her some breakfast and she screamed. I imagine she's scared, nervous, and exhausted."

A small crowd gathered around the car.

The girl regained her wits and snapped at the man who was questioning me: "What's it to you? None of your business, you old son-of-a-bee!"

The woman outside gasped audibly.

"I said *bee*," said the girl. "I didn't say nothin' else. Can I help it if you think somethin' worse?"

"Get a policeman!" said the woman. "Let 'im check up on 'em."

"You're all a buncha buttinskies," said the girl. "What's it to you? He"—meaning me—"told you the truth. He picked me up on the road. I was freezin' to death."

A policeman appeared and put a foot on the running-board and his elbows on the window on my side of the car. Fortunately, he was an intelligent man, and, asking me several questions and examining my driver's license and owner's certificate, presently indicated he believed my story.

"Who are you?" he asked the girl, then.

"Mrs. Wally Simpson!" she said, and laughed a bit.

"Quit your kidding," I said to her, "and answer the officer's questions."

"All right," she said, " 'Scuse me 'n' don' get sore at me, will you? Officer, my name is Hazel Leyton—L-e-y-t-o-n—*Mrs.* Leyton—and I'm on the bum—it's a long story—I was in a accident 'n' he picked me up, just like he says; now he wants to buy me breakfast 'n' he promised to take me far's Harrisburg. Everythin's just like he told you. I'm goin' to Baltimore, where somebody's gonna help me get a job 'n' set myself on my feet again."

The officer looked at her, then at me, then back at her. "You're pretty well bunged up, though."

"Yeah, but what's it to you? I can take it, don' worry about me; I'm tough."

The policeman grunted and turned to the crowd, "All right, move on! Leave 'em alone! There's nothin' to it." To a bystander who was in shirt sleeves and wore an apron, he remarked: "Let 'er get somethin' to eat, Nick, then let 'em get t'hell outa town. She's a tramp; he a damfool for pickin' 'er up. No use havin' 'spenses here with 'em."

Immediately on parking I had drawn a dollar bill out of my pocket; now I proffered it to my passenger, suggesting she go into the res·

taurant and breakfast. "I'll stay here in the car," I said, "and read the paper," which I had bought in Cleveland.

"You come with me!" she cried, panicky.

"I've had breakfast."

"Come 'n' have a cup of coffee, why don't you?" desperately.

"You go in yourself," I insisted, feeling mean and simultaneously trying to understand her panic.

"You'll drive off without me."

"I won't do anything of the sort."

"How do I know?"

"I'm telling you."

"You wanna get rid of me, 'n' I don't blame you. You're ashamed of me, 'n' I don't blame you; I pretty near got you in dutch; but—" Her voice broke with a threat of tears.

"All right, all right," I said, "I'll go in with you. I'm not ashamed of you," wondering how close I was to lying. "What put that into your head?"

"I wouldn't blame you if you was," she said. "But you're a white guy, no kiddin', and I believe you wouldna drove off without me, because you wouldna want to take my suitcase, if not because of anythin' else."

There was a lump in my midriff.

Going out of the car, the girl said, "Mind if I take your coat out and keep it 'round me?"

"No; go ahead."

The be-aproned proprietor of the dingy little eating-joint, a Pole or Slovak, asked no questions, and acted with an assumed matter-of-factness; showed Hazel to the washroom, then took her order—orange juice, cereal, bacon and eggs, rolls and jam, and coffee. She asked him whether he had a needle and some black thread, and he answered his wife had all that upstairs; and he went up and came back with a threaded needle; whereupon, while waiting for her food, Hazel stitched some of the worst tears in her outer garments.

I tried to read the paper, but Hazel, smoking, kept interrupting me with her condemnations of the "buttinskies" and with questions concerning the latest news about the king and Mrs. Simpson. She began to fascinate me, and I asked her, "Why did you say to the policeman that you were Mrs. Wally Simpson?"

"I don't know. I just said it. I bet he thought I was nuts. Say, I heard you tell the cop you was a writer, when he was askin' you. Are you for a fack, or was you just stringin' 'im?"

"I'm a writer."

"And you're goin' 'round the country for a magazine, writin' things up, like you told 'im? Gee, I wish I was a writer. I bet I could write a hot story. What do you write?"

"Books and things."

"I guess you must be pretty smart. But you know what? 'bout the time I graduated from grammar school I wrote a pome 'bout miners. My father was still alive then. Then he was killed in a cave-in." Pause. "He was a Austrian, but born in this country; his father came over long time ago. My mother was Welsh or somethin', but born here, too, 'n' she was all right long's my father was alive; then she cracked up or somethin' 'n' became no good—kinda crazy—married 'nother guy, who was a son-of-a-bee 'n' treated me awful. I was her only kid, and I lived with 'er 'n' the stepfather for six years, till I was fifteen; then I run away. She 'n' her new husband moved, 'n' I dunno where they're at now. Charming family, eh what, Edward darling? But I guess that's wrong; I read somewhere or somebody told me, that Wally calls the king Davie or Toots or Butch or somethin' like that. Ain't that wunnerful!"

She gulped the orange juice, then ate the rest of the meal. I warned her not to eat so fast, nor so much; it might harm her, since she had not eaten for two days; but she repeated she was tough and said food never harmed her except when she had none. She asked for a second cup of coffee and smoked two cigarettes. "You ever been on the bum?"

"A long time ago," I said, "after the war for a while."

"Been in the war? . . . Lotsa guys that pick me up was in it. How old was you when you was on the bum?"

"About twenty-one," I said.

"But was you as low-down on the bum as I am?"

"Hard to say. For one thing, I wasn't hurt in an accident."

"But you was broke and missed meals and spent nights outdoors?"

"Once or twice, for a while," I said; "it wasn't really bad."

"Gee! now here you are, buyin' me breakfast, wearin' good clothes, money in your pocket, and a swell car by the curb outside. Just goes to show *I* can do the same. Gee! I'll get off the bum sure's anythin'."

Hazel finished her coffee, I paid the check, and the proprietor said "Good luck" to her.

"Same to you," returned Hazel.

Outside it was sunny and warm, and she exclaimed, "Ain'tit wunnerful!" In the car we decided we did not need the heater any more. Hazel stayed wrapped in my topcoat.

I drove off and she fell asleep. Every once in a while her head and the upper part of her body swung toward me and onto the steering-wheel, and I pushed her back without waking her.

In Youngstown, while she slept, I wired my friend in Harrisburg I might not arrive till late afternoon or early evening. . . .

Hazel slept on.

She awakened with a start, but did not scream; and she looked at me. "Hi, there!"

"Hi, yourself!" I said. "How do you feel?"

"With my fingers," she replied, and laughed, adding: "Don't mind me; I'm silly. I guess I feel better than I have for a long time." She lighted a cigarette and took a few puffs in silence, looking out of the window. Then: "Where are we, anyhow?"

"In Pennsylvania—going toward Butler. The last place we went through was New Castle."

She sang again, *"I can't give you anything but love, baby ——"*

"You like that song, don't you?" I said.

"What song? Was I singin'?"

"Yes—*I can't give you anything but love, baby.*"

"Oh yeah, I 'member. Yeah, I like it"—confused. "Say, how much further to what-chuma-call-it—Harrisburg?"

"Six or seven hours, possibly longer."

"Then I'll be 't'out a home again."

"I've been thinking about you," I said, ". . . and when I let you out in Harrisburg I'll give you a little money, so you can ——"

"Say," sharply, "you're sorry for me."

"No, no," I said.

"You are, too!"

"I'm not. I guess I shouldn't have mentioned it now, but I thought you were worrying how you were to spend the night, and so on."

"You think I'm bad!"

"No, no; I don't think anything. It makes no difference to me if you're 'bad' or 'good.'"

"What'd you wanna give me money for?" She looked at me suspiciously. "I don' mean nothin' by that song, get me? I just sing it ——"

"You're crazy," I said. "Don't let it worry you what I think. You see, I'm a writer and having you in the car gives me an idea for a story."

"About me?"

"Yes, or about a girl like you. I don't know yet how I'll write it. I have only a rough idea. But when, and if, I write it, there'll probably be a chance of selling it to some magazine; and if I sell it ——"

"How much will you get for it?"

"I don't know. In fact, I'm not sure I'll sell it; but if I do, I'm liable to get very little, quite a bit, or a great deal, depending on what magazine will take it."

"How much do you want to give me?"

I told her.

"Honest?" she cried. "Gee! S'pose you don't sell it?"

"I'll put you in a book—a chapter in a book."

She was silent for a half-minute, pondering all this. Then: "But what can you write about me? You don't know my story, 'n' you even said you didn' wanna hear it 'cause maybe it wasn't interestin'—that's what you said, 'member?"

"Yes; but I've learned a great deal about you, none the less."

"What?"

"The sort of person you are."

"*What* sort of person am I?"—quickly.

"A little run down and 'groggy' or 'punch drunk' just now, as you put it yourself, but O.K., tough, proud—all I need to know."

"You don't know any facks."

It was futile to argue with her, and I regretted having told her I would write about her. What I should have done was to have kept silent till I let her out in Harrisburg, then have given her the money, and driven on.

"I told you 'bout my father," she went on, "he got buried in a mine accident, 'n' a little 'bout my mother . . . but you dunno what I did after I run away when I was fifteen.

"In a town called Port Jervis, in New York State near the Pee-ay border, a old lady took me in 'er home when I told 'er I was hungry. She had little store near the bus depot, sellin' candy 'n' cigarettes, pop, pies 'n' cake, newspapers 'n' magazines, 'n' she lived in backa the store. She wanted to know where was I from, who was my parents, but I wouldn' tell 'er. I only said I run away 'n' never want to go back, 'n' I cried. So she told me to stay, 'n' told the neighbors 'n' people that knowed 'er I was 'er niece from Hawley—that's a town in Pee-ay.

"She got to love me like I was 'er daughter, 'n' made me swear I was never to tell a soul we was no relation. My name was Hazel Culick, but after I come to Port Jervis I was Hazel Schugg—Schugg was the old lady's name—'n' I helped in the store; then, when she—I mean the old lady—took sick, I looked after 'er 'n' the store. I was there little more 'n two years, till she died. Gee! I felt terrible when she died. . . . She had nobody else in the world 'n' left me the store, 'n' I run it by myself 'n' lived alone in the backroom for six months. Then I got married to a Greyhound bus-driver that got nuts about me 'n' me about 'im. I was goin' on eighteen.

"Gee! he was wunnerful, 'n' we was awful happy"—her voice breaking a little. "He never found out the old lady was not my aunt; wasn't even interested in my family, he was so crazy about me. He was from Passaic, 'n' his name was Joe Sigafoos. He was on the Scranton-New York run, 'n' he was home every third night 'n' up to lunchtime the next day. Joe was in the war 'n' been gassed, so one day he come home with a cold 'n' fever, 'n' in three days he was dead. We wasn't married even a year. Gee! was terrible! I cried like I was goin' outa my nut.

"When I got over it a little, so I didn't cry all the time, I sold the store, got four hundred dollars for it, 'n' I went to New York on a bus 'n' was so miserable I got to talkin' with the driver, who knowed Joe. In fack, Joe 'n' this driver was friends. Then, to keep from bein' blue all the time, I went in for a good time in a big way; got some swell clothes at Gimbel's 'n' even bought a coupla things at Saks Fifth Avenue; 'n' I run around with bus-drivers, but I wasn't really bad—just wild 'n' crazy—just wasn't good—because I couldn't think of Joe 't'out bawlin' my head off when I was alone, because I loved 'im so. . . .

"I got a job as check-girl at Charles'—the night club, you know. I worked there coupla years, savin' my money. I went out with guys, to shows, to prize fights and races, to Lindy's for supper, and to the beach in summertime, that's all—honest. You believe me?"

"Yes, sure," I said. "Why shouldn't I believe you?"

"Is the story interestin'?"

"Yes—very."

"What did I tell you? But wait, best part's still to come. . . . I was savin' my money like I told you, thinkin' maybe some day another right guy'll come along; 'n' then one day I met this gob—Willis Leyton—who's in the pitcher you picked up in Ohio. Gee! he was good-lookin', big 'n' strong, 'n' he looked to be a wunnerful guy right through. I had a friend once, 'n' she married a sailor, 'n' he quit the navy after he married 'er 'n' went in business in Brooklyn, 'n' they was happy like nobody's business. Gee! they was happy; 'n' would you believe it, she got so respec'able she wouldn' see me any more. I knowed other gobs before that was O.K. So I thought this gob o' mine was, too, 'n' I said O.K. and we went to Hoboken and got married.

"This was last summer. I took a month off for honeymoon, he was on leave, 'n' we was both crazy to go drivin'; so we bought a new Plymouth—with my money. I loved 'im, gee! I was nuts about 'im, 'n' I didn' think there was anythin' fishy when he said we oughta buy the car in his name because he was a United States sailor 'n' sailors don't have to pay no sales tax. We saved forty dollars that way, 'n' I said O.K. Then we drove 'round for ten days, far up as Vermont and through upstate New York; 'n' we had that pitcher taken, 'n' had a wunnerful time. Gee! he was swell, no kiddin', 'n' I think he really loved me, but, like a lotta guys, he was also a heel inside.

"One morning I woke up in a tourist house near Troy, New York, 'n' there was no husband. He was gone with the car 'n' all the money 'cept three dollars and seventy-four cents he left in my purse. Big-hearted guy, eh what, Davie? . . . I'm just foolin'—Davie: Toots: that's what Wally Simpson calls the king. . . .

"Findin' myself alone like this, jilted 'n' robbed, this was worse'n the time my first husband died. Gee! I hated the son-of-a-bee, you know what I mean; but I was hurt, too, 'n' don't think I wasn't. I can't tell you what I went through. Gee! it hurt—maybe, bein' a writer, you can 'magine it. I guess writers can 'magine most anythin', that's why they're writers. I guess that's why you didn't care if I tell my story or not; you could 'magine it. . . .

"My first idea was to go to New London, Connecticut, where his ship was—a submarine—'n' make trouble for 'im. Then I changed my mind. I said to myself, I loved the guy; all right; now I never wanna see 'im again, or have anythin' to do with 'im. . . . I bet he wonders what's become of me—why I never made no trouble for 'im. Let 'im wonder. But I forgived 'im, long ago. . . .

"I was pretty sicka the whole thing, sicka New York, 'n' I didn't wanna go near anybody I knowed. I was afraid the girls and guys at Charles' 'd kid me: where was my gob? So I was through with 'em, too. I had fifty dollars left in postal-savings; I took that out 'n' got a room in a hotel on Madison Square, where nobody I know ever comes, 'n' I got drunk and stayed stiff for a week, all by myself, till the manager turned me over to the police . . . 'n' the police turned me over to a outfit for wayward girls. Can you 'magine?

"All I had in the world was a few dollars 'n' what was in this suitcase 'n' on my back . . . 'n' bingo! just like that, I decided to go to California. I always heard-a California—Los Angeles—Hollywood —what a swell place it was; so I slipped out of this house for wayward girls, where they tried to be nice to me, but I hated it, 'n' I got a bus through Holland Tunnel to Jersey City, then began to hitch—California, here I come! . . .

"That was middle-a September 'n' still warm—gee! it was wunnerful, with the leaves beginnin' to turn red in the country, 'n' I had no trouble gettin' picked up. I was good-lookin', if I say so myself, 'n' I wore good clothes; 'n' guys slammed on the brakes soon's they saw me.

"The first guy took me to Phillipsburg, New Jersey, where I quit 'im because he got fresh, you know what I mean. The next lift got

me far's Altoona, Pee-ay, and I slept there in a hotel. I had little over
five dollars left.

"Then . . . Cleveland . . . Chi . . . Kansas . . . Iowa . . . Colorado . . . New Mexico . . . Arizona——"

For a while after passing through Butler, Pennsylvania, I understood only a word or sentence now and then. She mumbled faintly,
intermittently, like a child falling asleep; then was silent. . . .

She awoke suddenly, eighty miles later.

"Where was I?" she asked.

I laughed. "You were just getting to Arizona."

"I musta fallen asleep for coupla minutes."

"You slept over two hours," I said.

"You wouldna kid me?"

"We're nearing Altoona."

"What do you know about that! I thought I just dozed off for a
minute or two while I was tellin' you about my travels."

We both laughed.

"I'm hungry," I said. "How about you?"

"Gonna treat me again?"

I nodded.

"I didn't ask you to, you know."

"No, you didn't ask me."

"I'm ready to eat, though, any time. Say, lookit that barn!" she cried,
suddenly.

I looked where she was pointing at a group of farm buildings a
stone-throw from the road, of which a large newly-painted barn was
the most striking—a veritable edifice.

"Ain'tit a beaut!" she exclaimed. "I seen lotsa barns in my travels
—thousands of 'em; in fack, I'm a expert on barns, 'n' when I say a
barn is beautiful, that barn is beautiful."

I drew up at a roadside "diner," and we had lunch. The man
behind the counter eyed us awhile, then evidently decided we were
none of his business.

Hazel picked up the narrative where she had left off:

". . . New Mexico . . . Arizona . . . This is one big country, let
me tell you. *Big*—B-I-G—and how! It took me three weeks to get to

Arizona, 'n' what I don't know about U.S.A.'s nobody's business. Wunnerful country!"

Her power of expression seemed to collapse. "I mean the land is wunnerful, 'cept where it was ruined by what-chuma-call-it—erosion 'n' windstorms. Even Arizona, what's mostly sand, is beautiful like anythin'. Such colors you see nowhere like in Arizona, Colorado, 'n' New Mexico. . . .

"People, that's 'nother story. . . . Guys that pick you up this side of Mississippi are mostly heels, you know what I mean, though you find some pretty good eggs 'mongst 'em, too. When they do you a favor, mosta 'em wanna get somethin' back; you know what I mean; you wasn't born yesterday. . . .

"Out West, you find heels, too; mosta 'em, though, are square-shooters, wunnerful guys, any way you take 'em. In Colorado 'n' New Mexico 'n' Arizona, they shoved money in my pocket when I wasn't lookin' or put it in my hand when they couldn' take me no further. One guy put a five-dollar bill in a chewin'-gum wrapper 'n' give it to me, pretendin' it was gum. 'Nother guy in Davenport, Iowa, 'n' one in Denver, took me to a hotel 'n' asked how much was the room, paid 'n' went away. I never saw either offum again.

"Out in Arizona a woman picked me up. She had a ranch somewhere; I guess was about fifty, but healthy, all brown 'n' hard 'n' beautiful; 'n' at a place called Flagstaff she got me a bag-a san'wiches 'n' oranges, 'n' put a silver dollar in the bag when I wasn't lookin'— first silver dollar I ever had. I wished she was my mother. She was worried 'bout me, 'n' said I was liable to have hard time gettin' to California, because Los Angeles cops was all over the desert, turnin' back people that had no money, 'n' beatin' 'em up, because California was fulla unemployed 'n' hobos 'n' good-f'r-nothin's that come here 'bout this time of the year when it starts gettin' cold other places.

"In Flagstaff I got picked up by a old what they call desert rat, maybe fifty, maybe more, 'n' he wanted to marry me 'n' make me his 'pardner'—that's what he said, his 'pardner.' He said he was lonely on the desert but had plentya money 'n' gold, 'n' would build us a house. I was tempted like anythin' to take 'im on, but then, like a fool, I don't know what made me say I was married 'n' was goin' to L.A. to meet my husband. I coulda kick myself, because he wouldof asked no questions—that's how those guys are out West when they're lonely 'n' gettin' on in years—no questions asked—'n' nobody wouldof ever knowed I was married to the gob, 'n' I coulda been all fixed by now, 'n' maybe I coulda learned to love 'im, I mean the old guy.

"He was sad like anythin' when I told 'im I was married, 'n' he took me far's Williams, Arizona, 'n' put me up at the little hotel there 'n' said good-by. I coulda cried when he was gone, gee! I was a dope.

"Next day I had a awful time gettin' a lift. Everybody said no use tryin' to cross the line to California—the L.A. bulls was sure to get me. They was all over, the bulls; some of 'em operatin' right in Arizona, even if it was against the law. Gee! I was scared 'n' wished the old desert rat would come back, so I could tell 'im I wasn't married 'n' was willin' to take 'im on. . . .

"By-'n'-by, though, a truck-driver took a chance on me 'n' said he'll smuggle me over the line to Bakersfield, California, which was where he was goin', if I didn' mind lyin' under a pile-a empty gunny sacks in backa the truck mosta the way, because he didn't know where the bulls was liable to stop 'im 'n' ask 'im if he had any hitchers or bums.

"I let 'im bury me under the sacks, 'n', gee! it was hot 'n' the sacks stunk . . . but we was only a little way past a town called Ash Fork, still in Arizona, when a coupla guys stopped us—they was in civvies 'n' drivin' a car with a Arizona license plate—'n' searched the truck 'n' found me under the sacks. I guess they was Arizona guys hired by L.A. cops to keep the likesa me outa California. One of 'em kicked me, slapped me more times 'n' I could count, pulled my hair, got fresh, 'n' threw me on the sand beside the road like a sack of potatoes or somethin'. The truck-driver called 'em a coupla son-of-a-bees, you know what I mean; 'n' swung on 'em, so then the two of 'em beat 'im up somethin' awful, but he could take it. They called me bad names; boy! what they called me—'n' him, too, the truck-driver—'n' they told 'im not to go to California, even if he had business there, because they was gonna notify the bulls ahead, 'n' they'll beat 'im up again, because he was tryin' to smuggle in people like me. So he turned around, the poor guy, all beat up 'n' black 'n' blue in the face, 'n' ast me to come with 'im if I wanted to.

"'Course I wanted to; what wouldof I been doin' there in the middle of the desert? He was mad like a hornet—not at me, though, but at the bulls and L.A. 'This useta be a free country,' he said. 'Look at it now!' . . .

"On t'other hand, though, when I cooled off and thought 'bout it, I couldn' blame L.A. for not wantin' the likesa me if the town and the whole state was, like everybody said, all full with all kindsa hard-luck people. Only they shouldnof beat me up, or the truck driver, or anybody else. Gee! I was sore, because that was first time anybody hit me since I run away from Simpson, Pee-ay, where my stepfather used to thrash me once in a while. Later, though, when I had time to think, it come to me that maybe they didn't like to beat me up, but did it so's to scare others, because they prob'ly figured I was gonna meet others 'n' tell 'em what to 'spect if they tried to get to California.

"Well, anyhow, we went back to Williams; 'n' would you believe it, this truck-driver—he was just a kid, 'bout twenty-four—made me take a dollar from 'im 'cause I was broke. He was a good egg, wasn't he, to be so kind after he got beat up because-a me. I coulda cried, no kiddin'. . . ."

We finished lunch and drove on. I felt a deep satisfaction in having picked her up—she obviously was a "good egg" herself.

She fell asleep again . . . awakened in Newport and talked to me the rest of the way to Harrisburg:

". . . In Williams, I met a lady from Baltimore; she was there on a ranch near town for her health, 'n' she got interested in me, 'n' I told 'er some-a the things I'm tellin' you, 'n' she thought I oughta go back East. There was more opportunities in the East, she said, 'n' I was liable to get on my feet quicker than in the West. I didn' wanna go back to New York, so she give me a note to a frienda hers that has a rest'rant in Baltimore 'n' maybe would give me a job. . . .

"Gee! I didn't know what to do 'n' wished that desert rat 'd come along again, but he didn't, though I hung around Williams for coupla days. I felt like a little girl, a little child, no kiddin'. I was so scared I shook inside.

". . . I took a lift from a guy with a California license plate who was goin' to Albuquerque, New Mexico, 'n' said he was a comyoonist —a red—'n' he tried to make me one, too. He gave me stuff to read 'n' said I was a victim of the capitalist system, 'n' there was lotsa other girls—millions of 'em—in the same fix like I was in, 'n' those

bulls that beat me up was servants of the capitalist system. . . . Boy!
he had everythin' figured out down to a *t* 'n' what he didn' all tell
me's nobody's business, no kiddin', but I couldn' unnerstand much
'cause it was all so new to me, 'n' deep's anythin'; 'n' besides, I didn'
like the guy, though it's meana me to say so, because he did give me
a lift 'n' didn't bother me at all, you know what I mean, 'n' bought
me san'wiches. He said he was a artist.

"But I could follow this guy when we talked about Mrs. Simpson.
She was liable to become queen, but don't let that worry me, he said
—I was as good as she was 'n' maybe a damsite better. Under the
capitalist system it was all a toss-up if a girl became Mrs. Simpson or
got on the bum like me; 'n' let me tell you, I been thinkin' 'bout that
ever since, 'n' it's true, it's true, though I dunno how come. It's a
toss-up, all right; mattera luck, mattera gettin' a break, the right kinda
schoolin' 'n' upbringin'; that's what it is. What do you think?"

I said there was something to what she was saying.

"You tell 'em!" she said. "That's why I told the cop in what-
chuma-call-it-town I was Wally Simpson. I *couldof* been her if I had
the breaks she had. . . . But never mind; I wanna tell you the rest
of the facks about my travels—are they interestin'?"

"Very," I said.

"See? What did I tell you, 'n' you wasn't sure if my story was
interestin'!" she reproached me.

"I didn't want to seem to pry—to pump you," I explained.

"But how was you gonna write 'bout me if you didn't know the
facks?"

"I could imagine many details."

"You couldnof 'magined things like I told you."

"Not exactly, but similar things."

"Gee! you're a funny guy. Don' mind me sayin' this, though. Everybody's funny."

Pause.

"Anyhow," she went on, "now you know the facks. . . . In Albuquerque I got a truck with a Kansas license plate. He was a fresh
guy, but I told 'im where I stand, so he apologized 'n' was O.K. after
that; 'n' we drove all afternoon 'n' night because he had to be in
Wichita, Kansas, a certain time 'n' he was late. He wasn't a bad guy,

though, married 'n' had kids, 'n' he told me to watch 'im so he don't fall asleep at the wheel, 'n' I fed 'im wakies——"

"Wakies?"

"Yeah, don't you know—wakies—that's pills, some kinda dope, truck-drivers take so they don't fall asleep. They pick up people like me so they got somebody to watch 'em 'n' feed 'em those pills—one every half-hour or so. Gee! it's no cinch to drive a truck on long hauls, let me tell you.

"Anyhow, in the mornin' we got to a little place called Raton, near the Raton Pass on the Colorado line, and the guy told me he can't take me no further. Gee! I tried to tell 'im I wasn't Mann Act, but he wasn't takin' no chances—so long!—'n' pulled out.

"That happened to me numbera times—guys ditched me just be- fore crossin' from one state to 'nother, 'n' you can't blame 'em. There's girls playin' the Mann Act all over, 'n' what I don't know 'bout that game's nobody's business. Guys told me of other guys that got played suckers, 'n' you know what?—big truckin' companies have standin' orders no driver can take a girl over any state line. . . . You took me over the Ohio-Pee-ay line. Wasn't you worried?"

"Just for a minute," I confessed. "Then I decided you were all right."

"What made you decide I was all right?"

"I just had a feeling."

My saying this pleased her.

"I go on hunches, too, only mine offen are all cockeyed. . . .

"Anyhow, in Raton, a man 'n' his wife picked me up, 'n' took me only over the Pass, to Trinidad, Colorado; 'n' there I caught 'nother truck all the way to Kansas City. The guy was like you, wasn't afraida me, 'n' took me over the Colorado-Kansas line. I popped a wakie in his mouth every so offen 'n' kept 'im awake.

"He let me off on the Missouri side of Kansas City, 'n' there a fellah with a Illinois license plate stopped for me—the worst heel I met durin' my travels, 'n' I didn' tell you much 'bout the other heels, because I just as soon forgot 'bout 'em. Well, this one was no good, had a dirty mind, 'n' so on, you know what I mean, 'n' was a little drunk 'n' jittery; 'n' after ridin' with 'im maybe half a hour I closed my eyes, thinkin' how I'll get 'im to let me off, when—*bang,* alla sudden, we hit somethin', I never found out what. My head went *bang* in the windshield 'n' the next thing I knowed I was in a police-station back in Kansas City, bleedin' outa two cuts on my face.

"What happened I guess was the guy crashed maybe in a telegraph pole, but didn' hurt himself or damage his car so much he couldn' use it. I was hurt, unconscious; so he drove on a way, then dumped me in a ditch behind a pile-a brush with my suitcase. He was scared I'd sue 'im. Then a traffic cop found me 'n' phoned for a police ambulance.

"Gee! was I in a mess! I wanted to die. I was good-lookin' once, if I say so myself; now these two gashes on my face! The doctor at the emergency station went through the motions of doctorin' me up, but that's all; then said there's nothin' the matter with me, though I had cuts and bruises all over, which I got maybe when the guy dumped me in the ditch. The idea was, I was no good, anyhow, just a little tramp or somethin' worse.

"Anyhow, I was out in the world again 'n' now guys was afraida me. I looked awful, like somethin' the cat dragged home, all black 'n' blue 'n' cut up; 'n' my dress 'n' coat was torn. I dunno, but I think I walked least a hundred miles a-tween Kansas City 'n' Cleveland the last ten days. The rest I made in short hitches, 'n' many of 'em that give me a lift got ridda me soon's they could, once they seen me up close. I looked worse every day. I didn' eat. The last time I ate before meetin' you was in Toledo; a truck-driver treated me.

"Then it got cold, gee! alla-sudden, 'specially on the stretch a-tween Toledo 'n' Cleveland. This was the only clothes I have, 'n' I shook 'n' my weight was fallin' down to nothin'. I seen leaves fall offa the trees 'n' I couldof cried; I wasn't even 's good as them leaves. . . .

"But it's partly my fault, though I can't help it. I'm not stuck up 'xactly, but I hate to crawl 'n' beg 'n' ask for handouts. I know that lotsa folks in Cleveland, if I knocked on their doors, maybe wouldof let me in 'n' feed me, 'n' let me get warm, but I couldn' bring myself to knock. It's one thing to bum rides, even when you look like the pitchera everythin' nobody wants to see, and it's somethin' else to crash in people's homes where they're happy—man 'n' wife 'n' children 'n' carpets on the floor 'n' things in the icebox—Say, do you think many people are really happy?"

"I guess some are," I said, "or they think they are, which is about the same thing."

"Are you?"

"I suppose."

"You married?"

"Yes."

"Where's your wife?"

"In New York."

"Gee! I bet you're happy——"

Late in the afternoon we approached Harrisburg.

"What river is this?" she asked.

"Susquehanna," I said.

"Oh yeah; beautiful ain'tit?"

"Yes. . . . But listen here," I went on. "I'm quite sure I'll sell the story about you or I'll put you in a book, so I'll give you double the amount I said I would give you."

"Charity!"

"No, no. What you told me is worth to me every cent I want to give you. Consider it a business proposition. You're going to Baltimore and see if you can get a job with the letter the lady gave you in Arizona?"

"Yeah."

"All right," I said. "Maybe you'll get fixed up in Baltimore, maybe not. I'll give you the money and my address. Eventually, if you feel like it, write to me and I'll tell you whether or not I sold the story. If you wish, consider this money a loan, which you can pay back sometime in the future if I don't sell the story, and which is annulled if I do sell it."

She was biting her lip.

"And," I continued, "I suggest you spend the night in Harrisburg and have a bath and a good night's sleep. I'm staying at some friends' house, but I'll take you to a hotel if you like. Also, it's just four-thirty, the stores are still open, and you should buy yourself some clothes, shoes, a hat, whatever else you need. Then in the morning take a bus to Baltimore. I'll come for you at the hotel about eight o'clock."

She burst out crying, and I felt like the devil, but let her cry awhile; then I chided her about saying she was tough, and she dried her eyes.

Next morning I took her to the bus depot. She had some new clothes and looked much better than she had the day before. She talked a good deal and said she had enjoyed a good breakfast. I had bought a newspaper: what was the latest about Mrs. Simpson? . . .

"How do I look?" she asked.

"Fine."

"Well, I feel like I was turnin' over a new leaf," she said. "Maybe meetin' you yesterday means I'm gonna be in for a little good luck from now on, for a change. Say you hope so," she said, almost desperately.

"I hope so very much."

"Gee!" Then, after a moment: "Too bad these darn cuts on my face will leave scars."

"Maybe they won't," I said.

Before going into the bus, she kissed me quickly; then said, "You don't mind, do you?"

"Don't be silly," I said.

"Tell your wife I kissed you, and tell 'er I kissed you in a way she wouldn' mind if she knew how I kissed you."

"All right. Good-by."

"Good-by!"

She waved to me from the bus.

I have not yet heard from her. Perhaps she lost my address and forgot my name. Or probably I did not break her spell of "hard luck" as she hoped I might have done. Or . . . God knows.

LANGSTON HUGHES Why he selected

POEMS of AMERICAN NEGRO LIFE

These poems I like because they are among those of mine most representative of the themes of difficulty and oppression, hope and dreams of the Negro people of whom I write.

New York, N. Y.   LANGSTON HUGHES
June, 1942

THE NEGRO

I AM a Negro:
   Black as the night is black,
Black like the depths of my Africa.

I've been a slave:
Caesar told me to keep his door-steps clean.
I brushed the boots of Washington.

I've been a worker:
Under my hand the pyramids arose.
I made mortar for the Woolworth Building.

I've been a singer:
All the way from Africa to Georgia
I carried my sorrow songs.
I made jazz.

I've been a victim:
The Belgiums cut off my hands in the Congo.
They lynch me now in Texas.

511

I am a Negro:
Black as the night is black.
Black like the depths of my Africa.

THE WEARY BLUES

DRONING a drowsy syncopated tune,
   Rocking back and forth to a mellow croon,
I heard a Negro play.
Down on Lenox Avenue the other night
By the pale dull pallor of an old gas light
   He did a lazy sway. . . .
   He did a lazy sway. . . .
To the tune of those Weary Blues.
With his ebony hands on each ivory key
He made that poor piano moan with melody.
   O, Blues!
Swaying to and fro on his rickety stool
He played that sad raggy tune like a musical fool.
   Sweet Blues!
Coming from a black man's soul.
   O, Blues!
In a deep song voice with a melancholy tone
I heard that Negro sing, that old piano moan—
   "Ain't got nobody in all this world,
   Ain't got nobody but myself.
   I'm gonna quit my frowin'
   And put my troubles on de shelf."
Thump, thump, thump, went his foot on the floor.
He played a few chords then he sang some more—
   "I got de Weary Blues
   And I can't be satisfied.
   Got de Weary Blues
   And can't be satisfied—
   I ain't happy no mo'
   And I wish that I had died."
Far into the night he crooned that tune.

The stars went out and so did the moon.
The singer stopped playing and went to bed.
While the Weary Blues echoed through his head
He slept like a rock or a man that's dead.

I, TOO

I, too, sing America.

I am the darker brother.
They send me to eat in the kitchen
When company comes,
But I laugh,
And eat well,
And grow strong.

Tomorrow,
I'll sit at the table
When company comes.
Nobody'll dare
Say to me,
"Eat in the kitchen,"
Then.

Besides,
They'll see how beautiful I am
And be ashamed—

I, too, am America.

MAXWELL ANDERSON

MIO and MIRIAMNE

Dear Whit Burnett:

I don't know what to nominate of my own for inclusion in your anthology for the reason that I don't like any well enough after it has been put through the rehearsal wringer. I should say choose what you like, if you like any.

You are certainly welcome to the scene from *Winterset* for the anthology.

All good luck with the book.

New York, N. Y.   MAXWELL ANDERSON
June 25, 1942

This scene from WINTERSET is the bank of a river under a bridge-head. A single street lamp is seen at the left—and a glimmer of apart-ment lights in the background beyond. It is an early, dark December evening.

MIO, the seventeen-year-old son of BARTOLOMEO ROMAGNA, the anarchist who was executed by false evidence, and MIRIAMNE, the fifteen-year-old sister of the man who could have saved him, meet each other for the first time in this scene. Neither one of them knows who the other is.

[ESDRAS, GAUNT *and* GARTH *enter the basement and shut the door.* TROCK *goes out with his men. After a pause* MIO *comes back from the right, alone. He stands at a little distance from Miriamne*]

Mio. Looks like rain.

[*She is silent*]

You live around here?

[*She nods gravely*]

I guess
you thought I meant it—about waiting here to meet me.

[*She nods again*]

I'd forgotten about it till I got that winter
across the face. You'd better go inside.
I'm not your kind. I'm nobody's kind but my own.
I'm waiting for this to blow over.

[*She rises*]

I lied. I meant it—
I meant it when I said it—but there's too much black
whirling inside me—for any girl to know.
So go on in. You're somebody's angel child
and they're waiting for you.

Miriamne. Yes. I'll go.

[*She turns*]

Mio. And tell them
when you get inside where it's warm,
and you love each other,
and mother comes to kiss her darling, tell them
to hang on to it while they can, believe while they can
it's a warm safe world, and Jesus finds his lambs
and carries them in his bosom.—I've seen some lambs
that Jesus missed. If they ever want the truth
tell them that nothing's guaranteed in this climate
except it gets cold in winter, nor on this earth
except you die sometime.

[*He turns away*]

Miriamne. I have no mother.
And my people are Jews.

Mio. Then you know something about it.

Miriamne. Yes.

Mio. Do you have enough to eat?

Miriamne. Not always.

Mio. What do you believe in?

Miriamne. Nothing.

Mio. Why?

Miriamne. How can one?

Mio. It's easy if you're a fool. You see the words
   in books. Honor, it says there, chivalry, freedom,
   heroism, enduring love—and these
   are words on paper. It's something to have them there.
   You'll get them nowhere else.

Miriamne. What hurts you?

Mio. Just that.
   You'll get them nowhere else.

Miriamne. Why should you want them?

Mio. I'm alone, that's why. You see those lights,
   along the river, cutting across the rain—?
   those are the hearths of Brooklyn, and up this way
   the love-nests of Manhattan—they turn their points
   like knives against me—outcast of the world,
   snake in the streets.—I don't want a hand-out.
   I sleep and eat.

Miriamne. Do you want me to go with you?

Mio. Where?

Miriamne. Where you go.

   [*A pause. He goes nearer to her*]

Mio. Why, you god-damned little fool—
   what made you say that?

Miriamne. I don't know.

Mio. If you have a home
   stay in it. I ask for nothing. I've schooled myself
   to ask for nothing, and take what I can get,
   and get along. If I fell for you, that's my look-out,
   and I'll starve it down.

Miriamne. Wherever you go, I'd go.

Mio. What do you know about loving?
   How could you know?
   Have you ever had a man?

Miriamne.
   [*After a slight pause*]
   No. But I know.
   Tell me your name.
Mio. Mio. What's yours?
Miriamne. Miriamne.
Mio. There's no such name.
Miriamne. But there's no such name as Mio!
   M.I.O. It's no name.
Mio. It's for Bartolomeo.
Miriamne. My mother's name was Miriam,
   so they called me Miriamne.
Mio. Meaning little Miriam?
Miriamne. Yes.
Mio. So now little Miriamne will go in
   and take up quietly where she dropped them all
   her small housewifely cares.—When I first saw you,
   not a half-hour ago, I heard myself saying,
   this is the face that launches ships for me—
   and if I owned a dream—yes, half a dream—
   we'd share it. But I have no dream. This earth
   came tumbling down from chaos, fire and rock,
   and bred up worms, blind worms that sting each other
   here in the dark. These blind worms of the earth
   took out my father—and killed him, and set a sign
   on me—the heir of the serpent—and he was a man
   such as men might be if the gods were men—
   but they killed him—
   as they'll kill all others like him
   till the sun cools down to the stabler molecules,
   yes, till men spin their tent-worm webs to the stars
   and what they think is done, even in the thinking,
   and they are the gods, and immortal, and constellations
   turn for them all like mill wheels—still as they are
   they will be, worms and blind. Enduring love,
   oh gods and worms, what mockery!—And yet

I have blood enough in my veins. It goes like music,
singing, because you're here. My body turns
as if you were the sun, and warm. This men called love
in happier times, before the Freudians taught us
to blame it on the glands. Only go in
before you breathe too much of my atmosphere
and catch death from me.

Miriamne. I will take my hands
and weave them to a little house, and there
you shall keep a dream—

Mio. God knows I could use a dream
and even a house.

Miriamne. You're laughing at me, Mio!

Mio. The worms are laughing.
I tell you there's death about me
and you're a child! And I'm alone and half mad
with hate and longing. I shall let you love me
and love you in return, and then, why then
God knows what happens!

Miriamne. Something most unpleasant?

Mio. Love in a box car—love among the children.
I've seen too much of it. Are we to live
in this same house you make with your two hands
mystically, out of air?

Miriamne. No roof, no mortgage!
Well, I shall marry a baker out in Flatbush,
it gives hot bread in the morning! Oh, Mio, Mio,
in all the unwanted places and waste lands
that roll up into the darkness out of sun
and into sun out of dark, there should be one empty
for you and me.

Mio. No.

Miriamne. Then go now and leave me.
I'm only a girl you saw in the tenements,
and there's been nothing said.

Mio. Miriamne.

[*She takes a step toward him*]

Miriamne. Yes.

    [*He kisses her lips lightly*]

Mio. Why, girl, the transfiguration on the mount
    was nothing to your face. It lights from within—
    a white chalice holding fire, a flower in flame,
    this is your face.

Miriamne. And you shall drink the flame
    and never lessen it. And round your head
    the aureole shall burn that burns there now,
    forever. This I can give you. And so forever
    the Freudians are wrong.

Mio. They're well-forgotten
    at any rate.

Miriamne. Why did you speak to me
    when you first saw me?

Mio. I knew then.

Miriamne. And I came back
    because I must see you again. And we danced together
    and my heart hurt me. Never, never, never,
    though they should bind me down and tear out my eyes,
    would I ever hurt you now. Take me with you, Mio,
    let them look for us, whoever there is to look,
    but we'll be away.

    [MIO *turns away toward the tenement*]

Mio. When I was four years old
    we climbed through an iron gate, my mother and I,
    to see my father in prison. He stood in the death-cell
    and put his hand through the bars and said, My Mio,
    I have only this to leave you, that I love you,
    and will love you after I die. Love me then, Mio,
    when this hard thing comes on you, that you must live
    a man despised for your father. That night the guards,
    walking in flood-lights brighter than high noon,
    led him between them with his trousers slit
    and a shaven head for the cathodes. This sleet and rain
    that I feel cold here on my face and hands
    will find him under thirteen years of clay

in prison ground. Lie still and rest, my father,
for I have not forgotten. When I forget
may I lie blind as you. No other love,
time passing, nor the spaced light-years of suns
shall blur your voice, or tempt me from the path
that clears your name—
till I have these rats in my grip
or sleep deep where you sleep.
   [*To Miriamne*]
I have no house,
nor home, nor love of life, nor fear of death,
nor care for what I eat, or who I sleep with,
or what color of calcimine the Government
will wash itself this year or next to lure
the sheep and feed the wolves. Love somewhere else,
and get your children in some other image
more acceptable to the State! This face of mine
is stamped for sewage!
   [*She steps back, surmising*]

Miriamne. Mio—

Mio. My road is cut
in rock, and leads to one end. If I hurt you, I'm sorry.
One gets over hurts.

Miriamne. What was his name—
your father's name?

Mio. Bartolomeo Romagna.
I'm not ashamed of it.

Miriamne. Why are you here?

Mio. For the reason
I've never had a home. Because I'm a cry
out of a shallow grave, and all roads are mine
that might revenge him!

Miriamne. But Mio—why here—why here?

Mio. I can't tell you that.

Miriamne. No—but—there's someone
lives here—lives not far—and you mean to see him—

you mean to ask him—
  [*She pauses*]
Mio. Who told you that?
Miriamne. His name
  is Garth—Garth Esdras—
Mio.
  [*After a pause, coming nearer*]
  Who are you, then? You seem
  to know a good deal about me.—Were you sent
  to say this?
Miriamne. You said there was death about you! Yes,
  but nearer than you think! Let it be as it is—
  let it all be as it is, never see this place
  nor think of it—forget the streets you came
  when you're away and safe! Go before you're seen
  or spoken to!
Mio. Will you tell me why?
Miriamne. As I love you
  I can't tell you—and I can never see you—
Mio. I walk where I please—
Miriamne. Do you think it's easy for me
  to send you away?
  [*She steps back as if to go*]
Mio. Where will I find you then
  if I should want to see you?
Miriamne. Never—I tell you
  I'd bring you death! Even now. Listen!
  [SHADOW *and* TROCK *enter between the bridge and the tenement
    house.* MIRIAMNE *pulls* MIO *back into the shadow of the rock to
    avoid being seen*]
Trock. Why, fine.

WILLIAM FAULKNER

THAT EVENING SUN

GO DOWN

Dear Mr. Burnett:

Choose anything of mine you want to, and that is convenient.

Oxford, Miss.   FAULKNER

July, 1942

MONDAY is no different from any other week day in Jefferson now. The streets are paved now, and the telephone and the electric companies are cutting down more and more of the shade trees —the water oaks, the maples and locusts and elms—to make room for iron poles bearing clusters of bloated and ghostly and bloodless grapes, and we have a city laundry which makes the rounds on Monday morning, gathering the bundles of clothes into bright-colored, specially made motor-cars: the soiled wearing of a whole week now flees apparition-like behind alert and irritable electric horns, with a long diminishing noise of rubber and asphalt like a tearing of silk, and even the Negro women who still take in white people's washing after the old custom, fetch and deliver it in automobiles.

But fifteen years ago, on Monday morning the quiet, dusty, shady streets would be full of Negro women with, balanced on their steady turbaned heads, bundles of clothes tied up in sheets, almost as large as cotton bales, carried so without touch of hand between the kitchen door of the white house and the blackened wash-pot beside a cabin door in Negro Hollow.

Nancy would set her bundle on the top of her head, then upon the bundle in turn she would set the black straw sailor hat which she wore Winter and Summer. She was tall, with a high, sad face sunken a little where her teeth were missing. Sometimes we would go a part

of the way down the lane and across the pasture with her, to watch
the balanced bundle and the hat that never bobbed nor wavered, even
when she walked down into the ditch and climbed out again and
stooped through the fence. She would go down on her hands and
knees and crawl through the gap, her head rigid, up-tilted, the bundle
steady as a rock or a balloon, and rise to her feet and go on.

Sometimes the husbands of the washing women would fetch and
deliver the clothes, but Jubah never did that for Nancy, even before
father told him to stay away from our house, even when Dilsey was
sick and Nancy would come to cook for us.

And then about half the time we'd have to go down the lane to
Nancy's house and tell her to come on and get breakfast. We would
stop at the ditch, because father told us to not have anything to do
with Jubah—he was a short black man, with a razor scar down his
face—and we would throw rocks at Nancy's house until she came to
the door, leaning her head around it without any clothes on.

"What you all mean, chunking my house?" Nancy said. "What
you little devils mean?"

"Father says for you to come and get breakfast," Caddy said.
"Father says it's over a half an hour now, and you've got to come this
minute."

"I ain't studying no breakfast," Nancy said. "I going to get my
sleep out."

"I bet you're drunk," Jason said. "Father says you're drunk. Are you
drunk, Nancy?"

"Who says I is?" Nancy said. "I got to get my sleep out. I ain't
studying no breakfast."

So after a while we quit chunking the house and went back home.
When she finally came, it was too late for me to go to school. So we
thought it was whiskey until that day when they arrested her again
and they were taking her to jail and they passed Mr. Stovall. He was
the cashier in the bank and a deacon in the Baptist church, and Nancy
began to say:

"When you going to pay me, white man? When you going to pay
me, white man? It's been three times now since you paid me a cent—"
Mr. Stovall knocked her down, but she kept on saying, "When you
going to pay me, white man? It's been three times now since—" until

Mr. Stovall kicked her in the mouth with his heel and the marshal caught Mr. Stovall back, and Nancy lying in the street, laughing. She turned her head and spat out some blood and teeth and said, "It's been three times now since he paid me a cent."

That was how she lost her teeth, and all that day they told about Nancy and Mr. Stovall, and all that night the ones that passed the jail could hear Nancy singing and yelling. They could see her hands holding to the window bars, and a lot of them stopped along the fence, listening to her and to the jailer trying to make her shut up. She didn't shut up until just before daylight, when the jailer began to hear a bumping and scraping upstairs and he went up there and found Nancy hanging from the window bar. He said that it was cocaine and not whiskey, because no nigger would try to commit suicide unless he was full of cocaine, because a nigger full of cocaine was not a nigger any longer.

The jailer cut her down and revived her; then he beat her, whipped her. She had hung herself with her dress. She had fixed it all right, but when they arrested her she didn't have on anything except a dress and so she didn't have anything to tie her hands with and she couldn't make her hands let go of the window ledge. So the jailer heard the noise and ran up there and found Nancy hanging from the window, stark naked.

When Dilsey was sick in her cabin and Nancy was cooking for us, we could see her apron swelling out; that was before father told Jubah to stay away from the house. Jubah was in the kitchen, sitting behind the stove, with his razor scar on his black face like a piece of dirty string. He said it was a watermelon that Nancy had under her dress. And it was Winter, too.

"Where did you get a watermelon in the Winter?" Caddy said.

"I didn't," Jubah said. "It wasn't me that give it to her. But I can cut it down, same as if it was."

"What makes you want to talk that way before these chillen?" Nancy said. "Whyn't you go on to work? You done et. You want Mr. Jason to catch you hanging around his kitchen, talking that way before these chillen?"

"Talking what way, Nancy?" Caddy said.

"I can't hang around white man's kitchen," Jubah said. "But white man can hang around mine. White man can come in my house, but I can't stop him. When white man want to come in my house, I ain't got no house. I can't stop him, but he can't kick me outen it. He can't do that."

Dilsey was still sick in her cabin. Father told Jubah to stay off our place. Dilsey was still sick. It was a long time. We were in the library after supper.

"Isn't Nancy through yet?" mother said. "It seems to me that she has had plenty of time to have finished the dishes."

"Let Quentin go and see," father said. "Go and see if Nancy is through, Quentin. Tell her she can go on home."

I went to the kitchen. Nancy was through. The dishes were put away and the fire was out. Nancy was sitting in a chair, close to the cold stove. She looked at me.

"Mother wants to know if you are through," I said.

"Yes," Nancy said. She looked at me. "I done finished." She looked at me.

"What is it?" I said. "What is it?"

"I ain't nothing but a nigger," Nancy said. "It ain't none of my fault."

She looked at me, sitting in the chair before the cold stove, the sailor hat on her head. I went back to the library. It was the cold stove and all, when you think of a kitchen being warm and busy and cheerful. And with a cold stove and the dishes all put away, and nobody wanting to eat at that hour.

"Is she through?" mother said.

"Yessum," I said.

"What is she doing?" mother said.

"She's not doing anything. She's through."

"I'll go and see," father said.

"Maybe she's waiting for Jubah to come and take her home," Caddy said.

"Jubah is gone," I said. Nancy told us how one morning she woke up and Jubah was gone.

"He quit me," Nancy said. "Done gone to Memphis, I reckon. Dodging them city po-lice for a while, I reckon."

"And a good riddance," father said. "I hope he stays there."

"Nancy's scaired of the dark," Jason said.

"So are you," Caddy said.

"I'm not," Jason said.

"Scairy cat," Caddy said.

"I'm not," Jason said.

"You, Candace!" mother said. Father came back.

"I am going to walk down the lane with Nancy," he said. "She says Jubah is back."

"Has she seen him?" mother said.

"No. Some Negro sent her word that he was back in town. I won't be long."

"You'll leave me alone, to take Nancy home?" mother said. "Is her safety more precious to you than mine?"

"I won't be long," father said.

"You'll leave these children unprotected, with that Negro about?"

"I'm going too," Caddy said. "Let me go, father."

"What would he do with them, if he were unfortunate enough to have them?" father said.

"I want to go, too," Jason said.

"Jason!" mother said. She was speaking to father. You could tell that by the way she said it. Like she believed that all day father had been trying to think of doing the thing that she wouldn't like the most, and that she knew all the time that after a while he would think of it. I stayed quiet, because father and I both knew that mother would want him to make me stay with her, if she just thought of it in time. So father didn't look at me. I was the oldest. I was nine and Caddy was seven and Jason was five.

"Nonsense," father said. "We won't be long."

Nancy had her hat on. We came to the lane. "Jubah always been good to me," Nancy said. "Whenever he had two dollars, one of them was mine." We walked in the lane. "If I can just get through the lane," Nancy said, "I be all right then."

The lane was always dark. "This is where Jason got scared on Hallowe'en," Caddy said.

"I didn't," Jason said.

"Can't Aunt Rachel do anything with him?" father said. Aunt Rachel was old. She lived in a cabin beyond Nancy's, by herself. She had white hair and she smoked a pipe in the door, all day long; she didn't work any more. They said she was Jubah's mother. Sometimes she said she was and sometimes she said she wasn't any kin to Jubah.

"Yes you did," Caddy said. "You were scairder than Frony. You were scairder than T.P. even. Scairder than niggers."

"Can't nobody do nothing with him," Nancy said. "He say I done woke up the devil in him, and ain't but one thing going to lay it again."

"Well, he's gone now," father said. "There's nothing for you to be afraid of now. And if you'd just let white men alone."

"Let what white men alone?" Caddy said. "How let them alone?"

"He ain't gone nowhere," Nancy said. "I can feel him. I can feel him now, in this lane. He hearing us talk, every word, hid somewhere, waiting. I ain't seen him, and I ain't going to see him again but once more, with that razor. That razor on that string down his back, inside his shirt. And then I ain't going to be even surprised."

"I wasn't scaired," Jason said.

"If you'd behave yourself, you'd have kept out of this," father said. "But it's all right now. He's probably in St. Louis now. Probably got another wife by now and forgot all about you."

"If he has, I better not find out about it," Nancy said. "I'd stand there and every time he wropped her, I'd cut that arm off. I'd cut his head off and I'd slit her belly and I'd shove—"

"Hush," father said.

"Slit whose belly, Nancy?" Caddy said.

"I wasn't scaired," Jason said. "I'd walk right down this lane by myself."

"Yah," Caddy said. "You wouldn't dare to put your foot in it if we were not with you."

II

Dilsey was still sick, and so we took Nancy home every night until mother said, "How much longer is this going to go on? I to be left alone in this big house while you take home a frightened Negro?"

We fixed a pallet in the kitchen for Nancy. One night we waked up, hearing the sound. It was not singing and it was not crying, coming up the dark stairs. There was a light in mother's room and we heard father going down the hall, down the back stairs, and Caddy and I went into the hall. The floor was cold. Our toes curled away from the floor while we listened to the sound. It was like singing and it wasn't like singing, like the sounds that Negroes make.

Then it stopped and we heard father going down the back stairs, and we went to the head of the stairs. Then the sound began again, in the stairway, not loud, and we could see Nancy's eyes half way up the stairs, against the wall. They looked like cat's eyes do, like a big cat against the wall, watching us. When we came down the steps to where she was she quit making the sound again, and we stood there until father came back up from the kitchen, with his pistol in his hand. He went back down with Nancy and they came back with Nancy's pallet.

We spread the pallet in our room. After the light in mother's room went off, we could see Nancy's eyes again. "Nancy," Caddy whispered, "are you asleep, Nancy?"

Nancy whispered something. It was oh or no, I don't know which. Like nobody had made it, like it came from nowhere and went nowhere, until it was like Nancy was not there at all; that I had looked so hard at her eyes on the stair that they had got printed on my eyelids, like the sun does when you have closed your eyes and there is no sun. "Jesus," Nancy whispered. "Jesus."

"Was it Jubah?" Caddy whispered. "Did he try to come into the kitchen?"

"Jesus," Nancy said. Like this: Jeeeeeeeeeeeeeeeesus, until the sound went out like a match or a candle does.

"Can you see us, Nancy?" Caddy whispered. "Can you see our eyes too?"

"I ain't nothing but a nigger," Nancy said. "God knows. God knows."

"What did you see down there in the kitchen?" Caddy whispered. "What tried to get in?"

"God knows," Nancy said. We could see her eyes. "God knows."

Dilsey got well. She cooked dinner. "You'd better stay in bed a day or two longer," father said.

"What for?" Dilsey said. "If I had been a day later, this place would be to rack and ruin. Get on out of here, now, and let me get my kitchen straight again."

Dilsey cooked supper, too. And that night, just before dark, Nancy came into the kitchen.

"How do you know he's back?" Dilsey said. "You ain't seen him."

"Jubah is a nigger," Jason said.

"I can feel him," Nancy said. "I can feel him laying yonder in the ditch."

"To-night?" Dilsey said. "Is he there to-night?"

"Dilsey's a nigger too," Jason said.

"You try to eat something," Dilsey said.

"I don't want nothing," Nancy said.

"I ain't a nigger," Jason said.

"Drink some coffee," Dilsey said. She poured a cup of coffee for Nancy. "Do you know he's out there to-night? How come you know it's to-night?"

"I know," Nancy said. "He's there, waiting. I know. I done lived with him too long. I know what he fixing to do 'fore he knows it himself."

"Drink some coffee," Dilsey said. Nancy held the cup to her mouth and blew into the cup. Her mouth pursed out like a spreading adder's, like a rubber mouth, like she had blown all the color out of her lips with blowing the coffee.

"I ain't a nigger," Jason said. "Are you a nigger, Nancy?"

"I hell-born, child," Nancy said. "I won't be nothing soon. I going back where I come from soon."

III

She began to drink the coffee. While she was drinking, holding the cup in both hands, she began to make the sound again. She made the sound into the cup and the coffee sploshed out on to her hands and her dress. Her eyes looked at us and she sat there, her elbows on her knees, holding the cup in both hands, looking at us across the wet cup, making the sound.

"Look at Nancy," Jason said. "Nancy can't cook for us now. Dilsey's got well now."

"You hush up," Dilsey said. Nancy held the cup in both hands, looking at us, making the sound, like there were two of them: one looking at us and the other making the sound. "Whyn't you let Mr. Jason telefoam the marshal?" Dilsey said. Nancy stopped then, holding the cup in her long brown hands. She tried to drink some coffee again, but it sploshed out of the cup, on to her hands and her dress, and she put the cup down. Jason watched her.

"I can't swallow it," Nancy said. "I swallows but it won't go down me."

"You go down to the cabin," Dilsey said. "Frony will fix you a pallet and I'll be there soon."

"Won't no nigger stop him," Nancy said.

"I ain't a nigger," Jason said. "Am I, Dilsey?"

"I reckon not," Dilsey said. She looked at Nancy. "I don't reckon so. What you going to do, then?"

Nancy looked at us. Her eyes went fast, like she was afraid there wasn't time to look, without hardly moving at all. She looked at us, at all three of us at one time. "You 'member that night I stayed in you all's room?" she said. She told about how we waked up early the next morning, and played. We had to play quiet, on her pallet, until father woke and it was time for her to go down and get breakfast. "Go and ask you maw to let me stay here to-night," Nancy said. "I won't need no pallet. We can play some more," she said.

Caddy asked mother. Jason went too. "I can't have Negroes sleeping in the house," mother said. Jason cried. He cried until mother said he couldn't have any dessert for three days if he didn't stop. Then Jason said he would stop if Dilsey would make a chocolate cake. Father was there.

"Why don't you do something about it?" mother said. "What do we have officers for?"

"Why is Nancy afraid of Jubah?" Caddy said. "Are you afraid of father, mother?"

"What could they do?" father said. "If Nancy hasn't seen him, how could the officers find him?"

"Then why is she afraid?" mother said.

"She says he is there. She says she knows he is there to-night."

"Yet we pay taxes," mother said. "I must wait here alone in this big house while you take a Negro woman home."

"You know that I am not lying outside with a razor," father said.

"I'll stop if Dilsey will make a chocolate cake," Jason said. Mother told us to go out and father said he didn't know if Jason would get a chocolate cake or not, but he knew what Jason was going to get in about a minute. We went back to the kitchen and told Nancy.

"Father said for you to go home and lock the door, and you'll be all right," Caddy said. "All right from what, Nancy? Is Jubah mad at you?" Nancy was holding the coffee cup in her hands, her elbows on her knees and her hands holding the cup between her knees. She was looking into the cup. "What have you done that made Jubah mad?" Caddy said. Nancy let the cup go. It didn't break on the floor, but the coffee spilled out, and Nancy sat there with her hands making the shape of the cup. She began to make the sound again, not loud. Not singing and not un-singing. We watched her.

"Here," Dilsey said. "You quit that, now. You get a-holt of yourself. You wait here. I going to get Versh to walk home with you." Dilsey went out.

We looked at Nancy. Her shoulders kept shaking, but she had quit making the sound. We watched her. "What's Jubah going to do to you?" Caddy said. "He went away."

Nancy looked at us. "We had fun that night I stayed in you all's room, didn't we?"

"I didn't," Jason said. "I didn't have any fun."

"You were asleep," Caddy said. "You were not there."

"Let's go down to my house and have some more fun," Nancy said.

"Mother won't let us," I said. "It's too late now."

"Don't bother her," Nancy said. "We can tell her in the morning. She won't mind."

"She wouldn't let us," I said.

"Don't ask her now," Nancy said. "Don't bother her now."

"They didn't say we couldn't go," Caddy said.

"We didn't ask," I said.

"If you go, I'll tell," Jason said.

"We'll have fun," Nancy said. "They won't mind, just to my house. I been working for you all a long time. They won't mind."

"I'm not afraid to go," Caddy said. "Jason is the one that's afraid. He'll tell."

"I'm not," Jason said.

"Yes, you are," Caddy said. "You'll tell."

"I won't tell," Jason said. "I'm not afraid."

"Jason ain't afraid to go with me," Nancy said. "Is you, Jason?"

"Jason is going to tell," Caddy said. The lane was dark. We passed the pasture gate. "I bet if something was to jump out from behind that gate, Jason would holler."

"I wouldn't," Jason said. We walked down the lane. Nancy was talking loud.

"What are you talking so loud for, Nancy?" Caddy said.

"Who; me?" Nancy said. "Listen at Quentin and Caddy and Jason saying I'm talking loud."

"You talk like there was four of us here," Caddy said. "You talk like father was here too."

"Who; me talking loud, Mr. Jason?" Nancy said.

"Nancy called Jason 'Mister,'" Caddy said.

"Listen how Caddy and Quentin and Jason talk," Nancy said.

"We're not talking loud," Caddy said. "You're the one that's talking like father—"

"Hush," Nancy said; "hush, Mr. Jason."

"Nancy called Jason 'Mister' aguh—"

"Hush," Nancy said. She was talking loud when we crossed the ditch and stooped through the fence where she used to stoop through with the clothes on her head. Then we came to her house. We were going fast then. She opened the door. The smell of the house was like the lamp and the smell of Nancy was like the wick, like they were waiting for one another to smell. She lit the lamp and closed the door and put the bar up. Then she quit talking loud, looking at us.

"What're we going to do?" Caddy said.

"What you all want to do?" Nancy said.

"You said we would have some fun," Caddy said.

There was something about Nancy's house; something you could smell. Jason smelled it, even. "I don't want to stay here," he said. "I want to go home."

"Go home, then," Caddy said.

"I don't want to go by myself," Jason said.

"We're going to have some fun," Nancy said.

"How?" Caddy said.

Nancy stood by the door. She was looking at us, only it was like she had emptied her eyes, like she had quit using them.

"What do you want to do?" she said.

"Tell us a story," Caddy said. "Can you tell a story?"

"Yes," Nancy said.

"Tell it," Caddy said. We looked at Nancy. "You don't know any stories," Caddy said.

"Yes," Nancy said. "Yes, I do."

She came and sat down in a chair before the hearth. There was some fire there; she built it up; it was already hot. You didn't need a fire. She built a good blaze. She told a story. She talked like her eyes looked, like her eyes watching us and her voice talking to us did not belong to her. Like she was living somewhere else, waiting somewhere else. She was outside the house. Her voice was there and the shape of her, the Nancy that could stoop under the fence with the bundle of clothes balanced as though without weight, like a balloon, on her head, was there. But that was all. "And so this here queen come walking up to the ditch, where that bad man was hiding. She was walking up the ditch, and she say, 'If I can just get past this here ditch,' was what she say. . . ."

"What ditch?" Caddy said. "A ditch like that one out there? Why did the queen go into the ditch?"

"To get to her house," Nancy said. She looked at us. "She had to cross that ditch to get home."

"Why did she want to go home?" Caddy said.

IV

Nancy looked at us. She quit talking. She looked at us. Jason's legs stuck straight out of his pants, because he was little. "I don't think that's a good story," he said. "I want to go home."

"Maybe we had better," Caddy said. She got up from the floor. "I bet they are looking for us right now." She went toward the door.

"No," Nancy said. "Don't open it." She got up quick and passed Caddy. She didn't touch the door, the wooden bar.

"Why not?" Caddy said.

"Come back to the lamp," Nancy said. "We'll have fun. You don't have to go."

"We ought to go," Caddy said. "Unless we have a lot of fun." She and Nancy came back to the fire, the lamp.

"I want to go home," Jason said. "I'm going to tell."

"I know another story," Nancy said. She stood close to the lamp. She looked at Caddy, like when your eyes look up at a stick balanced on your nose. She had to look down to see Caddy, but her eyes looked like that, like when you are balancing a stick.

"I won't listen to it," Jason said. "I'll bang on the floor."

"It's a good one," Nancy said. "It's better than the other one."

"What's it about?" Caddy said. Nancy was standing by the lamp. Her hand was on the lamp, against the light, long and brown.

"Your hand is on that hot globe," Caddy said. "Don't it feel hot to your hand?"

Nancy looked at her hand on the lamp chimney. She took her hand away, slow. She stood there, looking at Caddy, wringing her long hand as though it were tied to her wrist with a string.

"Let's do something else," Caddy said.

"I want to go home," Jason said.

"I got some popcorn," Nancy said. She looked at Caddy and then at Jason and then at me and then at Caddy again. "I got some popcorn."

"I don't like popcorn," Jason said. "I'd rather have candy."

Nancy looked at Jason. "You can hold the popper." She was still wringing her hand; it was long and limp and brown.

"All right," Jason said. "I'll stay a while if I can do that. Caddy can't hold it. I'll want to go home, if Caddy holds the popper."

Nancy built up the fire. "Look at Nancy putting her hands in the fire," Caddy said. "What's the matter with you, Nancy?"

"I got popcorn," Nancy said. "I got some." She took the popper from under the bed. It was broken. Jason began to cry.

"We can't have any popcorn," he said.

"We ought to go home, anyway," Caddy said. "Come on, Quentin."

"Wait," Nancy said; "wait. I can fix it. Don't you want to help me fix it?"

"I don't think I want any," Caddy said. "It's too late now."

"You help me, Jason," Nancy said. "Don't you want to help me?"

"No," Jason said. "I want to go home."

"Hush," Nancy said; "hush. Watch. Watch me. I can fix it so Jason can hold it and pop the corn." She got a piece of wire and fixed the popper.

"It won't hold good," Caddy said.

"Yes, it will," Nancy said. "You all watch. You all help me shell the corn."

The corn was under the bed too. We shelled it into the popper and Nancy helped Jason hold the popper over the fire.

"It's not popping," Jason said. "I want to go home."

"You wait," Nancy said. "It'll begin to pop. We'll have fun then." She was sitting close to the fire. The lamp was turned up so high it was beginning to smoke.

"Why don't you turn it down some?" I said.

"It's all right," Nancy said. "I'll clean it. You all wait. The popcorn will start in a minute."

"I don't believe it's going to start," Caddy said. "We ought to go home, anyway. They'll be worried."

"No," Nancy said. "It's going to pop. Dilsey will tell um you all with me. I been working for you all long time. They won't mind if you at my house. You wait, now. It'll start popping in a minute."

Then Jason got some smoke in his eyes and he began to cry. He dropped the popper into the fire. Nancy got a wet rag and wiped Jason's face, but he didn't stop crying.

"Hush," she said. "Hush." He didn't hush. Caddy took the popper out of the fire.

"It's burned up," she said. "You'll have to get some more popcorn, Nancy."

"Did you put all of it in?" Nancy said.

"Yes," Caddy said. Nancy looked at Caddy. Then she took the popper and opened it and poured the blackened popcorn into her apron and began to sort the grains, her hands long and brown, and we watching her.

"Haven't you got any more?" Caddy said.

"Yes," Nancy said; "yes. Look. This here ain't burnt. All we need to do is——"

"I want to go home," Jason said. "I'm going to tell."

"Hush," Caddy said. We all listened. Nancy's head was already turned toward the barred door, her eyes filled with red lamplight. "Somebody is coming," Caddy said.

Then Nancy began to make that sound again, not loud, sitting there above the fire, her long hands dangling between her knees; all of a sudden water began to come out on her face in big drops, running down her face, carrying in each one a little turning ball of firelight until it dropped off her chin.

"She's not crying," I said.

"I ain't crying," Nancy said. Her eyes were closed. "I ain't crying. Who is it?"

"I don't know," Caddy said. She went to the door and looked out. "We've got to go home now," she said. "Here comes father."

"I'm going to tell," Jason said. "You all made me come."

The water still ran down Nancy's face. She turned in her chair. "Listen. Tell him. Tell him we going to have fun. Tell him I take good care of you all until in the morning. Tell him to let me come home with you all and sleep on the floor. Tell him I won't need no pallet. We'll have fun. You remember last time how we had so much fun?"

"I didn't have any fun," Jason said. "You hurt me. You put smoke in my eyes."

v

Father came in. He looked at us. Nancy did not get up.

"Tell him," she said.

"Caddy made us come down here," Jason said. "I didn't want to."

Father came to the fire. Nancy looked up at him. "Can't you go to Aunt Rachel's and stay?" he said. Nancy looked up at father, her hands between her knees. "He's not here," father said. "I would have seen. There wasn't a soul in sight."

"He in the ditch," Nancy said. "He waiting in the ditch yonder."

"Nonsense," father said. He looked at Nancy. "Do you know he's there?"

"I got the sign," Nancy said.

"What sign?"

"I got it. It was on the table when I come in. It was a hog bone, with blood meat still on it, laying by the lamp. He's out there. When you all walk out that door, I gone."

"Who's gone, Nancy?" Caddy said.

"I'm not a tattletale," Jason said.

"Nonsense," father said.

"He out there," Nancy said. "He looking through that window this minute, waiting for you all to go. Then I gone."

"Nonsense," father said. "Lock up your house and we'll take you on to Aunt Rachel's."

" 'Twon't do no good," Nancy said. She didn't look at father now, but he looked down at her, at her long, limp, moving hands.

"Putting it off won't do no good."

"Then what do you want to do?" father said.

"I don't know," Nancy said. "I can't do nothing. Just put it off. And that don't do no good. I reckon it belong to me. I reckon what I going to get ain't no more than mine."

"Get what?" Caddy said. "What's yours?"

"Nothing," father said. "You all must get to bed."

"Caddy made me come," Jason said.

"Go on to Aunt Rachel's," father said.

"It won't do no good," Nancy said. She sat before the fire, her elbows on her knees, her long hands between her knees. "When even your own kitchen wouldn't do no good. When even if I was sleeping on the floor in the room with your own children, and the next morning there I am, and blood all——"

"Hush," father said. "Lock the door and put the lamp out and go to bed."

"I scared of the dark," Nancy said. "I scared for it to happen in the dark."

"You mean you're going to sit right here, with the lamp lighted?" father said. Then Nancy began to make the sound again, sitting before the fire, her long hands between her knees. "Ah, damnation," father said. "Come along, chillen. It's bedtime."

"When you all go, I gone," Nancy said. "I be dead to-morrow. I done have saved up the coffin money with Mr. Lovelady——"

Mr. Lovelady was a short, dirty man who collected the Negro insurance, coming around to the cabins and the kitchens every Saturday morning, to collect fifteen cents. He and his wife lived in the hotel. One morning his wife committed suicide. They had a child, a little girl. After his wife committed suicide Mr. Lovelady and the child went away. After a while Mr. Lovelady came back. We would see him going down the lanes on Saturday morning. He went to the Baptist church.

Father carried Jason on his back. We went out Nancy's door; she was sitting before the fire. "Come and put the bar up," father said. Nancy didn't move. She didn't look at us again. We left her there, sitting before the fire with the door opened, so that it wouldn't happen in the dark.

"What, father?" Caddy said. "Why is Nancy scared of Jubah? What is Jubah going to do to her?"

"Jubah wasn't there," Jason said.

"No," father said. "He's not there. He's gone away."

"Who is it that's waiting in the ditch?" Caddy said. We looked at the ditch. We came to it, where the path went down into the thick vines and went up again.

KATHERINE ANNE PORTER

Why she selected FLOWERING JUDAS

"Flowering Judas" was written between seven o'clock and midnight of a very cold December, 1929, in Brooklyn. The experiences from which it was made occurred several years before, in Mexico, just after the Obregon revolution.

All the characters and episodes are based on real persons and events, but naturally, as my memory worked upon them and time passed, all assumed different shapes and colors, formed gradually around a central idea, that of self-delusion, the order and meaning of the episodes changed, and became in a word fiction.

The idea first came to me one evening when going to visit the girl I call Laura in the story, I passed the open window of her living room on my way to the door, through the small patio which is one of the scenes in the story. I had a brief glimpse of her sitting with an open book in her lap, but not reading, with a fixed look of pained melancholy and confusion in her face. The fat man I call Braggioni was playing the guitar and singing to her.

In that glimpse, no more than a flash, I thought I understood, or perceived, for the first time, the desperate complications of her mind and feelings, and I knew a story; perhaps not her true story, not even the real story of the whole situation, but all the same a story that seemed symbolic truth to me. If I had not seen her face at that very moment, I should never have written just this story because I should not have known it to write.

The editor has asked for my favorite story. I have no favorites though there is perhaps one, a short novel, for which now and then I do feel a preference, for extremely personal reasons. I offer this story which falls within the stipulated length because it comes very near to being what I meant for it to be, and I suppose an author's choice of his own work must always be decided by such private knowledge of the margin between intention and the accomplished fact.

Boulder, Colo.   KATHERINE ANNE PORTER
July 13, 1942

BRAGGIONI sits heaped upon the edge of a straight-backed chair much too small for him, and sings to Laura in a furry, mournful voice. Laura has begun to find reasons for avoiding her own house until the latest possible moment, for Braggioni is there almost every night. No matter how late she is, he will be sitting there with a surly, waiting expression, pulling at his kinky yellow hair, thumbing the strings of his guitar, snarling a tune under his breath. Lupe the Indian maid meets Laura at the door, and says with a flicker of a glance towards the upper room, "He waits."

Laura wishes to lie down, she is tired of her hairpins and the feel of her long tight sleeves, but she says to him, "Have you a new song for me this evening?" If he says yes, she asks him to sing it. If he says no, she remembers his favorite one, and asks him to sing it again. Lupe brings her a cup of chocolate and a plate of rice, and Laura eats at the small table under the lamp, first inviting Braggioni, whose answer is always the same: "I have eaten, and besides, chocolate thickens the voice."

Laura says, "Sing, then," and Braggioni heaves himself into song. He scratches the guitar familiarly as though it were a pet animal, and sings passionately off key, taking the high notes in a prolonged painful squeal. Laura, who haunts the markets listening to the ballad singers, and stops every day to hear the blind boy playing his reed-flute in Sixteenth of September Street, listens to Braggioni with pitiless courtesy, because she dares not smile at his miserable performance. Nobody dares to smile at him. Braggioni is cruel to everyone, with a kind of specialized insolence, but he is so vain of his talents, and so sensitive to slights, it would require a cruelty and vanity greater than his own to lay a finger on the vast cureless wound of his self-esteem. It would require courage, too, for it is dangerous to offend him, and nobody has this courage.

Braggioni loves himself with such tenderness and amplitude and eternal charity that his followers—for he is a leader of men, a skilled revolutionist, and his skin has been punctured in honorable warfare —warm themselves in the reflected glow, and say to each other: "He has a real nobility, a love of humanity raised above mere personal affections." The excess of this self-love has flowed out, inconveniently for her, over Laura, who, with so many others, owes her comfortable situation and her salary to him. When he is in a very good humor, he tells her, "I am tempted to forgive you for being a *gringa. Gringita!*" and Laura, burning, imagines herself leaning forward suddenly, and with a sound back-handed slap wiping the suety smile from his face. If he notices her eyes at these moments he gives no sign.

She knows what Braggioni would offer her, and she must resist tenaciously without appearing to resist, and if she could avoid it she would not admit even to herself the slow drift of his intention. During these long evenings which have spoiled a long month for her, she sits in her deep chair with an open book on her knees, resting her eyes on the consoling rigidity of the printed page when the sight and sound of Braggioni singing threaten to identify themselves with all her re- membered afflictions and to add their weight to her uneasy premoni- tions of the future. The gluttonous bulk of Braggioni has become a symbol of her many disillusions, for a revolutionist should be lean, animated by heroic faith, a vessel of abstract virtues. This is nonsense, she knows it now and is ashamed of it. Revolution must have leaders, and leadership is a career for energetic men. She is, her comrades tell her, full of romantic error, for what she defines as cynicism in them is merely "a developed sense of reality." She is almost too willing to say, "I am wrong, I suppose I don't really understand the principles," and afterward she makes a secret truce with herself, determined not to surrender her will to such expedient logic. But she cannot help feeling that she has been betrayed irreparably by the disunion between her way of living and her feeling of what life should be, and at times she is almost contented to rest in this sense of grievance as a private store of consolation. Sometimes she wishes to run away, but she stays. Now she longs to fly out of this room, down the narrow stairs, and into the street where the houses lean together like conspirators under a single mottled lamp, and leave Braggioni singing to himself.

Instead she looks at Braggioni, frankly and clearly, like a good child who understands the rules of behavior. Her knees cling together under sound blue serge, and her round white collar is not purposely nun-like. She wears the uniform of an idea, and has renounced vanities. She was born Roman Catholic, and in spite of her fear of being seen by someone who might make a scandal of it, she slips now and again into some crumbling little church, kneels on the chilly stone, and says a Hail Mary on the gold rosary she bought in Tehuantepec. It is no good and she ends by examining the altar with its tinsel flowers and ragged brocades, and feels tender about the battered doll-shape of some male saint whose white, lace-trimmed drawers hang limply around his ankles below the hieratic dignity of his velvet robe. She has encased herself in a set of principles derived from her early training, leaving no detail of gesture or of personal taste untouched, and for this reason she will not wear lace made on machines. This is her private heresy, for in her special group the machine is sacred, and will be the salvation of the workers. She loves fine lace, and there is a tiny edge of fluted cobweb on this collar, which is one of twenty precisely alike, folded in blue tissue paper in the upper drawer of her clothes chest.

Braggioni catches her glance solidly as if he had been waiting for it, leans forward, balancing his paunch between his spread knees, and sings with tremendous emphasis, weighing his words. He has, the song relates, no father and no mother, nor even a friend to console him; lonely as a wave of the sea he comes and goes, lonely as a wave. His mouth opens round and yearns sideways, his balloon cheeks grow oily with the labor of song. He bulges marvelously in his expensive garments. Over his lavendar collar, crushed upon a purple necktie, held by a diamond hoop: over his ammunition belt of tooled leather worked in silver, buckled cruelly around his gasping middle: over the tops of his glossy yellow shoes Braggioni swells with ominous ripeness, his mauve silk hose stretched taut, his ankles bound with the stout leather thongs of his shoes.

When he stretches his eyelids at Laura she notes again that his eyes are the true tawny yellow cat's eyes. He is rich, not in money, he tells her, but in power, and this power brings with it the blameless ownership of things, and the right to indulge his love of small luxuries. "I have a taste for the elegant refinements," he said once, flourishing a yellow silk handkerchief before her nose. "Smell that? It is Jockey Club, imported from New York." Nonetheless he is wounded by life. He will say so presently. "It is true everything turns to dust in the hand, to gall on the tongue." He sighs and his leather belt creaks like a saddle girth. "I am disappointed in everything as it comes. Everything." He shakes his head. "You, poor thing, you will be disappointed too. You are born for it. We are more alike than you realize in some things. Wait and see. Some day you will remember what I have told you, you will know that Braggioni was your friend."

Laura feels a slow chill, a purely physical sense of danger, a warning in her blood that violence, mutilation, a shocking death, wait for her with lessening patience. She has translated this fear into something homely, immediate, and sometimes hesitates before crossing the street. "My personal fate is nothing, except as the testimony of a mental attitude," she reminds herself, quoting from some forgotten philosophic primer, and is sensible enough to add, "Anyhow, I shall not be killed by an automobile if I can help it.

"It may be true I am as corrupt, in another way, as Braggioni," she thinks in spite of herself, "as callous, as incomplete," and if this is so, any kind of death seems preferable. Still she sits quietly, she does not run. Where could she go? Uninvited she has promised herself to this place; she can no longer imagine herself as living in another country, and there is no pleasure in remembering her life before she came here.

Precisely what is the nature of this devotion, its true motives, and what are its obligations? Laura cannot say. She spends part of her days in Xochimilco, near by, teaching Indian children to say in English, "The cat is on the mat." When she appears in the classroom they crowd about her with smiles on their wise, innocent, clay-colored faces, crying, "Good morning, my titcher!" in immaculate voices, and they make of her desk a fresh garden of flowers every day.

During her leisure she goes to union meetings and listens to busy important voices quarreling over tactics, methods, internal politics. She visits the prisoners of her own political faith in their cells, where they entertain themselves with counting cockroaches, repenting of their indiscretions, composing their memoirs, writing out manifestoes and

KATHERINE ANNE PORTER

plans for their comrades who are still walking about free, hands in pockets, sniffing fresh air. Laura brings them food and cigarettes and a little money, and she brings messages disguised in equivocal phrases from the men outside who dare not set foot in the prison for fear of disappearing into the cells kept empty for them. If the prisoners confuse night and day, and complain, "Dear little Laura, time doesn't pass in this infernal hole, and I won't know when it is time to sleep unless I have a reminder," she brings them their favorite narcotics, and says in a tone that does not wound them with pity, "Tonight will really be night for you," and though her Spanish amuses them, they find her comforting, useful. If they lose patience and all faith, and curse the slowness of their friends in coming to their rescue with money and influence, they trust her not to repeat everything, and if she inquires, "Where do you think we can find money, or influence?" they are certain to answer, "Well, there is Braggioni, why doesn't he do something?"

She smuggles letters from headquarters to men hiding from firing squads in back streets in mildewed houses, where they sit in tumbled beds and talk bitterly as if all Mexico were at their heels, when Laura knows positively they might appear at the band concert in the Alameda on Sunday morning, and no one would notice them. But Braggioni says, "Let them sweat a little. The next time they may be careful. It is very restful to have them out of the way for a while." She is not afraid to knock on any door in any street after midnight, and enter in the darkness, and say to one of these men who is really in danger: "They will be looking for you—seriously—tomorrow morning after six. Here is some money from Vicente. Go to Vera Cruz and wait."

She borrows money from the Roumanian agitator to give to his bitter enemy the Polish agitator. The favor of Braggioni is their disputed territory, and Braggioni holds the balance nicely, for he can use them both. The Polish agitator talks love to her over café tables, hoping to exploit what he believes is her secret sentimental preference for him, and he gives her misinformation which he begs her to repeat as the solemn truth to certain persons. The Roumanian is more adroit. He is generous with his money in all good causes, and lies to her with an air of ingenuous candor, as if he were her good friend and confidant. She never repeats anything they may say. Braggioni never asks questions. He has other ways to discover all that he wishes to know about them.

Nobody touches her, but all praise her gray eyes, and the soft, round under lip which promises gayety, yet is always grave, nearly always firmly closed: and they cannot understand why she is in Mexico. She walks back and forth on her errands, with puzzled eyebrows, carrying her little folder of drawings and music and school papers. No dancer dances more beautifully than Laura walks, and she inspires some amusing, unexpected ardors, which cause little gossip, because nothing comes of them. A young captain who had been a soldier in Zapata's army attempted, during a horseback ride near Cuernavaca, to express his desire for her with the noble simplicity befitting a rude folk-hero: but gently, because he was gentle. This gentleness was his defeat, for when he alighted, and removed her foot from the stirrup, and essayed to draw her down into his arms, her horse, ordinarily a tame one, shied fiercely, reared and plunged away. The young hero's horse careered blindly after his stable-mate, and the hero did not return to the hotel until rather late that evening. At breakfast he came to her table in full charro dress, gray buckskin jacket and trousers with strings of silver buttons down the leg, and he was in a humorous, careless mood. "May I sit with you?" and "You are a wonderful rider. I was terrified that you might be thrown and dragged. I should never have forgiven myself. But I cannot admire you enough for your riding!"

"I learned to ride in Arizona," said Laura.

"If you will ride with me again this morning, I promise you a horse that will not shy with you," he said. But Laura remembered that she must return to Mexico City at noon.

Next morning the children made a celebration and spent their playtime writing on the blackboard, "We lov ar ticher," and with tinted chalks they drew wreaths of flowers around the words. The young hero wrote her a letter: "I am a very foolish, wasteful, impulsive man. I should have first said I love you, and then you would not have run away. But you shall see me again." Laura thought, "I must send him a box of colored crayons," but she was trying to forgive herself for having spurred her horse at the wrong moment.

A brown, shock-haired youth came and stood in her patio one night and sang like a lost soul for two hours, but Laura could think of nothing to do about it. The moonlight spread a wash of gauzy silver over the clear spaces of the garden, and the shadows were cobalt blue. The scarlet blossoms of the Judas tree were dull purple, and the names of the colors repeated themselves automatically in her mind, while she watched not the boy, but his shadow, fallen like a dark garment across the fountain rim, trailing in the water. Lupe came silently and whispered expert counsel in her ear: "If you will throw him one little flower, he will sing another song or two and go away." Laura threw the flower, and he sang a last song and went away with the flower tucked in the band of his hat. Lupe said, "He is one of the organizers of the Typographers Union, and before that he sold corridos in the Merced market, and before that, he came from Guanajuato, where I was born. I would not trust any man, but I trust least those from Guanajuato."

She did not tell Laura that he would be back again the next night, and the next, nor that he would follow her at a certain fixed distance around the Merced market, through the Zócolo, up Francisco I. Madero Avenue, and so along the Paseo de la Reforma to Chapultepec Park, and into the Philosopher's Footpath, still with that flower withering in his hat, and an indivisible attention in his eyes.

Now Laura is accustomed to him, it means nothing except that he is nineteen years old and is observing a convention with all propriety, as though it were founded on a law of nature, which in the end it might well prove to be. He is beginning to write poems which he prints on a wooden press, and he leaves them stuck like handbills in her door. She is pleasantly disturbed by the abstract, unhurried watchfulness of his black eyes which will in time turn easily towards another object. She tells herself that throwing the flower was a mistake, for she is twenty-two years old and knows better; but she refuses to regret it, and persuades herself that her negation of all external events as they occur is a sign that she is gradually perfecting herself in the stoicism she strives to cultivate against that disaster she fears, though she cannot name it.

She is not at home in the world. Every day she teaches children who remain strangers to her, though she loves their tender round hands and their charming opportunist savagery. She knocks at unfamiliar doors not knowing whether a friend or a stranger shall answer, and even if a known face emerges from the sour gloom of

that unknown interior, still it is the face of a stranger. No matter what
this stranger says to her, nor what her message to him, the very cells
of her flesh reject knowledge and kinship in one monotonous word.
No. No. No. She draws her strength from this one holy talismanic
word which does not suffer her to be led into evil. Denying everything, she may walk anywhere in safety, she looks at everything without amazement.

No, repeats this firm unchanging voice of her blood; and she looks
at Braggioni without amazement. He is a great man, he wishes to impress this simple girl who covers her great round breasts with thick
dark cloth, and who hides long, invaluably beautiful legs under a
heavy skirt. She is almost thin except for the incomprehensible fullness
of her breasts, like a nursing mother's, and Braggioni, who considers
himself a judge of women, speculates again on the puzzle of her
notorious virginity, and takes the liberty of speech which she permits
without a sign of modesty, indeed, without any sort of sign, which is
disconcerting.

"You think you are so cold, *gringita!* Wait and see. You will surprise yourself some day! May I be there to advise you!" He stretches
his eyelids at her, and his ill-humored cat's eyes waver in a separate
glance for the two points of light marking the opposite ends of a
smoothly drawn path between the swollen curve of her breasts. He is
not put off by that blue serge, nor by her resolutely fixed gaze. There
is all the time in the world. His cheeks are bellying with the wind of
song. "O girl with the dark eyes," he sings, and reconsiders. "But yours
are not dark. I can change all that. O girl with the green eyes, you
have stolen my heart away!" then his mind wanders to the song, and
Laura feels the weight of his attention being shifted elsewhere. Singing thus, he seems harmless, he is quite harmless, there is nothing to
do but sit patiently and say "No," when the moment comes. She
draws a full breath, and her mind wanders also, but not far. She dares
not wander too far.

Not for nothing has Braggioni taken pains to be a good revolutionist and a professional lover of humanity. He will never die of it. He
has the malice, the cleverness, the wickedness, the sharpness of wit,
the hardness of heart, stipulated for loving the world profitably. *He
will never die of it.* He will live to see himself kicked out from his

feeding trough by other hungry world-saviors. Traditionally he must sing in spite of his life which drives him to bloodshed, he tells Laura, for his father was a Tuscany peasant who drifted to Yucatan and married a Maya woman: a woman of race, an aristocrat. They gave him the love and knowledge of music, thus: and under the rip of his thumbnail, the strings of the instrument complain like exposed nerves.

Once he was called Delgadito by all the girls and married women who ran after him; he was so scrawny all his bones showed under his thin cotton clothing, and he could squeeze his emptiness to the very backbone with his two hands. He was a poet and the revolution was only a dream then; too many women loved him and sapped away his youth, and he could never find enough to eat anywhere, anywhere! Now he is a leader of men, crafty men who whisper in his ear, hungry men who wait for hours outside his office for a word with him, emaciated men with wild faces who waylay him at the street gate with a timid, "Comrade, let me tell you . . ." and they blow the foul breath from their empty stomachs in his face.

He is always sympathetic. He gives them handfuls of small coins from his own pocket, he promises them work, there will be demonstrations, they must join the unions and attend the meetings, above all they must be on the watch for spies. They are closer to him than his own brothers, without them he can do nothing—until tomorrow, comrade!

Until tomorrow. "They are stupid, they are lazy, they are treacherous, they would cut my throat for nothing," he says to Laura. He has good food and abundant drink, he hires an automobile and drives in the Paseo on Sunday morning, and enjoys plenty of sleep in a soft bed beside a wife who dares not disturb him; and he sits pampering his bones in easy billows of fat, singing to Laura, who knows and thinks these things about him. When he was fifteen, he tried to drown himself because he loved a girl, his first love, and she laughed at him. "A thousand women have paid for that," and his tight little mouth turns down at the corners. Now he perfumes his hair with Jockey Club, and confides to Laura: "One woman is really as good as another for me, in the dark. I prefer them all."

His wife organizes unions among the girls in the cigarette factories, and walks in picket lines, and even speaks at meetings in the evening. But she cannot be brought to acknowledge the benefits of true liberty. "I tell her I must have my freedom, net. She does not understand my point of view." Laura has heard this many times. Braggioni scratches the guitar and meditates. "She is an instinctively virtuous woman, pure gold, no doubt of that. If she were not, I should lock her up, and she knows it."

His wife, who works so hard for the good of the factory girls, employs part of her leisure lying on the floor weeping because there are so many women in the world, and only one husband for her, and she never knows where nor when to look for him. He told her: "Unless you can learn to cry when I am not here, I must go away for good." That day he went away and took a room at the Hotel Madrid.

It is this month of separation for the sake of higher principles that has been spoiled not only for Mrs. Braggioni, whose sense of reality is beyond criticism, but for Laura, who feels herself bogged in a nightmare. Tonight Laura envies Mrs. Braggioni, who is alone, and free to weep as much as she pleases about a concrete wrong. Laura has just come from a visit to the prison, and she is waiting for tomorrow with a bitter anxiety as if tomorrow may not come, but time may be caught immovably in this hour, with herself transfixed, Braggioni singing on forever, and Eugenio's body not yet discovered by the guard.

Braggioni says: "Are you going to sleep?" Almost before she can shake her head, he begins telling her about the May-day disturbances coming on in Morelia, for the Catholics hold a festival in honor of the Blessed Virgin, and the Socialists celebrate their martyrs on that day. "There will be two independent processions, starting from either end of town, and they will march until they meet, and the rest depends . . ." He asks her to oil and load his pistols. Standing up, he unbuckles his ammunition belt, and spreads it laden across her knees. Laura sits with the shells slipping through the cleaning cloth dipped in oil, and he says again he cannot understand why she works so hard for the revolutionary idea unless she loves some man who is in it. "Are you not in love with someone?" "No," says Laura. "And no one is in love with you?" "No." "Then it is your own fault. No woman need go begging. Why, what is the matter with you? The legless beggar woman in the Alameda has a perfectly faithful lover. Did you know that?"

Laura peers down the pistol barrel and says nothing, but a long, slow faintness rises and subsides in her; Braggioni curves his swollen fingers around the throat of the guitar and softly smothers the music out of it, and when she hears him again he seems to have forgotten her, and is speaking in the hypnotic voice he uses when talking in small rooms to a listening, close-gathered crowd. Some day this world, now seemingly so composed and eternal, to the edges of every sea shall be merely a tangle of gaping trenches, of crashing walls and broken bodies. Everything must be torn from its accustomed place where it has rotted for centuries, hurled skyward and distributed, cast down again clean as rain, without separate identity. Nothing shall survive that the stiffened hands of poverty have created for the rich and no one shall be left alive except the elect spirits destined to pro-create a new world cleansed of cruelty and injustice, ruled by benevolent anarchy: "Pistols are good, I love them, cannon are even better, but in the end I pin my faith to good dynamite," he concludes, and strokes the pistol lying in her hands. "Once I dreamed of destroying this city, in case it offered resistance to General Ortíz, but it fell into his hands like an overripe pear."

He is made restless by his own words, rises and stands waiting. Laura holds up the belt to him: "Put that on, and go kill somebody in Morelia, and you will be happier," she says softly. The presence of death in the room makes her bold. "Today, I found Eugenio going into a stupor. He refused to allow me to call the prison doctor. He had taken all the tablets I brought him yesterday. He said he took them because he was bored."

"He is a fool, and his death is his own business," says Braggioni, fastening his belt carefully.

"I told him if he had waited only a little while longer, you would have got him set free," says Laura. "He said he did not want to wait."

"He is a fool and we are well rid of him," says Braggioni, reaching for his hat.

He goes away. Laura knows his mood has changed, she will not see him any more for a while. He will send word when he needs her to go on errands into strange streets, to speak to the strange faces that will appear, like clay masks with the power of human speech, to mutter their thanks to Braggioni for his help. Now she is free, and she thinks, I must run while there is time. But she does not go.

Braggioni enters his own house where for a month his wife has spent many hours every night weeping and tangling her hair upon her pillow. She is weeping now, and she weeps more at the sight of him, the cause of all her sorrows. He looks about the room. Nothing is changed, the smells are good and familiar, he is well acquainted with the woman who comes toward him with no reproach except grief on her face. He says to her tenderly: "You are so good, please don't cry any more, you dear good creature." She says, "Are you tired, my angel? Sit here and I will wash your feet." She brings a bowl of water, and kneeling, unlaces his shoes, and when from her knees she raises her sad eyes under her blackened lids, he is sorry for everything, and bursts into tears. "Ah, yes, I am hungry, I am tired, let us eat something together," he says, between sobs. His wife leans her head on his arm and says, "Forgive me!" and this time he is refreshed by the solemn, endless rain of her tears.

Laura takes off her serge dress and puts on a white linen night-gown and goes to bed. She turns her head a little to one side, and lying still, reminds herself that it is time to sleep. Numbers tick in her brain like little clocks, soundless doors close of themselves around her. If you would sleep, you must not remember anything, the children will say tomorrow, good morning, my teacher, the poor prisoners who come every day bringing flowers to their jailor. 1-2-3-4-5—it is monstrous to confuse love with revolution, night with day, life with death —ah, Eugenio!

The tolling of the midnight bell is a signal, but what does it mean? Get up, Laura, and follow me: come out of your sleep, out of your bed, out of this strange house. What are you doing in this house? Without a word, without fear she rose and reached for Eugenio's hand, but he eluded her with a sharp, sly smile and drifted away. This is not all, you shall see—Murderer, he said, follow me, I will show you a new country, but it is far away and we must hurry. No, said Laura, not unless you take my hand, no; and she clung first to the stair rail, and then to the topmost branch of the Judas tree that bent down slowly and set her upon the earth, and then to the rocky ledge of a cliff, and then to the jagged wave of a sea that was not water but a desert of crumbling stone. Where are you taking me, she asked in wonder but without fear. To death, and it is a long way off, and we must hurry, said Eugenio. No, said Laura, not unless you take my hand. Then eat these flowers, poor prisoner, said Eugenio in a voice of pity, take and eat: and from the Judas tree he stripped the warm bleeding flowers, and held them to her lips. She saw that his hand was fleshless, a cluster of small white petrified branches, and his eye sockets were without light, but she ate the flowers greedily for they satisfied both hunger and thirst. Murderer! said Eugenio, and Cannibal! This is my body and my blood. Laura cried No! and at the sound of her own voice, she awoke trembling, and was afraid to sleep again.

JOHN DOS PASSOS   Why he selected

ESCAPE to the Proletariat

Picking a piece of your own work for purposes of exhibition is no easy matter. The pages in past books you remember so vividly as having turned out well have a way of going sour on you when you look them up again. Half the time you begin to feel unhappy before you've read ten lines. Maybe at first you skated along with proud enthusiasm over remembered excellences, but before you have gone very far you are sure to break through the slick surface into the quicksand of unfulfilled intentions that underlies every work of the imagination. You know you didn't succeed in doing what you were trying to do and the recollection of what you were attempting blocks out any satisfaction you might feel in that minimum of crowding reality you managed to get down on paper. I suppose it follows that the more of experience you were trying to encompass in the shortest possible space, the more chance you had of getting something halfway permanent down onto the printed page.

In this incident from *Adventures of a Young Man* I was particularly working to pack a great deal of undescribed background into one unbroken narrative. At that time I was particularly interested in the question of narrative pace. Narrative pace in a novel is, as I see it, the high tension wire upon which all the images and emotional pressures the writer wants to put over to the reader are transmitted.
Provincetown, Mass.   JOHN DOS PASSOS
May 30, 1942

TATTERS of cloud hurried across the sky that sagged low over the square. Glenn stood hesitating a moment on the box beside the small American flag. His breath caught in his windpipe as he looked out over the soggy caps and felt hats and heads of the street-meeting. The dark mass of people in overcoats, with a woman's dress making an occasional brighter patch, filled one corner of the square and thinned out along the curved asphalt path, where under the scrawny trees, men were slouched in rows on benches, or talking in knots, or walking hurriedly past. On the street beyond, cars and trucks moved in a shine of enamel and metal against the plateglass showwindows full of bright colors of cheap clothing stores, capped by biglettered signs that cut across the outlines of gawky old dingy-windowed buildings. He couldn't stand there like that. "I've come to tell you," he gasped out, "what I know about the great fight the underpaid Mexican workers are making against the sweatshop system in the state of Texas."

His voice rasped hollowly in his ears. They weren't looking at him. Youngsters and girls were chattering and giggling at the edge of the crowd. He had to make them laugh.

"When the pecanshellers complain that four cents an hour isn't a living wage the bosses say they don't need any more because they eat so many nuts." Several people laughed.

The caps and hats turned up now, he could see the white blur of faces, eyes were looking in his face. The crowd was all faces now. Glenn found himself picking out one face, a youngish ruddy face of a curlyhaired man who seemed to be going along with him, and talked straight at it. When he got to the part about the heroic fight the women and girls were making he told it all to a blackeyed Jewish girl in a green hat. He ended up with something about how nobody was going to help this poor and exploited foreign language group except their fellowworkers all over the country who must never forget that an injury to one was an injury to all. About half the people clapped when he stepped down.

It was beginning to drizzle. Glenn stood mopping his face while Irving Silverstone hurriedly announced a big meeting for the benefit of the pecanshellers' defence that night. A gust of sleety rain swept across the square and the crowd began to scatter. Walking away along the path littered with wet sheets of newspaper, past the searching stare of a brokennosed dick from the bombsquad, Irving took Glenn's arm and said it had been pretty good, but why on earth had he used that old I.W.W. slogan about an injury to one was an injury to all?

Wasn't it true, asked Glenn. Sure, said Irving, but it was bad tactics to remind the workers of the I.W.W., the I.W.W. was a thing of the past. Anarchosyndicalism was all washed up; and why hadn't he brought in something about John D. Rockefeller?

Glenn said, laughing, he couldn't see the connection and he didn't believe in personalities. It was the system that was wrong, wasn't it? It wasn't anybody's fault, was it? You had to put things concretely for the workers, muttered Irving.

Somebody was running after them through the driving rain calling Glenn, Glenn. It was Gladys, rosyfaced in a green raincoat. She threw herself into Glenn's arms and kissed him on the mouth. He'd been wonderful, Irving, hadn't he been wonderful? Here she was thinking Glenn had gotten to be a regular southern kukluxer and lyncher and she'd stopped to listen to the meeting and there he was talking to the workers. "Sure," said Irving patronizingly, "we can make a speaker out of him, if he'll only get over his petit-bourgeois ideology."

Then Irving said he had to go to a conference and, after telling Gladys to make sure that Glenn turned up at the meeting that night ready to speak for twenty minutes, he ran across the street dodging through the traffic and left the two of them standing there on the curb in the rain. "Let's go somewhere and talk. I want to talk to you about things," Gladys said in a businesslike tone. Glenn answered without looking at her, feeling his throat stiff. "Anywhere you say, Gladys. . . . Say, how's Boris?"

"Oh, he's fine. . . . No, he's terrible. Come along, I'm getting soaked."

They crossed the street and scampered acrosstown two blocks through crowded pavements, halfblinded by the rain as they hurried along with their heads lowered into the east wind, laughing and apologising when they bumped into people. "Boris is more of a social-fascist every day." Gladys spluttered out the words. "I'll tell you about it when we get inside. Let's go to the Royal and eat cheesecake."

It was warm and cigarsmoky inside the restaurant full of mittel-europa-looking people talking fast at round tables with stained white tablecloths. After they had ordered coffee and cheesecake of a gray elderly waiter Glenn sat at the table feeling his feet cold and wet, thinking of nothing, staring out in front of him without seeing any-

thing, while she went to the ladies' room to fix her hair that had been
sticking wet and spiky to her forehead and ears. She came back
looking tidy and smiling, her face glowing with the color in her lips
and cheeks and in the pink tip of an ear that showed where she had
combed her wavy short hair back over it. "Now tell me everything
you've been doing."

Glenn mumbled that there wasn't much to tell. His uncle had
gotten him a job in the bank down in Horton and he'd been fired for
acting as treasurer of the pecanworkers' defence committee, and as
soon as he'd hit town Irving had taken him in tow and made him go
to see Elmer Weeks, and Elmer Weeks had made him a big speech
about how he was the man to go down and organize the Mexican
workers, but Glenn had said he didn't know Spanish and he didn't
feel he had enough preparation. "But you've got the courage . . . you
know the system is rotten . . . all decentminded people agree with
you. What more do you want, Glenn?"

"I know, that's what Elmer Weeks said, but I couldn't make out
whether he was kidding himself or kidding me."

"He was telling the truth, Glenn," said Gladys, reaching over and
squeezing his hand that lay on the table beside his coffeecup. "Isn't
Comrade Weeks wonderful?"

Then she laughed and said, tossing her hair back, "I bet that
bank's failed already."

"The contradictions of capitalism are beginning to stick out like a
sore thumb," Glenn said. "But what's the matter with Boris?"

Boris was one of them, she said with a pout, she thought maybe
she ought to leave Boris for a while and give herself up to party work.
Glenn twisted his hand around and grabbed hers. The words were
out of his mouth before he knew it. "Come and live with me."

She didn't answer, but her eyes looked very big and dark. She
beckoned to the elderly waiter, who turned his facefull of sour disappointed wrinkles from one to the other, and ordered some more
coffee and cheesecake. The waiter was thinking of something else and
had to be told twice. Her voice trembled when she spoke. "I'll wager
he's a social democrat," she said after he'd gone. "I hate tired old jews."

Under the table Glenn felt her leg brush against his. He tried to
catch her foot with his feet but she pulled it back. Her eyes, so big and

so dark, were watching his lips. "Gosh, it would be the most wonderful luck," he said lamely.

Then he began talking his head off. What he was going to do was get a job in a mine or mill or something, he wanted to get plain hard laborer's work, live, eat, sleep like a worker. He was sick of this white-collar business. He hadn't any interest in the owning class, he was through with being a parlor pink. He was sick of it. It disgusted him. After this he was going to say what he thought and to hell with everything. "And what about the Party?" asked Gladys, reddening. Glenn clenched his fist and pounded on the table. He was going to join the Party as a worker and not as a whitecollar slave. When he was an honest to God worker he'd join the Party all right.

"I'm not a meeting," said Gladys. The little worried pout of her lips relaxed into a smile. "You talk just like I was a meeting." They both laughed and Glenn said, gosh, he'd better go and write his speech for tonight, why didn't she come and help him with it, he had a furnished room around the corner, he thought he could sneak her past the landlady. "I had things to do," said Gladys, "but I've forgotten what they were. . . . Oh, Glenn."

They walked, talking about politics in a brisk, businesslike way, the two blocks around to the tall brownstone house with pursedup windows and a blistered green door where Glenn had a furnished room. Inside, the hall was hot and smelt of stale cabbage and roach powder. They held their breath as they tiptoed up the creaky stairs to Glenn's hall bedroom. The room was dark and dense with the smell and hiss of steamheat. He closed the door gently behind them, shot the bolt and reached out his arms to her. She turned away from him, she seemed to be shivering. "Poor little girl," he whispered. Very gently he turned her head around until her lips were under his. She let him kiss her, and her arms tightened around his neck.

They raised a hundred and eight dollars at the meeting that night, although the hall was small. Afterwards, when they had gotten away from the others and were walking to the subway, Gladys said she'd have to go home to talk to Boris. Glenn asked hoarsely whether she thought he'd better go. No, she said, they were too good friends, it would be too great a strain on their comradeship. Boris would under-stand that she couldn't go on living with him and having him sneer at everything she believed in. Glenn made her feel strong like a real worker; it was terrible how scientists and engineers couldn't get over being the lackeys of capitalism. And poor Boris was such a sweet boy.

They took the East Side express together. Glenn held onto the strap with one hand; their arms were linked and she held on tight to his other hand as they lurched with the train closepacked in the crowd that pressed their two bodies together. "Gosh, we are going to be happy," Glenn whispered in her ear, "when we shake off our stiff old skins." "We'll go out to the country someplace and lie in the sun," she said in a little singsong voice. "And change our skins like snakes," he said, his lips touching her ear. "Oh, I'm scared of snakes." She giggled. "I don't believe in being scared of anything . . . especially not in the spring," said Glenn gravely. It was hard to talk above the clatter of the train.

Glenn went all the way to Brooklyn with her, though it was torture to sit beside her on the seat, after the crowd thinned away, with only their thighs touching and the edges of their hands, when all the time he wanted to have his arms around her. It was worse pacing up and down the empty draughty platform waiting for the train back to Manhattan after she'd given him a hurried peck on the chin and had run off up the steps.

When he went to bed he couldn't sleep. He was worrying about having only thirty dollars in his wallet, that meant he'd have to get a job mighty soon; and the bedbugs that the landlady had promised him only that morning she'd get rid of, had begun to come out and bite him; and he was racked with memories of Gladys, how Gladys' cheeks and Gladys' lips and Gladys' neck had felt under his lips, and the smell of her hair and the sound of her voice. At last he couldn't stand lying there any longer and dressed and went out.

The first gray of dawn gave a ghastly red flare to the streetlights. Garbage cans stood in groups between the unswept brownstone steps of old houses, with here and there a scrawnynecked cat scuttling out from between them. In the entrances of tenements the electric light shone wanly on tarnished rows of mailboxes. In the nightlife section on the West Side there was still a little stir; a few young drunks, a screaming girl in an eveningdress being helped into a taxicab, hackdrivers with their coatcollars turned up standing around outside of a busy bright whitetiled lunchroom in front of a row of freshpainted yellow cabs, shuffling panhandlers, and newsvendors flapping their arms over bundles of morning papers. Glenn walked around until it was day. Then he bought himself a cup of coffee and went back to the room and let himself drop on the bed with his overcoat on and went to sleep.

A knocking on his door woke him. He jumped to his feet. The landlady was standing at the foot of the bed grinning at him. She was a tiredlooking woman, with violet rings under sharp eyes in a face soft and wrinkled as a halfspent toy balloon, who wore her gray hair, dyed henna at the tips, in an oldfashioned pompadour. "Young lady to see yez," she said, squinting at him with her head on one side. "I says to her she's got to wait in the hall till you gits dressed and comes down. . . . Too bad, but I can't afford to allow no . . . no social life in my rooms, ye never kin tell where that sort of thing'll end. A house gits a bad name and first thing you know the vice squad comes around to shake you down for the protection."

"Yes, I understand," interrupted Glenn and closed the door on her to keep her gimlet eyes out of his face. He threw his things into a suitcase in a hurry and ran downstairs.

Gladys was sitting in the hall on the oak settee under the mirror with a little wicker suitcase beside her. She had been crying. He grabbed her and kissed her and said for God's sake they must get out of this town, they must have one day of living like human beings without feeling everything filthy and stinking around them. "That's what we're going to change, Glenn, all this dusty sordid life," she said in a funny coaxing tone, then she put her head on his shoulder and whispered, "Take me someplace, Glenn."

Fred Dyer had offered to lend Glenn his stone cottage up on the Delaware River for a weekend, so the first thing they did when they got their bags over to the Penn Station was to call him up. Glenn left Gladys sitting in the station reading while he went down on the subway to get the key from Fred at his office.

When he got back he ran breathless across the station. He was sure she'd be gone. But there she was sitting quietly where he'd left her. She was reading and eating a chocolatebar. She gave him a kiss that tasted of chocolate and said the station was the only place she'd ever found where she could read without people disturbing her. After this she was going to do all her reading in railroad stations. People on the benches around were beginning to stare at them, they were acting so excited, so they grabbed up their bags and hurried to the ticketoffice. A train was just leaving. When they clambered puffing into an almost empty daycoach, and felt the wheels begin to move under their feet, Glenn cried out, "Now I know I'm not dreaming."

They settled themselves and their bags and coats on two seats. "Did you tell Irving you'd come in for the meeting Saturday?" asked Gladys.

"I'll write him to wire Jed Farrington to come up. . . . He'd come up quick as a flash if we asked him to."

"Isn't he a degenerate?"

"That's all Irving's talk. He's an honest liberal lawyer who drinks too much. . . . He's a bright feller too." Gladys screwed up her face. "Sounds like a reformist politician trying to get ahead on the backs of the workers to me."

Her hands were in her lap in front of him, making a little wringing gesture as if they were moving without her knowing it. He put his hand over them and squeezed them tight. "Don't be unhappy, Gladys," he said. "Please don't. Don't think about anything except us. We're starting from the ground up, see. Nothing's ever happened to us before. We're going to come back from the farm and get us jobs and work our way up with the workers."

Glenn moved over from where he was sitting opposite to her and sat beside her. She put her arm around his waist and held him tight. He put his lips very close to her ear. "We've got to live real complete rounded lives. We ought to have kids. . . . God, I feel happy."

The train came out of the tunnel. Over the violet flats misty with smoking garbage dumps a thin spring sun shone pink over the girderwork of bridges, distant factory chimneys, silver oil tanks. They crossed a black river strung with rusty freighters with great patches of red on their hulls. Between rows of warped and smokegrimed wooden houses here and there a tree stood up in a pale flare of green. "Oh, there are flowers already," Gladys said. "Look at the yellow ones. I'm so glad I brought my painting things."

Glenn felt a chill go through him. "The first thing we want to do is live really human natural lives ourselves, before we start telling other people what to do." His voice sounded hollow in his ears. "Hell, that sounds cheesy, like the head of a boys' camp where I used to work, but you know what I mean." Gladys nodded quickly with her lips pressed together. He found himself stammering, "I've just led half a life . . . without anybody . . . you know what I mean. . . . Jesus, we need whole men at a time like this."

It cost them two dollars and a half for the taxi to go out to Fred Dyer's cottage, but it turned out to be a little stone house by a brook with a view of the river and daffodils in bloom in the grassy front yard. When they went in staggering under cartons of groceries with the longnosed taxidriver following them with their bags, Gladys shivered. "Oh, it's cold."

There was no wood chopped, so Glenn had to take off his coat and go after a pile of logs in the woodshed with an axe. He was awkward with the axe because it was a long time since he'd used one, but Gladys, who was standing around in the sun in front of the house with a blanket pulled over her shoulders on top of her overcoat, seemed to think he was wonderful to get the wood chopped at all.

It was only when he had the range started, and a roaring fire in the big fireplace in the old whiteplastered livingroom, that she'd come in out of the slanting afternoon sun. The air was already beginning to get chilly. She crouched shivering on the hearth with the blanket still around her and her damp shoes and stockings steaming beside her. He rubbed her feet to warm them. She couldn't seem to stop shivering.

When he made her some hot tea she felt better. By the time he had gotten ready their lunch of steak and boiled potatoes and fried onions, blue dusk was crowding in the windows. The room began to feel warm and cosy with the smell of the steak. There was no electric light and they'd forgotten to bring kerosene for the lamps so they had to eat by firelight.

Afterwards Glenn went out to bring in as much small wood as he could find in the dark while Gladys stacked the dishes and tidied things up. It was a clear chilly liquid spring night full of stars. Peepers and little frogs sounded like sleighbells from a pond down in the hollow somewhere. As he rummaged around in the dark woodshed he could see Gladys' slender little figure passing and repassing in front of the window lit pink by the firelight. When he came stumbling in the back door with his arms piled high she ran to him. "Oh, Glenn, I was getting scared; suppose there's a spook in the cottage." He let the wood drop with a thud in the woodbox. "That'll scare him away," he said, laughing.

There didn't seem to be a double bed in the house, so they got hold of two mattresses and laid them together in the middle of the floor in front of the fire. Rather solemnly they tucked in the sheets and spread the blankets. They sat side by side in front of the fire and gradually undressed. Suddenly Glenn pulled her to him and kissed her all over her face and neck. "Now we're not ashamed of anything, are we?" he whispered, very low. She jumped up. "There's nothing in life to be ashamed of except silly ideas and maybe bedbugs," she said oratorically. He laughed out, "You're right, by God, you're right." He stood up with his bare feet wide apart on the warm stones of the hearth and lifted her off the floor as he drew her to him.

In the morning Glenn was the first to wake up. He got up and after tucking the blanket carefully around the sleeping girl, pulled on his pants and shoes. Outside it was raining hard. A raw gust from the open window slapped him in the bare chest and arms. He built a fire in the range, put on coffee, and, taking off his shoes again so as not to wake her, made up the fire in the fireplace. The wood began to crackle. He couldn't help whistling as he worked around the stove after he'd washed himself all over at the kitchen pump. He cut some bread and put it on the hot stove to toast and started to sizzle some bacon in the skillet.

The rain stopped. Except for the roaring of the fire in the living room and in the range, the house was so quiet he could hear the drops drip off the eaves and the throaty gurgle of the little brook outside. A robin was whistling somewhere behind the house.

Beyond the stone wall he could see a hillside curve up vivid green with winter wheat. The smell of wet clay came in through the window and through it the smell of hot toast and coffee and frying bacon rose in streaks. "You're the only boy I ever knew who was the first up in the morning," came Gladys' voice. "It shows a very fine character." She was sitting up crosslegged on the mattress in front of the fire combing her hair.

After breakfast they put on rubbers and went out for a walk. Glenn

felt so good he couldn't keep his pace down and kept running ahead
of her, up muddy roads, past stone farms and fields full of last year's
stubble where they heard quail calling. He made her laugh by whistling bobwhite bobwhite at them and making them answer.

The sky cleared and the day became sunny and hot. They found a
little pool in the brook back of the house deep enough to take a dip in.
They dared each other to go in. The water was icy and they had to
run back to the house with their clothes bundled in their arms and
their shoes in their hands, to dry themselves in front of the fire. That
gave them a raging appetite for lunch so they ate up everything they
had in the house. After lunch they washed the dishes and swept the
floor and made up their bed, and then walked down to the village to
buy some groceries. On the way down Glenn began to talk about getting a job on a farm around there.

Next day he left Gladys painting watercolors and walked around to
several farms and asked if they needed a hired man. The farmers were
dutchmen mostly and seemed to think it was a great joke; no, they
never hired outsiders. Then he went down to the boxfactory he'd seen
behind the freightyard in the village. Nothing doing; they were laying
off hands every day. A couple of days later he went over to Bethlehem
on the train, and walked around to the employment office of one of
the steel companies. He'd no sooner gotten in the door than he caught
sight of a lettered sign on the bulletin board saying NO USE ASKING FOR
JOBS. THERE AREN'T ANY. THIS MEANS U.

After he'd bought some groceries and started up the hill with them
slung across his back in a canvas laundry bag he counted out his
money and found he had two dollars and sixtyeight cents, not enough
for their fare back to New York even if they'd wanted to go. Hell, he
told himself, tomorrow he'd have to wire Paul or Jed Farrington for
a loan. Gosh, Paul couldn't spare a cent he knew, he had two kids now
and Peggy had been sick. Jed seemed an openhanded guy, but you
never could tell. Boris would loan them the money soon enough, but
Christ, he couldn't ask him.

Glenn was tired and his shoes were caked with redbrown mud
when he got to the door of the stone house. He stopped to wipe his
shoes on the long grass around the big millstone that served for a doorstep and turned to look for a second at the yellow sunset laced with

slender salmoncolored bars of cloud behind the bulging purple and green hill of the wheatfield.

There were voices in the house. Somebody had come to see Gladys. Glenn opened the door and walked in and set his bag of groceries on the livingroom table. For a second he couldn't see who was there on account of the dusk and the dazzle of the sunset in his eyes. "Hello, Glenn," said Gladys in a stiff voice. "We need some more wood. We're freezing."

She was sitting on the mattress in front of the dying embers of the fire. Somebody was stretched out on the mattress with his head on her knees.

Glenn felt his whole body stiffen. He struck a match and lit the lamp on the table. "Boris has come for me . . . I'm going home with him. He's been very unhappy," Gladys was saying in a dreamy impersonalsounding tone of voice.

Glenn took a step towards them to put the lamp behind his back. Boris was stretched out with his eyes closed and his head on her lap. She was gently rubbing his temples with her fingers. "He's got a splitting headache. He's been working too hard," she said in the same low cooing tone as if she were talking to a child. "I'll go get some wood," Glenn said and walked out of doors.

As he chopped at the tough old pine boughs in the woodshed, he began not to tremble so. Walking back to the house, with his arms full of the resinsmelling wood, he found it was hard to keep his knees from knocking together. He went in by the kitchen door and stood looking at them.

He still had the axe in his hand. Gladys was sitting in the same place but Boris had gotten to his feet and stood with his back to Glenn whispering something to Gladys he couldn't catch.

Glenn felt his right hand tight round the axe handle. Boris' round skull with the curly hair cropped close on it was right in front of him. Glenn stood there feeling the sharp new axe heavy in his hand. Boris' big head looked fragile as a big egg on his small body. The axe was swinging a little in Glenn's hand.

Glenn found he was biting his lips. He turned sharp and put the axe outside the kitchen door. Then he went back into the livingroom without a word and began putting wood on the fire. Cold sweat had formed round the neck of his flannel shirt. When he'd gotten the fire going he turned and, standing on the hearth, with his hands that were still icy and trembling in his pockets, said in a controlled voice, "Hello, Boris, I thought you'd gone to Germany."

"I may go yet," said Boris, without moving a muscle of his face.

"Not without me," said Gladys with a hysterical titter. Boris ran his tongue over his lips. "You see she's done this before. . . . We might have known she'd get over it." Something warm and confiding came into his tone. "She's always gotten over it before in about a week."

Glenn cleared his throat. He was so relieved about the axe, he was thinking, he didn't give a damn about anything else. "Well, I guess it's up to me to butt out."

"Oh, it's beginning to rain. Isn't this weather horrid?" cried Gladys shrilly.

"Look," Glenn said, feeling the blood coming back into his arms and legs so that they felt less like wood, "you people take the key back to Fred Dyer when you're through with this little . . . this little lovenest."

"Yes, indeed," said Boris seriously. "I've got his address. That's how I found where Gladys was."

"Oh, but, Boris, I wrote you," whined Gladys.

"I had to know how to find the damn place. . . . As usual you didn't put any address on your letter, Gladdo, artistic temperament I guess."

"Be sure to lock everything up," said Glenn. "The axe is outside of the kitchen door. Don't leave it out in the rain."

Nobody said anything while Glenn walked back and forth across the room, collecting his things and stuffing them into his suitcase. Without looking at either one of them he put on his hat and overcoat, picked up his bag and left the house.

FRANK SULLIVAN Why he selected

 ## The JUKES FAMILY

"The Jukes Family" was written after I had been listening to a few samples of the soap opera, that depressing by-product of Marconi's creative efforts.

I was not in search of entertainment at the time. I was engaged in the rather morbid pastime of listening to radio commercials in order to find material for an article on the clichés of radio commercials. I got it all right.

After the commercial ended the soap opera would begin and I found myself listening with the same kind of paralyzed fascination that is said to grip a bird in the presence of a cobra.

They say that a large section of American womanhood listens daily to these messy, tear-stained, gushy, maudlin, sappy travesties on American home life. I cannot bring myself to believe that; I have too much respect for the intelligence of the American woman. If her I.Q. is really measured by the drool that gushes through the air in fifteen-minute spurts throughout the morning and afternoon, then God help the Republic.

The Jukes family portrayed in this burlesque is a typical specimen of the family portrayed in the average soap opera, except that if anything the Jukeses are more highly developed mentally, and much more charming.

Saratoga Springs, N. Y.   FRANK SULLIVAN
July 6, 1942

THE air is so cluttered with homely little radio programs recounting the daily heartaches and joys of a multitude of families—"The Green Family," "The Brown Family," "This Man's Family," "That Man's Family," and so on—that I have decided to climb on the band wagon with my own program, "The Jukes Family." It will recount, from day to day, the joys and sorrows of an average, homey, not-quite-bright family of the lower lower class.

The matriarch is Ma Jukes, a friendly old party of forty-five who has brought fifteen or twenty children into the world and has learned to take things as they come. She does the best she can to manage her unruly brood, each of whom has some characteristic that sets him or her apart from the herd. For instance, it has long been a subject of frank discussion in the family whether the ears on Laddie, the seventh boy, extend above the top of his head or whether the plateau of his head simply fails to rise to the top of his ears.

The fourth child, Slim, age twenty-two, has a penchant for bigamy which frequently brings upon him the good-natured raillery of the rest of the family. Another of the boys, Timmy, is doing a stretch in Sing Sing, and Mayzetta, the third girl, is in her sophomore year at the Dobbville Home for Delinquent Females. But the glamour girl of the Jukes Family is Babs—tall, striking, with dark, flashing eyes and a head of hair five and a half feet long. And every single strand of it a natural emerald green! Ma Jukes' family (she was a Cabot) all had hair of vivid yellow. Pa's folks' hair had been Alice blue. Nature's alchemy had combined the two colors happily in Babs.

Now then, as our first program opens, we find Ma Jukes setting a kettle of water to boil. A dozen or so of the youngsters, among them her first-born, Jeddie, a fine-looking chap of thirty with white hair and pink eyes, romp boisterously under her feet as she putters about the stove. There is a scuffle among the bairns. Ma intervenes.

"Monongahela!" she admonishes a strapping girl of about ten. "You give Jeddie back his doll. Ain't you ashamed to be playin' with dolls, a big gal like you. . . . Tarnation take it, git out from under my feet afore ye git scalded. Oh, it's you, Chub."

Chub is an attractive child of nineteen, always hanging around the stove because he *likes* to be scalded. Ma good-naturedly ladles a teaspoonful of hot water on him.

"Now, thar, that's enough. Git along an' quit pesterin' yer pore ole ma."

Chub scampers off with a happy scream of agony.

"I declar'," says Ma, philosophizing in the manner of all the Mas on the family radio programs, "I don't know what the younger generation's a-comin' to. When I was a young un we hung around our ma to git the scrapin's from the cake bowl, not to git hot water thrun on us. Now, whatever's a-keepin' yer pa?"

"I'm hongry," cries Eglantine Jukes, a comely sprite of fifteen without a chin.

Here the voice of Chuckles Gladsome, the announcer, is heard. Ma winces. In the cheery voice of the typical family-program announcer, Chuckles says that if little Eglantine is "hongry," she had just better get herself a good, big, heapin' ole dish of rich, creamy, juicy, delicious, nourishing Dwerps, the Sweetheart of Breakfast Foods. "So go to your corner grocery store tonight, or at the very latest tomorrow morning, etc., etc.," concludes Chuckles.

"I'm still hongry," says Eglantine.

"Well, yer pa oughta be here any minnit now with the chicken," says Ma. "Wonder what's a-keepin' him? Oh, here he is!"

Pa Jukes enters. He is a jovial soul who takes the responsibilities of a large family in his stride. His face, if you can call it a face, is unlined by the years, and its frank, open expression is enhanced rather than marred by an almost complete absence of chin.

"Howdy, Pa," says Ma. "Where's the chicken? You said you was a-goin' to snag us a chicken fer supper."

"Shucks, Ma, there ain't none," apologizes Pa. "Dad rat it, I was lucky I got out of Ole Man Eddy's hencoop 'thout gettin' a hideful o' buckshot."

Ma's face falls at this news, but only for an instant. She quickly hides her disappointment and presents a brave front to the children. All mothers on family programs are constantly presenting brave fronts in the face of domestic problems. "Tarnation take the ornery ole cuss!" she says. "Can't even leave a neighbor have a measly ole chicken. An' after the way we all pitched in an' helped, the night his barn took fire."

"Now, Ma," says Pa, "you know we wa'n't doin' no mor'n our plain duty in helpin' put that fire out. You know 's well 's I do, 'twas our Buster set that barn afire."

Buster is the firebug of the Jukes family, a gay, irresponsible Puck of thirteen with the typical Jukes no-chin, and regarded by the neighbors as quite a tease because of his habit of setting buildings afire every so often.

"Well," says Ma, "I kind o' had my face fixed fer chicken, but I guess we c'n manage. Here, Lump, you run down to Perkins' grocery and fetch up a few cans salmon an' any other vittles ye think might tech the spot."

"Not me," Lump says. "Jedge tole me ef I got caught swipin' any more stuff out'n stores, he'd send me to state's prison sure 'nough."

"That so, young Mister High-an'—Mighty!" snaps Pa Jukes. "Well, lemme tell you one thing, you young whippersnappers, ef state's prison's good enough fer yer brother Timmy, it's plenty good enough fer you."

"Now, Pa," says Ma, soothingly.

"Well, dad rat it, Ma, jest don't let him git so uppity, that's all. I don't know what's got into the younger generation lately. Why, there ain't a nicer crowd o' boys you'd want to meet than the boys at Sing Sing. Leastwise, 'twas so in my day thar."

"Pa, mebbe one o' the children that ain't never been pinched better go," advises Ma. "It'll look better."

There are shouts from the kiddies of "Me, Ma! Let me go! I wanna go, Ma."

At this point the door bursts open and in comes Wash Jukes, an attractive, coffee-colored lad of fourteen.

"Guess what, Ma!" Wash exults. "The jedge jes' pernounced me a ju-vile delinquent!"

Wash's brothers and sisters are agog with admiration and Ma glows with maternal pride, but Brother Lump is in the clutch of the green-eyed monster.

"Shucks!" says Lump. "I was a ju-vile delinquent when I was ten years old, wa'n't I, Ma?"

"Go on, po' white trash," sneers Wash.

"Wash Jukes!" Ma rebukes. "You lemme hear you call yer brother po' white trash again an' I'll slap ye down. Now git along to the store and fetch back some vittles." She sighs.

"What's wrong, Ma?" asks Pa.

"Pa, I'm a-worrit about Babs. I wa'n't fixin' to tell ye, because I didn't aim to fret ye none, but she ain't been hum now fer two days and two nights."

"Shucks, Ma, she prob'ly stopped off at some gal friend's house on her way hum from school."

"She hadn't oughta gone an' done it 'thout lettin' me know. I declar', I don't know what the younger generation's a-comin' to. When I was a gal Babs' age, ef I stayed away from hum fer moren't one night a-runnin', I got Hail Columbia from the matron."

"Don't ye fret none about Babs, Ma. She's just young an' full o' fun. Leave her have her fling. She'll be old soon enough."

"Mebbe yer right, Pa, but it seems to me the young uns don't pay no heed to their elders nowadays nohow. Mebbe I'm a-gettin' old-fashioned, but I kind o' like to know whar my children is o' nights. Say, that reminds me, I got a letter from Timmy today."

"Ye did? Then he's out o' solitary. They don't let ye write no letters when yer in solitary. Leastwise, they didn't in my day at Sing Sing. What's he say?"

"Tarnation take it, how do I know? That's why I'm a-waitin' for Babs to come hum, so's she can read it to me. Buster!"

"Yes, Ma?"

"Quit settin' fire to Chub!"

"But he ast me to set him afire, Ma," Buster says.

"Sure I did, Ma," says Chub.

"Makes no difference," says Ma, sternly. " 'Tain't good fer ye. Ye want to grow up all charred?"

"Yes," says Chub, eagerly.

"Well, I swan to glory, I don't know what the younger generation's a-comin' to. Pa, put out Chub, will ye?"

With a good-natured chuckle, Pa throws a pail of water over Chub just as Wash returns from his trip to Perkins' store. The hungry brood crowds around him eagerly.

"Any luck, Wash?" says Ma.

"Naw," says Wash. "Ole Perkins was a-watchin' me all the time. All I could git was this." He takes a ham from beneath his blouse.

"Well," says Ma, " 'tain't much, but it's somethin'."

"And this." Wash produces another package.

"A flitch o' bacon," says Ma. "Now, that's real nice." Ma's tone is cheery. She is presenting a brave front.

"And these," says Wash, and he unloads from various crannies of his person a quantity of canned goods, fresh vegetables, assorted table delicacies, a watermelon, and a case of soft drinks.

"That all ye got?" asks Ma, striving to keep the disappointment from her voice. "Well, ye done the best ye could. We'll manage somehow."

Now the door opens and who bursts in but Babs, her handsome eyes flashing and her green hair flying in the wind.

"Ma," cries Babs, "guess what!"

"Babs Jukes, whar you been?" says Ma, severely. "Go tidy up yer hair. Look at ye!"

"Ma!" cries Babs. "I got a job!"

Pa winces at the sound of the ugly three-letter word.

"Whar's the job?" Ma inquires, coldly, after a pause.

"In the circus! Lady Godiva!"

An artistic career! Well, that's different. Not quite to be classed as work. The alarm subsides, and the family is agog to hear about Babs' job.

"My sakes!" says Ma. "To think we got a real, gen-wine actress in the family!"

"Babs, c'n I have yer autograph?" asks little Monongahela.

Ma is thinking happily how she will come it over her neighbor up the alley, Mrs. Kallikak, who has been insufferable ever since her son got the hot squat for the axe murder of seven.

"Reason I ain't been hum," says Babs, "is I had to go to New York right away an' sign up. Guess they was afraid some other circus might grab me."

"I allus knew Babs'd go places," says Pa, with pride.

"Gee Whittaker, I'm tired," says Babs. "I set up on that train from New York the hull night."

"Set down, child," urges Ma. "I'll git ye a cup o' tea."

Babs sinks into a chair and the youngsters crowd around their distinguished sister, beseeching her for details of her new career and entreating her to get them jobs as freaks in the sideshow.

Suddenly, above the childish babble, there is heard a shriek, then a sinister crackling noise, and cries of alarm as the children scurry to safety.

"Buster! You quit that!" Ma shouts, as is her wont whenever she hears crackling, but it is too late. This time Buster's prank has succeeded all too well. By the time rescue measures have been taken, Babs' once-glorious mane is a smoldering ruin, naught of it remaining save a charred stubble.

Babs is inconsolable.

"Don't you fret none, dearie," Ma attempts to comfort her. "It'll grow in again in no time at all. Onct, when I had the type-ford fever ——"

But here the voice of Chuckles Gladsome interrupts Ma.

"Well, folks," says he, "all I can say is, if Babs Jukes wants that hair to grow again in time for her to join the circus, she had just better go tonight, or tomorrow morning at the very latest, to the nearest drugstore and get a bottle of Stickney's Famous Hair Restorer. Ladies, if your hair bothers you, if it is dull, dry, and hard to manage ——"

A shot rings out.

When the smoke clears, Ma Jukes is standing over poor Chuckles with Pa's shotgun in her right hand.

"Got him, by cracky!" she announces, with grim pleasure.

"Ma," Pa says. "Ye hadn't ought to o' gone an' done that. The law says 'tain't legal to shoot a buck announcer out o' season. Now ye've let ye'se'f in fer a good fine, and whar ye're a'gon' to raise the dough, I don't know."

Well, what will happen to Ma? Will any jury convict? Will any Fish and Game Commission slap a fine on her for shooting an announcer, in season or out? Is Ma on her way to the clink? And how about Babs' hair? Will it grow back in time for her to join the circus? Follow the adventures of that happy-go-lucky, madcap, lovable, charming, irresponsible bunch, the Jukes Family! Tune in on this station tomorrow afternoon at this same hour and find out what happened to Ma Jukes. Your announcer is Paul Parke, substituting for Chuckles Gladsome. Bi-ing ba-ang, bo-ong!

BOOTH TARKINGTON Why he

selected BRIDEWATER'S

HALF DOLLAR

There are few writers, and they are to be envied for their youth, who can be fond concerning works of their own construction already cold in print. Most of us prefer never if possible to be obliged to re-consider what is past recall; we do not relish the inevitable discovery of things that might have been otherwise, when it is too late to do much about it. Let the dead past bury its dead is our motto; though, being human, we can also feel a slightly fretful championage for whatever seems, unjustly, to be buried too deep.

Thus it is that readers should beware the anthology containing writings selected by the authors themselves, for such selections are only too likely to be things that "nobody else likes." Only the morbid reader, so to speak, will feel a genuine interest in such an anthology; but who shall say that the morbid reader is not, in essence, precisely the audience whom every writer, in his heart, hopes will attend?

In further extenuation of my choice of "Bridewater's Half Dollar" for reappearance here, I believe I should mention the fact that the only "fan letter" it evoked was from a gentleman who surprised me by extending his earnest congratulations upon my gallantry in defending dog poisoners, a class of people not so generally loved as they deserve to be, he maintained. It seems possible that this reprinting may find a reader who'd understand the tale in somewhat less completely inverse ratio to its intent.

Kennebunkport, Me.   BOOTH TARKINGTON
July 13, 1942

GEORGE BRIDEWATER looked upon a certain bench in Garfield Square as his own. The Square, a smoky screen parklet in the shabby, oldest part of the city, had a small central space of gravel about which were twelve benches, three on a side; and it was the middle bench on the north side, facing the sun, that Mr. Bridewater looked upon as his. The seven or eight other habitués respected his feeling, and, if a stranger loitered near, Bridewater yawned and extended both arms along the top of the bench, kept them there until the intruder either passed on or made another selection. He performed this manœuver, a little after five o'clock one afternoon of last May, to discourage an unknown saunterer whose appearance was that of a young workman out of a job; but, though he thus significantly stretched himself, Bridewater was interested in the conversation he was having with acquaintances upon other benches and didn't interrupt it.

"I'm fifty-four, Mr. Schleeman," he said, speaking loudly because he was addressing the seedy fat man who sat upon a bench across the graveled central space. "I'm fifty-four and I ain't never yet let no foreman work me to death. 'Who do you think I am?' I'd say. 'Don't get talky with me,' I'd say, 'or I'll put the heat on you! Give me my time and I'll go,' I'd say, 'but don't get talky!' I says just that the last job I had. It was in Nineteen Twenty-seven; and if they think they can take advantage of me now on account of the depression, make me work for nothin' and get talky with me, too, I'll show 'em!"

The loitering young workman sat down upon an unoccupied bench and addressed Mr. Bridewater. "I wouldn't," he said. "I wouldn't care how talky they got if they'd give me a job. Guess me and my family might all died if we hadn't got on Relief; but I sure am sick of bein' on it!"

Mr. Bridewater, Mr. Schleeman and the four other regulars present all looked at him coldly. They didn't mind listeners but disliked a talking stranger. This was the year 1935, and of course great public themes daily absorbed them, they were in accord upon the new politics, and, as views in opposition upset their nerves, they naturally didn't wish to hear any. An articulate stranger, therefore, was open to the suspicion of being a propagandist until he proved, by agreeing with them, that he wasn't.

"Listen!" Bridewater said. "You take Relief as long as you can get it. It's only the guvment givin' a man what's already his by rights. In this guvment one man's supposed to be as good as another, ain't he? Then it's logic he's entitled to as much as any other man is, ain't it? How do you get around that?"

"You can't!" Mr. Schleeman called across the open space. "One man's got the rights to the same as any other man; and it's a good thing for them politicians they're commencin' to see it, or we'd kick 'em all to hell out." He frowned. "What I don't like about this two-hundred-dollar-a-month plan, though, it's the sixty year clause. I don't begrudge anybody sixty years old from gettin' their money; but it ought to be widened at the base. Lots of people sixty years old's got better constitutions than some only fifty and fifty-five. It's too much regimentation, making it exackly sixty years old."

The other habitués looked at Mr. Schleeman respectfully; they admired him for language like "widened at the base" and "regimentation." Bridewater, however, ventured to take an argumentative tone. "No, no, Mr. Schleeman; that's a good plan. I only got six years to wait myself till I begin to draw the money; but to get right down to brass tacks, it's the other plan I favor the most. Five thousand dollars redistabution of wealth to everybody, paid down. Cold cash. That's what I say." He appealed to the others. "Five thousand dollars flat. Ain't that what you favor, gentlemen?"

On the next bench a gloomy man with a blade of grass waggling from his mouth shook his head, not in disagreement but in perplexity. "I ain't got the straight o' that yet, Mr. Bridewater. Are we all supposed to be going to get five thousand dollars—or is it three thousand?"

"Five."

"Well, then, is it five thousand dollars flat or five thousand dollars a year?"

"A year!" Bridewater exclaimed with emphasis. "They proved they can do it; proved it in cold figures over the radio."

"Who?" The young workman was skeptical. "Who proved they can give everybody five thousand dollars a year?"

"Who?" Mr. Bridewater gave him another cold look. "Don't you never listen to the radio? Ain't you read any litterchewer? The biggest men in this country's goin' to do it."

"How? How they goin' to do it?"

"How!" Bridewater exclaimed. "Why, by the redistabution of the wealth. All the guvment's got to do's put on taxes and take it away from everybody that's got over five thousand dollars a year and hand it to the rest of us that's got under that much. The guvment'll take all them stocks and bonds and highpriced cars and showoff jewelry from the wealthy and——"

"And pass 'em around?" the young man asked. "F'r instance, hand me a couple diamonds and part of a used limousine and some stock of a railroad that's in the red and——"

"No, sir!" Bridewater was irritated. "Any child knows the guvment can't do that and make a fair redistabution. What they'll do, they'll simply take all them things and sell 'em and then divide up the money fair and square, so that everybody all alike gets just exackly five——"

"Hold up!" the young man said. "Who they goin' to sell all them things *to*?"

"What?"

The disturber laughed harshly. "Who's goin' to buy 'em?"

Mr. Bridewater hadn't thought of this. Baffled, he stared in helpless annoyance at the young man; but Mr. Schleeman came to the rescue with a smile of pity for the questioner's ignorance. "Who's goin' to buy 'em? Why, Uncle Sam. The United States Guvment's goin' to buy 'em, that's who!"

"What with?" the young man asked derisively. "If the guvment's got the money to buy 'em, then it can already hand us out five thousand dollars a year right now without buyin' anything."

"What?"

"Why, certainly!" The intruder, once started, became disagreeably voluble. "On the other hand, if the guvment ain't got the money, why, it'd haf to buy all that stuff with paper currency. So if the paper currency's worth anything they could just as well hand *it* over to us, instead. So that proves this paper currency wouldn't be worth anything at all or else they'd do it. Besides, if the guvment could pay the rich for all their stocks and bonds and limousines and diamonds, then the rich'd have the money and be just as rich as they was before. How you goin' to get around that?"

"How?" Bridewater, flushed and frowning, made oratorical gestures. "Listen to me! Uncle Sam can do anything he wants to. He
can take the shirt right off your back if he wants to. He could lock
you up in jail this minute if he took the notion to. Uncle Sam'll simply take all that wealth and ——"

"Will he? Well, s'pose Uncle Sam does, what'll he do with it?
He can't sell it because there'd be nobody to buy it, and he can't
just hand around five thousand dollars a year for everybody because
he can't split diamonds and stocks and limousines up even; and they
wouldn't be worth anything much if they got split up. So listen here!
If any you guys got a good five cent cigar on you to trade, I'll sign
over my five thousand dollars a year to you right now, and I'll throw
in the two hundred dollars a month I'm goin' to get when I'm
sixty, just for extra; and then laugh in your face! Any takers?"

Pleased with himself, the talkative young workman burst into
loud laughter in which his hearers did not join. The gloomy man on
the bench next to Mr. Bridewater's began to murmur plaintively.

"I can't make nothin' of it," he said. "Sometimes it looks like a
man's goin' to get his rights in this world and then right away again
it don't. Take me now. I'm makin', say, an average of four to seven
dollars a week cuttin' grass, weedin' and so on. I got a second cousin,
Joe Entringer, never done a day's work in his life—nothin' but a
souse since the day he was weaned and got such a paunch on him
now he couldn't work if he wanted to. Yet he's foreman, settin' all
day on a stump with a bun on and smokin' cigars where they're raisin'
the levee up at Mill Creek. Eighty dollars a month! Does that look
right, with me only makin' twenty-eight, best I can do?"

"There's plenty worse off'n you," the man who shared the bench
with him responded. "On the other hand, look at the nice jobs floatin'
around if a man was only fixed to land one of 'em. Why, f'r instance,
I know a colored mulatto girl that gets twenty-five dollars a week,
guvment money—yes, sir, a cool hundred a month—just for handin'
out Relief. She's a high educated colored girl; but they'd ought to
hired some man with a family, instead. You know her, too, Mr. Bridewater—Ellamora Thompson that lives right across the street from your
house and always moves so kind of slow. Ain't it like I say?"

Mr. Bridewater did not reply. He was staring distastefully at the young workman and not listening. His mind was confused and he hadn't understood the interloper's argument; but he felt resentfully that here was an ominous force hostile to himself personally—somebody who wanted to deprive him of radiant prospects lately opened before him. "Listen here you!" he said, frowning heavily. "You sound like you're tryin' to argue in behalfs of them intanational Wall Street schemers. Their day's about over, let me tell you! My own dead father used to say over and over in his old age he hoped his chuldern'd never haf to work as hard as he had, and I never forgot it. What's the use a man's workin' himself to death and Wall Street gettin' all the money? The time's come for a turnover; we're goin' to get our rights and any man that comes around here arguin' against it——"

"Me?" The young man laughed ruefully. "I only wish them fairy stories was true!"

"Fairy stories!" Bridewater's voice was husky with anger. He rose and shook a lank forefinger at the young workman. "Listen here! You're the kind that wants to upset their own country just when it's gettin' straightened out the way it ought to be! Talkin' about fairy stories! You're the kind that wants to take bread out of the mouths of the poor! I bet you're paid for it! I bet you're hired by the banks to come around here and——"

"Paid? Hell, don't I wish I was, though!"

"I don't want no more truck with you!" Bridewater made a furiously obliterative gesture with his extended hand, turned abruptly and strode down a graveled path that led to Dellavan Avenue, the dismal west boundary of Garfield Square.

His shabby figure moved gauntly against the soiled gilt light of a sun edging its way downward into the western smoke of the sprawling city; and he muttered aloud as he walked. The mutterings were fragmentary; he conceived himself to be addressing the too talkative young workman. In more ways than one he called this creature a dog; he labeled him rodent also, and defied him. "Man to man now, just you try it! I been waitin' all my life for it, and now I got it and it's mine. Just you try get it away from me, you rat you!"

Naturally George Bridewater was in a state of rage. His always brittle temper, combined with his reverence for the hope so often expressed by his aged father, deceased, had led to long periods of moody idleness throughout his life. Now, at last virtual possessor of five thousand dollars a year, with two hundred dollars a month in prospect, all to be assured to him by Uncle Sam himself, he found upspringing dastards in his path, casting doubts that infuriated him because they frightened him. Talking about "fairy stories" and sneering at that bright income—when all the time millions and millions of people were going to help him get it, because they couldn't get theirs without seeing that he got his! Bridewater didn't care whether they got theirs or not, just so he got his.

"Sock in the jaw's what you need!" he said, as he crossed Dellavan Avenue. "Big Mouth!"

The house at the corner of Dellavan Avenue and Fourth Street added to his anger; he had always hated it without ever knowing anybody who lived in it. Opulently of the 'Seventies when the town was young, its white stone façade, its tall plate glass windows and its inside shutters of black walnut had been the front of high fortune and of "family"; but the twentieth century had long ago made the imposing house into an uncherished relic. Ill kept, dinged with years of soot, neighbored by lifeless "used car" salesrooms and a dead restaurant, it was now as apologetic as an old dress coat in a second-hand dealer's window. George Bridewater, annoyed in his youth by its early splendors, remained woodenly unaware of its slow complete change; his resentful mood still associated it with millionaires. Sheerly out of long habit he saw this pathetic house still enveloped in its same old air of bondholding superiority and exploiters' arrogance.

Therefore the lady who came forth from its front double doors of carved black walnut appeared arrogant to Bridewater, as he crossed the street. She was delicate-looking, pale, slender and elderly; but her little black hat, her brown shoes, her well-brushed tweed skirt and neat old brown cloth coat seemed to him offensively fashionable. What was worse and gave him a sense of being personally affronted, there capered and barked beside her, as she came down the stone steps, a long-haired little white dog obviously exclusive, high-toned and ill-disposed toward the common people. George Bridewater hated all dogs; but what he felt about this one can't respectably be even suggested. Horrid silver gleams came from its little collar; the preservation of its detested life was secured by a leather leash looped about the gloved wrist of its mistress.

Moreover, Bridewater knew this dog, both by sight and hearing, especially by hearing. His daughter's house, where he lived, faced upon Ackley Street, which was the next thoroughfare to Dellavan Avenue but unlike the Avenue had never been fashionable. The back yard of the hated mansion on Dellavan Avenue was separated by only a narrow alley from his daughter's back yard, and more than once George Bridewater's Sunday morning slumbers had been ruined by the egoistic barking of this little white dog, let out for air in the back yard of the pompous house.

The neat elderly lady and her noisy little pet, bound for a short airing in Garfield Square, came face to face with Bridewater at the corner of the crossing. "No, Rocket!" she said affectionately, as the dog made a short oblique dash toward Mr. Bridewater's left leg. Rocket, restrained by the leash, barked importantly at this moving leg; and his owner and the owner of the threatened limb exchanged a glance in passing—the briefest momentary gaze, but fateful.

Bridewater's eye was hard with old prejudice and with the new wrong being done him. This was not the first time he'd encountered the lady or been snapped at by Rocket. In them both he saw representatives of wealth, living in a wealthy house, luxurious aristocrats able to despise him because they had despoiled him. They'd better look out; he'd have his rights back from them before long!

The elderly lady's glance was a metallic one, too; she'd often noticed Bridewater about the neighborhood and disapproved of him, thinking him a surly loafer. She was a Miss Pency, a retired schoolteacher. She'd worked hard until she had passed sixty-five; and Bridewater was right in thinking her a bond-holder—invested savings brought her forty-two dollars a month. She and Rocket lived pretty sparsely in the struggling boarding-house that the grandiose mansion had long ago become.

Miss Pency lived there more sparsely than Rocket did. She had no relatives; her old friends, too, were all dead now, and except for him she was "alone in the world." She made every sacrifice for him and kept him happy. Failing sight no longer permitted her to read, and he was really more than the great thing in her life. She lived for him, and he, in return, though he was self-centered and conceited, loved only her—something no one else had ever done.

Rocket despised everybody in the world except Miss Pency and himself. As Bridewater, having given Miss Pency the one look, passed on his way, the little dog made plain in a final dart and snarl what he thought about that shabby leg. He believed he'd frightened off a marauder, and, barking with insufferable vanity, and looking all the way up to his mistress's face to reassure her of his protection, went on with her to the Square.

Bridewater, walking along dingy Fourth Street, toward Ackley Street, tasted gall. The unprovoked attack upon him by a high-living, costly, dangerous pet of the haughty rich woman who looked at him as if he were dirt burned in his heart with that other live coal, the young workman's argufying. Rocket's now distant, joyous barking epitomized into a sound all the forces that Bridewater had felt working against him throughout his life. "You! You!" that barking seemed to say. "You won't get it! Never! Not you!"

"I'd ought to kicked the liver out of him!" Bridewater said, pausing at the corner of Ackley and Fourth Streets; and, mentally conjoining Rocket and the young workman in the single pronoun, delivered the kick retrospectively to this hybrid. Then he saw upon the other side of the street a person with whom he wished to talk. He crossed over, dodging homeward-bound sedans, and approached her.

She was a comely young colored woman, sprightly in dress and much more expensively of the fashion than was Miss Pency, for instance. She sat, chewing gum absent-mindedly, upon the rather tumble-down front verandah of a small wooden house, and the verandah was so close to the street that Bridewater, halting upon the sidewalk before the house, could speak to her intimately and without raising his voice.

"Listen here, Ellamora," he said. "I been a good while tryin' to get a-hold of you for another little talk."

"That so?" Chewing her gum slowly, though at times allowing it to be visible, she seemed to feel a faint preoccupied interest in the passing sedans; none at all in Bridewater.

"Just like I told you the other day, Ellamora," he said, "you're gettin' a great big salary administrating Relief and I been a good family neighbor of yours a couple years now. Well, there must be some big money pass through your hands that the guvment's turning over to the people, so why oughtn't some of it to come my way just the same as it does to any other man that ain't got a job?" His voice, more than friendly, became insinuating. "You always been a nice good-lookin' girl, Ellamora. How about it?"

Ellamora turned her head to call into an open window behind her chair. "Gran'ma. You're allowing that skillet to remain exposed to the heated coals too long again. It causes the odor of scorching. Step on it, Gran'ma!" She looked forward again, over Bridewater's head, and seemed drowsily absorbed in her chewing-gum; but finally took cognizance of his question. "Well, no, Mr. Bridewater. I'm unable to see my way clear towards accommodating you like you been requesting me."

"Why not?" he asked urgently. "That guvment money all belongs to the people and ain't I ——"

"No," she said. "We don't favor the policies of handing out cash for the present time, Mr. Bridewater. I provide food and fuel exclusive only, and I'm already engaged with the total sum of one hundred and eleven families. I couldn't admit you inside this quota because I've made a ruling cases like you don't come under it."

"Why don't I?" She maddened him; but he contained himself, hoping to placate her. "Big Sam Lesloe told me yesterday him and his whole family been livin' on the guvment eight months now, and if you let Sam and his family in ——"

"No, I couldn't do it," Ellamora informed him languidly. "Mr. Lesloe and his family don't possess any property or any employment, so they come under the case; whereas you live with your daughter in a house owned in her name with an income from roomers. You're complete outside all our rulings and under the class of property owners."

"Listen!" Bridewater's voice was husky with his struggle to control it and still speak persuasively. "Them damn roomers owe their rent; they don't pay it. That house is mortgaged up to every cent it's worth and we ain't paid last October's taxes and don't never expect to. Big Sam Lesloe told me himself he turned down two jobs only last week because if he'd took 'em he'd had to get off guvment money. Listen here, Ellamora; if you let the Lesloes stay in and go on keepin' me out, ain't somebody liable to say it's because Lesloes is cousins of yours and I ain't? Big Sam's your cousin, ain't he?"

All he achieved was a further distention of his spleen. Ellamora looked at him sleepily, rose, yawned and turned toward the open doorway of the house. "I desire to lay down a while before supper, Gran'ma!" she called, as she went in. "Fix the sofa cushions for me. Step on it, Gran'ma!"

George Bridewater, in strong agitation upon the sidewalk, stared at the vacant verandah and uttered three words, two of them irreverent and the other hot with racial superiority.

It seemed to him that insult and outrage stalked him; that he was being used as a doormat by colored people, by rich women's dogs and by pseudo-workmen hired by the banks. He repeated the three words twice; then he turned and strode across the street to his own home, a wooden house somewhat larger than Ellamora Thompson's Grandma's but in greater disrepair. Half way across the street he encountered drifts of the smell of hot cabbage; the odor solidified as he penetrated farther into it, and, when he opened his front door, it filled his lungs, the orifices of his head and all the air spaces within his clothes.

His daughter, Effie Bridewater, met him in the narrow front hall. "I saw you across the street, Papa," she said, in an affectionate, tired voice. "Junior's home and I was just coming to call you. I got supper all ready now and I got a nice surprise for you, Papa."

"Surprise? Cabbage? You call that a——"

"No, we got cabbage soup; but you wait and see what else!" She took his hand and gazed up at him with a tender fondness. She was thirty but looked a driven and dried-up forty. "Come on, Papa. Junior's waiting for his supper."

She retained her father's hand until they had reached the hot little kitchen and sat down at the oilcloth-covered table, where her brother, Junior, had already helped himself to a plate of the cabbage soup. Junior, a thin boy of twenty-two with an unfortunate complexion, said nothing to either of them. He was always quiet at home, had no trade or profession but sometimes seemed to have a little money, which a girl in the next block always got away from him—something his father and sister had long ago learned they needn't hope to do. Once or twice a plainclothes man had come to the house inquiring about Junior when he was away, and sometimes Junior disappeared from home for as much as a month, but was stonily uncommunicative on his return.

He didn't get along well with his father, and, though he declined to argue with him, sometimes jeered at him a little. Junior was a Communist, and Bridewater hated all radicals, believed they were trying to ruin the country and might upset the great new plans for redistributing the wealth of the wealthy.

Effie didn't really care for Junior, either, though she supported him. All her life, for reasons lost in some fathomlessly obscure predilection of her infancy, her whole power to love had concentrated upon her father. To Effie her father was all that little Rocket was to Miss Pency, and, though Bridewater lacked Rocket's reciprocal intense devotion, the deepest feeling he had, except one, was for Effie.

"No, I ain't," he replied gruffly to an anxious question of hers, as he finished his soup. "I certainly ain't feelin' any too good this evening."

"You didn't eat anything disagreed with you this afternoon, Papa? A sangwich or anything?"

"How could I ate any sangwich without even a nickel on me?"

"Then what's the trouble, Papa?"

"Never you mind; I got enough! Where's this surprise you was talkin' so much about?"

"You'll see!" She removed the soup, brought fresh plates; then brightly set the surprise upon the table. "It's a steak, Papa! Just what you love the most. I thought for once we'd just splurge. Ain't it a dindy?"

His lowering brow lightened a little and he said he hoped so; but, when about half the steak had been placed upon his plate and he tested its quality, he made plain his disappointment. "Wha'd you pay for this steak?"

"Oh, my!" Effie cried, stricken. "They told me it was a tender one. Ain't it all right for your teeth, Papa?"

Bridewater clenched his fingers round the handle of his fork, stabbed the prongs heavily into the steak. "Might be all right for a dog's teeth," he said; and the thought of a dog made him sorer. "Leather!" He gave his slyly smiling son a hard glance. "Might be all right for them Russians' teeth, too. I hear they'll eat anything you care to give 'em."

Junior's eye showed a gleam of malicious mirth. "Say! You'd last about five minutes in Russia. Everybody's got to work there."

He put only a slight emphasis upon the word "got"; but the effect upon Bridewater was sufficient. "You shut your mouth!" he said. "I been all my life hopin' my chuldren wouldn't haf to work as hard as I have; but I never thought I'd bring a loafer into the world that'd try to upset the United States Guvment!"

"So it was you brought me into the world, was it?" Junior uttered a single harsh sound of laughter. "Glad I know who I got to thank for it. Done a lot for me since, too, haven't you?"

An impulse to violence swelled Bridewater's reddening neck. He seemed about to swing his long arm across the table; but Effie interposed hurriedly. "Here's fried potatoes, Papa. You always do love fried potatoes, dearie; and I got a dish of awful nice apple sauce for dessert, besides. I feel awful bad about the steak, Papa; but you eat all the fried potatoes because Junior and I can chew the steak all right and that's plenty for us. Won't you try to enjoy the fried potatoes and apple sauce, please, Papa?"

Bridewater, morose, made no vocal response; but ate all of the fried potatoes, almost all of the apple sauce and also drank two cups of a brownly transparent fluid Effie called coffee. Junior, rising, gave his father a brief, unbearable glance of amusement and departed; was heard ascending the creaky stairway in the hall, on his way to his own quarters in the attic. Effie washed the dishes, glancing now and then placatively at her father. He remained broodingly in his chair at the table, and sometimes his thoughts caused him to breathe so heavily that she heard the sound. When this happened she sighed deeply with a loving compassion, and, when she had finished the dishes, she sat down beside him and looked at him entreatingly.

"Papa, I got a feeling something's gone awful wrong with you to-day. Couldn't you tell me about it, dearie?"

"On top of everything else," he said, "think of my havin' a son like that! Sometimes I get so sick of——" He paused and looked toward the open window through which there came from the dusk beyond a repeated sharp little sound that seemed to sting him. "A man can't hear himself talk in his own house!"

"It's only that little white dog in the yard behind our alley," Effie said soothingly. "They always let him out now for a few minutes, and again about ten o'clock; but just for a little while. There; he's stopped. They've took him in the house again. Go on, Papa, tell me what you was goin' to. Won't you, dearie?"

"I'm sick of this life!" he said. "I ain't goin' to put up with it no longer. If it ain't goin' to change right from now on, I'm through!"

The desperation in his voice and in his face alarmed her. "Oh, Papa, don't say that! You don't mean you'd—you'd——"

"I mean just what I say, I can tell you! If things don't look like gettin' better right from now on, what I got to live for? I ain't goin' to put up with it, gettin' balked and flouted and high-hatted and bit at and walked on and treated like I ain't got a word to say in this world. I'm ready to quit, I tell you!"

"No, no, dearie; don't talk like this!" Effie implored him. "It's my fault. I'd ought to made sure that steak was going to be tender; I'd ought to paid a few cents more and got a better cut. I can't stand for you to feel so bad. I'd give you anything in the world, Papa, if I had it. I'd give my life's blood to have you feel happier. You know I would, don't you, dearie?"

"Would you?" He looked at her penetratingly. "You honest mean you would, Effie?"

"Of course I would. A thousand times!"

At that, his mood seemed to lighten a little; his frown relaxed and he gave her a kind look. "Listen, honey. For a good while back I been thinkin' over ways to make things better, and it's just begun to look to me like I've worked out a plan to where I could swing it. All I need's a little ready money. Less'n three hundred dollars would do it."

She looked frightened. "Would do what, Papa?"

"Would give me something to go on," he explained. "Money to live on. Honey, I'm so sick and tired of goin' around without a cent in my pocket—not a single solitary red penny!—I just can't stand it no longer, Effie. I don't ask much—just a few dollars in my pants, enough to feel like a human bein', anyhow, and get my shoes patched and buy a cigar or a sangwich if I wanted to, and take a 'bus ride somewheres maybe. A man can't go forever without even a nickel on him, honey!"

Her fright increased as she stared at him. "Papa, you don't mean the house, do you? You ain't talking about that again?"

"Yes, I am," he said; and now his tone became earnestly persuasive. "Honey, I got it all figured out, prackly to the dot. We ain't got long to wait for that redistabution of the wealth to be worked out. It'll be six years before I get my two hundred dollars a month; but the biggest men in the country are workin' every minute right now, fixin' to give everybody five thousand dollars a year; and it's just like wildfire. Nine-tenths of everybody you talk to's for it, and anybody in Congress or anywheres else that stands against it's goin' to get what's comin' to 'em! All I want's a little to go on while we're waitin' for the big money to begin comin' in. That's all I'm askin' you to do, Effie—just enough to tide me over till then."

"Oh, Papa, if I only had it! If I only ——"

"But you have!" he urged. "Anyways you could lay hands on it inside of a few days. I was down at them real estate men's, Smith and Angel's, this morning again; and they says yes, they still got this client that's buyin' up depression property and they're still willin' to take over the mortgage and on top of it pay you cash down two hundred and eighty-five dollars for your equity in this house."

"Papa!" she gasped. "I can't!"

"Yes, you can." He was increasingly urgent. "Wait till you see the beauty of it! The minute we don't own the house no longer, we go on Relief and get all our food and fuel. Ellamora Thompson as good as told me this evening she couldn't keep us off Relief if we didn't own the house. And we'd rent the house from Smith and Angel and go on livin' here just the same, but not pay only just part of the first month's rent, and after that, under this new law, Smith and Angel couldn't evict us out for over a year anyways. And all the time we'd have close on three hundred dollars to be spendin' any way we please, pure velvet! And by that time the redistabution plan'll be workin' and we'll be livin' a life *worth* livin' and ——"

"Oh, Papa dear!" Effie cried pleadingly, in sharpest distress. "I

can't! Don't ask me that. You know I told Mamma before she died
I'd always try to hold on to the house and keep our little family together. I haven't told you; but the roomers been payin' a little better
lately. I'm keepin' up the mortgage interest all right, and only this
afternoon I was down at the Treasurer's Office and paid off the taxes."

"What!" Bridewater shouted; and, electrified by a sudden anguish,
sprang to his feet. "The taxes? You paid 'em? You didn't!"

"Yes, I did."

Bridewater called loudly upon his Creator and began to pace the
floor. "Threw it away when you knew I was walkin' the streets without a nickel to my name! Yes, and just when we're goin' to sell the
house and them real estate men would had to pay the taxes and we
needn't ever even *thought* about 'em again! Threw it away just when
we could had that much more money to spend as we please and ——"

"But I *can't* sell the house!" Effie cried. "I can't! I can't! I just
can't!"

"Why not?"

Effie began to cry. "Papa, it was mostly for you I worked so hard
to buy it. Eight years workin' in that laundry to save the money and
always thinkin' I'd have a nice place for you and me to live anyhow,
no matter what else happened! Anyways, we got a roof over our heads
and we *mustn't* give it up, Papa. Don't push me to sell it, Papa; please
don't! Suppose this redistribution got stopped some way and didn't
come about and ——"

"Quit that talk!" he bellowed at her. "I had enough of that this
afternoon from a smart-aleck in Garfield Square and I won't hear not
another damn word against the United States Guvment doin' what
it's goin' to do, and got to do, and *better* do—else it'll get a revolution
and be *made* to do it! All I want to know now is just this. Are you
goin' to do like I say or aren't you?"

"Wait!" Effie ran into her small pantry, whence there issued, a
moment later, a thin sound of tinkling. She came out extending toward her father eagerly but with trembling fingers a silver half dollar.
"Take it, Papa. I know it's awful mean for you to go around without
anything at all on you. I been too close with you, I know; but I been
so terrible scared over the taxes and interest. It's fifty cents, Papa;
won't you take it?"

"Half a dollar!" With bitterest irony Bridewater faced his tragedy —denied close on three hundred dollars and offered fifty cents! His passionate open palm struck the coin from Effie's shaking fingers; it rolled upon the floor. "Half a dollar! Now by God I *am* through! Said you'd give your life's blood for me, and then go and fiddle me out half a dollar! Half a dollar!"

Effie began to sob aloud. "I would—I would give you my life's blood. You know I would!" She sank down in the chair he'd left vacant, put her arms upon the table and her head, face downward, upon her arms. "I can't let the house go, Papa! It seems like I hear Mamma always whispering me to keep it for you. I can't! I can't! I can't!"

"I'm through, I tell you" Bridewater shouted. "I don't haf to stand such a life and I won't! I'll do something! By God I will! I'll go crazy if I don't do something now!"

Effie, shaking all over and sobbing, could only protest babblingly, not lifting her head. To these incoherent sounds there came no other response than a brief scuffling of Bridewater's shoes upon the wooden floor. Then, while she still moaned to him entreatingly, the flimsy house felt the shock of the front door's being hurled shut with a crash. Bridewater had gone; but his daughter continued to sob upon her desolate arms.

After a while, still sniffling, she rose, took a dish cloth from a nail upon the wall and wiped the oilcloth of the table where her tears had trickled. "Oh, Papa dearie" she moaned, and, moaning, looked wetly about, searching the floor for the fallen half dollar. She couldn't find it, and, when she understood that he must have retrieved it and taken it with him, she was a little cheered for a time; but later had a thought that disquieted her. Once in her mind, that thought grew, did more than disquiet her; slowly became sinister.

At nine o'clock she went up to the attic, where her brother, still dressed, lay stretched upon his bed reading a pamphlet. She stood at the foot of the bed, trembling, her fingers twitching and her eyes staring.

"Junior, I'm scared about Papa!"

Junior looked at her amusedly over the top of his pamphlet. "What for? Is he goin' to commit suicide some more?"

"Junior, I'm scared! Will you help me go look for him?"

He didn't move. "Will you buy me a pack of cigarettes if I do?"

"Yes, I will, Junior. I'm scared."

"O.K." He smiled with one side of his mouth, congratulating himself on an easy bargain, and rolled himself lazily off the bed. "Bet you a quarter he's down at Abe Trissel's Place on First Street watchin' a pool game."

Effie didn't take the bet, though not because she knew she wouldn't be paid if she won it; she only asked him to hurry. On the street Junior objected to the pace she set. "What's the use breakin' your neck? He ain't goin' to do anything to himself, not that guy! What you pantin' like that for? He'll be settin' there all right; you'll see."

Junior was mistaken. Bridewater wasn't at Abe Trissel's Place and hadn't been there; nor was he at Johnny March's Café or at Frank's Bar, Junior's other suggestions. "Quit that pantin', can't you?" he said, as they came out of Frank's Bar. "There's one other place he hangs around sometimes; so that's where he *got* to be. It's Horling's out on West Eighth, quite a ways unless you want to get big-hearted and give us a trolley ride."

"No, no," she said. "We can walk it just as easy, and you say he's sure to be there anyways, Junior, so——"

He laughed bleakly. "O.K. Come on, then, if we got to hoof it."

Neither Bridewater nor any news of him was at Horling's; and, when they came out to the street, Effie was weeping as well as panting. Junior again complained of her emotion.

"But that's all the places he ever goes; you told me so!" she explained, defending herself. "You don't *know* the state he was in, Junior; you didn't hear him when he went out. You didn't——"

"Say, listen! I know the kind that do that; he ain't built that way."

"Maybe not most the time, Junior," she whimpered; "but he's different to-night. You didn't hear his voice when he said he was through and was goin' crazy if he didn't do something. You didn't——"

"Say! Listen, I'm tired. How's he goin' to do it, suppose even he tries to? He hasn't got a gun, and if he went over to the river he couldn't let himself stop swimmin', even if he did take a notion to jump in and wet himself. He hasn't got any money, so he couldn't go to a drug store and——"

"Oh, but he has!" Effie cried. "He's got money. I gave him fifty cents."

"Went haywire, did you?" Junior asked, sardonic. "Just throwin' your money around! Short life but a merry one, what? Tell me next time you get that way, will you? Come on; we got to hoof it all the way back home."

"No, no! I want to—I want to ask at the drug store if he—if he bought anything like that. Let's go to Hait's drug store."

"Hait's? Nopy," Junior said. "He can't go there because he talked 'em into givin' him credit last January. If he wanted to buy carbolic to drink his own health in, they prob'ly wouldn't sell it to him except some place where they know him, and Hait's is the only place they do."

"No, it isn't. Mr. Kleever, that used to have the bedroom over the kitchen, clerks at Brown's Cash Drug Store, corner Ackley and Sixth, and he knows Papa. We got to go there, Junior."

Junior consented. "It's on the way home anyhow," he said; and presently was again objecting to the speed at which she kept him scurrying through the long, darkling streets. But when finally they reached the place they sought, she faltered outside the lighted doorway, and with twisting fingers clutched her brother's sleeve.

"You ask Mr. Kleever. I'm—I'm too scared to. You just ask him if Papa's been there, and, if he has, you—you ask Mr. Kleever if he bought anything. I'm scared. I'll wait here, Junior."

Junior grinned at her. "Goofy, huh? O.K., I'll ask him." He slouched into the drug store; but Effie didn't watch him through either the doorway or the broad bright window beside it. Instead, she stood with her back to these areas of light, faced the melancholy street and twisted her fingers. When Junior came out he was smoking another of the cigarettes she'd bought for him at Abe Trissel's. "Come on," he said, taking her arm. "No place else to go; me for home. It's only a couple blocks. Come on."

She came with him slowly, and her voice was weak when she contrived to use it. "Junior, you—you never took a-hold of my arm before. Did—did they say——"

"Walk on," he said. "I told you he wouldn't do it, and they haven't got me believin' so yet."

"Yet? Then they—then they did——"

"Don't get so excited!" Junior's voice was a little unsteady. "If he was goin' to do it, why wouldn't he done it soon's he got outside the store? Had the stuff in his hand, so why not?"

Effie uttered a gulping outcry. "Then he did——"

"Yep. Kleever says he come in the drug store about half past nine. Told Kleever he wanted strychnine pills for his heart, and Kleever sold 'em to him. I give a laugh and asked if they'd do him any harm; and Kleever said no, not unless he took about half of 'em all at once. Says then it might be pretty bad; but says the old man knew all about that himself. Here! What you——"

Effie cried out again. *"Papa!"* and began to run.

Junior ran with her. Side by side they reached the gate in the picket fence that was the decrepit barrier between their home and the public sidewalk. "Look in the yard," Junior said, panting now himself. "Look in the yard. If I was goin' to do anything like that I'd do it in the yard, not in the house—most likely the back yard. He *might* be out here—somewheres."

The yard was small, mangily patched with grass, here and there, and without trees. The light from street lamps showed no form extended upon the forepart of this limited, unlovely expanse; and the brother and sister passed round the house to the thicker darkness that was in the rear. Effie, convulsive all over, clutched at her throat and shoulders, shut her eyes and ceased to go forward.

"You'll—you'll haf to do the looking," she sobbed. "But you tell me if——"

She could say no more, stood praying within herself; then she heard a sickish laugh from Junior.

"Come here," he said; and, when she stumblingly had come beside him, he pointed to the unshuttered kitchen window. "Look a-yonder!"

The saving Effie had turned out the electric bulb in the kitchen before she left the house; but the warm little room was lighted now. In the sufficient illumination from above his head, Bridewater sat tilted back in a chair and had his shoeless feet on the table. He smoked a five cent cigar and read a magazine of Hollywood full of alluring pictures of ladies. His expression was placid. After all the arguments and insults and barkings he'd had to bear, this hard day, he seemed at peace.

Outside in the darkness Effie clung feebly to Junior. "Poor Papa!" she said, sobbing no longer but weeping gently in thankfulness. "He never told me his heart give him any trouble. I won't be so close with him after this. I got to find ways to make him happier."

George Bridewater had already found one way to make himself happier. That is to say, he just now felt comparatively satisfied, and, in a measure, avenged upon the wealthy—at least temporarily. He had saved his reason by doing that something he had declared he must do or go crazy.

Effie's ninety-nine cent clock on the wall behind him showed the time to be about twenty minutes of eleven; and at ten o'clock there had been the usual sprightly barking in the yard beyond the alley. The sound had stopped abruptly when the scampering Rocket came upon a bit of toughish steak near the alley fence. Thence onward he was quiet. Nevermore would that gay spirit disturb honest neighbors at bedtime or break the peace of a Sabbath morning.

Now, through the darkness of the yard of the pompous Dellavan Avenue mansion there groped a broken-hearted old schoolteacher, stifling her faint outcries to whisper bits of loving baby-talk. She walked stoopingly, holding her dead little white dog close to her under a shawl. Miss Pency hoped to evade the landlady and to get up to her own meager room unseen, so that she could have this one last night with Rocket.

V

THE DUST WHICH IS GOD

EDNA ST. VINCENT MILLAY

FIFTEEN SONNETS

Another rereading of work by this poet, that has for many years sustained rereading many times, has led me to the belief that in this particular collection it would be best to represent her by the finest of her. sonnets, and leave the culling of her lyrics for a later day. It is hard to sacrifice such poems from *Second April*, one of the most beautiful of her books (first published over twenty years ago), as "Elegy Before Death," "Weeds," "The Poet and His Book," and "Exiled." In these lyrics, as elsewhere throughout her career, there are immortal lines, as well as an extraordinary—and inspired—faithfulness of natural observation. The last line of "Weeds"—"The Blood too bright, the brow accurst"—is as amazing as any line to be found among the Elizabethans. In another vein, her need for the ocean off the coast of Maine, as expressed in "Exiled," in its second through its sixth verses, as perfectly conveys everything noted by the senses in a particular scene as any poem we have in the language. Among the sonnets I have chosen, Number XXXVI is another example of this god-given precision of language applied to a scene remembered.

The limitations of the reviewers of Miss Millay's poetry in the sonnet form have spoken for themselves. The fact is that she remains today the greatest living master of the sonnet in the English language. It may be a form that future poetry will discard or expand into something unrecognizable. She has accepted its convention, in the main, though she has also experimented with final heptameter lines and with sonnets in tetrameter. Accepting that convention, she has filled the form again and again with new force and fire, with great wit, emotion, and a marvelous dexterity of art that conceals art. Her work has sometimes been assailed as a nostalgic for the classical and mediaeval, traditional in phraseology, unmodern in idiom. A characteristic love of the tapestry of legend will be found in the sonnet "Women have loved before as I love now—," which however refers directly to the living present. One of the greatest of her sonnets introduces again the much-used myth of Endymion, but in a new and passionately actual instance. Being an artist and a lover of beauty she has never desired to destroy the art of the past, like the modern vandal. She has but turned it to her own great uses. She has lived vividly in the present world, as must be amply apparent to anyone with intelligence, and in the realm of the imagination she is fitted to discourse with the deathless dead.

New York, N. Y.   WILLIAM ROSE BENÉT
August, 1942

I SHALL forget you presently, my dear,
    So make the most of this, your little day,
Your little month, your little half a year,
Ere I forget, or die, or move away,
And we are done forever; by and by
I shall forget you, as I said, but now,
If you entreat me with your loveliest lie
I will protest you with my favourite vow.
I would indeed that love were longer-lived,
And oaths were not so brittle as they are,
But so it is, and nature has contrived
To struggle on without a break thus far,—
Whether or not we find what we are seeking
Is idle, biologically speaking.

CHERISH you then the hope I shall forget
    At length, my lord, Pieria?—put away
For your so passing sake, this mouth of clay,
These mortal bones against my body set,
For all the puny fever and frail sweat
Of human love,—renounce for these, I say,
The Singing Mountain's memory, and betray

The silent lyre that hangs upon me yet?
Ah, but indeed, some day shall you awake,
Rather, from dreams of me, that at your side
So many nights, a lover and a bride,
But stern in my soul's chastity, have lain,
To walk the world forever for my sake,
And in each chamber find me gone again!

PITY me not because the light of day
    At close of day no longer walks the sky;
Pity me not for beauties passed away
From field and thicket as the year goes by;
Pity me not the waning of the moon,
Nor that the ebbing tide goes out to sea,
Nor that a man's desire is hushed so soon,
And you no longer look with love on me.
This have I known always: Love is no more
Than the wide blossom which the wind assails,
Than the great tide that treads the shifting shore,
Strewing fresh wreckage gathered in the gales:
Pity me that the heart is slow to learn
What the swift mind beholds at every turn.

WHAT lips my lips have kissed, and where, and why,
    I have forgotten, and what arms have lain
Under my head till morning; but the rain
Is full of ghosts tonight, that tap and sigh
Upon the glass and listen for reply,
And in my heart there stirs a quiet pain
For unremembered lads that not again
Will turn to me at midnight with a cry.
Thus in the winter stands the lonely tree,
Nor knows what birds have vanished one by one,

Yet knows its boughs more silent than before:
I cannot say what loves have come and gone,
I only know that summer sang in me
A little while, that in me sings no more.

EUCLID alone has looked on Beauty bare.
   Let all who prate of Beauty hold their peace,
And lay them prone upon the earth and cease
To ponder on themselves, the while they stare
At nothing, intricately drawn nowhere
In shapes of shifting lineage; let geese
Gabble and hiss, but heroes seek release
From dusty bondage into luminous air.
O blinding hour, O holy, terrible day,
When first the shaft into his vision shone
Of light anatomized! Euclid alone
Has looked on Beauty bare. Fortunate they
Who, though once only and then but far away,
Have heard her massive sandal set on stone.

NOT that it matters, not that my heart's cry
   Is potent to deflect our common doom,
Or bind to truce in this ambiguous room
The planets of the atom as they ply;
But only to record that you and I,
Like thieves that scratch the jewels from a tomb,
Have gathered delicate love in hardy bloom
Close under Chaos—I rise to testify.
This is my testament: that we are taken;
Our colours are as clouds before the wind;
Yet for a moment stood the foe forsaken,
Eyeing Love's favour to our helmet pinned;
Death is our master,—but his seat is shaken;
He rides victorious,—but his ranks are thinned.

ON HEARING A SYMPHONY OF BEETHOVEN

SWEET sounds, oh, beautiful music, do not cease!
　　Reject me not into the world again.
With you alone is excellence and peace,
Mankind made plausible, his purpose plain.
Enchanted in your air benign and shrewd,
With limbs a-sprawl and empty faces pale,
The spiteful and the stingy and the rude
Sleep like the scullions in the fairy-tale.
This moment is the best the world can give:
The tranquil blossom on the tortured stem.
Reject me not, sweet sounds! oh, let me live,
Till Doom espy my towers and scatter them.
A city spell-bound under the aging sun,
Music my rampart, and my only one.

WOMEN have loved before as I love now;
　　At least, in lively chronicles of the past—
Of Irish waters by a Cornish prow
Or Trojan waters by a Spartan mast
Much to their cost invaded—here and there,
Hunting the amorous line, skimming the rest,
I find some woman bearing as I bear
Love like a burning city in the breast.
I think however that of all alive
I only in such utter, ancient way
Do suffer love; in me alone survive
The unregenerate passions of a day
When treacherous queens, with death upon the tread,
Heedless and wilful, took their knights to bed.

MOON, that against the lintel of the west
   Your forehead lean until the gate be swung,
Longing to leave the world and be at rest,
Being worn with faring and no longer young,
Do you recall at all the Carian hill
Where worn with loving, loving late you lay,
Halting the sun because you lingered still,
While wondering candles lit the Carian day?
Ah, if indeed this memory to your mind
Recall some sweet employment, pity me,
That with the dawn must leave my love behind,
That even now the dawn's dim herald see!
I charge you, goddess, in the name of one
You loved as well: endure, hold off the sun.

LOVE is not all: it is not meat nor drink
   Nor slumber nor a roof against the rain;
Nor yet a floating spar to men that sink
And rise and sink and rise and sink again;
Love can not fill the thickened lung with breath,
Nor clean the blood, nor set the fractured bone;
Yet many a man is making friends with death
Even as I speak, for lack of love alone.
It well may be that in a difficult hour,
Pinned down by pain and moaning for release,
Or nagged by want past resolution's power,
I might be driven to sell your love for peace,
Or trade the memory of this night for food.
It well may be. I do not think I would.

HEARING your words, and not a word among them
   Tuned to my liking, on a salty day
When inland woods were pushed by winds that flung them
Hissing to leeward like a ton of spray,

I thought how off Matinicus the tide
Came pounding in, came running through the Gut,
While from the Rock the warning whistle cried,
And children whimpered, and the doors blew shut;
There in the autumn when the men go forth,
With slapping skirts the island women stand
In gardens stripped and scattered, peering north,
With dahlia tubers dripping from the hand:
The wind of their endurance, driving south,
Flattened your words against your speaking mouth.

EVEN in the moment of our earliest kiss,
     When sighed the straitened bud into the flower,
Sat the dry seed of most unwelcome this;
And that I knew, though not the day and hour.
Too season-wise am I, being country-bred,
To tilt at autumn or defy the frost:
Snuffing the chill even as my fathers did,
I say with them, "What's out tonight is lost."
I only hoped, with the mild hope of all
Who watch the leaf take shape upon the tree,
A fairer summer and a later fall
Than in these parts a man is apt to see,
And sunny clusters ripened for the wine:
I tell you this across the blackened vine.

OH, SLEEP forever in the Latmian cave,
     Mortal Endymion, darling of the Moon!
Her silver garments by the senseless wave
Shouldered and dropped and on the shingle strewn,
Her fluttering hand against her forehead pressed,
Her scattered looks that trouble all the sky,
Her rapid footsteps running down the west—

Of all her altered state, oblivious lie!
Whom earthen you, by deathless lips adored,
Wild-eyed and stammering to the grasses thrust,
And deep into her crystal body poured
The hot and sorrowful sweetness of the dust:
Whereof she wanders mad, being all unfit
For mortal love, that might not die of it.

THE SECOND OF TWO SONNETS IN MEMORY OF
SACCO AND VANZETTI

WHERE can the heart be hidden in the ground
    And be at peace, and be at peace forever,
Under the world, untroubled by the sound
Of mortal tears, that cease from pouring never?
Well for the heart, by stern compassion harried,
If death be deeper than the churchmen say,—
Gone from this world indeed what's graveward carried,
And laid to rest indeed what's laid away.
Anguish enough while yet the indignant breather
Have blood to spurt upon the oppressor's hand;
Who would eternal be, and hang in ether
A stuffless ghost above his struggling land,
Retching in vain to render up the groan
That is not there, being aching dust's alone?

ONLY the diamond and the diamond's dust
    Can render up the diamond unto Man;
One and invulnerable as it began
Had it endured, but for the treacherous thrust
That laid its hard heart open, as it must,
And ground it down and fitted it to span
A turbaned brow or fret an ivory fan,
Lopped of its stature, pared of its proper crust.

So Man, by all the wheels of heaven unscored,
Man, the stout ego, the exuberant mind
No edge could cleave, no acid could consume,—
Being split along the vein by his own kind,
Gives over, rolls upon the palm abhorred,
Is set in brass on the swart thumb of Doom.

WILLIAM ROSE BENÉT Why he

selected From THE DUST WHICH

IS GOD

What follows are excerpts from a novel in verse founded for the most part upon the author's own life, but with many episodes invented and only true in spirit to what actually happened. To a certain extent *The Dust Which Is God* is a *roman à clef*. The character of Sylvia Chantry is modelled upon the late poet and novelist, Elinor Wylie, though the circumstances of Sylvia's life are her own, and for the most part invented. The first extract here, "Souvenirs of Sylvia," is from pages 400-402 in *The Dust Which Is God*, in the section entitled "Cupid Is a Casuist." In it the protagonist of the story, Raymond Fernandez, is imagined remembering his wife after her death. The extract, "Naphthalene River," is from the section of that name, pages 417-420 in the book, in which Raymond is engaged in drinking at a real, but thinly-disguised bistro on 52nd Street, New York City. The third extract, "The Galilean," is from an attempt in a section called "The Avatars" (of which these are pages 473-475) to assess the weight of influence of modern ideologies, and return, incidentally, to "the forgotten man."

Like the writer, Raymond has been imagined as of partly Spanish and Minorcan ancestry. *The Dust Which Is God* is the story of a life seen as a spiritual as well as a carnal adventure. The medium used is a foundation of modernized blank verse both rhymed and unrhymed, and interspersed with lyrical movements. Its background is the Twentieth Century in its first forty-two years.

New York, N. Y. WILLIAM ROSE BENÉT
July 31, 1942

SOUVENIRS OF SYLVIA

WE WILL look at the local views
 artistically reproduced
in sepia collotype
and say   that was the manor with its cows
under the oak abrowse
and say   that was the bridge across the brook
the thick and furry trees   and look
those were the forest ponies on the lawn
there was the Pound Farm Pond
with the summer road beyond
the school wood and the Cross
the bicycle leaned against the little shop
England her England   dark with tobacco tins
and ashplants   or next take up the neat
card-map that shows curving New Compton Street
Step through Church Passage   Are you at a loss?
The second restaurant from Charing Cross
near Palace Theatre   Shaftesbury Avenue
"Italian catering to perfection"
Of myriad memories these two
"The bearer is accompanied by his wife. . ."
Tony sends out for wine
"This passport good for travel
this visa valid for faery lands forlorn. . ."
Bliss beyond care or cavil
Chianti in the cup and honey in the horn
So what is your predilection
now that so perfectly we dine?
Thrust back with nervous hands the waves of hair
that hide the small pale ears and frame your face
Tense your boyish shoulders with the grace
of something alert and wild
lift perfect throat and chin
and stare with eyes of a child

that turn bleak hawklike   being but blind
to ordinary walls   seeing within the mind
lozenges of harlequin
designs all silverpoint and pearl
or ice flowers or flower forms of words
lustrously clustered. . .
while the sleek man of the City over there
mutters above his beef and mustard
some "Ha!" joke to the equine woman in the other chair. . .

the Pont Royale is gleaming in the rain
the bookstalls are shuttered on the Seine
the aproned garçon piles the saucers high
breakneck taxis slither by
like musical valkyrie crying
Our cigarettes are withering to embers
crushed in a dish   like bright confetti flying
all about us in a private storm
the thoughts   fond dreams that keep us warm
and fugitive delights the flesh remembers. . .
voices   faces   bright or sorrowful places
grimace of Furies   garlands of the Graces. . .
The glassy flickering cell
of the lift in its shaft from the lobby of the hotel
rises to floors above. . .
quatrième étage   we are alone with love
in our strange large room   the taxis still are crying
far off and faint   the night is flaring and dying
to dream   to deep darkness   to heavenly wells. . .

and sunlight is a warrior in the room
and there is a maddening carillon of bells. . .

NAPHTHALENE RIVER

HE FELT so swell he'd just drop in at Tony's
and have one modest Daiquiri   or a brandy
before going to dinner   it was dull

eating alone at some small restaurant
and people were amusing at a bar
or into Behr and Bull's *Club Cavalier*
to view the new snobocracy and see
the many funny signs above the bottles
and in the "johnny" Tod de Tocqueville's murals
Watteau girls   chamber-pots   and What-ho men
indelicate delicacy   for his style
was brilliant   Old black Cyrus brushed you off
"Yes *suh!*"   a brandy and soda   and another. . .
most girls make up so badly   and the men
have nothing much but money   Charley Copley
with the red-blonde over there   He's getting fat
but funny still   Voluminous Redwood Roome
smile and "Hiya!"   the only columnist
with absolute independence   talking talking
in his slow drawl   and there's Beau Brummagem
chronicler of café society
so dear to the celebrity-hounds and slick
restaurateurs with their fantastic prices—
Tory of Tories   connoisseur of wines
eyelids a little weary . . .
                         Eurydice
out of the Subway!   fleeing from her shepherd
trod on a snake in the grass   and through the cave
of Taenarus to the Tartarian realm
came limping   with a hound   but not three-headed
One is enough   with a crew cut   and he ordered
straight rye   Daintily hesitating she
made hers a Clover Club
                         Mirabel Carter
(the Mink to friends) with desolating eyes
sized up Nick Velie in a corner scared
of being caught with his polemics down. . .
A couple of Thracian maenads sipping Scotch
not noticing Tantalus . . . a Fury's cheeks
actually wet with tears . . . a psychopath
a Wall Street paranoiac   another victim

of our manic-depressive economic cycle—
a schizoid there pursuing his one aim
to make the brunette baby-doll—syntonic
obviously—so perfectly attuned
to his environment   At the next table
a Hollywood director talking montage. . .
Moronia's praetorian guard!   An insect
like *culex pipiens*—swart little man
all in the know   lisping against the bragging
of Scaramouch the Socialite. . . Herbivorous
brontosaurus!   Three gals with orange lipstick
three Graces?   Fates? Furies?   or Daughters of
Danaus   taking waters in a sieve—
sieves for strong waters!

                                        The fifth brandy asserted
authority
                        A florid dinner-coat
was saying "—crowded him over the side-boards—saw it!
trying to trip his pony . . . saw it myself!"

"When?"
                        "The sixth chukker"
                                                "Doubt he'll ever go
to Meadowbrook"
                                        Another man was asking
three glasses down the bar: "You saw the obit?
They had a shirt-tail on him because he mixed
with Francie Roland seven years ago. . .
Might have been a Governor of the Exchange. . .
What? Oh pneumonia I think and heart. . .
Isthmian at St. Paul's when I was Shattuck
In 1912 with Squire Hurst and Coe
then it was Skelly Hurst and Coe   and then
it was B. F. Skelly   Boy was that a lulu
the Roland case!"
                                "—ivory duchess satin
The bodice trimmed with rose point lace   My *dear!*

and lilies of the valley—" said a girl
Another said "It's just two-skin kolinsky—
Gawd I could rape a walrus   leave us eat!"
Smooth liquid skin that molds you in does not
restrict or bind   red disagreeable mouth
and blank insulting eyes
                            O little sister
Eumenidean   white meat of the iguana—
follow that night-hawk's erratic bat-like flight
and nasal note!
                        Sweet mystery of life!
Though the Department of Anatomy
succeeded at two hundred below zero
in fixing life's most microscopical
structure   its protoplasm   in positions
of life   its living tissue being composed
of tiny cells that through the microscope
resemble grapes   watches   or bits of string
or dice   and all transparent   and each having
a nucleus   a small gray-looking sac
shiny fat droplets   granules and thin threads
and many other little objects seen
that also are parts of the process that they call
Life   What are they made of?   How are they placed?
Could we create a living protoplasm
in a laboratory?   Can we extend the span
of life?   In the University of Chicago
tissue still living is plunged into pentane
or high-test gasoline   in a second's fraction
frozen solid   there is little distortion
of the tissue cells   the frozen tissue placed
in a vacuum   the water is dried out
the chalkwhite tissue now resembles snowflakes
delicate snowflakes falling on your heart
like lace. . .
                        "Lousy old bastard" said a girl
"he thinks he's going to make—"

He couldn't hear
the rest   the smoke swayed gently now   he thought
of a funny parody   his brain began:

Bid me to live and I will live
thy Humanist to be
but bid me love and I will give
an Inner Check to thee. . .

it sounded like
something he really didn't quite remember
but honestly   those Humanists!   He'd put it
in that compendium of all delights
"rare and refinèd workes of woorthy knights
gentlemen   masters of arts and braue schollers"
his column in the *Book Review*
                                         "Another
brandy and soda! . . .
                         I wrote *Daffodil Time
in New Zealan'!*" he said suddenly to a man
he had never seen before   "It goes like iss
Iss daffodil time in New Zealan'
sang in Weimar a poet name Wielan'—
rhymesh not exac' nor is it a fac'
in New Zealan' 'at Wielan'—hrrnch!—I beg yer pardon!"

with dignity he produced his wallet   paid
his friend behind the bar   and very erect
wove from the room. . .

THE GALILEAN

YET one from Galilee   who did not say
     "Kill them for treason   kill them for sabotage
Kill them that hinder my agrarian scheme
Exile and liquidate them who dispute

my view   my way!"
                        In the Day of the Lie
withdraw the nails   support the body down. . .

and in the twilit garden   terribly
hushed   wash the body   take from off the head
the crown of scorns   and sprinkle all the body
with spice and tie it in a winding sheet. . .

"Woman, why weepest thou?   Whom seekest thou?"

"Because I know not where. . ."

                        "Mary!"
                                "Rabboni!"

. . . such dry-mouthed terror in that utter darkness
and now such light. . .

                    \ outside the old walled city
of Caiaphas
                        outside the old walled city
of Lutetia a town in Gaul
                                outside the city
walled and called Londinium of old time. . .

Love one another
                        . . . and the streams of blood. . .

The upper room   the wine   loaves without leaven
"This do in remembrance of me—!"

He took the cup. . .

"Lord is it I?"
                        . . . by whom the son of **Man**
is again betrayed

                    It had been good for him
if he had not been born   for he shall live
only forever with jackals of the night. . .
And after they had crucified Him
the Parthians revolted against the Legions
the Britons rebelled and massacred the Romans
Gaul rose   and Nero gabbled near his end
and the Spanish proclaimed Galba   and Nero fled
from the Golden House   and Galba entered Rome
but brought no peace   Soon the Praetorians killed him
and proclaimed Otho
                         and there was sound of war
on the Rhine   the Danube   the Po   the Tiber
the shore of the North Sea   Caligula
the incestuous epileptic screamed for earthquake
and pestilence   and Asia and Achaia
and Macedonia   and Naples   and Pompeii
shook with earthquake   and the whole Campagna
screamed for terror. . .
                         In the fulness of time
were the signs fulfilled . . .
                         But who shall mend for us
the fishers' nets on the Capernaum shore . . . ?

LOUIS UNTERMEYER Why

he selected THREE POEMS

If you would like to represent me in my role as poet, I think I would choose the three poems enclosed herewith. I select them partly because they seem to be the three most often quoted, partly because two of them have become something like "texts" for these times. Both "Prayer" and "Caliban" express a social consciousness which is also a social protest, an expression which is eliciting more response today than when the poems were written some twenty-five years ago.
Elizabethtown, N. Y.   LOUIS UNTERMEYER
May 20, 1942

PRAYER

GOD, though this life is but a wraith,
   Although we know not what we use,
Although we grope with little faith,
   Give me the heart to fight—and lose.

Ever insurgent let me be,
   Make me more daring than devout;
From sleek contentment keep me free,
   And fill me with a buoyant doubt.

Open my eyes to visions girt
   With beauty, and with wonder lit—
But let me always see the dirt,
   And all that spawn and die in it.

Open my ears to music; let
  Me thrill with Spring's first flutes and drums—
But never let me dare forget
  The bitter ballads of the slums.

From compromise and things half-done,
  Keep me, with stern and stubborn pride.
And when, at last, the fight is won,
  God, keep me still unsatisfied.

THE DARK CHAMBER

THE brain forgets, but the blood will remember.
  There, when the play of sense is over,
The last, low spark in the darkest chamber
  Will hold all there is of love and lover.

The war of words, the life-long quarrel
  Of self against self will resolve into nothing;
Less than the chain of berry-red coral
  Crying against the dead black of her clothing.

What has the brain that it hopes to last longer?
  The blood will take from forgotten violence,
The groping, the break of her voice in anger.
  There will be left only color and silence.

These will remain, these will go searching
  Your veins for life when the flame of life smolders:
The night that you two saw the mountains marching
  Up against dawn with the stars on their shoulders—

The jetting poplars' arrested fountains
  As you drew her under them, easing her pain—
The notes, not the words, of a half-finished sentence—
  The music, the silence. . . . These will remain.

CALIBAN IN THE COAL MINES

GOD, we don't like to complain;
   We know that the mine is no lark.
But—there's the pools from the rain;
   But—there's the cold and the dark.

God, You don't know what it is—
   You, in Your well-lighted sky—
Watching the meteors whizz;
   Warm, with a sun always by.

God, if You had but the moon
   Stuck in Your cap for a lamp,
Even You'd tire of it soon,
   Down in the dark and the damp.

Nothing but blackness above
   And nothing that moves but the cars.
God, if You wish for our love,
   Fling us a handful of stars!

CHRISTOPHER MORLEY Why he

selected A SONG FOR EROS

I hope it will not startle you if I say I think I should prefer to enter your caravan as a poet rather than in other possible disguises. In the matter of prose the various excerpts that I can think of would suffer, I think, by being used in that way.

To carry the matter a stage further I enclose four selections in verse. I have chosen them as representing four quite different moods of the deponent. If spoken to suddenly and sharply I would perhaps identify them as lyric ("A Song for Eros"), frolic ("The Nightpiece to Herrick"), somewhat cerebral ("Dogwood Tree"), and elegiac ("Hampstead Coach").

"Nightpiece to Herrick" has never been printed. "Hampstead Coach" was printed only in a college magazine. The other two are deducted from two of my books as marked on the copy.

If you are puzzled at my having chosen some selections in verse, I may say I did so because poetry was and remains my first love; I write a good deal more of it than I have any intention of printing; and I occasionally weary of seeing my least skillful pieces the only ones noticed.

New York, N. Y.   CHRISTOPHER MORLEY
April 6, 1942

A SONG FOR EROS

IF, IN days of sullen air,
      Dark with anger, dull with grief,
Merciful and unaware

There transpire for thy relief
            Lighter mood or cleaner sky—
            Look no further: it is I.
Bandaged close and held apart
            Are thy mortal wounds that bleed,
Yet some subtle healer's art
            Touches on thy secret need:
                  What physician, then, to bless?
                  I it was, eased thy distress.

Beauty never guessed before
            Now is casual to the gaze:
Laughter copious to restore
            All the waste of barren days:
                  Cistern water turned to wine—
                  Yea, these miracles are mine.

Under Zeus' immortal nod
            I am passion undefiled:
I, the child that is a god
            And the god that is a child.
                  Canst thou not identify
                  Thy magician? It is I.

THE NIGHTPIECE TO HERRICK

O HERRICK, parson of my heart
      I'll go to church with thee
And bear a humble willing part
      In thy sweet liturgy.

The Trinity by thee confessed,
      Thy book of common prayer,
Are Julia's leg, Anthea's breast,
      And Dianeme's hair.

DOGWOOD TREE

FOUNTAIN of snow, tossed up in morning light,
    Light brims those tilted vanes of bloom,
Sheets of petalled spindrift, poising spouts
Burst like the creamed explosion of a sea,
A spume of argent, geysered up in sway
On the warm slope of sunny air.
Light meets its equal wave-length there
And rests in clotted crisps and gouts
Upon my reveillé of snow.
Thought, the shrill mongrel with a curly scut
Runs wild with clamor in the thorny scrub.
Tie him, for silence, to the dogwood tree.
The trunk, the bole, a single spring
Of upwardness, rounded in stiff desire and crackled bark.
Then parted, spread, sweet groins and forks of living,
Comings together and divisions dear
And from the health of all those mimic loins
Flashing a dazzled outburst of relief.
All the other fifty weeks a year
The dumb and level Tuesdays, Thursdays, Sundays
For this one crest of rapture,
Quaternions of snow!
Snow's too white a thought, silver is too shiny:
Love-child of gold and silver, or the tone
Of summer's thighs by summer sunlight kissed
And then in moonlight seen. Or the tender glow
Of a child's clear forehead near the hair.

HAMPSTEAD COACH

February 3, 1820

HE RODE to town, that day false-mildest still
    In all our treacherous almanac of spring;
My dowsing rod, he thought, a forked quill,
Feels the deep twitch of fresh imagining.
A play for Drury Lane? Or verse diffused
With all St. Agnes' colors (O bright star!)
And if it's good enough to be abused
I'll sign it—like La Belle Dame—*Caviare.*

February filldyke: that night, frost,
The perjured crocus sleeted in the mud
And Hampstead Hill slow-climbed in gale and torrent.
Why he looks radiant; but the eyes are glossed
With fever.
           "Rode outside? No coat? Good God—"
"Brown, let me see that blood. . . .
                    It's my death warrant."

(JAMES) BRANCH CABELL

Why he selected   DEDICATIONS in

                ACROSTICS

Inasmuch as a forty-year-old devotion to the doctrine that the main purpose of art is to divert the artist entails some reminiscence of respect, even at a period when art falters between disregard and decease, I have picked, from the enormous bulk of my time-wasting in Philistia, that portion which has most entertained me, and, for symmetry's sake, have arranged all in alphabetical order, according to each book's title.

Ophelia, Va.   (JAMES) BRANCH CABELL
June 29, 1942

1: BEYOND LIFE

GARRULITY again begets
Unconscionable dreadful debts ...

You that have piped to-day must dance;
Herein beholding maintenance
Of arguments about Romance
(Like fountains falling whence they spring)
To you revert its eddying.

2: HAMLET HAD AN UNCLE

HERE is your story steadfastly retold
    And freed of fancy, seeking nor to lend
Music where music was not, nor to mould
Less frankly your remissions, but to mend,
Even as you mended, error, and to hold
Truth as you held it even to the end.

3: JURGEN

BEFORE each taradiddle,
    Uncowed by sciolists,
Robuster persons twiddle
Tremendously big fists.

    "Our gods are good," they tell us;
"Nor will our gods defer
Remission of rude fellows'
Ability to err."

    So this, your JURGEN, travels
Content to compromise
Ordainments none unravels
Explicitly . . . and sighs.

4: LADIES AND GENTLEMEN

REGARDING the famed dead herein allied
In letters as in proverbs: Ye abide
Concernless now, and heed not, in the grave,
How once ye postured—and thereafter died.

And yet, lest such epistolary flings
Rehearsing your lost lives seem flippant things
Devoid of grace and tenderness, I crave
Benignancy of you—queens, knaves, and kings.

Unite in pardon if I utter aught
To mar your splendors; for indeed I sought,
Long and all loyally, with truth for guide
Even in my jestings, but to mar misthought
Regarding the famed dead herein allied.

Grant me forgiveness if perchance I name
Lightly or rashly your yet-living fame
And smile upon your hurtless sins, which rest
Eternally beyond all cure or blame.

Nay, ye will pardon me—but not that wide
Zoölogy of zanies who deride
Exaltedly such fribblers as would jest
Regarding the famed dead herein allied.

5: PREFACE TO THE PAST

GAILY we shared long labors, each with each,
Until at last there was not any showing
Your thought from mine, your speaking from my speech.

Hardly we knew, that had no need of knowing,
One from another; and all went to lend
Life to our MANUEL—and to his going
Thus far, with you alone, past Storisende.

6: SMIRE

HEREINAFTER we dismiss
Usage for some little time,
Noting that in dreamland this
Takes the randomness of rhyme.

Every law which dreamland knows
Riots and leads all askance,
So that saneliest one goes
Toward dreamland's fond romance
As the fallen, unforlorn
God of Branlon goes—with chance
Guiding through carved gates of horn.

7: SMIRT

GRANTING dullness might esteem
Egoistic any dream
Of an author's loves and laurels,
Rightly I recite its morals . . .

Gifted, SMIRT forever finds
Everywhere inferior minds;
Testing, SMIRT provokes insanely

Each and all reared less urbanely;
And, derided, SMIRT derides.

None the less, SMIRT too decides
Neither wit nor erudition
Amply bolsters SMIRT's position . . .

Thereupon, with heart unhurt,
He perceives that SMIRT stays SMIRT,
And attests this by imploring
Naught of dullness save ignoring.

8: SMITH

JAUNTILY as Mr. SMITH
   Ordains that Branlon be a jumble,
      Heaven makes each man a myth—
Narrow-minded, ardent, humble,
Loosely-living, love-led, mean,
Opinionated, greedy, grieving,
Timid, noble, gay, obscene,
Trustless; and in self-deceiving
Illimitably past believing.

Equably as Mr. SMITH
Regards his children's odd appearance,
Canny persons traffic with
All their kindred's incoherence.

Brethren need not criticize
Each the other's variant metal
Loudly—nor in any wise
Let x the pot flout y the kettle.

9: SONNETS FROM ANTAN

TO TREAD as others have trodden by faith controlled
Handfast with hearsay—these hardly heeding how they
Inevitably wane toward white through gray,
Subtly, as shadows dwindle—and tread with bold,
Inexplicable, unquestioning, manifold,
Superb unreason, keeps best our fathers' way
Nowhere unfollowed, save where pride need slay
One or some two, it may be . . . even as of old.

Nowhere unfollowed (saving but through pride)
Survives the inveterate wayfaring which men
Endure as did their fathers—though long denied,
Nowhere unfollowed, saving only when
Some two (or three, it may be) in mirth allied
Evade the unbreakable snares of faith . . . again.

10: SPECIAL DELIVERY

"GOOD and evil, blending,"
Earnest persons say,
"Obscurely work at sending
Rewards on Judgment Day."

"Good and evil, blending,"
Elsewhere others bray,
"Take no thought of ending,
Keep no ordered way—
Eternally at play,
Aim but at interplaying . . ."

Thirdly, some offend
Ineffably by saying,
Not without shrugs, "My friend,
Good and evil blend."

11: THE FIRST GENTLEMAN OF AMERICA

AS, BUT for you, this book had not been done
Justly, I need (at outset) to proclaim
How opulent has been your aid.
                              —Whereon
(As, but for you, this book had not been done)
Nature demands, all-justly, that your name
Now head this Story of NEMATTANON
And of His Flight into Oblivion.

12: THE KING WAS IN HIS COUNTING HOUSE

HERE is youth's journey, and that journey's end,
As he recalls it that had love to lend
Zest to his living, and held faith his friend
Eternally, in Branlon's dim dear wood—
Lost love that revelled with large lustihood,
Lost faith that found and then unfound all good
Under the sway of Branlon's swaggering king's
Kindly ordaining of high happenings—
Ere love with faith lay slain by Time, who brings
Relentlessly, against the half-poet's prime
And too-brief laughter and futile ripples of rhyme,

Silence and gray cold wits, to aid cold Time
Coldly to hale these weaklings one by one
Out of fair Branlon, through carved gates, whereon
Each carving speaks of faith and love fordone.

13: THESE RESTLESS HEADS

JOURNEYS end in lovers meeting;
　Only June may follow May;
　　Hearts like muffled drums are beating;
Not a dog but has his day.

　　Absence makes the heart grow fonder;
Learn to look before you leap;
Blondes are better yet when blonder;
Early sow and early reap.

　　Rules like these, with others not of
Themes less varied, I pursue
Mindful of what more I wot of
Axioms thus trite yet true
Controverted by a lot of
Younger folk than I or you.

14: THE SILVER STALLION

COULD but one luring dream rest dead forever
    As dreamers rest at last, with all dreams done,
Redeemers need not be, and faith need never
Lease, for the faithful, homes beyond the sun.

Victoriously that dream—above the sorrow
And subterfuge of living—still lets fail
No heart to heed its soothing lure . . . *To-morrow*
Dreams will be true, and faith and right prevail.

Out of the bright—and, no, not vacant!—heavens
Redeemers will be coming by-and-by,
En route to make our sixes and our sevens
Neat as a trivet or an apple-pie.

ROBINSON JEFFERS Why he selected

TAMAR DANCING

This passage is chosen chiefly for the sake of perspective, because "Tamar" was written twenty years ago. Probably I have done better since then . . . and worse . . . but the poem seems nearer my mind than many later things.

Carmel, Cal.   ROBINSON JEFFERS
May 6, 1942

THIS was the high plateau of summer and August waning; white vapors
Breathed up no more from the brown fields nor hung in the hills; daily the insufferable sun
Rose, naked light, and flaming naked through the pale transparent ways of the air drained gray
The strengths of nature; all night the eastwind streamed out of the valley seaward, and stars blazed.
The year went up to its annual mountain of death, gilded with hateful sunlight, waiting rain.
Stagnant waters decayed, the trickling springs that all the misty-hooded summer had fed
Pendulous green under the granite ocean-cliffs dried and turned foul, the rock-flowers faded,
And Tamar felt in her blood the filth and fever of the season. Walking beside the house-wall
Under her window, she resented sickeningly the wounds in the cypress bark, where Andrews
Climbed to his tryst, disgust at herself choked her, and as a fire by water
Under the fog-bank of the night lines all the sea and sky with fire, so her self-hatred
Reflecting itself abroad burned back against her, all the world growing hateful, both her lovers

631

Hateful, but the intolerably masculine sun hatefulest of all. The heat
    of the season
Multiplied centipedes, the black worms that breed under loose rock,
    they call them thousand-leggers,
They invaded the house, their phalloid bodies cracking underfoot with
    a bad odor, and dropped
Ceiling to pillow at night, a vile plague though not poisonous. Also
    the sweet and female sea
Was weak with calm, one heard too clearly a mounting cormorant's
    wing-claps half a mile off shore;
The hard and dry and masculine tyrannized for a season. Rain in
    October or November
Yearly avenges the balance; Tamar's spirit rebelled too soon, the
    female fury abiding
In so beautiful a house of flesh. She came to her aunt the ghost-seer.
    "Listen to me, Aunt Stella.
I think I am going mad, I must talk to the dead; Aunt Stella, will
    you help me?" That old woman
Was happy and proud, no one for years had sought her for her talent.
    "Dear Tamar, I will help you.
We must go down into the darkness, Tamar, it is hard and painful
    for me." "I am in the darkness
Already, a fiery darkness." "The good spirits will guide you, it is easy
    for you; for me, death.
Death, Tamar, I have to die to reach them." "Death's no bad thing,"
    she answered, "each hour of the day
Has more teeth." "Are you so unhappy, Tamar, the good spirits will
    help you and teach you." "Aunt Stella,
To-night, to-night?" "I groan when I go down to death, your father
    and brother will come and spoil it."
"In the evening we will go under the rocks by the sea."
    "Well, in the evening." "If they talk to us
I'll buy you black silk and white lace."

      In and out of the little fjord swam the weak waves
Moving their foam in the twilight. Tamar at one flank, old Stella at
    the other, upheld poor Jinny

Among the jags of shattered granite, so they came to the shingle. Rich,
    damp and dark the sea's breath
Folding them made amend for days of sun-sickness, but Jinny among
    the rubble granite
(They had no choice but take her along with them, who else would
    care for the idiot?) slipped, and falling
Gashed knees and forehead, and she whimpered quietly in the dark-
    ness. "Here," said Tamar, "I made you
A bed of seaweed under the nose of this old rock, let Jinny lie beside
    you, Aunt Stella,
I'll lay the rug over you both." They lay on the odorous kelp, Tamar
    squatted beside them,
The weak sea wavered in her rocks and Venus hung over the west
    between the cliff-butts
Like the last angel of the world, the crystal night deepening the sea
    and the three women
Kept silence, only Tamar moved herself continually on the fret of her
    taut nerves,
And the sea moved, on the obscure bed of her eternity, but both were
    voiceless. Tamar
Felt her pulse bolt like a scared horse and stumble and stop, for it
    seemed to her a wandering power
Essayed her body, something hard and rounded and invisible pressed
    itself for entrance
Between the breasts, over the diaphragm. When she was forced back-
    ward and lay panting, the assault
Failed, the presence withdrew, and in that clearance she heard her old
    Aunt Stella monotonously muttering
Words with no meaning in them; but the tidal night under the cliff
    seemed full of persons
With eyes, although there was no light but the evening planet's and
    her trail in the long water.
Then came a man's voice from the woman, saying, "Que quieres
    pobrecita?" and Tamar, "Morir,"
Trembling, and marveling that she lied for no reason, and said, "Es
    porque no entiendo,

Anything but ingles." To which he answered, "Ah pobrecita," and
was silent. And Tamar

Cried, "I will talk to that Helen." But instead another male throat
spoke out of the woman's

Unintelligible gutturals, and it ceased, and the woman changing voice,
yet not to her own:

"An Indian. He says his people feasted here and sang to their Gods
and the tall Gods came walking

Between the tide-marks on the rocks; he says to strip and dance and
he will sing, and his Gods

Come walking." Tamar answered, crying, "I will not, I will not, tell
him to go away and let me

Talk to that Helen." But old Stella after a silence: "He says No, no,
the pregnant women

Would always dance here and the shore belongs to his people's ghosts
nor will they endure another

Unless they are pleased." And Tamar said, "I cannot dance, drive him
away," but while she said it

Her hands accepting alien life and a strange will undid the fastenings
of her garments.

She panted to control them, tears ran down her cheeks, the male voice
chanted

Hoarse discords from the old woman's body, Tamar drew her beauty

Out of its husks; dwellers on eastern shores

Watch moonrises as white as hers

When the half-moon about midnight

Steps out of her husk of water to dance in heaven:

So Tamar weeping

Slipped every sheath down to her feet, the spirit of the place

Ruling her, she and the evening star sharing the darkness,

And danced on the naked shore

Where a pale couch of sand covered the rocks,

Danced with slow steps and streaming hair,

Dark and slender

Against the pallid sea-gleam, slender and maidenly

Dancing and weeping . . .

It seemed to her that all her body

Was touched and troubled with polluting presences
Invisible, and whatever had happened to her from her two lovers
She had been until that hour inviolately a virgin,
Whom now the desires of dead men and dead Gods and a dead tribe
Used for their common prey . . . dancing and weeping,
Slender and maidenly . . . The chant was changed,
And Tamar's body responded to the change, her spirit
Wailing within her. She heard the brutal voice
And hated it, she heard old Jinny mimic it
In the cracked childish quaver, but all her body
Obeyed it, wakening into wantonness,
Kindling with lust and wilder
Coarseness of insolent gestures,
The senses cold and averse, but the frantic too-governable flesh
Inviting the assaults of whatever desired it, of dead men
Or Gods walking the tide-marks,   .
The beautiful girlish body as gracile as a maiden's
Gone beastlike, crouching and widening,
Agape to be entered, as the earth
Gapes with harsh heat-cracks, the inland adobe of sun-worn valleys
At the end of summer
Opening sick mouths for its hope of the rain,
So her body gone mad
Invited the spirits of the night, her belly and her breasts
Twisting, her feet dashed with blood where the granite had bruised
     them,
And she fell, and lay gasping in the sand, on the tide-line. Darkness
Possessed the shore when the evening star was down; old Stella
Was quiet in her trance; old Jinny the idiot clucked and parroted to
     herself, there was none but the idiot
Saw whether a God or a troop of Gods came swaggering along the
     tide-marks unto Tamar, to use her
Shamefully and return from her, gross and replete shadows, swagger-
     ing along the tide-marks
Against the sea-gleam. After a little the life came back to that fallen
     flower; for fear or feebleness

She crept on hands and knees, returning so to the old medium of this
  infamy. Only
The new tide moved in the night now; Tamar with her back bent
  like a bow and the hair fallen forward
Crouched naked at old Stella's feet, and shortly heard the voice she
  had cried for. "I am your Helen.
I would have wished you choose another place to meet me and milder
  ceremonies to summon me.
We dead have traded power for wisdom, yet it is hard for us to wait
  on the maniac living
Patiently, the desires of you wild beasts. You have the power." And
  Tamar murmured, "I had nothing,
Desire nor power." And Helen, "Humbler than you were. She had
  been humbled, my little Tamar.
And not so clean as the first lover left you, Tamar. Another, and half
  a dozen savages,
Dead, and dressed up for Gods." "I have endured it," she answered.
  Then the sweet disdainful voice
In the throat of the old woman: "As for me, I chose rather to die."
  "How can I kill
A dead woman," said Tamar in her heart, not moving the lips but the
  other listened to thought
And answered, "O, we are safe, we shan't fear murder. But, Tamar,
  the child will die, and all for nothing
You were submissive by the river, and lived, and endured fouling.
  I have heard the wiser flights
Of better spirits, that beat up to the breast and shoulders of our Father
  above the star-fire,
Say, 'Sin never buys anything.'" Tamar, kneeling, drew the thickness
  of her draggled hair
Over her face and wet till it seemed heavy with blood; and like a
  snake lifting its head
Out of a fire, she lifted up her face after a little and said, "It will live,
  and my father's
Bitch be proved a liar." And the voice answered, and the tone of the
  voice smiled, "Her words

Rhyme with her dancing. Tamar, did you know there were many of
    us to watch the dance you danced there,
And the end of the dance? We on the cliff; your mother, who used
    to hate me, was among us, Tamar.
But she and I loved each only one man, though it were the same. We
    two shared one. You, Tamar,
Are shared by many." And Tamar: "This is your help, I dug down
    to you secret dead people
To help me and so I am helped now. What shall I ask more? How it
    feels when the last liquid morsel
Slides from the bone? Or whether you see the worm that burrows up
    through the eye-socket, or thrill
To the maggot's music in the tube of a dead ear? You stinking dead.
    That you have no shame
Is nothing: I have no shame: see I am naked, and if my thighs were
    wet with dead beasts' drippings
I have suffered no pollution like the worms in yours; and if I cannot
    touch you I tell you
There are those I can touch. I have smelled fire and tasted fire,
And all these days of horrible sunlight, fire
Hummed in my ears, I have worn fire about me like a cloak and
    burning for clothing. It is God
Who is tired of the house that thousand-leggers crawl about in, where
    an idiot sleeps beside a ghost-seer,
A doting old man sleeps with dead women and does not know it,
And pointed bones are at the doors
Or climb up trees to the window. I say He has gathered
Fire all about the walls and no one sees it
But I, the old roof is ripe and the rafters
Rotten for burning, and all the woods are nests of horrible things,
    nothing would ever clean them
But fire, but I will go to a clean home by the good river." "You danced,
    Tamar," replied
The sweet disdainful voice in the mouth of the old woman, "and now
    your song is like your dance,
Modest and sweet. Only you have not said it was you,
Before you came down by the sea to dance,

That lit a candle in your closet and laid
Paper at the foot of the candle. We were watching.
And now the wick is nearly down to the heap,
It's God will have fired the house? But Tamar,
It will not burn. You will have fired it, your brother
Will quench it, I think that God would hardly touch
Anything in that house." "If you know everything,"
Cried Tamar, "tell me where to go.
Now life won't do me and death is shut against me
Because I hate you. O believe me I hate you dead people
More than you dead hate me. Listen to me, Helen.
There is no voice as horrible to me as yours,
And the breasts the worms have worked in. A vicious berry
Grown up out of the graveyard for my poison.
But there is no one in the world as lonely as I,
Betrayed by life and death." Like rain breaking a storm
Sobs broke her voice. Holding by a jag of the cliff
She drew herself full height. God who makes beauty
Disdains no creature, nor despised that wounded
Tired and betrayed body. She in the starlight
And little noises of the rising tide
Naked and not ashamed bore a third part
With the ocean and keen stars in the consistence
And dignity of the world. She was white stone,
Passion and despair and grief had stripped away
Whatever is rounded and approachable
In the body of woman, hers looked hard, long lines
Narrowing down from the shoulder-bones, no appeal,
A weapon and no sheath, fire without fuel,
Saying, "Have you anything more inside you
Old fat and sleepy sepulchre, any more voices?
You can do better than my father's by-play
And the dirty tricks of savages, decenter people
Have died surely. I have so passed nature
That God himself, who's dead or all these devils
Would never have broken hell, might speak out of you
Last season thunder and not scare me." Old Stella

Groaned but not spoke, old Jinny lying beside her
Wakened at the word thunder and suddenly chuckling
Began to mimic a storm, "Whoo-whoo" for wind
And "boom-boom-boom" for thunder. Other voices
Wakened far off above the cliff, and suddenly
The farm-bell ringing fire; and on the rock-islets
Sleepy cormorants cried at it. "Why, now He speaks
Another way than out of the fat throat,"
Cried Tamar, and prayed, "O strong and clean and terrible
Spirit and not father punish the hateful house.
Fire eat the walls and roofs, drive the red beast
Through every wormhole of the rotting timbers
And into the woods and into the stable, show them,
These liars, that you are alive." Across her voice,
The bell sounded and old Jinny mimicking it,
And shouts above the cliff. "Look, Jinny, look,"
Cried Tamar, "the sky'll be red soon, come and we'll dress
And watch the bonfire." Yet she glanced no thought
At her own mermaid nakedness but gathering
The long black serpents of beached seaweed wove
Wreaths for old Jinny and crowned and wound her. Meanwhile
The bell ceased ringing and Stella ceased her moan.
And in the sudden quietness, "Tamar," she said
In the known voice of Helen so many years
Dead, "though you hate me utterly, Tamar, I
Have nothing to give back, I was quite emptied
Of hate and love and the other fires of the flesh
Before your mother gave the clay to my lover
To mould you a vessel to hold them." Tamar, winding
Her mindless puppet in the sea-slough mesh
Said over her shoulder, hardly turning, "Why then
Do you trouble whom you don't hate?" "Because we hunger
And hunger for life," she answered. "Did I come uncalled?
You called me, you have more hot and blind, wild-blooded
And passionate life than any other creature.
How could I ever leave you while the life lasts?
God pity us both, a cataract life

Dashing itself to pieces in an instant.
You are my happiness, you are my happiness and death eats you.
I'll leave you when you are empty and cold and join us.
Then pity me, then Tamar, me flitting
The chilly and brittle pumice-tips of the moon,
While the second death
Corrodes this shell of me, till it makes my end."

WILLIAM CARLOS WILLIAMS

Why he selected SOME FLOWER STUDIES

The thing has been with me to work the language in order to find what new may be done with it. Not merely does one chase after newness for the sake of sensation or abandon the old because it is stale. There is a necessity to reinvestigate our means of expression in every age. For in the forms of the arts many things get locked up, some of them permanent and invaluable and some of them stultifying if allowed to remain fixed. Unless every age claims the world for its own and makes it so by its own efforts in its own day and unless the mark of this effort and success is left upon all the forms of that age including those formal expressions which we call art, no one can be said to have lived in any age or at any time. These pieces show my own efforts to possess my world thought which, when successful, the life of my day has breathed whatever value they have into them.

Rutherford, N. J.   WILLIAM CARLOS WILLIAMS
June 14, 1942

DAISY

THE day's eye hugging the earth
in August, ha! Spring is
gone down in purple,
weeds stand high in the corn,
the rainbeaten furrow
is clotted with sorrel
and crabgrass, the
branch is black under
the heavy mass of the leaves—

The sun is upon a
slender green stem
ribbed lengthwise.
He lies on his back—
it is a woman also—
he regards his former
majesty and
round the yellow center,
split and creviced and done into
minute flowerheads, he sends out
his twenty rays—a little
and the wind is among them
to grow cool there!

One turns the thing over
in his hand and looks
at it from the rear: brownedged,
green and pointed scales
armor his yellow.

But turn and turn,
the crisp petals remain
brief, translucent, greenfastened,
barely touching at the edges:
blades of limpid seashell.

PRIMROSE

YELLOW, yellow, yellow, yellow!
     It is not a color.
It is summer!
It is the wind on a willow,
the lap of waves, the shadow
under a bush, a bird, a bluebird,
three herons, a dead hawk
rotting on a pole—
Clear yellow!

It is a piece of blue paper
in the grass or a threecluster of
green walnuts swaying, children
playing croquet or one boy
fishing, a man
swinging his pink fists
as he walks—
It is ladysthumb, forget-me-nots
in the ditch, moss under
the flange of the carrail, the
wavy lines in split rock, a
great oaktree—
It is a disinclination to be
five red petals or a rose, it is
a cluster of birdsbreast flowers
on a red stem six feet high,
four open yellow petals
above sepals curled
backward into reverse spikes—
Tufts of purple grass spot the
green meadows and clouds the sky.

QUEEN-ANN'S-LACE

HER body is not so white as
anemone petals nor so smooth—nor
so remote a thing. It is a field
of the wild carrot taking
the field by force; the grass
does not raise above it.
Here is no question of whiteness,
white as can be, with a purple mole
at the center of each flower.
Each flower is a hand's span
of her whiteness. Wherever
his hand has lain there is
a tiny purple blemish. Each part

is a blossom under his touch
to which the fibres of her being
Stem one by one, each to its end,
until the whole field is a
white desire, empty, a single stem,
a cluster, flower by flower,
a pious wish to whiteness gone over—
or nothing.

MARIANNE MOORE

Why she selected WHAT ARE YEARS?

"What Are Years?" partly written in 1931 and finished in 1939, is elegiac.

The desperation attendant on mortal fallibility is mitigated for me by admitting that the most willed and resolute vigilance may lapse, as with the Apostle Peter's denial that he could be capable of denial; but that failure, disgrace, and even death have now and again been redeemed into inviolateness by a sufficiently transfigured courage.

Brooklyn, N. Y.   MARIANNE MOORE
March 22, 1942

WHAT is our innocence,
       what is our guilt? All are
naked, none is safe. And whence
is courage: the unanswered question,
the resolute doubt,—
dumbly calling, deafly listening—that
in misfortune, even death,
       encourages others
       and in its defeat, stirs

the soul to be strong? He
sees deep and is glad, who
       accedes to mortality
and in his imprisonment, rises
upon himself as
the sea in a chasm, struggling to be
free and unable to be,

in its surrendering
finds its continuing.

So he who strongly feels,
behaves. The very bird,
    grown taller as he sings, steels
his form straight up. Though he is captive,
his mighty singing
says, satisfaction is a lowly
thing, how pure a thing is joy.
        This is mortality,
        this is eternity.

MURIEL RUKEYSER

Why she selected Song from

"MEDITERRANEAN"

The song from *Mediterranean* was written on the boat on the way
home from Spain after the first days of the war.
New York, N. Y.   MURIEL RUKEYSER
July 20, 1942

I SAW Europe break apart
   and artifice or martyr's will
cannot anneal this war, nor make
the loud triumphant future start
shouting from its tragic heart.

Cover away the fighting cities
but still your death-afflicted eyes
must hold the print of flowering guns,
bombs whose insanity craves size,
the lethal breath, the iron prize.

Once the fanatic image shown,
enemy to enemy,
past and historic peace wear thin;
we see Europe break like stone,
hypocrite sovereignties go down
before this war the age must win.

H. D. Why she selected The ISLANDS

As to what I like—I don't at the moment much like anything I have done. I am now in London and if *"The Islands"* is enough for the collection, that suits me.

London   H. D.

July, 1942

WHAT are the islands to me,
      what is Greece,
what is Rhodes, Samos, Chios,
what is Paros facing west,
what is Crete?

What is Samothrace,
rising like a ship,
what is Imbros, rending the storm-waves
with its breast?

What is Naxos, Paros, Milos,
what the circle about Lycia,
what, the Cyclades'
white necklace?

What is Greece . . .
Sparta, rising like a rock,
Thebes, Athens,
what is Corinth?

What is Euboia
with its island violets,
what is Euboia, spread with grass,

set with swift shoals,
what is Crete?

What are the islands to me,
what is Greece?

II

What can love of land give to me
that you have not . . .
what do the tall Spartans know,
and gentler Attic folk?

What has Sparta and her women
more than this?

What are the islands to me
if you are lost . . .
what is Naxos, Tinos, Andros,
and Delos, the clasp
of the white necklace?

III

What can love of land give to me
that you have not,
what can love of strife break in me
that you have not?

Though Sparta enter Athens,
Thebes wrack Sparta,
each changes as water,
salt, rising to wreak terror
and fall back.

IV

"What has love of land given to you
that I have not?"

I have questioned Tyrians
where they sat
on the black ships,
weighted with rich stuffs,
I have asked the Greeks
from the white ships,
and Greeks from ships whose hulks
lay on the wet sand, scarlet
with great beaks.
I have asked bright Tyrians
and tall Greeks . . .
"what has love of land given you?"
And they answered . . . "peace."

V

But beauty is set apart,
beauty is cast by the sea,
a barren rock,
beauty is set about
with wrecks of ships,
upon our coast, death keeps
the shallows . . . death waits
clutching toward us
from the deeps.

Beauty is set apart;
the winds that slash its beach,
swirl the coarse sand
upward toward the rocks.

Beauty is set apart
from the islands
and from Greece.

VI

In my garden
the winds have beaten

the ripe lilies;
in my garden, the salt
has wilted the first flakes
of young narcissus,
and the lesser hyacinth,
and the salt has crept
under the leaves of the white hyacinth.

In my garden
even the wind-flowers lie flat,
broken by the wind at last.

VII

What are the islands to me
if you are lost,
what is Paros to me
if your eyes draw back,
what is Milos
if you take fright of beauty,
terrible, torturous, isolated
a barren rock?

What is Rhodes, Crete,
what is Paros facing west,
what, white Imbros?

What are the islands to me
if you hesitate,
what is Greece if you draw back
from the terror
and cold splendour of song
and its bleak sacrifice?

WALLACE STEVENS Why he selected

DOMINATION of BLACK

The themes of life are the themes of poetry. It seems to be, so clearly, that what is the end of life for the politician or the philosopher, say, ought to be the end of life for the poet, and that his important poems ought to be the poems of the achievement of that end. But poetry is neither politics nor philosophy. Poetry is poetry, and one's objective as a poet is to achieve poetry, precisely as one's objective in music is to achieve music. There are poets who would regard that as a scandal and who would say that a poem that had no importance except its importance as poetry had no importance at all, and that a poet who had no objective except to achieve poetry was a fribble and something less than a man of reason.

Hartford, Conn.   WALLACE STEVENS
August, 1942

A T NIGHT, by the fire,
    The colors of the bushes
And of the fallen leaves,
Repeating themselves,
Turned in the room,
Like the leaves themselves
Turning in the wind.
Yes: but the color of the heavy hemlocks
Came striding.
And I remembered the cry of the peacocks.

The colors of their tails
Were like the leaves themselves

Turning in the wind.
In the twilight wind.
They swept over the room,
Just as they flew from the boughs of the hemlocks
Down to the ground.
I heard them cry—the peacocks.
Was it a cry against the twilight
Or against the leaves themselves
Turning in the wind,
Turning as the flames
Turned in the fire,
Turning as the tails of the peacocks
Turned in the loud fire,
Loud as the hemlocks
Full of the cry of the peacocks,
Or was it a cry against the hemlocks.

Out of the window,
I saw how the planets gathered
Like the leaves themselves
Turning in the wind.
I saw how the night came,
Came striding like the color of the heavy hemlocks.
I felt afraid.
And I remembered the cry of the peacocks.

VI
THE MASTERS

HORACE

The best of Agnes Repplier is not preceded by the usual author's foreword for the reason set forth in the following letter by Mrs. Lightner Witmer, niece of the author.

"My aunt, Agnes Repplier, received your letter, but she has been ill for the last two years, very weak and frail and confined to her bed. She is not able to write and I have had charge of her correspondence. I think Aunt Agnes should be represented in the anthology, and I talked to her about it yesterday and she agreed.

"When Miss Repplier published her *Eight Decades* in 1937, she was asked then to include in that publication those of her essays which she deemed the best. This she did, and I remember asking her at the time if 'Horace' was not her first choice, and she said, 'yes.' I spoke to her of it yesterday, and she agreed, adding that there would never be a time when people would not want to read about Horace.

"Aunt Agnes is too ill to formulate or write a paragraph, but we could quote what she has often said to us on the subject—if that would do."

THAT a poet should survive two thousand years is not remarkable. Whatever changes two thousand more may bring about, they will not affect the standing of Homer or of Virgil. *"Ce n'est que le premier pas qui coûte."* If you survive your first thousand, the others will fall into line. But that a poet writing two thousand years ago should today be the helpmate and spokesman of humanity is in the nature of a miracle. It can be accounted for only by the fact that Horace was a man wholly disillusioned, and wholly good-tempered.

No word in our language has been so misused in the past nineteen years as the word "disillusionment." It has come to mean the perpetual grouch of men still deeply resentful that the World War was not in the nature of a garden party, and that the World Peace was not a highway to Utopia. Every crime and every folly have been excused on this ground. Even the kaleidoscopic divorces of Reno, the suspension of privacy, the repeal of reticence, have been accounted for by the disillusionment of youth at the way the world was run when it was too young to run it, as the natural result of a war which saw greater acts of heroism and of supreme self-sacrifice than had ever before purified the souls of men.

The disillusionment of Horace was not of this order. It meant that he had awakened from the noble dreams of youth to the equally noble realities of manhood. He saw life as a whole, and this educational process taught him that it is not easy to find happiness in ourselves, and that it is not possible to find it elsewhere. Reason, moderation, content, a wide mental horizon, a firm foundation of principle—these were the gifts of the gods (and Horace reverenced his gods) to men of good purpose and sobriety.

His upbringing was of the best. His father, though but a freedman who had received his name, Horatius, either because he had been the property of some member of the patrician family of Horatii, or because his birthplace, Venusia, was part of their vast estates in Apulia, was sanely ambitious for his promising young son. He took him to Rome to be educated—an extravagance he could ill afford—provided for him liberally, and watched over him with care. We hear nothing of the mother, so presumably she was dead. Rome was more concerned with the functions of motherhood than was Greece. She could not have endowed the world with her two great gifts, the sanctity of the family and the majesty of the law, she could not have given to it, as she did, a life morally worth the living, if she had not looked sharply after her women, emphasizing their duties rather than their privileges. But she was far from being a matriarchy like the United States. She was not a nation of husbands, but a nation of men. The foundation of the family was the father. He had undisputed authority, unshared responsibility, and often unlimited devotion.

Certain it is that Horace pays a tribute of gratitude to the father who begrudged him nothing that it was in his power to give. He permitted the boy to be freely flogged by his severe master, Orbilius, having the male parent's insensitiveness in this regard; but he protected him alike from folly and from misdoing. "He kept me chaste," wrote Horace in after years, "free from shameful deeds, and from the breath of dishonour."

His Roman schooling over, young Horace was sent to Athens, still the thrice superb teacher of the world; and there, free from his father's restraining hand, he did what all young men of spirit have done since the beginning of time—he went to the wars. The profitless murder of Julius Caesar had brought Brutus to Greece. Horace, being twenty-two, an age singularly sensitive to oratory, joined the republican army, and was given the post of military tribune—a circumstance usually mentioned as proof of his talent, but which seems rather to indicate a shortage of trained soldiers. If we may trust to his recollections, as embodied in his lines to Pompeius Varus, his military experiences were not altogether unpleasant. There were hours of relaxation to compensate for hours of peril:

> "Full oft we sped the lingering day,
>   Quaffing bright wine as in our tents we lay,
>   With Syrian spikenard on our glistening hair."

It is an agreeable picture of campaigning; but the curtain fell on the desolate field of Philippi. Brutus and Cassius died by their own hands; and Horace, convinced that his was not a military genius, profited by the general amnesty to return to Rome.

It was a hard home-coming. His father was dead, his small estate in Venusia had been confiscated—which was to have been expected—and he himself was under suspicion as a pardoned enemy of the state. He had much to live down, and he had much to build up. He secured his daily bread by working as a scribe in the quaestor's office, and he began his career as poet. Naturally he began it by writing satires. What else should a brilliant and bitterly disappointed young man have written? And just as naturally he regretted many of these satires when time had brought him reason.

We all remember how Byron strove to blot out of existence his outbreak of ill-temper, "English Bards and Scotch Reviewers," and how he found out that as soon as English readers discovered they could no longer get that particular poem they were all possessed by a desire to have it. Horace would have liked to blot out his early satires. They were not his métier. The concentrated anger of Juvenal or of Swift was utterly foreign to his nature. Swift was a great and powerful humorist, and Juvenal was esteemed a wit; but in their two souls "rage accumulated like water behind a dam," and burst into devastating floods. Horace had not even the tenacity of wrath which made an indifferent poet like Lucilius a fairly great satirist; but in its place he had a gift which was slowly maturing—a balanced and delicate irony, playful but with a rapier's point. The charming picture of country life, simple, serene and self-respecting, which the moneylender, Alfius, contemplates with unction but decides not to live, is a perfect example of the ironical, of the laughter that is so low-pitched it seems—for one mistaken moment—to be kindly. As admirable in its more worldly way is his epistle to the young Tiberius, heir to the throne, introducing a persistent acquaintance who will not be set aside. This is the ninth epistle of the first book. As there are few of us who have not suffered a somewhat similar experience, its study cannot fail to be of service.

In the fifth epode we find the first direful picture of the witch, Canidia, a singularly disgusting person. It is at once the most tragic and the most dramatic poem that Horace ever wrote. Curiously dramatic, for it opens with the outbreak of terrified anger from the patrician child who has been trapped into the witches' den, there to die in slow torment for the better making of a love philtre; and it closes with the curse which the doomed boy hurls at his destroyers. Fear has left him, and fury has taken its place. He bids the hags remember that no magic can alter right and wrong, or avert retribution. He, dying at their hands, will pursue them to their shameful deaths. The rabble will pelt them with heavy stones, and fling their unblessed bodies to the wolves:

> "This shall my parents see,
> Alas! surviving me."

Horace was always concerned with witches and sorcerers; but the trend of his mind was sceptical. He reached the sane conclusion that they were malignant but impotent.

All this time he was making friends of an agreeable order. The reign of the great Augustus, even the consulship of the great Octavius, was singularly favourable to brilliant young men. Rome was extravagant and immoral; but it was full of artistic and intellectual fervour.

Horace's personality was charming, his attainments were remarkable. Virgil, whose own estate had been confiscated and restored, was his intimate companion; and it was Virgil who presented him to Maecenas, the minister and confidential adviser of Octavius. From this introduction and the friendship that followed sprang one of the most perfect interchanges of gifts the world has ever known. Maecenas gave Horace a farm in the Sabine hills, and the very modest independence he desired. Horace gave Maecenas an immortality that can never be disassociated from his own. The more we think about it, the more sure we are that the fates—kindly for once—put these two men in the same place at the same time for the perfecting of their lives.

Augustus would have taken the accomplished young poet for one of his own secretaries, and would in all likelihood have treated him with the generosity he lavished upon Virgil; but Horace, lacking ambition, was not of the stuff out of which good courtiers are made. His political views had undergone a sobering change. He began to understand the mighty mission of Rome; the need of her to hold the western world together; her policy of conciliating and amalgamating conquered nations; her "thrice-hammered hardihood" which nothing human could resist. No pride of citizenship ever equalled hers; and even her politicians still retained some measure of disinterested patriotism. Her monumental achievement, her lasting gift to the world she ruled, was law.

In the strengthening of imperial Rome, Maecenas played an important rôle. He was of Etruscan descent and a very great gentleman, scholarly, hospitable, public-minded. Where the superb basilica of Santa Maria Maggiore now stands, there stood his villa. Thither Augustus when ill had himself carried, to recover in purer air and more spacious quarters than his own palace, simple and plain, afforded him. The self-indulgence of the Roman emperors had no example in him. Since the lamentable Ides of March which saw the murder of Caesar, Maecenas had guided, supported, and restrained Caesar's nephew and heir. Many are the stories told of him, the most characteristic being that of his prompt action in the Forum when Octavius in an unrelenting mood was sentencing one political offender after another to death. Unable to approach the tribune on account of the crowd that surged about it, Maecenas wrote on his tablets, *Surge tandem Carnifex!*

("Butcher, break off!") and flung them straight into the ruler's lap. Octavius read the words, rose silently, and quitted the judgment seat which he had been pronounced unworthy to fill.

Under the protection of Maecenas, Horace lived his life serenely, and his talents ripened to perfection. His lovely odes gave the same delight then that they give now; his Roman soul venerated what was admirable, and strove for what was attainable. He spent the best months of the year in the country, where, unhurried by engagements and unharassed by acquaintances, he wrote with delight and deliberation. Like Marcus Aurelius, he was able to be alone; but he was far too wise to make of himself that lopsided thing called a recluse. He felt with Montaigne the rare delight of dividing his life between the solace afforded him by nature and the stimulus afforded him by men.

It must be admitted that he had uncommon luck in his dealings with both. Most of us could live in stable harmony with nature if our meeting place were a beautiful and fertile corner of Italy. What did Horace know of the malignant nature that rules supreme over wilderness and jungle, desert and swamp? What of disastrous nature hurling tornadoes and dust storms at her helpless children? What of relentless nature that hates a farmer, and sends sodden floods, or blighting droughts, or armies of pestiferous insects, to ruin him? The casual fashion in which the poet alludes to unfavourable weather conditions proves how small a part they played in his life. Not for nothing has Italy been called the sweetheart of the world. Horace's farm was small, thirteen hundred feet above the sea, and surrounded by beautiful woods. It produced corn, olives and vines, though he thought poorly of the wine made from its grapes. It was managed by a bailiff, and cultivated by five families of freedmen. All its owner had to do was to eat and drink its products. He had also eight slaves to wait upon him, and, like most Roman slaves, they had uncommonly little to do. Even his modest meals of pancakes, lentils, and peas were served to him by three young slaves, smiling boys with whom he occasionally conversed. It was what was then called the simple life; but, as compared with the crude and elemental thing which goes by that name in this our land today, it is recognizable as the austere luxury of a very cultivated poet.

Rome, too, had its simplicities as well as its grandeurs. The citizen who stepped from his silken litter into a Roman street might be tripped into the gutter by one of the pigs that, like the happy Plantagenet pigs of London (at a later date), enjoyed unmolested the freedom of the city. Horace preferred on the whole the free and roving pig to the free and roving dog. The pig was at least sane. The dog might be rabid, and snap at him as it ran by. His satires, which grew at once keener and kinder as he approached his thirty-sixth birthday (they were given to the world collectively in 29 B.C.), describe for us the follies and extravagances of Rome; and, as unmitigated seriousness is always out of place in human affairs, these follies and extravagances amuse us as they amused the satirist two thousand years ago, as they must always amuse as well as instruct the student of human nature. It was from Horace that Thackeray learned how to people the canvas of "Vanity Fair." "To Thackeray," says Sir Theodore Martin, "Horace was a breviary."

"Out of Plato," says Emerson, "come all things that are still written or debated among men of thought." And if this be true, we may add one word more. Out of Horace come most things that are still enjoyed and respected by men of feeling. The clear-sighted do not rule the world, but they sustain and console it. It is not in human nature to be led by intelligence. An intelligent world would not be what it is today; it would never have been what it has been in every epoch of which we have any knowledge. Horace had no illusions on this score. He did not pass his life in ignorance of the ills about him. Men lived on their elemental instincts then as now. They wanted to keep what they had, or they wanted to get what their neighbours had, just as they do today. Horace knew this, and he invented no fancy phrases to decorate a bald fact. To understand life was, indeed, a classic form of consolation, a mental austerity which Pope failed to take into account when he wrote:

> "Horace still charms with graceful negligence,
> And, without method, talks us into sense."

Yet the little Queen Anne man had a deep admiration for the poet who distilled philosophy from life, and whose counsel of perfection is based upon the feasibility of performance. There was none of Goethe's "negative and sceptical neutrality" about Horace. He knew that Rome was the best possible means for ordering a large fraction of humanity. He knew that discipline at home and invulnerability abroad were necessary for this end. He loved with a passionate intensity of devotion the greatness of Roman traditions, and the memory of the mighty dead. Two notes of admonition he struck. One is in the tenth ode of the second book, where he warns Licinius, and through him all Romans, of the unwisdom of plotting against the state: "Reef your sails while there is yet time." The other is the third ode of the third book, one of the great Alcaics on which the fame of the poet securely rests. In it Juno herself sings the praises and the triumphs of Rome—Rome destined to unite the severed countries of the world, provided only that she paid no heed to her own rabble (Horace and Shakespeare held the same opinion as to the intelligence of mobs), and curbed her own cupidity:

> "Riches the hardy soldiers must despise,
> And look on gold with undesiring eyes."

It is not clear why this ode is held by most commentators to refer to the hidden treasure of Darius (which, by the way, still awaits discovery). It seems to allude merely to the gold which all men knew to be buried deep in mines, and which wise men believed had much better be left there.

"The understanding sadness of Horace," says Edith Hamilton, "tempers the gaiety of his verse into something infinitely endearing." The sobering truth which he bore ever in mind he expressd with customary terseness:

> "We may be wise, or rich, or great,
> But never can be blest."

Therefore he sang unceasingly the praises of sweet content which springs from "those deep regions of self where the issues of character are decided." This tenderness combined with disillusion has made him a helpmate for two thousand years. Cheerfulness and melancholy can be, and usually are, equally odious; but a sad heart and a gay temper hold us in thrall. Even the amatory odes, which are so perfect and so unweighted by passion, have in them an undertone of regret. Commentators, always immersed in sentiment, have concluded that Cinara was to Horace what Lucy was to Wordsworth—a lost love and

a lasting memory. But all we know is that she died young, and that
Horace regretted with tempered sadness her early loss:

"I am not the man I was under the reign of Cinara."

Lucy has no rival in the field. Cinara shares the canvas with shy
Chloe, and false Neaera, and forward Glycera, and heartless Barine,
and that accomplished flirt, Pyrrha,

"Plain in her neatness."

and Lydia, the lady of an ode as fragile and as flawless as a butterfly,
which has been entitled in English "The Reconciliation." It has been
translated by many lovers of Horace, never better perhaps than by
Ben Jonson, though its sentiment is far from the direct and powerful
emotions of the Elizabethans and of their immediate successors. It
accords with the grace of the cavaliers, the playtime of the Restoration.
Sir Charles Sedley should have translated it. Lovelace might have
written it. Horace opens the dialogue. He is reproachful, but far from
downcast, as he reminds Lydia that once he was her chosen lover.
Lydia replies with spirit that when she reigned in his heart and in his
song she asked no happier fate; but that she is not prepared to play
second fiddle to Chloe. Horace admits the impelling power of Chloe,
her sweetness, and her skill with the lyre. Of course his heart is hers.
Lydia, not to be outdone in inconstancy, avows her love for Calais,
Calais the son of Ornytus, a youth so engaging she would gladly die
for him. Horace, an old hand at the game of love, asks what would
happen should he discard bright Chloe, and return a suppliant to his
earlier love. Lydia, in a suspiciously sudden surrender, responds with a
cry of joy; though Calais be fairer than a star, and Horace inconstant
and rough as the sea,

"Yet should I wish to love, live, die with thee."

Horace, like Virgil, remained contentedly unmarried. He had the
uneasy married lives of Augustus and of Maecenas by way of warning.
His interest in women was an undertone. The stifling problem (it is
called a problem) of sex which excites half the world to frenzy, and
bores the other half to extinction, resolves itself in his hands into its
simplest elements. His great emotions lay elsewhere, and he held even

his great emotions in control. The supreme Roman virtue was patriotism—to serve the state and to die for it. Yet in what temperate language Horace clothes his maxims, the very triteness of which proves them immortal. *Dulce et decorum est pro patria mori*. Not a flourish! Not a gesture! Yet life becomes a thing of value and of sweetness because men can renounce it with dignity. And there is nothing in the written history of the world to outstrip Horace's description, in the fifth ode of the third book, of Regulus returning to Carthage: " 'Tis said he put away his chaste wife's kisses and his little children, as one bereft of civil rights, and bent his gaze upon the ground till he should strengthen the Senate's wavering purpose by advice never before given, and turn his steps to exile."

Next to the unswerving loyalty to Rome came the love which Horace bore his friends, and, above and beyond all other friends, to Maecenas, whose bread he ate, and whose heart he held in his keeping. "Remember," said the dying Maecenas to the Emperor Augustus, who stood sorrowing by his bedside, "remember Flaccus as you would remember me."

There was no need for this entreaty. In three weeks Horace followed his friend, and was buried by his side on the Esquiline Hill. This was as he had always foretold. "When the blow falls it will crush us both; and to whatever bourne you lead the way, I shall follow." Fifty-seven years the poet had lived, enjoying the ripeness of middle age, and escaping the frosts that ensue. He had achieved the utmost renown that Rome could give. A great lyric poet; a philosopher whose epistles embody all pagan wisdom and a perfect understanding of humanity. The writer of the Secular Hymn had become the arbiter of taste, the spokesman of the Emperor, the persuasive exponent of a reasonable life, the clear, sad thinker who led no man astray. His death was so sudden that he had no time to summon a scribe and dictate a will. Therefore he made it orally, bequeathing his modest estate to the Emperor. Such wills held good in Roman law, where many simplicities survived; but, in view of the uncertainties attendant upon men's recollections, it was wise to leave all to the throne. If ever an oral will was sure to be remembered rightly, it was when Augustus was the heir.

Horace not only reverenced his gods, but he believed that he had been kindly treated by them. He was disposed to see something above and beyond nature in the protection afforded him. When he was a little lost child in the forest, and the leaves drifted upon him as he slept, he felt sure that the birds had covered him, as in later years they covered the hapless Babes in the Wood. The falling tree that grazed but did not harm him, the wolf that turned from his path when he was wandering in the Sabine hills, composing an ode to Lalage—these things did not happen by chance. Maecenas, too, had in his day been snatched from danger; but mighty Jove conceived it his duty to look after Maecenas; whereas

> "Pan, who keeps watch
> O'er easy souls like mine,"

had turned smiling to the aid of Horace. Therefore it behooves Maecenas to build a shrine and offer tribute; but Horace will sacrifice a young lamb to the sylvan god.

The poet was the most hospitable of men. He dearly loved the companionship of friends; and, having a perfectly correct sense of values, he saw no reason why Maecenas should not leave his stately home, which so far exceeded in splendour the Emperor's palace, and spend his birthday by the Sabine fireside, where Virgil had been content to sit. The preparations for his coming were of a joyous rusticity. Horace does not appear to have had the furniture polished, as when the advocate, Torquatus, came to visit him; but the silver vessels were burnished brightly, garlands were gathered, the altar wreathed with sacred leafage, the kitchen fires roared hospitably, and a jar of Alban wine, nine years old, was waiting to be unsealed. Horace had the poorest possible opinion of water drinkers, and was convinced that not one of them ever wrote a song that lived.

It behooved the poet to be out of the way a goodly portion of his time, because he was too much wanted in Rome. Maecenas wanted him and the Emperor wanted him; and these two august and powerful men thought it right that they should have what they desired. Horace thought otherwise. He clung tenaciously to his liberty, and he achieved it because he stood ready to sacrifice, if need be, all luxuries, comforts, and pleasures for its sake. He would not write his verse and he would not live his life to order. In a very determined and very delicate fashion he makes this known to Maecenas in the seventh epistle

of the first book. He has left Rome for a week and he has stayed away
a month—greatly to his friend's displeasure. After all, the month was
August, and August is a season when anyone would be well advised
to stay away from Rome. Horace says so plainly. It is the season, he
writes, when the first figs and the mounting sun keep the undertaker
busy. His health requires the cooler air, and, what is more important,
his soul requires the freedom to make its own choice. "Every man
must measure himself by his own rule and standard."

With Augustus the task was more difficult. The Emperor wanted
to be sung, and he wanted to be sung in an intimate and homely
strain. Horace wrote his most noble odes to celebrate the triumphs
of Rome. He wrote charming songs to celebrate the peace and plenty
which Augustus ensured to the Romans: "The ox roams the pastures
in safety, Ceres makes plentiful the crops, the sea is calm, the shrines
are sacred, the home is unpolluted." He also wrote the Secular Hymn
at the instigation of the ruler. But that was as far as he would go. He
never lessened the distance between the Emperor and the subject. He
never affected an easy intimacy with the throne, though Augustus
had asked him mockingly if he were ashamed of such a friendship.
We cannot conceive him addressing the Caesar as the courtiers of
Charles the Second addressed their easygoing monarch. And in all this
he was more than worldly-wise. He was safeguarding his own self-
respect, and preserving a fine and delicate standard of personal honour.

Of the poet's second home at Tibur we know little save that he
loved it, and that it was surpassingly beautiful. The villa probably
belonged to Maecenas, who slept more sweetly to the sound of falling
waters, and Horace lived in it, off and on, for nineteen years. The
Franciscan monks, with that unerring eye for beauty which all the
religious orders have displayed, built the monastery of San Antonio
on the site of his villa. It stood on the borderland between the Sabine
country and the Campagna. Catullus, who lived near by, was wont
to say that if his friends wished to mock at him as a rustic, they called
him a Sabine. If they wished to imply that he was a gentleman, they
called him a Tiburtine.

For Tibur, now Tivoli, is an older city than Rome, and was once
its equal. In its earlier phase it was a city of smiths who fashioned and
sharpened swords for the perpetual warfare of the day. The surround-

ing soil is more fertile than in the hill country. It grows better vines and more abundant crops. If Horace missed the Fountain of Bandusia, that leaping cascade which he was wont to climb so far to see, and to whose guardian deity he sacrificed a flower-decked kid, he had in its stead the falling waters of the Anio; the Cascata Grande, not then the torrent it is now, and the lovely Cascatelle streaming down the hillside in broken threads of silver. The orchards of Tibur were wet with spray, and the Tiburtine Sibyl delivered her oracles to the sound of many waters. Even Italy had nothing better to give. Small wonder that Horace wrote with a sigh of content, "May Tibur, founded by Argive wanderers, be the home of my old age and my final goal."

The scholars of the last century believed firmly that the classics offer us both a training for life and a help in living it. This is the hold that Horace has had on humanity, and his fashion of speech is such that educated youth gladly accepts his spokesmanship. We are told that a hundred years ago most public-school boys in England, and almost all Etonians, knew their Horace if they knew nothing else. It was not unusual for a lad of intelligence to have most of the odes by heart. The twentieth century has many new voices (some of them very insistent), but no one of them speaks to us with the accent of Horace. Hugh Macnaghten, for many years a master at Eton, and a translator of the classics, tells us a pleasant story in this regard. In the second year of the World War he had a letter from a former student, Henry Evelyn Platt, then fighting in France. It requested—of all things in the world— a copy of Horace, a small book, "with perhaps a crib for the hard words," and it gave the reason why. Young Platt was one of three Etonians in that line of trenches, and they had recently been joined by a Harrovian who was always quoting Horace. The Etonians were not so preoccupied with the deadly details of their lives as to be indifferent to this challenge. Come what might, they would reread their Horace for their own satisfaction, and for the honour of Eton.

Surely the soul of Horace, wherever it is located, was made glad by that letter. It was just what he had foretold. Death for the pagan was a dismal thing. The bright gods dwelt on Olympus; but they shared their bliss with none, and the realm of Pluto was but a poor exchange for Athens or for Rome. But Horace knew that he would triumph over death. *Non omnis moriar* ("Not all of me shall die"). He spoke as prophets speak, piercing the future. While Rome lived, he would live. "As long as the Pontiff climbs the Capitol with the silent Vestal by his side, I shall be famed, and beyond the boundaries of Rome I shall travel far."

"Barbarians unborn my name shall know."

We know it and are glad.

EDGAR LEE MASTERS Why he

selected TO-MORROW IS MY

BIRTHDAY

I don't say that in this poem I reached my most satisfactory expression, though I think it is one of my best in blank verse.

New York, N. Y.　　　　　　　　　　　EDGAR LEE MASTERS
May 13, 1942

WELL, then, another drink! Ben Jonson knows,
　　So do you, Michael Drayton, that to-morrow
I reach my fifty-second year. But hark ye,
To-morrow lacks two days of being a month—
Here is a secret—since I made my will.
Heigh ho! that's done too! I wonder why I did it?
That I should make a will! Yet it may be
That then and jump at this most crescent hour
Heaven inspired the deed.

　　　　　　　　　　　　　As a mad younker
I knew an aged man in Warwickshire
Who used to say, "Ah, mercy me," for sadness
Of change, or passing time, or secret thoughts.
If it was spring he sighed it, if 'twas fall,
With drifting leaves, he looked upon the rain
And with doleful suspiration kept
This habit of his grief. And on a time
As he stood looking at the flying clouds,
I loitering near, expectant, heard him say it,
Inquired, "Why do you say 'Ah, mercy me,'
Now that it's April?" So he hobbled off
And left me empty there.

671

                                      Now here am I!
Oh, it is strange to find myself this age,
And rustling like a peascod, though unshelled,
And, like this aged man of Warwickshire,
Slaved by a mood which must have breath—"Tra-la!"
That's what I say instead of "Ah, mercy me."
For look you, Ben, I catch myself with "Tra-la"
The moment I break sleep to see the day.
At work, alone, vexed, laughing, mad or glad
I say, "Tra-la" unknowing. Oft at table
I say, "Tra-la." And 'tother day, poor Anne
Looked long at me and said, "You say, 'Tra-la'
Sometimes when you're asleep; why do you so?"
Then I bethought me of that aged man
Who used to say, "Ah, mercy me," but answered:
"Perhaps I am so happy when awake
The song crops out in slumber—who can say?"
And Anne arose, began to keel the pot,
But was she answered, Ben? Who know a woman?

To-morrow is my birthday. If I die,
Slip out of this with Bacchus for a guide,
What soul would interdict the poppied way?
Heroes may look the Monster down, a child
Can wilt a lion, who is cowed to see
Such bland unreckoning of his strength—but I,
Having so greatly lived, would sink away
Unknowing my departure. I have died
A thousand times, and with a valiant soul
Have drunk the cup, but why? In such a death
To-morrow shines and there's a place to lean.
But in this death that has no bottom to it,
No bank beyond, no place to step, the soul
Grows sick, and like a falling dream we shrink
From that inane which gulfs us, without place
For us to stand and see it.

                                     Yet, dear Ben,
This thing must be; that's what we live to know
Out of long dreaming, saying that we know it.
As yeasty heroes in their braggart teens
Spout learnedly of war, who never saw
A cannon aimed. You drink too much to-day,
Or get a scratch while turning Lucy's stile,
And like a beast you sicken. Like a beast
They cart you off. What matter if your thought
Outsoared the Phoenix? Like a beast you rot.
Methinks that something wants our flesh, as we
Hunger for flesh of beasts. But still to-morrow,
To-morrow and to-morrow and to-morrow
Creeps in this petty pace—O, Michael Drayton,
Some end must be. But 'twixt the fear of ceasing
And weariness of going on we lie
Upon these thorns!

                              These several springs I find
No new birth in the Spring. And yet in London
I used to cry, "O, would I were in Stratford;
It's April and the larks are singing now.
The flags are green along the Avon river;
O, would I were a rambler in the fields.
This poor machine is racing to its wreck.
This grist of thought is endless, this old sorrow
Sprouts, winds and crawls in London's darkness. Come
Back to your landscape! Peradventure waits
Some woman there who will make new the earth,
And crown the spring with fire."
                                  So back I come.
And the springs march before me, say, "Behold
Here are we, and what would you, can you use us?"
What good is air if lungs are out, or springs
When the mind's flown so far away no spring,
Nor loveliness of earth can call it back?
I tell you what it is: in early youth

The life is in the loins; by thirty years
It travels through the stomach to the lungs,
And then we strut and crow. By forty years
The fruit is swelling while the leaves are fresh.
By fifty years you're ripe, begin to rot.
At fifty-two, or fifty-five or sixty
The life is in the seed—what's spring to you?
Puff! Puff! You are so winged and light you fly.
For every passing zephyr, are blown off,
And drifting, God knows where, cry out "tra-la,"
"Ah, mercy me," as it may happen you.
Puff! Puff! away you go

                                        Another drink?
Why, you may drown the earth with ale and I
Will drain it like a sea. The more I drink
The better I see that this is April time. . . .

Ben! There is one Voice which says to everything:
"Dream what you will, I'll make you bear your seed.
And, having borne, the sickle comes among ye
And takes your stalk." The rich and sappy greens
Of spring or June show life within the loins,
And all the world is fair, for now the plant
Can drink the level cup of flame where heaven
Is poured full by the sun. But when the blossom
Flutters its colors, then it takes the cup
And waves the stalk aside. And having drunk
The stalk to penury, then slumber comes
With dreams of spring stored in the imprisoned germ,
An old life and a new life all in one,
A thing of memory and of prophecy,
Of reminiscence, longing, hope and fear.
What has been ours is taken, what was ours
Becomes entailed on our seed in the spring,
Fees in possession and enjoyment too. . . .

The thing is sex, Ben. It is that which lives
And dies in us, makes April and unmakes,
And leaves a man like me at fifty-two,
Finished but living, on the pinnacle
Betwixt a death and birth, the earth consumed
And heaven rolled up to eyes whose troubled glances
Would shape again to something better—what?
Give me a woman, Ben, and I will pick
Out of this April, by this larger art
Of fifty-two, such songs as we have heard,
Both you and I, when weltering in the clouds
Of that eternity which comes in sleep,
Or in the viewless spinning of the soul
When most intense. The woman is somewhere,
And that's what tortures, when I think this field
So often gleaned could blossom once again
If I could find her.

                       Well, as to my plays:
I have not written out what I would write.
They have a thousand buds of finer flowering.
And over "Hamlet" hangs a teasing spirit
As fine to that as sense is fine to flesh.
Good friends, my soul beats up its prisoned wings
Against the ceiling of a vaster whorl
And would break through and enter. But, fair friends,
What strength in place of sex shall steady me?
What is the motive of this higher mount?
What process in the making of myself—
The very fire, as it were, of my growth—
Shall furnish forth these writings by the way,
As incident, expression of the nature
Relumed for adding branches, twigs and leaves? . . .

Suppose I'd make a tragedy of this,
Focus my fancied "Dante" to this theme,
And leave my halfwrit "Sappho," which at best

Is just another delving in the mine
That gave me "Cleopatra" and the Sonnets?
If you have genius, write my tragedy,
And call it "Shakespeare, Gentleman of Stratford,"
Who lost his soul amid a thousand souls,
And had to live without it, yet live with it
As wretched as the souls whose lives he lived.
Here is a play for you: Poor William Shakespeare,
This moment growing drunk, the famous author
Of certain sugared sonnets and some plays,
With this machine too much to him, which started
Some years ago, now cries him nay and runs
Even when the house shakes and complains, "I fall,
You shake me down, my timbers break apart.
Why, if an engine must go on like this
The building should be stronger."

                                                                    Or to mix,
And by the mixing, unmix metaphors,
No mortal man has blood enough for brains
And stomach too, when the brain is never done
With thinking and creating.

                                                                    For you see,
I pluck a flower, cut off a dragon's head—
Choose twixt these figures—lo, a dozen buds,
A dozen heads out-crop. For every fancy,
Play, sonnet, what you will, I write me out
With thinking "Now I'm done," a hundred others
Crowd up for voices, and, like twins unborn
Kick and turn o'er for entrance to the world.
And I, poor fecund creature, who would rest,
As 'twere from an importunate husband, fly
To money-lending, farming, mulberry trees,
Enclosing Welcombe fields, or idling hours
In common talk with people like the Combes.
All this to get a heartiness, a hold

On earth again, lest Heaven Hercules,
Finding me strayed to mid-air, kicking heels
Above the mountain tops, seize on my scruff
And bear me off or strangle.

                                  Good, my friends,
The "Tempest" is as nothing to the voice
That calls me to performance—what I know not.
I've planned an epic of the Asian wash
Which slopped the star of Athens and put out,
Which should all history analyze, and present
A thousand notables in the guise of life,
And show the ancient world and worlds to come
To the last blade of thought and tiniest seed
Of growth to be. With visions such as these
My spirit turns in restless ecstasy,
And this enslavéd brain is master sponge,
And sucks the blood of body, hands and feet.
While my poor spirit, like a butterfly
Gummed in its shell, beats its bedraggled wings,
And cannot rise.

                      I'm cold, both hands and feet.
These three days past I have been cold, this hour
I am warm in three days. God bless the ale.
God did do well to give us anodynes. . . .
So now you know why I am much alone,
And cannot fellow with Augustine Phillips,
John Heminge, Richard Burbage, Henry Condell,
And do not have them here, dear ancient friends,
Who grieve, no doubt, and wonder for changed love.
Love is not love which alters when it finds
A change of heart, but mine has changed not, only
I cannot be my old self. I blaspheme:
I hunger for broiled fish, but fly the touch
Of hands of flesh.

I am most passionate,
And long am used perplexities of love
To bemoan and to bewail. And do you wonder,
Seeing what I am, what my fate has been?
Well, hark you; Anne is sixty now, and I,
A crater which erupts, look where she stands
In lava wrinkles, eight years older than I am,
As years ago, but I am a youth afire
While she is lean and slippered. It's a Fury
Which takes me sometimes, makes my hands clutch out
For virgins in their teens. O sullen fancy!
I want them not, I want the love which springs
Like flame which blots the sun, where fuel of body
Is piled in reckless generosity. . . .
You are most learned, Ben, Greek and Latin know,
And think me nature's child, scarce understand
How much of physic, law, and ancient annals
I have stored up by means of studious zeal.
But pass this by, and for the braggart breath
Ensuing now say, "Will was in his cups,
Potvaliant, boozed, corned, squiffy, obfuscated,
Crapulous, inter pocula, or so forth.
Good sir, or so, or friend, or gentleman,
According to the phrase or the addition
Of man and country, on my honor, Shakespeare
At Stratford, on the twenty-second of April,
Year sixteen-sixteen of our Lord was merry—
Videlicet, was drunk." Well, where was I?—
Oh yes, at braggart breath, and now to say it:
I believe and say it as I would lightly speak
Of the most common thing to sense, outside
Myself to touch or analyze, this mind
Which has been used by Something, as I use
A quill for writing, never in this world
In the most high and palmy days of Greece,
Or in this roaring age, has known its peer.
No soul as mine has lived, felt, suffered, dreamed,

Broke open spirit secrets, followed trails
Of passions curious, countless lives explored
As I have done. And what are Greek and Latin,
The lore of Aristotle, Plato to this?
Since I know them by what I am, the essence
From which their utterance came, myself a flower
Of every graft and being in myself
The recapitulation and the complex
Of all the great. Were not brains before books?
And even geometrics in some brain
Before old Gutenberg? O fie, Ben Jonson,
If I am nature's child am I not all?
Howe'er it be, ascribe this to the ale,
And say that reason in me was a fume.
But if you honor me, as you have said,
As much as any, this side idolatry,
Think, Ben, of this: That I, whate'er I be
In your regard, have come to fifty-two,
Defeated in my love, who knew too well
That poets through the love of women turn
To satyrs or to gods, even as women
By the first touch of passion bloom or rot
As angels or as bawds.

Bethink you also
How I have felt, seen, known the mystic process
Working in man's soul from the woman soul
As part thereof in essence, spirit and flesh,
Even as a malady may be, while this thing
Is health and growth, and growing draws all life,
All goodness, wisdom for its nutriment.
Till it become a vision paradisic,
And a ladder of fire for climbing, from its topmost
Rung a place for stepping into heaven. . . .

This I have known, but had not. Nor have I
Stood coolly off and seen the woman, used

Her blood upon my palette. No, but heaven
Commanded my strength's use to abort and slay
What grew within me, while I saw the blood
Of love untimely ripped, as 'twere a child
Killed i' the womb, a harpy or an angel
With my own blood stained.

                                        As a virgin shamed
By the swelling life unlicensed needles it,
But empties not her womb of some last shred
Of flesh which fouls the alleys of her body,
And fills her wholesome nerves with poisoned sleep,
And weakness to the last of life, so I
For some shame not unlike, some need of life
To rid me of this life I had conceived
Did up and choke it too, and thence begot
A fever and a fixed debility
For killing that begot.

                        Now you see that I
Have not grown from a central dream, but grown
Despite a wound, and over the wound and used
My flesh to heal my flesh. My love's a fever
Which longed for that which nursed the malady,
And fed on that which still preserved the ill,
The uncertain, sickly appetite to please.
My reason, the physician to my love,
Angry that his prescriptions are not kept
Has left me. And as reason is past care
I am past cure, with ever more unrest
Made frantic-mad, my thoughts as madmen's are,
And my discourse at random from the truth,
Not knowing what she is, who swore her fair
And thought her bright, who is as black as hell
And dark as night.

But list, good gentlemen,
This love I speak of is not as a cloak
Which one may put away to wear a coat,
And doff that for a jacket, like the loves
We men are wont to have as loves or wives.
She is the very one, the soul of souls,
And when you put her on you put on light,
Or wear the robe of Nessus, poisonous fire,
Which if you tear away you tear your life,
And if you wear you fall to ashes. So
'Tis not her bed-vow broke, I have broke mine,
That ruins me; 'tis honest faith quite lost,
And broken hope that we could find each other,
And that mean more to me and less to her.
'Tis that she could take all of me and leave me
Without a sense of loss, without a tear,
And make me fool and perjured for the oath
That swore her fair and true. I feel myself
As like a virgin who her body gives
For love of one whose love she dreams is hers,
But wakes to find herself a toy of blood,
And dupe of prodigal breath, abandoned quite
For other conquests. For I gave myself,
And shrink for thought thereof, and for the loss
Of myself never to myself restored.
The urtication of this shame made plays
And sonnets, as you'll find behind all deeds
That mount to greatness, anger, hate, disgust,
But, better, love.

           To hell with punks and wenches,
Drabs, mopsies, doxies, minxes, trulls and queans,
Rips, harridans and strumpets, pieces, jades.
And likewise to the eternal bonfire lechers,
All rakehells, satyrs, goats and placket fumblers,
Gibs, breakers-in-at-catch-doors, thunder tubes.
I think I have a fever—hell and furies!

Or else this ale grows hotter i' the mouth.
Ben, if I die before you, let me waste
Richly and freely in the good brown earth,
Untrumpeted and by no bust marked out.
What good, Ben Jonson, if the world could see
What face was mine, who wrote these plays and sonnets?
Life, you have hurt me. Since Death has a veil
I take the veil and hide, and like great Cæsar
Who drew his toga round him, I depart.

Good friends, let's to the fields—I have a fever.
After a little walk, and by your pardon,
I think I'll sleep. There is no sweeter thing,
Nor fate more blessed than to sleep. Here, world,
I pass you like an orange to a child
I can no more with you. Do what you will.
What should my care be when I have no power
To save, guide, mould you? Naughty world you need me
As little as I need you: go your way!
Tyrants shall rise and slaughter fill the earth,
But I shall sleep. In wars and wars and wars
The ever-replenished youth of earth shall shriek
And clap their gushing wounds—but I shall sleep,
Nor earthy thunder wake me when the cannon
Shall shake the throne of Tartarus. Orators
Shall fulmine over London or America
Of rights eternal, parchments, sacred charters
And cut each others' throats when reason fails—
But I shall sleep. This globe may last and breed
The race of men till Time cries out "How long?"
But I shall sleep ten thousand thousand years.
I am a dream, Ben, out of a blessed sleep—
Let's walk and hear the lark.

CARL VAN DOREN Why he selected

~~~~ SWIFT and VANESSA

(The story of a passion which for a time contended with Swift's lifelong affection for Esther Johnson whom he called Stella.)

The piece of writing I would most like to be represented by is to be found in my *Swift* (Viking, 1930) beginning with the words "He had met Vanessa" on page 147 and running to the bottom of page 167. Please call it: "Swift and Vanessa."

As to my reasons: I think I am better in biography than in any other form, and better in *Swift* and *Franklin* than in any other of my biographical writings. The Vanessa episode is more nearly independent than any other in either of these two books and loses less by being separated from the whole. Moreover I think I have here come nearest to setting forth a complete situation and fully characterizing the persons involved.

New York, N. Y.   CARL VAN DOREN
February 16, 1942

JONATHAN SWIFT had met Vanessa (Esther Vanhomrigh) early in 1708 in London, where her mother was living with her children. It pleased the mother to call the daughter younger than she was, and it did not displease the daughter. She was a sleepy girl, still, at twenty, undecided between the nursery and the drawing-room, moody, idle, intelligent. Swift, at first considering her a child, discovered in her a mind, and was irresistibly, humorously impelled to shape it. "She had good principles," he wrote three years later, "and I have corrected all her faults." She had, however, the passion of sleepy women, not the obedience of Stella.

To that passion Swift was blind, first carelessly, then deliberately. No doubt he felt it. He had put his entire energy into his pride. His

683

senses, no matter how cold towards women, must have learned that the relationship with Stella, no matter how close and kind, was sometimes dry and mild. She was nearly a wife, and some routine had got into their companionship. Vanessa was younger. Vanessa was new. Swift, for all his prudence, enjoyed the tumult in her disposition. Because he held her, as he seems always to have done, at a safe arm's-length, he was obtuse to her eagerness. Obtuse and insufficiently concerned. Being forty, he could not quite resist such warmth from a girl, did not have quite the courage to put out such a fire or leave it. Too scrupulous or too temperate to make the full use of Vanessa's passion, he went on idling within its perilous range. He was surprised when he found that he had on his hands a mistress as extraordinary as the wife he had in Ireland.

Stella the extraordinary wife. Vanessa the extraordinary mistress. Swift the extraordinary husband and lover. No other terms will bound the extraordinary triangle. Gossip then and gossip since has wasted its strength in trying to find out whether Swift was technically lover or husband to either of the women. What if he was? What if he was not? The drama remains the same.

Stella was for nearly forty years, child and woman, "the truest, most virtuous and valuable friend that I," Swift said, "or perhaps any other person, ever was blessed with." Call Stella his wife or be pedantic. Vanessa was for fifteen years his occasional companion, his delight, his torment, to whom he wrote—in bad French—that there was no merit nor any proof of his good taste in his finding in her all that nature had given any mortal in the way of honour, virtue, sense, wit, tenderness, agreeableness, and firmness of spirit. Call Vanessa his mistress or be pedantic. One side of Swift looked towards a wife, one towards a mistress. He maintained between them a singular course, but it was no more singular than his character. He was, after all, only one man loved by two women.

The friendship begun in 1708 between Swift and Vanessa, anxious to be possessed but willing to be taught, was kept up during that stay in England and, by letters, during his next absence in Ireland. When he returned to become a Tory in 1710 he had so lavish a welcome from the Vanhomrighs that their house became almost his. He lived near them, dined with them often and then more often, and had a small room there in which to read and write.

Stella, hearing about them, seems to have sniffed. "You say they are of no consequence," he answered her. "Why, they keep as good female company as I do male. I see all the drabs of quality at this end of the town with them." He spoke in his journal rather of the mother or of the whole family than of Vanessa.

When, having taken to Chelsea in the spring of 1711, he walked more or less daily to London and back, he kept his best gown and periwig at the Vanhomrigh house, and called twice a day to change. Vanessa, with the family, possibly visited him in Chelsea, as she probably did at Kensington in the summer of the year after. The Vanhomrighs certainly visited Swift at Windsor in September 1712, and Vanessa was on some score disappointed. "Why then," he wrote, "you should not have come, and I knew that as well as you."

So far any strong feelings there may have been in either of them had not risen into words. He teased her for her dawdling, for her chiding, for her jealousy of her younger sister, for her habit of coaxing him for political secrets. She complained, rather childishly, of his neglect of her when he was out of London. Their letters might have been between Swift and any young woman of his acquaintance.

But when he went to Ireland in June 1713, sick of England, Vanessa could not endure the stern break which suited him. The four letters she wrote before she got an answer were disconsolate. "I find no conversation on earth comparable but yours." She had heard of his illness. "Oh! what would I give to know how you do at this instant. My fortune is too hard. Your absence was enough, without this cruel addition." "How could you be so cruel, to defer telling me the thing of the world I wished most to know? If you think I write too much, your only way is to tell me so, or at least to write to me again, that I may know you don't quite forget me; for I very much fear that I never employ a thought of yours now, except when you are reading my letters, which makes me ply you with them. . . . If you are very happy it is ill-natured of you not to tell me, except 'tis what is inconsistent with mine."

Swift could not mistake this last clause. In seven words Vanessa made plain that she was wondering whether he could be happy without her, asking whether he was by any dreadful chance happy with some one else, announcing that she thought of him and her as having their happiness in common. His answer put cold oceans between them.

"I had your last spleenatic letter. I told you when I left England I would endeavour to forget everything there, and would write as seldom as I could. I did indeed design one general round of letters to my friends, but my health has not yet suffered me. I design to pass the greatest part of the time I stay in Ireland here in the cabin where I am now writing; neither will I leave the kingdom till I am called for; and if they have no further service for me I will never see England again. At my first coming I thought I should have died with discontent, and was horribly melancholy while they were installing me. But it begins to wear off and change to dulness. My river walk is extremely pretty, and my canal in great beauty, and I see trouts playing in it."

Her ardour, that is, he saw as spleen. He meant to forget her along with all the others. If he were to go back it would be to politics. He was dull but not melancholy. Vanessa would be glad to know that there were fish in his canal.

Politics called Swift back in September, to London and to Vanessa. There are no letters belonging to that winter, but there is the poem, apparently written then, in which Swift told the story of Cadenus (that is *Decanus*, dean) and Vanessa.

He began lightly, with the graces of a contemporary wit. The shepherds and the nymphs, he said, had gone to law before the court of Venus, the nymphs accusing the shepherds of resisting love, the shepherds defending themselves by the counter-accusation that, thanks to the nymphs, "modern love" was no longer

> *"A fire celestial, chaste, refined,*
> *Conceived and kindled in the mind,"*

but had become a "gross desire," moving through caprice and folly. Venus, unable to decide the suit, had undertaken an experiment, and had endowed Vanessa, happily new-born, with all the virtues which the Queen of Love—or Swift—thought most "lovely in the female kind": "a sweetness above all perfumes," a cleanliness "incapable of outward stains," a mind as modest as "the speech of prudes," and a "gentle, soft, engaging air." Not yet satisfied, Venus had fooled Pallas into thinking that the baby was a boy, and had obtained for her the other virtues "for manly bosoms chiefly fit": "knowledge, judgment, wit," "justice, truth, and fortitude," "honor which no breath can stain," "open heart and bounteous hand," and, since "meat must be with money bought," as Pallas knew, "some small regard for state and wealth" and a useful fortune of five thousand pounds.

The romantic Venus, when all this was done, had looked for the restoration of her power. The realistic Pallas—

> *"For how can heavenly wisdom prove*
> *An instrument to earthly love?"*—

had, though enraged by the deceit, left "all things to their natural course." And Pallas was justified. The beaux, when Vanessa came to town, listened to her hermaphroditic discourses—

> *"Through nature and through art she ranged,*
> *And gracefully her subject changed"*—

and thought her tiresome. The belles, disgusted by her lack of interest in clothes and gossip, thought her old-fashioned.

> *"To copy her few nymphs aspired;*
> *Her virtues fewer swains admired."*

Vanessa hardened her heart and turned her back on the world.

Was the actual Vanessa, when she had read this far, pleased with the figure she cut in the fable? Or did the actual Cadenus, if he read it to her, notice that she twisted in her chair?

The verses went on. Cupid, zealous for his mother's credit, resolved to conquer the adamant Vanessa. At first he wasted shaft after shaft. Cadenus, the girl's tutor, protected her by "placing still some book

betwixt" her and the mischievous god. Cupid saw he must include
the tutor in his revenge. At a time when Cadenus—

> *"Grown old in politics and wit,*
> *Caressed by ministers of state,*
> *Of half mankind the dread and hate"—*

was reading to her, on her demand, from his "poetic works," Cupid
shot a dart of such length that it pierced the volume and, carrying with
it "some lines more moving than the rest," reached Vanessa's heart.
Unlucky Vanessa.

> *"Cadenus, common forms apart,*
> *In every scene had kept his heart,*
> *Had sighed and languished, vowed and **writ**,*
> *For pastime, or to shew his wit,*
> *But books and time and state affairs*
> *Had spoiled his fashionable airs.*
> *He now could praise, esteem, approve,*
> *But understood not what was love.*
> *His conduct might have made him **styled***
> *A father, and the nymph his child.*
> *That innocent delight he took*
> *To see the virgin mind her book*
> *Was but the master's secret joy*
> *In school to hear the finest boy."*

Not having seen the malevolent arrow, he was amazed at the sudden change in his pupil. She seemed to listen more than ever but she
could not keep her mind on what he said. Modestly he conjectured
that he had bored her with studies too grave for her "tender sex and
age." He should have known better. "Nature must be nature still." If
she would excuse him, he would take his leave. But Vanessa, it soon
appeared, had learned what he had taught her.

> *"Now, said the nymph, to let you see*
> *My actions with your rules agree,*

> *That I can vulgar forms despise,*
> *And have no secrets to disguise . . .*
> *Your lessons found the weakest part,*
> *Aimed at the head but reached the heart."*

Cadenus was overwhelmed with "shame, disappointment, guilt, surprise." He could not doubt her words, but he thought he must pretend to, out of policy. The difference in their ages was too great. Love between them would be a scandal. He told her she must not seem so tragic when, as he knew, she was only joking.

Vanessa was too good a disputant to be put off. Reason, she insisted, was her guide in love. In loving him she was only loving the virtues and merits which she had observed in him and had made her own. Her love was as strong as self-love, for it was that. She had seen him full of "love, esteem, and awe" for dead geniuses. Surely he would have felt the same emotions if he had lived when they did. Then consider her case. She lived in the same age with a great genius. It was as much her duty as her instinct to adore him.

> *"Cadenus answers every end,*
> *The book, the author, and the friend.*
> *The utmost her desires will reach*
> *Is but to learn what he can teach.*
> *His converse is a system fit*
> *Alone to fill up all her wit,*
> *While every passion of her mind*
> *In him is centred and confined."*

In that flood of reasons Cadenus wavered. They were his own reasons, thrown back at him with his skill. He could not think them bad reasons. He was proud of his pupil for her eloquence. His pride, called up by her, stayed to caress him. If he had been preferred to all the "colonels, lords, and beaux" by "so bright a nymph" whom he had never thought of courting, he must have the qualities which she saw in him.

> *" 'Tis an old maxim in the schools*
> *That flattery's the food of fools,*

> *Yet now and then your men of wit*
> *Will condescend to take a bit."*

Cadenus could not withstand her tribute. Love, of course, was out of the question.

> *"Love why do we one passion call*
> *When 'tis a compound of them all?*
> *Where hot and cold, where sharp and sweet,*
> *In all their equipages meet,*
> *Where pleasure mixed with pains appear,*
> *Sorrow with joy, and hope with fear,*
> *Wherein his dignity and age*
> *Forbid Cadenus to engage."*

But he could offer friendship, "a constant, rational delight," which was rooted in virtue and so could last, as shifting love could not. "Gratitude, respect, esteem": those she could have to make up for his want of passion. He talked high about friendship.

Vanessa brought him down. If he was to give her "devotion, duty, and respect," their rôles would be changed. She would, however, take him at his word. He could be pupil and she be tutor, though she could see already that he would have a hard time with the science she had in mind for him. Any fool knew more than Cadenus about love.

The actual Vanessa, reading or listening, must have nodded, not with sleep. Did she stamp when the poem broke off?

> *"But what success Vanessa met*
> *Is to the world a secret yet*
> *Whether the nymph to please her swain*
> *Talks in a high romantic strain,*
> *Or whether he at last descends*
> *To act with less seraphic ends,*
> *Or, to compound the business, whether*
> *They temper love and books together,*
> *Must never to mankind be told,*
> *Nor shall the conscious Muse unfold."*

Did the reader or the listener follow the last lines of the fable, in which, with another flourish of contemporary grace, Venus decided against the shepherds, said her experiment had failed, left the world in the hands of her son, "harnessed her doves, and flew to heaven"?

The tragedy of Vanessa was that Swift saw their drama as a comedy. Experience had fortified him against this scene. With Stella—

> *"When men began to call me fair*
> *You interposed your timely care"*—

Swift had already played Cadenus. If his temper had ever inclined him to love, or if his years had left him more audacity, or if he had been less absorbed in the great campaign of his pride, he might have responded to Vanessa—or if, of course, he had felt for her that kind of passion which makes the sun, or the moon, of a fresh love seem to shine on an earth just created. He met none of these conditions. He had an impulse to regulate her mind, but not to possess her person. He even believed that the desire he had was more important than the one he lacked. Cold towards Vanessa as flesh and blood, he was warm only towards the idea of being loved by her.

It was his pride which glowed. If, at the declaration, he had either loved or hated Vanessa he would have known what to do. He would have taken her or he would have gone from her, in the storm of any consequences. As it was, he let his pride seduce him as she could not. Its device was simple. It argued with him, as no doubt Vanessa did, that her fiery need of him obliged him to be kind. He hesitated. She was quick to snatch at her advantage. Give her the present, and she would not worry about the future. Give her what he could give, and she would not ask for more. These were promises which no shrewd man would have trusted. He would have seen through them to what lay behind: the hope that if he could be held he could be won: the assurance that any kindness he might show would be more than kindness, would be the selfishness which she longed to find in him. Swift was not shrewd. Moved if not convinced, he agreed to do what he could to please her, not realizing how much it was to indulge himself.

Then, almost as if to clear himself of a last annoying suspicion, he told the story of Cadenus and Vanessa in the bold but humorous light in which he saw it. Such lucidity as his would have overpowered a stronger woman than Vanessa. Whether his version was at all points accurate or not, she had to fall into the place which his comedy had assigned her.

But she could struggle. The rest of her life was largely taken up by her efforts to get out of the poem and nearer to the poet. Swift, having made the blunder of undertaking to meet love with kindness, could never undo it. Vanessa pursued him like the ghost of his blunder. In August 1714, when he had sullenly retired to Berkshire, she surprised him with a visit. "You should not have come by Wantage for a thousand pound. You used to brag you were very discreet. Where is it gone?" As soon as he had settled in Ireland, Vanessa followed. Her mother, having died, had left the daughters something of a fortune, including a handsome house at Celbridge eleven miles out of Dublin. From her house in the country or from occasional lodgings in town Vanessa implored him.

"Once I had a friend that would see me sometimes, and either commend what I did or advise me what to do, which banished all my uneasiness. But now, when my misfortunes are increased by being in a disagreeable place, amongst strange, prying, deceitful people, whose company is so far from an amusement that it is a very great punishment, you fly me, and give me no reason but that we are amongst fools and must submit. I am very well satisfied that we are amongst such, but know no reason for having my happiness sacrificed to their caprice. You once had a maxim, which was to act what was right and not mind what the world said. I wish you would keep to it now. Pray what can be wrong in seeing and advising an unhappy young woman? I can't imagine. You can't but know that your frowns make my life insupportable. You have taught me to distinguish and then you leave me miserable."

Swift answered only that he had "ever feared the tattle of this nasty town, and told you so." He begged her to be easy if he saw her still less often. "These are accidents in life that are necessary and must be submitted to."

Vanessa was not so frantic that she could mistake disinclination for discretion. "You bid me be easy, and you'd see me as often as you could. You had better said as often as you could get the better of your inclinations so much, or as often as you remembered that there was such a one in the world. If you continue to treat me as you do you will not be made uneasy by me long. 'Tis impossible to describe what I have suffered since I saw you last. I am sure I could have bore the rack better than those killing, killing words of yours. Sometimes I have resolved to die without seeing you more; but those resolves, to your misfortune, did not last long. . . . The reason I write to you is because I cannot tell it you, should I see you. For when I begin to complain, then you are angry, and there is something in your look so awful that it strikes me dumb. . . . I say as little as ever I can. Did you but know what I thought I am sure it would move you. Forgive me, and believe I cannot help telling you this and live."

There are ways to get rid of importunate Vanessas, but they are ways unknown to men who can try to be kind to women desperately in love with them. Swift, with his variations of temper, was the worst man in the world for this Vanessa. In one letter he could write: "A fig for your letters and messages"; and in another: "I cannot see you, I fear, today, having affairs of my place to do; but pray think it not want of friendship or tenderness, which I will always continue to the utmost." Vanessa, prying into every sentence to see what might be hidden in it, turning every word over and over with a lover's feverish research, could arrive at the security neither of hope nor of despair.

The affair dragged on, irresistible passion matched with immovable affection. Swift was Dean of St. Patrick's, known to be the friend, and by some gossips thought to be the husband, of Stella, who, though she did not live at the deanery, was the centre of such life as it had. He refused to give the world the least excuse for regarding Vanessa as his mistress. He smothered her with discretion, hating it yet unable to take a final stand at one extremity or another. When he had snubbed her long enough to put an end to any ordinary suit, he would turn kind, would insist upon his esteem and admiration, and so would once more rouse her. He could or would not learn that her love and his kindness were oil and water.

During the half-dozen dark years after he left the Court for Ireland he perversely relished the secret drama, whatever form it took, and let himself be drawn into various cautious meetings with Vanessa. When, towards the end of that eclipse, he began to be more thoroughly himself, he became less cautious. His whole nature, as if by some rejuvenation, expanded. He took up the cause of Ireland against the Whigs. He wrote verses, tender, intimate, teasing, to Stella. As if he thought the conflict between him and Vanessa was settled, he tried to get back to the old footing.

Instantly her desire flared up. "I here tell you," she wrote to him, "that I have determined to try all manner of human arts to reclaim you." He did what he could to laugh off her seriousness, even to praising the art with which she wrote. Nothing would now quiet her. His least kindness intoxicated her. When he told her to use assumed names in her letters, which he was afraid might be opened, and dashes for "everything that may be said to Cad—— at beginning or conclusion," she was suddenly in raptures over sharing secrets with him. "———— Cad——, you are good beyond expression, and I will never quarrel again if I can help it." Swift did not take warning.

"What would you give," he asked her in August 1720, "to have the history of Cad—— and —— exactly written, through all its steps, from the beginning to this time? I believe it would do well in verse, and be as long as the other. I hope it will be done. It ought to be an exact chronicle of twelve years, from the time of spilling the coffee to drinking of coffee, from Dunstable to Dublin, with every single passenger since. There would be the chapter of the blister; the chapter of Madam going to Kensington; the chapter of the Colonel's going to France; the chapter of the wedding, with the adventure of the lost key; of the strain; of the joyful return; two hundred chapters of madness; the chapter of long walks; the Berkshire surprise; fifty chapters of little times; the chapter of Chelsea; the chapter of swallow and cluster; a hundred whole books of myself and so low; the chapter of hide and whisper; the chapter of Who made it so? My sister's money."

Vanessa, answering that "it would be too much once to hope for such a history," asked him "did those circumstances crowd on you, or did you recollect them to make me happy?" But, though she might suspect that he had meant to please her, she could not help exulting that he had remembered. She was not sure friendship had such a memory. She knew love had.

Swift had suggested that he might, for the first time, visit her at Celbridge. "Is it possible you will come and see me? I beg for God's sake you will." He did visit her. Back in Dublin he advised her to take more exercise, be cheerful, "read pleasant things that will make you laugh, and not sit moping with your elbows on your knees on a little stool by the fire."

Vanessa was out of hand. "I . . . here declare that 'tis not in the power of art, time, or accident to lessen the unexpressible passion which I have for — — —. Put my passion under the utmost restraint, send me as distant from you as the earth will allow, yet you cannot banish those charming ideas which will ever stick by me whilst I have the use of memory. Nor is the love I bear you only seated in my soul, for there is not a single atom of my frame that is not blended with it. . . . For heaven's sake tell me what has caused this prodigious change in you which I have found of late. If you have the least remains of pity for me left, tell me tenderly. No, don't tell it so that it may cause my present death; and don't suffer me to lead a life like a languishing death, which is the only life I can lead if you have lost any of your tenderness for me."

Swift did not reply. The death of Vanessa's sister revived the correspondence, which went on with the same disparity. "The worst thing in you and me," he wrote, "is that we are too hard to please, and whether we have not made ourselves is the question. . . . We differ prodigiously in one point: I fly from the spleen to the world's end, you run out of your way to meet it." He urged her—Swift of all men— to accept what came and be pleased with it. She did her best to be the kind of philosopher he specified, but "I find the more I think the more unhappy I am."

In his last surviving letter to her he reminded her of the pleasant episodes "of Windsor, Cleveland Row, Ryder Street, St. James's, Kensington, the Sluttery, the Colonel in France. . . . Cad thinks often of these, especially on horseback, as I am assured. What a foolish thing is time, and how foolish is man who would be as angry if time stopped as if it passed." This was in August 1722. Vanessa died in June 1723.

The end of the story is all gossip. It says that Vanessa, unable to endure her jealousy, wrote to Swift, or to Stella, asking if it were true that Stella was Swift's wife. It says in one account that Stella answered that she was, in another that she sent the letter to Swift to answer. It says that Swift took the letter from Vanessa to Stella, or to him, and with it rode savagely to Celbridge, entered the room where Vanessa was, threw down the letter, gave Vanessa a look which for the last time struck her dumb and, without one of his "killing, killing words," left the house. It says that Vanessa thereupon changed her will, leaving her fortune to strangers, not to Swift, and died.

All gossip, any of it true, or none. Vanessa did leave her fortune to strangers and did not mention Swift among the friends to whom she gave small legacies to buy mourning rings. Something had parted Cadenus and Vanessa before she died. The parting was natural, but tragically late. She had loved a man whose thoughts, she said, "no human creature is capable of guessing at, because never any one living thought like you." She had spent her life trying to win him, and he had let her spend it. Dying, she planned what revenge was left to her, the publication of his poem about Cadenus and Vanessa and of the letters between them.

When the poem, though not the letters, appeared in 1726 to the comfort of his enemies, Swift kept silence. It had been, he told a friend, a "cavalier business," "a private humoursome thing which by an accident inevitable and the baseness of particular malice" had been made public. "I never saw it since I writ it." He refused to "use shifts or arts" to justify himself, "let people think of me as they please. . . . I have borne a great deal more." He had gone through what was comedy for him and tragedy for Vanessa. Others must make up their own minds, if they had them, about who was to blame, if there must be blame, when a universal Héloïse encountered a special Abélard.

HENDRIK WILLEM VAN LOON

Why he selected BEETHOVEN

I am very bad—I am happy to say—at writing things about my own literary products and always leave it to outsiders. Haven't you got some clever boy or girl who could do that job nicely? I don't mind the labor involved, but that book has now "left home" and we are more or less strangers.

Old Greenwich, Conn. HENDRIK WILLEM VAN LOON
June 20, 1942

AFTER Wolfgang Amadeus Mozart came another subject of their Imperial and Royal Apostolic Majesties of Vienna, by the name of Ludwig van Beethoven.

To little Wolfgang, Papa had always come next to God. To little Ludwig, the word "father" was synonymous with the Devil. For the author of his being was a shiftless, drunken, ill-tempered hack musician, who during the soberer days of his youth had held a minor position in the choir of the Archbishop Elector of Cologne. But having heard of the success of the little Mozart boy (as who had not?) he decided to do likewise with his own offspring. At the age of five he started to teach him the fiddle and got nowhere at all. For Ludwig was no Wolferl. He was as obstinate as a dozen mules, and all his life long he was as independent of spirit as a truck weaving its way through a post road full of flivvers.

These qualities were his good right. They had come to him as part of his racial heritage. You know perhaps what a great role the city of Antwerp has played in the history of painting. It has been either the birthplace or the home of Quentin Matsys, Frans Hals, Jordaens, Rubens, Van Dyck, and the two Pieter Breughels. In the middle of the seventeenth century a little music was added to this rather un-balanced artistic diet. The family of the Van Beethovens made its appearance among the list of citizens.

It was Ludwig's grandfather who had moved from Antwerp to Cologne. He too had been a musician and so had his son, the tipsy tenor. And so his grandson was going to be, if blood and tradition counted for anything. The grandfather died in 1774 when Ludwig was only four years old, but he always remembered him kindly. He also retained happy memories of his mother. She had been a very simple woman, a servant in the household of the Elector. She too had deserted him when he was most in need of her love and her care. For it must have been dreadfully humiliating for a boy of his type, proud and independent and conscious of his superior ability, to feel that his father was an object of pity and contempt in the sight of his neighbors. In a little city like Bonn everybody knew everything about everybody else, and the fact that young Ludwig was entrusted with his father's wages because otherwise (as the authorities knew only too well) all the money would be spent on liquor must have been common knowledge in that old and gossipy city on the Rhine.

There were several other relatives. They played quite a role in Ludwig's life, for they became an everlasting source of nuisance. When they did well for themselves they never lifted a finger to help their queer brother. When in need, they unceremoniously dropped all their troubles in his lap and shrieked like hungry harpies for his support "because he must remember that he was their brother." And finally they left him with a nephew who was perhaps not quite as black a sheep as posterity has made him out to be but who was a dull and lazy fellow and therefore always in some sort of trouble. Nothing very wicked. Nothing very scandalous. Just annoying trifles, such as spending more than he should spend or marrying the wrong girl at the wrong moment.

But lawsuits and police-court proceedings do not go well with symphonies and sonatas. No one of the Beethoven family, however, seems to have worried about that. They had not the slightest conception of their brother's greatness. All they knew was that he was on intimate personal terms with some of the greatest names of the Austrian Empire. A man who had the entree, so to speak, of all the palaces of the imperial capital should be able to do something for his loving brothers and sisters. He need not live in a couple of shabby rooms in a shabby street and go about in shabby clothes with long, wild hair (he surely could afford an occasional visit to the barber!) and holes in the soles of his boots. He could keep a servant so that his rooms would not look like a pigsty and that he might be fed decently and at regular hours. And above all things, he should use his influence to get favors for his own kith and kin. Those dedications to all sort of excellencies and highnesses were all very well but cash in hand would have been much pleasanter.

A pretty sordid tragedy. But a very common one since that unhappy day when the arts and life parted company, which they began to do during the end of the eighteenth century.

I here must introduce a word which no American can ever hope to "feel" quite as deeply as a European. Compared to Europe we are still in that happy stage of our economic development where we can truthfully claim that we are not conscious of any definite "classes." Birds of a feather will always flock together. The man with an income of a hundred thousand a year will live a different existence from the man with only a thousand. But in America even today the road is not definitely blocked against the poor devil with twenty-five dollars a week. His chances may be very slim, but they exist. In the Austria (and for that matter, in the Europe) of the eighteenth century, there was no way of escape. All the lower middle class could hope to do was to maintain itself without losing ground and slipping down into the subbasement of those who were only *Volk*—just "people."

As the royal patron was rapidly going out of fashion, now that artists were beginning to deal in a commodity that was to be at everybody's disposal, a career as an artist meant a highly risky voyage into the realm of uncertainty. But uncertainty was the nightmare of all respectable shopkeepers and of all minor officials and of all the thousand and one groups whose trades or professions allowed them to cling to the idea of their still being *anständige Bürger*—respectable citizens. In Austria, where even today after a whole series of socialistic forms of government, the feudal system has survived for so much longer than anywhere else, an artist—a person blessed by the divine touch—could still occasionally be treated as an equal by his social superiors who ruled their fellow men by the divine right of having been born as their fathers' children.

As many of the aristocrats of the end of the Rococo period happened to be men of taste and discrimination, and as all of them were more or less tinged with a touch of the dangerous Rousseau doctrines about "equality," Beethoven had an easier time of it than those who came after him. Besides, absurd though it may seem to modern ears, that "van" made it a little easier to associate with him than with a plain Herr Mozart. The "van" meant the same thing it means in my own name—just exactly nothing. But it could be abbreviated into a single small "v." A symphony by Ludwig v. Beethoven looked much more imposing than one by plain Johann Kuhnau. As you may remember, even poor Sebastian Bach had not been able to escape from the illusion that the title of a "royal court *Kapellmeister*" would help him in his struggles with the town counselors and church authorities of Leipzig.

The Beethoven brothers had the same name and yet, as you may well object, did not do them any good. Of course not. They were just common, ordinary people. But a small "v." plus genius—that was a combination which meant a great deal in Vienna during the beginning of the nineteenth century. It even meant that Beethoven (who today would have been seriously suspected of leanings toward the Left) could get away with his rudeness and on occasions could even afford to be grossly and unnecessarily rude to a Royal Majesty without suffering any unpleasant consequences. "What do you expect? He's just poor old Beethoven, one must take him as he is. After all, he's a genius." And so the Austrian aristocracy tolerated the old fellow (who was not really old at all, but a man who had never been young) and were kind to him when he had been insufferably boorish and overbearing on account of some imaginary slight. When he died, they had to call out the army to keep order in the streets through which the coffin passed. Everybody was there. For it was he, old Ludwig, who had avenged all the humiliations which Austria had suffered at the hands of the Corsican usurper.

In his younger days, full of hope and enthusiasm for the cause of liberty and equality, he had written a symphony in honor of General Bonaparte, the prophet of these new revolutionary ideals. Then General Bonaparte made himself the Emperor Napoleon, and liberty and equality were removed from the battle flags of the republic. The will of a single capital letter *N* was henceforth to be the law of an entire continent. Whereupon Ludwig van Beethoven, the old radical, took the manuscript of his symphony (the third one, as we now count them) and scratched out all reference to the Judas who had betrayed the cause of popular government. He scribbled across the cover: "A Heroic Symphony to Celebrate the Memory of a Great Man." And in this way, Napoleon's final obituary was written a dozen years before he suffered defeat at Waterloo.

Beethoven came to Vienna in the year 1792. He was sent there by the Archbishop Elector of Cologne who wanted this talented young man to have the best training that was to be had. As Vienna at that time was the center of music, it was to Vienna that he must go. His teachers were old Papa Haydn, who just kept on living and working and smiling his pleasant smile, and Salieri, who had been such a bitter enemy of poor Mozart, now dead and buried in his nameless grave.

The reason why Haydn was chosen was a personal one. The old gentleman on his way to England had passed through Bonn and had there heard some of Ludwig's compositions. And the Archbishop had used the occasion to recommend his young protégé to one whom all the world then regarded as the founder of the "new music."

A word about that new music which introduces the (to me) hopelessly difficult subject of harmony. First of all, what is harmony? The accepted definitions will not help me very much. They merely substitute one set of terms for another. Here is the way one of the standard musical dictionaries defines harmony: "Harmony," so it writes, "as a general term means an agreeable combination of tones. More exactly, any simultaneous sounding of tones as opposed to melody, or concord as opposed to discord." If this were true, if harmony were indeed "any agreeable combination of tones," how ought we to define the music of Hindemith or Schönberg, both of whom are "harmonists" (for do they not belong to the contrapuntal school)? Yet neither of whom apparently is in the least little bit interested in pro-

ducing tone combinations that are "agreeable" to the ears of most
of their contemporaries.

I am not writing this in a critical spirit of disapproval, for I realize
how rapidly we can attune our ears to what at first strikes us as an
offensive combination of sounds. I am only too conscious of the fact
that when I heard Debussy's *Cathédrale engloutie* for the first time it
was quite as much of a torture as sitting through Stravinski's *Fire-
bird*. Yet today I can listen to these compositions quite happily and
they sound about as tame and inoffensive as an aria by Pergolesi or
Rossini. If I live another thirty years I shall perhaps feel the same
way about some of the latest products of the atonality specialists
whose work now reminds me of a child of three or four in one of our
modern schools, where the little darlings are supposed to "express
themselves," hammering away at a piano with one hand and eating
a piece of cake with the other. But I may learn. Besides, none of these
problems, involving our personal tastes, can ever hope to be settled by
the application of an esthetic slide rule.

All this, however, does not get me any nearer to an explanation of
the word "harmony." Let me try to do it this way. Try for a moment
to think of music in the form of lines. The old polyphonic music, the
music that was written from the beginning of time until the days of
Bach (the last of the polyphonic musicians) would then be represented
by horizontal lines:

———————   ———————   ———————

———————   ———————   ———————

While the newer form of music, that harmony which only goes back
to the days of Bach's successors, would then be represented by vertical lines:

| | | | | |

Or, instead of many voices that sang independently of each other
(but each one adhering to certain very strict rules and always keeping the correct interval), they now moved in chord formation. This
produced a fuller and freer method but not so pure as that which had
gone before. And therefore there is something strict and formal in the
music of Bach and Handel and all their predecessors which we miss in

the music of the "harmonic" masters. But again I shall have to ask you to let some competent musician explain this to you on the piano. He can accomplish more in five minutes while giving you a few concrete examples to which you can listen than I can hope to do with a million words which you are obliged to read.

The same stories were being told since the beginning of time but the mode of expression was a different one. Shakespeare and Chaucer had just as much to say as Eugene O'Neill and Sinclair Lewis. But they spoke in a different language.

Harmony, of course, is not something that was invented one fine day by some great musical genius. It developed very slowly and took centuries to be recognized for what it was. Here and there in medieval music we occasionally hear something that sounds to us very much like a harmonic color effect. But harmony in our modern sense of the word does not really make its appearance until the latter half of the eighteenth century and it was then identified with the "great Bach" as Karl Philipp Emanuel was called by his contemporaries who knew him much better than they did his father, Johann Sebastian.

Philipp Emanuel was a good and dutiful son, well aware of his father's great abilities, as proof whereof I offer you his attempts to get the old man's *Art of the Fugue* engraved and printed—a disastrous publishing venture which ended with the sale of exactly thirty copies. His father had trained him to be a harpsichord virtuoso and as such he was engaged at the court of Frederick the Great to accompany His Majesty when he played the flute. From Berlin he went to Hamburg to succeed Georg Philipp Telemann as general director of church music, and there he died in 1788.

Many of his contemporaries hated him most bitterly, for he was the first man who had ever written a handbook on the art of playing the piano, in which the technique of that instrument (growing originally out of the technique for the lute or the violin) was now made the subject of certain definite laws of digital behavior, such as an equal development of both the left hand and the right, a regular way of playing scales, and numberless other little items which give children without talent such an intense dislike for that big black box in the front parlor.

This same Philipp Emanuel Bach is also often mentioned as the great prophet of the new "harmonic" school of composition, and his recommendations for this honor came from sources that are entirely beyond reproach. For Haydn, Mozart, and Beethoven, all three in great harmonic unison, sang his praises as the father of the new music . . .

Beethoven was fortunate in that he got a thorough grounding in both the old and the new style of music. In Bonn, his first teacher, Neefe, made him study Bach's *Well-Tempered Clavichord* until he knew that work by heart. Afterwards in Vienna, Salieri and Albrechtsberger, both of them excellent teachers, drilled him until there was no form of music, old or new in which he was not completely at home. And so, in contrast to Mozart and other precociously clever children, he did not really begin to compose until he knew his craft and knew it inside out and outside in.

Like Bach and Kant and Rembrandt, he never felt the need of visiting foreign countries in order to widen his own horizon. He sometimes withdrew to one of the villages near Vienna that he might be able to compose without interruptions on the part of either welcome friends or unwelcome admirers. But for the rest he was quite content to "live within himself." This may explain the modern craze for travel. When there is nothing to explore at home, one must find solace in contemplating the scenery of distant lands.

The statistical data in connection with his life are very simple. He was never very rich and never quite as poor as he made out to be. His brothers and sisters-in-law and afterwards his beloved but worthless nephew cost him a lot of money and, being a very bad financier, he was always hard up. Nor, I am sorry to say, was he himself always entirely scrupulous in dealing with his patrons, especially with his devoted and generous admirers in England. But his complaints about the neglect with which his contemporaries treated him, about his shabby clothes, about his days and nights without a crust of bread to still the pangs of hunger—all these belong to the realm of, let us call it, "musical license."

He was in his own manners, in his entire way of living, as shiftless as his drunken father. His rooms were always in a mess. Pianos covered with dirty dishes and manuscript sheets of the Ninth Symphony, a bed that had not been made for days or weeks, a washstand dangerously balancing itself on three legs, coats and shirts (none too clean) on the chairs and on the only sofa, more sheets of manuscript paper on the floor, scores of other people's music (sent to him for his approval) lying on top of the cupboard, covered with a heavy layer of dust, and rarely a window open for air, for the Master believed that fresh air was very bad for his bronchitis. Once in a while a slatternly servant would make her appearance to try to put some semblance of order into this mess. But old Ludwig would haggle with her over a groschen she was supposed to have wasted on his sauerkraut and the slavey would vanish again amidst a volley of loud vituperations, for like all members of his class (accustomed to that degrading miserliness which is the result of generations which have never had quite enough for their daily needs), Beethoven was never so angry as when he thought that someone in his employ had cheated him out of one of his hard-earned pennies. Meanwhile he himself squandered the pounds with a noble gesture of abundance—but only for the benefit of his own relatives. In his respectable little middle-class world, the family remained the beginning and end of all things.

Garrets are common enough in the history of the arts. Loneliness is part of the penalty every true artist pays for being different from the rest of his fellow men. But surely few people have lived as strange a life as this scowling and uncouth barbarian whose manners were those of a Flemish peasant, whose soul was that of a sensitive child, and whose genius created a new sort of music of such stark beauty and such vast dimensions that our own little everyday world seems to rattle around in it like one pea in a pod.

I shall not stress the fact that during the last dozen years of his life he was stone-deaf and therefore never heard the last of his great works. As early as the year 1800 he had noticed that he was beginning to be hard of hearing. What caused this deafness, nobody knows. The ailments of Beethoven have never been correctly diagnosed, but after his thirtieth year he rarely enjoyed a whole month of good health and his deafness was only part of his suffering. He bravely fought this most terrible of all misfortunes, and it was not really until the year 1822, after that ghastly episode when he tried to conduct a dress rehearsal of his own opera *Fidelio* and had not the slightest idea of what was happening on the stage, that he refrained from attending any further public performances of his own works. However, there are a great number of musicians with perfectly good ears who never go to a concert out of their own free will. But in the case of a man as sensitive as Ludwig van Beethoven, it was his deafness that made him avoid the companionship of his fellows. By nature he was really a very congenial soul who liked to have his friends around him and who was very fond of going to parties and meeting people and who (may Heaven have mercy upon his soul!) was particularly devoted to very poor practical jokes.

There are, in the former Royal Library in Berlin, a number of boxes that contain almost eleven thousand scraps of paper, covered with the pothooks and scrawls of L. v. B. For that was the only way in which the poor man could now communicate with the outside world, questions and answers on little pieces of paper—all of them jotted down by the nervous hand of a man who was constantly irritated by being cut off from society. The first of these little scraps go back to the year 1816. Beethoven did not die until 1827. During the last years of his life, therefore, he dwelt in perpetual silence. But out of this silence there arose such melodies as the world had never yet heard.

Perhaps Nature inspired him to write these by way of compensation. For Beethoven suffered as much as mortal man could bear. He fell in love repeatedly and every time was brutally rebuffed. Not through any particular cruelty on the part of the women upon whom he bestowed his affections. They sometimes liked him well enough, but the idea of marrying him was out of the question. It was all very well for an Austrian aristocrat to be on friendly terms with a personage whom all the world recognized as a genius. Their doors were open to Beethoven the composer, the piano virtuoso who by sheer strength of his ability had forced emperors and kings to listen when he spoke to them in his own language. But the very idea of such a man as a possible son-in-law was preposterous. His middle-class background, his drunken father, his dreadful brothers, the terrible nephew who was always under foot, his endless lawsuits with his sisters-in-law, his quarrels with his benefactors and, even worse, his everlasting suspicion of being slighted, his arrogant resentment of anything that might be construed as a reflection upon his greatness—all of these combined to make him a person whom one could admire and revere, but only within his own sphere.

Socially speaking, the Von Breunings and the Guicciardis and the Von Brunswicks would just as soon have given their daughters to their valets as to the man who in a most painful outburst of passion would dedicate one of his works to the object of his affections (the "Moonlight" Sonata bears the name of Giulietta Guicciardi) and who the next moment could be guilty of such a gross breach of decorum that everybody present turned pale with rage or wept with pity. No, it could not be done. And after Beethoven had lost his hearing, he realized that the case was hopeless. He still loved. But he had learned discretion. From that time on his music spoke the words his lips dared not utter.

In most lives of Beethoven you will come across a threefold division. The first part begins in 1783 and ends in 1803. During this period he is still learning his trade and is entirely under the influence of Haydn and Mozart. He brings about certain innovations. Instead of the minuet which Haydn and Mozart had deemed a necessary part of their symphonies, he gives his hearers a scherzo, but for the rest his work does not yet bear any signs of that highly pronounced Beethoven style so typical of the works of the second period which comes to an end in 1815. Then there are several years during which it sometimes seems that he has fulfilled his destiny and that his self-appointed task has been performed. But in the meantime strange things are taking place in the soul of this man of sorrows.

Like all the people of his time who took a deep interest in the world around them, he had risen from the depths of despondency to the highest summits of hope, only to be cast back into an even deeper and darker despair by the rapid political changes that had taken place since the beginning of the great French Revolution. Had he been an ordinary human being, he would have turned cynical. He would have bade his fellow men destroy themselves in any way they pleased. But when he had recovered from the shock he was ready to do further battle. Like that great French general who was responsible for the final victory in the late war, his left wing had been broken, his right wing had been smashed, his center had given way, and he therefore made ready to attack. While all around him people bowed to the inevitable, Beethoven alone refused to surrender. Steeped in the works of the greatest of his predecessors, strengthened by the rugged courage of a Bach and a Mozart, he gave the signal to reassemble and in unmistakable terms reaffirmed his belief in the ultimate victory of mankind. And that is the way the Ninth Symphony came to be written.

No longer is destiny knocking at the gate as it did in the Fifth Symphony. No longer is the master concerned about the fate of his hero, his failure or success, as he was in the "Eroica." No longer does he occupy his mind with the beauties of nature as he had done in the "Pastoral" Symphony nor does he try to write the apotheosis of the dance, which found its fulfillment in the Seventh. He leaves all these common concerns behind him. In his Ninth Symphony the man who has been recognized as the most versatile manipulator of orchestral effects goes back to the oldest of all instruments. He goes back to the human voice to give expression to his unshakable faith in that freedom of the spirit which all through his life had been his dearest and proud· est possession.

JOSEPH WOOD KRUTCH Why he

selected The SECOND PART of

"DON QUIXOTE"

The five essays from one of which this selection is taken were written to see what I could do in a form I have always liked—namely the mixed biographical-critical essay in which one deals with only those parts of a man's life which seem to throw some definite light on his writings. In recent years high-brow critics have tended to be very scornful of such loose interpretive-impressionistic-half-historical-half-critical essays but I still think that when well done they furnish the best introduction to a great writer. I don't know how well these particular essays were done but I have not changed my opinions concerning the subjects and if I had the essays to do over again I would only want to do the same thing better. I have never thought that any one critical instrument or method was all-sufficient or the only really legitimate one. I prefer to write, as I prefer to read, discussions in which each of the various instruments and methods is used as each seems, for the occasion, most useful. A great writer is more than his doctrine, more than his technique, more than his psycho-analytical determinants, more than his social significance. He is, indeed, more than the sum of all of these. An "interpretive" essay doesn't get all of him, but it at least is more likely than the formal analysis of any one aspect to keep the reader in mind of the fact that the subject *is* complex.

Bethel, Conn.   JOSEPH WOOD KRUTCH
August, 1942

THIS First Part of "The Ingenious Gentleman Don Quixote de la Mancha" was issued at the beginning of the year 1605. Cervantes sold the manuscript to a bookseller and the fact that the latter secured his rights only so far as a part of Spain (Castile) was concerned has been taken to mean that he set no great store by the prospects of its popularity. But if such were indeed the case, then the bookseller was wrong and another publisher hastened to profit by his fellow's mistake. In a very short time "Don Quixote" had covered all Spain and even, though in those days fame was slow to cross national boundaries, overflowed into other countries. In 1607 an edition read eagerly over northern Europe was printed in Brussels and there are various references in English books of about the same time to show that the countrymen of Shakespeare had also become thoroughly familiar with the adventures of the Knight of the Rueful Countenance. Cervantes received but little financial profit from his success but for the first time in his life he was a famous man.

Under the circumstances one would naturally expect the speedy appearance of the Second Part. When a poverty-stricken author captures the imagination of the public as completely as Cervantes had done, when his next work seems mapped out for him and the way is prepared, not only for greater fame but for greater profit as well, one expects him to seize his opportunity. Yet Cervantes did nothing of the sort. First months and then years passed. He presented to the public his "Exemplary Novels"—a collection of short stories—and he even renewed with less success than before his effort to write plays; but while everyone else was talking about Don Quixote he had nothing more to say concerning the adventures of the man whom he had abandoned in mid-career.

Authors are sometimes hurt almost as much as they are pleased by the success of some one of their works and find themselves famous for reasons not entirely welcome. Thus Boccaccio had been led away from his own genius by the pressure of his age and it is difficult not to believe that Cervantes was all but diverted in similar fashion. He was essentially a grave and thoughtful man. He loved beautiful letters—poetry perhaps above all—and if he had created something very beautiful its beauty was of a sort too new for even him to understand. What he had done was certainly not what he had once planned. Perhaps the raucous laughter of the populace which found his hero merely funny hurt him in some half-understood way and certainly he had not intended to crown his difficult and arduous life with a farce.

This sense of failure was, moreover, fostered by the critical canons of his time. He was a man of the Renaissance and to say that is to say that he was the inheritor of a long literary tradition with which "Don Quixote" broke. The revival of interest in literature as a conscious art, accompanied as it was by a renewed study of classical models, had led to the establishment of certain recognized forms of literary expression and "Don Quixote" belonged to none of them. Men had recognized the two faces which life presents and they had evolved a class of literature appropriate to the presentation of each, but, holding as they did that a certain purity of tone was the distinguishing characteristic of true art, they were inclined to regard any mingling of forms or spirits as essentially vulgar. One might, for example, write (in either prose or verse) an epic as Homer and Virgil had done; but the epic had its laws: it scorned vulgar things and vulgar people, it recounted none but great deeds, and it was marked by an unfailing grandeur of style. And if, on the other hand, one wished to describe the adventures of common people one had not only the tale in the Italian style which Boccaccio had brought to perfection but one had besides the picaresque romance which recounted in an amusing and realistic way the rough-and-tumble adventures of a rogue living by his wits at the bottom of society. But the epic must never sink and the picaresque romance must never soar. Each was what we should call highly artificial and yet each could be brought to a certain perfection by virtue of the very fact that neither sought to comprehend any emotions not immediately consonant with the general tone of the work.

Now in the "Galatea" Cervantes had written a respectably "pure" work of art since he had adopted for it that pastoral form which was recognized in respectable literature. Toward the end of his life he was to set great store by another "pure" work—this time a heroic romance —which to us is duller if possible than the "Galatea" itself. But he could not, on the other hand, be other than aware that "Don Quixote" violated the literary canons of his age. Outwardly it was nearer to the picaresque romance than to anything else—it was strung upon a thread of comic misadventures and it not only dealt realistically with common people but carried such realism further than it had ever been carried before—yet it touched upon high things which had no place among the vulgarities of the picaresque romance and it seemed to strive for that synthesis of the comedy and the tragedy of life, which we recognize as the distinguishing mark of the modern novel but which, to the contemporaries of Cervantes, must have seemed to constitute something dangerously like a mere defiance of the ideal of stylistic purity which was thought of as distinguishing serious literature from the formlessness of mere vulgar story-telling.

And so Cervantes, much as he must have loved "Don Quixote" and clearly as he must, at moments, have perceived its greatness, hesitated to finish what he had begun. Like Boccaccio he refused to recognize the nature of his genius and like Boccaccio he turned his back upon it even after he had written his masterpiece. Though he, more than any one else, created the modern novel he continued to dream of the pure pastoral or the pure drama or the pure heroic romance and he let ten long years slip by between the publication of the first and second parts of his great work while filling the time with unsuccessful efforts to do far lesser things.

At last, however, he did send the Don forth upon new adventures. The untimely appearance of a spurious "Second Part" seems to have speeded his pen for he spoke of the bogus continuation with great bitterness and it is possible that it taught him to realize more fully how great his own work was. In any event "Don Quixote, Part Two," was concluded in time to be issued from the press in the latter part of 1615, when its author was already in his sixty-ninth year.

Hardly have we begun to read this Second Part when we realize that important developments have taken place in the method of the work and that it is everywhere more ambitious and more rich than before, as though Cervantes, having resigned himself to the necessity of expressing himself in the form which the world had approved, was determined to make it afford a scope for every power which he possessed and every idea which he held.

On the one side the book becomes, even more completely than it was before, a realistic novel marked by a vivid fidelity never approached before and never surpassed since. Certain scenes—that for example which occurs in the fifth chapter of the Second Part where Sancho discusses his plans with his wife—might have been signed by any of those writers from Fielding to George Eliot to whom we sometimes give credit for the invention of the method by which humble character is realistically represented with humorous fidelity. And yet, while the realistic background is drawn with more consummate skill than before, the change which has taken place in the two chief characters is one which lifts them still further above the merely human level, and the greatest of the miracles wrought by Cervantes is that by which a unity is achieved under conditions which might seem to make such unity impossible.

Though these characters move through a world which is essentially a literal reflection of the one in which the readers of the book lived— though the characters themselves seem to have part of their existence in that same plane—they also transcend it. Sancho becomes, even more than he was before, an empirical philosopher and the Don, even more than he was before, his Platonistic opponent. The latter is still mad, still incapable that is to say of interpreting the evidence of his senses in the same way as his fellows, but his delusions (if such they be) are systematized into a philosophy and he comes even nearer than before to the point where he himself is able to recognize them, not as delusions, but as forms of thought. Thus the transformation which had begun to take place in the "First Part" was completed during the interval which elapsed between its publication and the beginning of the "Second Part." Far from remaining a mere object of ridicule, Don Quixote has gradually assumed qualities which make him first loved and then respected until at last Cervantes has come so near to identifying himself with his creation that he can permit the latter to speak for him. That which he had created out of a whim, sent forth into the world as a character, and received back from it as a symbol had become eventually himself.

Those readers who have enjoyed "Don Quixote" chiefly because of those elements which relate it to the picaresque romance have sometimes maintained that the "Second Part" is inferior to the first. They have pointed out that the farcical adventures follow one another in less rapid succession and they seem sometimes unable to appreciate the fact that the enormously increased richness of the background and the substitution of the comedy of character for mere burlesque would in itself much more than compensate for any diminished emphasis upon those rough-and-tumble adventures which, indeed, tend rather to weary than amuse most modern readers. But the truth of the matter is that by the time the beginning of the "Second Part" was reached "Don Quixote" had almost completely outgrown the form in which it was originally cast and ceased to have any essential relation to the picaresque romance. Cervantes had begun it as such, intending, perhaps, no more than a diversion and almost certainly unaware that it was to be the major work of his lifetime, but as he began to put more and more into it he was compelled to create a form which would serve a purpose entirely outside the scope of the simple *genre* to which he had first thought of it as belonging.

Doubtless it would be impossible to put one's finger upon any one paragraph and say: "At this point Cervantes was for the first time aware of the implications of his story. From here on it is evident that he was, to some degree at least, aware that if he followed the adventures of his hero far enough he would be brought face to face with all the problems of his life." But once he had divined the nature of the hold which the Don had upon his affection, once he had perceived that the madness of the latter was the result, not of a mere perversity, but of a determination to see the world in a fashion more acceptable to his spirit than that adopted by those who took the senses as the sole arbiter of truth, it was inevitable that all the cruxes of Renaissance thought should be involved.

In the first place the presence of a hero who sees giants where others see windmills and who is called "mad" for no other reason than that he cannot agree with his fellows as to the interpretations to be put upon the sensations which he receives through his eyes and ears, raises at once the fundamental and much canvassed question of the dependability of these same senses. Every effort to penetrate the nature of reality must begin with some definition, tacit or explicit, of the attitude toward the validity of the evidence which they offer and Cervantes was consciously aware of this fact. Orthodox medieval philosophy had accepted their evidence as far as it went but Renaissance Platonism had sometimes questioned it. And Cervantes himself had been driven, by the very unsatisfactoriness of his own relations with the physical world, to wish, at least, that he too might dismiss the universe in which his body had its being as mere delusion.

Nor do we, indeed, have anything except the weight of vulgar opinion—surely no very satisfactory criterion of truth—to convince us that the things which the eye sees are more real than those which the imagination conceives. If the "madness" of Don Quixote were common and the "sanity" of Sancho Panza were rare then their roles would be reversed. It would be the Sanchos whom we should believe deprived of their wits, since it is only by a sort of popular vote that we can decide whether a thing "really is" a windmill or a giant and since, for all we know, the world may bear no direct relation to what anybody sees there, "sanity" may be, after all, only that species of madness which happens to be most prevalent.

But this is only the crude and obvious aspect of the problem, for even if we grant that the world as Sancho sees it corresponds more closely than does the world as Don Quixote sees it to certain realities, the question still remains whether or not those realities are the only or even the most important ones. Not even the Aristotelianism of the Middle Ages, firmly as it accepted common sense as its starting point, ever conceived the possibility that the senses revealed all or that demonstrations such as those which Sancho gave were conclusive so far as the ultimate reality and importance of things was concerned, while to Plato, whose influence had grown enormously with the Renaissance, the world of senses was only a world of distorted shadows and the realest reality could only be reached by reason when reason refused to be misled by vain appearance.

And even if, to grant still another concession, the world of Sancho's is the only world existing outside of man, are there not worlds which he has created for himself which may be no less important for him than those which he shares with the beasts? By acting as though love were more than lust and life less important than honour he has succeeded to a certain degree in making them so. If he has not actually transformed windmills into giants he has performed other miracles of the imagination and of the will no less striking by creating chivalry out of free-booting and the mystical devotion of Dante out of the animal instinct for generation.

Now the task of Cervantes was in part, as has already been hinted, one which had to do with the creation of a literary form capable of expressing a sense of the complex nature of human experience more adequately than was possible by either the satiric or the romantic *genre* which the current canons of taste recognized as legitimate. But the need for such a form grew out of the fact that his vision of life was complicated by the extent to which he had assimilated the perplexities of Renaissance thought and to which its problems—the dependability of the senses, the reality of the supersensual world, and the power of persistent idealism to create values not originally existing in the world of nature—were present to him in a form not to be solved as simply as they had been solved by either the dogmatic faith of the medieval Christian or the naïve materialism of the Renaissance sceptics.

To such a one as Boccaccio and his hard-headed fellows who may stand for this materialism in its simplest form, the medieval world of Dante had seemed a world of the merest quixoticism. Opposing the senses to the imagination, they had called upon eyes and ears to bear witness to their contention that this was a world not of giants but of windmills and that it should be treated as such. But the effect of their protest was not so much to establish their point of view as to raise a problem by making it necessary for every man either to choose between the two or to find for himself some satisfactory conception of the relations between them.

The authority of the Church finally succumbed to critical attacks and in certain departments of thought the materialists won unequivocal victories as when, for example, experience (i.e. experiment) replaced metaphysics as the method of natural science. But they did not succeed in making humanity at large content with the world of pure nature nor convince it that this world of nature was *all*. They merely drove their opponents to subtler defences of supersensual values and raised up in Cervantes the first great modern champion of that realism which finds in natural fact a challenge to discover hidden realities. Humanism, the name which we give to the most characteristic philosophy of the Renaissance during its period of highest development was not, essentially, either that revival of classical learning or that materialistic scepticism with both of which it has sometimes been identified, but rather an attempt to realize the implications of the fact that life is led upon two planes—the human and the natural—which intersect but do not coincide. It attempted to determine where the assumption that man is merely a shrewder sort of animal was fruitful and where it was not, and "Don Quixote" is a statement of this problem in comic terms.

When Cervantes wrote, it had already been discussed for at least two hundred and fifty years and he had acquired (as recent and thorough study of his work has demonstrated) a wide if not systematic familiarity with the most important expressions of Renaissance thought. Not only were his own experiences as hero calculated to provoke in him meditations upon the relative worth of such principles as led to the chivalric actions of his own youth and such as might have resulted in a more comfortable old age, but his reading had been of a kind which made it inevitable that the figures of Sancho and Don Quixote should become, as soon as he created them, symbols of the realistic and the idealistic currents of Renaissance thought. Sancho becomes essentially the representative of that realistic and critical spirit of which Boccaccio is the first great exponent and the Don rises to the point where he is able to comprehend the real reason behind his unwillingness to let the senses set the limits of his world. Thus the quixoticism of Don Quixote is more than mere chivalry and more than a generous folly in dealing with persons or events. It is the expression of a faith in the power of the human being to create values by virtue of his faith in them and to generate a world above the world of nature in which his human as opposed to his natural life may be led. His, in a word, is that philosophy more recently called the philosophy of "As If" and that philosophy achieves its defence by making the "mad" hero of the story more admirable than any of his sane adversaries.

In the second part of the work a kindly duchess is entertaining the Don and, hoping to plumb his madness, she turns the conversation upon the Lady Dulcinea—the country wench whom he has chosen as his mistress and whom he insists upon endowing with all beauty and all virtue. "If," she says, "we are to believe the history of Don Quixote which has come out here lately with general applause, it is to be inferred from it, if I mistake not, that you never saw the Lady Dulcinea, and that the said lady is nothing in the world but an imaginary lady, one that you yourself begot and gave birth to in your brain, and adorned with whatever charms and perfections you chose." To this charge the Don replies, not as a mad man defending his delusions, but merely as one who has chosen to see the world through poetic imagination, for it is thus (the italics are mine) that he retorts: "There is a good deal to be said on that point. God knows whether there be any Dulcinea or not in the world, or whether she is imaginary or not imaginary; these are things the proof of which must not be pushed to extreme lengths. I have not begotten nor given birth to my lady *though I behold her as she needs must be.*" And in saying that he committed himself to the world of poetry rather than to the world of fact, to that world which critics had defined when they said that it is not the business of the poet to recount things as they are but as they ought to be.

Thus Cervantes, speaking now through the mouth of Don Quixote, now through that of Sancho Panza, drew a picture of *the world as it is* traversed by *man as he ought to be*; and giving his credence to the hard-headed materialists of Italy, he reserved his affections for those who are willing to act *as though* the mind and the imagination were the supreme realities. No mere slave of fact could have drawn a more meticulously real or living picture of the society of his day and he never (with one exception to be noted later) failed to distinguish between the two planes upon which the action of his story moves, so that his background never loses the sharpness of its realistic outline, never wavers between fact and fancy. But in one heroic figure he embodies everything which that background is not and the effects of this glaring contrast between the realism of the setting and the fantastic poetry of the central character constitutes a harmonious whole for the simple reason that its existence in the form of the ever present contrast between fact and aspiration is the thing of which our experience in living makes us most persistently aware.

Even this fact does not, however, comprise all the greatness of the author for the form which he created to express what was for him the most important duality of the moral universe was one which was ready to be used in a thousand ways. Not for another century and a quarter, not, that is to say, until the rise of the great English novel, did another man appear who could handle it, but Cervantes had discovered for himself how to give to fiction a quality which it had never had before. Doubtless he was not the first to perceive that some kind of emotional complexity differentiates the experience of living from the one which we undergo when we read a *conte* of Boccaccio. Others must have recognized before him that when one lives through an experience one does not feel it to belong to any pure literary *genre* or to be, that is to say, as Boccaccio would have made it, indubitably comic or indubitably sad and nothing else. But he was the first successfully to attempt a piece of prose fiction in which the simplification of the tale was discarded in favour of a more complicated form capable of suggesting this emotional ambiguity of life.

Critics who discuss the modern novel sometimes describe this peculiar excellence which Cervantes introduced as a "three-dimensional quality" and the metaphor implied is more appropriate than it might seem at first blush to be. The plastic appearance of a natural object, the sense of depth which we experience when we regard it, arises as a result of the fact that each of our two eyes sees it from an angle of its own. In some mysterious fashion the brain fuses the two flat but slightly disparate images which the two retinas receive and from that fusion is generated the sense that the object exists, not on a plane, but in space. Now what Cervantes and what, after him, all the masters of Eighteenth and Nineteenth Century fiction accomplished, was something exactly analogous. Instead of accepting a sort of monocular vision as inevitable in fiction, instead of adopting, as all previous authors of the prose tale had done, some one point of view—satiric, or romantic, or heroic or what not—he was able to see his material from the two different angles which are necessary for a stereoscopic picture. Sancho Panza and Don Quixote are the names of the two eyes through which he looked forth and in some fashion or other the account which describes what the two of them see is made to do the work of the brain. Thanks to it the two do not contradict but rather supplement each other—they are fused. And out of that fusion comes a sense of solidity in the moral realm which is utterly new in Cervantes.

Doubtless he himself did not know just what it was that he had accomplished and it was perfectly possible for him to write in the older, simpler style. Thus in "The Exemplary Novels," already referred to, there is no suggestion of his supreme excellence and if one will turn either to them or to the various tales interspersed between the chapters of "Don Quixote" one will perceive very clearly what that excellence is. So strong were his own romantic predilections that even in the midst of his masterpiece he was compelled to take occasional refuge in pure romance, to compose the interludes which he called "The Story of the Shepherdess Marcela," "The Ill-Advised Curiosity" etc., and in them he slipped back into the manner of the primitive novella. They seem flat and, in comparison with the richness of the main story, almost silly, but no sooner has he finished one than he seems without effort to re-enter the far more substantial world of his two heroes. It would be fantastic to suppose that he wrote these minor tales deliberately to call attention by contrast to the virtues of his great work, but certainly they can be made to serve that purpose.

No other man whose name is remembered in the history of story-telling ever did so much to advance the art which he practised. It is no little thing to have stated, as he did, the chief intellectual problem of his age in a novel and if, to the realization of this achievement he added a realization of the fact that he painted the realistic details of everyday life with a hitherto unapproached fidelity, one can hardly hesitate to award him a place in the front rank of the fiction writers of all time. And yet neither of these things is so important as that subtler creation which we must still call "three-dimensional fiction." Every writer who achieves it in narrative is modern; whoever cannot may possibly write memoirs or be content with one or another of the styles of tale-writing which have survived, but he cannot be what we call a novelist because the power to suggest the emotional and intellectual complexity of any series of events is the very essence of the art of the modern novel.

Cervantes was in his sixty-ninth year when the Second Part of "Don Quixote" was published. About a year before he had given us in the Prologue of "The Exemplary Novels" a pen portrait of himself with his "aquiline visage," his "smooth unruffled brow," his "silver beard" and the teeth which were "not important" because he had "but six of them and those in an ill condition and worse placed because they do not correspond the one with the other." No information seems available concerning the amount of financial profit which he received from his new publication but it was not great and there were not many years left him through which he might endure poverty.

Yet he had no intention of resigning the pen before death should snatch it from him. Instead of resting upon his laurels he was startlingly—perhaps febrilly—fertile of projects. One of them, the "heroic" and unreadable romance of "Persiles and Sigismunda," was actually executed but of the others, including the long-promised continuation of the "Galatea," not a trace has been found. Apparently he still hesitated to rest his whole claim for fame upon anything as "irregular" as "Don Quixote" but failing strength cut short the expressions of his allegiance to older standards.

In the Prologue to the "Persiles" (published after his death) he tells us of a ride along the road from Esquivivia to Madrid and recounts with obvious pleasure a chance meeting with a bespectacled student who, upon learning his name, saluted him as the "joy of the muses" and then proceeded to diagnose his ailment as dropsy. This ride (if not imaginary) was probably the last which the joy of the muses was permitted to take. About the same time in a letter to a patron he had remarked that his malady increased "so greatly that I think it will make an end of me, though not of my gratitude" and on April 18, 1616 he received supreme unction. Next day he rallied sufficiently to compose the dedication to the "Persiles" and four days after he died. He was buried in the habit of a Franciscan, for Cervantes, like a good Spaniard and a good Catholic, had punctiliously arranged for a decent termination to his life by becoming a tertiary of the order some two weeks before. If he felt that his country had wronged him he never revealed the feeling and if his speculations were sometimes bold he had never permitted himself an expression of which the Church could disapprove.

All the supreme creations of character—Pantagruel, Falstaff, Hamlet and Crusoe—have an existence independent of the work in which they first appear. We know more about them than Rabelais, Shakespeare, and Defoe have told us because these characters, refusing to be confined within the pages of a book, have walked out into the world to take a place there as real as that occupied by any man who ever left a memory behind him. Every critic who has discussed them, every reader upon whose imagination they have taken hold, has added something; their symbolic significance has been enriched by every thought to which they have given rise and men have been glad to father their own fancies upon characters already so substantial.

Legends have grown up around them as they have grown up around the most appealing of historical characters, and the Falstaff who now belongs to the universal imagination is almost as much greater than the Falstaff of Shakespeare's plays as the Cleopatra of the universal imagination is greater than she of history. When one of these magic names is mentioned our minds are flooded with light, not all of which comes from the author who created the character, and filled with a harmony to which countless overtones are added from the countless imaginations which have responded with sympathetic vibrations to the original chord.

Each, moreover, has been enriched by what the Greeks called "pathos"—each, that is to say, is surrounded by an aura composed in part of the memory of those who have cherished it. When a character has passed through many inferior hands it becomes hackneyed and cheap but when many noble minds have concerned themselves with it it is not worn but enriched. Like an heirloom it becomes more precious because of those who have possessed it, and something of those who have touched it adheres. What many men have wept over is the sadder for their tears and what many men have laughed over is made not merrier, to be sure, but more precious by the echoes of that dead laughter. Thus the great figures of legend and literature grow more meaningful as they endure. When we touch them we touch not only them, but also and at the same time all those who have felt for them, making ourselves part of a great continuous tradition of human sensibility.

And though Don Quixote shares with these other great figures the distinction of being greater than anything which even the imagination of Cervantes or of any other one man could compass, he is nevertheless unique in one respect. His creator, having sent him forth into the world, took him up again after he had become a legend and himself completed what he had begun.

No other author ever quite did just this with any conception before. Perhaps Shakespeare came nearest to it when he carried Falstaff through three plays, but it is generally admitted that the Falstaff of the "Merry Wives" is less rather than more than the Falstaff of the other plays and it can hardly be said that Shakespeare fully utilized the legend he had created. But Cervantes took full advantage of his opportunity. He gave Don Quixote to the world in the first part of his romance and then took him back again to be completed after the world had already made more of him than an author unaided could have done.

Thus Don Quixote is the genius of Cervantes, plus the genius of his Spain, plus the eager imagination of all Europe during the three hundred years which have elapsed since he first went gloriously mad. Some laugh when his adventures are read and some weep; but no one has yet definitely answered the riddle which he propounds. Nor will it ever be answered until we know for sure whether madness be not, after all, the highest wisdom.

VII
THE DRAMA

GEORGE JEAN NATHAN

Why he selected AESTHETIC

JURISPRUDENCE

My nomination for the anthology is the chapter called "Aesthetic Jurisprudence" from my book *The Critic and the Drama*, published by Knopf. Though written some long years ago, it still accurately reflects my feeling and my attitude toward my profession and its various practitioners. Were I to rewrite it, there are several passages I would edit literarily, but there would be no changes whatsoever as to the implicit thought.

New York, N. Y.   GEORGE JEAN NATHAN
February 14, 1942

I

ART is a reaching out into the ugliness of the world for vagrant beauty and the imprisoning of it in a tangible dream. Criticism is the dream book. All art is a kind of subconscious madness expressed in terms of sanity; criticism is essential to the interpretation of its mysteries, for about everything truly beautiful there is ever something mysterious and disconcerting. Beauty is not always immediately recognizable as beauty; what often passes for beauty is mere infatuation; living beauty is like a love that has outlasted the middle-years of life, and has met triumphantly the test of time, and faith, and cynic meditation. For beauty is a sleep-walker in the endless corridors of the wakeful world, uncertain, groping, and not a little strange. And criticism is its tender guide.

Art is a partnership between the artist and the artist-critic. The former creates; the latter re-creates. Without criticism, art would of course still be art, and so with its windows walled in and with its lights extinguished would the Louvre still be the Louvre. Criticism is the windows and chandeliers of art: it illuminates the enveloping darkness in which art might otherwise rest only vaguely discernible, and perhaps altogether unseen.

Criticism, at its best, is a great, tall candle on the altar of art: at its worst, which is to say in its general run, a campaign torch flaring red in behalf of æsthetic ward-heelers. This campaign torch motif in criticism, with its drunken enthusiasm and raucous hollering born of ignorance, together with what may be called the Prince Albert motif, with its sober, statue-like reserve born of ignorance that, being well-mannered, is not so bumptious as the other, has contributed largely to the common estimate of criticism as a profession but slightly more exalted than Second Avenue auctioneering if somewhat less than Fifth. Yet criticism is itself an art. It might, indeed, be well defined as an art within an art, since every work of art is the result of a struggle between the heart that is the artist himself and his mind that is the critic. Once his work is done, the artist's mind, tired from the bitterness of the struggle, takes the form of a second artist, puts on this second artist's strange hat, coat and checkered trousers, and goes forth with refreshed vigour to gossip abroad how much of the first artist's work was the result of its original splendid vitality and how much the result of its gradually diminished vitality and sad weariness. The wrangling that occurs at times between art and criticism is, at bottom, merely a fraternal discord, one in which Cain and Abel belabour each other with stuffed clubs. Criticism is often most sympathetic when it is apparently most cruel: the propounder of the sternest, hardest philosophy that the civilized world has known never failed sentimentally to kiss and embrace his sister, Therese Elisabeth Alexandra Nietzsche, every night at bed-time. "It is not possible," Cabell has written, "to draw inspiration from a woman's beauty unless you comprehend how easy it would be to murder her." And—"Only those who have firmness may be really tender-hearted," said Rochefoucauld. One may sometimes even throw mud to tonic purpose. Consider Karlsbad.

Art is the haven wherein the disillusioned may find illusion. Truth is no part of art. Nor is the mission of art simple beauty as the text books tell us. The mission of art is the magnification of simple beauty to proportions so heroic as to be almost overpowering. Art is a gross exaggeration of natural beauty: there was never a woman so beautiful as the Venus di Milo, or a man so beautiful as the Apollo Belvedere of the Vatican, or a sky so beautiful as Monet's, or human speech so beautiful as Shakespeare's, or the song of a nightingale so beautiful as Ludwig van Beethoven's. But as art is a process of magnification, so criticism is a process of reduction. Its purpose is the reducing of the magnifications of art to the basic classic and æsthetic principles, and the subsequent announcement thereof in terms proportioned to the artist's interplay of fundamental skill and overtopping imagination.

The most general fault of criticism lies in a confusion of its own internal processes with those of art: it is in the habit of regarding the business of art as a reduction of life to its essence of beauty, and the business of criticism as an expansion of that essence to its fullest flow. The opposite is more reasonable. Art is a beautiful, swollen lie; criticism, a cold compress. The concern of art is with beauty; the concern of criticism is with truth. And truth and beauty, despite the Sunday School, are often strangers. This confusion of the business of art and that of criticism has given birth to the so-called "contagious," or inspirational, criticism, than which nothing is more mongrel and absurd. Criticism is designed to state facts—charmingly, gracefully, if possible—but still facts. It is not designed to exhort, enlist, convert. This is the business not of the critic, but of those readers of the critic whom the facts succeed in convincing and galvanizing. Contagious criticism is merely a vainglorious critic's essay at popularity: facts heated up to a degree where they melt into caressing nothingness.

But if this "criticism with a glow" is not to be given countenance, even less is to be suffered the criticism that, in its effort at a fastidious and elegant reserve, leans so far backward that it freezes its ears. This species of criticism fails not only to enkindle the reader, but fails also—and this is more important—to enkindle the critic himself. The ideal critic is perhaps much like a Thermos bottle: full of warmth, he suggests the presence of the heat within him without radiating it. This inner warmth is essential to a critic. But this inner warmth, where it exists, is automatically chilled and banished from a critic by a protracted indulgence in excessive critical reserve. Just as the professional frown assumed by a much photographed public magnifico often becomes stubbornly fixed upon his hitherto gentle brow, so does the prolonged spurious constraint of a critic in due time psychologically hoist him on his own petard. A writer's work does not grow more and more like him; a writer grows more and more like his work. The best writing that a man produces is always just a little superior to himself. There never was a literary artist who did not appreciate the difficulty of keeping up to the pace of his writings. A writer is dominated by the standard of his own writings; he is a slave *in transitu*, lashed, tormented, and miserable. The weak and inferior literary artist, such a critic as the one alluded to, soon becomes the helpless victim of his own writings: like a vampire of his own creation they turn upon him and suck from him the warm blood that was erstwhile his. A pose in time becomes natural: a man with a good left eye cannot affect a monocle for years without eventually coming to need it. A critic cannot write ice without becoming in time himself at least partly frosted.

Paraphrasing Pascal, to little minds all things are great. Great art is in constant conflict with the awe of little minds. Art is something like a wonderful trapeze performer swinging high above the heads of the bewildered multitude and nervous lest it be made to lose its balance and to slip by the periodic sudden loud marvellings of the folk below. The little mind and its little criticism are the flattering foes of sound art. Such art demands for its training and triumph the countless preliminary body blows of muscular criticism guided by a muscular mind. Art and the artist cannot be developed by mere back-slapping. If art, according to Beulé, is the intervention of the human mind in the elements furnished by experience, criticism is the intervention of the human mind in the elements furnished by æsthetic passion. Art and the artist are ever youthful lovers; criticism is their chaperon.

II

I do not believe finally in this or that "theory" of criticism. There are as many sound and apt species of criticism as there are works to be criticized. To say that art must be criticized only after this formula or after that, is to say that art must be contrived only out of this formula or out of that. As every work of art is an entity, a thing in itself, so is every piece of criticism an entity, a thing in itself. That "Thus Spake Zarathustra" must inevitably be criticized by the canons of the identical "theory" with which one criticizes "Tristan and Isolde" is surely difficult of reasoning.

To the Goethe-Carlyle doctrine that the critic's duty lies alone in discerning the artist's aim, his point of view and, finally, his execution of the task before him, it is easy enough to subscribe, but certainly this is not a "theory" of criticism so much as it is a foundation for a theory. To advance it as a theory, full-grown, full-fledged and flapping, as it has been advanced by the Italian Croce and his admirers, is to publish the preface to a book without the book itself. Accepted as a theory complete in itself, it fails by virtue of its several undeveloped intrinsic problems, chief among which is its neglect to consider the undeniable fact that, though each work of art is indubitably an entity and so to be considered, there is yet in creative art what may be termed an æsthetic genealogy that bears heavily upon comprehensive criticism and that renders the artist's aim, his point of view and his execution of the task before him susceptible to a criticism predicated in a measure upon the work of the sound artist who has just preceded him.

The Goethe-Carlyle hypothesis is a little too liberal. It calls for qualifications. It gives the artist too much ground, and the critic too little. To discern the artist's aim, to discern the artist's point of view, are phrases that require an amount of plumbing and not a few foot-notes. It is entirely possible, for example, that the immediate point of view of an artist be faulty, yet the execution of his immediate task exceedingly fine. If carefully planned triumph in art is an entity, so also may be undesigned triumph. I do not say that any such latter phenomenon is usual, but it is conceivable, and hence may be employed as a test of the critical hypothesis in point. Unschooled, without aim or point of view in the sense of this hypothesis, Schumann's compositions at the age of eleven for chorus and orchestra offer the quasi-theory some resistance. The question of the comparative merit of these compositions and the artist's subsequent work may not strictly be brought into the argument, since the point at issue is merely a theory and since theory is properly to be tested by theory.

Intent and achievement are not necessarily twins. I have always perversely thought it likely that there is often a greater degree of accident in fine art than one is permitted to believe. The aim and point of view of a bad artist are often admirable; the execution of a fine artist may sometimes be founded upon a point of view that is, from an apparently sound critical estimate, at striking odds with it. One of the finest performances in all modern dramatic writing, upon its critical reception as such, came as a great surprise to the writer who almost unwittingly had achieved it. Art is often unconscious of itself. Shakespeare, writing popular plays to order, wrote the greatest plays that dramatic art has known. Mark Twain, in a disgusted moment, threw off a practical joke, and it turned out to be literature.

A strict adherence to the principles enunciated in the Goethe-Carlyle theory would result in a confinement of art for all the theory's bold aim in exactly the opposite direction. For all the critic may accurately say, the aim and point of view of, say, Richard Strauss in "Don Quixote" and "A Hero's Life," may be imperfect, yet the one critical fact persists that the executions are remarkably fine. All things considered, it were perhaps better that the critical theory under discussion, if it be accepted at all, be turned end foremost: that the artist's execution of the task before him be considered either apart from his aim and point of view, or that it be considered first, and then—with not too much insistence upon them—his point of view and his aim. This would seem to be a more logical æsthetic and critical order. Tolstoi, with a sound, intelligent and technically perfect aim and point of view composed second-rate drama. So, too, Maeterlinck. Synge, by his own admissions adjudged critically and dramatically guilty on both counts, composed one of the truly first-rate dramas of the Anglo-Saxon stage.

In its very effort to avoid pigeon-holing, the Goethe-Carlyle theory pigeon-holes itself. In its commendable essay at catholicity, it is like a garter so elastic that it fails to hold itself up. That there may not be contradictions in the contentions here set forth, I am not sure. But I advance no fixed, definite theory of my own; I advance merely contradictions of certain of the phases of the theories held by others, and contradictions are ever in the habit of begetting contradictions. Yet such contradictions are in themselves apposite and soundly critical, since any theory susceptible of contradictions must itself be contradictory and insecure. If I suggest any theory on my part it is a variable one: a theory that, in this instance, is one thing and in that, another. Criticism, as I see it—and I share the common opinion—is simply a sensitive, experienced and thoroughbred artist's effort to interpret, in terms of æsthetic doctrine and his own peculiar soul, the work of another artist reciprocally to that artist and thus, as with a reflecting mirror, to his public. But to state merely what criticism is, is not to state the doctrine of its application. And herein, as I see it, is where the theorists fail to cover full ground. The anatomy of criticism is composed not of one theory, but of a theory—more or less generally agreed upon—on which are reared in turn other theories that are not so generally agreed upon. The Goethe-Carlyle theory is thus like a three-story building on which the constructor has left off work after finishing only the first story. What certain aspects of these other stories may be like, I have already tried to suggest.

I have said that, if I have any theory of my own, it is a theory susceptible in practice of numerous surface changes. These surface changes often disturb in a measure this or that phase of what lies at the bottom. Thus, speaking as a critic of the theatre, I find it impossible to reconcile myself to criticizing acting and drama from the vantage point of the same theory, say, for example, the Goethe-Carlyle theory. This theory fits criticism of drama much better than it fits criticism of acting, just as it fits criticism of painting and sculpture much more snugly than criticism of music. The means whereby the emotions are directly affected, and soundly affected, may at times be critically meretricious, yet the accomplishment itself may be, paradoxically, artistic. Perhaps the finest acting performance of our generation is Bernhardt's Camille: its final effect is tremendous: yet the means whereby it is contrived are obviously inartistic. Again, "King Lear," searched into with critical chill, is artistically a poor instance of playmaking, yet its effect is precisely the effect striven for. Surely, in cases like these, criticism founded strictly upon an inflexible theory is futile criticism, and not only futile but eminently unfair.

Here, of course, I exhibit still more contradictions, but through contradictions we may conceivably gain more secure ground. When his book is once opened, the author's mouth is shut. (Wilde, I believe, said that; and though for some peculiar reason it is today regarded as suicidal to quote the often profound Wilde in any serious argument, I risk the danger.) But when a dramatist's play or a composer's symphony is opened, the author has only begun to open his mouth. What results, an emotional art within an intellectual art, calls for a critical theory within a critical theory. To this composite end, I offer a suggestion: blend with the Goethe-Carlyle theory that of the afore-mentioned Wilde, to wit, that beauty is uncriticizable, since it has as many meanings as man has moods, since it is the symbol of symbols, and since it reveals everything because it expresses nothing. The trouble with criticism—again to pose a contradiction—is that, in certain instances, it is often too cerebral. Feeling a great thrill of beauty, it turns to its somewhat puzzled mind and is apprised that the thrill which it has unquestionably enjoyed from the work of art might conceivably be of pathological origin, a fremitus or vibration felt upon percussion of a hydatid tumour.

The Goethe-Carlyle theory, properly rigid and unyielding so far as emotional groundlings are concerned, may, I believe, at times safely be chucked under the chin and offered a communication of gipsy ardour by the critic whose emotions are the residuum of trial, test and experience.

III

Coquelin put it that the footlights exaggerate everything: they modify the laws of space and of time; they put miles in a few square feet: they make minutes appear to be hours. Of this exaggeration, dramatic criticism—which is the branch of criticism of which I treat in particular—has caught something. Of all the branches of criticism it is intrinsically the least sober and the least accurately balanced. It always reminds me somehow of the lash in the hands of Œacus, in "The Frogs," falling upon Bacchus and Xanthus to discover which of the two is the divine, the latter meantime endeavouring to conceal the pain that would betray their mortality by various transparent dodges. Drama is a two-souled art: half divine, half clownish. Shakespeare is the greatest dramatist who ever lived because he alone, of all drama-tists, most accurately sensed the mongrel nature of his art. Criticism of drama, it follows, is similarly a two-souled art: half sober, half mad. Drama is a deliberate intoxicant; dramatic criticism, aromatic spirits of ammonia; the re-creation is never perfect; there is always a trace of tipsiness left. Even the best dramatic criticism is always just a little dramatic. It indulges, a trifle, in acting. It can never be as impersonal, however much certain of its practitioners may try, as criticism of painting or of sculpture or of literature. This is why the best criticism of the theatre must inevitably be personal criticism. The theatre itself is distinctly personal; its address is directly personal. It holds the mirror not up to nature, but to the spectator's individual idea of nature. If it doesn't, it fails. The spectator, if he is a critic, merely holds up his own mirror to the drama's mirror: a reflection of the first reflection is the result. Dramatic criticism is this second reflection. And so the best dramatic criticism has about it a flavour of the unconscious, grotesque and unpremeditated. "When Lewes was at his business," Shaw has said, "he seldom remembered that he was a gentleman or a scholar." (Shaw was speaking of Lewes' free use of vulgarity and impudence whenever they happened to be the proper tools for his job.) "In this he showed himself a true craftsman, intent on making the measurements and analyses of his criticism as accurate, and their expression as clear and vivid, as possible, instead of allowing himself to be distracted by the vanity of playing the elegant man of letters, or writing with perfect good taste, or hinting in every line that he was above his work. In exacting all this from himself, and taking his revenge by expressing his most laboured conclusions with a levity that gave them the air of being the unpremeditated whimsicalities of a man who had perversely taken to writing about the theatre for the sake of the jest latent in his own outrageous unfitness for it, Lewes rolled his stone up the hill quite in the modern manner of Mr. Walkley, dissembling its huge weight, and apparently kicking it at random hither and thither in pure wantonness."

Mr. Spingarn, in his exceptionally interesting, if somewhat overly indignant, treatise on "Creative Criticism," provides, it seems to me, a particularly clear illustration of the manner in which the proponents of the more modern theories of criticism imprison themselves in the extravagance of their freedom. While liberating art from all the old rules of criticism, they simultaneously confine criticism with the new rules—or ghosts of rules—wherewith they free art. If each work of art is a unit, a thing in itself, as is commonly agreed, why should not each work of criticism be similarly a unit, a thing in itself? If art is, in each and every case, a matter of individual expression, why should not criticism, in each and every such case, be similarly and relevantly a matter of individual expression? In freeing art of definitions, has not criticism been too severely defined? I believe that it has been. I believe that there may be as many kinds of criticism as there are kinds of art. I believe that there may be sound analytical, sound emotional, sound cerebral, sound impressionistic, sound destructive, sound constructive, and other sound species of criticism. If art knows no rules, criticism knows no rules—or, at least, none save those that are obvious. If Brahms' scherzo in E flat minor, op. 4, is an entity, a work in and of itself, why shouldn't Huneker's criticism of it be regarded as an entity, a work in and of itself? If there is in Huneker's work inspiration from without, so, too, is there in Brahms': if Brahms may be held a unit in this particular instance with no consideration of Chopin, why may not Huneker with no consideration of Brahms?

If this is pushing things pretty far, it is the Spingarns who have made the pushing necessary. "Taste," says Mr. Spingarn, "must reproduce the work of art within itself in order to understand and judge it; and at that moment æsthetic judgment becomes nothing more or less than creative art itself." This rings true. But granting the perfection of the taste, why define and limit the critical creative art thus born of reproduction? No sooner has a law been enunciated, writes Mr. Spingarn, than it has been broken by an artist impatient or ignorant of its restraints, and the critics have been obliged to explain away these violations of their laws or gradually to change the laws themselves. If art, he continues, is organic expression, and every work of art is to be interrogated with the question, "What has it expressed, and how completely?", there is no place for the question whether it has conformed to some convenient classification of critics or to some law derived from this classification. Once again, truly put. But so, too, no sooner have laws been enunciated than they have been broken by critics impatient or ignorant of their restraints, and the critics of critics have been obliged to explain away these violations of the laws, or gradually to change the laws themselves. And so, too, have these works of criticism provided no place for the question whether they have conformed to some convenient classification of the critics of criticism or to some law derived from this classification.

"Criticism," said Carlyle, his theories apart, "stands like an interpreter between the inspired and the uninspired, between the prophet and those who hear the melody of his words, and catch some glimpse

of their material meaning, but understand not their deeper import."
This is the best definition that I know. It defines without defining;
it gives into the keeping of the interpreter the hundred languages of
art and merely urges him, with whatever means may best and properly
suit his ends, to translate them clearly to those that do not understand;
it sets him free from the very shackles which Carlyle himself, removing
from art, wound in turn about him.

EUGENE O'NEILL Why he selected

THE GREAT GOD BROWN

Rereading *The Great God Brown*, written in 1925, which I haven't looked at for ten years or more, I still consider this play one of the most interesting and moving I have written. It has its faults, of course, but for me, at least, it does succeed in conveying a sense of the tragic mystery drama of *Life* revealed through the *lives* in the play. And this, I think, is the real test of whether any play, however excellent its structure, characterization, dialogue, plot, social significance, or what not —is true drama or just another play.

I choose this particular scene for the anthology because it is one of the best, and the most self-sufficient when taken out of its context.

Danville, Cal.   EUGENE O'NEILL
May 24, 1942

SCENE. *Cybel's parlor. An automatic, nickel-in-the-slot player-piano is at center, rear. On its right is a dirty gilt second-hand sofa. At the left is a bald-spotted crimson plush chair. The backdrop for the rear wall is cheap wall-paper of a dull yellow-brown, resembling a blurred impression of a fallow field in early spring. There is a cheap alarm clock on top of the piano. Beside it her mask is lying.*

DION *is sprawled on his back, fast asleep on the sofa. His mask has fallen down on his chest. His pale face is singularly pure, spiritual and sad.*

The player-piano is groggily banging out a sentimental medley of "Mother—Mammy" *tunes.*

CYBEL *is seated on the stool in front of the piano. She is a strong, calm, sensual, blonde girl of twenty or so, her complexion fresh and healthy, her figure full-breasted and wide-hipped, her movements slow and solidly languorous like an animal's, her large eyes dreamy with the reflected stirring of profound instincts. She chews gum like a sacred cow forgetting time with an eternal cud. Her eyes are fixed, incuriously, on* DION's *pale face.*

CYBEL. (*as the tune runs out, glances at the clock, which indicates midnight, then goes slowly over to* DION *and puts her hand gently on his forehead*) Wake up!

DION. (*stirs, sighs and murmurs dreamily*) "And He laid His hands on them and healed them." (*Then with a start he opens his eyes and, half sitting up, stares at her bewilderedly*) What—where—who are you? (*He reaches for his mask and claps it on defensively*).

CYBEL. (*placidly*) Only another female. You was camping on my steps, sound asleep. I didn't want to run any risk getting into more trouble with the cops pinching you there and blaming me, so I took you in to sleep it off.

DION. (*mockingly*) Blessed are the pitiful, Sister! I'm broke—but you will be rewarded in Heaven!

CYBEL. (*calmly*) I wasn't wasting my pity. Why should I? You were happy, weren't you?

DION. (*approvingly*) Excellent! You're not a moralist, I see.

CYBEL. (*going on*) And you look like a good boy, too—when you're asleep. Say, you better beat it home to bed or you'll be locked out.

DION. (*mockingly*) Now you're becoming maternal, Miss Earth. Is that the only answer—to pin my soul into every vacant diaper? (*She stares down at his mask, her face growing hard. He laughs*) But please don't stop stroking my aching brow. Your hand is a cool mud poultice on the sting of thought!

CYBEL. (*calmly*) Stop acting. I hate ham fats. (*She looks at him as if waiting for him to remove his mask—then turns her back indifferently and goes to the piano*) Well, if you simply got to be a regular devil like all the other visiting sports, I s'pose I got to play with you. (*She takes her mask and puts it on—then turns. . . . mask is the rouged and eye-blackened countenance of the hardened prostitute. In a coarse, harsh voice*) Kindly state your dishonorable intentions, if any! I can't sit up all night keeping company! Let's have some music! (*She puts a plug in the machine. The same sentimental medley begins to play. The two masks stare at each other. She laughs*) Shoot! I'm all set! It's your play, Kid Lucifer!

DION. (*slowly removes his mask. She stops the music with a jerk. His face is gentle and sad—humbly*) I'm sorry. It has always been such agony for me to be touched!

CYBEL. (*taking off her mask—sympathetically as she comes back and sits down on her stool*) Poor kid! I've never had one, but I can guess. They hug and kiss you and take you on their laps and pinch you and want to see you getting dressed and undressed—as if they owned you— I bet you I'd never let them treat one of mine that way!

DION. (*turning to her*) You're lost in blind alleys, too. (*Suddenly holding out his hand to her*) But you're strong. Let's be friends.

CYBEL. (*with a strange sternness, searches his face*) And never nothing more?

DION. (*with a strange smile*) Let's say, never anything less! (*She takes his hand. There is a ring at the outside door bell. They stare at each other. There is another ring*).

CYBEL. (*puts on her mask,* DION *does likewise. Mockingly*) When you got to love to live it's hard to love living. I better join the A. F. of L. and soap-box for the eight-hour night! Got a nickel, baby? Play a tune. (*She goes out.* DION *puts a nickel in. The same sentimental tune starts.* CYBEL *returns, followed by* BILLY BROWN. *His face is rigidly composed, but his superior disgust for* DION *can be seen.* DION *jerks off the music and he and* BILLY *look at each other for a moment,* CYBEL *watching them both—then, bored, she yawns*) He's hunting for you. Put out the lights when you go. I'm going to sleep. (*She starts to go —then, as if reminded of something—to* DION) Life's all right, if you let it alone. (*Then mechanically flashing a trade smile at* BILLY) Now you know the way, Handsome, call again! (*She goes*).

BROWN. (*after an awkward pause*) Hello, Dion! I've been looking all over town for you. This place was the very last chance. . . . (*Another pause—embarrassedly*) Let's take a walk.

DION. (*mockingly*) I've given up exercise. They claim it lengthens your life.

BROWN. (*persuasively*) Come on, Dion, be a good fellow. You're certainly not staying here——

DION. Billy would like to think me taken in *flagrante delicto*, eh?

BROWN. Don't be a damn fool! Listen to me! I've been looking you up for purely selfish reasons. I need your help.

DION. (*astonished*) What?

BROWN. I've a proposition to make that I hope you'll consider favorably out of old friendship. To be frank, Dion, I need you to lend me a hand down at the office.

DION. (*with a harsh laugh*) So it's the job, is it? Then my poor wife did a-begging go!

BROWN. (*repelled—sharply*) On the contrary, I had to beg her to beg you to take it! (*More angrily*) Look here, Dion! I won't listen to you talk that way about Margaret! And you wouldn't if you weren't drunk! (*Suddenly shaking him*) What in hell has come over you, anyway! You didn't use to be like this! What the devil are you going to do with yourself—sink into the gutter and drag Margaret with you? If you'd heard her defend you, lie about you, tell me how hard you were working, what beautiful things you were painting, how you stayed at home and idolized the children!—when everyone knows you've been out every night sousing and gambling away the last of your estate. . . . (*He stops, ashamed, controlling himself*).

DION. (*wearily*) She was lying about her husband, not me, you fool! But it's no use explaining. (*Then, in a sudden, excitable passion*) What do you want? I agree to anything—except the humiliation of yelling secrets at the deaf!

BROWN. (*trying a bullying tone—roughly*) Bunk! Don't try to crawl out! There's no excuse and you know it. (*Then as DION doesn't reply—penitently*) But I know I shouldn't talk this way, old man! It's only because we're such old pals—and I hate to see you wasting yourself—you who had more brains than any of us! But, damn it, I suppose you're too much of a rotten cynic to believe I mean what I've just said!

DION. (*touched*) I know Billy was always Dion Anthony's friend.

BROWN. You're damn right I am—and I'd have proved it long ago if you'd only given me half a chance! After all, I couldn't keep chasing after you and be snubbed every time. A man has some pride!

DION. (*bitterly mocking*) Dead wrong! Never more! None whatever! It's unmoral! Blessed are the poor in spirit, Brother! When shall I report?

BROWN. (*eagerly*) Then you'll take the—you'll help me?

DION. (*wearily bitter*) I'll take the job. One must do something to pass away the time, while one is waiting—for one's next incarnation.

BROWN. (*jokingly*) I'd say it was a bit early to be worrying about that. (*Trying to get* DION *started*) Come along, now. It's pretty late.

DION. (*shakes his hand off his shoulder and walks away from him —after a pause*) Is my father's chair still there?

BROWN. (*turns away—embarrassed*) I—I don't really remember, Dion—I'll look it up.

DION. (*taking off his mask—slowly*) I'd like to sit where he spun what I have spent. What aliens we were to each other! When he lay dead, his face looked so familiar that I wondered where I had met that man before. Only at the second of my conception. After that, we grew hostile with concealed shame. And my mother? I remember a sweet, strange girl, with affectionate, bewildered eyes as if God had locked her in a dark closet without any explanation. I was the sole doll our ogre, her husband, allowed her and she played mother and child with me for many years in that house until at last through two tears I watched her die with the shy pride of one who has lengthened her dress and put up her hair. And I felt like a forsaken toy and cried to be buried with her, because her hands alone had caressed without clawing. She lived long and aged greatly in the two days before they closed her coffin. The last time I looked, her purity had forgotten me, she was stainless and imperishable, and I knew my sobs were ugly and meaningless to her virginity; so I shrank away, back into life, with naked nerves jumping like fleas, and in due course of nature another girl called me her boy in the moon and married me and became three mothers in one person, while I got paint on my paws in an endeavor to see God! (*He laughs wildly—claps on his mask*) But that Ancient Humorist had given me weak eyes, so now I'll have to foreswear my quest for Him and go in for the Omnipresent Successful Serious One, the Great God Mr. Brown, instead! (*He makes him a sweeping, mocking bow*).

BROWN. (*repelled but cajolingly*) Shut up, you nut! You're still drunk. Come on! Let's start! (*He grabs* DION *by the arm and switches off the light*).

DION. (*from the darkness—mockingly*) I am thy shorn, bald, nude sheep! Lead on, Almighty Brown, thou Kindly Light!

CURTAIN

ROBERT E. SHERWOOD

Why he selected The ELECTION
of LINCOLN*

The playwright's chief stock in trade is feelings, not facts. When he writes of a subject out of history or out of today's news, he cannot be a scholarly recorder or a good reporter; he is, at best, an interpreter, with a certain facility for translating all that he has heard in a manner sufficiently dramatic to attract a crowd. He has been granted by tradition considerable poetic license to distort and embellish the truth . . . However, in the case of a play . . . about Abe Lincoln, a strict regard for the plain truth is more than obligatory; it is obviously desirable. His life as he lived it was a work of art, forming a veritable allegory of the growth of the democratic spirit, with its humble origins, its inward struggles, its seemingly timid policy of "live and let live" and "mind your own business," its slow awakening to the dreadful problems of reality, its battles with and conquest of those problems, its death at the hands of a crazed assassin, and its perpetual renewal caused by the perpetual human need for it. Furthermore, just as Lincoln's life needs no adornments of symbolism to make it pertinent, his character needs no romanticizing, no sentimentalizing, no dramatizing.

Lincoln's great achievement, most of which was accomplished by the echo of his words, long after his death, was the solidification of the American ideal. In "Abe Lincoln in Illinois" he did not set out to make a play about his achievement; rather to make a play about the solidification of Lincoln himself—a long, uncertain process, affected by influences some of which came from within his own reasoning mind, some from his surrounding circumstances, some from sources which we cannot comprehend.

New York, N. Y.   Robert E. Sherwood
August 9, 1942

* The penultimate scene of *Abe Lincoln in Illinois*.

Lincoln campaign headquarters in the Illinois State House. The evening of Election Day, November 6, 1860.

It is a large room with a tall window opening out on to a wide balcony. There are doors upper right and upper left. At the left is a table littered with newspapers and clippings. There are many chairs about, and a liberal supply of spittoons.

At the back is a huge chart of the thirty-three states, with their electoral votes, and a space opposite each side for the posting of bulletins. A short ladder gives access to Alabama and Arkansas at the top of the list.

On the wall at the left is an American flag. At the right is a map of the United States, on which each state is marked with a red, white or blue flag.

ABE is sitting at the table, with his back to the audience, reading newspaper clippings. He wears his hat and has spectacles on. MRS. LINCOLN is sitting at the right of the table, her eyes darting nervously from ABE, to the chart, to the map. She wears her bonnet, tippet and muff.

ROBERT LINCOLN is standing near her, studying the map. NINIAN EDWARDS is sitting at the left of the table and JOSH SPEED is standing near the chart. They are both smoking cigars and watching the chart.

The door at the left is open, and through it the clatter of telegraph instruments can be heard. The window is partly open, and we can hear band music from the square below, and frequent cheers from the assembled mob, who are watching the election returns flashed from a magic lantern on the State House balcony.

Every now and then, a telegraph operator named JED comes in from the left and tacks a new bulletin up on the chart. Another man named PHIL is out on the balcony taking bulletins from JED.

SCENE XI

ROBERT

What do those little flags mean, stuck into the map?

JOSH

Red means the state is sure for us. White means doubtful. Blue means hopeless.

(ABE *tosses the clipping he has been reading on the table and picks up another.*)

(JED *comes in and goes up to pin bulletins opposite Illinois, Maryland and New York.*)

NINIAN (*rising to look*)

Lincoln and Douglas neck and neck in Illinois.
(JOSH *and* ROBERT *crowd around the chart.*)

JOSH

Maryland is going all for Breckenridge and Bell. Abe—you're nowhere in Maryland.

MARY (*with intense anxiety*)

What of New York?

JED (*crossing to the window*)

Say, Phil—when you're not getting bulletins, keep that window closed. We can't hear ourselves think.

PHIL

All right. Only have to open 'er up again. (*He closes the window.*)

MARY

What does it say about New York?
(JED *goes.*)

NINIAN

Douglas a hundred and seventeen thousand—Lincoln a hundred and six thousand.

MARY (*desperately, to* ABE)

He's winning from you in New York, Abe!

JOSH

Not yet, Mary. These returns so far are mostly from the city where Douglas is bound to run the strongest.

ABE (*interested in a clipping*)

I see the New York *Herald* says I've got the soul of a Uriah Heep encased in the body of a baboon. (*He puts the clipping aside and starts to read another.*)

NINIAN (*who has resumed his seat*)

You'd better change that flag on Rhode Island from red to white, Bob. It looks doubtful to me.

(ROBERT, *glad of something to do, changes the flag as directed.*)

MARY

What does it look like in Pennsylvania, Ninian?

NINIAN

There's nothing to worry about there, Mary. It's safe for Abe. In fact, you needn't worry at all.

MARY (*very tense*)

Yes. You've been saying that over and over again all evening. There's no need to worry. But how can we help worrying when every new bulletin shows Douglas ahead.

JOSH

But every one of them shows Abe gaining.

NINIAN (*mollifying*)

Just give them time to count all the votes in New York and then you'll be on your way to the White House.

MARY

Oh, why don't they hurry with it? Why don't those returns come in?

ABE (*preoccupied*)

They'll come in—soon enough.

(BILLY HERNDON *comes in from the right. He has been doing a lot of drinking but has hold of himself.*)

BILLY

That mob down there is sickening! They cheer every bulletin that's flashed on the wall, whether the news is good or bad. And they cheer every picture of every candidate, including George Washington, with the same, fine, ignorant enthusiasm.

JOSH

That's logical. They can't tell 'em apart.

BILLY (*to* ABE)

There are a whole lot of reporters down there. They want to know what will be your first official action after you're elected.

NINIAN

What do you want us to tell 'em, Abe?

ABE (*still reading*)

Tell 'em I'm thinking of growing a beard.

JOSH

A beard?

NINIAN (*amused*)

Whatever put that idea into your mind?

ABE (*picking up another clipping*)

I had a letter the other day from some little girl. She said I ought to have whiskers, to give me more dignity. And I'll need it—if elected.
(JED *arrives with new bulletins.* BILLY, NINIAN, JOSH *and* ROBERT *huddle around* JED, *watching him post the bulletins.*)

MARY

What do they say now?
(JED *goes to the window and gives some bulletins to* PHIL.)

MARY

Is there anything new from New York?

NINIAN

Connecticut—Abe far in the lead. That's eleven safe electoral votes anyway. Missouri—Douglas thirty-five thousand—Bell thirty-three— Breckenridge sixteen—Lincoln, eight. . . .

(*Cheers from the crowd outside until* PHIL *closes the window.* JED *returns to the office at the left.*)

MARY

What are they cheering for?

BILLY

They don't know!

ABE (*with another clipping*)

The Chicago *Times* says, "Lincoln breaks down! Lincoln's heart fails him! His tongue fails him! His legs fail him! He fails all over! The people refuse to support him! They laugh at him! Douglas is champion of the people! Douglas skins the living dog!"

(*He tosses the clipping aside.* MARY *stands up.*)

MARY (*her voice is trembling*)

I can't stand it any longer!

ABE

Yes, my dear—I think you'd better go home. I'll be back before long.

MARY (*hysterical*)

I won't go home. You only want to be rid of me. That's what you've wanted ever since the day we were married—and before that. Anything to get me out of your sight, because you hate me! (*Turning to* JOSH, NINIAN *and* BILLY.) And it's the same with all of you—all of his friends—you hate me—you wish I'd never come into his life.

JOSH

No, Mary.

(ABE *has stood up, quickly, at the first storm signal. He himself is in a fearful state of nervous tension—in no mood to treat* MARY *with patient indulgence. He looks sharply at* NINIAN *and at the others.*)

ABE

Will you please step out for a moment?

NINIAN

Certainly, Abe.

(*He and the others go into the telegraph office.* JOSH *gestures to* ROBERT *to go with them.* ROBERT *casts a black look at his mother and goes. . . .* ABE *turns on* MARY *with strange savagery.*)

ABE

Damn you! Damn you for taking every opportunity you can to make a public fool of me—and yourself! It's bad enough, God knows, when you act like that in the privacy of our own home. But here—in front of people! You're not to do that again. Do you hear me? You're never to do that again!

(MARY *is so aghast at this outburst that her hysterical temper vanishes, giving way to blank terror.*)

MARY (*in a faint, strained voice*)

Abe! You cursed at me. Do you realize what you did? You cursed at me.

(ABE *has the impulse to curse at her again, but with considerable effort, he controls it.*)

ABE (*in a strained voice*)

I lost my temper, Mary. And I'm sorry for it. But I still think you should go home rather than endure the strain of this—this Death Watch.

(*She stares at him, uncomprehendingly, then turns and goes to the door.*)

MARY (*at the door*)

This is the night I dreamed about, when I was a child, when I was an excited young girl, and all the gay young gentlemen of Springfield were courting me, and I fell in love with the least likely of them. This is the night when I'm waiting to hear that my husband has become President of the United States. And even if he does—it's ruined, for me. It's too late. . . .

(She opens the door and goes out. ABE looks after her, anguished, then turns quickly, crosses to the door at the left and opens it.)

ABE *(calling off)*

Bob!
(ROBERT comes in.)
Go with your Mother.

ROBERT

Do I have to?

ABE

Yes! Hurry! Keep right with her till I get home.
(ROBERT has gone. ABE turns to the window. PHIL opens it.)

PHIL

Do you think you're going to make it, Mr. Lincoln?

ABE

Oh—there's nothing to worry about.

CROWD OUTSIDE *(singing)*

Old Abe Lincoln came out of the wilderness
Out of the wilderness
Out of the wilderness
Old Abe Lincoln came out of the wilderness
Down in Illinois!
(NINIAN, JOSH, BILLY, AND JED come in, the latter to post new bulletins. After JED has communicated these, PHIL again closes the window. JED goes.)

NINIAN

It looks like seventy-four electoral votes sure for you. Twenty-seven more probable. New York's will give you the election.
(ABE walks around the room. JOSH has been looking at ABE.)

JOSH

Abe, could I get you a cup of coffee?

ABE

No, thanks, Josh.

NINIAN

Getting nervous, Abe?

ABE

No. I'm just thinking what a blow it would be to Mrs. Lincoln if I should lose.

NINIAN

And what about me? I have ten thousand dollars bet on you.

BILLY (scornfully)

I'm afraid that the loss to the nation would be somewhat more serious than that.

JOSH

How would you feel, Abe?

ABE (sitting on the chair near the window)

I guess I'd feel the greatest sense of relief of my life.
(JED comes in with a news despatch.)

JED

Here's a news despatch. (He hands it over and goes.)

NINIAN (reads)

"Shortly after nine o'clock this evening, Mr. August Belmont stated that Stephen A. Douglas has piled up a majority of fifty thousand votes in New York City and carried the State."

BILLY

Mr. Belmont be damned!
(CRIMMIN comes in, smoking a cigar, looking contented.)

CRIMMIN

Good evening, Mr. Lincoln. Good evening, gentlemen—and how are you all feeling *now*?

(*They all greet him.*)

NINIAN

Look at this, Crimmin. (*He hands the despatch to* CRIMMIN.)

CRIMMIN (*smiles*)

Well—Belmont is going to fight to the last ditch, which is just what he's lying in now. I've been in Chicago and the outlook there is cloudless. In fact, Mr. Lincoln, I came down tonight to protect you from the office-seekers. They're lining up downstairs already. On the way in I counted four Ministers to Great Britain and eleven Secretaries of State.

(JED *has come in with more bulletins to put on the chart and then goes to the window to give* PHIL *the bulletins.*)

BILLY (*at the chart*)

There's a bulletin from New York! Douglas a hundred and eighty-three thousand—Lincoln a hundred and eighty-*one* thousand!

(JED *goes.*)

JOSH

Look out, Abe. You're catching up!

CRIMMIN

The next bulletin from New York will show you winning. Mark my words, Mr. Lincoln, this election is all wrapped up tightly in a neat bundle, ready for delivery on your doorstep tonight. We've fought the good fight, and we've won!

ABE (*pacing up and down the room*)

Yes—we've fought the good fight—in the dirtiest campaign in the history of corrupt politics. And if I have won, then I must cheerfully pay my political debts. All those who helped to nominate and elect me must be paid off. I have been gambled all around, bought and sold a hundred times. And now I must fill all the dishonest pledges made in my name.

NINIAN

We realize all that, Abe—but the fact remains that you're winning. Why, you're even beating the coalition in Rhode Island!

ABE

I've got to step out for a moment. (*He goes out at the right.*)

NINIAN (*cheerfully*)

Poor Abe.

CRIMMIN

You gentlemen have all been close friends of our Candidate for a long time so perhaps you could answer a question that's been puzzling me considerably. Can I possibly be correct in supposing that he doesn't want to win?

JOSH

The answer is—yes.

CRIMMIN (*looking toward the right*)

Well—I can only say that, for me, this is all a refreshingly new experience.

BILLY (*belligerently*)

Would *you* want to become President of the United States at this time? Haven't you been reading the newspapers lately?

CRIMMIN

Why, yes—I try to follow the events of the day.

BILLY (*in a rage*)

Don't you realize that they've raised ten thousand volunteers in South Carolina? They're arming them! The Governor has issued a proclamation saying that if Mr. Lincoln is elected, the State will secede tomorrow, and every other state south of the Dixon line will go with it. Can you see what this means? War! Civil War! And *he'll* have the whole terrible responsibility for it—a man who has never wanted anything in his life but to be let alone, in peace!

NINIAN

Calm down, Billy. Go get yourself another drink.
(JED *rushes in.*)

JED

Mr. Edwards, here it is! (*He hands a news despatch to* NINIAN, *then rushes to the window to attract* PHIL's *attention and communicate the big news.*)

NINIAN (*reads*)

"At 10:30 tonight the New York *Herald* conceded that Mr. Lincoln has carried the state by a majority of at least twenty-five thousand and has won the election!" (*He tosses the despatch in the air.*) He's won! He's won! Hurrah!
(*All on the stage shout, cheer, embrace and slap each other.*)

BILLY

God be praised! God be praised!

CRIMMIN

I knew it! I never had a doubt of it!
(JED *is on the balcony, shouting through a megaphone.*)

JED

Lincoln is elected! Honest Old Abe is our next President!
(*A terrific cheer ascends from the crowd below.* ABE *returns. They rush at him.* BILLY *shakes hands with him, too deeply moved to speak.*)

NINIAN

You've carried New York, Abe! You've won! Congratulations!

CRIMMIN

My congratulations, Mr. President. This is a mighty achievement for all of us!
(JED *comes in and goes to* ABE.)

JED

My very best, Mr. Lincoln!

ABE (*solemnly*)

Thank you—thank you all very much.
(*He comes to the left.* JOSH *is the last to shake his hand.*)

JOSH

I congratulate you, Abe.

ABE

Thanks, Josh.

NINIAN

Listen to them, Abe. Listen to that crazy, howling mob down there.

CRIMMIN

It's all for you, Mr. Lincoln.

NINIAN

Abe, get out there and let 'em see you!

ABE

No. I don't want to go out there. I—I guess I'll be going on home, to tell Mary. (*He starts toward the door.*)
(*A short, stocky officer named* KAVANAGH *comes in from the right. He is followed by two soldiers.*)

CRIMMIN

This is Captain Kavanagh, Mr. *President*.

KAVANAGH (*salutes*)

I've been detailed to accompany you, Mr. Lincoln, in the event of your election.

ABE

I'm grateful, Captain. But I don't need you.

KAVANAGH

I'm afraid you've got to have us, Mr. Lincoln. I don't like to be alarming, but I guess you know as well as I do what threats have been made.

ABE (*wearily*)

I see . . . Well—Good night, Josh, Ninian—Mr. Crimmin—Billy. Thank you for your good wishes.

(*He starts for the door. The others bid him good night, quietly.*)

KAVANAGH

One moment, Sir. With your permission, I'll go first.

(*He goes out,* ABE *after him, the two other soldiers follow. The light fades.*)

STARK YOUNG Why he selected

MEI LAN-FANG

I chose this article for the anthology because it may be of service to a great artist, whom I admired and am grateful to, and because he liked it so much that he sent sixty-two copies to poets, scholars, and friends in China.

Austin, Tex.   STARK YOUNG
June, 1942

Mei Lan-fang and his Company, in Repertory. Forty-ninth Street Theater, February 17, 1930.

WE KNOW how much, ordinarily, is seen in the arts—very little indeed by the average eye; and how much rubbish is talked, rubbish that is somewhat insincere, faddish, imitative, or else fetched up from sentiments within the speaker and not from any perception of the work of art. How much more chance, then, a review of Mei Lan-fang has of being oblique, bluffing or fatuous! In his case more than in most, a criticism is apt to be mere autobiography on the critic's part.

In an art that belongs within the tradition of an old race, and in the presence of an artist considered by them a great artist, a good part of our attendance must be taken up with humility. I spent a fair part of my time, during this performance of the Chinese company, trying merely to learn, as one learns a language. We see what we can, and must be thankful for what perception is granted us. In this performance of Mei Lan-fang I saw enough to see that for me it was the highest point in the season's theater and in any season since Duse's visit and the Moscow Art Theater's production of Chekhov's plays.

As to the Chinese theater, we perceive in the first place that it is an art based on music, or at least musically seen, and is a complete art consisting of music, speech and dancing in the full sense, which includes dance movement, gymnastics, pantomime and gesture. Most of the music was lost on me, of course, with its foreign scale and intention, but I was surprised to find how much of it takes on meaning for an outsider and how often the themes are easily distinguishable. But most of all I was struck by the mingling of music and action that I saw on the stage, the admirable accentuation of gesture by music, the way in which the music gave the tempo to the acting; and by the security of an effect achieved through such delicate means. I could tell, however foreign the music, or rather his tone, by a curious brightness and metal, that Mei Lan-fang's voice was highly unusual, and that the poetic wholeness of his art arose from an astonishing unity of time, tone, emotional rhythm and bodily control.

This Chinese art is, in the second place, stiffened and syllabled with conventions; some of which are familiar to us and thought of largely with naïve, indulgent humor, but many of which, not known at all, underlie, like an alphabet, the entire theatrical occasion. The masks of these faces, painted with black predominating where fierceness is to be symbolized, with blue for cruelty, red for the heroic, and so on; the stage properties, where moving a chair may imply another apartment, through whose imaginary door you bend to pass; the duster of horse hair, denoting the divine, the heroic, the holy; the whip standing for the horse; the elaborate usages for the sleeve; the use of the eyes and hands; the prologue on the actor's entrance, the couplet following; there are these and numberless other conventional symbols. Foreigners seize on them for harmless discussions—the easiest way out of so far-off an art, and we can read of them in the voluminous notes supplied by George Kin Leung for the brochure of information that is given out with the programs. We cannot dwell upon them here, but it is interesting to consider their relation to us. There is one element to them, the visual, that we can take for the aesthetic qualities obviously present. The other element in them—whether we know their implications or not—is the symbolistic. When purely symbolistic, these conventions represent—without reproducing—ideas, actions, things, exactly as words do, which in themselves are nothing but sound. There is this difference, however, between these symbols and words: a movement or object symbolizing a beautiful idea, personage, place, tends to be created into something in itself more beautiful and worthy of the association, whereas a word remains the same, plus perhaps our efforts to put beauty into its employment. These Chinese conventions in themselves have doubtless, therefore, taken on a greater and greater perfection.

It is interesting, also, to note the Greek and Elizabethan parallels in this Chinese theater, the obvious and slighter Elizabethan ones, mostly theater mechanics, and the more profound Greek characteristics. One of these Greek similarities consists of the scenes, developed over and over again and falling into types, the Parting Scenes, Recognition Scenes, Ironic Scenes, and so on. The other is the method, practised always by the Greeks—a method that is based on our physical nature— we rise to song with an access of vitality—and that has always seemed to me inevitable in the highest development of the theater—I mean the rising into music where the pitch of the dramatic idea and emotion seems to require it.

It is interesting to note the antiquity of this Chinese theater, going back almost thirty centuries perhaps; to note the continuity and innovations in its history, its deep relation to the Chinese soul, the innovations and inventions that are credited to Mei Lan-fang; and to note the fact that the Chinese see these plays from time to time throughout their lives, which means listening to and learning a perfection—something like great music heard many times, always different, always the same— which is one of the signs of excellence in any work of art, and of sophistication rather than semi-barbarism in a theater public.

Of Mei Lan-fang himself, such facts as that he is the greatest actor in China, a public idol, with the highest honors, "The Foremost of the Pear Orchard" and the head of the Ching-Chung Monastery, that he was an accomplished musician at seven, a success in feminine roles at twelve, and that his house, collections and position in Chinese culture today are known over China—these things we can read in a hundred places and in more than one language.

Taking him—in the way an actor as a dramatic medium must be taken—as we take a musical instrument or the pigment for a painter, we see that Mei Lan-fang is of medium height, slender, with sure, close-knit muscles, small, supple wrists, superb support in the waist— from which the fine movements and gestures of the torso proceed—a remarkable control of the neck, and perfect poise and suspension in the ankles. His face is the classic Chinese oval, with highly expressive eyes. His make-up, that overlay of carmines and darker tones, is the most beautiful I have ever seen in the theater. The diction is sharp and always pointed. The famous hands are curiously like those in Botticelli, Simone Martini and other painters of the fifteenth century. They are rather tense in form, with long fingers, squarish-tipped; not so much our ideal of the hand, which is based on the seventeenth century of Rubens and Van Dyke, but incredibly trained in the conventions and dance of the Chinese actor's art. And even with no knowledge of that art, you can see with what perfection Mei Lan-fang begins his speech, prolongs the word that gives the musicians the cue to begin, retards the words by which the music is warned to stop.

For our purposes, however, it seems to me that all this is unimportant compared to one point that bears on all art basically. I mean the relation of the art of Mei Lan-fang—the greatest in his field—to reality. That question of the relation of art to reality is the greatest of all questions with regard to art. It parallels—to employ the terms closest to us humanly—the relation of the spirit to the body, or, to go the other way round, the relation of the passing to the permanent, of the casual in the moment to the flower of it.

On this subject much has been written about Chinese art and about this actor that is misleading. We will stick to Mei Lan-fang. About this actor we are told to note his impersonation of women and his impersonation of various emotions. Words are weak and dependent things, and nothing could be more confusing than these are likely to be. In the first place, there is no attempt to impersonate a woman. The female roles are the most important in the Chinese theater; and he, in the kind of female role that he presents, strives only to convey the essence of the female quality, with all its grace, depth of feeling, its rhythm of tenderness and force. This distillation that he employs of the material into its inherent and ideal qualities, Mei Lan-fang does with an economy both brilliant and secure, a studious care, delicacy and inner music. The impression is one of a perfection, at once fragile and secure, that is astonishing.

But even more important—for the Chinese critics have already often warned us not to go astray with regard to these female roles—even more important for us is the matter of his realism in general. I found myself most impressed in this regard during the piece from the Ming

Dynasty, where the princess stabs the general who had destroyed her family, and then kills herself with his sword. This seemed to me more satisfying than the play about the husband's return, for in the last it was easy to see the movement away from the older, high style. What we must say about the realism and abstraction and stylization of Mei Lan-fang's art is that, exactly as is the case in the classic Chinese art, we are astonished at the precision of its realistic notations and renderings, and are dazzled by the place these take in the highly stylized and re-moved whole that the work of art becomes. These movements of Mei Lan-fang, that way he has of keeping the whole body alive, even in the stillest moments of the action, of putting that continuous move-ment or vibration into the head as it springs from the neck; that voice that in its sheer tone moves away from actuality; that sophisticated, poetic use of the eyes, those expressions of fear, pity, murderous resolu-tion, despair, and so on, that come over his face; none of these is im-personation or reality in the usual sense. They are real only in the sense that great sculptures or paintings are real, through their motion in repose, their impression of shock, brief duration and beautiful finality. Every now and then—very rarely—in acting we see this happen; I mean a final creation, free from merely incidental matter, of an essential quality in some emotion, the presentation of that truth which confirms and enlarges our sense of reality. But I have never seen it so securely and repeatedly achieved as in Mei Lan-fang.

THORNTON WILDER Why

he selected The HAPPY JOURNEY

to TRENTON and CAMDEN

The form in which this play is cast is not an innovation but a revival. The healthiest ages of the theatre have been marked by the fact that there was least literally representative scenery. The sympathetic participation of the audience was most engaged when their collaborative imagination was called upon to supply a large part of the background.

It is perhaps a sad commentary on the kind of people who go in for amateur stage production to say that in the many productions of the play I have seen "Ma" has been permitted, or directed, to play her role sentimentally, and the closing moments have been drenched in tears, ostentatious piety and a kind of heroic self-pity. The play is a testimonial of homage to the average American mother who brings up her children as instinctively as a bird builds its nest and whose strength lies in the fact that whatever stress arrives from the circumstances of life, she strives to maintain an atmosphere of forward-looking industry and readiness.

New Haven, Conn.   THORNTON WILDER
April 13, 1942

No scenery is required for this play. Perhaps a few dusty flats may be seen leaning against the brick wall at the back of the stage.
The five members of the Kirby family and the Stage Manager *compose the cast.*
The Stage Manager not only moves forward and withdraws the few

*properties that are required, but he reads from a typescript the
lines of all the minor characters. He reads them clearly, but with
little attempt at characterization, scarcely troubling himself to alter
his voice, even when he responds in the person of a child or a
woman.*

As the curtain rises the Stage Manager *is leaning lazily against the
proscenium pillar at the audience's left. He is smoking.*

Arthur *is playing marbles in the center of the stage.*

Caroline *is at the remote back right talking to some girls who are
invisible to us.*

Ma Kirby *is anxiously putting on her hat before an imaginary mirror.*

MA. Where's your pa? Why isn't he here? I declare we'll never get
started.

ARTHUR. Ma, where's my hat? I guess I don't go if I can't find my
hat.

MA. Go out into the hall and see if it isn't there. Where's Caroline
gone to now, the plagued child?

ARTHUR. She's out waitin' in the street talkin' to the Jones girls.—
I just looked in the hall a thousand times, ma, and it isn't there. (*He
spits for good luck before a difficult shot and mutters:*) Come on,
baby.

MA. Go and look again, I say. Look carefully.

Arthur *rises, runs to the right, turns around swiftly, returns to
his game, flinging himself on the floor with a terrible impact
and starts shooting an aggie.*

ARTHUR. No, ma, it's not there.

MA. (*serenely*). Well, you don't leave Newark without that hat,
make up your mind to that. I don't go no journeys with a hoodlum.

ARTHUR. Aw, ma!

Ma *comes down to the footlights and talks toward the audience
as through a window.*

MA. Oh, Mrs. Schwartz!

THE STAGE MANAGER (*consulting his script*). Here I am, Mrs.
Kirby. Are you going yet?

MA. I guess we're going in just a minute. How's the baby?

THE STAGE MANAGER. She's all right now. We slapped her on the back and she spat it up.

MA. Isn't that fine!—Well now, if you'll be good enough to give the cat a saucer of milk in the morning and the evening, Mrs. Schwartz, I'll be ever so grateful to you.—Oh, good afternoon, Mrs. Hobmeyer!

THE STAGE MANAGER. Good afternoon, Mrs. Kirby, I hear you're going away.

MA (*modest*). Oh, just for three days, Mrs. Hobmeyer, to see my married daughter, Beulah, in Camden. Elmer's got his vacation week from the laundry early this year, and he's just the best driver in the world.

Caroline *comes "into the house" and stands by her mother.*

THE STAGE MANAGER. Is the whole family going?

MA. Yes, all four of us that's here. The change ought to be good for the children. My married daughter was downright sick a while ago——

THE STAGE MANAGER. Tchk—Tchk—Tchk! Yes. I remember you tellin' us.

MA. And I just want to go down and see the child. I ain't seen her since then. I just won't rest easy in my mind without I see her. (*To Caroline*) Can't you say good afternoon to Mrs. Hobmeyer?

CAROLINE (*blushes and lowers her eyes and says woodenly*). Good afternoon, Mrs. Hobmeyer.

THE STAGE MANAGER. Good afternoon, dear.—Well, I'll wait and beat these rugs until after you're gone, because I don't want to choke you. I hope you have a good time and find everything all right.

MA. Thank you, Mrs. Hobmeyer, I hope I will.—Well, I guess that milk for the cat is all, Mrs. Schwartz, if you're sure you don't mind. If anything should come up, the key to the back door is hanging by the ice box.

ARTHUR AND CAROLINE. Ma! Not so loud. Everybody can hear yuh.

MA. Stop pullin' my dress, children. (*In a loud whisper*) The key to the back door I'll leave hangin' by the ice box and I'll leave the screen door unhooked.

THE STAGE MANAGER. Now have a good trip, dear, and give my love to Loolie.

MA. I will, and thank you a thousand times.

She returns "into the room."

What can be keeping your pa?

ARTHUR. I can't find my hat, ma.

Enter Elmer *holding a hat.*

ELMER. Here's Arthur's hat. He musta left it in the car Sunday.

MA. That's a mercy. Now we can start.—Caroline Kirby, what you done to your cheeks?

CAROLINE (*defiant-abashed*). Nothin'.

MA. If you've put anything on 'em, I'll slap you.

CAROLINE. No, ma, of course I haven't. (*hanging her head*) I just rubbed'm to make'm red. All the girls do that at High School when they're goin' places.

MA. Such silliness I never saw. Elmer, what kep' you?

ELMER (*always even-voiced and always looking out a little anxiously through his spectacles*). I just went to the garage and had Charlie give a last look at it, Kate.

MA. I'm glad you did. I wouldn't like to have no breakdown miles from anywhere. Now we can start. Arthur, put those marbles away. Anybody'd think you didn't want to go on a journey to look at yuh.

They go out through the "hall," take the short steps that denote going downstairs, and find themselves in the street.

ELMER. Here, you boys, you keep away from that car.

MA. Those Sullivan boys put their heads into everything.

The Stage Manager has moved forward four chairs and a low platform. This is the automobile. It is in the center of the stage and faces the audience. The platform slightly raises the two chairs in the rear. Pa's *hands hold an imaginary steering wheel and continually shift gears.* Caroline *sits beside him.* Arthur *is behind him and* Ma *behind* Caroline.

CAROLINE (*self-consciously*). Goodbye, Mildred. Goodbye, Helen.

THE STAGE MANAGER. Goodbye, Caroline. Goodbye, Mrs. Kirby. I hope y'have a good time.

MA. Goodbye, girls.

THE STAGE MANAGER. Goodbye, Kate. The car looks fine.

MA (*looking upward toward a window*). Oh, goodbye, Emma!

(*modestly*) We think it's the best little Chevrolet in the world.—Oh, goodbye, Mrs. Adler!

THE STAGE MANAGER. What, are you going away, Mrs. Kirby?

MA. Just for three days, Mrs. Adler, to see my married daughter in Camden.

THE STAGE MANAGER. Have a good time.

> *Now* Ma, Caroline, *and the* Stage Manager *break out into a tremendous chorus of goodbyes. The whole street is saying goodbye.* Arthur *takes out his pea shooter and lets fly happily into the air. There is a lurch or two and they are off.*

ARTHUR (*in sudden fright*). Pa! Pa! Don't go by the school. Mr. Biedenbach might see us!

MA. I don't care if he does see us. I guess I can take my children out of school for one day without having to hide down back streets about it.

> Elmer *nods to a passerby.*

> Ma *asks without sharpness:*

Who was that you spoke to, Elmer?

ELMER. That was the fellow who arranges our banquets down to the Lodge, Kate.

MA. Is he the one who had to buy four hundred steaks? (Pa *nods.*) I declare, I'm glad I'm not him.

ELMER. The air's getting better already. Take deep breaths, children.

> *They inhale noisily.*

ARTHUR. Gee, it's almost open fields already. *"Weber and Heilbronner Suits for Well-dressed Men."* Ma, can I have one of them some day?

MA. If you graduate with good marks perhaps your father'll let you have one for graduation.

CAROLINE (*whining*). Oh, Pa! do we have to wait while that whole funeral goes by?

> Pa *takes off his hat.*

> Ma *cranes forward with absorbed curiosity.*

MA. Take off your hat, Arthur. Look at your father.—Why, Elmer, I do believe that's a lodge-brother of yours. See the banner? I suppose this is the Elizabeth branch.

Elmer *nods.* Ma *sighs: Tchk—tchk—tchk. They all lean forward and watch the funeral in silence, growing momentarily more solemnized. After a pause,* Ma *continues almost dreamily:*

Well, we haven't forgotten the one that we went on, have we? We haven't forgotten our good Harold. He gave his life for his country, we mustn't forget that. (*She passes her finger from the corner of her eye across her cheek. There is another pause.*) Well, we'll all hold up the traffic for a few minutes some day.

THE CHILDREN (*very uncomfortable*). Ma!

MA (*without self-pity*). Well I'm "ready," children. I hope everybody in this car is "ready." (*She puts her hand on Pa's shoulder*). And I pray to go first, Elmer. Yes. (Pa *touches her hand.*)

·THE CHILDREN. Ma, everybody's looking at you. Everybody's laughing at you.

MA. Oh, hold your tongues! I don't care what a lot of silly people in Elizabeth, New Jersey, think of me.—Now we can go on. That's the last.

There is another lurch and the car goes on.

CAROLINE. *"Fit-Rite Suspenders. The Working Man's Choice."* Pa, why do they spell Rite that way?

ELMER. So that it'll make you stop and ask about it, Missy.

CAROLINE. Papa, you're teasing me.—Ma, why do they say *"Three Hundred Rooms Three Hundred Baths?"*

ARTHUR. *"Miller's Spaghetti: The Family's Favorite Dish."* Ma, why don't you ever have spaghetti?

MA. Go along, you'd never eat it.

ARTHUR. Ma, I like it now.

CAROLINE (*with gesture*). Yum-yum. It looks wonderful up there. Ma, make some when we get home?

MA (*dryly*). "The management is always happy to receive suggestions. We aim to please."

The whole family finds this exquisitely funny. The children scream with laughter. Even Elmer *smiles.* Ma *remains modest.*

ELMER. Well, I guess no one's complaining, Kate. Everybody knows you're a good cook.

MA. I don't know whether I'm a good cook or not, but I know

I've had practice. At least I've cooked three meals a day for twenty-five years.

ARTHUR. Aw, ma, you went out to eat once in a while.

MA. Yes. That made it a leap year.

This joke is no less successful than its predecessor. When the laughter dies down, Caroline *turns around in an ecstasy of well-being and kneeling on the cushions says:*

CAROLINE. Ma, I love going out in the country like this. Let's do it often, ma.

MA. Goodness, smell that air will you! It's got the whole ocean in it.—Elmer, drive careful over that bridge. This must be New Brunswick we're coming to.

ARTHUR *(jealous of his mother's successes)*. Ma, when is the next comfort station?

MA *(unruffled)*. You don't want one. You just said that to be awful.

CAROLINE *(shrilly)*. Yes, he did, ma. He's terrible. He says that kind of thing right out in school and I want to sink through the floor, ma. He's terrible.

MA. Oh, don't get so excited about nothing, Miss Proper! I guess we're all yewman-beings in this car, at least as far as I know. And, Arthur, you try and be a gentleman.—Elmer, don't run over that collie dog. *(She follows the dog with her eyes.)* Looked kinda peakèd to me. Needs a good honest bowl of leavings. Pretty dog, too. *(Her eyes fall on a billboard.)* That's a pretty advertisement for Chesterfield cigarettes, isn't it? Looks like Beulah, a little.

ARTHUR. Ma?

MA. Yes.

ARTHUR *("route" rhymes with "out")*. Can't I take a paper route with the Newark *Daily Post?*

MA. No, you cannot. No, sir. I hear they make the paper boys get up at four-thirty in the morning. No son of mine is going to get up at four-thirty every morning, not if it's to make a million dollars. Your *Saturday Evening Post* route on Thursday mornings is enough.

ARTHUR. Aw, ma.

MA. No, sir. No son of mine is going to get up at four-thirty and miss the sleep God meant him to have.

ARTHUR (*sullenly*). Hhm! Ma's always talking about God. I guess she got a letter from him this morning.

Ma *rises, outraged*.

MA. Elmer, stop that automobile this minute. I don't go another step with anybody that says things like that. Arthur, you get out of this car. Elmer, you give him another dollar bill. He can go back to Newark, by himself. I don't want him.

ARTHUR. What did I say? There wasn't anything terrible about that.

ELMER. I didn't hear what he said, Kate.

MA. God has done a lot of things for me and I won't have him made fun of by anybody. Go away. Go away from me.

CAROLINE. Aw, Ma,—don't spoil the ride.

MA. No.

ELMER. We might as well go on, Kate, since we've got started. I'll talk to the boy tonight.

MA (*slowly conceding*). All right, if you say so, Elmer. But I won't sit beside him. Caroline, you come, and sit by me.

ARTHUR (*frightened*). Aw, ma, that wasn't so terrible.

MA. I don't want to talk about it. I hope your father washes your mouth out with soap and water.—Where'd we all be if I started talking about God like that, I'd like to know! We'd be in the speak-easies and night-clubs and places like that, that's where we'd be.—All right, Elmer, you can go on now.

CAROLINE. What did he say, ma? I didn't hear what he said.

MA. I don't want to talk about it.

They drive on in silence for a moment, the shocked silence after a scandal.

ELMER. I'm going to stop and give the car a little water, I guess.

MA. All right, Elmer. You know best.

ELMER (*to a garage hand*). Could I have a little water in the radiator—to make sure?

THE STAGE MANAGER (*in this scene alone he lays aside his script and enters into a rôle seriously*). You sure can. (*He punches the tires.*) Air, all right? Do you need any oil or gas?

ELMER. No, I think not. I just got fixed up in Newark.

MA. We're on the right road for Camden, are we?

THE STAGE MANAGER. Yes, keep straight ahead. You can't miss it. You'll be in Trenton in a few minutes.

He carefully pours some water into the hood.

Camden's a great town, lady, believe me.

MA. My daughter likes it fine,—my married daughter.

THE STAGE MANAGER. Ye'? It's a great burg all right. I guess I think so because I was born near there.

MA. Well, well. Your folks still live there?

THE STAGE MANAGER. No, my old man sold the farm and they built a factory on it. So the folks moved to Philadelphia.

MA. My married daughter Beulah lives there because her husband works in the telephone company.—Stop pokin' me, Caroline!—We're all going down to see her for a few days.

THE STAGE MANAGER. Ye'?

MA. She's been sick, you see, and I just felt I had to go and see her. My husband and my boy are going to stay at the Y.M.C.A. I hear they've got a dormitory on the top floor that's real clean and comfortable. Had you ever been there?

THE STAGE MANAGER. No, I'm Knights of Columbus myself.

MA. Oh.

THE STAGE MANAGER. I used to play basketball at the Y though. It looked all right to me.

He has been standing with one foot on the rung of Ma's chair. They have taken a great fancy to one another. He reluctantly shakes himself out of it and pretends to examine the car again, whistling.

Well, I guess you're all set now, lady. I hope you have a good trip; you can't miss it.

EVERYBODY. Thanks. Thanks a lot. Good luck to you.

Jolts and lurches.

MA (*with a sigh*). The world's full of nice people.—That's what I call a nice young man.

CAROLINE (*earnestly*). Ma, you oughtn't to tell'm all everything about yourself.

MA. Well, Caroline, you do your way and I'll do mine.—He looked kinda thin to me. I'd like to feed him up for a few days. His mother lives in Philadelphia and I expect he eats at those dreadful Greek places.

CAROLINE. I'm hungry. Pa, there's a hot dog stand. K'n I have one?

ELMER. We'll all have one, eh, Kate? We had such an early lunch.

MA. Just as you think best, Elmer.

ELMER. Arthur, here's half a dollar.—Run over and see what they have. Not too much mustard either.

Arthur *descends from the car and goes off stage right.*

Ma *and* Caroline *get out and walk a bit.*

MA. What's that flower over there?—I'll take some of those to Beulah.

CAROLINE. It's just a weed, ma.

MA. I like it.—My, look at the sky, wouldya! I'm glad I was born in New Jersey. I've always said it was the best state in the Union. Every state has something no other state has got.

They stroll about humming.

Presently Arthur *returns with his hands full of imaginary hot dogs which he distributes. He is still very much cast down by the recent scandal. He finally approaches his mother and says falteringly:*

ARTHUR. Ma, I'm sorry. I'm sorry for what I said.

He bursts into tears and puts his forehead against her elbow.

MA. There. There. We all say wicked things at times. I know you didn't mean it like it sounded.

He weeps still more violently than before.

Why, now, now! I forgive you, Arthur and tonight before you go to bed you . . . (*she whispers.*) You're a good boy at heart, Arthur, and we all know it.

Caroline *starts to cry too.*

Ma *is suddenly joyously alive and happy.*

Sakes alive, it's too nice a day for us all to be cryin'. Come now, get in. You go up in front with your father, Caroline. Ma wants to sit with her beau. I never saw such children. Your hot dogs are all getting wet. Now chew them fine, everybody.—All right, Elmer, forward march.—Caroline, whatever are you doing?

CAROLINE. I'm spitting out the leather, ma.

MA. Then say: Excuse me.

CAROLINE. Excuse me, please.

MA. What's this place? Arthur, did you see the post office?

ARTHUR. It said Laurenceville.

MA. Hhm. School kinda. Nice. I wonder what that big yellow house set back was.—Now it's beginning to be Trenton.

CAROLINE. Papa, it was near here that George Washington crossed the Delaware. It was near Trenton, mama. He was first in war and first in peace, and first in the hearts of his countrymen.

MA (*surveying the passing world, serene and didactic*). Well, the thing I like about him best was that he never told a lie.

The children are duly cast down.

There is a pause.

There's a sunset for you. There's nothing like a good sunset.

ARTHUR. There's an Ohio license in front of us. Ma, have you ever been to Ohio?

MA. No.

A dreamy silence descends upon them.

Caroline *sits closer to her father.*

Ma *puts her arm around* Arthur.

ARTHUR. Ma, what a lotta people there are in the world, ma. There must be thousands and thousands in the United States. Ma, how many are there?

MA. I don't know. Ask your father.

ARTHUR. Pa, how many are there?

ELMER. There are a hundred and twenty-six million, Kate.

MA (*giving a pressure about* Arthur's *shoulder*). And they all like to drive out in the evening with their children beside'm.

Another pause.

Why doesn't somebody sing something? Arthur, you're always singing something; what's the matter with you?

ARTHUR. All right. What'll we sing? (*He sketches:*)

"In the Blue Ridge mountains of Virginia,
    On the trail of the lonesome pine . . ."

No, I don't like that any more. Let's do:

"I been workin' on de railroad
    All de liblong day.
    I been workin' on de railroad

Just to pass de time away."

Caroline *joins in at once.*

Finally even Ma *is singing.*

Even Pa *is singing.*

Ma *suddenly jumps up with a wild cry:*

MA. Elmer, that signpost said Camden, I saw it.

ELMER. All right, Kate, if you're sure.

Much shifting of gears, backing, and jolting.

MA. Yes, there it is. Camden—five miles. Dear old Beulah.—Now children, you be good and quiet during dinner. She's just got out of bed after a big sorta operation, and we must all move around kinda quiet. First you drop me and Caroline at the door and just say hello, and then you men-folk go over to the Y.M.C.A. and come back for dinner in about an hour.

CAROLINE (*shutting her eyes and pressing her fists passionately against her nose*). I see the first star. Everybody make a wish.

Star light, star bright,

First star I seen tonight.

I wish I may, I wish I might

Have the wish I wish tonight.

(*then solemnly*) Pins. Mama, you say "needles."

She interlocks little fingers with her mother.

MA. Needles.

CAROLINE. Shakespeare. Ma, you say "Longfellow."

MA. Longfellow.

CAROLINE. Now it's a secret and I can't tell it to anybody. Ma, you make a wish.

MA (*with almost grim humor*). No, I can make wishes without waiting for no star. And I can tell my wishes right out loud too. Do you want to hear them?

CAROLINE (*resignedly*). No, ma, we know'm already. We've heard'm. (*She hangs her head affectedly on her left shoulder and says with unmalicious mimicry:*) You want me to be a good girl and you want Arthur to be honest-in-word-and-deed.

MA (*majestically*). Yes. So mind yourself.

ELMER. Caroline, take out that letter from Beulah in my coat pocket by you and read aloud the places I marked with red pencil.

CAROLINE (*working*). "*A few blocks after you pass the two big oil tanks on your left . . .*"

EVERYBODY (*pointing backward*). There they are!

CAROLINE. "*. . . you come to a corner where there's an A and P store on the left and a firehouse kitty-corner to it . . .*"

They all jubilantly identify these landmarks. "*. . . turn right, go two blocks, and our house is Weyerhauser St. Number 471.*"

MA. It's an even nicer street than they used to live in. And right handy to an A and P.

CAROLINE (*whispering*). Ma, it's better than our street. It's richer than our street.—Ma, isn't Beulah richer than we are?

MA (*looking at her with a firm and glassy eye*). Mind yourself, missy. I don't want to hear anybody talking about rich or not rich when I'm around. If people aren't nice I don't care how rich they are. I live in the best street in the world because my husband and children live there.

> *She glares impressively at* Caroline *a moment to let this lesson sink in, then looks up, sees* Beulah *and waves.*

There's Beulah standing on the steps lookin' for us.

> Beulah *has appeared and is waving.*
> *They all call out:* Hello, Beulah—Hello.
> *Presently they are all getting out of the car.*
> Beulah *kisses her father long and affectionately.*

BEULAH. Hello, papa. Good old papa. You look tired, pa.—Hello, mama.—Lookit how Arthur and Caroline are growing!

MA. They're bursting all their clothes!—Yes, your pa needs a rest. Thank Heaven, his vacation has come just now. We'll feed him up and let him sleep late. Pa has a present for you, Loolie. He would go and buy it.

BEULAH. Why, pa, you're terrible to go and buy anything for me Isn't he terrible?

MA. Well, it's a secret. You can open it at dinner.

ELMER. Where's Horace, Loolie?

BEULAH. He was kep' over a little at the office. He'll be here any minute. He's crazy to see you all.

MA. All right. You men go over to the Y and come back in about an hour.

BEULAH (*as her father returns to the wheel, stands out in the street beside him*). Go straight along, pa, you can't miss it. It just stares at yuh. (*She puts her arm around his neck and rubs her nose against his temple.*) Crazy old pa, goin' buyin' things! It's me that ought to be buyin' things for you, pa.

ELMER. Oh, no! There's only one Loolie in the world.

BEULAH (*whispering, as her eyes fill with tears*). Are you glad I'm still alive, pa?

> She kisses him abruptly and goes back to the house steps.
>
> The Stage Manager *removes the automobile with the help of* Elmer *and* Arthur *who go off waving their goodbyes.*

Well, come on upstairs, ma, and take off your things.

Caroline, there's a surprise for you in the back yard.

CAROLINE. Rabbits?

BEULAH. No.

CAROLINE. Chickens?

BEULAH. No. Go and see.

> Caroline *runs off stage.*
>
> Beulah *and* Ma *gradually go upstairs.*

There are two new puppies. You be thinking over whether you can keep one in Newark.

MA. I guess we can. It's a nice house, Beulah. You just got a *lovely* home.

BEULAH. When I got back from the hospital, Horace had moved everything into it, and there wasn't anything for me to do.

MA. It's lovely.

> The Stage Manager *pushes out a bed from the left. Its foot is toward the right.* Beulah *sits on it, testing the springs.*

BEULAH. I think you'll find the bed comfortable, ma.

MA (*taking off her hat*). Oh, I could sleep on a heapa shoes, Loolie! I don't have no trouble sleepin'. (*She sits down beside her.*) Now let me look at my girl. Well, well, when I last saw you, you didn't know me. You kep' saying: *When's mama comin'? When's mama comin'?* But the doctor sent me away.

BEULAH (*puts her head on her mother's shoulder and weeps*). It was awful, mama. It was awful. She didn't even live a few minutes, mama. It was awful.

MA (*looking far away*). God thought best, dear. God thought best. We don't understand why. We just go on, honey, doin' our business.

> *Then almost abruptly—passing the back of her hand across her cheek.*

Well, now, what are we giving the men to eat tonight?

BEULAH. There's a chicken in the oven.

MA. What time didya put it in?

BEULAH (*restraining her*). Aw, ma, don't go yet. I like to sit here with you this way. You always get the fidgets when we try and pet yuh, mama.

MA (*ruefully laughing*). Yes, it's kinda foolish. I'm just an old Newark bag-a-bones. (*She glances at the backs of her hands.*)

BEULAH (*indignantly*). Why, ma, you're good-lookin'! We always said you were good-lookin'.—And besides, you're the best ma we could ever have.

MA (*uncomfortable*). Well, I hope you like me. There's nothin' like being liked by your family.—Now I'm going downstairs to look at the chicken. You stretch out here for a minute and shut your eyes. —Have you got everything laid in for breakfast before the shops close?

BEULAH. Oh, you know! Ham and eggs.

> *They both laugh.*

MA. I declare I never could understand what men see in ham and eggs. I think they're horrible.—What time did you put the chicken in?

BEULAH. Five o'clock.

MA. Well, now, you shut your eyes for ten minutes.

> Beulah *stretches out and shuts her eyes.*

> Ma *descends the stairs absent-mindedly singing:*

"There were ninety and nine that safely lay
 In the shelter of the fold,
 But one was out on the hills away,
 Far off from the gates of gold. . . ."

And the curtain falls.

WILLIAM SAROYAN Why he selected

A PREFACE

This piece, strictly without form, essentially neither essay nor story nor autobiography, is a "saying" piece, consequently there is little I could add to its saying, excepting I said something altogether whole and separate, and not about the piece, but about something else. It is a piece in which a man talks to whoever will listen, or can't escape listening. It is also a lucky piece, as Saroyan is a lucky writer. I doubt if you will find a luckier piece in this whole book. It is lucky in that it is simultaneously artless and artful, if somebody kind will tell you what that means. If I may be that person, this is what that means: the "writing" here did not make the "saying" here. What needed to be said was said, and was therefore the writing, not the other way around. That's the artless part, which means that that's the extremely artful part, too—both. These things can't be talked about much—people either know about them or don't. I do. I have little use for any other kind of writing, unless it is my own, in which case I am devoted to the stuff. This is so because I have such an intelligent view of things. If I wrote it, let me not pretend that it could ever be the work of any but the finest and greatest of writers. So it is—and they go about angry or laughing because it *is* so. But so it is, so it is.

New York, N. Y.   WILLIAM SAROYAN
July 24, 1942

TO "HELLO OUT THERE," A ONE-ACT PLAY (DEDICATED TO GEORGE BERNARD SHAW)

THIS play was written early in August, 1941. It was produced at the Lodbero Theatre in Santa Barbara on Wednesday, September 10, 1941, as the curtain raiser to George Bernard Shaw's *The Devil's Disciple*. Miss Phyllis Walker played the part of the girl, and Harry Bratsburg the part of the young man. John Houseman staged the play and Kate Drain Lawson did the set. Harry Bratsburg, who played the part of the mailman in *My Heart's in the Highlands*, is in my opinion one of the finest actors in the American theatre. Miss Walker is a newcomer for whom good things are predicted.

Before this play was written I had spent almost four months loafing. When I came home from New York after having produced and directed *The Beautiful People* I decided not to work for a while and if possible to get out in the sun. I hadn't gotten out in the sun in years. I hadn't had any time to get out in it. I had always planned to get out, but I had always had the bad luck of getting a story or a play going just when I wanted to quit work and start loafing, and I had always stayed with the story or play until it had been written. Then I had planned to rush right out and get in the sun, only to run headlong into another story or play, and I had always gone to work and written this one, too. That is the only way I have ever been able to take care of anything that wanted to be written. Beginning any time of the day or night I have gone to work and written it—all at once if possible, but if not, as soon as possible. I have never given myself time to sit down and not have anything else on my mind.

I have never worked at writing, although I have come to refer to writing as my work. I am as excited about writing as I was when I was a kid, and I have not yet been able to write anything expressly for the purpose of making money. This is so because I cannot write that way. I have given away any number of pieces especially written on specific themes, but I have written these pieces because the themes have been challenging and because I have not been able to resist them. Furthermore, I have never had any limitations imposed on my writing other than my own. Every new piece I see in a magazine makes me happy, and every new book that comes from the presses is something I behold with wonder, awe and amazement. I shall probably never get over the delight of writing and being published.

Even so, a good deal of my interest is away from writing, and for over ten years now I have been planning to spend a winter somewhere in the woods, camping and hunting, but have not done so; I have planned to spend a year driving all over America slowly, with especial interest in out-of-the-way towns, but have never done so; I have planned to take a leisurely trip around the world, and have never done so; I have planned to go back to work on a vineyard for a winter, and

have never done so; I have planned to read all the books I have always
wanted to read, and have never done so; I have planned to study the
works of every composer of the world, the music of all the peoples of
the world, and the songs of all the folk of the world, and I have never
done so; I have planned to take a year out to learn from actual painting how to paint, and I have never done so; I have planned to learn
to read and write Armenian, and perhaps translate the works of my
favorite Armenian writers, and have never done so; I have wanted to
buy an expensive microscope and study the forms of the smallest of
things, and have never done so; I have planned to perfect my new
theatre—a globe device with the basic colors and forms, capable of
creating an inexhaustibly varied drama of objects and colors and
relationships, accompanied by their related sounds—and have never
done so; I have planned to walk from San Francisco to Mexico City,
and have never done so; I have planned to ride a bicycle from San
Francisco to New York, by way of El Paso, New Orleans, Jacksonville
and Oceana, and have never done so; I have planned to marry the
most beautiful woman in the world and bring up a family, and have
never done so; I have never met her—how could I do so? I have
planned to read *The Bible* and the books of all other religions, and
have never done so; and I have planned to buy a hundred acres of
fertile land with a stream running through it, have the house I have
always wanted built on it, and on the land plant as many kinds of
trees as I can get hold of, and watch them grow, and I have never
done it.

I have also planned to get out in the sun and get rid of the urban
pallor which has become my normal complexion, and until this summer
I have not done so. But this summer I managed to make it. Of course
I was temporarily sidetracked in this ambition by the writing of the
play *Jim Dandy*, by the reading and correcting of manuscript and
proofs of two books, by a simultaneous hunger for loafing in San
Francisco dives, and by cards, horses and dice. But finally I got away
and went to Fresno and got out in the sun.

During the four months since my return from New York I have
gone to Fresno four times—the shortest visit being a three-day visit,
and the longest being a one-month one. Gradually the pallor gave way

to a fairly deep tan, but nothing like the tan of Young Corbett, with whom I went fishing a number of times at Mendota and Friant.

Young Corbett runs the best saloon (or cocktail lounge) in my home town. The sun is very close to the earth in Fresno, its rays very direct and penetrating, the heat very great and magnificent, but if you expose yourself to all this suddenly, you are apt to be cooked. I know, because that is what happened to me every day until Corbett explained that you had to rub yourself with a mixture composed of two parts olive oil and one part vinegar. After that, instead of getting cooked every day and not being able to sleep all night and having the skin peel off after a week or so, taking the color with it and bringing out a fresh layer of pallor, the sun-color moved in slower and deeper and stayed there. I still have some of this color, although it is beginning to fade, and now winter is coming. But I got out into the sun, just as I had planned, and had a lot of fun watching Corbett try to catch a fish, which he never did. Later, though, he got a big one off the coast of Santa Cruz, and to prove it he had the photograph printed in the papers. I hadn't talked to Corbett since we had sold the *Fresno Evening Herald* together, along about twenty-five years ago, when Buzz Martin was our boss and pal, Mr. York in charge of street sales, and Mayor Toomey a big easy-going man who made a special trip to the sand-lot at Kern and L Streets to give an informal talk to the newsboys of the town. I remember that this man, Mayor Toomey, is the first important man in the world whom I didn't dislike. He came to the sand-lot, the kids all gathered around, and he stood there and talked to them. He didn't make a speech and he didn't say anything momentous, but his coming down that way, bothering with a bunch of hoodlums, made me like him and remember him as a great man. Maybe he wasn't really great, but as I *remember* it he was. I don't think Corbett remembered me as well as I remembered him, but after loafing around together a while it was practically the same as in the old days. After having been the best fighter of his time in his division, I found him great-hearted, easy-going, boyishly eager about fishing and getting out to the country, full of high spirits, a fair singer of popular ballads, and a good drinking companion. I have found few places as pleasant to loaf around in, anywhere in the world, as my home town,

no bar with a better atmosphere than Young Corbett's, and no company more pleasant than his.

By the end of July I figured it was time for me to go back to San
Francisco. After I got home this play was one of the first things I
wrote.

Now, having a play on the same bill with a play by the one and
only, the good and great, the impish and noble, the man and super-
man, George Bernard Shaw, is for me an honor, and I think a most
fitting thing. While I have never read *The Devil's Disciple,* and
while the only play of Shaw's I have ever seen has been *St. Joan*—and
I saw that from the last row of the gallery from whence it was a
pageant and not a play, since I could hear nothing said—I have long
known of Mr. Shaw, read his plays and prefaces, and loved him. I
admire heroic effort. Accomplishment I love. What I am about to say
is no invention, and I am putting it down for whatever it may be
worth to the historian of literature and for the student of influences
of men on men, and because it is true and must therefore be made
known. As a boy, charging pell-mell through literature, reading everything I could lay hands on in the Public Library of Fresno, I found
many men to whom I felt deeply grateful—especially Guy de Mau-
passant, Jack London and H. L. Mencken—but the first man to whom
I felt definitely related was George Bernard Shaw. This is a presumptuous or fatuous thing to mention, perhaps, but even so it must
be mentioned.

I myself, as a person, have been influenced by many writers and
many things, and my writing has felt the impact of the writing of
many writers, some relatively unknown and unimportant, some downright bad. But probably the greatest influence of them all when an
influence is most effective—when the man being influenced is nowhere
near being solid in his own right—has been the influence of the great
tall man with the white beard, the lively eyes, the swift wit and the
impish chuckle. I have read Dickens with fascination and wonder. I
have read Schopenhauer at the age of twelve with no bewilderment
and no contempt for his contempt for the world and its strange
inhabitant, and no contempt for the strange inhabitant himself. I have
read writing without regard for the name or quality of the writer—
just writing, just print, just books. I have read Mark Twain and Walt

Whitman. I have read the Russians, Chekhov, Andreyev and Gorki. I have read Sherwood Anderson and Carl Sandburg, Gertrude Stein and Ernest Hemingway. I have read Ibsen and Oscar Wilde. I have read *Poetry Magazine* and any of the little magazines I have been able to find in the second-hand bookstores of Fresno. I have read anything and everything—Ambrose Bierce and Bret Harte, and books in French and German and Spanish without being able to understand a word of it, simply because they were books and because something was being said, even if it was in a language I did not know. I have read books about the behavior of mobs—*The Mob* by Le Bon, if I remember rightly, was one—about crime in children, and about genius in them, about the greatest bodies of things, and about the littlest of them. I have been fascinated by it all, grateful for it all, grateful for the sheer majesty of the existence of ideas, stories, fables and paper and ink and print and books to hold them all together for a man to take aside and examine alone. But the man I liked most and the man who seemed to remind me of myself—of what I really was and would surely become— was George Bernard Shaw.

When, at the age of eighteen, I was night manager of the Postal Telegraph office at 21 Taylor Street in San Francisco I remember having been asked by the clerk there, a man named Clifford, who the hell I thought I was. And I remember replying very simply and earnestly somewhat as follows: If you have ever heard of George Bernard Shaw, if you have ever read his plays or prefaces, you will know what I mean when I tell you that I am that man by another name.

Who is *he?* I remember the clerk asking.

George Bernard Shaw, I replied, is the tonic of the Christian peoples of the world. He is health, wisdom, and comedy, and that's what I am, too.

How do you figure? the clerk said.

Don't bother me, I said. I'm night manager of this office and when I tell you something it's final.

H. L. Mencken's *Prejudices* and George Jean Nathan's suave and lively spoofing had a fine effect on me, too. I liked the men who were most like bad boys, having fun all the time, playing pranks, talking out of turn, acting up, making fun of fools and frauds, ridiculing the

pompous and phoney, howling with laughter or sitting by after ruining the works and being dead-pan and innocent about the whole
thing—and beyond all this being very wise and very serious, and
knowing how to write—knowing that you couldn't be serious and
dull at the same time and still be effective. Mencken's stuff made me
bust out laughing in the Public Library. Sometimes it even made me
jump up out of my chair and walk around the place whispering things
at people I didn't know.

This is not the place or time, however, for me to go into detail
about the men and writing and ideas which have influenced my life
and writing.

All I know is that it is right for a one-act play by William Saroyan
to serve as curtain-raiser to a play by George Bernard Shaw. To show
you the importance of this, the inevitability of it in fact, let me reveal
how, finally, this event came to be, and how close it came not to be.
Let me reveal the series of accidental and fortuitous events—all of them
always closer to not taking place than to taking place—which finally,
one by one, resulted in this most appropriate and inevitable circumstance.

When I stepped out of the sun of Fresno and came home to the
gloom of San Francisco, although I felt the time was ripe for the
writing of something good, nothing presented itself to me. Therefore,
I made no effort, but spent my time loafing, playing pin-ball games for
hours, sitting around in little bars, listening to juke-box music, drinking and talking. After three days of this I sat down one night at two
o'clock in the morning with the intention of typing a title and a few
ideas I didn't want to forget. But I did not get up until I had written
this play. I had been drinking a good deal, but I was not drunk. There
are nights of such drinking. Instead of getting drunk a man gets sober.
He gets very sober. That was how it was that night. I didn't know at
the time that I had a play to write, but I must have had it to write,
because I wrote it.

The very writing of the play was an accident, even if it was an
inevitable one. Of course we all know that accidents are compelled.
I know this from having read in my Public Library days an essay
about the mystical behavior of Hindus, and from having watched
this matter carefully, and considered it from one year to another. I

know accidents are avoidable. Even when I was the fastest messenger in Fresno, and the one who took the most chances, I had very few accidents, and these were only mild. I was once forced to knock down a brewery horse by butting it with my head because I was going too fast and couldn't stop and the horse was blocking the alley down which I was racing. While racing down the alley I had reasoned that if somebody stepped out into my path I would have no trouble going through with no harm to him or to myself; if an automobile crossed this path I would pace my speed to swerve around it and go on my way; if something immovable blocked my way I would lift the whole front part of the bicycle, fall backwards, and probably hurt my back but not be instantly killed; and if something moving slowly appeared in my way and I could not pace around it I would—at this point, while I was going about twenty miles an hour, a brewery horse appeared and completely blocked the alley, moving much too slowly. Without any further reasoning I tightened up on the bicycle, feet tight in toeclips, muscles taut, head down. It was an accident and there had been nothing else to do. My head butted the horse in the side, the horse exhaled, its front feet buckled and it went down. I was a little scared—especially of the horse, which was very big—but I wasn't hurt.

There were some other accidents. Chains broke on me a couple of times while I was sprinting and sprawled me out on the pavement. A cop intentionally caught my arm at the elbow as I shot through between him and a truck, spinning me around and almost ruining my bicycle. And a couple of bad drivers ran into me from behind and knocked me off my bicycle. Each of these accidents could have been avoided. I know it. The one involving the horse could have been avoided but only if I was willing to agree not to speed, and I wasn't. The chains that broke had been weak and should have been attended to. The cop was a dog anyway; I knew it, and I could have avoided the accident by not challenging him and thinking I could get away with it. And the people who drove their cars into my bike should never have been credited with wakefulness by me. I had overestimated them and I had been recklessly optimistic. But the accidents could have been avoided.

Getting the title of the play was an accident too. A clownish friend of mine named Stanley Rose one night on a street corner in Fresno began calling out as if he were in the wilderness—Hello out there! Hello out there! I liked the sound and enjoyed the absurdity of it, but immediately forgot all about it.

Next, it was an accident that I went to the opening of *Anna Christie* in San Francisco; an accident that I met the director of the play, John Houseman; an accident that he asked if I had a one-act play; an accident that I had one, *this* one, just written; and an accident that I promised to put it in the mail for him the next day. It was no accident that I did, though.

On the other side of things, to begin with I had no idea what other plays would be presented with my play. I imagined they would be new plays by one or another of the American writers of plays. It turned out that there would be only one other play, and that this play was *The Devil's Disciple* by George Bernard Shaw. But this was also an accident. It seems that Mr. Shaw was allowing no further production of his plays until after the war. The production of this play had just barely gotten under the wire, but under the wire is under the wire, and my work has finally appeared on the same bill with the work of George Bernard Shaw.

Such progressions as these are important to record. A few critics with bad breath and fallen arches and a few other things of this sort are going to come forward with an attack upon Mr. Shaw himself, by way of once again annihilating me, as they have been doing these seven years, God love them. It shall seem to these critics most frightful of me to associate my name with George Bernard Shaw's, but let me simplify everything by making known very clearly that if it matters wnich of the writing men I have felt close to, and by whom my writing has been influenced, that man has not been Ernest Hemingway, as Mr. Edmund Wilson seems to feel, but George Bernard Shaw. Now, if Mr. Shaw and Mr. Saroyan are poles apart, no comparison between the two, one great and the other nothing, one a genius and the other a charlatan, let me repeat that if you must know which writer has influenced my writing when influences are real and for all I know enduring, then that writer has been George Bernard Shaw. I shall in my own day influence a young Shaw or two somewhere or other, and you need not worry about that.

Young Shaw, hello out there.

CLIFFORD ODETS   Why he selected

ROCKET to the MOON

It is difficult to give you a paragraph about why I chose to be represented by the first act of *Rocket to the Moon*. It is just because it seems to me to be excellent writing, representative of the best in our modern theatre, as it is in the body of my own writing. Is it my *best* writing? No, my best writing is still to come! And I am as anxious as the next fellow to see it and hear it played, when it comes.

Hollywood, Cal.   CLIFFORD ODETS
August 4, 1942

ACT ONE

TIME: *The Present.*

PLACE: *A dentist's waiting room in a New York office building. A door to the elevators at the left. On the right side is a window. At the back are two doors, one leading to the dentist's office, the other open and showing the dentist's chair and apparatus. There is also a small hall, up right, which leads to another dentist's office.*

The curtain rises on the waiting room during an early hot June afternoon. Present are DR. BEN STARK *and his wife,* BELLE. *At the moment there is a strain and coolness between them, resulting from a family discussion on economics. In the silence* STARK *puffs strongly on his pipe as he looks at a page of a dental magazine in his hand.* BELLE *is depressed but hides it well.*

STARK (*finally*): You've had your last word. There's nothing more to say.

BELLE: No, I want you to make up your own mind, or see that I'm right.

STARK: Aren't you always right, Belle?

BELLE: Ben, dear, such remarks are uncalled for.

STARK: You know I've wanted to specialize all my life. Yesterday your father proposes that I open a new office in a suitable neighborhood. He offers to bear all the expense, new equipment and all that. Look at that outfit—this x-ray unit! All night I didn't sleep thinking about it!

BELLE: Ben, you mustn't over-simplify ——

STARK (*breaking in*): Let's forget it, Belle.

BELLE: Poppa would pay the initial cost, but the rent there would be three times what it is here.

STARK: A little over two.

BELLE: A little less than three. You know the people here won't come uptown. It's too far away and that expensive neighborhood would frighten them off. It takes years to develop a practice. We had the experience twice ——

STARK (*breaking in*): You win, you win!

BELLE (*earnestly*): It's not that I want to win, Ben. Don't you see that, Ben? Don't you see it?

STARK (*harshly, standing up*): *I told you let's forget it. It's settled!* (*Moodily, after a pause.*) I was a pioneer with Gladstone in orthodontia, once. Now I'm a dentist, good for sixty dollars a week, while men with half my brains and talents are making their twenty and thirty thousand a year!—I came over to the water cooler and I can't remember what for.

BELLE: To take a drink. . . .

STARK: I wanted to do something . . . what was it? Not a drink. . . . Oh, the flowers! (*He fills a paper cup, puts his pipe between his teeth and tries without success, one hand full, to fill a second cup.*)

BELLE: Try one at a time, dear.

STARK (*coolly*): One at a time is a good idea. (*At the window, right, he pours the water on a window box of drooping petunias. As he turns for more water he faces* BELLE *who has brought him the second cupful.*) Thanks.

BELLE (*smiling*): Any day now I'm expecting to have to powder and diaper you. (*Without an answer,* STARK *turns from the window and sits on the couch. After further silence, to make conversation*):

STARK: I like flowers.

BELLE (*to ease the tension*): You missed your profession, Ben.

STARK (*soberly*): Botany?

BELLE: No, a florist shop.

STARK: I don't think you'd have married a florist.

BELLE: Why not? The way Poppa and Mamma were always quarreling?—My nerves mincemeat? The way I felt when I married you,
I'd have married a shoemaker almost.

STARK: I have a bunch of answers for that, but I won't give them.

BELLE: But he would have had to be calm and quiet, the way you were.
You have such dignity, Ben . . . even when you're angry.

STARK (*annoyed*): I'm not angry, dear.

BELLE (*softly*): I know what it means to you. . . . (*Seductively.*) Don't
you think I know?

STARK: I know you know. . . .

BELLE: Tell Poppa what you decided. Is he coming here?

STARK: Some time this afternoon.

BELLE: Is it settled?

STARK: It's settled.

BELLE (*cautiously*): Did Poppa bring up the question of moving in
with us again?

STARK: Yes. . . .

BELLE: Don't encourage him.

STARK (*half indignantly*): I don't, but I must say I can't understand
how a father and daughter can be on the outs for so many years.

BELLE: If you'd seen the life of hell he gave my mother, you'd understand.

STARK: All right, but your mother's been dead a year. He's an old man,
lonely ——

BELLE: He'll manage—he's been to school.

STARK: I only mean that he's alone in the world ——

BELLE (*seriously*): A man and his wife should live alone, always. Poppa
would be an intruder in our house. We wouldn't have a minute to
ourselves. And out of sheer respect for my mother's memory ——

STARK: Your father isn't a villain ——

BELLE: Why do you take his part?

STARK (*again indignantly*): I'm not, but after all, a man wants to spend
thousands of dollars putting me in a better practice and you expect
me to think he's a villain?

BELLE: Now, Ben, you know he'd be in the way, don't you?

STARK (*reluctantly, after a pause*): I guess so. . . .

BELLE: Don't you know it?

STARK (*with a faint ironic smile*): Yes, ma'm. . . .

BELLE (*moving around the irony*): Then it's settled.

STARK (*nodding his head*): Umm.

BELLE (*crossing for purse*): Where's the girl, your new secretary? My, my, two hours for lunch—a fancy lady, indeed! That girl isn't working out!

STARK: She's new at the job, dear. Give her time.

BELLE: She's taking plenty, two hours for lunch. And then the third week here you raise her salary. I don't understand you, Ben Stark.

STARK: Can a girl live on twelve dollars a week?

BELLE: I could manage if I had to, for the both of us.

STARK: Thank God we don't have to ——

BELLE: It's not God who keeps us off the dole.

STARK: It's you, Belle. I don't know what I'd do without you! (*He puts his arms around her.*)

BELLE: Take the pipe out of my face. (*He moves his pipe and they kiss.*) And now your terrible wife is going to give you another push. Did you put the ad in the paper? If we don't sublet the apartment soon, we'll have it on our hands all summer, and we can't afford it.

STARK: That's why Miss Singer's late. I asked her to put the ad in while she was out to lunch.

BELLE: She'll forget.

STARK: I'll eat my hat if she does. (DR. COOPER *enters from up right and crosses to the water cooler, where he drinks.*)

COOPER: Hot day.

BELLE: Yes.

COOPER (*crossing back*): Beer makes you hotter. It's not a hot-weather drink like they think. (*Exits right again.*)

BELLE (*lowering her voice*): I didn't know Dr. Cooper was in his office.

STARK: He's pouring some model or something. He's got his own troubles.

BELLE: How much does he owe us?

STARK (*sotto voce*): Not so loud, Belle.

BELLE (*dropping her voice*): How much?

STARK (*trying to remember*): He hasn't paid his rent for three months.

BELLE: Four. Charity's a fine trait.

STARK: But it begins at home?

BELLE: You think it shouldn't? . . . Move the pipe away. Stop being soft-hearted. Will you be able to take a vacation this summer?

STARK: Why, we're taking a bungalow at the beach.

BELLE: That's a substitute for a vacation. Why can't we do what Jack and Milly Heitner do? Go to the Rockies, or to Europe in the summer? But you're considerate of others. Not of yourself or your wife!

STARK (*slowly*): I never thought of it that way.

BELLE: A woman wants to live *with* a man—not next to him. I see you three or four hours a night—in the morning you're gone before I get up. I'll elope some day. Then you'll cry your blue eyes black.

STARK: Every once in awhile I see something I didn't see before.

BELLE: What vision hit you now?

STARK: That being a dentist's wife is no joke——

BELLE: That's an old story——

STARK (*with sudden buoyancy*): I wish I could change everything. I'd buy Aladdin's lamp for a thousand dollars if I could. We'd rub it up, we'd rub it down— Slam! We'd be in China——!

BELLE: I'll settle for Lake George— (*The door, left, opens. An elderly man walks in, quickly takes in the scene, and hastily exits.* BELLE's *back is to the door, but she catches* STARK's *glance.*) Who was that?

STARK: Your father.

BELLE: Where?

STARK (*going to the door*): He looked in and walked right out again.

BELLE: Don't call him. He'll be back in his own sweet time . . . in case you should both want to discuss me.

STARK (*surprised*): Discuss you? Why?

BELLE: I heard him make a remark to you once: "The mother ate sour grapes and the daughter's teeth are set on edge." Ben, don't let Poppa turn you against me. Explain to him why you can't accept his offer——

STARK: Say, I see I've walked into something today.

BELLE: I happen to have been feeling blue all morning.

STARK: Why?

BELLE: Never mind. . . .

STARK: Tell me why.

BELLE: It doesn't matter, Ben . . . if you don't remember it.

STARK: What?

BELLE: Did you really forget, Ben? (STARK *is puzzled and tries to joke away her distressed look.*)

STARK (*with a boyish twinkle*): It's not your birthday and we were married in the winter. Or is it *my* birthday? . . . (*Then suddenly.*) Oh . . .

BELLE: What?

STARK: You're thinking about . . . the boy?

BELLE: Yes.

STARK (*putting his arms around her*): Well . . . it's not as if we had him . . . he died at birth. . . .

BELLE: Three years ago this morning. I had him, I felt I had him. . . .

STARK: Don't think about it, dear.

BELLE: But never to be able to have another one . . . well . . .

STARK: Don't think about it, Belle.

BELLE: We could adopt a boy . . . if you wanted. . . .

STARK: Someone else's?

BELLE: If you wanted. . . .

STARK: We'll talk about it some other time, dear.

BELLE: Ben, you have to love me all the time. I have to know my husband's there, loving me and needing me.

STARK (*wanting to escape further involvement*): Which I do, Belle, you know I do. Come on downstairs and let me buy you an ice cream soda.

BELLE: You know as much about women as the man in the moon!

STARK: I admit it. . . .

BELLE: No wonder your women patients don't like you.

STARK: They like me.

BELLE: Who? (CLEO SINGER *enters the waiting room.* STARK *quickly looks from secretary to wife and back again.*)

STARK (*sternly, for his wife's sake*): You're late, Miss Singer ——

CLEO: Late? Good afternoon, Mrs. Stark.

STARK: You're not supposed to take two hours for lunch.

CLEO: The buses take so long. . . . I'm sorry.

BELLE: Are you eating lunch in the Waldorf Astoria these days?

STARK: No, she went down to put the ad in.

CLEO: Ad? . . .

BELLE (*watching her closely*): Eat your hat—she forgot it!

STARK: Did you?

CLEO: I meant to . . . Yes, it seems ——

STARK: You're not very efficient, Miss Singer.

CLEO: It's so hot today.

BELLE: But how about the whole week? You had a whole week to clean the instruments and cut some cotton rolls for Dr. Stark.

CLEO (*helplessly*): I'm going to do that right now, Mrs. Stark.

BELLE: No, right now you're going to take the ad to the *Times*.

STARK (*to* BELLE): She'd better stay here now. I'll send the ad down with a messenger boy. (*To* CLEO.) You'd better change into your uniform.

CLEO: Right away, Dr. Stark. (CLEO *escapes into the office and closes the door behind her.*)

STARK (*in a low voice*): Let's not discuss her now.

BELLE: She has to be told ——

STARK: Not now, Belle, not in front of her.

BELLE: Why not?

STARK: Belle, don't you think the girl has feelings? You and I are going downstairs. A soda for you, pipe tobacco for me. (*Seeing her face.*) What's the matter, Belle?

BELLE: Go without me. I want to talk to her a minute.

STARK: Belle . . .

BELLE: On your way, Dr. Stark. (*He looks at her, shrugs his shoulders and starts for the door.*) Put your street jacket on—be professional, Ben. (STARK *changes his dentist's gown for a street jacket, looks at his wife again and exits left. Clearing her voice and then calling.*) Miss Singer!

CLEO (*within*): Yes.

BELLE: Are you changing?

CLEO: Yes.

BELLE: I want to have a few words with you.

CLEO (*opening the door but standing behind it*): I'll be out in just a sec', Mrs. Stark.

BELLE: You're dressed to kill, Miss Singer.

CLEO: That's one of my ordinary everyday dresses—angel-skin satin.

BELLE: It looks hot.

CLEO (*coming into the waiting room in her uniform*): It's one of my coolest dresses.

BELLE: Is that why you don't wear stockings?

CLEO: Yes.

BELLE (*disapprovingly*): I thought maybe to save money.

CLEO: I come from a well-to-do family.

BELLE: How well to do?

CLEO: I really don't need this job.

BELLE (*archly*): Nevertheless, as long as you have the job, you should wear stockings in the office.

CLEO: Yes?

BELLE: Yes, it looks sloppy and it makes a very bad impression on the patients. Why do you wear your hair up in the air like that?

CLEO: Don't you like it this way?

BELLE: You're not modeling dresses now, Miss Singer.

CLEO: Oh, did Dr. Stark tell you ——

BELLE: Dr. Stark tells me everything. The bills have to be sent out.

CLEO: I know that.

BELLE: Also, the reminder cards ——

CLEO: I know that.

BELLE (*overly patient*): If you know so much, why don't you do it?

CLEO (*flustered*): You see, I was . . . (DR. COOPER *enters again from his office off right. He is wearing the usual dentist's gown. He is a big man, hot and troubled at present. He speaks and moves in irregular unexpected rhythms, but his manner is always frank and winning. He is boyish and uncomplex, but worried.*)

COOPER: Did the phone ring just now? Did I hear a phone ring?

BELLE: No, you didn't, Dr. Cooper.

COOPER: I must be imagining things. (*Goes to water cooler to drink.*)

CLEO: Probably.

COOPER: What?

CLEO (*innocently*): I said probably. (*Seeing* BELLE *give her a strong look.*) I'll start on the bills now. (*She exits into the office, closing the door behind her.*)

COOPER (*drinking*): Municipal champagne! (*Sitting heavily.*) Bills!—She thinks people pay bills! I'm expecting a call. What did you say?

BELLE: Nothing. . . .

COOPER: I'm hot—hot hot hot! In my younger days I was inclined to poetry. In my older days I'm inclined to poverty.

BELLE: What are your plans for the summer?

COOPER: What are the plans of a horse?

BELLE: You sound discouraged.

COOPER: My boy fell on his skates yesterday and broke his arm.

BELLE: I'm sorry to hear that.

COOPER: And that's the only break I've had in years! Yes, I went through the whole war and nothing happened to me. They could have left me there ——

BELLE: You . . . owe us a few months' rent here.

COOPER: You have my sympathies.

BELLE: I know it's a bad time to remind you ——

COOPER: To tell the truth, I'm waiting for a call from the loan company. I'll see what they have to say.

BELLE (*not unkindly*): Why do you drink so much?

COOPER: Who drinks so much?

BELLE: Maybe it's coffee I smell.

COOPER: Yeah, Scotch coffee.

BELLE: Fair is fair, and if you share an office with another dentist, you have to share expenses. You won't do that by letting patients smell liquor on your breath, will you?

COOPER: What're you doing? Bawling me out?

BELLE: I'm telling you what I think.

COOPER: Maybe I'm not interested.

BELLE: My husband lets people walk all over him—Don't you think you're taking advantage of his good nature?

COOPER: That's a real nervy remark!

BELLE (*quietly*): You don't meet your obligations.

COOPER: Sure, but give a man a chance!

BELLE: Dr. Cooper, to drink his practice away?

COOPER (*wrathfully*): Who're you talking to? I'm not some shyster, some drunken bum!

BELLE (*patient, as with a child*): Please don't shout.

COOPER: Is that what I am? A bum? Is that how I look to you?

BELLE: Nothing of the sort——

COOPER (*after a pause*): I don't blame you.

BELLE: For what?

COOPER (*sitting again*): For looking out for your husband's interests. A civilized person can't tolerate me. Business won't pick up till after Labor Day. But if the loan company decides to— (*Within the office the telephone rings.* COOPER *quickly opens the door and takes the telephone from* CLEO's *hands.*) Hello? . . . Yes, this is your party . . . . yes . . . yes . . . yes . . . (COOPER *hangs up the telephone and trails back into the waiting room.* BELLE *sees* CLEO *staring out with curiosity and closes the office door on her.*) No, no dice . . . no shoes for baby. . . . I don't know what I'll do with my boy— Children are not like furniture— You can't put them in storage. If his mother was alive . . .

BELLE (*genuinely touched by his abject attitude*): Stay another month. . . .

COOPER (*slowly*): The summer'll be dead. Excuse me for the rumpus before. When I'm happy I'm a different person. You'd be surprised —everybody likes Phil Cooper. (*He moves to the outer door, left.*)

BELLE: Where are you going?

COOPER: For a drink of coffee, Scotch coffee. (COOPER *exits.* BELLE *goes to the side table for her purse and gloves. From there she reaches up to the electric fan and slows it down a notch. Then she calls to* CLEO.)

BELLE: Miss Singer?

CLEO (*opening the office door*): Yes, Mrs. Stark?

BELLE: I'm going now. Tell Dr. Stark his terrible wife expects him home at seven. Good-bye.

CLEO: Good-bye. (*In crossing the room* BELLE *picks up the dental magazine which* STARK *left on the couch.*)

BELLE: Oh, one more thing. (*Handing over the magazine.*) Put this in the office, like a good girl.

CLEO: Surely.

BELLE: Good-bye. (*As she looks* CLEO *over.*)

CLEO: Good-bye, Mrs. Stark. (*As* BELLE *goes to the door it is opened from the outside.* MR. PRINCE, BELLE's *father, enters again. He is near sixty, wears an old panama hat, a fine Palm Beach suit of twenty years ago and a malacca cane. There is about him the dignity and elegant portliness of a Jewish actor, a sort of aristocratic air. He is an extremely self-confident man with a strong sense of humor which, however, is often veiled. He is very alive in the eyes and mouth, the rest of him relaxed and heavy.* BELLE *looks at her father, who looks back at her with the same silence. He holds the door open for her as she exits.* MR. PRINCE *slowly crosses and seats himself, leaning on his cane with both hands.*)

PRINCE (*with genuine curiosity*): Who are you?

CLEO (*timidly*): Who are you?

PRINCE (*pointing to the door*): I am the old father of that lady, so called.

CLEO: Mr. Prince?

PRINCE (*with suave gravity*): Yes.

CLEO: I heard of you.

PRINCE: From who?

CLEO: Frenchy.

PRINCE: Who?

CLEO: Frenchy—Dr. Jensen.

PRINCE (*moving restlessly around the room*): You mean the foot doctor down the hall.

CLEO: Yes. Don't you speak to her?

PRINCE: No.

CLEO: Why?

PRINCE (*grandly*): I am the American King Lear. (*Seeing her bewildered look.*) Where is Dr. Stark?

CLEO: He'll be back in a minute.

PRINCE: And who are you?

CLEO: I'm the new secretary.

PRINCE: Hmm . . . what are your opinions?

CLEO: On what?

PRINCE: On anything. (*Taking newspaper from side table.*) Here's the paper. Do you read? What are you? A communist? A fascist? A democrat?

CLEO: I don't know about all these things.

PRINCE (*glancing at the paper*): Here it says in India a snake swallowed a man. What is your opinion of that, Miss . . . ?

CLEO: Singer.

PRINCE: What is that book in your hand?

CLEO: A dental magazine.

PRINCE: Leave it here—I like to look at pictures. (CLEO *gives him the magazine.*) Are you afraid of me?

CLEO: No. . . .

PRINCE: Then why do you act nervous before me?

CLEO: I'm not nervous.

PRINCE: What's your first name?

CLEO: Cleo. . . .

PRINCE: Yes, Miss Cleo. . . . That's a name for a dancer. Do you dance?

CLEO: Yes.

PRINCE: You don't say!

CLEO: I've been with several shows.

PRINCE: You don't say! A dancer? What is the secret of life? Do you know?

CLEO: The secret?

PRINCE: I don't chew my cabbage twice, Miss Cleo. Let us pass on to my opinion of this (*Indicating the newspaper*) front page. Are you listening?

CLEO: Yes.

PRINCE: In my opinion the universe is governed by a committee; one man couldn't make so many mistakes. (*Seeing* CLEO *laugh heartily.*) Is that funny?

CLEO: Yes.

PRINCE (*smiling*): I like to make people laugh. My daughter calls me a clown. The two of them, my wife included—with their bills they ate holes in me like Swiss cheese, but I was a clown!

CLEO: Mrs. Stark is very observant.

PRINCE: She annoys you?

CLEO (*withdrawing*): I wouldn't say that.

PRINCE: Speak freely, Miss Cleo——

CLEO: Excuse me for being so personal before.

PRINCE: Everything that's healthy is personal.

CLEO: You're a very peculiar man, Mr. Prince.

PRINCE: Because I joke?

CLEO: Are you joking?

PRINCE (*twisting his hand from the wrist*): Yes and no, hot and cold, like a shower. Do you have a gospel?

CLEO (*warily puzzled*): What?

PRINCE: Every woman wants to convert a man to the gospel of herself. Fact? Fact! What is your gospel?

CLEO (*after a pause*): I don't understand a word you're saying, Mr. Prince.

PRINCE: It doesn't matter— I'm only a minor person in life. But I see you're honest.

CLEO (*narrowly*): You're making fun of me!

PRINCE (*raising a hand*): God forbid! You know something? . . . often I wished I was a young girl. I'd get somebody to support me —no worries about money——

CLEO (*flashingly*): Nobody supports me!

PRINCE: A beautiful girl like you? Nobody supports you?

CLEO: No!

PRINCE: My remark makes you angry?

CLEO: Yes! I come from a very good home——

PRINCE: Miss Cleo, I think you need a revision of your philosophy——

CLEO: I heard enough from you! In fact I heard enough all day! I don't need this job. They burn your ears off around here for sixteen dollars a week. That's chicken feed!

PRINCE (*more than agreeing*): Less! *Pigeon* feed!

CLEO (*excited beyond diplomacy*): I don't have to stand in Macy's window and let people throw rocks at me!

PRINCE (*calmly agreeing*): Of course not.

CLEO: Am I the kind of girl who lets anybody make suggestive remarks to her?

PRINCE: No!

CLEO: Your daughter thinks——

PRINCE: Refer to her in the impersonal.

CLEO: Mrs. Stark, she thinks I'm a dummy. Do this, do that!—I'm a person!

PRINCE: One of the nicest I met in many years. Yes, Miss Cleo——

CLEO: And you?—You're an old fool!

PRINCE (*piously*): What is age? A matter of psychology. Am I decrepit in my psychology?

CLEO (*tossing her head*): I can't say!

PRINCE: The answer is no.

CLEO: And I don't care! If nobody cares for me I don't care for them!

PRINCE: Fair enough.

CLEO: I thought Dr. Stark was a nice man when I came here. But his wife just twists him around her little finger, like a spit curl.

PRINCE: Correct! And any woman could do the same.

CLEO: He stands there like a big shepherd dog and she tells him what to do!

PRINCE: Correct!

CLEO: He's afraid of his own shadow!

PRINCE: Correct!

CLEO (*excitedly*): You can't get in my good graces by agreeing with me in everything I say. I see right through you, Mr. Prince, like cellophane.

PRINCE (*calmly*): And when you look through the cellophane, what do you see?

CLEO: Never mind! How dare you say I have no opinions!

PRINCE: Did I say that?

CLEO: You insinuated that I was stupid——

PRINCE: Miss Cleo, I feel I know you for a lifetime.

CLEO (*scornfully*): Thanks for the compliment!

PRINCE: You know something? You're just like me——

CLEO: Oh, no I'm not!

PRINCE: So you're not. Then who are you like?

CLEO: Like myself, like Cleo Singer! And I'm good and mad!

PRINCE (*suddenly snapping out*): Calm down!

CLEO: What?

PRINCE (*sharply*): Calm down. You have expressed yourself enough! You work here in an office—a regular insect society—so don't act like a tiger. Unless you don't want the job.

CLEO (*immediately contrite*): Did I raise my voice?

PRINCE (*calmly*): You don't know the facts of life, Miss Cleo.

CLEO: I'm not thinking of the job, but I'm sorry I hurt your feelings. Please excuse me.

PRINCE: Always address your elders with respect. They could leave you a fortune.

CLEO: I didn't mean to say all those things——

PRINCE: Do you get along well with people?

CLEO: No.

PRINCE: Why?

CLEO (*changing her mind*): I get along with them.

PRINCE: Which is it?

CLEO (*distressed*): I'm sorry I said so much. . . .

PRINCE: Are you going to cry, Miss Cleo?

CLEO: No.

PRINCE: I see dewdrops. . . .

CLEO: Something's in my eye.

PRINCE (*drawing a white silk handkerchief from breast pocket*):
Where? Which one?

CLEO: This.

PRINCE: Take your finger away. Look up. I won't hurt you. (*Delicately
working on the eye.*) Don't move. . . . (*Unseen by them* DR. STARK
opens the door. He watches the scene with disapproval.)

PRINCE: Is it out?

CLEO (*blinking*): I . . . think so.

PRINCE (*standing off a little*): Don't rub it.

CLEO (*blinking*): No.

PRINCE: You use nice toilet water. It smells like thousands of flowers
——

CLEO: Gardenia.

PRINCE: Pleasant.

CLEO: Forty dollars an ounce.

PRINCE: Unpleasant.

CLEO: That's a beautiful handkerchief.

PRINCE: You like it? Have it.

CLEO: Oh, no ——

PRINCE (*spying* STARK): Here is Benny, the shepherd dog. (CLEO *whirls
around, guilt written all over her.*)

STARK: Hello, Poppa. . . .

CLEO (*rapidly*): There was something in my eye and Mr. Prince——

STARK: Is it out now?

CLEO: It was nothing ——

PRINCE: A glass splinter . . . from my daughter's heart.

STARK (*with a slight frown, to* CLEO): I think you'd better take that ad down to the *Times*, Miss Singer. Just slip your coat on . . . (*In the silence* CLEO *takes her coat and goes to the door, left.*)

CLEO (*lamely*): Mrs. Stark says she expects you home at seven o'clock. She told me to tell you. . . . (*She exits.*)

STARK (*lightly*): What was going on here?

PRINCE (*sitting*): Just like she told you. (STARK *is changing jackets.*)

STARK: You're a great hand with the girls, Poppa.

PRINCE: It's the last thing in my mind.

STARK: But you mustn't talk that way about Belle in front of strangers.

PRINCE: Bad taste?

STARK: It doesn't happen to be true.

PRINCE: How old is Miss Cleo?

STARK (*smiling*): None of your business. Where did you disappear to before?

PRINCE (*sauntering to the window*): I often meant to ask you— What is that over there?

STARK: The back of the Hotel Algiers.

PRINCE: Hmm, I know a bookie in there. What must go on in those rooms at night . . .

STARK: What does it matter?

PRINCE: You got a decrepit psychology, Benny. Sometimes you talk like an old lady. (*Going back to his seat.*) Do they rent out rooms to couples?

STARK: Riffraff.

PRINCE: Some night I'll come and look . . . just as if it interests me!

STARK: Tell me, what interests you, Poppa?

PRINCE: I love to gamble; cards, the races, the market . . .

STARK: Wine, women and song.

PRINCE: In all my life I never took a drink, and I don't sing. Yes, Benny, *I* started from an idealist, too, believe it or not. Now I'm a villain. . . . What does your friend Shakespeare say on this point?

STARK: What point?

PRINCE: The point of all points—happiness! Where is she hiding, happiness? (*After giving* STARK *a quizzical glance.*) So when do you expect to move?

STARK (*nervously*): Move?

PRINCE (*picking up the dental magazine*): I see you turned down the pages—the machinery——

STARK: That Ritter outfit is a beauty. . . .

PRINCE (*seeing the other's hesitation*): But?

STARK: I've decided to stay here for the present, Poppa. Not that your kindness——

PRINCE: Why?

STARK: Belle thought . . . she thinks it won't be wise.

PRINCE (*pursing his lips*): I see. And you, what do you think?

STARK: After all, it's an economic risk. . . . (*He flushes off into silence.*)

PRINCE (*almost vehemently*): Crazy boy, I offer it to you on a silver platter——

STARK (*painfully*): That's how it is, Poppa.

PRINCE: Your nose is just the right shape to fit your wife's hand!

STARK: Is that a right thing to say?

PRINCE: Well, it's your life—yours and Mrs. Belle Stark!

STARK: Why do you insist, Poppa?

PRINCE: Because I like to do some good to a man who needs it! A lovable being!

STARK: Why don't you make it up with Belle?

PRINCE (*with a smile*): How's business?

STARK (*smiling*): Slow. . . .

PRINCE: The summer slump?

STARK: Yes. Why don't you get along with Belle, Poppa?

PRINCE (*wryly*): It's a pleasant June afternoon, Benny.

STARK: It grieves her very much.

PRINCE (*reluctantly*): Benny, my daughter don't like me; she claims I ruined her mother's life. I claim her mother ruined *my* life!

STARK: How?

PRINCE: There are two kinds of marriages, Benny—where the husband quotes the wife, or where the wife quotes the husband. Fact? Fact!

STARK: But you didn't speak to her for ten years.

PRINCE: Because she insulted my soul, me, a first-class man, a lover of his brother man——

STARK: And his sister!

PRINCE: Never! *But never!* Not once did I make a sexual deviation!

And what did I ask from my wife? To be a companion, to help me succeed ——

STARK: You did—you're worth a fortune.

PRINCE: In spite of her! I shouldn't be ambitious. Go work for somebody else for twenty dollars a week—a man with my brains! Play safe! A housewife's conception of life! In the bargain, she had more respectability under the blankets than you have on Fifth Avenue! A man of my strength, my fire! (*Now masking his feelings again.*) Drip, drip, the matrimonial waters go, and a man wears away. My wife is dead, I'm an old man who missed his boat. Ida Prince had her revenge . . . her husband has disappeared in the corner, with the dust, under the rug.

STARK (*grinning*): Nonsense! You haven't disappeared, Poppa. You're a very dominant person ——

PRINCE (*passionately*): Without marriage I would have been one of the greatest actors in the world! . . . You don't believe it?

STARK (*having heard this before*): I believe it. . . .

PRINCE (*suddenly*): All my life I wanted to do something. . . . Pfu! . . . We'll talk of something pleasant.

STARK: After all is said and done, Poppa, Belle is your only child.

PRINCE: I'm her only father.

STARK: She's very lonely since Momma died. I feel sure she wants to bury the axe.

PRINCE (*cynically*): Certainly. . . . Right in my head! I have a certain respectable mania for the truth—we don't like each other.

STARK: And yet you want to live with us.

PRINCE: You I like, Benny. But in my whole life one sensible woman came to my attention—she killed herself. She left a note, "I am a pest."

STARK (*shaking his head*): You're in a bad mood today. . . .

PRINCE (*mopping his brow with the silk handkerchief and looking out at the Hotel Algiers again*): True, true— (*Turning back from the window.*) I made six thousand dollars this morning.

STARK: ! ? !

PRINCE: The more money I make, the more heartache. Who'll I leave all my money to? Mrs. Belle Stark, née Prince?

STARK (*smiling*): I know a certain orphan home in Philadelphia, where I was raised . . . they'd use it.

PRINCE: I don't know . . . maybe I'll leave it to Jascha Heifetz.

STARK: You going to Saratoga this summer?

PRINCE: Why should I drink Saratoga waters?—It only prolongs my life. (*Smiling slyly and winking.*) Am I wrong? . . . Hotel Algiers. A man is a mirror. He tells me his wife is wonderful. . . . I look in his face to see the truth.

STARK (*uncomfortably*): What do you see in my face?

PRINCE: A better liar than I gave you credit for. Is this the life you dreamed for yourself?

STARK: It's not Belle's fault.

PRINCE: One answer at a time. Is it?

STARK (*evasively, after a pause*): I don't know what you mean.

PRINCE: A life where every day is Monday. There used to be a week-end, but now it's always Monday. Awnings up, awnings down, coat on, coat off. Sweat in summer, freeze in winter—a movie, a bridge game, an auto ride to Peekskill. Gas is twenty cents a gallon, worry about the bills, write a budget—the maid is too expensive—you bought a pair of shoes *last* month. You're old, you're getting old— she's old. Yesterday you didn't look in my face. Tomorrow you forgot I'm here. Two aspirin pills are good for headaches. The world is getting . . . so dull, let me sleep, let me sleep! You sneeze, you have a cold. No, that was last month. No, it's now. Which is now and which is then? Benny . . . you used to be a clever boy! (*A silence follows, which* STARK *finally breaks.*)

STARK (*defiantly*): Yes, a certain man once said that in our youth we collect materials to build a bridge to the moon; but in our old age, he says, we use the materials to build a shack.

PRINCE (*looking around the room*): Yes, *this is it!* But you, you gradu-ated first in the class! You played tennis, you were full of life and plans. Look, you don't even resent me now.

STARK (*slowly*): I'm what I am . . . it's not Belle's fault!

PRINCE: What are you?

STARK: Not unhappy. . . .

PRINCE: You fell asleep at the switch. But Belle is worried——

STARK: Is she?

PRINCE: She's intelligent. You don't have children to hold you together. You're almost forty . . . a time for special adventures.

STARK (*stung, with sudden hotness*): You have no right to speak this way! We're happy——

PRINCE (*cutting in*): You're happy? You're sure of your future? You go home with a happy face at night?

STARK: Don't make trouble, Poppa!

PRINCE (*half smiling*): Whose voice do you hear in your ear? Mine or yours? (*And then he smiles.*)

STARK (*slowing down*): Gee, Poppa, I never know when you're serious.

PRINCE: A housewife rules your destiny. You love her?

STARK: Of course!

PRINCE: She's got you where she wants you. . . . Like an iceberg, three-quarters under water. . . . (*Pause.*) I mightn't live forever. I want you to know what I think. (*He starts for the door.*)

STARK: You going home?

PRINCE: To my brokers and watch the board. My electric shares are going up. Your secretary uses too much paint and powder.

STARK: She'll tone it down.

PRINCE (*suddenly turning, hand on door knob, pointing his cane at STARK and lowering his voice to a near whisper*): Iceberg, listen . . . why don't you come up and see the world, the sea gulls and the ships to Europe? (*Coming back into the room.*) When did you look at another woman last? The year they put the buffalo nickel on the market? Why don't you suddenly ride away, an airplane, a boat! Take a rocket to the moon! Explode! What holds you back? You don't want to hurt Belle's feelings? You'll die soon enough——

STARK: I'll just have to laugh at that!

PRINCE: Laugh. . . . But make a motto for yourself: "Out of the coffin by Labor Day!" Have an affair with—with—with this girl . . . this Miss Cleo. She'll make you a living man again.

STARK (*laughing*): You're a great joker, Poppa. (PRINCE *follows* STARK'S *laughter; both men laugh together.*)

PRINCE: . . . Never look away from a problem, Benny.

STARK: I never know when you're serious.

PRINCE: When you look away from the problem, it don't disappear. But maybe *you* might disappear! Remember I told you! (PRINCE *abruptly exits.* STARK *is still laughing; now he suddenly stops, mouth half open. He is not feeling humorous and he realizes it in a flash. Rather he is now depressed, even frightened a little. Twice he mutters to himself.*)

STARK: "Sonofagun! . . . Sonofagun! . . ." (*Now* DR. JENSEN, *a chiropodist with office down the hall, commonly called Frenchy, breezes into the waiting room. He is an American of Swedish parents, aged thirty, realistic and alert, fast and practical. He has an active wiry body; wears a white jacket. Now he pins the door back.*)

FRENCHY: Hello, Doc. Pin back the door—it's hot. (*Goes to water cooler.*)

STARK (*abstracted*): Hello, Frenchy.

FRENCHY: Some day, when I can afford it, I'll get a water cooler. You don't mind me running in and out like that, do you? (*He sits.*)

STARK (*depressed*): Of course not, Frenchy.

FRENCHY: The Palm Beach kid was here again.

STARK: Who?

FRENCHY: Mr. Prince. He gave me a gloomy hello in the hall.

STARK: He's a gloomy man.

FRENCHY: Why?

STARK: I can't make out. He disturbs me.

FRENCHY: Why?

STARK: Every time he drops in here I'm depressed for hours after.

FRENCHY: Make a phonograph record—let me listen.

STARK: You wouldn't understand. You have to be married first.

FRENCHY: I see.

STARK: Do you know something about women?

FRENCHY: What?

STARK: No, I mean do you know anything about women?

FRENCHY: I'll be explicit: no!

STARK (*musingly*): A man falls asleep in marriage. And after a time he wants to keep on sleeping, undisturbed. I'm surprised how little I've thought about it. Gee!—What I don't know would fill a book.

FRENCHY (*watching him*): You look like helplessness personified.

STARK: He tries to tell me I'm dissatisfied with my married life——

FRENCHY: Maybe you are. . . .

STARK: He's very persuasive in some things, but I know he's incorrect. (*Suddenly grinning.*) Do I look like an unhappy man?

FRENCHY (*after a pause, soberly*): You'd know that better than me, Doc.

STARK (*shaking his head again*): Sonofagun! . . . Don't all married couples argue and disagree? Even the joke papers tell us that. A man would be a mad idealist to want a honeymoon all his life.

FRENCHY: No, he'd be a woman. A man can't be both lover and banker, enchanter and provider. But the girls want those combined talents. . . . The man who worries for the bucks is not the one to kiss his wife behind the ear.

STARK: Yes. . . . (*But continuing with his own thoughts.*) There's something positively *sinister* about that man!

FRENCHY: Prince? *Cynical.*

STARK: I don't understand human nature, not the off-color things. Suddenly he tells me he wants to be an actor! I like normal people, like you.

FRENCHY: Hell, who's normal nowadays! Take that kid of yours, that Cleo ——

STARK: Sometimes people embarrass me. The most ordinary people suddenly become sinister ——

FRENCHY: Sinister? They're just sleepy.

STARK: What about Miss Singer? You were saying—(COOPER *enters the waiting room, distracted and brooding.*)

FRENCHY (*with a glad shout*): Here's Coop! Let's hear what he has to say.

COOPER (*sitting heavily*): What?

FRENCHY: What's your opinion of women, Coop?

COOPER: Who's got time to think about women! I'm trying to make a living!

FRENCHY (*turning to* STARK *with a laugh*): You see!

COOPER: Is there a man in our generation with time to think about women? Show me that man and I'll show you a loafer!—(*To* STARK.) Did anybody call me while I was out?

STARK: No.

COOPER: This morning I had a hunch there'd be some business. Nobody called?

STARK: No. (*Notice here* FRENCHY's *constant activity of watching people, listening and probing them, watching their reactions to things he says and does. It must be confessed: He is a self-educated, amateur student of human nature in all its aspects.*)

COOPER (*after a pause*): It's gonna be a hot summer. . . .

STARK: Nothing on your calendar today?

COOPER (*with a snort*): Yeah! At four o'clock a distant relative is coming in for a free cleaning. (*Mopping his brow.*) I'm dead! (*Pause.*) Your wife made me a proposition, to put up or get out.

STARK: When? !

COOPER: Recently. She almost chewed my head off. Before.

STARK (*embarrassed, trying to explain*): She thinks people take advantage of me. . . .

FRENCHY: You're doing those W.P.A. boys' work for half price—that's advantage.

STARK: I hope she doesn't hear about it.

FRENCHY: It's her business to hear about it: every generous impulse on your part brings her closer to insecurity.

COOPER (*defensively, annoyed*): You're a big busybody, Frenchy!

STARK (*protestingly*): You can't let poor boys like that just walk out.

FRENCHY: I know plenty who let them walk.

COOPER: Walk yourself, please—I have to talk business here.

FRENCHY (*giving* COOPER *a shrewd look*): *Excuséz moi.* . . . I'll go back and take a nap.

STARK: In the middle of the day?

FRENCHY (*going to the door*): Why not? Just had my lunch. A snake eats a rabbit and falls asleep, don't it? Why should I be better than a snake? (FRENCHY *laughs and exits left.*)

COOPER: He's a madman. (*An uncomfortable silence ensues*): Who wears the pants in your family, Stark?

STARK (*indignantly*): Belle had no right to tell you that!

COOPER (*humble in the face of necessity*): Tell her you decided to let me stay in the office till after Labor Day. How is that for a request? (*After waiting for an answer.*) She might object . . . ?

STARK: I'll decide that, Phil!

COOPER: Well, that's my problem in a nutshell. You'll have an empty office on your hands if I leave.

STARK: Where would you go?

COOPER: In the park and eat grass.

STARK (*shocked back to attention*): As bad as that? (*After another uncomfortable pause.*) Can't you pay anything, Phil?

COOPER: No. . . .

STARK: I mean . . . you know . . .

COOPER: Sure. . . .

STARK (*finally*): . . . You'd better stay here till something happens. You can't move now.

COOPER: In July I'll pay a month—I'll get the money.

STARK (*uncomfortably*): You know how it is. . . .

COOPER: So it's settled?

STARK: Yes.

COOPER (*with a joy of relief*): You gave me a new lease on life! You're good, you're kind, you're generous to the nth degree!

STARK (*embarrassed*): No, I'm not. . . .

COOPER: Hail, Ben Stark!

STARK: Stop it, Phil. . . .

COOPER: No, I mean it, every word!

STARK: I hope things pick up for you.

COOPER: You're a pride to me, a pleasure! Now I'll go down for a shave. Again, thanks. (*He offers his hand, which* STARK *takes.*)

STARK: Shhh! (*With a laugh and a wave of his hand,* COOPER *starts for the exit, right.* CLEO SINGER *enters,* COOPER *almost knocking her down.*)

COOPER: Miss Singer, you're a lovely girl. Take any messages for me. (COOPER *exits, left.* CLEO *stands in her place a moment, surprised.* STARK *looks at her as if he had never seen her before, secretly examining her throughout the following scene. Because of his previous scene with* PRINCE *she now presents a challenge to him which he might never have come to alone.*)

CLEO: Why did he say that?

STARK: He's feeling good.

CLEO (*taking off her coat*): I almost roasted to death in this coat. They call weather like this earthquake weather in California.

STARK: Were you ever there?

CLEO: Surely, several times. (*Hanging up the coat.*) The more expensive kinds of camel hair don't wear well, do they?

STARK: Did you put the ad in?

CLEO: I don't forget my duties twice, Dr. Stark.

STARK (*appeased by her attractive humble air*): I owe you an apology for the way I shouted at you before.

CLEO (*pleasantly*): Into every life a little rain must fall. I don't mind.

STARK (*hesitantly*): You'd be much more attractive . . . if . . . you didn't . . . use so much lipstick.

CLEO: Too much? . . . It's so dark at this mirror here. (*Goes to the wall mirror.*)

STARK: It's only my opinion, Cleo ——

CLEO (*turning rapidly*): Do you realize that's the first time you've called me Cleo since I've been here? !

STARK (*taken aback*): Is there any reason why I shouldn't?

CLEO: Oh, no! Certainly not!

STARK: How old are you, Cleo?

CLEO (*coquetting slightly*): Don't you think that's a personal question?

STARK: I have no personal motives. . . .

CLEO (*smiling back*): Mr. Prince asked me the same thing. He's a terrible flirt, isn't he?

STARK (*frowning*): That's his way. He tries to be interesting ——

CLEO: Lots of men are trying to be interesting.

STARK: Are they?

CLEO (*she starts for the office door but stops short*): Would you mind if I don't wear stockings in the office in the summer? Mr. Bernstein at Chelsea-Pontiac didn't mind.

STARK: Well . . .

CLEO (*hastily*): If you say not to ——

STARK (*ditto*): It's quite all right.

CLEO: Your wife might object.

STARK: Why should she?

CLEO: I may be wrong, but so many wives like to keep an eye on their husband's secretary.

STARK: Mrs. Stark runs my home. I run the office.

CLEO: After all, we must keep cool, mustn't we? May I say this?—I like you, Dr. Stark. Maybe that's too personal, but everything that's healthy is personal, don't you think?

STARK (*ponderously*): Very possible. . . . (CLEO *stops at the side table on her way to the office again.*)

CLEO: Looking at this newspaper makes me think—the universe must be ruled by a committee; one man couldn't be so stupid.

STARK (*smiling*): That's a very witty remark!

CLEO (*pleased*): I'm glad you think so, Dr. Stark.

STARK (*looking at his watch*): Mrs. Nelson will be here any minute. You'd better clean up the instruments, particularly the scalers.

CLEO: The scalers? . . . Which are those, Dr. Stark? I know, but I want to make sure.

STARK (*taking one from his top pocket*): These.

CLEO: I'll cut some cotton rolls, too.

STARK: Always dry an instrument when you remove it from the sterilizer. It'll clean easier.

CLEO: That's a very good hint.

STARK (*dryly*): I wasn't hinting. Patients like clean instruments.

CLEO: Of course. (*Stopping at the operating room door.*) Your wife was very angry with me before.

STARK (*impatiently*): Mrs. Stark is not the terrible person many people think she is!

CLEO (*dismayed*): Oh, I didn't mean anything. . . .

STARK (*almost savagely*): She's one of the most loyal, sincere and helpful persons I've ever met!

CLEO (*in a small voice*): I'm sure she is, I'm sure of that. . . . (CLEO *now disappears into the operating room. For a moment* STARK *stands there, wagging his head. His eye falls on the dental magazine. He picks it up, looks at the ad and then throws the magazine across the room. As he begins to fill his pipe his glance turns to the window, right. He moves over to the window and looks out at the Hotel Algiers.* CLEO's *voice from the operating-room threshold turns him around with a guilty start. In a small contrite voice.*) Pardon me . . . did I tell you before? Your wife expects you home at seven.

STARK (*annoyed*): Yes, thanks—you told me—thanks!

CLEO (*meekly*): You're welcome, Dr. Stark. (CLEO *disappears into the operating room again.* STARK *looks after her, annoyed. For a moment he stands reflectively. Finally he strikes a match and begins to light his pipe.*)

Slow Curtain

E. E. CUMMINGS Why he selected

 SPEECH from a PLAY

please honour my contribution by surrounding it with a little silence. Silence is lively; and deathful is doubletalk, eg la guerre

Silver Lake, N. H.   E. E. CUMMINGS
August, 1942

O MY voices, don't forget me; voices, come to me, I am afraid; I am nothing, nothing without you—you are myself which I shall never know, for to know is to hold: O but you are what everyone may not keep, the poor are not poorer than the rich, the sick are not weak and the well are not strong and captains are soldiers of this who will never be commanded; but this is you, you—and it is much brighter than everything will be very dark and not anyone believes me: women are not so women and men so men that they may imagine the wonder of it, and without wonder they are noone; for this wonder is themselves: all of them can be less than nothing; but each may be more than any someone, each may be everywhere and forever and each may be alive: each of them may become this wonder wholly and the here of this wonderful now and its beautiful moving—O my voices, not all the boys who shall ever die can take you from all the girls who were ever born; and if the young moon sleeps your hands are under her sky (but without you the first star does not breathe) and your fingers are waking the earth

. . . silence.

Then carefully I'll remember how I found you; it was a summer day, the earth was made of sky and the sun was full of bells but in the bells are cries, and then into the air came another brightness; everything around me climbed and fell like a heart, my life flew and swam. She was a little girl, my life. After a while it was a summer day; then she stood, she did not swim and fly, she was not trembling for she was me; and near me were my animals, who are kind and who are not afraid, who do not hate and who cannot lie because their minds are in their eyes. "Jehanne is going" my life tells them "someone is calling me, his name is Michael, he is slender and shining and his armor fits him like water; beside him are two ladies who live before the altar sometimes, they are very beautifully tall but I know their names, Margaret and Catharine. If these three speak to a little girl, she is made of flowers." My animals look at me and look at me and they understand; they are my friends. "Flowers" I tell them "flowers" and their eyes do not need to speak. —But you took me from these friends, O my voices, and you put me on a wide road into the dark world; and I went through cities as if they were clouds, and I came to a silence and in the silence was a fire and men and women stood in this fire. Perhaps the silence was a palace, I don't know; perhaps the fire was torches, fifty torches, a thousand, a hundred, I don't know; I only looked and looked: and in the center of the fire moved men and women beautifully dressed. Then someone whispered "where is he whom you seek?" and now those three who are my voices came to me bright and clear—brighter, much brighter, than music and a little brighter than the morning; they are so bright, no one but me can see their words: they are so clear, noone but me can hear this light who sings "don't fear, Jehanne, for the fire is not a man, Jehanne, but in the fire is the only man." And (smiling) someone who I am went up into it and flames are all above me and all around her, but we were not afraid, for she sees him only, although he was dressed like the others, he has no crown and no sceptre: but I knew she had found him. And I stand before that man. And I say "you are the king."

Silence . . .

ah—how they laughed: the haters, not men and not women; the goddams, which do not fear or dare, the English; which are awake if they are asleep and asleep if they are awake: swarming under a blue steep sky by thousands of tens of thousands they come, laugh-

ing and laughing; laughing because we are so few, so very few—
yes: but beyond this colour you are breathing and above it is a
silence, and I tell you the silence is full of armies and these armies
are my armies; I tell you my armies are hundreds of thousands and
thousands of hundreds of thousands: I say "you cannot see them;
these armies are so huge, only I can see these armies." Yes, the few
around me are amazed; breathing, they stare and stare at nothing
and at nothing: the air is the air; these men can breathe but these
men cannot see, and they are less amazed than I who see and do not
breathe. No—it is a dream: no; only blue air is shining and is shining
and before me the lice of England come laughing. Her men look at
Jehanne. And (trembling) I ask my life "who has spoken?" and my
life answers "me." —Then Jehanne The Maid cries to her soldiers
"do you believe?" and all together like one man these men answer
her "yes!" and the world spoke arrows and a bird sang and the
earth opened. Who rides first, in clear armor, lifting high the whiteness of a banner which is wings? Jehanne: and around Jehanne
men without wings live to their shoulders in the smoke of bursting
bellies, and behind Jehanne men who cannot swim skate on the ice
of English brains; and beyond me and above me perfectly are
charging millions whom no life but only mine has dreamed. . . .
Then how those haters leaped through their laughter and tripped
—look, the lines writhe; see: the shapes wince and cringe—now
they run: everywhere before us not women who are not men are
running, they are running; stumbling, are tumbling; as we lop hit
and chop stab smite until down down they go bubbling and down
screaming whose flesh wilts under us (their heads are not laughing
these teeth bite through these necks) and why? This has no why:
this now is more than ours, here we are not some shadows called
ourselves, now we are in God together you and I; His are such
armies as will fill our blood with always: this is His meaning and
our own, my friends; now we are made of one secret. —O for those
armies over me again and over you, my soldiers; you thrusting
yanking you grappling hacking mowing you diving through dead
laughter, you and the good stink of you and the tough blaze of
your eyes, yes; and a yell of steel split and clean wriggling of bright
flags all grabbed with new sunlight and all the roaring of a high

battle around us all with souls dying and walls falling, and the floating of a black horse under me!

. . . silence . . .

someone is lost, someone I must find. Where is she; where? I only look and look, but there is nothing and this nothing neither moves nor does not move—and then within this nothing is another, a nothing which is something. Or someone? It has eyes. Hush. Speak very softly: whisper: can this be the someone whom you seek? No. No; for my someone was made of flowers, and they move—flowers grow and open and they close and disappear; this someone does not die or live, this someone only seems: it cannot grow. Only this something is not asleep but it is dreaming; it is dreaming but it is speaking—I hear words; hark: I hear it saying "Jehanne who has knocked bigfisted knights out of their armor, Jehanne who has smashed princes into smithereens, Jehanne who has seen a man kneeling and a king rising and him, only him, standing: crowned with a crown and sceptred with a sceptre, while people cried and laughed and danced and fell down and the bells swung out into the mountains and the rivers of France melted." These are the words I hear in its dream; and I am afraid. —You less than noone; you something within a nothing: where are my good friends gone, my true kind friends who cannot hate and who do not fear? It dreams, but it speaks. —Where have they gone, and their eyes which cannot lie, only who understand me and whom I understand: where? It looks, but it does not see. Answer: who are you? —Me? No—! Don't look: take your eyes into your eyes again! You not—you it—could you have been . . . my Jehanne? O can I have dreamed a king? Were those bells crashing and were those dancers living in my head and falling down and were those people laughing in my heart and crying? Creatures which are not men and are not women— have I dreamed them? Was there ever any fire and any silence and any summer day? You—you with the murdered hair—tell me; was there once any someone in armor like water and ladies much taller than sunlight, calling to me gently and very sweetly crying, until a little girl is made of flowers?

silence.

—But they believed! My soldiers did not see, no; they could only
breathe, yes; but they believed. Now I can only breathe; now I can
believe: I am a soldier now; I am not a dream—someone else is
gone, someone else is dead and the someone who I am is all alone:
no . . . no, now she can hear a little girl crying and crying, and
saying "help me—I am lost: I am standing in a dark place, I am
terribly afraid of this dark, I am my heart falling and climbing but
everywhere is dark; dark—speak to me, my voices! O speak! The
great doctors have faces like books and I cannot read: speak! —O
my voices, their faces which are not faces hate me only because I
love you: these are not dead, they are not even English—they are
things: I am in the power of things which have no hands and no
feet: things follow me everywhere; they listen to my dreaming when
I am asleep, things are picking my one red life into large little
pieces; hear me, my voices—things undress me with their deaf eyes
and I am cold when they cover me with questions. Tell me—it is
Jehanne—speak to her, you voices: have I come to die among things
because I would not become a thing?" —So the little girl cries and
cries; and I am not dead. Once upon a time she was made of
flowers. Therefore the big faces which I cannot read will eat me. And
still I shall not read. I shall not know. Ever; for to know is to hold.
I shall only understand . . . quietly. —But you shall live, but nothing
shall ever hurt you, my voices, who are everything beautiful and
everything free; perfectly you are gladness and singing, you are
spring when she touches the first tree with her eyes and the fields
dance, you are all the white brooks who laugh and cry and the green
hills who grow—anywhere sun and stars and the moon are only
alive because your light is their light and they play in your day,
which is always much nearer than near, nearer than is, nearer than
nearer and nearest and now and nearer than how the birds swim
through the air and why the fish fly through the sea

     —Thanks!

O I am not afraid, my voices! You shall be very proud of me, for
I will be very beautiful for you: I will dress myself carefully in

thick red fire and in sharp white fire and in round blue cool fire. Now it is not dark and there is no world: perfectly begins to grow a brighter brightness than all of the sky and of the sea and of the earth; everywhere Jehanne only is alive, everywhere this climbing wonderfully mighty only colour is her gladness. And in her gladness rising, taller than everyone than everything than nothing, stands He Whom she may know: hark—to only Him, to Him, her life is calling and crying and singing "my Love! my Love! out of all this light which is my joy comes to You a woman who is more than every queen: look, her wings begin to open—King Of All Kings, put your great eyes around me as I climb beyond the steepest flower which breathes—see; now all of the little flames are lifting me higher than tomorrow in all of their hands—Man Who Is God! take from these alive fingers quickly one shining bird"

VIII
KITCHEN BOUQUET

IRVIN S. COBB Why he selected

"SPEAKING

of OPERATIONS—"

As a correspondent for *The Saturday Evening Post* I came back from the Western Front early in 1915, nursing a small umbilical hernia which I'd acquired lifting wounded soldiers and prisoners out of box-cars in Northern France.

I caught up with my writing. Then, practically without either pre-meditation or provocation, I went on a so-called lecture tour. Then I went into a hospital where my rupture was scientifically "reduced" so that thereafter it was only about four times as outstanding as it had been before. In all other respects, the operation was a pronounced success—as soon as I had paid various bills for professional services rendered.

Being convalescent, I was moved to do a piece about what had been my first experience with invalidism in my entire life. The subject was fresh in my mind; the newly-formed scar tissue still itched. So I sat down and in three sittings of approximately four hours apiece, the tale was written. You might say it wrote itself. All the facts were there where I could put my hands on them.

It appeared first as an article in *The Saturday Evening Post.* Immediately, a publisher put it in book form. It proved to be a best-seller. It is still selling. I believe it has broken some record for this type of book. After nearly twenty-seven years it continues to enjoy some demand. The last time I heard from it, the job had gone into its thirty-ninth edition. Or maybe it was the twenty-ninth—anyhow, somewhere around there.

For its length—and breadth—it has yielded more in royalties than any other book of mine did. Perhaps that explains why I chose it for inclusion in this volume. It also explains my present attitude toward it, which is favorable, not to say affectionate.

It may be a little old fashioned by now. But then, so am I.

Santa Monica, Cal.   IRVIN S. COBB
April 14, 1942

NOW that the last belated bill for services professionally rendered has been properly paid and properly receipted; now that the memory of the event, like the mark of the stitches, has faded out from a vivid red to a becoming pink shade; now that I pass a display of adhesive tape in a drug-store window without flinching—I sit me down to write a little piece about a certain matter—a small thing, but mine own—to wit, That Operation.

For years I have noticed that persons who underwent pruning or remodeling at the hands of a duly qualified surgeon, and survived, like to talk about it afterward. In the event of their not surviving I have no doubt they still liked to talk about it, but in a different locality. Of all the readily available topics for use, whether among friends or among strangers, an operation seems to be the handiest and most dependable. It beats the Tariff, or Roosevelt or Bryan, or when this war is going to end, if ever, if you are a man talking to other men; and it is more exciting even than the question of how Mrs. Vernon Castle will wear her hair this season, if you are a woman talking to other women.

For mixed companies a whale is one of the best and the easiest things to talk about that I know of. In regard to whales and their peculiarities you can make almost any assertion without fear of successful contradiction. Nobody ever knows any more about them than you do. You are not hampered by facts. If someone mentions the blubber of the whale and you chime in and say it may be noticed for miles on a still day when the large but emotional creature has been moved to tears by some great sorrow coming into its life, everybody is bound to accept the statement. For after all how few among us really know whether a distressed whale sobs aloud or does so under its breath? Who, with any certainty, can tell whether a mother whale hatches her own egg her own self or leaves it on the sheltered bosom of a fjord to be incubated by the gentle warmth of the midnight sun? The possibilities of the proposition for purposes of informal debate, pro and con, are apparent at a glance.

The weather, of course, helps out amazingly when you are meeting people for the first time, because there is nearly always more or less weather going on somewhere and practically everybody has ideas about it. The human breakfast is also a wonderfully good topic to start up during one of those lulls. Try it yourself the next time the conversation seems to drag. Just speak up in an offhand kind of way and say that you never care much about breakfast—a slice of toast and a cup of weak tea start you off properly for doing a hard day's work. You will be surprised to note how things liven up and how eagerly all present join in. The lady on your left feels that you should know she always takes two lumps of sugar and nearly half cream, because she simply cannot abide hot milk, no matter what the doctors say. The gentleman on your right will be moved to confess he likes his eggs boiled for exactly three minutes, no more and no less. Buckwheat cakes and sausage find a champion and oatmeal rarely lacks a warm defender.

But after all, when all is said and done, the king of all topics is operations. Sooner or later, wherever two or more are gathered together it is reasonably certain that somebody will bring up an operation.

Until I passed through the experience of being operated on myself, I never really realized what a precious conversational boon the subject is, and how great a part it plays in our intercourse with our fellow beings on this planet. To the teller it is enormously interesting, for he is not only the hero of the tale but the rest of the cast and the stage setting as well—the whole show, as they say; and if the listener has had a similar experience—and who is there among us in these days that has not taken a nap 'neath the shade of the old ether cone?—it acquires a double value.

"Speaking of operations—" you say, just like that, even though nobody present has spoken of them; and then you are off, with your new acquaintance sitting on the edge of his chair, or hers as the case may be and so frequently is, with hands clutched in polite but painful restraint, gills working up and down with impatience, eyes brightened with desire, tongue hung in the middle, waiting for you to pause to catch your breath, so that he or she may break in with a few personal recollections along the same line. From a mere conversation it resolves itself into a symptom symposium, and a perfectly splendid time is had by all.

If an operation is such a good thing to talk about, why isn't it a good thing to write about, too? That is what I wish to know. Besides, I need the money. Verily, one always needs the money when one has but recently escaped from the ministering clutches of the modern hospital. Therefore I write.

It all dates back to the fair, bright morning when I went to call on a prominent practitioner here in New York, whom I shall denominate as Doctor X. I had a pain. I had had it for days. It was not a dependable, locatable pain, such as a tummyache or a toothache is, which you can put your hand on; but an indefinite, unsettled, undecided kind of pain, which went wandering about from place to place inside of me like a strange ghost lost in Cudjo's Cave. I never knew until then what the personal sensations of a haunted house are. If only the measly thing could have made up its mind to settle down somewhere and start light housekeeping I think I should have been better satisfied. I never had such an uneasy tenant. Alongside of it a woman with the moving fever would be comparatively a fixed and stationary object.

Having always, therefore, enjoyed perfectly riotous and absolutely unbridled health, never feeling weak and distressed unless dinner happened to be ten or fifteen minutes late, I was green regarding physicians and the ways of physicians. But I knew Doctor X slightly, having met him last summer in one of his hours of ease in the grand stand at a ball game, when he was expressing a desire to cut the umpire's throat from ear to ear, free of charge; and I remembered his name, and remembered, too, that he had impressed me at the time as being a person of character and decision and scholarly attainments.

He wore whiskers. Somehow in my mind whiskers are ever associated with medical skill. I presume this is a heritage of my youth, though I believe others labor under the same impression. As I look back it seems to me that in childhood's days all the doctors in our town wore whiskers.

I recall one old doctor down there in Kentucky who was practically lurking in ambush all the time. All he needed was a few decoys out in front of him and a pump gun to be a duck blind. He carried his calomel about with him in a fruit jar and when there was a cutting job he stropped his scalpel on his bootleg.

You see, in those primitive times germs had not been invented yet, and so he did not have to take any steps to avoid them. Now we know that loose, luxuriant whiskers are unsanitary, because they make such fine winter quarters for germs; so, though the doctors still wear whiskers, they do not wear them wild and waving. In the profession bosky whiskers are taboo; they must be landscaped. And since it is a recognized fact that germs abhor orderliness and straight lines they now go elsewhere to reside, and the doctor may still retain his traditional aspect and yet be practically germproof. Doctor X was trimmed in accordance with the ethics of the newer school. He had trellis whiskers. So I went to see him at his offices in a fashionable district, on an expensive side street.

Before reaching him I passed through the hands of a maid and a nurse, each of whom spoke to me in a low, sorrowful tone of voice, which seemed to indicate that there was very little hope.

I reached an inner room where Doctor X was. He looked me over, while I described for him as best I could what seemed to be the matter with me, and asked me a number of intimate questions touching on the lives, works, characters and peculiarities of my ancestors; after which he made me stand up in front of him and take my coat off, and he punched me hither and yon with his forefinger. He also knocked repeatedly on my breastbone with his knuckles, and each time, on doing this, would apply his ear to my chest and listen intently for a spell, afterward shaking his head in a disappointed way. Apparently there was nobody at home. For quite a time he kept on knocking, but without getting any response.

He then took my temperature and fifteen dollars, and said it was an interesting case—not unusual exactly, but interesting—and that it called for an operation.

From the way my heart and other organs jumped inside of me at that statement I knew at once that, no matter what he may have thought, the premises were not unoccupied. Naturally I inquired how soon he meant to operate. Personally I trusted there was no hurry about it. I was perfectly willing to wait for several years, if necessary. He smiled at my ignorance.

"I never operate," he said; "operating is entirely out of my line. I am a diagnostician."

He was, too—I give him full credit for that. He was a good, keen, close diagnostician. How did he know I had only fifteen dollars on me? You did not have to tell this man what you had, or how much. He knew without being told.

I asked whether he was acquainted with Doctor Y—Y being a person whom I had met casually at a club to which I belong. Oh, yes, he said, he knew Doctor Y. Y was a clever man, X said—very, very clever; but Y specialized in the eyes, the ears, the nose and the throat. I gathered from what Doctor X said that any time Doctor Y ventured below the thorax he was out of bounds and liable to be penalized; and that if by any chance he strayed down as far as the lungs he would call for help and back out as rapidly as possible.

This was news to me. It would appear that these up-to-date practitioners just go ahead and divide you up and partition you out among themselves without saying anything to you about it. Your torso belongs to one man and your legs are the exclusive property of his brother practitioner down on the next block, and so on. You may belong to as many as half a dozen specialists, most of whom, very possibly, are total strangers to you, and yet never know a thing about it yourself.

It has rather the air of trespass—nay, more than that, it bears some of the aspects of unlawful entry—but I suppose it is legal. Certainly, judging by what I am able to learn, the system is being carried on generally. So it must be ethical.

Anything doctors do in a mass is ethical. Almost anything they do singly and on individual responsibility is unethical. Being ethical among doctors is practically the same thing as being a Democrat in Texas or a Presbyterian in Scotland.

"Y will never do for you," said Doctor X, when I had rallied somewhat from the shock of these disclosures. "I would suggest that you go to Doctor Z, at such-and-such an address. You are exactly in Z's line. I'll let him know that you are coming and when, and I'll send him down my diagnosis."

So that same afternoon, the appointment having been made by telephone, I went, full of quavery emotions, to Doctor Z's place. As soon as I was inside his outer hallway I realized that I was nearing the presence of one highly distinguished in his profession.

A pussy-footed male attendant, in a livery that made him look like a cross between a headwaiter and an undertaker's assistant, escorted me through an anteroom into a reception-room, where a considerable number of well-dressed men and women were sitting about in strained attitudes, pretending to read magazines while they waited their turns, but in reality furtively watching one another.

I sat down in a convenient chair, adhering fast to my hat and my umbrella. They were the only friends I had there and I was determined not to lose them without a struggle. On the wall were many colored charts showing various portions of the human anatomy and what ailed them. Directly in front of me was a very thrilling illustration, evidently copied from an oil painting, of a liver in a bad state of repair. I said to myself that if I had a liver like that one I should keep it hidden from the public eye—I would never permit it to sit for its portrait. Still, there is no accounting for tastes. I know a man who got his spleen back from the doctors and now keeps it in a bottle of alcohol on the what-not in the parlor, as one of his most treasured possessions, and sometimes shows it to visitors. He, however, is of a very saving disposition.

Presently a lady secretary, who sat behind a roll-top desk in a corner of the room, lifted a forefinger and silently beckoned me to her side. I moved over and sat down by her; she took down my name and my age and my weight and my height, and a number of other interesting facts that will come in very handy should anyone ever be moved to write a complete history of my early life. In common with Doctor X she shared one attribute—she manifested a deep curiosity regarding my forefathers—wanted to know all about them. I felt that this was carrying the thing too far. I felt like saying to her:

"Miss or madam, so far as I know there is nothing the matter with my ancestors of the second and third generations back, except that they are dead. I am not here to seek medical assistance for a grandparent who succumbed to disappointment that time when Samuel J. Tilden got counted out, or for a great-grandparent who entered into Eternal Rest very unexpectedly and in a manner entirely uncalled for as a result of being an innocent bystander in one of those feuds that were so popular in my native state immediately following the Mexican War. Leave my ancestors alone. There is no need of your shaking my family tree in the belief that a few overripe patients will fall out. I alone—I, me, myself—am the present candidate!"

However, I refrained from making this protest audibly. I judged she was only going according to the ritual; and as she had a printed card, with blanks in it ready to be filled out with details regarding the remote members of the family connection, I humored her along.

When I could not remember something she wished to know concerning an ancestor I supplied her with thrilling details culled from the field of fancy. When the card was entirely filled up she sent me back to my old place to wait. I waited and waited, breeding fresh ailments all the time. I had started out with one symptom; now if I had one I had a million and a half. I could feel goose flesh sprouting out all over me. If I had been taller I might have had more, but not otherwise. Such is the power of the human imagination when the surroundings are favorable to its development.

Time passed; to me it appeared that nearly all the time there was passed and that we were getting along toward the shank-end of the Christian era mighty fast. I was afraid my turn would come next and afraid it would not. Perhaps you know this sensation. You get it at the dentist's, and when you are on the list of after-dinner speakers at a large banquet, and when you are waiting for the father of the Only Girl in the World to make up his mind whether he is willing to try to endure you as a son-in-law.

Then some more time passed.

One by one my companions, obeying a command, passed out through the door at the back, vanishing out of my life forever. None of them returned. I was vaguely wondering whether Doctor Z buried his dead on the premises or had them removed by a secret passageway in the rear, when a young woman in a nurse's costume tapped me on the shoulder from behind.

I jumped. She hid a compassionate smile with her hand and told me that the doctor would see me now.

As I rose to follow her—still clinging with the drowning man's grip of desperation to my hat and my umbrella—I was astonished to note by a glance at the calendar on the wall that this was still the present date. I thought it would be Thursday of next week at the very least.

Doctor Z also wore whiskers, carefully pointed up by an expert hedge trimmer. He sat at his desk, surrounded by freewill offerings from grateful patients and by glass cases containing other things he had taken away from them when they were not in a condition to object. I had expected, after all the preliminary ceremonies and delays, that we should have a long séance together. Not so; not at all. The modern expert in surgery charges as much for remembering your name between visits as the family doctor used to expect for staying up all night with you, but he does not waste any time when you are in his presence.

I was about to find that out. And a little later on I was to find out a lot of other things; in fact, that whole week was of immense educational value to me.

I presume it was because he stood so high in his profession, and was almost constantly engaged in going into the best society that Doctor Z did not appear to be the least bit excited over my having picked him out to look into me. In the most perfunctory manner he shook the hand that has shaken the hands of Jess Willard, George M. Cohan and Henry Ford, and bade me be seated in a chair which was drawn up in a strong light, where he might gaze directly at me as we conversed and so get the full values of the composition. But if I was a treat for him to look at he concealed his feelings very effectually.

He certainly had his emotions under splendid control. But then, of course, you must remember that he probably had traveled about extensively and was used to sight-seeing.

From this point on everything passed off in a most businesslike manner. He reached into a filing cabinet and took out an exhibit, which I recognized as the same one his secretary had filled out in the early part of the century. So I was already in the card-index class. Then briefly he looked over the manifest that Doctor X had sent him. It may not have been a manifest—it may have been an invoice or a bill of lading. Anyhow, I was in the assignee's hands. I could only hope it would not eventually become necessary to call in a receiver. Then he spoke:

"Yes, yes-yes," he said; "yes-yes-yes! Operation required. Small matter—hum, hum! Let's see—this is Tuesday? Quite so. Do it Friday!

Friday at"—he glanced toward a scribbled pad of engagement dates at his elbow—"Friday at seven A. M. No; make it seven-fifteen. Have important tumor case at seven. St. Germicide's Hospital. You know the place?—up on Umpty-umph Street. Go' day! Miss Whoziz, call next visitor."

And before I realized that practically the whole affair had been settled I was outside the consultation-room in a small private hall, and the secretary was telling me further details would be conveyed to me by mail. I went home in a dazed state. For the first time I was beginning to learn something about an industry in which heretofore I had never been interested. Especially was I struck by the difference now revealed to me in the preliminary stages of the surgeons' business as compared with their fellow experts in the allied cutting trades—tailors, for instance, not to mention barbers. Every barber, you know, used to be a surgeon, only he spelled it chirurgeon. Since then the two professions have drifted far apart. Even a half-witted barber—the kind who always has the first chair as you come into the shop—can easily spend ten minutes of your time thinking of things he thinks you should have and mentioning them to you one by one, whereas any good, live surgeon knows what you have almost instantly.

As for the tailor—consider how wearisome are his methods when you parallel them alongside the tremendous advances in this direction made by the surgeon—how cumbersome and old-fashioned and tedious! Why, an experienced surgeon has you all apart in half the time the tailor takes up in deciding whether the vest shall fasten with five buttons or six. Our own domestic tailors are bad enough in this regard and the Old World tailors are even worse.

I remember a German tailor in Aix-la-Chapelle in the fall of 1914 who undertook to build for me a suit suitable for visiting the battle lines informally. He was the most literary tailor I ever met anywhere. He would drape the material over my person and then take a piece of chalk and write quite a nice long piece on me. Then he would rub it out and write it all over again, but more fully. He kept this up at intervals of every other day until he had writer's cramp. After that he used pins. He would pin the seam together, uttering little soothing, clucking sounds in German whenever a pin went through the goods and into me. The German cluck is not so soothing as the cluck of the English-speaking peoples, I find.

At the end of two long and trying weeks, which wore both of us down noticeably, he had the job done. It was not an unqualified success. He regarded it as a suit of clothes, but I knew better; it was a set of slip covers, and if only I had been a two-seated runabout it would have proved a perfect fit, I am sure; but I am a single-seated design and it did not answer. I wore it to the war because I had nothing else to wear that would stamp me as a regular war correspondent, except, of course, my wrist watch; but I shall not wear it to another war. War is terrible enough already; and, besides, I have parted with it. On my way home through Holland I gave that suit to a couple of poor Belgian refugees, and I presume they are still wearing it.

So far as I have been able to observe, the surgeons and the tailors of these times share but one common instinct: If you go to a new surgeon or to a new tailor he is morally certain, after looking you over, that the last surgeon you had, or the last tailor, did not do your cutting properly. There, however, is where the resemblance ends. The tailor, as I remarked in effect just now, wants an hour at least in which to decide how he may best cover up and disguise the irregularities of the human form; in much less time than that the surgeon has completely altered the form itself.

With the surgeon it is very much as it is with those learned men who write those large, impressive works of reference which should be permanently in every library, and which we are forever buying from an agent because we are so passionately addicted to payments. If the thing he seeks does not appear in the contents proper he knows exactly where to look for it. "See appendix," says the historian to you in a footnote. "See appendix," says the surgeon to himself, the while humming a cheery refrain. And so he does.

Well, I went home. This was Tuesday and the operation was not to be performed until the coming Friday. By Wednesday I had calmed down considerably. By Thursday morning I was practically normal again as regards my nerves. You will understand that I was still in a state of blissful ignorance concerning the actual methods of the surgical profession as exemplified by its leading exponents of today. The knowledge I have touched on in the pages immediately preceding was to come to me later.

Likewise Doctor Z's manner had been deceiving. It could not be that he meant to carve me to any really noticeable extent—his attitude had been entirely too casual. At our house carving is a very serious matter. Any time I take the head of the table and start in to carve it is fitting to remove the women and children to a place of safety, and onlookers should get under the table. When we first began housekeeping and gave our first small dinner-party we had a brace of ducks cooked in honor of the company, and I, as host, undertook to carve them. I never knew until then that a duck was built like a watch—that his works were inclosed in a burglarproof case. Without the use of dynamite the Red Leary-O'Brien gang could not have broken into those ducks. I thought so then and I think so yet. Years have passed since then, but I may state that even now, when there are guests for dinner, we do not have ducks. Unless somebody else is going to carve, we have liver.

I mention this fact in passing because it shows that I had learned to revere carving as one of the higher arts, and one not to be approached except in a spirit of due appreciation of the magnitude of the under- taking, and after proper consideration and thought and reflection, and all that sort of thing.

If this were true as regards a mere duck, why not all the more so as regards the carving of a person of whom I am so very fond as I am of myself? Thus I reasoned. And finally, had not Doctor Z spoken of the coming operation as a small matter? Well then?

Thursday at noon I received from Doctor Z's secretary a note stating that arrangements had been made for my admission into St. Germicide that same evening and that I was to spend the night there. This hardly seemed necessary. Still, the tone of the note appeared to indicate that the hospital authorities particularly wished to have me for an overnight guest; and as I reflected that probably the poor things had few enough bright spots in their busy lives, I decided I would humor them along and gladden the occasion with my presence from dinner-time on.

About eight o'clock I strolled in very jauntily. In my mind I had the whole programme mapped out. I would stay at the hospital for, say, two days following the operation—or, at most, three. Then I must be up and away. I had a good deal of work to do and a number of people to see on important business, and I could not really afford to waste more than a week-end on the staff of St. Germicide's. After Monday they must look to their own devices for social entertainment. That was my idea. Now when I look back on it I laugh, but it is a hollow laugh and there is no real merriment in it.

Indeed, almost from the moment of my entrance little things began to come up that were calculated to have a depressing effect on one's spirits. Downstairs a serious-looking lady met me and entered in a book a number of salient facts regarding my personality which the previous investigators had somehow overlooked. There is a lot of bookkeeping about an operation. This detail attended to, a young man, dressed in white garments and wearing an expression that stamped him as one who had suffered a recent deep bereavement, came and relieved me of my hand bag and escorted me upstairs.

As we passed through the upper corridors I had my first introduction to the hospital smell, which is a smell compounded of iodoform, ether, gruel, and something boiling. All hospitals have it, I understand. In time you get used to it, but you never really care for it.

The young man led me into a small room tastefully decorated with four walls, a floor, a ceiling, a window sill and a window, a door and a doorsill, and a bed and a chair. He told me to go to bed. I did not want to go to bed—it was not my regular bedtime—but he made a point of it, and I judged it was according to regulations; so I undressed and put on my night clothes and crawled in. He left me, taking my other clothes and my shoes with him, but I was not allowed to get lonely.

A little later a ward surgeon appeared, to put a few inquiries of a pointed and personal nature. He particularly desired to know what my trouble was. I explained to him that I couldn't tell him—he would have to see Doctor X or Doctor Z; they probably knew, but were keeping it a secret between themselves.

The answer apparently satisfied him, because immediately after that he made me sign a paper in which I assumed all responsibility for what was to take place the next morning.

This did not seem exactly fair. As I pointed out to him, it was the surgeon's affair, not mine; and if the surgeon made a mistake the joke would be on him and not on me, because in that case I would not be here anyhow. But I signed, as requested, on the dotted line, and he departed.

After that, at intervals, the chief house surgeon dropped in, without knocking, and the head nurse came, and an interne or so, and a ward nurse, and the special nurse who was to have direct charge of me. It dawned on me that I was not having any more privacy in that hospital than a goldfish.

About eleven o'clock an orderly came, and, without consulting my wishes in the matter, he undressed me until I could have passed almost anywhere for September Morn's father, and gave me a clean shave, twice over, on one of my most prominent plane surfaces. I must confess I enjoyed that part of it. So far as I am able to recall, it was the only shave I have ever had where the operator did not spray me with cheap perfumery afterward and then try to sell me a bottle of hair tonic.

Having shaved me, the young man did me up amidships in a neat cloth parcel, took his kit under his arm and went away.

It occurred to me that, considering the trivial nature of the case, a good deal of fuss was being made over me by persons who could have no personal concern in the matter whatsoever. This thought recurred to me frequently as I lay there, all tied in a bundle like a week's washing. I did not feel quite so uppish as I had felt. Why was everybody picking on me?

Anon I slept, but dreamed fitfully. I dreamed that a whole flock of surgeons came to my bedside and charted me out in sections, like one of those diagram pictures you see of a beef in the Handy Compendium of Universal Knowledge, showing the various cuts and the butcher's pet name for each cut. Each man took his favorite joint and carried it away, and when they were all gone I was merely a recent site, full of reverberating echoes and nothing else.

I have had happier dreams in my time; this was not the kind of dream I should have selected had the choice been left to me.

When I woke the young sun was shining in at the window, and an orderly—not the orderly who had shaved me, but another one—was there in my room and my nurse was waiting outside the door. The orderly dressed me in a quaint suit of pyjamas cut on the half shell and buttoning stylishly in the back, *princesse mode*. Then he rolled in a flat litter on wheels and stretched me on it, and covered me up with a white tablecloth, just as though I had been cold Sunday-night supper, and we started for the operating-room at the top of the building; but before we started I lit a large black cigar, as Gen. U. S. Grant used to do when he went into battle. I wished by this to show how indifferent I was. Maybe he fooled somebody, but I do not believe I possess the same powers of simulation that Grant had. He must have been a very remarkable man—Grant must.

The orderly and the nurse trundled me out into the hall and loaded me into an elevator, which was to carry us up to the top of the hospital. Several other nurses were already in the elevator. As we came aboard one of them remarked that it was a fine day. A fine day for what? She did not finish the sentence.

Everybody wore a serious look. Inside of myself I felt pretty serious too—serious enough for ten or twelve. I had meant to fling off several very bright, spontaneous quips on the way to the table. I thought them out in advance, but now, somehow, none of them seemed appropriate. Instinctively, as it were, I felt that humor was out of place here.

I never knew an elevator to progress from the third floor of a building to the ninth with such celerity as this one on which we were traveling progressed. Personally I was in no mood for haste. If there was anyone else in all that great hospital who was in a particular hurry to be operated on I was perfectly willing to wait. But alas, no! The mechanism of the elevator was in perfect order—entirely too perfect. No accident of any character whatsoever befell us en route, no dropping back into the basement with a low, grateful thud; no hitch; no delay of any kind. We were certainly out of luck that trip. The demon of a joyrider who operated the accursed device jerked a lever and up we soared at a distressingly high rate of speed. If I could have had my way about that youth he would have been arrested for speeding.

Now we were there! They rolled me into a large room, all white, with a rounded ceiling like the inside of an egg. Right away I knew what the feelings of a poor, lonely little yolk are when the spoon begins to chip the shell. If I had not been so busy feeling sorry for myself I think I might have developed quite an active sympathy for yolks.

My impression had been that this was to be in the nature of a private affair, without invitations. I was astonished to note that quite a crowd had assembled for the opening exercises. From his attire and general deportment I judged that Doctor Z was going to be the master of the revels, he being attired appropriately in a white domino, with rubber gloves and a fancy cap of crash toweling. There were present, also, my diagnostic friend, Doctor X, likewise in fancy-dress costume, and a surgeon I had never met. From what I could gather he was going over the course behind Doctor Z to replace the divots.

And there was an interne in the background, playing caddy, as it were, and a head nurse, who was going to keep the score, and two other nurses, who were going to help her keep it. I only hoped that they would show no partiality, but be as fair to me as they were to Doctor Z, and that he would go round in par.

So they placed me right where my eyes might rest on a large wall cabinet full of very shiny-looking tools; and they took my cigar away from me and folded my hands on the wide bowknot of my sash. Then they put a cloth dingus over my face and a voice of authority told me to breathe. That advice, however, was superfluous and might just as well have been omitted, for such was my purpose anyhow. Ever since I can recall anything at all, breathing has been a regular habit with me. So I breathed. And, at that, a bottle of highly charged sarsaparilla exploded somewhere in the immediate vicinity and most of its contents went up my nose.

I started to tell them that somebody had been fooling with their ether and adulterating it, and that if they thought they could send me off to sleep with soda pop they were making the mistake of their lives, because it just naturally could not be done; but for some reason or other I decided to put off speaking about the matter for a few minutes. I breathed again—again—agai——

I was going away from there. I was in a large gas balloon, soaring up into the clouds. How pleasant! . . . No, by Jove! I was not in a balloon—I myself was the balloon, which was not quite so pleasant. Besides, Doctor Z was going along as a passenger; and as we traveled up and up he kept jabbing me in the midriff with the ferrule of a large umbrella which he had brought along with him in case of rain. He jabbed me harder and harder. I remonstrated with him. I told him I was a bit tender in that locality and the ferrule of his umbrella was sharp. He would not listen. He kept on jabbing me. . . .

Something broke! We started back down to earth. We fell faster and faster. We fell nine miles, and after that I began to get used to it. Then I saw the earth beneath and it was rising up to meet us.

A town was below—a town that grew larger and larger as we neared it. I could make out the bonded indebtedness, and the Carnegie Library, and the moving-picture palaces, and the new dancing parlor, and other principal points of interest.

At the rate we were falling we were certainly going to make an awful splatter in that town when we hit. I was sorry for the street-cleaning department.

We fell another half mile or so. A spire was sticking up into the sky directly beneath us, like a spear, to impale us. By a supreme effort I twisted out of the way of that spire, only to strike squarely on top of the roof of a greenhouse back of the parsonage, next door. We crashed through it with a perfectly terrific clatter of breaking glass and landed in a bed of white flowers, all soft and downy, like feathers.

And then Doctor Z stood up and combed the débris out of his whiskers and remarked that, taking it by and large, it had been one of the pleasantest little outings he had enjoyed in the entire course of his practice. He said that as a patient I was fair, but as a balloon I was immense. He asked me whether I had seen anything of his umbrella and began looking round for it. I tried to help him look, but I was too tired to exert myself much. I told him I believed I would take a little nap.

I opened a dizzy eye part way. So this was heaven—this white expanse that swung and swam before my languid gaze? No, it could not be—it did not smell like heaven. It smelled like a hospital. It was a hospital. It was my hospital. My nurse was bending over me and I caught a faint whiff of the starch in the front of her crisp blue blouse. She was two-headed for the moment, but that was a mere detail. She settled a pillow under my head and told me to lie quiet.

I meant to lie quiet; I did not have to be told. I wanted to lie quiet and hurt. I was hurty from head to toe and back again, and crosswise and cater-cornered. I hurt diagonally and lengthwise and on the bias. I had a taste in my mouth like a bird-and-animal store. And empty! It seemed to me those doctors had not left anything inside of me except the acoustics. Well, there was a mite of consolation there. If the over-hauling had been as thorough as I had reason to believe it was from my present sensations, I need never fear catching anything again so long as I lived, except possibly dandruff.

I waved the nurse away. I craved solitude. I desired only to lie there in that bed and hurt—which I did.

I had said beforehand I meant to stay in St. Germicide's for two or three days only. It is when I look back on that resolution I emit the hollow laugh elsewhere referred to. For exactly four weeks I was flat on my back. I know now how excessively wearied a man can get of his own back, how tired of it, how bored with it! And after that an-other two weeks elapsed before my legs became the same dependable pair of legs I had known in the past.

I did not want to eat at first, and when I did begin to want to they would not let me. If I felt sort of peckish they let me suck a little glass thermometer, but there is not much nourishment really in thermome-ters. And for entertainment, to while the dragging hours away, I could count the cracks in the ceiling and read my temperature chart, which was a good deal like Red Ames' batting average for the past season—ranging from ninety-nine to one hundred and four.

Also, through daily conversations with my nurse and with the sur-geons who dropped in from time to time to have a look at me, I learned, as I lay there, a great deal about the medical profession—that is, a great deal for a layman—and what I learned filled me with an abiding admiration for it, both as a science and as a business. This surely is one profession which ever keeps its face to the front. Burying its past mistakes and forgetting them as speedily as possible, it pushes straight forward into fresh fields and fresh patients, always hopeful of what the future may bring in the way of newly discovered and highly expensive ailments. As we look backward upon the centuries we are astonished by its advancement. I did a good deal of looking back-wards upon the centuries during my sojourn at St. Germicide's.

Take the Middle Ages now—the period when a barber and a sur-geon were one and the same. If a man made a failure as a barber he turned his talents to surgery. Surgeons in those times were a husky breed. I judge they worked by the day instead of by piecework; anyhow the records show they were very fond of experiments, where somebody else furnished the raw material.

When there came a resounding knock at the tradesman's entrance of the moated grange, the lord of the manor, looking over the portcullis and seeing a lusty wight standing down below, in a leather apron, with his sleeves rolled up and a kit of soldering tools under his arm, didn't know until he made inquiry whether the gentle stranger had come to mend the drain or remove the cook's leg.

A little later along, when gunpowder had come into general use as a humanizing factor of civilization, surgeons treated a gunshot wound by pouring boiling lard into it, which I would say was calculated to take the victim's mind off his wound and give him something else to think about—for the time being, anyhow. I assume the notion of applying a mustard plaster outside one's stomach when one has a pain inside one's stomach is based on the same principle.

However, one doesn't have to go clear back to medieval times to note the radical differences in the plan of treating human ailments. A great many persons who are still living can remember when the doctors were not nearly so numerous as they are now. I, for one, would be the last to reverse the sentence and say that because the doctors were not nearly so numerous then as they are now, those persons are still living so numerously.

In the spring of the year, when the sap flowed and the birds mated, the sturdy farmer felt that he was due to have something the matter with him, too. So he would ride into the country-seat and get an almanac. Doubtless the reader, if country raised, has seen copies of this popular work. On the outside cover, which was dark blue in color, there was a picture of a person whose stomach was sliced four ways, like a twenty-cent pie, and then folded back neatly, thus exposing his entire interior arrangements to the gaze of the casual observer. However, this party, judging by his picture, did not appear to be suffering. He did not even seem to fear that he might catch cold from standing there in his own draught. He was gazing off into space in an absent-minded kind of way, apparently not aware that anything was wrong with him; and on all sides he was surrounded by interesting exhibits, such as a crab, and a scorpion, and a goat, and a chap with a bow and arrow—and one thing and another.

Such was the main design of the cover, while the contents were made up of recognized and standard varieties in the line of jokes and the line of diseases which alternated, with first a favorite joke and then a favorite disease. The author who wrote the descriptions of the diseases was one of the most convincing writers that ever lived anywhere. As a realist he had no superiors among those using our language as a vehicle for the expression of thought. He was a wonder. If a person wasn't particular about what ailed him he could read any page at random and have one specific disease. Or he could read the whole book through and have them all, in their most advanced stages. Then the only thing that could save him was a large dollar bottle.

Again, in attacks of the breakbone ague or malaria it was customary to call in a local practitioner, generally an elderly lady of the neighborhood, who had none of these latter-day prejudices regarding the use of tobacco by the gentler sex. One whom I distantly recall, among childhood's happy memories, carried this liberal-mindedness to a point where she not only dipped snuff and smoked a cob pipe, but sometimes chewed a little natural leaf. This lady, on being called in, would brew up a large caldron of medicinal roots and barks and sprouts and things; and then she would deluge the interior of the sufferer with a large gourdful of this pleasing mixture at regular intervals. It was efficacious, too. The inundated person either got well or else he drowned from the inside. Rocking the patient was almost as dangerous a pastime as rocking the boat. This also helps to explain, I think, why so many of our forebears had floating kidneys. There was nothing else for a kidney to do.

By the time I attained to long trousers, people in our town mainly had outgrown the unlicensed expert and were depending more and more upon the old-fashioned family doctor—the one with the whisker-jungle—who drove about in a gig, accompanied by a haunting aroma of iodoform and carrying his calomel with him in bulk.

He probably owned a secret calomel mine of his own. He must have; otherwise he could never have afforded to be so generous with it. He also had other medicines with him, all of them being selected on the principle that unless a drug tasted like the very dickens it couldn't possibly do you any good. At all hours of the day and night he was to be seen going to and fro, distributing nuggets from his private lode. He went to bed with his trousers and his hat on, I think, and there was a general belief that his old mare slept between the shafts of the gig, with the bridle shoved up on her forehead.

It has been only a few years since the old-time general practitioner was everywhere. Just look round and see now how the system has changed! If your liver begins to misconduct itself the first thought of the modern operator is to cut it out and hide it some place where you can't find it. The oldtimer would have bombarded it with a large brunette pill about the size and color of a damson plum. Or he might put you on a diet of molasses seasoned to taste with blue mass and quinine and other attractive condiments. Likewise, in the spring of the year he frequently anointed the young of the species with a mixture of mutton suet and asafetida. This treatment had an effect that was distinctly depressing upon the growing boy. It militated against his popularity. It forced him to seek his pleasures outdoors, and a good distance outdoors at that.

It was very hard for a boy, however naturally attractive he might be, to retain his popularity at the fireside circle when coated with mutton suet and asafetida and then taken into a warm room. He attracted attention which he did not court and which was distasteful to him. Keeping quiet did not seem to help him any. Even if they had been blindfolded others would still have felt his presence. A civet-cat suffers from the same drawbacks in a social way, but the advantage to the civet-cat is that as a general thing it associates only with other civet-cats.

Except in the country the old-time, catch-as-catch-can general practitioner appears to be dying out. In the city one finds him occasionally, playing a limit game in an office on a back street—two dollars to come in, five to call; but the tendency of the day is toward specialists. Hence the expert who treats you for just one particular thing. With a pain in your chest, say, you go to a chest specialist. So long as he can keep the trouble confined to your chest, all well and good. If it slips down or slides up he tries to coax it back to the reservation. If it refuses to do so, he bids it an affectionate adieu, makes a dotted mark on you to show where he left off, collects his bill and regretfully turns you over to a stomach specialist or a throat specialist, depending on the direction in which the trouble was headed when last seen.

Or, perhaps the specialist to whom you take your custom is an advocate of an immediate operation for such cases as yours and all others. I may be unduly sensitive on account of having recently emerged from the surgeon's hands, but it strikes me now that there are an awful lot of doctors who take one brief glance at a person who is complaining, and say to themselves that here is something that ought to be looked into right away—and immediately open a bag and start picking out the proper utensils. You go into a doctor's office and tell him you do not feel the best in the world—and he gives you a look and excuses himself, and steps into the next room and begins greasing a saw.

Mind you, in these casual observations as compiled by me while bedfast and here given utterance, I am not seeking to disparage possibly the noblest of professions. Lately I have owed much to it. I am strictly on the doctor's side. He is with us when we come into the world and with us when we go out of it, oftentimes lending a helping hand on both occasions. Anyway, our sympathies should especially go out to the medical profession at this particular time when the anti-vivisectionists are railing so loudly against the doctors. The anti-vivisection crusade has enlisted widely different classes in the community, including many lovers of our dumb-animal pets—and aren't some of them the dumbest things you ever saw!—especially chow dogs and love birds.

I will admit there is something to be said on both sides of the argument. This dissecting of live subjects may have been carried to extremes on occasions. When I read in the medical journals that the eminent Doctor Somebody succeeded in transferring the interior department of a pelican to a pointer pup, and vice versa, with such success that the pup drowned while diving for minnows, and the pelican went out in the back yard and barked himself to death baying at the moon, I am interested naturally; but, possibly because of my ignorance, I fail to see wherein the treatment of infantile paralysis has been materially advanced. On the other hand, I would rather the kind and gentle Belgian hare should be offered up as a sacrifice upon the operating table and leave behind him a large family of little Belgian heirs and heiresses—dependent upon the charity of a cruel world—than that I should have something painful which can be avoided through making him a martyr. I would rather any white rabbit on earth should have the Asiatic cholera twice than that I should have it just once. These are my sincere convictions, and I will not attempt to disguise them.

Thanks, too, to medical science we know about germs and serums and diets and all that. Our less fortunate ancestors didn't know about them. They were befogged in ignorance. As recently as the generation immediately preceding ours people were unacquainted with the simplest rules of hygiene. They didn't care whether the housefly wiped his feet before he came into the house or not. The gentleman with the drooping, cream-separator mustache was at perfect liberty to use the common drinking cup on the railroad train. The appendix lurked in its snug retreat, undisturbed by the prying fingers of curiosity. The fever-bearing skeeter buzzed and flitted, stinging where he pleased. The germ theory was unfathomed. Suitable food for an invalid was anything the invalid could afford to buy. Fresh air, and more especially fresh night air, was regarded as dangerous, and people hermetically sealed themselves in before retiring. Not daily as at present was the world gladdened by the tidings that science had unearthed some new and particularly unpleasant disease. It never occurred to a mother that she should sterilize the slipper before spanking her offspring. Babies were not reared antiseptically, but just so. Nobody was aware of microbes.

In short, our sires and our grandsires abode in the midst of perils. They were surrounded on all sides by things that are immediately fatal to the human system. Not a single one of them had a right to pass his second birthday. In the light of what we know, we realize that by now this world should be but a barren waste, dotted at frequent intervals with large graveyards and populated only by a few dispossessed and hungry bacteria, hanging over the cemetery fence singing: Driven From Home!

In the conditions generally prevalent up to twenty-five years ago, most of us never had any license, really, to be born at all. Yet look how many of us are now here. In this age of research I hesitate to attempt to account for it, except on the entirely unscientific theory that what you don't know doesn't hurt you. Doubtless a physician could give you a better explanation, but his would cost you more than mine has.

But we digress. Let us get back to our main subject, which is myself. I shall never forget my first real meal in that hospital. There was quite a good deal of talk about it beforehand. My nurse kept telling me that on the next day the doctor had promised I might have something to eat. I could hardly wait. I had visions of a tenderloin steak smothered in fried onions, and some French-fried potatoes, and a tall table-limit stack of wheat cakes, and a few other incidental comfits and kickshaws. I could hardly wait for that meal.

The next day came and she brought it to me, and I partook thereof. It was the white of an egg. For dessert I licked a stamp; but this I did clandestinely and by stealth, without saying anything about it to her. I was not supposed to have any sweets.

On the occasion of the next feast the diet was varied. I had a sip of one of those fermented milk products. You probably know the sort of thing I mean. Even before you've swallowed it, it tastes as though it had already disagreed with you. The nurse said this food was predigested but did not tell me by whom. Nor did I ask her. I started to, but thought better of it. Sometimes one is all the happier for not knowing too much.

A little later on, seeing that I had not suffered an attack of indigestion from this debauch, they gave me junket. In the dictionary I have looked up the definitions of junket. I quote:

JUNKET. *v.* I. *t.* To entertain by feasting; regale. II. *i.* To give or take part in an entertainment or excursion; feast in company; picnic; revel. JUNKET, *n.* A merry feast or excursion; picnic.

When the author of a dictionary tries to be frivolous he only succeeds in making himself appear foolish.

I know not how it may be in the world at large, but in a hospital, junket is a custard that by some subtle process has been denuded of those ingredients which make a custard fascinating and exciting. It tastes as though the eggs, which form its underlying basis, had been laid in a fit of pique by a hen that was severely upset at the time.

Hereafter when the junket is passed round somebody else may have my share. I'll stick to the mince pie *à la mode.*

And the first cigar of my convalescence—ah, that, too, abides as a vivid memory! Dropping in one morning to replace the wrappings

Doctor Z said I might smoke in moderation. So the nurse brought me a cigar, and I lit it and took one deep puff; but only one. I laid it aside. I said to the nurse:

"A mistake has been made here. I do not want a cooking cigar, you understand. I desire a cigar for personal use. This one is full of herbs and simples, I think. It suggests a New England boiled dinner, and not a very good New England boiled dinner at that. Let us try again."

She brought another cigar. It was not satisfactory either. Then she showed me the box—an orthodox box containing cigars of a recognized and previously dependable brand. I could only conclude that a root-and-herb doctor had bought an interest in the business and was introducing his own pet notions into the formula.

But came a day—as the fancy writers say when they wish to convey the impression that a day has come, but hate to do it in a commonplace manner—came a day when my cigar tasted as a cigar should taste and food had the proper relish to it; and my appetite came back again and found the old home place not so greatly changed after all.

And then shortly thereafter came another day, when I, all replete with expensive stitches, might drape the customary habiliments of civilization about my attenuated frame and go forth to mingle with my fellow beings. I have been mingling pretty steadily ever since, for now I have something to talk about—a topic good for any company; congenial, an absorbing topic.

I can spot a brother member a block away. I hasten up to him and give him the grand hailing sign of the order. He opens his mouth to speak, but I beat him to it.

"Speaking of operations—" I say. And then I'm off.

Believe me, it's the life!

CORNELIA OTIS SKINNER

Why she selected THE BODY

 BEAUTIFUL

While it is a little embarrassing for me to pick out what I think is my best writing, I can say, however, that one of the most popular ones is the article that appeared in *Reader's Digest* called "The Body Beautiful." This was, of necessity, published in cut-down form, but the entire article is included in my book *Soap Behind the Ears*, which has a collection of many short stories.

New York, N. Y. CORNELIA OTIS SKINNER

June 2, 1942

AT LEAST three times a year the average woman tries on dresses in a shop. She finds herself standing before one of those fitting-room mirrors with movable side-panels suggestive of a primitive triptych . . . that is, if she has sufficient imagination to turn the triple reflection of herself in a pink slip into a trio of medieval saints. Such mirrors afford one a lot of seldom beheld angles of one's self and the sudden sight of them comes in the nature of a shock. You find you're staring at yourself rather than at the clothes you're buying; at your profile which somehow isn't at all the way you'd remembered it; at that curious three-quarter view when your face appears to be the shape of a Jordan almond, and at that alarming, almost indecent exposure of the back of your neck. When, furthermore, your eye travels earthward from the nape and is suddenly arrested, not without horror, by the reflection of that portion of the anatomy of which you catch a good glimpse only on these sartorial occasions, and which since the last shopping trip appears to have taken on distressing prominence, you reach the grim conclusion that it's almost too late for clothes to matter.

A recently beheld panorama of myself in the clear, cold light of

846

Bloomingdale's most relentless mirror filled me with such panic, I felt I must do something immediately. Recalling the ads of those numerous "slimming salons" which assure you that within a few weeks and for a price unnamed they can change you from a model for Helen Hokinson into a stand-in for Katherine Hepburn, I decided to take my troubles and my protuberances to one of them. Ever since the days of boarding-school, when I used to send for every free sample from henna rinses to stove-polish, I have always fallen for ads. The sweetheart of J. Walter Thompson, I have a peasant-like belief in whatever miracle they profess to effect.

I made inquiries among my better-shaped acquaintances and was told that an establishment in the East Fifties was among the best. The place, though small, was impressive. The façade was what is known as "moderne." Instead of the usual show window, it had sort of port-holes in which terra-cotta dryads (they might even have been hamadryads) danced amid bottles of perfume. On the ground floor was a sales and reception room where were displayed cosmetics, evening bags and (although a blizzard was raging outside) dark glasses and sun-tan oil. The place, decorated in Louis something style, had such an air of luxe and "parfum" about it you felt that, instead of streamlining you, they ought to turn you out looking like a Boucher. (Why didn't I live at that time, anyway?) A marquise disguised as a saleswoman was sitting behind the sort of table at which de Sévigné must have written her letters. It now held an enormous appointment book, some atomizer bottles and a very pure white phone. She asked if there were anything she could do for me and I said, "Yes. Reduce my rear," which shocked her very much; but, being of the aristocracy, she managed to smile politely. "Have you made an appointment for a consultation with Mme. Alberta?" "Mme. Alberta?" I echoed. "I'm afraid I haven't heard about her." From the expression of the marquise I might have said I hadn't heard about the Duchess of Windsor.

"I don't think I need any consultation," I said. "I just want to reduce my . . ." her eyebrows flickered ever so slightly and I ended lamely, "I just want to lose a few inches."

"All our clients have a consultation first with Mme. Alberta," was her reply. "She happens to be disengaged at the moment. If you'll please go upstairs I'll phone her you're coming." I climbed a mauve carpeted stair, wondering what sort of consultation lay in store for me. Would Mme. Alberta greet me with a stethoscope or would she be discovered gazing into a crystal? A pretty woman, youngish and frighteningly smart was seated at another period table. I gathered she was Mme. Alberta for she said "How do you do?" She had a very strenuous smile and her accent was so determined to be English it broadened every "a" . . . even in the case of such words as *hand* and *ankle*. It was hard to know how to address her. "Mme. Alberta" sounded embarrassing. She didn't look much like an Alberta and to call her plain *Madam* was unthinkable. She was one of those women who are so well-groomed they are positively "soignée" . . . In their immaculate presence you feel as if you had several runs in your stockings. She motioned me to a chair and listened to the story of my proportions as if it were a case history. She then quoted me prices and after accepting my check took out a card resembling a hospital chart. On it she wrote my name and address and some things that struck me as being singularly irrelevant in the matter of hip reduction . . . when my child was born, what sicknesses I'd ever had, the current lie about my age, and my blood-pressure which, like my Social Security number, is something I can never remember.

"Now, then, we'll see about your weight."

"I know what I weigh," I said, and added recklessly, "and I don't care. All I'm after is to reduce my . . ."

"Weight and measurements must be taken every treatment." Her tone, though polite, implied she didn't think I was quite bright. "There's the dressing room. Will you disrobe kindly?" I went to what seemed to be a daintily furnished sentry box and disrobed kindly. I felt somehow I was up for a woman's branch of the Army. A trim mulatto brought me a sheet and a pair of paper slippers that were the shape and texture of peanut bags. I tried to drape the sheet so I'd look like a Tanagra figure but it wouldn't work, so I arranged it along the more simple lines of a Navajo blanket and emerged with caution. Mme. Alberta, who was waiting, told me to "come this way" and I followed her down a corridor, not without a vague apprehension that at the finish of the trip I might find myself confronted by an anaesthetist. She led me behind a screen, whisked off my sheet in the manner of a mayor unveiling a statue and placed me on a scale, naked as Lot's wife . . . nakeder, because that lady could at least boast of a good coating of salt.

"But I tell you, I *know* what I weigh," I protested weakly and told her. She shed on me the indulgent smile a night nurse might give a psychopathic patient, took my weight which turned out to be exactly what I'd said and then told *me*. "Now for those measurements," she said. "Miss Jones, will you please come here?" Miss Jones proved to be a lovely young thing in a wisp of sky blue tunic. She was of such bodily perfection one had the suspicion that "Miss Jones" was incognito for "Miss America." We were formally introduced . . . Miss Jones in her bright blue suit, I in my bright pink skin. She handed Mme. Alberta a tape measure in exchange for which Mme. Alberta gave her a pencil and my hospital chart.

"Please mark as I call them, Miss Jones," and as if she hadn't already sufficiently humiliated me, Mme. Alberta began calling out my measurements to the world at large. She measured everything. She even measured my neck, my ankle and the length of my arm. I began to wonder if a suit of acrobat fleshings were thrown in with the course.

"I hardly think you need go to all that trouble," I interposed. "It's just my . . ."

"We take all measurements," Mme. Alberta said somewhat acidly and continued to encompass me with the tape measure which was a flexible metal affair . . . very cold and with a tendency to tickle. She accompanied her work with a flow of exclamations that might be taken any way. "Well, *well!*" she'd murmur, or "I *thought* so!" and at times shook her pretty head and went "Tsk! Tsk!"

Having completed her survey, she turned me over to Miss Jones, who had me don a baggy little lemon colored suit . . . the sort of thing that in my girlhood was known as an Annette Kellerman. It contrasted cruelly with her own trim tunic, and I felt more humble than I had in my recent nakedness. She led the way to an exercise room that contained a mat, a gramophone and far too many mirrors, ordered me onto the mat and proceeded to put me through twenty minutes of hard labor. I rolled and thumped. I stretched and kicked. I jumped and pranced. I also puffed and panted. I stood on my shoulders with my feet in the air; that is, Miss Jones hoisted my feet into the air while I rose up onto a fast-breaking neck and screamed. She never paused to allow me to catch a breath which by now was of such weakened quality it hardly seemed worth while trying to catch it. I tried to take time out . . . to divert her with harmless chatter. But Miss Jones is very strict. Now and then when total collapse seemed imminent, using the therapy of the brass band spurring on exhausted troops, she'd play a lively record on the gramophone calling out "one *and* two *and* three *and* four" as if it were a battle cry. She herself was tireless. She'd do awful things such as picking up her ankle with one hand and holding her foot above her head like a semaphore, and expected me to do likewise. I'm one of those rigid types who, since early childhood, has never been able to lean over and touch my toes—not that I've ever wanted to especially. Moreover, I not only can't raise my foot above my head, I can't even bend far enough to get my hand anywhere near my ankle. Miss Jones tells me I'm seriously hamstrung . . . a nasty expression that makes me feel they've been keeping me in the smoke-house all these years.

It's hard to feel cozy with Miss Jones. She is not only strict, she's exceptionally refined. What I call "middle" she calls diaphragm, what I call *stomach* with her goes whimsey and becomes *tummy*, and what I call something else she refers with averted eyes to as *derrière*.

The time dragged almost as heavily as my limbs. Finally Miss Jones said I was a good girl and had done enough for the day (the dear Lord knows the day had done enough for me!) and I might go have my massage. I staggered out and into the capable arms of a Miss Svenson who looked like Flagstad dressed up as a nurse. She took me into a small room, flung me onto a hard table and for forty-five minutes went to work on me as if I were material for a taffy-pulling contest. She kneaded me, she rolled me with a hot rolling pin, she did to me what she called "cupping" which is just a beauty-parlor term for good old orthodox spanking. After she'd gotten me in shape for the oven she took me into a shower-room and finished me up with that same hose treatment by which they subdue the recalcitrant inmates of penitentiaries.

I was then permitted to return to my sentry-box and my clothes. Once I'd recaptured my breath I felt extraordinarily full of radiant health and rugged appetite. It was time for lunch and visions of beefsteak danced in my head. But Mme. Alberta was lying in wait for me outside. "Here is your diet," she said, handing me an ominous little slip of paper which I fully expected to be marked ℞.

"I don't really care about a diet," I stammered. "You see, it isn't my weight, it's just my . . ."

"We'd like you to try it," she said.

It was a tasty little menu with the usual well done dab of chop-meat, a few fruit juices and some lettuce garnished by a rousing dressing made with mineral oil. I was to dine at the Colony that eve-ning and could just imagine Eugene's expression if I were to ask him to bring me an order of green salad mixed with Nujol. However, I pocketed the darn thing and used the back of it for a shopping list.

Part of the system at Mme. Alberta's consists in doing quite a lot of extra curricula work. Employing the honor system, Miss Jones expects one to go through a daily routine of prescribed gymnastics at home. For this end (that end I've been referring to) she has tried to lure me into purchasing a mat of purple satin but with Jeffersonian sim-plicity I maintain that I can gyrate just as unsuccessfully on the moth-honored surface of my old college blanket. Exercise in the privacy of one's domicile is a brisk and splendid idea provided one has any amount of domicile and any modicum of privacy. Space in my apart-ment is by no means magnificent and the only reasonable expanse of it is in the living-room which in lieu of a door has an open archway and is exposed in every portion to the hall. Having no yellow Annette Kellerman at home I generally gird myself for my exertions in nothing more confining than a pair of old pink rayon bloomers. This means that whenever the door-bell rings I am obliged to leap for sanctuary behind the sofa and I don't always hear the bell—which makes it pretty fascinating for whoever comes to the door. Once, in all inno-cence and semi-nudity, I gave a private performance for the window-cleaner; since when, on the occasions of his monthly visit, if we have the misfortune to meet, we pass each other with lowered eyes.

A problem that confronts me more, perhaps, than most people is that much of my time is spent in travel. The rooms in the newer of what are known as the "leading" hotels are often of dimensions akin to those of a Pullman roomette. To find a sufficient number of square feet in which to spread out one's blanket and one's self becomes a problem in engineering. Often as not I have to lie with head and shoulders under the bed, one arm beneath the bureau and the other half-way across the sill of the bathroom—a pretty picture indeed for the chambermaid or house detective, should they take the notion to enter with their pass-keys. The over-shadowing proximity of furniture is a constant menace. During the course of leg-flinging, rolling upside-down, bicycling, and the rest of Miss Jones' required antics, I have cracked shins on the corners of tables, dislocated digits on the rockers of chairs, stunned myself into momentary insensibility against radiators and kicked cuspidors about like medicine balls. An important feature in reducing the—well, you know—is the thump—double thump, single thump and just plain boops-a-daisy. When executed with sufficient enthusiasm, thumping can produce considerable strain on the structure of the room and there is always the fear that the plaster in the ceiling underneath will start falling and prove fatal to some distinguished traveler like Mrs. Roosevelt or Nelson Eddy.

Reducing, if one goes by the doctrines of the Mme. Alberta school, is a twenty-four-hour job. Aside from the list of more or less stereo-typed exercises, one is shown any number of everyday contortions that can, supposedly, be indulged in anywhere, any time. You can, for ex-ample, improve your posture by straightening out your spine along the edge of the nearest available door even if, to the casual observer, you appear to be scratching an itching back. You can also, while standing, do those thumps against the handiest walls—say those of the elevator, thereby bringing a moment of diversion into the monotonous life of the operator. Then there are a few less inconspicuous numbers such as standing on tiptoe and stretching up the hands ("Reaching for cherries" is Miss Jones' pretty term for it), leaning over side-ways from the waist, deep-knee bending and a movement dignified by the name of "abdominal control" that curiously resembles the beginnings of the "danse du ventre." These you are expected to burst forth with at odd hours of the day and night even at the risk of starting the grim rumor that you're coming down with St. Vitus. Then one must walk. "Walk like a goddess" is Miss Jones' advice. So I do. I walk like mad if not particularly like a goddess. Walking in New York is simple pursuit but in strange towns it leads to any number of surprises. Setting out for the residential section, I suddenly find myself in the thick of the colored population; or, aiming for a public park, discover that, with the unerring instinct of the homing pigeon, I'm back at the railroad yards. At other times I realize I'm striding enthusiastically down one of those streets of a nature that isn't even questionable. There remains nothing to do but hasten back to the hotel and walk round and round the block until the local policeman begins to grow suspicious.

However, all things come to she who weighs and I discover that I'm tipping the scales to a much lesser degree. Thanks to Miss Jones and Miss Svenson and my own shining determination, the last time Mme. Alberta encircled me with that glacial little measuring tape she found signs of considerable shrinkage and told me she was pleased with me— which made me glow with pride. I doubt if anyone viewing me from the neck down would as yet mistake me for Hedy Lamarr but I'm no longer so horrified by the reflection of myself in a triple mirror and what is more satisfying my clothes are beginning to look like the hand-me-downs of an older and fatter sister. And that is dejà quelque chose.

ROBERT BENCHLEY

Why he selected The TREASURER'S

REPORT

Dear Mr. Burnett:

I am afraid that I am lukewarm over the whole idea of an author picking his "best" work. It presents a rather horrid picture of an authors' tea after about the third highball . . . The only reason that I took Dottie Parker's suggestion of "The Treasurer's Report" was that it typifies what I have been doing for twenty years in print and on the Silver Screen—cashing in on being an amateur. I always tried to keep from thinking of myself as an author, and God knows I try to keep from thinking of myself as an actor, and to sit down and pick out two or three pieces of my own as my "favorites" or "best work" would be not only tiring but distasteful. The ones that I would probably pick (like the treatise on Dendrophilism or some other parodies) are impressive to me only because they are the ones that I spent any time on—in other words, that I re-wrote. Anything that I re-wrote *must* have been better than the others . . . but "The Treasurer's Report" is the best I can do for you if you insist.

New York, N. Y.   Robert Benchley

June 23, 1942

AUTHOR'S NOTE

ABOUT eight years ago (eight, to be exact) I was made a member of a committee to plan a little Sunday night entertainment for some newspapermen who wanted to act. The committee was supposed to meet at a certain time, each member with some suggestions for sketches or song-numbers. (In order to get out of this morass of pussy-footing which I have got myself into, I will come right out and say that the "certain time" at which the committee was to meet was 8 P.M. on Sunday night.) At 7:15 P.M. I suddenly realized that I had no suggestions to offer for the entertainment.

As all the other members of the committee were conscientious workers, I felt considerably abashed. But as they were also charming and indulgent fellows, I knew that they would take my dereliction in good part if I could only take their minds off the business of the meeting and possibly put them in good humor with a comical story or a card-trick. So, on the way up in the taxi, I decided to make believe, when they called on me for my contribution, that I had misunderstood the purpose of the committee-meeting and had come prepared to account for the year's expenditures. These I jotted down on the back of an old shirt.

As is always the case with such elaborate trickery, my plan to escape censure by diverting the minds of the committee fell flat. They listened to my temporizing report and voted me a droll chap, but then they said: "And now what are your suggestions for the entertainment?" As I had to confess that I had none, it was agreed that, *faute de mieux,* I should elaborate the report I had just offered and perhaps acquire some skill in its delivery, and give that as my share of the Sunday night entertainment. At this moment my entire life changed its course.

I guess that no one ever got so sick of a thing as I, and all my friends, have grown of this Treasurer's Report. I did it every night and two matinees a week for nine months in the Third Music Box Revue. Following that, I did it for ten weeks in vaudeville around the country, I did it at banquets and teas, at friends' houses and in my own house, and finally went to Hollywood and made a talking movie of it. In fact, I have inflicted it on the public in every conceivable way except over the radio and dropping it from airplanes. But I have never written it. I have been able to throw myself into a sort of trance while delivering it, so that the horrible monotony of the thing made no impression on my nerve cells, but to sit down and put the threadbare words on paper has always seemed just a little too much to bear.

I am writing it out now more as a release than anything else. Perhaps, in accordance with Freudian theories, if I rid myself of this thing which has been skulking in the back of my mind for eight years, I shall be a normal man again. No one has to read it. I hope that no one does, for it doesn't read at all well. All I want to do is get it on paper and out of the way. I feel better already, just from having told all this. And please let's never bring the matter up again.

*   *   *

The report is delivered by an Assistant Treasurer who has been called in to pinch-hit for the regular Treasurer who is ill. He is not a very good public-speaker, this assistant, but after a few minutes of confusion is caught up by the spell of his own oratory and is hard to stop.

I shall take but a very few moments of your time this evening, for I realize that you would much rather be listening to this interesting entertainment than to a dry financial statement . . . but I *am* reminded of a story—which you have probably all of you heard.

It seems that there were these two Irishmen walking down the street when they came to a—oh, I should have said in the first place that the parrot which was hanging out in *front* of the store—or rather belonging to one of these two fellows—the *first* Irishman, that is—was —well, *any*way, this parrot——

(*After a slight cogitation, he realizes that, for all practical purposes, the story is as good as lost; so he abandons it entirely and, stepping forward, drops his facile, story-telling manner and assumes a quite spurious businesslike air.*)

Now, in connection with reading this report, there are one or two points which Dr. Murnie wanted brought up in connection with it, and he has asked me to bring them up in connec—to bring them up.

In the first place, there is the question of the work which we are trying to do up there at our little place at Silver Lake, a work which we feel not only fills a very definite need in the community but also fills a very definite need—er—in the community. I don't think that many members of the Society realize just how big the work is that we are trying to do up there. For instance, I don't think that it is generally known that most of our boys are between the age of fourteen. We feel that, by taking the boy at this age, we can get closer to his real nature —for a boy *has* a very real nature, you may be sure—and bring him into closer touch not only with the school, the parents, and with each other, but also with the town in which they live, the country to whose flag they pay allegiance, and to the—ah—(*trailing off*) town in which they live.

Now the fourth point which Dr. Murnie wanted brought up was that in connection with the installation of the new furnace last Fall. There seems to have been considerable talk going around about this not having been done quite as economically as it might—have—been —done, when, as a matter of fact, the whole thing *was* done just as economically as possible—in fact, even *more* so. I have here a report of the Furnace Committee, showing just how the whole thing was handled from start to finish.

(*Reads from report, with considerable difficulty with the stiff covers.*)

Bids were submitted by the following firms of furnace contractors, with a clause stating that if we did not engage a firm to do the work for us we should pay them nothing for submitting the bids. This clause alone saved us a great deal of money.

The following firms, then, submitted bids:

Merkle, Wybigant Co., the Eureka Dust Bin and Shaker Co., The Elite Furnace Shop, and Harris, Birnbauer and Harris. The bid of Merkle, Wybigant being the lowest, Harris Birnbauer were selected to do the job.

(*Here a page is evidently missing from the report, and a hurried search is carried on through all the pages, without result.*)

Well, that pretty well clears up that end of the work.

Those of you who contributed so generously last year to the floating hospital have probably wondered what became of the money. I was speaking on this subject only last week at our up-town branch, and, after the meeting, a dear little old lady, dressed all in lavender, came up on the platform, and, laying her hand on my arm, said: "Mr. So-and-so (calling me by name) Mr. So-and-so, what the hell did you do with all the money we gave you last year?" Well, I just laughed and pushed her off the platform, but it has occurred to the committee that perhaps some of you, like that little old lady, would be interested in knowing the disposition of the funds.

Now, Mr. Rossiter, unfortunately our treasurer—or rather Mr. Rossiter our *treasurer, unfortunately* is confined at his home tonight with a bad head-cold and I have been asked (*he hears someone whispering at him from the wings, but decides to ignore it*) and I have been asked if I would (*the whisperer will not be denied, so he goes over to the entrance and receives a brief message, returning beaming and laughing to himself*). Well, the joke seems to be on *me*! Mr. Rossiter has *pneumonia*!

Following, then, is a summary of the Treasurer's Report:

(*Reads, in a very businesslike manner.*)

During the year 1929—and by that is meant 1928—the Choral Society received the following donations:

B. L. G.	$500
G. K. M.	500
Lottie and Nellie W——	500
In memory of a happy summer at Rye Beach	10
Proceeds of a sale of coats and hats left in the boat-house..	14.55
And then the Junior League gave a performance of "Pinafore" for the benefit of the Fund which, unfortunately, resulted in a deficit of	$300
Then, from dues and charges	2,354.75
And, following the installation of the new furnace, a saving in coal amounting to $374.75—which made Dr. Murnie very happy, you may be sure.	
Making a total of receipts amounting to	$3,645.75

This is all, of course, reckoned as of June.

In the matter of expenditures, the Club has not been so fortunate. There was the unsettled condition of business, and the late Spring, to contend with, resulting in the following—er—rather discouraging figures, I am afraid.

Expenditures	$23,574.85
Then there was a loss, owing to—several things—of.......	3,326.70
Car-fare	4,452.25

And then, Mrs. Rawlins' expense account, when she went
   down to see the work they are doing in Baltimore, came
   to $256.50, but I am sure that you will all agree that it
   was worth it to find out—er—what they are doing in
   Baltimore.
And then, under the general head of Odds and Ends...... 2,537.50
Making a total disbursement of ...(*hurriedly*) $416,546.75
or a net deficit of—ah—several thousand dollars.

Now, these figures bring us down only to October. In October my
sister was married, and the house was all torn up, and in the general
confusion we lost track of the figures for May and August. All those
wishing the *approximate* figures for May and August, however, may
obtain them from me in the vestry after the dinner, where I will be
with pledge cards for those of you who wish to subscribe over and
above your annual dues, and I hope that each and every one of you
here tonight will look deep into his heart and (*archly*) into his
pocketbook, and see if he can not find it there to help us to put this
thing over with a bang (*accompanied by a wholly ineffectual gesture
representing a bang*) and to help and make this just the biggest and
best year the Armenians have ever had . . . I thank you.

   (*Exits, bumping into proscenium*)

OGDEN NASH Why he selected

TWO and ONE Are a PROBLEM

Mr. Burnett has asked me to tell why the verses which follow this headstone are my favorites. This is difficult because they are not, and I'm afraid I can't remember having written any that are. I enjoy writing these things, but reading them is another matter, and if it weren't for the occasional need to collect pieces for a book, I think that I should never look at a verse of mine again after having mailed it to an editor. Once the first flush of creation has departed, I find myself too often wondering why no one ever taught me the proper function of a wastebasket in a writer's life. As I am now too old to learn this, I have chosen six pieces for inclusion here. These six are all about different things: love birds, growing old, beaches, profuse apologies, moodiness, and a cow. If anyone is interested in my gamut, this is probably it.

Salisbury, Md.   OGDEN NASH
August, 1942

DEAR Miss Dix, I am a young man of half-past thirty-seven.
My friends say I am not unattractive, though to be kind and true is what I have always striven.
I have brown hair, green eyes, a sensitive mouth and a winning natural exuberance,
And, at the waist, a barely noticeable protuberance.
I am open-minded about beverages so long as they are grape, brandy or malt,
And I am generous to practically any fault.
Well Miss Dix not to beat around the bush, there is a certain someone who thinks I am pretty nice,
And I turn to you for advice.

You see, it started when I was away on the road
And returned to find a pair of lovebirds had taken up their abode
    in my abode.
Well I am not crazy about lovebirds, but I must say they looked very
    sweet in their gilded cage,
And their friendship had reached an advanced stage,
And I had just forgiven her who of the feathered fiancés was the
    donor of
When the houseboy caught a lost lovebird in the yard that we couldn't
    locate the owner of.
So then we had three, and it was no time for flippancy,
Because everybody knows that a lovebird without its own lovebird to
    love will pine away and die of the discrepancy,
So we bought a fourth lovebird for the third lovebird and they sat
    around very cozily beak to beak
And then the third lovebird that we had provided the fourth lovebird
    for to keep it from dying died at the end of the week,
So we were left with an odd lovebird and it was no time for flippancy,
Because a lovebird without its own lovebird to love will pine away
    and die of the discrepancy,
So we had to buy a fifth lovebird to console the fourth lovebird that
    we had bought to keep the third lovebird contented,
And now the fourth lovebird has lost its appetite, and, Miss Dix, I am
    going demented.
I don't want to break any hearts, but I got to know where I'm at;
Must I keep on buying lovebirds, Miss Dix, or do you think it would
    be all right to buy a cat?

A LADY THINKS SHE IS THIRTY

UNWILLINGLY Miranda wakes,
    Feels the sun with terror,
One unwilling step she takes,
Shuddering to the mirror.

Miranda in Miranda's sight
Is old and gray and dirty;

Twenty-nine she was last night;
This morning she is thirty.

Shining like the morning star,
Like the twilight shining,
Haunted by a calendar,
Miranda sits a-pining.

Silly girl, silver girl,
Draw the mirror toward you;
Time who makes the years to whirl
Adorned as he adored you.

Time is timelessness for you;
Calendars for the human;
What's a year, or thirty, to
Loveliness made woman?

Oh, Night will not see thirty again,
Yet soft her wing, Miranda;
Pick up your glass and tell me, then—
How old is Spring, Miranda?

PRETTY HALCYON DAYS

HOW pleasant to sit on the beach,
    On the beach, on the sand, in the sun,
With ocean galore within reach,
And nothing at all to be done!
No letters to answer,
No bills to be burned,
No work to be shirked,
No cash to be earned.
It is pleasant to sit on the beach
With nothing at all to be done.

How pleasant to look at the ocean,
Democratic and damp; indiscriminate;
It fills me with noble emotion
To think I am able to swim in it.
To lave in the wave,
Majestic and chilly,
Tomorrow I crave;
But today it is silly.
It is pleasant to look at the ocean;
Tomorrow, perhaps, I shall swim in it.

How pleasant to gaze at the sailors,
As their sailboats they manfully sail
With the vigor of vikings and whalers
In the days of the viking and whale.
They sport on the brink
Of the shad and the shark;
If it's windy they sink;
If it isn't, they park.
It is pleasant to gaze at the sailors,
To gaze without having to sail.

How pleasant the salt anæsthetic
Of the air and the sand and the sun;
Leave the earth to the strong and athletic,
And the sea to adventure upon.
But the sun and the sand
No contractor can copy;
We lie in the land
Of the lotus and poppy;
We vegetate, calm and æsthetic,
On the beach, on the sand, in the sun.

THE COW

THE cow is of the bovine ilk;
One end is moo, the other, milk.

JUST KEEP QUIET AND NOBODY WILL NOTICE

THERE is one thing that ought to be taught in all the colleges,
    Which is that people ought to be taught not to go around always
    making apologies.
I don't mean the kind of apologies people make when they run over
    you or borrow five dollars or step on your feet,
Because I think that kind is sort of sweet;
No, I object to one kind of apology alone,
Which is when people spend their time and yours apologizing for
    everything they own.
You go to their house for a meal,
And they apologize because the anchovies aren't caviar or the partridge
    is veal;
They apologize privately for the crudeness of the other guests,
And they apologize publicly for their wife's housekeeping or their
    husband's jests;
If they give you a book by Dickens they apologize because it isn't by
    Scott,
And if they take you to the theater, they apologize for the acting and
    the dialogue and the plot;
They contain more milk of human kindness than the most capacious
    dairy can,
But if you are from out of town they apologize for everything local
    and if you are a foreigner they apologize for everything American.
I dread these apologizers even as I am depicting them,
I shudder as I think of the hours that must be spent in contradicting
    them,
Because you are very rude if you let them emerge from an argument
    victorious,
And when they say something of theirs is awful, it is your duty to
    convince them politely that it is magnificent and glorious,
And what particularly bores me with them,
Is that half the time you have to politely contradict them when you
    rudely agree with them,
So I think there is one rule every host and hostess ought to keep with

the comb and nail file and bicarbonate and aromatic spirits on
  a handy shelf,
Which is don't spoil the denouement by telling the guests everything
  is terrible, but let them have the thrill of finding it out for them-
  self.

SO PENSEROSO

COME, megrims, mollygrubs and collywobbles!
  Come, gloom that limps, and misery that hobbles!
Come also, most exquisite melancholiage,
As dark and decadent as November foliage!
I crave to shudder in your moist embrace,
To feel your oystery fingers on my face.
This is my hour of sadness and of soulfulness,
And cursed be he who dissipates my dolefulness.
The world is wide, isn't it?
The world is roomy.
Isn't there room, isn't it,
For a man to be gloomy?
Bring me a bathysphere, kindly,
Maybe like Beebe's,
Leave me alone in it, kindly,
With my old heebie-jeebies.
I do not desire to be cheered,
I desire to retire, I am thinking of growing a beard,
A sorrowful beard, with a mournful, a dolorous hue in it,
With ashes and glue in it.
I want to be drunk with despair,
I want to caress my care,
I do not wish to be blithe,
I wish to recoil and writhe,
I will revel in cosmic woe,
And I want my woe to show.
This is the morbid moment,
This is the ebony hour.
Aroint thee, sweetness and light!

I want to be dark and sour!
Away with the bird that twitters!
All that glitters is jitters!
Roses, roses are gray,
Violets cry Boo! and frighten me.
Sugar is diabetic,
And people conspire to brighten me.
Go hence, people, go hence!
Go sit on a picket fence!
Go gargle with mineral oil,
Go out and develop a boil!
Melancholy is what I brag and boast of,
Melancholy I mean to make the most of,
You beaming optimists shall not destroy it.
But while I am it, I intend to enjoy it.
Go, people, feed on kewpies and soap,
And remember, please, that when I mope, I mope!

S. J. PERELMAN Why he selected

KITCHEN BOUQUET

Best suited to represent me is a short treatise called "Kitchen Bouquet" which first appeared in *The New Yorker*. In general, I feel that any exegesis of humor is both fatal and dull, but if I show some slight preference for this piece, it is because of its underlying note of desperation. It marks a troubled period when I almost gave up writing to become a charwoman. I'm still not sure I made the more profitable choice.

Erwinna, Pa.   S. J. PERELMAN
June, 1942

YESTERDAY morning I awoke from a deep dream of peace compounded of equal parts of allonal and Vat 69 to find that autumn was indeed here. The last leaf had fluttered off the sycamore and the last domestic of the summer solstice had packed her bindle and caught the milk train out of Trenton. Peace to her ashes, which I shall carry up henceforward from the cellar. Stay as sweet as you are, honey, and don't drive through any open drawbridges is my Christmas wish for Leota Claflin. And lest the National Labor Relations Board (just plain "Nat" to its friends, of whom I am one of the staunchest) summon me to the hustings for unfair employer tactics, I rise to offer in evidence as pretty a nosegay of houseworkers as ever fried a tenderloin steak. Needless to say, the characters and events depicted herein are purely imaginary, and I am a man who looks like Ronald Colman and dances like Fred Astaire.

The first reckless crocus of March was nosing up through the lawn as I sprang from the driver's seat, spread my cloak across a muddy spot, and obsequiously handed down Philomène Labruyère—colored, no laundry. Philomène was a dainty thing, built somewhat on the order of Lois De Fee, the lady bouncer. She had the rippling muscles of a panther, the stolidity of a water buffalo, and the lazy insolence of a shoe salesman. She stood seventy-five inches in her stocking feet, which I will take my Bible oath were prehensile. As she bent down to lift her suitcase, she picked up the car by mistake and had it halfway down the slope before I pointed out her mistake. She acknowledged the reproof with a glance of such sheer hatred that I knew at once I should have kept my lip buttoned. After all, perhaps the woman wanted my automobile in her bedroom for some purpose of her own.

"You—you can take it up with you if you want," I stammered, thinking to retrieve her esteem. "I've got plenty of others—I mean I've got plenty of nothing—I mean—" With my ears glowing, I attempted to conceal my *gaffe* by humming a few bars of "Summertime," but her cold, appraising glance told me that Philomène had me pegged.

"Whuh kine place *is* this?" she rumbled suspiciously. "You mus' be crazy."

"But aren't we all?" I reminded her with a charming smile. *"C'est la maladie du temps*—the sickness of the times—don't you think? *Fin-de-siècle* and lost generation, in a way. 'I should have been a pair of ragged claws scuttling across the floors of silent seas.' How well Eliot puts it! D'ye ever see any of the old *transition* crowd?" I skipped along doing my best to lighten her mood, carried her several hatboxes, and even proffered a reefer, but there was no doubt in either of our minds who had the upper hand.

That Philomène was a manic-depressive in the downhill phase was, of course, instantly apparent to a boy of five. Several boys of five, who happened to be standing around and were by way of being students of psychopathology, stated their belief to me in just those words: "Manic-depressive, downhill phase." At the close of business every evening, Philomène retired to her room, armed with a sixteen-inch steak knife, doubtless to ward off attack by the dancing men. She then spent the best part of an hour barricading her door with dressers, armoires, and other heavy furniture, preparatory to sleeping with the lights on. I say "sleeping" utterly without conviction; she undoubtedly molded lead statues of her employer and crooned to them over a slow fire.

But if her behavior was erratic, there was no lack of consistency in Philomène's cuisine. Meat loaf and cold fried chicken succeeded each other with the deadly precision of tracer bullets. At last, when blood and sinew could stand no more and I was about to dissolve the union. I suddenly discovered that this female Paul Bunyan had grown to womanhood under the bright skies of Martinique, and I knew a moment of elation. I let it be bruited through the servants' hall that I would look tolerantly on fried plantain, yams, and succulent rice dishes. That afternoon the kitchen was a hive of activity. The air was heavy with saffron, pimento, and allspice. I heard snatches of West Indian Calypsos, caught a glimpse of Philomène's head swathed in a gay bandanna. With the care befitting a special occasion, I dressed negligently but with unimpeachable taste in whites and cummerbund, mixed myself several excellent stengahs, and sauntered in to dinner for all the world like an up-country tea planter. A few moments later, Philomène entered with what might be called a smoking salver except for the circumstance that it was stone cold. On it lay the wing and undercarriage of an even colder chicken, flanked by two segments of meat loaf.

After five minutes of reflection, during which, I am told, my features closely resembled a Japanese print, I arose and, throwing out my tiny chest, marched into the kitchen. The maledictions withered on my lips. Seated at the table, my black hibiscus blossom was tucking in a meal consisting of *potage Parmentier avec croûtons,* a crisp *gigot, salade fatiguée,* and *pot de crème au chocolat.*

"You—thing," I said at length, and five minutes later Philomène was on her way back to St. Pierre.

Her successor was a chapfallen Australian cadaver who had reached his zenith as steward of a country club in Pompton Lakes and treated me and mine with the tired fatalism of a social worker. For some reason I never could fathom, unless it was that I occasionally wore a Tattersall vest, William persisted in regarding me as a racing man. He could recall every entry in the Cesarewitch Sweepstakes since 1899 and did, but faced with a pot roast, he assumed a wooden incomprehension that would have done credit to a Digger Indian. It was William's opinion, freely given, that cooked food was dead food and that I would triple my energy by living on fronds. He knew a hundred different ways of preparing bran, each more ghastly than the last. For an avowed vegetarian (or "raw-fooder," as he described himself), he spent his leisure in a puzzling enough fashion, polishing and whetting the superb collection of Swedish-steel carving knives which was the one relic of his former magnificence.

William hadn't been with us long before I began to feel uneasy, but I attributed my disquiet to Edmund Pearson's admirable study of the Lizzie Borden case, which I was reading at the time. And then, on the sultry morning of August 4th—by an uncanny coincidence the forty-seventh anniversary of the Fall River holocaust—I came down to find awaiting me an exact duplicate of the breakfast which had been served on Second Street that fateful morning: warmed-over mutton soup, cold mutton, and bananas. I am not unduly superstitious, but there is no sense flying in the face of history. I left the check and the usual reference on William's bureau and hid in the woods until traintime.

The time had now come, I felt, for plain speaking. I inserted two and a half inches in the metropolitan press setting forth my special needs. I wanted something stout and motherly, with floury hands and a hot apple pie cooling on the window sill. What I got was an ancient Latvian beldam, named Ilyeana, who welcomed the idea of living in the country with such alacrity I was convinced she must be a fugitive from justice. Her cooking did nothing to contradict the impression; three nights hand running she served mulligan and coffee made in a tin and seemed strangely familiar with the argot of hobo jungles. How near I was to the bull's-eye was revealed a week later with the arrival of a letter sent to Ilyeana by relatives in Canada. She ripped open the envelope and a newspaper clipping slipped out and fell to the floor. I picked it up and was about to hand it to her when I saw the sinister heading, "Missing Man Believed Found." The Mounties, idly dragging a lake near Moose Jaw, Saskatchewan, had recovered some parcels which, laid end to end, turned out to be the body of a man. "The victim's sister, whom the authorities would like to question," the account added, "is at present thought to be in Latvia." Far from being in Latvia, the victim's sister was standing at that exact moment peering over my shoulder in good old Tinicum Township, Pennsylvania. I cleared my throat and edged a little closer to the fire tongs.

"What do you make of this, Ilyeana?" I asked. I knew damn well what she made of it, but you have to begin *somewhere*.

"Ah, this happen every time I get good job," she said. "Always pickin' on me. Well, I guess I go up there and take a look at him. I know that head of hair anywhere."

At the station, Ilyeana bought a ticket to Savannah, which would seem a rather circuitous route to the Dominion, but nobody was surprised, least of all the passenger agent. What with people winging through to Martinique, Australia and similar exotic climes, that little New Jersey depot could give cards and spades to Shepheard's Hotel in Cairo. And speaking of spades, could anybody put me on to one named Uncle Pompey, with a frizzy white poll and a deft hand for grits?

JAMES THURBER Why he selected

The NIGHT the GHOST GOT IN

Plain fact is, the house I used to live in often assumed the strange cloaks of fantasy. There actually was a ghost (families in the house before we moved in, we learned later, had heard the walking around and the step on the stair). There also actually was a guinea pig that slept on a zither. In this story, more than in any other, are assembled the weird commonplaces of my life in Columbus.

New York, N. Y.   JAMES THURBER
July 24, 1942

THE ghost that got into our house on the night of November 17, 1915, raised such a hullabaloo of misunderstandings that I am sorry I didn't just let it keep on walking, and go to bed. Its advent caused my mother to throw a shoe through a window of the house next door and ended up with my grandfather shooting a patrolman. I am sorry, therefore, as I have said, that I ever paid any attention to the footsteps.

They began about a quarter past one o'clock in the morning, a rhythmic, quick-cadenced walking around the dining-room table. My mother was asleep in one room upstairs, my brother Herman in another; grandfather was in the attic, in the old walnut bed which, as you will remember, once fell on my father. I had just stepped out of the bathtub and was busily rubbing myself with a towel when I heard the steps. They were the steps of a man walking rapidly around the dining-room table downstairs. The light from the bathroom shone down the back steps, which dropped directly into the dining-room; I could see the faint shine of plates on the plate-rail; I couldn't see the table. The steps kept going round and round the table; at regular

intervals a board creaked, when it was trod upon. I supposed at first
that it was my father or my brother Roy, who had gone to Indianapolis
but were expected home at any time. I suspected next that it was a
burglar. It did not enter my mind until later that it was a ghost.

After the walking had gone on for perhaps three minutes, I tiptoed
to Herman's room. "Psst!" I hissed, in the dark, shaking him. "Awp,"
he said, in the low, hopeless tone of a despondent beagle—he always
half suspected that something would "get him" in the night. I told

He always half suspected that something would get him.

him who I was. "There's something downstairs!" I said. He got up
and followed me to the head of the back staircase. We listened together. There was no sound. The steps had ceased. Herman looked at
me in some alarm: I had only the bath towel around my waist. He
wanted to go back to bed, but I gripped his arm. "There's something
down there!" I said. Instantly the steps began again, circled the dining-
room table like a man running, and started up the stairs toward us,
heavily, two at a time. The light still shone palely down the stairs;
we saw nothing coming; we only heard the steps. Herman rushed to
his room and slammed the door. I slammed shut the door at the stairs

top and held my knee against it. After a long minute, I slowly opened
it again. There was nothing there. There was no sound. None of us
ever heard the ghost again.

The slamming of the doors had aroused mother: she peered out of
her room. "What on earth are you boys doing?" she demanded. Herman ventured out of his room. "Nothing," he said, gruffly, but he was,
in color, a light green. "What was all that running around downstairs?" said mother. So she had heard the steps, too! We just looked
at her. "Burglars!" she shouted, intuitively. I tried to quiet her by
starting lightly downstairs.

"Come on, Herman," I said.

"I'll stay with mother," he said. "She's all excited."

I stepped back onto the landing.

"Don't either of you go a step," said mother. "We'll call the police."
Since the phone was downstairs, I didn't see how we were going to
call the police—nor did I want the police—but mother made one of
her quick, incomparable decisions. She flung up a window of her bedroom which faced the bedroom windows of the house of a neighbor,
picked up a shoe, and whammed it through a pane of glass across the
narrow space that separated the two houses. Glass tinkled into the
bedroom occupied by a retired engraver named Bodwell and his wife.
Bodwell had been for some years in rather a bad way and was subject
to mild "attacks." Most everybody we knew or lived near had *some*
kind of attacks.

It was now about two o'clock of a moonless night; clouds hung
black and low. Bodwell was at the window in a minute, shouting,
frothing a little, shaking his fist. "We'll sell the house and go back to
Peoria," we could hear Mrs. Bodwell saying. It was some time before
Mother "got through" to Bodwell. "Burglars!" she shouted. "Burglars
in the house!" Herman and I hadn't dared to tell her that it was not
burglars but ghosts, for she was even more afraid of ghosts than of
burglars. Bodwell at first thought that she meant there were burglars
in his house, but finally he quieted down and called the police for
us over an extension phone by his bed. After he had disappeared from
the window, mother suddenly made as if to throw another shoe, not
because there was further need of it but, as she later explained, because

the thrill of heaving a shoe through a window glass had enormously taken her fancy. 1 prevented her.

The police were on hand in a commendably short time: a Ford sedan full of them, two on motorcycles, and a patrol wagon with about eight in it and a few reporters. They began banging at our front door. Flashlights shot streaks of gleam up and down the walls, across the yard, down the walk between our house and Bodwell's. "Open up!" cried a hoarse voice. "We're men from Headquarters!" I wanted to go down and let them in, since there they were, but mother wouldn't hear of it. "You haven't a stitch on," she pointed out. "You'd catch your death." I wound the towel around me again. Finally the cops put their shoulders to our big heavy front door with its thick beveled glass and broke it in: I could hear a rending of wood and a splash of glass on the floor of the hall. Their lights played all over the living-room and crisscrossed nervously in the dining-room, stabbed into hall-ways, shot up the front stairs and finally up the back. They caught me standing in my towel at the top. A heavy policeman bounded up the steps. "Who are you?" he demanded. "I live here," I said. "Well, whattsa matta, ya hot?" he asked. It was, as a matter of fact, cold; I went to my room and pulled on some trousers. On my way out, a cop stuck a gun into my ribs. "Whatta you doin' here?" he demanded. "I live here," I said.

The officer in charge reported to mother. "No sign of nobody, lady," he said. "Musta got away—whatt'd he look like?" "There were two or three of them," mother said, "whooping and carrying on and slamming doors." "Funny," said the cop. "All ya windows and doors was locked on the inside tight as a tick."

Downstairs, we could hear the tromping of the other police. Police were all over the place; doors were yanked open, drawers were yanked open, windows were shot up and pulled down, furniture fell with dull thumps. A half-dozen policemen emerged out of the darkness of the front hallway upstairs. They began to ransack the floor: pulled beds away from walls, tore clothes off hooks in the closets, pulled suit-cases and boxes off shelves. One of them found an old zither that Roy had won in a pool tournament. "Looky here, Joe," he said, strumming it with a big paw. The cop named Joe took it and turned it over. "What is it?" he asked me. "It's an old zither our guinea pig used to sleep on," I said. It was true that a pet guinea pig we once had would never sleep anywhere except on the zither, but I should never have said so. Joe and the other cop looked at me a long time. They put the zither back on a shelf.

Police were all over the place.

"No sign o' nuthin'," said the cop who had first spoken to mother. "This guy," he explained to the others, jerking a thumb at me, "was nekked. The lady seems historical." They all nodded, but said nothing; just looked at me. In the small silence we all heard a creaking in the attic. Grandfather was turning over in bed. "What's 'at?" snapped Joe. Five or six cops sprang for the attic door before I would intervene or explain. I realized that it would be bad if they burst in on grandfather unannounced, or even announced. He was going through a phase in which he believed that General Meade's men, under steady hammering by Stonewall Jackson, were beginning to retreat and even desert.

When I got to the attic, things were pretty confused. Grandfather had evidently jumped to the conclusion that the police were deserters from Meade's army, trying to hide away in his attic. He bounded out of bed wearing a long flannel nightgown over long woolen underwear, a nightcap, and a leather jacket around his chest. The cops must have realized at once that the indignant white-haired old man belonged in the house, but they had no chance to say so. "Back, ye cowardly dogs!" roared grandfather. "Back t' the lines, ye goddam lily-livered cattle!" With that, he fetched the officer who found the zither a flat-handed smack alongside his head that sent him sprawling. The others beat a retreat, but not fast enough; grandfather grabbed Zither's gun from its holster and let fly. The report seemed to crack the rafters; smoke filled the attic. A cop cursed and shot his hand to his shoulder. Somehow, we all finally got downstairs again and locked the door against the old gentleman. He fired once or twice more in the darkness and then went back to bed. "That was grandfather," I explained to Joe, out of breath. "He thinks you're deserters." "I'll say he does," said Joe.

The cops were reluctant to leave without getting their hands on somebody besides grandfather; the night had been distinctly a defeat for them. Furthermore, they obviously didn't like the "layout"; something looked—and I can see their viewpoint—phony. They began to poke into things again. A reporter, a thin-faced, wispy man, came up to me. I had put on one of mother's blouses, not being able to find anything else. The reporter looked at me with mingled suspicion and interest. "Just what the hell is the real lowdown here, Bud?" he asked. I decided to be frank with him. "We had ghosts," I said. He gazed at me a long time as if I were a slot machine into which he had, without results, dropped a nickel. Then he walked away. The cops followed him, the one grandfather shot holding his now-bandaged arm, cursing and blaspheming. "I'm gonna get my gun back from that old bird," said the zither-cop. "Yeh," said Joe. "You—and who else?" I told them I would bring it to the station house the next day.

"What was the matter with that one policeman?" mother asked, after they had gone. "Grandfather shot him," I said. "What for?" she demanded. I told her he was a deserter. "Of all things!" said mother. "He was such a nice-looking young man."

Grandfather was fresh as a daisy and full of jokes at breakfast next morning. We thought at first he had forgotten all about what had happened, but he hadn't. Over his third cup of coffee, he glared at Herman and me. "What was the idee of all them cops tarryhootin' round the house last night?" he demanded. He had us there.

LUDWIG BEMELMANS Why he

selected SACRE DU PRINTEMPS

I started to write "Sacre du Printemps" when Hitler came back from one of his *Parteitage* in Nuremberg and when I observed the little girls marching and singing Battle Hymns. I made some pictures which I loosely sketched on the stone top of a table in the Cafe Luitpold in Munich, and then I thought I'd throw the idea away, because it seemed a little too crass, at the time. I thought, something will happen, it will pass—I wrote the story soon after.

Several weeks after in Munich when I returned to my hotel after a visit to the Castle of Nymphenburg, I had witnessed a performance there that left me astounded for a whole week. Some thousand fat, uniformed, and middle-aged *Gauleiters* in uniform were marched out into the beautiful old park of the castle. The officers at the heads of the various groups gave the signal to halt, and then the command to stand at ease, and then they dismissed the men with the order that "for half an hour we will admire nature." The companies disbanded and the men dutifully looked at trees, the water in the canal, at birds and butterflies. At the end of half an hour the command to fall in was given, and the stout buddies faced about and tramped back to Munich, all of them singing.

It was particularly interesting to see that among this group there was not a single Nazi youth. They were the citizenry of Munich, the embodiment of *Gemuetlichkeit*, and the funny paper type of Bavarian —solid beerdrinkers, honest butchers, bakers, and manufacturers of porcelain and *Lebkuchen*. I had always hoped that in them would be some rebellion, some scoffing, a subdued growl. It was as bitter to watch, this performance, as it was to look at the Swastika hanging from the rafters of that cathedral of well-being, the great hall of the

Hofbrauhaus, in which the Horst Wessel song was the new *Te Deum*.

New York, N. Y.   LUDWIG BEMELMANS
June, 1942

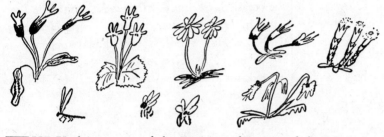

THE Undersecretary of the Division of Spring of the Ministry of the Four Seasons unrolled an ivy-green runner on the balcony of the Ministry of Strength-Through-Joy at the precise moment that the Undersecretary of the Ministry of Discipline and Order placed thereon his microphone; then both listened to the bells strike seven in the morning and opened the door behind which stood in proper uniform, with all buttons buttoned, the Ministers of Spring, of Discipline and Order, and of Strength-Through-Joy. The Minister of the Four Seasons and the Minister of Discipline and Order announced the beginning of Spring.

Dutifully, with dispatch and promptness, there appeared blossoms in their proper colors on all trees in the land, buttercups growing orderly along the brooks opened their little faces to the sun, forget-me-nots in the forests, heather in the marshes, daisies among the fields and even Edelweiss high up in the mountains.

In the windowboxes of the workingmen, geraniums bloomed, tulips in the gardens of the civil servants of the classes 1, 2, 3, 4, 5, and roses in the classes from six to twelve. Above that, in classes thirteen to fifteen, there was no need of Spring—flowers were in bloom the year round in the winter-gardens of generals, bishops, directors of banks and gas factories. Heartwarming and admirable was the success with which the State and particularly the Ministers of Joy and Strength, the Division of Spring of the Ministry of the Four Seasons, and the Ministry of Order had succeeded in the administration for all details down to the orderly joy of the little girls, who marched out into the lovely greenery in proper white starched dresses and in battalion formation, starting at seven-thirty in the morning, the smallest in front, the tallest in back.

There the little girls stopped to sing the appropriate songs, simple *Lieder* written for the occasion. On this day they were sung: The *Lied* of the *Lindenbaum* for the *Lindenbaeume*, the song of the *Heideroeslein*, for the little wild rose. How good! How without problems was life ahead for the little blonde girls! How provident was the Ministry of the Four Seasons and, for that matter, the Ministry of Youth, of Motherhood, and even of Love!

No one was forgotten. The railroads ran extra trains to take each and every citizen out into the Spring. And even the railroad was an example of the forethought and order of the provident State. There were first class carriages with red plush upholstery and cerise curtains; there were second class compartments with green herringbone sailcloth; third class (a) with wooden seats, soft wood tailored to conform to the curves of the body; and third class (b) with hard wooden benches, non-conforming; and sixth class carriages, to stand up in.

Malcontents, enemies of the government, and scoffers told of a sixth class carriage that had no floor—just a roof and sides—in which the passengers had to run along the tracks. That, of course, was not so. Besides, there were no malcontents.

The unsleeping vigilance of the Ministry of Justice had run all non-conformists into the ground, or successfully converted them. That is, all but one man, the Outsider, the One, by name Kratzig, Emil, who walked alone in his own disorderly path.

When all the citizens were out in the Spring, Emil Kratzig sat at home with his curtains drawn and read forbidden books, and again when all were snug at home in the Winter, singing the songs of the "Oven," "Grandfather's clock, tick, tock, tick tock," or *"Ich bin so gern, so gern daheim, daheim in meiner stillen Klause"* he ran around outside in the snow and whistled.

There was a long official report under K. Kratzig, Emil. But while the Political Police shadowed him, they nevertheless left him alone.

They did not disturb him. "We must save him," said the Minister of Justice. "He is the last one; we may need him as an example." Besides,

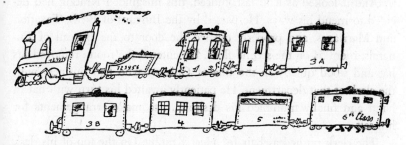

Emil Kratzig was an old man, and a foreigner: his maternal great grandfather had been a Frenchman.

So Emil Kratzig lived apart and sat alone. And on the street the Policeman, Umlauf, who was stationed at the City Hall square to keep him under surveillance, filled his little notebook with the discordant reports of the going and coming of the dissenter.

The leaves in the official notebook of Policeman Umlauf, pages 48 to 55, carry the story of the sad end of the incorrigible, insubordinate Emil Kratzig. . . .

On the sunlit morning of a green May day, when all in the city went out to look at the blossoms, take deep breaths and sing in the new, light-flowered prints designed by the Ministry of Dress and Underwear, Kratzig, wrapped in a muffler, burdened with galoshes and heavy wintercoat, fled alone to the meanest landscape he could find, a district that contained the Municipal Gas Factory, the garbage trucks and the streetcleaning apparatuses. There he spent the day in crossing and recrossing over the cobblestones, in wild tirades, made free with the name of ministers, the Government, the nation as a whole, and that night came home and slept with open windows. That night, of course, there was a frost, and it was this frost which took many blossoms and reached out also for the life of Emil Kratzig.

The next day Emil Kratzig was ill. A cold turned to pleurisy of the left lobar cavity, and the Government doctor who came the following day and ordered him to stay in bed, shook his head as he left the house. But Emil Kratzig got up again, in violation of the doctor's orders, and with a high fever ran to the City Hall.

"Aha," said Policeman Umlauf, and in his notebook he remarked: "The end is near and Herr Kratzig is coming to heel."

And it looked as if at last, indeed, this misguided Kratzig had decided to mend his ways. He passed by the Bureaus of Birth, Taxation and Marriages, and properly opened the door to the Bureau of Funerals, room 54 on the second floor. He entered the room, removed his hat and stood quietly in the line of Citizens who had business with the clerk of that department. He patiently awaited his turn with hat in hand and finally mumbled his desire . . . to make arrangements for himself.

The clerk pushed a chair for Herr Kratzig. On the top of his desk was a large album. He opened it for Emil Kratzig's inspection.

The chief clerk appeared and pushed a platoon of Under Clerks away. With his own lips he blew dust from the funeral album (this album was used only in extraordinary cases); he washed his hands in the air with anticipation, patted Kratzig on the shoulder, cleared his throat, and opened the cover.

"Now this," said the Chief Clerk, "is the first class funeral—but not for you. It is for the classes 13 to 15 of the Civil Service."

He pointed however to the first of the many pictures and recited, "The first class funeral is composed of the wagon, first class," he

pointed with the rubber end of his pencil at the four angels of Annunciation carved in the teakwood, who stood at the four corners of the wagon, at the rubber tires, at the betasselled curtains of black brocade.

"This wagon is drawn by six horses, with black cloaks and black plumes. They wear this silver harness. There is besides a bishop and two priests, sixty *Saengerknaben*, a band, the bells of all the churches ring, there is a salute of guns, incense, and, at the high mass, twelve of these golden candelabra are used with scented bees-wax candles."

He turned the page of the second class funeral. "Here we have the same car, rubber tires, four horses with black cloaks, black plumes and silver harness, three priests, but no bishop, forty *Saengerknaben*, incense, six of the first class candelabra at the high mass, the bells of

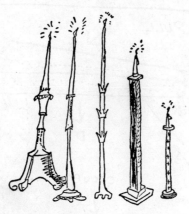

half the churches, no guns, and, on the first class candelabra, plain un-cented candles."

Again he turned a huge page. "Now we come to the third class funeral," he continued. "There is a different wagon, but also very nice, with one mourning angel sitting on top, cretonne curtains, two horses with nickel harness, black cloaks and plumes, two priests, no *Saenger-knaben*, but a male quartet, nickel candelabra, of course no guns but the two bells of the cemetery chapel and one priest with two apprentice priests, incense, and a very nice grade of candles, not bees-wax but scented. But that is not for you either."

He shifted the weight of his body to his left foot and his voice changed. "The fourth class funeral is somewhat plainer. We have here the wagon of the third class, one horse with cloak and plume and nickel harness, one priest, one singer, two altar boys and incense. For the bass, organ music and two candelabra with candles.

"The fifth class funeral," he went on, "is here." And he turned the page. "Here is a strong solid wagon, and one horse, no cloak, no plume, but it is a black horse, an apprentice priest, and one singer, one altar boy, incense, no music at the mass, and two wooden candelabra with used candles."

He paused.

"And finally we come to the sixth class funeral," he said. "Here again you get the wagon of the fifth class, the black horse, an apprentice priest, no singer, one altar boy, two wooden candelabra with used sub-

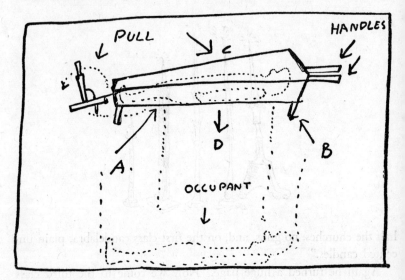

stitute-wax candles, a little bell." And he turned the page to show a drawing, "and with this funeral goes a rental coffin—it saves you buying one."

A working drawing of this imaginative, melancholy piece of black carpentry was attached, also photographs showing its economic performance. It looked like any other frugal coffin, but had an ingenious device—two doors at the bottom opened when a lever was pulled. Once occupied and having been carried to its destination, the coffin opened at the bottom and the occupant was dropped into the grave. So the rental coffin could be used over and over again.

"Very simple, after all," said the clerk and turning, he left the sentence open, because Emil Kratzig was gone.

Emil Kratzig was not seen again until the middle of next night. Policeman Umlauf, standing in the center of the market square, saw a pale man coming toward him. The man was dressed in a long, white night shirt. On his head was a top hat. Tied to it with a piece of crêpe was a black plume. In his hand he held two burning candles and he carried a shovel under his arm.

"What is your name?" asked Policeman Umlauf.

"I am Emil Kratzig," said the man. "I died last night. I am going up to the cemetery. This is a seventh class funeral."

IX

THEY WEREN'T GOING TO DIE

IRWIN EDMAN Why he selected

M. PLATON

I have chosen "M. Platon" as my contribution to this anthology in answer to a request to choose "the best" thing that I had written. One's own judgment in these matters is notoriously questionable, and "best" always implies "best for what?" I am assuming "best" in this instance to mean "most characteristic" or "most representative."

This chapter seems to me to bring together most of my interests. Its subject is a humanistic philosopher, and my own interest in philosophy is primarily humanistic. The chapter is largely a dialogue, and, taking my cue from Plato, I think the best of philosophy is conversation. The subject matter of the conversation is the relationship of poetry and philosophy, of life and culture, of tradition and sensibility. These are the matters I find myself thinking about when I am free to play over things I most care about.

I have selected this chapter also because I judge from responses to it that it has entertained and been persuasive to more people than any other single thing I have written. Finally, it happens to be able to stand alone and does not give the impression of being the torn and bleeding heart of a larger work.

New York, N. Y.
June 3, 1942

IRWIN EDMAN

YOU had better come with us to Italy," said my friends as I left them at Vézelay, where the grandiose Abbaye and its superb spaces and capitals and the June weather and the pleasures of reunion (I had been away a year) had given us a very good time together.

"No, I have made up my mind to see Autun," I insisted. "There's a fine Romanesque cathedral there." And I began to recite its simple unadorned charm, its historical importance, the beauty of the surrounding country, the Roman theatre where the Comédie Française came to play in the summer. I had been reading the *Guide Bleu* with care.

I knew I had made no mistake even before seeing the cathedral, for the Hôtel St.-Louis was one of those inns on the Continent which make one find a reason for staying in a town longer than one had intended. It was then well over a hundred years old; they show you the room where Napoleon slept. It has an inner courtyard where the stage-coaches and carriages used to draw up. My room under the eaves seemed singularly homelike and comfortable and had a bath, which Napoleon's room did not. I arrived late in the afternoon and had a glimpse of the cathedral before dark. The *Guide Bleu* had not exaggerated. I took a walk out of town through rolling green country that reminded me at once of the Cotswolds and of Vermont. "This," I said to myself, "is just the place to stay for a couple of weeks of reading and writing."

I was sure of it that night at dinner. Apparently Autun was now on one of the main motor roads to the South, and for all its sleepy, comforting isolation had a good deal of passing tourist traffic. The *cuisine* was *renommée*. So was the wine. I was lonely without my friends and drank considerable of it. I felt wonderful. "Why did nobody tell me of Autun before?" I thought as I was falling asleep.

Next morning I wished I had never heard of it. The *cuisine renommée*, the *vin superbe*, had done for me. I was sure I had ptomaine poisoning. I asked the *valet de chambre* to send the friendly manager, whom the evening before I had complimented on his food, his wine, his country, and the room that Napoleon had slept in.

"Is it," I said wanly when he appeared, "that there is a doctor in Autun?"

"But yes, monsieur," he said briskly. "M. Platon."

"But you are joking, monsieur, *c'est de la blague,* not really M. Platon." Even though I had ptomaine poisoning, I wouldn't believe there was anybody named Plato in a French provincial town.

"Yes, M. Platon," the innkeeper said simply, "an excellent family physician; he has attended my own family for twenty years now; a physician of the first order."

"Send M. Platon," I said weakly, wondering whether ptomaine poisoning was fatal. I remembered that Aristotle, anyway, was a physician and that there was a good deal about the humours of the body

in Plato; and a physician, Erixymachus, appears in one of the dialogues. Maybe this Platon chap was all right after all.

Twenty minutes later—I was growing more and more sure it was
ptomaine poisoning—I heard a hearty voice down the corridor. "*Alors,*
where is the American?" The voice sounded almost threatening. Perhaps these provincial doctors still believed in blood-letting.

There entered my room not the diminutive Frenchman I had
somehow expected but a tall, heavy man with bushy hair and eyebrows
(he turned out to have originated in the Basque country); very brisk
and energetic in his movements and an impatient firmness in his eye.
He looked not at all like the busts of Plato, though he did have a broad
brow.

"If you will permit me, sir," he said, and, much to my surprise,
took from my table some galley-proofs of the *Journal of Philosophy*
that I had hoped to read in the course of the morning. *Journal of Philosophy* was printed at the top of each galley.

"English," he said, pointing accusingly to the innocent words, "is
simply French badly spelt. I do not, monsieur, speak English, or, as I
could easily demonstrate, not very well. I do not read it very well
either. But I read it well enough to see that English is simply French
badly spelt and badly pronounced, and badly constructed. *Journal de
la Philosophie, n'est-ce pas?* Monsieur, I am a philosopher not only in
name but in nature. You must translate that article for me. It seems to
be something that concerns the æsthetic. Is it, perhaps, your own?"

"Yes, monsieur."

"Then all the more reason: translate it for me at once."

"But, doctor, I am not feeling very well," I protested. Sight translation, or second sight translation, of even one's own prose in the
midst of an attack of ptomaine poisoning was not a project that captured my imagination for the moment. Yet M. Platon looked men-
acing, and, after all, the request was an unexpected compliment from
an unexpected source.

The doctor sat down by my bedside and I proceeded in a feeble
voice—and, I fear, rather feeble French—to translate my ideas, which
had, as I remember it, something to do with the relations of poetry

consideration of a doctor's convenience and they have all chosen this week to be sick at once. I said to myself: 'Of course, an American tourist, who has not the equipment to, or the education to, digest our excellent French food.' I did not look forward to the prospect of seeing you. But, sir, you are a humanist, an itinerant humanist. I am a humanist, too, but, alas, my profession keeps me here in Autun where there are very few. Now, had you arrived in this city in the Middle Ages, it would have been clear at once that you were a humanist. You would have worn a special costume; you would have spoken Latin. All the world would have known you were a humanist and you would at once have had access to the humanists of Autun—there are probably half a dozen and you shall now know them all. As it is, to whom have you spoken; to whom would you have spoken, if this wretched digestion of yours had not brought me by sheer accident to your bedside? Monsier, there should be formed a Society of Itinerant Humanists—you and I will found it now—so that in the future when a cultivated gentleman arrives anywhere in the world he will at once be welcomed by his fellows and his peers. It will add to the interchange of ideas; it will bring kindred spirits into contact; it will prevent such as you from moving through France as if it were merely a picture book. I shall now make the usual examination, ask you the usual questions, make out the usual prescription (I think I could do it safely without the examination or the questions), and call upon you tomorrow when I expect you to be well. Then you must dine with me and, later in the week, meet one of our fellow-humanists. Do not thank me; it is in just this way that our proposed Society of Itinerant Humanists will function in the future. It is a pity that Latin is no longer the international language; *hélas,* not everyone speaks French, though they should. It is the language of the mind and, I may add, of the soul."

He asked his questions, he made his examination, he made out his prescription and hastily rose to depart. . . . I could not resist thanking him, or asking him how he came to be called Platon.

"It is the name of my father," he said brusquely and, picking up his satchel, departed.

I saw a good deal of M. Platon the next week or two. As he had predicted, in a day or two I was better; even before his examination I was already convinced that it was not ptomaine poisoning.

My third day in Autun I went to M. Platon's house to dinner. He was a widower; his small son was away at school. He lived in a house filled with massive eighteenth-century furniture, and on the walls were several nineteenth-century paintings, including one silvery early Corot. We had an excellent dinner, with a sauce for the fish which had been invented by the humanist, so Doctor Platon said, whom I should meet later in the week, and which included a touch of honey of Hymettus, for the inventor, of course, loved Greece. Remembering my recent disaster, I grew a little diffident at the succession of courses and of wines. My host observed it. He reminded me that while I might study the Stoics I was dining with an Epicurean. Over the brandy and coffee in his library he took as his theme the life of the spirit in the provinces.

"All provincial towns are alike," he said, "be they in France or America. You have read *Madame Bovary*; I have read *Main Street*. There are a few free spirits in every such town, and in France they are chiefly lawyers and physicians. There are some others: sometimes a priest, sometimes a bookseller, a librarian. In Autun there are about half a dozen, and one of them lives out in the country some ten kilometres from Autun. We must drive over to see him. He is a philologist and would like to be a novelist. During the war he served four years and carried throughout the war the Homeric hymns in his pocket. They saved him from being killed once and they kept him alive always. There is no one else in the town to talk to about the things one really cares to talk about. I go off to Paris sometimes in desperation, but I feel like a foreigner there now with so many English and Americans about, and sometimes to get as good service as a foreigner does, I pretend I am a Hollander using English as an intermediate language. It is good luck that has brought you here; perhaps I could contrive that that hotel of yours mildly poison each client who seems to be an itinerant humanist. Yet they would hardly know which to poison. The Comédie Française comes here occasionally during the summer and plays Racine in the Roman theatre. Some of the actors are cultivated people. I wrote a long poem about that theatre once."

He produced it and read a long section. It may have been better than English poetry but I had had too much food and wine to know or even completely to understand.

I took my leave. Would *monsieur le docteur* come to dine with me at the hotel? . . . I could not offer him as good a dinner, but they did very well. He would come gladly, but on one condition: frankly, he must choose his own wine. I was not stupid, but I was an American where the *vin du pays* was whisky, and where even that was forbidden.

A few days later Doctor Platon and I drove out at a wild pace to a neat, almost English-looking cottage on a wooded upland. M. Houvat, he explained, lived on a tiny income; he had been incapacitated during the war and could not carry on his university duties. He had had a novel or two published, but the philologist had got in the way of the artist. But he was a humanist in essence.

He was indeed such. It was a bright June day. We had tea and then wild strawberries, and M. Houvat, pale, slender, with one arm (the other had been lost in the trenches), talked of poetry, of Homer, and of the Homeric hymns. That was all he seemed to care to remember of the war.

"Would you like to see an amputation?" said the doctor as we drove back to town. "I must perform one now." I shuddered. "A philosopher should see everything," he said. I declined. He shrugged his shoulders.

The last night I was to be in Autun I again dined with the doctor. He had called for me to take a little stroll before going to his house. As we walked down the main street of the town he bowed almost continuously.

"You know everyone, doctor," I said. "If I walked along this street alone it would be simply a post-card view. You probably could tell me a story about everyone in this town, as you have already told me some about many of them."

"Everyone in this town is my friend, or my enemy; but they all know me. Only a nonentity remains unknown."

Toward the close of the evening, M. Platon again broached his project of the itinerant humanists. "We really should do something about it," he said. "There is only one country—it is that of people of intelligence. Its citizens are few; they should be acquainted."

I thanked my host for all his kindnesses and in the flush of the wine and the dinner said: "Doctor, I have seen a corner and an aspect of France not open to many travellers. I wonder if I might ask a favour. I have a friend who comes to Paris about once a year. He is a journalist. He meets the editors and politicians; he never leaves Paris. Might he come to Autun? Might he greet you?"

M. Platon regarded me firmly. "Your friend, you say, is a journalist? You will pardon me—I will not receive him. *Un philosophe, voilà une chose; un journaliste, c'est tout autre chose. Je regrette; je ne reçois pas votre camarade. . . . Il n'est pas humaniste itinérant.*"

PIERRE VAN PAASSEN

Why he selected The STREET of

OUR LADY

Probably it was a nostalgic feeling that moved me to select some passages from my French village diary for your anthology. Seeking repose and escape from the ceaseless nervous tension that grips us all, I turned with relief to the days I lived in that little village near Paris. So calmly and evenly did time flow in Bourg-en-Forêt that the very silence of those days still re-echoes in my memory. Yet in re-reading this passage I am convinced that it is the best I have ever done.

On quiet Sundays we would start at break of day in order not to miss the miracle of the rising mist, when the whole world would be sprinkled with diamonds for a few moments before the sun dried up the dew. The milkish vapors of the dawn would first lift from the ground and from around the basements of the houses we passed. Little by little the doorsteps and the lower lintels of the windows would become visible, then the upper sills and the rain pipes running along the eaves, until at last there was but a small plumelike tuft of white clinging to the chimney. When this suddenly evaporated, it was as if some one with invisible hands had slowly pulled their sleeping clothes from the cottages and in a final gesture had lifted their nightcaps . . . .

Today the future weighs upon us as a terrible, often incomprehensible burden under which scarcely any one dares to look ahead. By day and by night innumerable thoughts and questions come to harrow and torment us.

And Bourg-en-Forêt, filled though it was with human troubles and tragedies, recalls the days when one awaited each dawn joyfully, with new hope.

Bronxville, N. Y. PIERRE VAN PAASSEN
July, 1942

I

WHEN we moved from Paris to the village of Bourg-en-Forêt in
1929, we soon discovered that we had done more than change
our residence. It was like another world. As a fog sometimes lingers
over a swamp long after the sun is up, so the past still seemed to linger
in Bourg-en-Forêt. True, the elementary gods had not failed to work
their havoc; most of the houses were decrepit; their roofs sagged
and the doors hung crooked; the rains of centuries had completely
obliterated the features of the sculptured saints in the portal of the
church, but life had remained untouched by the tumult with which
the modern metropolis seeks to hide its secret anguish. Those peasants amongst whom we lived for almost ten years were poor in
worldly goods; they had no automobiles or radios, but neither did
they envy those who had them. Thoughts of tomorrow did not torture them. They did not lament when death came, nor were they
afraid of life. And yet they had a remarkably clear conception of
the problems of our time and did not hesitate to take definite stands
when occasion demanded it. Their rule was to cultivate their own
gardens. I think that the serenity of their existence, which often
evoked the envy of strangers who watched them, resided in the fact
that they insisted on being men before social beings. They were in-
dividualists. They were content to be human. Thus they had retained
something of that fundamental dignity which is the sole condition of
human happiness because it is both our physiological norm and the
law of nature.

In Bourg life moved with a slower, perhaps a more graceful,
rhythm than in Paris. The parish priest, who became our friend, had
not visited the capital in a quarter century, although the distance
was but an hour by rail and on a clear day you could, by climbing
the perilous stairway of a ruined mill, see the Eiffel Tower trace its
lacy silhouette against the southern sky.

About eight or nine in the evening the peasants harnessed their
heavy dray horses to the carts, hung a lantern on the whippletree,
and settled down to sleep on a sack of straw in the front seat of
their covered wagons. They let the horses find their own way to the
night market in Paris. They were back before the larks winged their

way to heaven and we heard the rumble of their empty carts on the dirt road as they passed our house. These men never saw Paris in the daytime. Indeed, to most families in the village a trip to the capital was still an event of importance for which provisions had to be prepared on the previous day—bread and sausage and chicken—as if no restaurants existed in the capital! Stiff Sunday clothes were worn on such occasions. Umbrellas, the device by which a French peasant thinks he raises himself to the rank of a bourgeois, never used in the village itself, not even in the heaviest downpour, were taken from the cupboards and carried for decorative purposes. Relatives went along as far as the station to see the voyagers off and stood waiting in the same place a few hours later to welcome them back home again. One morning one of my neighbors, "Papa" Vessières, a man well over seventy, who was the father of a professor at the Sorbonne, one of the greatest living authorities on tropical diseases, finding himself alone in the train compartment with me, whispered in evident distress, "Monsieur Pierre, when we come to the Gare du Nord, would you mind if I take your arm? I am afraid something might happen to me. *Les bicyclettes, vous savez, et puis les taxis. Ah, mon Dieu, mon Dieu, quelle horreur!*"

Our house stood on the Rue Notre-Dame de Bonne-Nouvelle. It was hidden from the road by a hedge of intertwining willows and by an eight-foot wall. In the rear it overlooked a rolling expanse of meadows and farmland bounded on the distant horizon by the somber mass of the forest of Montmorency. From the upstairs windows and from the garden which sloped down to a small stream, we watched the color of the valley change from the dull ocher of winter to an immense beggar's blanket with all the varieties of green in square patches. Ribbons of red, where the poppies grew, marked off the borders of the wheat fields. In midsummer the entire plain was overspread by a light sheen of azure caused by the millions of bluebottles and cornflowers pushing up in the pale oats and the ripening grain. A few weeks later, on the edge of the forest far away, appeared the first sprinkle of heather purple.

You could pick out the river by letting your eyes follow a line of stately poplars, which our Abbé called the most feminine of trees. The stream gleamed like a strip of blue mirror in the evening when the sun went down. On still evenings, too, you could sometimes see the miracle of the corn suddenly beginning to sway as if an invisible hand had brushed over it. The quiver communicated itself from field to field as often happens when a sudden squall darkens a portion of the ocean's surface on a seemingly windless day. . . . To the west were farmhouses, their gray roofs visible above clusters of oak and chestnut. Not a sound penetrated into our solitude except the whistle of the train which we saw crawling along the bottom of the valley, puffing out its smoke clouds as seriocomically as a man forcing his pipe to draw.

In my more philosophic moods I have sometimes wondered if we must not see in France's valleys of abundance a source of the enduring enmity of the Germans? Could it not be, I thought, that the knowledge, or the surmise, that to the west of them, where the rivers widen and the earth is watered more copiously, soil more nourishing and a scene more colorful than the dreary monotony of their own pine forests and arid swamps could be found, so roused their Teutonic imagination and cupidity that they came again and again in the course of history, breaking down the barriers the Caesars had originally erected, smashing their way with unbridled fury towards the fat and pleasant habitations of the Celts?

If this be contrary to the doctrine of economic determinism, so much the worse for that doctrine!

After the roar of cities and years of imprisonment between their tower-high stone walls, we rediscovered the land and stilled the nostalgia which gnaws silently at the heart of every city dweller. In our home the quiet of morning was disturbed only by the occasional rattle of a passing cart or the distant clangor of the blacksmith's hammer on the anvil. The bells in the stunted, moss-grown tower tolled out the hours of day a little sadly. But most of the time we were up at daylight and out in the fields. A peach tree in bloom, a cluster of wild strawberry shrubs, a mole heap with its labyrinth of galleries accidentally disturbed by the plow, the nests that the swallows built under our eaves—these were the marvels before which we halted in admiration. We learned again to wonder and to admire the virtues which have almost been banished by the frenzied agitation of modern life. For when a man is alone with nature he is astonished, he admires alone and at leisure. What do we know in our hectic cities of the sweetness and consolation of a flower, which is nevertheless as vast as space! There were moments when we felt prodigiously rich in the divine distraction of soil and sky and in the mere contemplation of the changing weather.

"Do you know," once asked Henri Bataille, "what is needed to shelter all the love under heaven, the greatest sorrow and the most pressing cares of earth? A solitary tree, on one of whose low-hanging branches sits a magpie blinking at the passing clouds!"

Before the open windows on those long summer evenings we watched the lamps being lit in the mansions of the Lord. It was at times as if we caught a breath of eternity: the riddle of human existence, the sense, the purpose and the mystery of life presented itself ineluctably to my spirit. From the Abbé de la Roudaire, our friend, whose hobby was astronomy, and who often brought his instruments to make his calculations by our window, I learned that it takes the light from one of those stars fifty million years to reach us, and that our life on the earth, which is but "an insignificant fragment of a grain of sand in millions of oceans of sand," is a pure accident.

Intuition violently contradicted the priest's calm rationalism. Like Tagore, I never felt myself a stranger on this earth, but rather that we are here for a definite purpose and that it is our task to discover that purpose and to explain and arrange the world in accordance with it. I cannot tolerate the idea of a planless universe, or that the weary road of mankind is frustration and the end of the journey universal death. I believe that human instinct, the instinct of immortality included, never deceives.

How far removed we seemed in our rural retreat from the pandemonium of Paris and the heartbreaking struggle of the millions for bread and happiness! When you thought of it, which was frequently, it poisoned your life and made you ashamed of your privileged position and your own enjoyment of peace. No matter how I tried, I have never been able to conquer that anguish. It was a sorrow implanted in me from birth. It turned moments that should have been the happiest into bitterness and gall. I felt guilty of egoism, of desertion, of seeking an escape from the reality of life. What good is it, asked Renan once, when *I* live passably well but *humanity* suffers? And yet I wanted to go on dreaming forever in the charmed stillness of our valley where everything was sweetness and voluptuousness. . . .

II

Everybody met at the weekly market and you could learn all the scandal and gossip of the neighborhood. There were always a few idlers on hand, who, in exchange for a glass of wine at the zinc-covered counter in one of the taverns on the square, volunteered to give away men's innermost secrets: which of the merchants and farmers most assiduously frequented the state brothel; what was going on at the château on those winter evenings when long lines of limousines from Paris were halted in the park; what was the real situation between the curé of a neighboring hamlet and the widow of a rich grocer whom he visited—most of it lies, of course, but it was good to hear them talk.

For a political debate the Café of the Golden Lion was the place. There Monsieur Tisserand had his permanent seat. "Un annarsheest" the villagers called him. If you wanted to hear him at his best you had to wait for the afternoon when the pharmacist and the rest of the Radicals dropped in. Monsieur Tisserand was the administrator of the public library from which he *"systématiquement,"* as he was wont to say, kept away "the poison of clericalism and religion," something that was his right and even his duty, I dare to say, under a republican regime which, as Viviani once exclaimed, has extinguished the heavenly lights. The clergy did not like Monsieur Tisserand, although no two men greeted each other with a greater flourish of hats and deep bows than he and the Abbé de la Roudaire when they met on the streets. From time to time these two citizens exchanged lengthy letters on a burning question of the day, and watched from behind the curtains in their respective parlors, as the mail carrier deposited the epistles in each other's letter boxes, for they lived vis-à-vis. I do not know who started that correspondence, but I suspect it was Monsieur Tisserand. He literally boiled over with indignation or enthusiasm, depending on the occasion, to inform his clerical neighbor of his views on a political event of importance. In those letters he let off steam. They ran into dozens of pages and were read in public in

the café by Monsieur Antoine Tisserand himself: those of the Abbé
in a voice that betrayed pitiful condescension, the copies of his own in
the tone of majestic finality. He quoted voluminously from Voltaire
and the philosophers of the Encyclopédie, but his hero was a certain
Pierre Leroux, a Utopian freethinker of the seventies. In those missives
to the Abbé, the librarian never failed to include citations from Lamen-
nais, Alfred Loisy and other priests who had left the church. To these
pinpricks the Abbé replied invariably with the assurance that he never
ceased praying for the salvation of M. Tisserand's soul, as well as for
the souls of those departed apostates, a remark that made the recipient
of the letter as furious as a riled rooster.

III

I was kept informed of the deaths in the community by Camille
Villetorte, the gravedigger, whose place of work I passed every time
I had to go to Paris.

"Today it's Monsieur Thurandot's turn," Camille greeted me when
I hailed him one morning from the road.

"I don't know your Monsieur Thurandot," I said, stopping by the
fence.

"Sure, Monsieur knows him, the cross-eyed little grocer with the
long nose from the Rue de la Buanderie? Monsieur remembers?"

"He of the two beautiful daughters?"

"Precisely, the father of Lucienne and Suzanne." This with a wink.

"That reminds me: I don't see her around any more, the little
Suzanne. She used to come by some evenings with a young man."

"Ah, no wonder, Monsieur, no wonder. She is in Paris. Monsieur
had not heard of it? But yes, she is in the great city."

Camille dropped his spade on the bottom of the grave he was
squaring off and clambered to the surface. He walked to the foot of
a weeping willow, pulled a bottle of *pinard* from his haversack which
lay there in the shade and took a swig.

"The whole commune is talking of that affair," he went on,
sucking his moustaches. "I am surprised that Monsieur has not
heard . . . It appears she is making little steps to and fro in the
neighborhood of the Porte St. Denis. . . . Monsieur the collector of

the direct imposts was telling me, *voilà,* two or three months ago. It appears he had to be in Paris one day, Monsieur the collector, ha, ha, and *tiens!* whom does he see there, but the *petite* Suzanne of the grocer. Wasn't that a coincidence? He's a man of fine instincts, this Monsieur the tax collector. He knows what's good. . . . I wonder if she'll be at the funeral *tout é heure,* the little Suzanne. . . . A fine shape she has, that girl, and of such a father! To be sure, one can never tell."

Camille dropped back into the hole, but presently threw two skulls and some human bones to the surface.

"What's this?" I asked in surprise. "What are you doing now?"

"They are a little crowded down here, Monsieur. I am throwing them out for the time being, till after the funeral. Then they go back. This is the head of *le père* Cochard, a rich farmer. Monsieur did not know him. He died before Monsieur's time. A scoundrel and a villain if ever there was one. He left not a sou to charity."

"What I don't understand," I said, "is how these skulls get out of coffins. How long ago was he buried, this Monsieur Cochard?"

"That must be going on to forty years, Monsieur, since we put *le père* Cochard away. My father dug his grave. . . . It's a moist patch down here. The pine boards don't hold, Monsieur. They rot away in no time. And then, the worms in France always had good teeth. . . ."

"Well, Monsieur Camille, I must be on my way!"

"To Paris, Monsieur Pierre?"

"To Paris!"

"Politics, Monsieur?"

"Not politics exactly. I must go to the Foreign Office!"

"Who's there now at the Quai d'Orsay, Laval or Tardieu?"

"Monsieur Laval is now the Foreign Minister."

"Ah, *le salaud!* It's that rascal and his gang who will bring misery upon us yet, mark my words! Ah, *les salauds!*" The gravedigger shook his head. "A dirty job *la politique,* Monsieur Pierre, a very foul business!"

IV

We were not the only foreigners living in Bourg. About a quarter of a mile out of the village, on the road towards Clamercy, was a farm occupied by a Russian *émigré*. Unlike the other peasant cottages, his house did not border the roadway but stood a good distance inland and was almost completely hidden from view in summertime by clusters of shrubbery and the foliage of a small woods of willow trees. You reached the place by a sunken dirt road which followed the bends of a shallow creek formed by the seepage from the adjoining pastures. In the fall the road turned into a sea of mire and remained that way: virtually impassable till the warm weather of the following year. Yet, a small amount of money, a few loads of pebbles and sand and a little grading, altogether a few days' work, would have easily repaired the damage. But of this the proprietor would not hear. The *cantonnier* had spoken to him on the subject of the road more than once. He had dismissed the official every time with the remark that it was his own private property and that he could do with it as he liked; moreover, he wanted the road that way because it reminded him of Russia.

The farmer's name was Platon Klioutchevsky. A heavy-set individual with a small reddish beard and blue eyes, he must have been in his early fifties. He was something like our local man of mystery. There was a light in the window of his house at all times of the night, for he always neglected to close the shutters. Peasants driving by in their carts to or from the market in Paris said that some nights they had heard the Russian sing at the top of his voice. Often, too, they had been on the point of driving up the dirt road to investigate what was going on at the lonely farm house where they could see the vehemently gesticulating silhouette of the man moving against the light of the lamp or hear the crash of furniture, the screams of a woman and the raucous cursing voice of Klioutchevsky. What was going on at the house? Why were they always quarreling?

Madame Klioutchevsky was much younger than her husband. She was a woman of simple grace, not unattractive: tall, Titian-haired with soft jade-colored eyes and a skin as white as alabaster. She was obviously of genteel birth, for she spoke French in that melodious drawl affected by the former Russian upper classes. She carried herself with the dignity of a born aristocrat and although her clothes were old she always made a presentable appearance. When she came into the village to do her shopping, the women stood still to see her go by and then whispered: Was she Klioutchevsky's wife or was she his mistress? Why did she stay with such a brutal man?

"He beats her," said the men, "so she must be his legal wife. All Russians beat their wives. . . ."

Still others held that Klioutchevsky had been a general in the Russian army—every second Russian in France is either a general or a prince. But that surmise was based on nothing more authentic than that M. Klioutchevsky was invariably dressed in an old blouse with a broad leather belt around the waist and that he wore a pair of mud-splashed riding boots. There was nothing military in his bearing. He had a rather slouchy walk and always kept his hands in his trouser pockets. It is true that he kept a saber in his house. This I knew from Louise, our *femme de ménage*, who had served the Klioutchevsky family before she came to us.

"A funny kind of a farmer, that Monsieur Klioutchevsky," Louise would say. "For one thing, he never gets up till eleven in the morning, and then only to sit drinking one cup of cocoa after the other and smoking cigarettes till the room is white with smoke. If it were not for his wife the horses would never get fed. He'd let them starve!"

"When does he work?"

"*Eh bien,* he must work at nights—he does not stir out of the house till three or four in the afternoon when he is not drunk. When he is drunk he remains indoors altogether."

Drink, that was the trouble with M. Klioutchevsky. But for his drinking there was a primary cause. When he staggered around the village from one taproom to the other, or sat all by himself in a corner of the Lion d'Or with a somber stare on his face, contemplating the glass in front of him, the other customers shook their heads. "*C'est la douleur des hommes russes,*" they would say.

"He's a White and as such I can have no sympathy with him," said Monsieur Tisserand, "but he is human just the same. . . . How would we feel far away from France in some strange country without hope of ever returning? The thought is enough to drive a man to drink and to insanity. But such is life. Those Russians we have here in France are paying for the sins of their fathers. There is retributive justice in this world after all. With a few noble exceptions, men like Tolstoy and the like, their class lived a life of leisure and affluence

on the back of the long-suffering moujik, the same good-natured fellow
as our own *Jacques Bonhomme* whom our nobles exploited like cattle.
Until the *Jacquerie* revolts came and the manor houses went up in
flame and the heads of the squires were carried around on pikes. That
is the way it went in Russia. The jug goes down the well until it
breaks."

I never had any personal dealings with M. Klioutchevsky except
one day when he came to the house, in the fall of the year 1931. He
had learned, he said, that I had been on a visit to his native country
and would be glad if I could tell him some of my impressions.

I asked him inside and gave him a brief description of what I had
seen: the mournful aspect of Leningrad and the general down-at-the-
heels appearance of the population. On the other hand, there had
been an enormous amount of building and construction in cities like
Moscow, Kiev and Rostov-on-the-Don, and feverish activity on the
collective farms.

I told him of the huge crowds of kulaks I had seen sleeping in the
streets of Leningrad near the Finland station. They were mostly
Ukrainians who were on their way to the forests of Karelia. They
were being removed to break up the sullen hostility against Stalin's
agrarian reforms. But I also told him of the enormous amount of
study and reading that was going on, the splendid theatrical experiments, and the spirit of daring and innovation in the science and architecture. "Step by step," I said, "painfully at times, no doubt, the
peoples of Russia are being imbued with a new vision. The difference
between Russia and the rest of Europe is that whereas in countries
like Germany and Italy culture is on the decline, and the standard
of living going down, in Russia it is going up, imperceptibly almost,
but going up just the same."

"Do you know any Russian?" he asked.

"I speak a little Ruthenian," I said, "and those with whom I came
in contact understood me quite well."

"You were treated well, I mean not officially, but in chance meetings with people who did not know you were a foreign journalist?"

"Exceptionally well," I said. "I think the Russians are the most
brotherly people on earth."

"And the army?"

"What I saw of the army gave me an impression of power and efficiency . . . But I do not like armies, the Red army no more than any other. The only good thing that can be said about Soviet militarism is that the leaders do not glory in their country's military prowess, but that they look upon armaments and all the rest of the killing game as an unavoidable evil. They would much sooner devote the wealth that is being produced to the improvement of the people's condition. But the others do not allow them. They must arm because they are menaced from all sides."

He sat silent for a while, rubbing his hand over his mouth and beard, looking out of the window.

All at once he said, "I feel like asking you to give me a blow on the head!" He rose from his chair. *"Je vous en prie, je vous en prie, flanquez-moi une gifle au moins."*

"Why should I strike you, M. Klioutchevsky? This is a most extraordinary request: a man comes to my house . . ."

"Ah, you don't know," he replied, and buried his face in his hands. "Don't you see," he said, turning up his tear-stained face, "that's where I belong, over there. . . . The revolution was right. . . . There was hunger and there had to be a change. . . . Why did not I see it earlier? How can I get back now? I would do anything: sweep floors, the dirtiest work if only I could see Russia again, hear my own people talk. . . . I detest them, you understand. I have an unutterable contempt for everything Russian, but I am dying without Russia . . . Do you think they will give me a visa, these others?"

"The Bolsheviks, you mean? Why not? Many are going back. I understand there is a standing invitation to the exiles to return." And I told him of the case of Prince Mirsky, who had given up his position as professor of Slavonic languages in the University of London to return to Moscow where he had become the literary critic on one of the great dailies.

But Klioutchevsky did not return to Russia, although he entered into negotiations with the Soviet embassy in Paris for a return visa, and he did sell his farm on the strength of the good news he heard there.

It was the money he received for his property that brought about the tragedy. Unknown to his wife he had hidden the bank notes in the bottom of the stove. One day while he was away in Paris to make arrangements for their departure, the woman lit the fire and the money vanished.

Klioutchevsky came home around seven in the evening. From a distance he saw the smoke rising from the chimney. Those who met him on the road said that his face was terrible to behold, the face of a maniac. He bellowed like an ox in the abattoir as he raced along the road.

What happened when he reached the house the gendarmes learned from Madame Klioutchevsky just before she died the following day. Finding that his money had been burned, he had tied his wife's hands to the kitchen table and chopped them off with an ax.

v

In Bourg-en-Forêt the market was a weekly joy from which we returned light of heart and loaded with parcels. Its approach never failed to give me a holiday feeling. On Thursday, the school holiday in France, the atmosphere in the "grand" square was reminiscent of a kermis in Flanders than which, I think, there is nothing more joyous on earth. In the narrow alleys between the booths and stalls a dense crowd of peasants, rich and poor, from the surrounding district milled about with their wives and children. Their carts and horses cluttered up the side streets. You saw the notables, the school-teachers, the notaries, the mayors and officials from all the hamlets and villages in the neighborhood. The clergy were also present. Those priests, generally the sons of peasants themselves, examined the cattle with the eyes of connoisseurs, and their counsel was frequently sought when it came to making a purchase after hours of haggling. *Les paysannes* made you taste their butter from the point of a knife. When you bought a supply of potatoes for the winter you concluded the bargain by drinking a glass of white wine with the salesman in one of the taverns. Merchants and hucksters shouted their wares. "Ah, this good linen, ah, the delicious nougat from Montélimar!" Quacks sold remedies against all conceivable ills. According to the learned diagnosis of one rural Aesculapius, most of our maladies are due to the presence of worms in the human organism. There are worms, he would say, which eat away at your brain, causing premature senility; other worms gnaw away at a person's heart when a love affair does not run smoothly. This doctor, who wore a silk hat and a shining frock coat, had a sheet of linen spread out against the back of the stall on which was painted a worm of boa-constrictor dimensions gorging himself with a chunk of a blood-red human heart. It was a most convincing picture. He called the peasants over to his booth: "*Messieurs-dames, approchez-vous, approchez-vous,* health is within your grasp!" If they protested that they enjoyed perfect health, he made the peasants spit on their caps and then held a magnifying glass above the saliva which at once became alive with maggots. "And what do you think of your health, now, Monsieur? You are chock-full of worms!" The peasants looked aghast. It was nothing short of magic!

It takes a French peasant a long time to make up his mind before making a purchase. That is why the merchants poured forth an endless stream of sales talk which they shrewdly mixed with the bait of indiscreet references to prominent personalities of the neighborhood: "Now this pair of bed sheets—have a feel of the material, dear madam—one pair for the master and his goodwife, one pair for the children and one for the maid. . . . At the château the maids do not get sheets on the bed. *C'est pas nécessaire, d'ailleurs* . . . they crawl into the seigneur's bed. . . . The six sheets for two hundred francs. . . . Now is the best time to buy. . . . In a week the government is going to raise prices. The price of bread is going up, the price of bed sheets is going up. . . . *Monsieur le ministre* has discovered a new danseuse. . . . She's as poor as a church mouse, but from what I hear she has compensating qualities, *o là, là!* what that demoiselle needs is a trousseau. . . . You are going to pay for it, if you don't buy now . . . *Vive la République!* . . . For good measure I throw in this fine rope to tie up the dog. . . . Where will you get such a bargain?"

One of the most popular personages in the market place was a troubadour who operated a wheezy harmonica. He was an ex-soldier, *une gueule cassée* whose face had been twisted into a horrible smirk by a piece of shrapnel. One eye was fully an inch lower than the other. This gave you the impression that he looked at you from a house with two storeys. He sang through his nose in the Parisian slang to which the peasants listened with a religious solemnity. His chants were mostly laments on the fate of dimple-cheeked milkmaids in the dens of evil in Montmartre. Sometimes, I thought, he exaggerated. Often, too, he repeated himself, which was understandable in the course of human events. But his moral code was beyond reproach: like Calvin Coolidge's preacher, he was against sin. . . .

Two or three bookstalls before which the intellectuals and the clergy met were a perpetual delight. They had a fresh stock of secondhand literature each week. One of the book merchants had the most vivid blue eyes of any man I ever saw. Next to the pharmacist, I was his best customer. He sold me some French pamphlets which had been printed in Holland in the sixteenth and seventeenth centuries. Their contents would have sent their authors before the execution squad in half a dozen European and American countries today.

And then there were the soothsayers and the dispensers of contraceptive medicine. They had to hide their illicit trade behind some innocuous false front. Madame Gabrielle, for instance, had her son, the pimply-faced Marcel, stand outside her little booth to urge you to have your photo taken, seated in a tin airplane. But once inside, she laid the cards for you and hinted in a mysterious whisper that she knew an address or two in the neighborhood where one could be *tranquil* in an *intérieur exotique* with a rural daughter of Venus who was said to be an expert in *caresses délicieuses* and all the games of love. If the farmers could get rid of their wives and children, leave them somewhere in a waffle booth or haggling with a Jew about the price of a mechanical eggbeater or a goatskin, they sneaked away to Madame Gabrielle. That woman was rich. She came to the market in her own automobile.

From one of the streets leading to the market square, the Rue Danès de Montardart, named after a long-since-departed citizen who had left his money to the poor, ran a narrow alley known as the Passage of the Sirens. In this alley were two "houses of illusion," easily recognizable by the red lanterns and the large numbers on their doors. The inmates of these temples, dedicated to a mercenary Aphrodite, leaned their bosoms on the open windows or strolled out amidst the crowds at the fair, triumphantly leading a customer off now and then to their haunts. They were no longer young, these ladies, and no longer fresh—Montmartre had left its traces—but they could do wonders with cosmetics. The farmers stared at them openmouthed and followed at a distance, swallowing hard, their eyes glistening.

We ended our day at the market by having a late lunch in the restaurant-kitchen of Mother Lunette which was located in one of the side streets off the square. Her house leaned against the church so that when the hours struck in the clock tower you could feel the walls of the dining room tremble. "Mama" Lunette, queen of French cooks, personally supervised the service in her establishment. The shoulder of mutton with string beans, the *ragoût de veau*, the *sole meunière* with wine sauce, or the omelet with mushrooms which she prepared in a corner of the room under the big chimney, came to the table so perfect, so well cooked, so appetizingly dished up that it made your mouth water. And with it a crackling loaf of bread, not wrapped in cellophane, thank heaven! and a choice of Burgundy, Haut Sauterne and Beaujolais. All of it for ten francs—thirty cents in our money.

"I do not expect to taste better in Paradise," the Abbé de la Roudaire used to sigh as he took his napkin from under his chin.

LOUIS BROMFIELD Why he selected

The RAINS CAME

The following passage concerns four or five of the principal characters in *The Rains Came* at moments of crisis in their lives. Although the book was written over five years ago the implications of the passage chosen were never so clear as they are today in relation to the world in general and the social background of Great Britain in particular.

I have selected the passage from *The Rains Came* as it seems to represent to me as much as any other passage I have written what I seek to do in writing a novel, briefly—to deal with characters and the interplay of characters against a background or environment which in itself plays a definite part in their motivation and the moulding of their thoughts and actions. For me characters must not be imposed upon a plot but rather the *story* must grow out of the characters, their environment and background. I have also chosen the passage as a good representation of what I aim to achieve in style—that each sentence be clear, simply constructed however long it may be, and carrying if possible a definite rhythm and sense of the imminence of background. For me a sentence which must be read twice in order to extract the meaning is a bad sentence. Words were meant primarily and eternally for communication of ideas and pictures between man and man, and a good style is one which accomplishes this communication with as little friction and blundering as possible.

I think the passage stands up well as a unit.

Lucas, Ohio   LOUIS BROMFIELD
June 1, 1942

T HE rain had stopped for a moment and as he drove across the square by the cinema the whole place came suddenly to life, with people rushing out of shops and houses to take advantage of the respite —servants on errands, women bound for the bazaar, merchants bartering, washerwomen hurrying to the great tank. From the square he turned past the music school into the Engineering School Road. It was actually called Beaconsfield Avenue but nobody ever used that name. It was always spoken of as Engineering School Road. And then as if God had pulled the chain of a gigantic shower bath the rain began again in a flood, and a little ahead of him on the right he spied the figure of Miss Dirks trudging along in a mackintosh and a man's felt hat. He thought, "I'll stop and ask the poor old thing if she wants a lift. If she refuses then I'll never have to ask her again."

She must have been thinking of something very far away as she trudged along through the rain, for when he drew up beside her and called out she looked at him in a startled way, almost without recognition, as if she had come back from a great distance.

"Can I give you a lift?" he asked.

She did not smile. She said, "Good morning. No thank you. I like walking. I get so little exercise."

(All right then, walk! I'll be damned if I ever ask you again!)

As she spoke her face grew suddenly flushed in the most extraordinary way so that Ransome wondered if speech with a man always affected her thus. He had put his foot on the clutch to start on his way to El-Kautara when she spoke again.

"It's funny," she said, "I was just thinking of you." Then she coughed and said, "Could I come and see you this afternoon?"

His first impulse was to make an excuse, but pity for her and curiosity checked him. Something about her made him feel suddenly very English. He was aware of the closeness of his blood to that of the grim spinster and he felt suddenly their loneliness in this rain-drenched town where nothing was what it seemed to be. He saw that both of them were in a way exiles from everything that touched them closely.

He said, "Of course. But I could save you the trouble. I could come to you."

But she objected quickly: "No. It had better be at your house. At home we wouldn't be alone. . . ." Again she coughed: "You see, it's rather personal."

"All right . . . as you like. What time? Will you come for tea?"

"Yes. That will be fine. I couldn't get away from school before then."

"I'll expect you about five."

The flush went suddenly out of her face, leaving it the color of death. She said, "It's very kind of you. Good day," and awkwardly, abruptly she turned and went on her way.

The road toward Mount Abana was thick with mud, and beneath the new bridges built by the Swiss engineer the yellow water slid past with only an inch or two of clearance. He thought, "They should have been built with higher arches. If there was a flood they would only act as dams to the water."

Slowly as he drove along the road the great mountain appeared out of the rain, taking form above the flat plain like a gigantic pyramid. There were few pilgrims now that the rains had come, and the great stairway which led from the plain to the summit crowned with temples was no longer crowded with worshiping Jains from every part of India, going up and coming down in an endless pageant of color. At the top of the mountain in this season the priests were living a damp solitary existence—a good life, thought Ransome, if it were not for all the other priests.

He was forced to drive slowly because of the thick mud and the danger of slipping off the road, but after two hours he arrived at the huge ruined gateway of El-Kautara. It was made of red sandstone and the elaborate Mogul carvings were half-hidden by the tangle of vines and small thrusting plants. It stood at the very base of the mountain, this dead and silent city, its thick walls surrounded by a wide ruined moat which had filled with water, so that for a moment he had an illusion of what the city must have been like in the days when its squares and mosques were filled with merchants and soldiers, courtesans and dancing girls, horses and elephants. But the illusion passed quickly. It was a dead and ruined place which the earth had begun to claim again as its own.

Among the ruins in the streets and squares a path had been cleared just wide enough for a motor to pass and along this Ransome drove slowly, avoiding the deep pools of water that stood here and there. In the courtyards and sometimes within the walls of palaces and houses wild fig trees and banyans had sprung up, cracking and thrusting aside the tiles that had been brought long ago from the north, from Delhi and Agra and Lahore.

As history went in India it was not an ancient city; it could not have been more than a hundred and fifty years since the last Mogul subject looked back for the last time at its deserted walls. But already it was lost, its history swallowed up. No one knew why it had been abandoned and allowed to die. India was like that, thought Ransome. It swallowed up everything, human ambition and faith, cities and conquerors, fame and glory. Only Akbar survived and his successors who, as time went in the East, had lived only yesterday. Asoka and the great Alexander and the rest were already legendary, half-man, half-god, like Rama and Krishna. In the empty courtyards the trees were hung with flying foxes waiting for nightfall to sweep in clouds across the plains toward Ranchipur. Again and again, where the fragment of a roof still remained, he caught a swift and sinister glimpse of a wild face framed with long greasy black hair peering at him from behind a ruined arch, and presently he came to have the feeling that as he drove along the empty streets he was being watched. They were the Bhils, the wild aboriginal people from the hills beyond Abana, who when the rains came sought the shelter of the ruined mosques and temples for their children and their goats.

At last in the great square before a huge ruined mosque he stopped the car and sat there for a long time, filled at last with a sense of peace, the sickness gone from him. In the solitude there was bitterness and a kind of sinister pleasure, for the spectacle said to him, "See! Here was once a rich and powerful city. It is gone now as all the others which followed it must go." It seemed to say to all the world—the dictators, the politicians, the bankers, the "great men" of the world—"See! This is what you must come to through greed and folly and evil! See! One day what you have built will fall and its ruins will be the haunt of bats and panthers and savages."

When she was dressed and everyone had gone away, even Bates, Edwina went into Esketh's room and sat for a long time, watching and thinking. She did not sit beside the bed but in a chair across the room, from which he appeared to her objectively, free from any bond of any kind. He did not stir when she came in and gave no sign of knowing that she was there. He simply lay bloated and heavy, his face swollen and more purple than it had been three hours earlier. Major Safti had told her that she should not enter the room until Esketh's illness had been properly diagnosed. If it were plague, he said, it would be dangerous for her. But she had no feeling about the danger because deep within her there was a consciousness, like the belief which some soldiers have in battle, that nothing would touch her. And she was by nature a gambler. If she was to have the plague, she would have it anyway.

She had been driven to return to the room by a kind of horrid fascination which Esketh, ill and unconscious, seemed to have for her. And because it gave her a perverse pleasure to look at him, helpless, downed, beaten for the first time. And while she sat there she thought: "There you are—not the great swaggering Lord Esketh, boasting and bullying and buying what you want, but just plain, vulgar Albert Simpson, the son of a small building contractor in Liverpool, who got beyond himself. You've never done a good deed for anyone unless it brought you profit and glory. And you've ruined men and women who trusted you for the sake of power and money. Oh, you've given money to charities in large lumps well advertised in your newspapers, but it never cost you anything. You never missed it and it made people who didn't know you say you were generous, and it served to whitewash your character and cover up a lot of sculduggery and stifle the criticism of your enemies. You'd betray your own country if it would bring in another shilling or another ounce of power. Long ago you sold rifles and shells to Turks to kill at Gallipoli boys who came from your own country, men better than yourself who went off to their death while you stayed at home and made money out of the tragic needs of your own people and wrote wild leaders in your own papers to keep the war going. And now, only a fortnight ago in Delhi, you wrote a leader to be printed in all the Esketh papers that was certain to make ill feeling and bitterness and lead to more wars. It cost you a nice lot to cable it all the way from Delhi but that didn't matter because if there was a war you'd get back the money a billion times over. You didn't know that I read it first, but I did. There are so many things you don't know about me and what I know of you. Bates and I together could write a biography of you that would put

you in jail or in an asylum for mad men. Oh, you're very shrewd . . .
using your newspapers, your mines, your factories, your steamships,
round and round in an endless chain, turning out profit for yourself
at the expense of workman, of shareholders, of humanity itself. You've
never had a friend that you didn't buy. You even bought your own
wife and a bad bargain she was—probably the worst bargain you ever
made. What was it that happened long ago, perhaps when you were
a small child, that made you want all those things for which you sacrificed everything decent? Were you thinking about all this long ago
when you were selling cheap knives and watches in Malaya? Who
hurt you? Who put into your head the idea that all this power and
all this money were the only things worth having in life? What made
you think that you could buy things in life—things like love and
fidelity and respect and breeding? What are you like inside? What
must it be like to be *you*? What does it feel like to be so ruthless, so
bitter, so alone, hating everybody who does not lick your boots?
You'll never tell anyone because you don't know yourself how it feels.
You've never known. You can't know, because you're like a man
born with a horrible physical deformity who can never know what it
is like to be fine and straight and young and beautiful. Your brain,
your soul must have some horrible deformity which is all the worse
because it cannot be seen. You must have been a horrible child—
grasping and calculating how to make money even out of your mother.
But it's all destroyed you too. Because you're a finished man, Albert
Simpson. The world is finished with you and you are sick of yourself
and tired and worn down by the thing you built up with so much
trickery and ambition. You're going to die in the India which you
hate, of a loathsome disease; and no one will ever care, not one person
in the world, not even your wife or your servant or the secretary you
sent ahead to Bombay. That wonderful private railway carriage which
you thought made you seem greater than other men will go back
without you. Maybe your ashes will go home on that swift beautiful
boat and maybe they won't. But you're finished. God-damn you!
You'll never get out of that horrible bed alive, to sleep with me again
like an animal. You'll never again shout at servants as if they were
dogs. You'll never again make me ashamed in public that I ever knew
you. You did something horrible to me, to my very soul. Oh, I let you

do it because I was tired and didn't care, but you could have helped me a little. You might have seen what I needed—oh, so little—to have saved me, but you didn't see. You never had time. All you did was shove money at me. Well, you're finished. You're going to die and rot and in a few years nobody will remember who you were. You haven't even an heir to leave behind you. I'm glad that vile blood of yours won't go on living because I bore you a child. I'm glad I saw to that. You're finished and nobody cares. Go on, slobber and snore, like the gross animal you are. There were times when you thought you could break my pride and make me as coarse as yourself, but you never did. In the end I've won. Even last night I won when I sent you skulking out of my room. You hadn't any kindness or any morals or any ethics, so nobody could touch you but me. I knew you well enough to know where it would hurt, and you made me use my knowledge. You forced me to do it. I'm not sorry. I wish it had been more cruel. Oh, if you only knew how many times I'd betrayed you, and never once with a man who wasn't better than yourself—kinder, warmer, more decent, more beautiful. Yes, and every one of them was a better lover than you. People grow to look like what they are, Albert. You were a hog and you've grown to look like a hog, lying there, snoring and slobbering in your own spittle. Well, you're going to die. This is the end of you; and the whole world—even little brats in the streets of India and China—will be happier and have a better life because you are dead."

And presently she felt a wild desire to cross the room and spit on him, but she did not do it because it occurred to her almost immediately that such a spectacle would only be extremely funny. "What's happened to me?" she thought. "Perhaps I'm going to be ill too. I shouldn't be here in this room. But even if I caught something, what difference would it make? I shouldn't care. Why should I suddenly care so profoundly about Albert's nastiness? Why should I be hysterical?"

Leaving him, she went back to her own room and threw herself down on the bed, and in a moment she found that she was crying without making a sound. The tears streamed down her face and made a nasty little puddle on the pillow of pink *crêpe de Chine*. She could not think why she was weeping; certainly it was neither for Esketh nor from fear of death. She had never been afraid of that, not half so afraid as she had been of growing old and losing the white smooth- ness of her skin and the shine of her blond hair. She could not remem- ber having wept since she was a schoolgirl and now this was the same sort of weeping, from nerves, over nothing at all, a relaxing, satisfac- tory performance, touched by the same voluptuousness and melancholy.

"But I've never had nerves," she thought. "It must be this damned country and this damned climate—the bloody rain and heat and bore- dom."

After a time she felt better and, sitting up, she took her mirror and looked at herself, a little shocked that her hair was in such disarray and her eyes so red and swollen. Looking at her reflection she thought, "Is that really me? It can't be," for what she saw was a woman who was no longer elegant and smooth and beautiful, but a rather plain disheveled creature on the verge of middle age. And then in fright she put down the mirror.

"What if I should never escape? What if I should have to stay in this awful country forever? If my looks go what will I have to offer a man?" "No," she thought, "I must be quick. I must snatch every- thing while I can." And she wondered whether she looked to Major Safti as she had looked just now in the mirror. She had wanted to look her best because he was more attractive than she had remembered. But for him she would pack up and leave now. To hell with Albert! To hell even with the Major! She leaned across the little table to push the bell for the maid, to tell her to begin packing at once, but in the middle of the gesture she stopped herself. You couldn't do that, even to Albert.

Miss Dirks was late for tea, not because she had failed to leave the high school in plenty of time but because she had stopped a great deal on the way—in shops, at the library and even at the museum where she pretended to be looking for some new Persian designs which the younger girls might use in their embroidery and water-color work. When she had first come to Ranchipur, people—even Indians who are rarely astonished by anything—had turned and looked after her in the street, not only because of her strange sexless appearance but because there was something about her which set her apart from other people, something direct and determined; duty was a master little known and scarcely recognized among Indians. But now they no longer noticed her because she had become a kind of fixture, like the statue of Queen Victoria on the middle buttress of the Zoological Gardens bridge.

It was not an easy thing for her to do—this going to have tea with Ransome. A half-dozen times she very nearly lost her courage and would have turned back save that her sense of obligation amounted to an obsession. She had engaged herself for tea and Mr. Ransome was waiting for her to arrive and in order not to fail him she would have passed through fire and water, battle and plague.

For the first time in twenty-five years she was calling on a European and for the first time in her life she was calling on a man. A year or two earlier, when she felt strong as a horse, it would have been easier for her, but now when she was weak and tired there were moments as she walked through the rain when she felt a strange animal desire to crawl into a thicket of bamboo and quietly die, alone, leaving the world to deal with all the troubles which tormented her, to lie down and quit like a faithful old horse who could not go one step further. As she trudged along in her heavy boots the temptation became an obsession, the kind of luxury which one would encounter only in heaven. And her weariness seemed too to drag her back and back across all the years of isolation into her childhood as if she were already a very old woman, so ancient that she forgot what happened yesterday and remembered only those things which had occurred when she was very young. She wasn't any longer Miss Sarah Dirks, distinguished and able head-mistress of the Maharani's High School for Girls who had done an extraordinary job under the most discouraging circumstances, but plain awkward Sally Dirks, daughter of the Nolham draper, going to the castle to help at the annual bazaar for the benefit of the orphanage.

At the prospect of having tea with Ransome the same vague awe and confusion filled the heart of this tired woman of fifty which had filled the same heart at the age of seventeen. It all returned to her with remarkable clearness, the whole picture of the castle, the great lawn with the little booths all about it and the showers which always interrupted the gayeties, and in the midst of the scene Ransome's mother,

Lady Nolham, all in lace with a big picture hat, moving about fussily and aimlessly, always in spite of everything a stranger, greeting the townspeople. She could remember too the figure of the child of three or four who clung to her hand, a good-looking child with dark curly hair, the youngest of the family, who had grown up into Tom Ransome.

It was absurd, she told herself, that she should be upset at the prospect of calling upon a man who was young enough to be her son. She tried to argue herself out of the feeling but in spite of every argument she still felt herself to be what she had been at seventeen, pale, unattractive and shy, the daughter of the village draper permitted inside the grounds of the Castle on the occasion of the annual bazaar and horticultural show. For three hundred years the people of the Castle had looked after the people of the village conscientiously and well.

At five-thirty she arrived at last, her heart beating wildly to find Ransome waiting for her on the verandah, drinking brandy. "He looks like his father," she thought. "But his drinking is beginning to tell." She thought he looked tired and middle-aged. The drinking probably came from his mother. In the last letter she ever had from Nolham her sister had written that Lady Nolham (so she had heard) was unhappy and drank secretly.

For a moment it seemed to her that she had not the strength to climb the five steps to the verandah, not only because she felt tired and ill but because she was bearing the weight of a whole flood of new memories, which had come rushing back to her at sight of him.

He was very kind to her and put an extra cushion into the deep chair when he had taken her mackintosh. He did it gracefully and with sincerity of feeling. "They were always great gentlemen," she thought. He did it just as his father would have done. She could remember old Lord Nolham well, coming into her father's shop to pass the time of day. He too had had that same quiet look of desperation. He was, she remembered, a very handsome man who wore side-whiskers like Lord Lonsdale.

She said, "I hope I haven't been a nuisance, coming in like this?" and at the sound of her own voice she felt her confidence returning a little.

He laughed pleasantly, showing very white teeth, and it struck her that it was a pity so handsome a young man should apparently be set upon destroying himself by dissipation.

"I've nothing to do," he said; "I never have. After all, life in Ranchipur is very simple, especially when you have nothing to do like me."

John the Baptist appeared with the tea, silent, but observing everything out of his large dark ox-eyes, and Miss Dirks said, "Shall I pour it?"

"Please. No, I won't have any."

She poured her own tea, her big bony hands shaking with weakness and excitement. "I heard that you painted," she said; and again he laughed: "No, not really. I haven't any talent. I do it to kill time."

It was not easy at first. There were little halts and pauses, and he discovered that in her shyness Miss Dirks had developed a stammer which made it difficult sometimes to understand what she was saying. It was awkward because they were both waiting for something—Miss Dirks to tell the reason for her visit, and Ransome to discover what it was. They talked of the rains and the cholera, of the school and the Maharajah's impending departure, and after a time Ransome began to feel that weariness which came over him when he talked with people who were not frank but held back a part of themselves. It always gave him a sense of fencing with a shadowy opponent, of trying to find something which he knew was there but could not find. All the while Miss Dirks sat bolt upright, with an air of authority, as if she were conducting a class. He noticed that now and then the muscles of her face would contract with sudden harshness and she would grow deathly pale.

John the Baptist returned presently to take away the tea things and then Miss Dirks plunged.

She said, "How long has it been since you last saw Nolham?"

At the mention of the name he put down his brandy glass suddenly:

"Nolham? Oh, ten years at least. What do you know about Nolham?"

"Do you remember Mr. Dirks, the draper?"

"Old 'Dacy' Dirks? Of course I do. Oh, I see. You're some relation?"

924   LOUIS BROMFIELD

"I'm his daughter. He only had two children. My sister still lives in Nolham and keeps the shop."

The thing was done now, the barrier broken down and she felt suddenly free. All at once it was as if they were old friends, and Miss Dirks felt a wild desire to cry.

"Why didn't you ever tell me before?"

"Well, you see, I scarcely knew you. I couldn't think that it mattered very much, really. I thought it would be . . ." She hesitated miserably and then said, "I thought it would seem presumptuous."

"You should have told me. I never connected the names—yours and Nolham, I mean. I never thought of it. You see, your father died when I was still a boy and I haven't been back to Nolham since my brother succeeded."

"My father has been dead twenty-one years this autumn."

"That's right. I must have been about eighteen. I remember the funeral. I went to it with my father. I was home on leave."

"Yes, he died after I came out here."

"What do you hear from Nolham?"

A shadow crossed the grim face of Miss Dirks. "I don't hear much," she said. "You see, I've rather gotten out of the habit of writing home. I haven't had a letter for a good many years." After twenty-five years, she still thought of Nolham, with its green common and the little river full of reeds alongside, as home. India was still "out here."

"I know," he said. "One does lose contact. It's been three or four years since I've had any news from there. The last was from Banks, the estate agent, about some things my father left me."

"Not old Morgan Banks? He's not still alive?"

"No, his nephew . . . you remember, the red-headed one."

They were getting on now. Miraculously, suddenly, they had slipped back into the ancient relationship from which they had both broken away so long ago. Nothing had really changed that feeling between Castle and Village. It was exactly the same as if neither of them had ever left Nolham and they had met now by chance in the Peacock Tea Room instead of on the verandah of a house in Ranchipur.

They talked about characters in the town, about the changes which had taken place since they both had left. There was something in her eagerness which made him feel inexpressibly sad. She flushed and grew excited and at last she confessed, "You don't know how I sometimes longed to talk with you about Nolham, but I couldn't get up my courage. You see Elizabeth—that's Miss Hodge—had never seen Nolham. She comes from Birmingham. She's city bred. She'd never understand what Nolham was like."

He had quite forgotten that she had come to see him about a matter which was "personal" until she grew suddenly rather stern again and said, "But that wasn't really what I came for. It was to talk about something else—to talk about Major Safti, to be exact."

"He's a great friend of mine."

"Well. That's just it. You see I've been ill for several months." She flushed and added, "I may have to have an operation. I wanted to know about him."

"There's no better surgeon in India."

Again a wave of color came over her face: "I didn't mean that. I know that. I meant what kind of a man is he?"

Then slowly the preposterousness of what she was seeking struck him. He felt a ribald desire to laugh and managed to translate it into a reassuring smile.

"Oh, he's a fine gentleman," he said, "one of the finest I've ever known. Charming and human too." And in order to make it clear he added, "He's immensely understanding and his attitude toward things like that is absolutely scientific and professional."

"Then you'd advise me to go to him?"

"I should think he was the one man in all India to go to. You needn't feel shy with him. He won't make you feel shy."

(My God! Now I'm becoming adviser to old maids with female complaints.)

"Well," said Miss Dirks, "I must say I've never heard anything against him. It was only that he was Indian. I've never gotten over feeling that Indians are a little strange."

"He's the same race as you and I. Even his eyes are blue."

"I know . . . I know," said Miss Dirks, "but they always *seem* different."

He had thought that she meant to leave but she remained, slipping off again, temporizing, talking about his garden and John the Baptist.

At last she said, "That wasn't all I wanted to ask you. There was another thing . . . about Miss Hodge."

"If I can help in any way, I'll be delighted."

The color rushed back again into Miss Dirks' face: "You see, we've been friends for a great many years and she has come to be dependent upon me—rather too dependent. She doesn't even think for herself any more except"—she hesitated for a moment and then plunged—"except in moments of rebellion; and at such times she hasn't any judgment or balance. She's like someone who tries to get up and walk for the first time after having been in bed for years." She fumbled with the worn handbag in her lap and looked away from him: "Lately she's been getting worse. You see at times it seems almost as if she were a little . . . well, unbalanced." She hurried on as if she were forcing herself: "You see, I've lost touch with all my friends and relations at home and the same thing has happened to her. What I'm worried about is if I should have to have an operation and anything should happen to me."

Tears rose suddenly to her eyes, but they did not fall. It was the gnawing pain and the weakness which made her cry. With a terrible effort she stopped the tears almost before they had begun to flow. Ransome, listening, thought, "If only she could say all that is in her heart. If only once she could let herself go." But it was too late now. She, like Miss Hodge, was paralyzed, but in a different way.

"You see," she went on, "if anything did happen to me, Elizabeth would be left all alone in the world. Whatever money I have, I'm leaving to her. It isn't much but it's enough to make her comfortable— a little I've saved and what my sister paid me for my share of the shop in Nolham. You see, there were only two of us and my father left it to us jointly. My sister . . . she married Tom Atwood, son of the chemist. Maybe you remember."

"Of course. Perfectly."

"Well, she wanted to buy my share, so I sold it to her. But to get back to the point . . . I can't think of Elizabeth being left out here all alone. She's so nervous and flighty. You see, what I wanted to ask you about was finding someone who might act as a kind of trustee for her to look after the money and see that she didn't get into some scrape or other. I came to you because you were the only possible person. It isn't only that we really don't know anyone out here, but you were the only one I could think of who might understand. If anything happened to me, I'd prefer to have Elizabeth go back to England. I hope it's not too presumptuous . . . I hope . . ."

Ransome said, "I couldn't do it myself. I'm not what you'd call a responsible person And I might clear out and leave Ranchipur for good at any time, but I could ask the family solicitor to take the responsibility. He'd do it for me and then you could be sure that her income would always be safe."

Again the tears rose for an instant in the clear blue eyes: "That's so good of you. You don't know what a relief it is. You see, I feel responsible for Elizabeth. I feel as if it were my fault, as if I'd brought her out here where she's lost touch with everyone at home. I was always the strongest and I've always had wonderful health. I never thought that something would happen to me first. I never thought that anything like this would happen. It's very kind of you. It makes everything much easier."

"You can trust him. He'll know exactly what to do."

"Some of the money is at Lloyd's in Bombay and the rest is at home in England. There's enough here to get her safely back." Again she hesitated for a moment: "Of course it's not all as simple as that. If anything did happen to me, it's quite possible that it would throw Elizabeth completely off her balance, for a time anyway. I was wondering if you could look out for her and see that she was treated kindly and got back to England all right. I know I'm asking a great deal, but I didn't know who to turn to. I worried about it for a long time and then I thought of Nolham. . . ."

He said, "I'm sure that there's no need to think about anything happening to you. I'm sure everything will be all right, especially with the Major. You can trust him."

He divined what it was she thought although she never quite said it, perhaps because she did not understand it quite clearly and had not the words to express it. In her extremity she had gone back to her roots, to a system, a civilization which had almost vanished, from which both of them had cut loose long ago; she had come up from the Village to find help at the Castle, and ironically she had come to him, the one member of the family who had revolted and refused to accept the responsibility. He was pleased that she had come to him and at the same time he was ashamed of the half-feudal pleasure he found in it. It was at once warming and deceptive to be thrust suddenly into the patriarchal position of the Lord of the Manor. And he thought suddenly of his grandmother at home in her great turreted house in Grand River, seeing her in the same circumstances, accepting the responsibility of Miss Hodge and of helping poor Miss Dirks, not as something medieval but as something simple and human. If she were only here now there was so much that she could do to help these two poor lonely old maids which he could never do because he was a man and because, in spite of everything, neither he nor they could ever quite forget the relationship of the Castle to the Village.

"I think now," she was saying, "that perhaps we were wrong in living so much apart. Sometimes Elizabeth did want to call on people and ask people to tea, but in the end, somehow, we never did it and so now we really don't know anyone."

While she was speaking his mind slipped quickly and naturally from his grandmother to Aunt Phoebe and from Aunt Phoebe to the Smileys, and then he saw exactly the course to take. The Smileys were precisely the ones to care for Miss Hodge if anything happened to Miss Dirks. One more burden he knew, would scarcely be noticed by them. And they would do it simply and kindly, as if Miss Hodge were a neighbor just across the street who had fallen ill. He found himself saying, "Maybe it's not too late. Maybe it would be a good idea to have Miss Hodge come to know some of the nice people." He saw that she winced a little as he said "nice people," but he went on: "I'm sure nothing is going to happen to you, but if it did, then she wouldn't find herself quite alone. Maybe it would be a good idea if I gave a tea party. Would you come and bring Miss Hodge?"

She did not answer him at once, for she was struggling again with the terror and paralysis which attacked her whenever the question of human contacts arose. At last she said, "That would be very nice of you." And then the seamed harsh face went white: "But I'm afraid it's impossible. You see there are so many people who wouldn't come if they knew we were going to be there."

"Oh, I'm sure that you imagine that."

She looked at him directly, searchingly, as if judging whether he would understand what she had to say and then, like Fern Simon, she found in his face something which gave her courage and she plunged: "You see, some of the people here have spread nasty stories about Miss Hodge and me."

He smiled, "Oh, I hadn't meant to ask those people. I never see them myself. I had meant to ask friends of mine—the Smileys and Mrs. Smiley's aunt and Miss MacDaid and Major Safti and maybe Raschid Ali Khan and his wife. Raschid might be very useful to Miss Hodge."

The whiteness left her face and she hesitated for a moment on account, he knew, of the Indians. Then she said, "Yes, that would be very nice. And then perhaps we could give a party too at home. I think that would make Elizabeth quite happy. For years she's wanted people to see the house and how very attractive she's made it."

"Very well, then. I'll do it. I'll let you know what day I can get them all together."

She rose now and took up the mackintosh, and when he helped her with it he saw that she was trembling from head to foot with the effort the visit had cost her:

"And I'll speak to my friend the Major about an examination. I know he'll see you whenever you like. You needn't be afraid of him. He's a kind man and very understanding."

"That would be very good of you. You've helped me so much today."

"It wasn't much I've done. We must have another talk soon about Nolham. It's made me homesick." And he knew at once that he had said the wrong thing because he had raised up for her a picture of the little town which her spirit had never left and her body would never see again. She choked and said, "Yes, sometimes I get very homesick for the common and the river and my father's shop."

She would not let him drive her home but went alone down the drive into the rain, leaving him with his brandy and soda; and when she had gone out of sight he himself returned to Nolham which had come back to him with extraordinary vividness. Talking about old "Dacy" Dirks and Morgan Bates and Tom Atwood, the chemist, had suddenly peopled the common, the square, the "pub," with figures, alive and moving about within that frame which none of them had ever left. It was far enough away now for him to forget the things he had hated—the awful patronizing Victorian qualities of his father, the arrogance and snobbery of his older brother, the bewildered unhappiness of his ineffectual mother whose money it was that kept Nolham intact, the quality of lifeless, paralyzing artificiality which he always felt on his return from the easy freedom of Grand River—all that rigid feeling of caste which he found even in the scullery. All these things seemed unimportant now and, sentimentally, he saw only the virtues of a system into which he had never fitted—the stability, the peace, the sense of obligation accepted alike by Castle and Village. But even that was already going. They were represented by a Socialist M. P. and bit by bit the land had been sold until there remained only one or two farms and the vast useless park which surrounded the castle. Even his mother's American fortune, dug long ago by his grandfather out of the hills of Nevada, was not enough to preserve it.

Out of all the figures from his boyhood old "Dacy" Dirks the draper emerged the clearest of all, perhaps because there had always been about him a sinister quality almost of menace, standing in the doorway of his shop, clad in the unchanging long-skirted coat and white tie, looking angrily across the little square toward the "Hare and the Jug" where so many fine young men were being ruined. "It was extraordinary," Ransome thought, "how well I divined, on that day at Mr. Jobnekar's, the background out of which Miss Dirks had come—divined it without even so much as a hint."

Old "Dacy" belonged to the Plymouth Brethren and in his household there was never any fun. The rooms back of the shop where "Dacy" and his family lived must have been as dreary and sunless as the shop itself. On the Sabbath there was never anything but the Bible. His daughters never saw any boys their own age and they were taught that all men save "Dacy" were predatory creatures and that love was an unfortunate necessity like going to the privy in the back garden. Out of that Miss Dirks had stumbled only a little way, crippled and hampered, to die at last in India on the other side of the world from green quiet Nolham, having never known any pleasure save the grim tyrannical satisfaction of having done her duty.

For she was going to die. He knew while she sat there talking to him that he had entertained at tea a woman who was already dead. He was wrong only in the supposition that she herself did not know it.

PEARL BUCK Why she selected

The OLD DEMON

I chose "The Old Demon" for your anthology because it represents for me the source of China's strength which is in her country people, who are four-fifths of all of them. Then, too, China's women are a source of her strength. They are strong and fearless and indomitable, and they seem to grow finer as they grow older. The incident of opening the dikes is a true one. Dikes were opened in many places and fields were flooded as a weapon against the enemy.

Perkasie, Pa.   PEARL BUCK
April 20, 1942

OLD Mrs. Wang knew of course that there was a war. Everybody had known for a long time that there was war going on and that Japanese were killing Chinese. But still it was not real and no more than hearsay since none of the Wangs had been killed. The Village of Three Mile Wangs on the flat banks of the Yellow River, which was old Mrs. Wang's clan village, had never even seen a Japanese. This was how they came to be talking about Japanese at all.

It was evening and early summer, and after her supper Mrs. Wang had climbed the dike steps, as she did every day, to see how high the river had risen. She was much more afraid of the river than of the Japanese. She knew what the river would do. And one by one the villagers had followed her up the dike, and now they stood staring down at the malicious yellow water, curling along like a lot of snakes, and biting at the high dike banks.

"I never saw it as high as this so early," Mrs. Wang said. She sat down on a bamboo stool that her grandson, Little Pig, had brought for her, and spat into the water.

"It's worse than the Japanese, this old devil of a river," Little Pig said recklessly.

"Fool!" Mrs. Wang said quickly. "The river god will hear you. Talk about something else."

So they had gone on talking about the Japanese. . . . How, for instance, asked Wang, the baker, who was old Mrs. Wang's nephew twice removed, would they know the Japanese when they saw them?

Mrs. Wang at this point said positively, "You'll know them. I once saw a foreigner. He was taller than the eaves of my house and he had mud-colored hair and eyes the color of a fish's eyes. Anyone who does not look like us—that is a Japanese."

Everybody listened to her since she was the oldest woman in the village and whatever she said settled something.

Then Little Pig spoke up in his disconcerting way. "You can't see them, Grandmother. They hide up in the sky in airplanes."

Mrs. Wang did not answer immediately. Once she would have said positively, "I shall not believe in an airplane until I see it." But so many things had been true which she had not believed—the Empress, for instance, whom she had not believed dead, was dead. The Republic, again, she had not believed in because she did not know what it was. She still did not know, but they had said for a long time there had been one. So now she merely stared quietly about the dike where they all sat around her. It was very pleasant and cool, and she felt nothing mattered if the river did not rise to flood.

"I don't believe in the Japanese," she said flatly.

They laughed at her a little, but no one spoke. Someone lit her pipe—it was Little Pig's wife, who was her favorite, and she smoked it.

"Sing, Little Pig!" someone called.

So Little Pig began to sing an old song in a high quavering voice, and old Mrs. Wang listened and forgot the Japanese. The evening was beautiful, the sky so clear and still that the willows overhanging the dike were reflected even in the muddy water. Everything was at peace. The thirty-odd houses which made up the village straggled along beneath them. Nothing could break this peace. After all, the Japanese were only human beings.

"I doubt those airplanes," she said mildly to Little Pig when he stopped singing.

But without answering her, he went on to another song.

Year in and year out she had spent the summer evenings like this on the dike. The first time she was seventeen and a bride, and her husband had shouted to her to come out of the house and up the dike, and she had come, blushing and twisting her hands together to hide among the women while the men roared at her and made jokes about her. All the same, they had liked her. "A pretty piece of meat in your bowl," they had said to her husband. "Feet a trifle big," he had answered deprecatingly. But she could see he was pleased, and so gradually her shyness went away.

He, poor man, had been drowned in a flood when he was still young. And it had taken her years to get him prayed out of Buddhist purgatory. Finally she had grown tired of it, what with the child and the land all on her back, and so when the priest said coaxingly, "Another ten pieces of silver and he'll be out entirely," she asked, "What's he got in there yet?"

"Only his right hand," the priest said, encouraging her.

Well, then, her patience broke. Ten dollars! It would feed them for the winter. Besides, she had had to hire labor for her share of repairing the dike, too, so there would be no more floods.

"If it's only one hand, he can pull himself out," she said firmly.

She often wondered if he had, poor silly fellow. As like as not, she had often thought gloomily in the night, he was still lying there, waiting for her to do something about it. That was the sort of man he was. Well, some day, perhaps, when Little Pig's wife had had the first baby safely and she had a little extra, she might go back to finish him out of purgatory. There was no real hurry, though. . . .

"Grandmother, you must go in," Little Pig's wife's soft voice said. "There is a mist rising from the river now that the sun is gone."

"Yes, I suppose I must," old Mrs. Wang agreed. She gazed at the river a moment. That river—it was full of good and evil together. It would water the fields when it was curbed and checked, but then if an inch were allowed it, it crashed through like a roaring dragon. That was how her husband had been swept away—careless, he was, about his bit of the dike. He was always going to mend it, always going to pile more earth on top of it, and then in a night the river rose and broke through. He had run out of the house, and she had climbed on the roof with the child and had saved herself and it while he was drowned. Well, they had pushed the river back again behind its dikes, and it had stayed there this time. Every day she herself walked up and down the length of the dike for which the village was responsible and examined it. The men laughed and said, "If anything is wrong with the dikes, Granny will tell us."

It had never occurred to any of them to move the village away from the river. The Wangs had lived there for generations, and some had always escaped the floods and had fought the river more fiercely than ever afterward.

Little Pig suddenly stopped singing.

"The moon is coming up!" he cried. "That's not good. Airplanes come out on moonlight nights."

"Where do you learn all this about airplanes?" old Mrs. Wang exclaimed. "It is tiresome to me," she added, so severely that no one spoke. In this silence, leaning upon the arm of Little Pig's wife, she descended slowly the earthen steps which led down into the village, using her long pipe in the other hand as a walking stick. Behind her the villagers came down, one by one, to bed. No one moved before she did, but none stayed long after her.

And in her own bed at last, behind the blue cotton mosquito curtains which Little Pig's wife fastened securely, she fell peacefully asleep. She had lain awake a little while thinking about the Japanese and wondering why they wanted to fight. Only very coarse persons wanted wars. In her mind she saw large coarse persons. If they came one must wheedle them, she thought, invite them to drink tea, and explain to them, reasonably—only why should they come to a peaceful farming village . . . ?

So she was not in the least prepared for Little Pig's wife screaming at her that the Japanese had come. She sat up in bed muttering, "The tea bowls—the tea ——"

"Grandmother, there's no time!" Little Pig's wife screamed. "They're here—they're here!"

"Where?" old Mrs. Wang cried, now awake.

"In the sky!" Little Pig's wife wailed.

They had all run out at that, into the clear early dawn, and gazed up. There, like wild geese flying in autumn, were great birdlike shapes.

"But what are they?" old Mrs. Wang cried.

And then, like a silver egg dropping, something drifted straight down and fell at the far end of the village in a field. A fountain of earth flew up, and they all ran to see it. There was a hole thirty feet across, as big as a pond. They were so astonished they could not speak, and then, before anyone could say anything, another and another egg began to fall and everybody was running, running . . .

Everybody, that is, but Mrs. Wang. When Little Pig's wife seized her hand to drag her along, old Mrs. Wang pulled away and sat down against the bank of the dike.

"I can't run," she remarked. "I haven't run in seventy years, since before my feet were bound. You go on. Where's Little Pig?" She looked around. Little Pig was already gone. "Like his grandfather," she remarked, "always the first to run."

But Little Pig's wife would not leave her, not, that is, until old Mrs. Wang reminded her that it was her duty.

"If Little Pig is dead," she said, "then it is necessary that his son be born alive." And when the girl still hesitated, she struck at her gently with her pipe. "Go on—go on," she exclaimed.

So unwillingly, because now they could scarcely hear each other speak for the roar of the dipping planes, Little Pig's wife went on with the others.

By now, although only a few minutes had passed, the village was in ruins and the straw roofs and wooden beams were blazing. Everybody was gone. As they passed they had shrieked at old Mrs. Wang to come on, and she had called back pleasantly:

"I'm coming—I'm coming!"

But she did not go. She sat quite alone watching now what was an extraordinary spectacle. For soon other planes came, from where she did not know, but they attacked the first ones. The sun came up over the fields of ripening wheat, and in the clear summery air the planes wheeled and darted and spat at each other. When this was over, she thought, she would go back into the village and see if anything was left. Here and there a wall stood, supporting a roof. She could not see her own house from here. But she was not unused to war. Once bandits had looted their village, and houses had been burned then, too. Well, now it had happened again. Burning houses one could see often, but not this darting silvery shining battle in the air. She understood none of it—not what those things were, nor how they stayed up in the sky. She simply sat, growing hungry, and watching.

"I'd like to see one close," she said aloud. And at that moment, as though in answer, one of them pointed suddenly downward, and, wheeling and twisting as though it were wounded, it fell head down in a field which Little Pig had ploughed only yesterday for soybeans. And in an instant the sky was empty again, and there was only this wounded thing on the ground and herself.

She hoisted herself carefully from the earth. At her age she need be afraid of nothing. She could, she decided, go and see what it was. So, leaning on her bamboo pipe, she made her way slowly across the fields. Behind her in the sudden stillness two or three village dogs appeared and followed, creeping close to her in their terror. When they drew near to the fallen plane, they barked furiously. Then she hit them with her pipe.

"Be quiet," she scolded, "there's already been noise enough to split my ears!"

She tapped the airplane.

"Metal," she told the dogs. "Silver, doubtless," she added. Melted up, it would make them all rich.

She walked around it, examining it closely. What made it fly? It seemed dead. Nothing moved or made a sound within it. Then, coming to the side to which it tipped, she saw a young man in it, plumped into a heap in a little seat. The dogs growled, but she struck at them again and they fell back.

"Are you dead?" she inquired politely.

The young man moved a little at her voice, but did not speak. She drew nearer and peered into the hole in which he sat. His side was bleeding.

"Wounded!" she exclaimed. She took his wrist. It was warm, but inert, and when she let it go, it dropped against the side of the hole. She stared at him. He had black hair and a dark skin like a Chinese and still he did not look like a Chinese.

"He must be a Southerner," she thought. Well, the chief thing was, he was alive.

"You had better come out," she remarked. "I'll put some herb plaster on your side."

The young man muttered something dully.

"What did you say?" she asked. But he did not say it again.

"I am still quite strong," she decided after a moment. So she reached in and seized him about the waist and pulled him out slowly, panting a good deal. Fortunately he was rather a little fellow and very light. When she had him on the ground, he seemed to find his feet; and he stood shakily and clung to her, and she held him up.

"Now if you can walk to my house," she said, "I'll see if it is there."

Then he said something, quite clearly. She listened and could not understand a word of it. She pulled away from him and stared.

"What's that?" she asked.

He pointed at the dogs. They were standing growling, their ruffs up. Then he spoke again, and as he spoke he crumpled to the ground. The dogs fell on him, so that she had to beat them off with her hands.

"Get away!" she shouted. "Who told *you* to kill him?"

And then, when they had slung back, she heaved him somehow onto her back, trembling, half carrying, half pulling him, she dragged him to the ruined village and laid him in the street while she went to find her house, taking the dogs with her.

Her house was quite gone. She found the place easily enough. This was where it should be, opposite the water gate into the dike. She had always watched that gate herself. Miraculously it was not injured now, nor was the dike broken. It would be easy enough to rebuild the house. Only, for the present, it was gone.

So she went back to the young man. He was lying as she had left him, propped against the dike, panting and very pale. He had opened his coat and he had a little bag from which he was taking out strips of cloth and a bottle of something. And again he spoke, and again she understood nothing. Then he made signs and she saw it was water he wanted, so she took up a broken pot from one of many blown about the street, and, going up the dike, she filled it with river water and brought it down again and washed his wound, and she tore off the strips he made from the rolls of bandaging. He knew how to put the cloth over the gaping wound and he made signs to her, and she followed these signs. All the time he was trying to tell her something, but she could understand nothing.

"You must be from the South, sir," she said. It was easy to see that he had education. He looked very clever. "I have heard your language is different from ours." She laughed a little to put him at his ease, but he only stared at her somberly with dull eyes. So she said brightly, "Now if I could find something for us to eat, it would be nice."

He did not answer. Indeed he lay back, panting still more heavily, and stared into space as though she had not spoken.

"You would be better with food," she went on. "And so would I," she added. She was beginning to feel unbearably hungry.

"It occurred to her that in Wang, the baker's, shop there might be some bread. Even if it were dusty with fallen mortar, it would still be bread. She would go and see. But before she went she moved the soldier a little so that he lay in the edge of shadow cast by a willow tree that grew in the bank of the dike. Then she went to the baker's shop. The dogs were gone.

The baker's shop was, like everything else, in ruins. No one was there. At first she saw nothing but the mass of crumpled earthen walls. But then she remembered that the oven was just inside the door, and the door frame still stood erect, supporting one end of the roof. She stood in this frame, and, running her hand in underneath the fallen roof inside, she felt the wooden cover of the iron caldron. Under this there might be steamed bread. She worked her arm delicately and carefully in. It took quite a long time, but, even so, clouds of lime and dust almost choked her. Nevertheless she was right. She squeezed her hand under the cover and felt the firm smooth skin of the big steamed bread rolls, and one by one she drew out four.

"It's hard to kill an old thing like me," she remarked cheerfully to no one, and she began to eat one of the rolls as she walked back. If she had a bit of garlic and a bowl of tea—but one couldn't have everything in these times.

It was at this moment that she heard voices. When she came in sight of the soldier, she saw surrounding him a crowd of other soldiers, who had apparently come from nowhere. They were staring down at the wounded soldier, whose eyes were now closed.

"Where did you get this Japanese, Old Mother?" they shouted at her.

"What Japanese?" she asked, coming to them.

"This one!" they shouted.

"Is he a Japanese?" she cried in the greatest astonishment. "But he looks like us—his eyes are black, his skin ——"

"Japanese!" one of them shouted at her.

"Well," she said quietly, "he dropped out of the sky."

"Give me that bread!" another shouted.

"Take it," she said, "all except this one for him."

"A Japanese monkey eat good bread?" the soldier shouted.

"I suppose he is hungry also," old Mrs. Wang replied. She began to dislike these men. But then, she had always disliked soldiers.

"I wish you would go away," she said. "What are you doing here? Our village has always been peaceful."

"It certainly looks very peaceful now," one of the men said, grinning, "as peaceful as a grave. Do you know who did that, Old Mother? The Japanese!"

"I suppose so," she agreed. Then she asked, "Why? That's what I don't understand."

"Why? Because they want our land, that's why!"

"Our land!" she repeated. "Why, they can't have our land!"

"Never!" they shouted.

But all this time while they were talking and chewing bread they had divided among themselves, they were watching the eastern horizon.

"Why do you keep looking east?" old Mrs. Wang now asked.

"The Japanese are coming from there," the man replied who had taken the bread.

"Are you running away from them?" she asked, surprised.

"There are only a handful of us," he said apologetically. "We were left to guard a village—Pao An, in the county of——"

"I know that village," old Mrs. Wang interrupted. "You needn't tell me. I was a girl there. How is the old Pao who keeps the teashop in the main street? He's my brother."

"Everybody is dead there," the man replied. "The Japanese have taken it—a great army of men came with their foreign guns and tanks, so what could we do?"

"Of course, only run," she agreed. Nevertheless she felt dazed and sick. So he was dead, that one brother she had left! She was now the last of her father's family.

But the soldiers were straggling away again leaving her alone.

"They'll be coming, those little black dwarfs," they were saying. "We'd best go on."

Nevertheless, one lingered a moment, the one who had taken the bread, to stare down at the young wounded man, who lay with his eyes shut, not having moved at all.

"Is he dead?" he inquired. Then, before Mrs. Wang could answer, he pulled a short knife out of his belt. "Dead or not, I'll give him a punch or two with this——"

But old Mrs. Wang pushed his arm away.

"No, you won't," she said with authority. "If he is dead, then there is no use sending him into purgatory all in pieces. I am a good Buddhist myself."

The man laughed. "Oh well, he is dead," he answered; and then, seeing his comrades already at a distance, he ran after them.

A Japanese, was he? Old Mrs. Wang, left alone with this inert figure, looked at him tentatively. He was very young, she could see, now that his eyes were closed. His hand, limp in unconsciousness, looked like a boy's hand, unformed and still growing. She felt his wrist but could discern no pulse. She leaned over him and held to his lips the half of her roll which she had not eaten.

"Eat," she said very loudly and distinctly. "Bread!"

But there was no answer. Evidently he was dead. He must have died while she was getting the bread out of the oven.

There was nothing to do then but to finish the bread herself. And when that was done, she wondered if she ought not to follow after Little Pig and his wife and all the villagers. The sun was mounting and it was growing hot. If she were going, she had better go. But first she would climb the dike and see what the direction was. They had gone straight west, and as far as eye could look westward was a great plain. She might even see a good-sized crowd miles away. Anyway, she could see the next village, and they might all be there.

So she climbed the dike slowly, getting very hot. There was a slight breeze on top of the dike and it felt good. She was shocked to see the river very near the top of the dike. Why, it had risen in the last hour!

"You old demon!" she said severely. Let the river god hear it if he liked. He was evil, that he was—so to threaten flood when there had been all this other trouble.

She stooped and bathed her cheeks and her wrists. The water was quite cold, as though with fresh rains somewhere. Then she stood up and gazed around her. To the west there was nothing except in the far distance the soldiers still half-running, and beyond them the blur of the next village, which stood on a long rise of ground. She had better set out for that village. Doubtless Little Pig and his wife were there waiting for her.

Just as she was about to climb down and start out, she saw something on the eastern horizon. It was at first only an immense cloud of dust. But, as she stared at it, very quickly it became a lot of black dots and shining spots. Then she saw what it was. It was a lot of men—an army. Instantly she knew what army.

"That's the Japanese," she thought. Yes, above them were the buzzing silver planes. They circled about, seeming to search for someone.

"I don't know who you're looking for," she muttered, "unless it's me and Little Pig and his wife. We're the only ones left. You've already killed my brother Pao."

She had almost forgotten that Pao was dead. Now she remembered it acutely. He had such a nice shop—always clean, and the tea good and the best meat dumplings to be had and the price always the same. Pao was a good man. Besides, what about his wife and his seven children? Doubtless they were all killed, too. Now these Japanese were looking for her. It occurred to her that on the dike she could easily be seen. So she clambered hastily down.

It was when she was about halfway down that she thought of the water gate. This old river—it had been a curse to them since time began. Why should it not make up a little now for all the wickedness it had done? It was plotting wickedness again, trying to steal over its banks. Well, why not? She wavered a moment. It was a pity, of course, that the young dead Japanese would be swept into the flood. He was a nice-looking boy, and she had saved him from being stabbed. It was not quite the same as saving his life, of course, but still it was a little the same. If he had been alive, he would have been saved. She went over to him and tugged at him until he lay well near the top of the bank. Then she went down again.

She knew perfectly how to open the water gate. Any child knew how to open the sluice for crops. But she knew also how to swing open the whole gate. The question was, could she open it quickly enough to get out of the way?

"I'm only one old woman," she muttered. She hesitated a second more. Well, it would be a pity not to see what sort of a baby Little Pig's wife would have, but one could not see everything. She had seen a great deal in this life. There was an end to what one could see, anyway.

She glanced again to the east. There were the Japanese coming across the plain. They were a long clear line of black, dotted with thousands of glittering points. If she opened this gate, the impetuous water would roar toward them, rushing into the plains, rolling into a wide lake, drowning them, maybe. Certainly they could not keep on marching nearer and nearer to her and to Little Pig and his wife who were waiting for her. Well, Little Pig and his wife—they would wonder about her—but they would never dream of this. It would make a good story—she would have enjoyed telling it.

She turned resolutely to the gate. Well, some people fought with airplanes and some with guns, but you could fight with a river, too, if it were a wicked one like this one. She wrenched out a huge wooden pin. It was slippery with silvery green moss. The rill of water burst into a strong jet. When she wrenched one more pin, the rest would give way themselves. She began pulling at it, and felt it slip a little from its hole.

"I might be able to get myself out of purgatory with this," she thought, "and maybe they'll let me have that old man of mine, too. What's a hand of his to all this? Then we'll——"

The pin slipped away suddenly, and the gate burst flat against her and knocked her breath away. She had only time to gasp, to the river:

"Come on, you old demon!"

Then she felt it seize her and lift her up to the sky. It was beneath her and around her. It rolled her joyfully hither and thither, and then, holding her close and enfolded, it went rushing against the enemy.

JOHN GUNTHER Why he selected

The OUTBREAK of INTER-
NATIONAL GANGSTERISM

I've always liked "Death of Dollfuss" partly because of the agitated circumstances in which it was written. Things moved fast in Austria that week. I had my newspaper, the Chicago *Daily News*, to cover with daily cables. I was out most of the day, grabbing at rumors and information and then putting it all on the phone to Paris. But before the story was a day old I felt that it must have more permanent form, at least for my own intrinsic satisfaction. I wanted to figure out the how and why of these events, to fit them into a larger pattern, to have them on the record. I cabled my New York agent asking if he could place an article on the assassination, the *Putsch*, and its attendant crises. He fished around and a couple of American magazines turned the idea down. I remember how broke I was and how expensive my cables were. Then finally *Harper's* said they would take the piece. So I began to write it, while the events I was describing were still boiling and unfolding. Each evening I would squeeze myself into my office, which was the small servants' room on Neulinggasse, and try to write a consecutive narrative of all that occurred while, at the same time, giving it true body and perspective. I had to change the lead a dozen times. No sooner did I finish one version than our spies and tipsters (to say nothing of various muddled officials of the Austrian government) gave us new information, false or true. This I sought to weigh. My friend, M. W. Fodor, was of inestimable service and so was a splendid Netherlands newspaper man named Nypels. The technical difficulties were enormous. I don't think I ever worked so hard on an article. It was the first political article of this type that I had ever attempted. The manuscript was a patched-up mass of tangled cuts and inserts. Finally a sixth or seventh draft was ready. There was no time to retype it and I hurried down to the Westbahn station and threw it at the boat train. I felt that I had been salting the tail of history. I went home, happy, and had three beers.

New York, N. Y.   JOHN GUNTHER

July, 1942

THE murder of Dollfuss in 1934 marked the entrance of gangsterism into European politics on an international basis. On June 30, inside Germany, the Nazis imitated Al Capone, and on July 25 these methods crossed into a neighboring land. The assassination was a deliberate exercise in policy; the Nazis had to murder Dollfuss because every other method to defeat him failed. The story of the Dollfuss killing is that of an organized conspiracy to murder.

All the Putschists seem to have been members of the eighty-ninth SS regiment, one of four SS (Hitlerite guard) detachments which secretly existed on Austrian soil. The rank and file of the plotters were former non-commissioned officers or privates of the regular Austrian army who had been dismissed from the service for their Nazi sympathies. Also among them were active officers of the Vienna police whose surreptitious Nazi activities had escaped detection—an extremely important point.

The plotters looked for support in three directions. (1) In Germany there were Frauenfeld and Habicht, the exiled leaders of the Austrian section of the Nazi party. (2) In Vienna there was a group of high police executives and officials who were later arrested or fled the country. (3) In Rome there was "King Anton" Rintelen. There was another leader, a mysterious civilian whose *nom-de-complot* was Kunze, of whom more later.

Dr. Anton Rintelen, a white-cropped man of fifty-eight, who looked less like a conspirator than almost anyone I ever met, was promoted by Dollfuss to be Austrian minister in Rome in order to get him out of the country. He was too powerful to be overtly sacked. For ten years Rintelen had been governor of Styria, the turbulent province south of Vienna. He was clever and cold and ambitious and, though named by the Nazis to be their chancellor, he was not a Nazi. He was Rintelen. Years before he flirted with the socialists, hoping to reach power by a socialist coalition. When the socialists faded and the Nazis rose he intrigued with the Nazis. It is not the least of the ironies of July 25th that this chief actor should have been motivated by aims so crass. He ran with the Nazis not because he loved Hitler but because he wanted a job and loved power. The Nazis, on their side, needed him. He was "respectable" and they knew they could most easily gain Austria through the medium of a transitory coalition government. Rintelen was to be the Austrian Papen.

Various Styrian industrialists were friends of Rintelen. In their factories, like the Alpine Montangesellschaft, the largest industrial concern in Austria, the workmen were secretly organized on an SA basis. Here the Styrian rebels hid their arms.

Germany fed the springs of dissatisfaction and treachery with a powerful stream of gold; for instance it spent 75,000,000 marks in Austria for propaganda in the seventeen months between January, 1933 and July, 1934. Of German moral responsibility for the Dollfuss murder there was no doubt. Munich day in, day out, preached violence. And plenty of indication of German foreknowledge of the actual plot may be cited. As witness:

(1) The Munich headquarters of the Nazi party, according to the official *Wiener Zeitung*, had a special airplane ready at nine A.M. on the 25th for the victorious flight of Habicht and Frauenfeld to Vienna.

(2) As early as July 21st, a Berlin photo agency sent out pictures of Rintelen marked "New Austrian Chancellor—Hold for Release."

(3) A Nazi named Aberger, arrested in Innsbruck and later sentenced to life imprisonment for bomb smuggling, testified that on July 22nd, three days before the murder, he was informed by courier from Munich that an armed rising was scheduled in Austria for the 25th.

(4) Italian secret agents reported movements of the Austrian Legion (Austrian Nazis on German soil) to the frontier on the evening of the 24th. The Legion was to take posts two miles behind the border.

(5) Most striking of all, the official German news agency, the

Deutsches Nachrichten Büro, issued at ten-forty-five A.M. on July 25th instructions to all German papers to use only official German accounts of the news anticipated from Austria *that day.* Later this same agency prepared and distributed a story of the "successful" Austrian revolt, although at this time the *Putsch* had barely started.

The Nazi were in a hurry because Dollfuss planned to visit Mussolini in Riccioni, an Italian seaside resort, later that week, and they feared that some new agreement between Mussolini and Dollfuss would finally beat them. One story is that the *Putsch* was first planned for July 24th, but was postponed a day when secret information came to the plotters that Dollfuss' last cabinet session in Austria would take place on the 25th, not on the 24th as first believed. It was the intention of the conspirators to capture the whole cabinet. Rintelen had arrived in Vienna from Rome on July 23rd, ostensibly on a holiday.

So much for the setting. The actual events of July 25th began as follows:

At about eleven A.M. the conspirators assembled at various points in the streets of Vienna. Their organization was excellent and they acted with the utmost smoothness and precision. One group gathered, man by man, on the sidewalk of the Kolowrat Ring. They had received weapons from their leaders the night before, and some had found cards in their letter boxes notifying them of the rendezvous. Not all the plotters knew who the higher-ups were; the password was the number "89." Fourteen started from the Kolowrat Ring for Ravag, the radio headquarters, where the signal for the *Putsch* was given. They were not disguised and they went on foot. Loitering on the Johannesgasse, where Ravag is situated, were two uniformed policemen, members of the gang, who "covered" them and led them to the door.

A larger group meantime assembled at the gymnasium of the German Athletic Club on Siebensterngasse. This building, it is interesting to note, directly adjoins an army barracks. The plot had been organized with such sureness that one of the conspirators confessed later to having been informed by open telegram where to come and what to do. The group numbered one hundred and forty-four, of whom no fewer than one hundred and six were former army non-coms or privates, and ten were *active* police. The hour of attack was chosen with beautiful precision so that the plotters would reach the chancellery at the moment of the changing of the guard, when it was most vulnerable.

At about ten A.M. a police officer named Dobler who was also a prominent (secret) Nazi turned traitor to the Nazis and in a very befuddled and Viennese way betrayed the plot to the authorities.[1] Had they acted promptly, Dollfuss would never have been shot. But the police who were loyal had been fatigued by a plethora of false alarms, and the disloyal police sabotaged attempts to take precautions.

Dobler's movements that morning form a fascinating record. Trying to notify the authorities without giving himself away, he and intermediaries of the most astoundingly fortuitous variety succeeded, between ten and eleven-thirty, in holding meetings with public officials in at least three different—of course—coffee-houses. By about eleven-fifteen Major Wrabel, the aide-de-camp to Major Fey, minister of public security, had heard the gist of the matter. He sent a trusted detective, Marek, to Siebensterngasse to investigate. Fey seems to have been informed, "rather vaguely," at eleven-forty-five. He acted promptly and at once informed the cabinet, but it was too late.

The detective, Marek, arrived at the Siebensterngasse barracks and saw the plotters, but the presence of uniformed police threw him off the track. The whole plot was made possible by the factor of disguise Nevertheless his suspicions grew and three times he telephoned to Wrabel between twelve-ten and twelve-thirty, once from a public phone-booth, once from a coffee-house, once from a furniture shop. Wrabel transmitted the alarm to the public security officials, but police headquarters were only informed later. Meantime loyal police had been misled by clever and daring spies who reported that an attack on Dollfuss was being prepared in a different part of town.

After his third call Marek was seized by the conspirators. He was dragged into the hall, where he saw the men changing into army uniform, the uniform of the crack Vienna *Deutschmeister* regiment. The rebels clambered into three private trucks which they had hired, one marked BUTTER AND EGGS, and started for the chancellery. They did not know what to do with Marek and so (amazing cheek)

---

[1] Dobler later committed suicide or was murdered by either loyal or Nazi police. The full story is in the official Austrian version of the events, translated into English as *The Death of Dollfuss.*

they took him with them. When they were a block from the chancellery
Marek jumped out, and none of the Nazis, for fear of raising the
alarm, dared shoot him. The reader may well ask how three trucks
full of "soldiers" could traverse a dozen blocks of a crowded city
at noon without attracting attention; but troop movements were not
uncommon in Vienna at this time, and the uniformed police on the
running-boards allayed suspicion.

The plotters reached the chancellery at twelve-fifty-three P.M. The
scene was set for dramatic and terrible events. But first there is the
Ravag episode to tell.

Revolt on the Ether

July 25th was a hot day, though not sunny, and I wanted to go
swimming. I had finished my morning's work, and put on my hat to
leave for lunch when at seven minutes past one the telephone rang.
One of my tipsters said in a low voice, "Have you heard the radio?"
The Vienna radio has just made this announcement: *'The government
of Dr. Dollfuss has resigned. Dr. Rintelen has assumed power.* It may
be a joke, I don't know. I'll check it up and call in a minute."

I put in a call for Paris at once (we sent our stories by phone) and
while waiting for it I telephoned (*a*) the American Legion, (*b*) a
friend, M. W. Fodor, of the *Manchester Guardian*, with whom I
worked closely, (*c*) the Bundeskanzleramt or chancellery. The legation had heard the radio announcement and was investigating. Fodor
rushed to meet me downtown. The Bundeskanzleramt—interesting!—
did not answer. Then Telegrafen-Compagnie, a local news service,
called with the radio announcement and said that a Nazi *Putsch* was
in progress. I wrote a brief story and finished it just when the Paris
call came through. It was one-nineteen. I still had my hat on.

I lost about ten minutes because a police officer stopped me and
made me drive him to his headquarters. A general alarm had been
sounded, he said, but he didn't know about what. I got to the
Bundeskanzleramt at about one-thirty-five. The tawny oak doors
were shut and a few policemen were outside, but otherwise nothing
seemed wrong. I assumed that the government had locked itself in,
preparing defense.

An armored car passed by and with a couple of other newspapermen I followed in pursuit. It turned away from the Bundeskanzleramt and lurched round the Ring to the Johannesgasse, the Ravag headquarters. The locale is comparable to Forty-third or Forty-fourth street in New York. The car got into position and the police on the turret ducked inside the steel shell. Then I heard revolver-shooting and machine-gun fire. The police were storming Ravag to blast out the Nazi Putschists there. I had a feeling that it was all monstrously unreal. The police pushed us back, but we were eager to see; it isn't often you get a pitched battle in the heart of downtown Vienna. Then PRPRPRFFBUM we heard exploding hand-grenades. A waiter in a white-duck jacket slid through the crowd with a platter of beers.

What had happened at Ravag was this. At two minutes to one the fourteen plotters from Kolowrat Ring entered the building. They shot the loyal policeman on guard and the chauffeur of the Ravag director who were lounging in the doorway. Four Nazis reached the studio, where a broadcast of phonograph records was going on. They grabbed the announcer, put a gun in his ribs, and made him give their message. This was the signal for the *Putsch*. All over Austria it throbbed.

But a courageous telephone girl had had time to sound an alarm, although all the lines to police headquarters—an interesting point—were "busy." And an official with great presence of mind cut the wires to Bisamberg, the sending station, so that the Nazis were unable to give a second message. Their plan had been to repeat "Dollfuss has resigned; Rintelen is chancellor" every ten minutes, interspersing this aerial tattoo with instructions to the country, false news, and so on, which would have paralyzed any defense action of the government. I remember that a British radio expert told me years before how marvelously a revolution might be organized by radio.

An unfortunate actor rehearsing a broadcast skit became hysterical with excitement, started to scream, and was shot. The police broke into the building and another policeman was killed, also the Nazi leader. Of the five who died, three bled to death because no doctor was available. Outside we waited till the police, victorious, began to drag out their captives at about three-twenty. I proceeded home and wrote my story, longer this time, and put in my Paris call.

I went to the Bundeskanzleramt again at about three-fifty. On the way I ran into G. E. R. Gedye of the New York *Times*, who was returning from Ravag, and we stopped a second, both saying, "Well, it seems to be all over." We certainly were wrong, but very few people knew then that anything was amiss except at Ravag. I had passed the Bundeskanzleramt myself before, and it looked entirely normal except for the closed doors. Feeling a flicker of doubt, I said to Gedye, "You know, a government doesn't usually lock itself in at a moment of great crisis." He agreed. "Funny." And we remembered that the phone had not answered. I walked toward the building. A patrol had been flung around the area and I couldn't get in. Then the story burst.

Policy by Murder

The Bundeskanzleramt, or Federal Chancellery, is the old Metternich palace where the Congress of Vienna met in 1815. Certainly from that day to this it can have witnessed no more dramatic and agitated a situation. A stately baroque building, its cream-colored façade opens on the Ballhausplatz. Grilled balconies of graceful iron project twenty feet over the sidewalk. Directly opposite is a post office built into the heavy walls of the Hofburg, the former imperial palace, and on the west side a high gate leads to the green meadow of the Burg garden.

The hundred and forty-four Nazis from Siebensterngasse, sweeping into the courtyard, had seized those members of the government within, Dollfuss, Fey, and Fey's assistant Karwinsky, and about one hundred and fifty members of the staff, civil servants, clerks, and so on. The guards in the building, sixty of them, suspected nothing or at least put up no resistance and were disarmed and arrested. The police plotters knew well the corridors and rooms of the complicated building (some of them, indeed, had previously been posted there on duty), and the occupation was quick and thorough. The analogy for America would be the seizure of the White House, since the Bundeskanzleramt was the central ganglion of government in Austria.

Nothing whatever of these events was known to the small group outside the building. Among the newspapermen who, having heard the radio signal, had arrived by one-fifteen and stayed till nightfall were Nypels of the Amsterdam *Algemeen Handelsblad*, Diez of the New York *Herald-Tribune*, Werner of the A.P., two Hungarians, one Albanian, and one Czech. They did not succumb to the temptation to follow the armored car which led me away to Ravag. They saw the whole story, and from a correlation of their records I made the following chronology.

The very first arrival on Ballhausplatz after Nypels was a tall blond youthful German photographer, who—remarkable coincidence if coincidence it was—had arrived in Vienna from Berlin the day before. Calmly he set up his tripod. At one-twenty-five some plain-clothes detectives and four uniformed police wearing steel helmets and carrying rifles arrived. A shout pierced the basement window, "Go away or we shoot." At one-fifty-five a Heimwehr lieutenant arrived, unarmed and alone, and smashed his fists against the door, shouting with quixotic magnificence, "I give you five minutes to open the door, or I will blow it up." This gesture accomplished, he went away and was not seen again.

(Dollfuss was already bleeding to death by this time, the blood pumping from the hole in his throat, but no one knew. . . .)

Several other officers arrived, looked about, decided that nothing was wrong, and went away again. Traffic was still entirely normal. Then, at five minutes past two, came Dr. Funder, the venerable editor of the government organ *Reichspost*. A voice from inside was heard, *"Machen Sie sich keine Sorgen."* (Don't be alarmed.) "Rintelen is chancellor and a new police chief is coming from Berlin." Funder hurried away. Many Heimwehr men and police had now arrived. At about two-thirty began a series of ultimatums that lasted the whole day. A Heimwehr officer knocked on the door at two-thirty-five and said, "We give you twenty minutes and then we blow up the building." "Go away or we shoot," a voice, distorted and hollow, answered through the door. The impression was now general that the whole government had been taken prisoner.

At three o'clock Major Baar, a Heimwehr officer and vice-governor of Lower Austria, arrived. A police officer told him, "I don't know what to do. I was awaiting reënforcements and orders." The Heimwehr were now massed along the road to the Burg Theater, but the police pushed them back. "Who is inside?" Baar was asked. He answered, "Dollfuss, Fey, and Karwinsky are inside, prisoners of the Putschists. A new government has been formed and is meeting at the war ministry on Stubenring." Police reënforcements came and a courteous officer said, "Look here, gentlemen, this is not a good place to stand because here you are in the direct line of fire." At three-forty-five traffic was finally stopped and the little group of onlookers were a compact island in the broad empty pond of the square.

At three-fifty-seven Major Fey, who has a face like a battle-ax, appeared for the first time on the balcony. He was pale as paper. He wrung his hands as if to free them from dust on the doorhandle. With him was Holzweber, the leader of the rebels, a bespectacled little man who looked like a clerk on a stool despite his captain's uniform, blazing with decorations. The crowd started to shout, and Fey called in a low voice, *"Ruhe!"* (Quiet.)

Everyone thought at once, "It is a *Putsch* made by Fey and the regular army."

Fey called, "Where is the commandant?" He could not be found, but a policeman walked up and saluted respectfully. "Who are you?" Fey asked. "I am Captain Eibel, awaiting orders," the policeman said. Holzweber whispered to Fey and Fey said, "Come without weapons to the back door." Eibel nodded and Holzweber called after him, "Be sure you are without arms and come alone."

Heimwehr men in the square had recognized Fey and they began to shout, "Fey! Our Fey!"

At eight minutes past four Eibel returned from the back door on Metastasiogasse. He was running hard, his helmet was off, and his hair was damp and disorderly. He grabbed an open alarm phone. Everyone heard what he said, talking to headquarters:

"I've been inside, I've spoken with Fey. The Bundeskanzler [Dollfuss] is apparently badly wounded. He has resigned. There is a new government, and Fey remains vice-chancellor." Headquarters asked something and Eibel replied, "They are disciplined and look like the military. The staff of the chancellery, one hundred and fifty men and women, are under guard in the courtyard."

By this time the commandant, Hofrat Humpel, had turned up and he said to Eibel, "If the chancellor is wounded he should have a physician. Run to the back door and offer to bring a doctor." Eibel came back: "I knocked and the sentry said, 'No need for a physician any more.'" So it was known to this limited group that the chancellor was dead.

At four-twenty Fey appeared on the balcony again, Holzweber at his elbow. The idea that it was a *Putsch* with Fey in charge was exploded because obviously Holzweber was in command and giving Fey orders. Fey called, *"Ruhe!"* (Quiet.) Then, bending over the balcony, he called, "Where is Rintelen?" The Heimwehr started to shout to the Nazis inside:

"Woe to you if you harm our Fey. Touch our Fey, and we will hang every one of you on these trees."

Fey shouted: *"Nichts unternehmen!* (Take no action.) Nothing may be done until I give the order. I am in command here." He beckoned to Humpel and ordered him around to the back door. A big Heimwehr man, just under the balcony, crossed his hands like a seat and gestured to Fey to jump. Humpel came back in about twenty minutes and shouted, "Rintelen is chancellor, Fey is vice-chancellor. They are waiting for Rintelen, who will come in a few minutes."

On the Balcony

But it was not Rintelen who came; it was quite another person. Neustädter-Stürmer, a member of Dollfuss' cabinet. He waited a few moments and then Fey appeared on the balcony again and called, "Where is Rintelen?"

Neustädter-Stürmer shouted, standing in the street, *"Rintelen kommt nicht!"* (Rintelen is not coming.)

Astonished, Fey turned to Holzweber at his elbow and a Heimwehr man called, "Shall we storm the building?"

Fey shouted down: "No, nothing is to be done. Take no action without my orders."

Neustädter-Stürmer answered: "A new government has been formed and I represent it. In the name of the government I promise a safe conduct to the rebels. They will be conducted to the German frontier. If you do not surrender in twenty minutes we storm the building."

Fey called: "No. You will not storm the building. I am state secretary of public security and you are to take no action without my authority."

Neustädter-Stürmer, looking up (sharply): *"Sie irren Sich,* Herr Fey! (You are mistaken.) The members of the government who are prisoners are under duress and not competent to give orders. It is now five-twenty-eight. At five-forty-eight the building will be stormed."

When the ultimatum expired everyone took cover, but there was no shooting. Neustädter-Stürmer kept pacing up and down and Fey had disappeared. "It was just an Austrian ultimatum," someone joked. But the tension was terrific. At four minutes past six Fey came out again and said that the rebels agreed to surrender but asked what guaranty there was of safe conduct. They wanted military protection to the border. "That can be arranged," Neustädter-Stürmer replied, and Fey, speaking for Hudl (another rebel on the balcony), called, "Can we have fifteen minutes more?" A civilian shouted, "They mustn't harm anyone in the building."

At six-thirty Fey came out once more. He tried to talk to General Zehner, the under-secretary of state for war, who had taken charge. There was such a tumult that no one could hear. Police, journalists, Heimwehr, lookers-on were all under the balcony, shouting. So Zehner and Neustädter-Stürmer went round to meet Fey at the back door. Then Dr. Reith, the German minister, arrived. At about six-fifty Zehner reappeared and announced, "They will get military protection to the frontier under the command of a staff officer."

At about seven-thirty Fey came out the back door. He walked up to Neustädter-Stürmer and said, "Give me a cigarette." A journalist called, "*Pfui* on their safe-conduct!" Fey, lifting his voice with effort, said, "Quiet!" Neustädter-Stürmer asked him, "Is it true that Dollfuss is dead?" Fey said: "Yes. I spoke to him just before he died. When I came in he was lying on a divan wounded and bleeding." He crushed the cigarette in his hand and said, "Give me another cigarette."

At seven-forty Reith and Karwinsky came out. Schuschnigg, the new prime minister, arrived and led Fey, Zehner, and Neustädter-Stürmer into the Burg garden. The police closed the gates behind them and, standing there on the grass, in the dusk, they held a cabinet meeting. By now twenty military trucks were lined up along the Ballhaus, and police streamed into the building to disarm the rebels and conduct them to the frontier. The rebels came out cocky and confident. Everyone thought their free passage to Germany was assured. They thought so too. But they were wrong.

Death

Dollfuss had opened his last cabinet meeting at eleven. Among the items on the agenda were—of all things—regulations governing a famous Vienna theater devoted to comic opera. The warning did not reach the cabinet till after eleven. Vienna *Schlamperei*, as well as treason, is probably responsible for the fact that the chancellery doors were not shut in time. Once he got the alarm, Dollfuss acted with great energy and coolness. He dismissed the cabinet and ordered the ministers to scatter to their separate offices, only Fey and Karwinsky remaining. This saved Austria, because if Schuschnigg and Neustädter-Stürmer had not been outside the building the *Putsch* would probably have succeeded.

By twelve-fifty-five the rebels were inside the gates, one hundred and forty-four of them. "We arrest you in the name of President Miklas," they falsely shouted.

Officials at the chancellery told me the next day that they first thought a surprise military drill was in progress. The uniforms seemed genuine and the men were disciplined. Then, along each tier of offices, rude voices shouted: "Come out! Hands up!" Doors were battered down and the staff herded into the courtyard. The more prominent officials were imprisoned in a small room and told that they were the first batch of hostages who would be shot if the plot miscarried. A second batch was then chosen to be shot after the first batch. It became clear that the men were Nazis when the first thing they did was to open the telephone switchboard to get in touch with the German legation. And one rebel told a friend of mine: "Curious, are you? In half an hour you'll hear all about it on the Munich radio."

Immediately on disarming the guard one detachment of rebels went up the main staircase, ignoring other objectives, to search the state departments, find Dollfuss, and murder him. There is little doubt but that this group was specifically charged with this duty. It was led by an ex-corporal in the army, Otto Planetta, with a chin like a boxing-glove. Dollfuss was given no chance to escape. He might easily, like Fey and the others, have been captured alive. But the rebels had one predominant aim, to kill him. They entered the building at twelve-fifty-five and two minutes past one at the latest he was shot.

Having dismissed the cabinet Dollfuss retired to his private study, a small room papered in yellow silk. His valet, Hedvicek, looked out of the window and saw the rebel trucks unloading in the courtyard. He told Dollfuss to try to escape through a passage that led through the complicated web of archives rooms upstairs. Briskly the chancellor left the yellow room and started across an oyster-white room toward the famous congress hall. The oyster-white room has three doors. One gives on the main staircase, and here the rebels entered. The door to the congress hall was locked and Hedvicek fumbled with the key. Dollfuss, a small man, reached for the knob and at a range of about twenty inches Planetta shot him in the exposed armpit. The chancellor reeled and Planetta fired again, this time in the throat, at about a distance of eight inches. The chancellor fell. ("How his head cracked on the floor!" Hedvicek said.)

"*Hilfe, Hilfe!*" Dollfuss muttered. ("Help, help.")

Planetta said, "Stand up."

"I cannot," Dollfuss whispered.

They picked him up and laid him on the rose-and-cream Louis XV divan. Servants were still sucking up the dust and blood with vacuum cleaners when I saw the room next morning. On the embroidery of the divan were three large blood spots, almost exactly the shape and color of large oak leaves.

Fey, who was detained near by, had heard the shots but did not know their meaning. At about two-thirty a group of Nazis summoned him and led him to the room where Dollfuss was still dying. The chancellor recognized him and whispered weakly:

"I charge you to take care of my family if I die."

The rebels had a revolver in Fey's ribs and permitted him to say nothing. Dollfuss went on, very faintly:

"Where is Schuschnigg?"

Fey shook his head and, mustering strength, Dollfuss whispered, "Try to settle this without bloodshed. Tell Rintelen to make peace."

Fey was hustled out of the room. He appealed to the rebels to get a doctor or at least a priest. They refused, although they asked the prisoners if a doctor were among them, and one of them gave the dying chancellor a glass of water. Dollfuss must have thought he had been betrayed by his own army; not only that the *Putsch* had succeeded, but that his own men had killed him. Later he apparently believed that loyal troops, not rebels, were surrounding him, staring at his shrunken face, because he whispered, "*Kinder* [children], you are so good to me. Why are the others not as you are? I wanted only peace. May God forgive the others." The last blood was now streaming from his small body. A basin to catch it was put under the divan. At three-forty-five he died.

The rebels thought they had won, until about five P.M. At four-thirty Hudl, the second in command, told the prisoners in the courtyard that a new government had been formed and that Rintelen, the new chancellor, would arrive at once. Thereupon about twenty officials gave him the Hitler salute and others called out, "*Heil* Hitler." Hudl testified at his trial that Wrabel, who was caught inside the building, gave him his card and said, "Call me *du*." (The familiar form of the second person.)

After five, when Neustädter-Stürmer was outside, the morale of the rebels began to break. Holzweber went to Fey and said frankly: "There has been some hitch. I do not know what to do." Fey shrugged. Then, a characteristically Viennese touch, Holzweber proceeded, "Aah! I shall telephone the Café Eiles and ask if Herr Kunze is there." So with the chancellor dead, the government disrupted, Austria convulsed, and Europe at the ragged edge of war, the leader of the rebels rang up a coffee-house, to ask if a man who *might* be there could tell him what to do.

Kunze was a civilian who had been at Siebensterngasse. Holzweber led the first truck and Hudl the second and Kunze was to have been in the third. But he never arrived. No one knows for sure what happened to him or how he disappeared. The Viennese police think he was a Nazi lawyer who ratted at the extreme last moment, fled to Germany.

At about six the rebels decided to surrender, following the promise of safe conduct. All the one hundred and fifty hostages would be shot, Holzweber declared, if free passage was not given. Fey said to the government negotiator, "Do not allow considerations of my safety to influence you one way or another." Then Hudl suggested telephoning to Dr. Reith, the German minister, as witness for the safe conduct. Fey explained the business over the telephone, and Reith asked him whether or not to come. Fey said, "It is not my business to give you orders or dissuade you. I have only to pass on these men's demand." Reith came, the negotiations were completed, and the exodus began.

Still the mass of the imprisoned hostages did not know the chancellor was dead. Leaving the building, one of the rebels called out, "We've left a dead one in the corner room upstairs." An official rushed up and found Dollfuss there. The body had completely shriveled like a raisin and was clammy blue. The face was uncovered and wore an expression of extremest agony. A piece of canvas covered part of the body. There was a terrible wound in the throat. Underneath the divan, spilled beyond the basin, was a lake of blood.

The Missing Chief

And now about Rintelen. Why did Rintelen not come? Why did the *Putsch* fail?

He did not come because he was arrested. He was arrested not by the police or government, but by his old friend Dr. Funder, the editor of the *Reichspost*, who, leaving the chancellery at ten minutes past two, went straight to the Hotel Imperial where Rintelen was staying and on his own responsibility persuaded him to give himself up at the war ministry, in order to avert scandal. Owing to his position as a minister he was not searched. It is said that the Ravag got through to Rintelen at about one-fifty and asked him to deny the radio report naming him chancellor. "I have no authority to do that," Rintelen answered, and rang off. At midnight that night he shot himself. The wound was not mortal, though so dangerous that the actual heart had to be stitched up.

About the position of Fey there will probably be dispute as long as the story is told. I do not think he knew anything about this particular plot. But if he was not a traitor, he behaved like a poltroon. No one knows exactly what passed between Fey and the rebels when they first arrested him; but the evidence of both police officers who entered the building is that they understood that Fey, with Dollfuss dead hardly a minute, was vice-chancellor in the new Rintelen régime. On the other hand, Fey can hardly be blamed for telling the loyalist forces not to bombard the building. He had not only his own life to save but he was responsible for the safety of the one hundred and fifty other prisoners. If Fey had shouted early in the afternoon, "They have murdered the chancellor; storm the building even if we die," it would have been a magnificent gesture but it would have cost much bloodshed. One must remember that Fey knew nothing of what was going on outside. He thought Rintelen *was* chancellor. Even so, if he had greeted Neustädter-Stürmer's appearance with a whisper of pleasure instead of a reiterated demand for Rintelen his reputation for loyalty and courage would not have suffered such a severe setback.

There was much bad feeling about the withdrawal of the safe conduct. The rebels were shipped, not to the German frontier, but to the Marokanner police barracks hardly a mile away. The government defended what was certainly bad faith by saying (*a*) Fey was not authorized to give a safe conduct, and (*b*) Neustädter-Stürmer gave it unaware that the rump cabinet at five o'clock made it conditional on no casualties. I imagine the final decision not to free the Nazis was taken at the cabinet meeting outside the chancellery at seven-thirty. Here Schuschnigg was informed for the first time of the circumstances of Dollfuss' death and he decided simply not to let the murderers go. Neustädter-Stürmer said at Holzweber's trial: "Yes, I gave my soldier's word of honor. But a soldier's word of honor is given to other soldiers, not to men who deny medical aid and priestly services to a mortally wounded man."

Another reason for the failure of the *Putsch* was that the country as a whole did not rise. In Styria and Carinthia, where the Nazis had arms, there was severe but brief fighting, but nowhere else. For a year all of us were deluded into believing that the Nazis were fifty or sixty per cent of the country. Possibly this was true, but at the critical moment the Nazis did not take action. The rebel signal had reverberated through the land; for four hours there was no regular government; but nothing happened. The Nazis had not bothered to arm their adherents, feeling sure that the army would mutiny and provide weapons; but the army remained loyal. Thus they lost their supreme chance.

Above all, the *Putsch* failed because Hitler welshed. The one hundred and forty-four conspirators were betrayed three times on July 25th; by their own higher-ups, chiefly Kunze; by the promise of safe conduct; above all, by Germany. For a year and a half the Germans had incited their Austrian cousins to violence and rebellion and then, at the crisis, they let them down. The Austrian Legion did not march; instead, as soon as the *Putsch* was seen to have failed, it was disbanded. Habicht was dismissed from his post as Hitler's "Inspector" for Austria, and Frauenfeld disappeared. Dr. Reith was summarily fired, to give way to Franz von Papen. Instantly it was known that Mussolini had mobilized and would march into Austria if the *Putsch* succeeded, and this was clear by six P.M. of the 25th, the Germans wretchedly crawled and washed their hands of the whole business, and ever since have sought to evade responsibility.

Thirteen of the Putschists were hanged, including four of the traitorous policemen, and, of course, Holzweber and Planetta. I have seldom seen a court-room more stirred than when Holzweber, just before his sentence, rose and said:

"I was assured that there would be no bloodshed. I was told that I should find Rintelen at the chancellery and that the new government was already formed. Not meeting the leader of the operation at the chancellery, I disclosed myself at once to Major Fey. I told him, 'Here I stand, and I do not know what to do.' "

Three hours later he and Planetta were hanged. Both died bravely, and both with the words, "*Heil* Hitler," on their lips. But Hitler did not hear them. In East Prussia President von Hindenburg was dying. And Hitler was busy becoming President of Germany.

Rintelen, seven months later, went on trial and was sentenced to life imprisonment on a charge of high treason. After serving a brief time in the penitentiary he was transferred to a sanatorium, under police surveillance. The evidence against him at the trial was not particularly concrete. As a result rumors rose that Rintelen had come to Vienna expecting to take part in a *different* revolt against Dollfuss, in which Fey too allegedly was involved. The July 25 *Putsch* was, it was said, made by Habicht, to forestall a Rintelen-Fey *Putsch* scheduled for about the same time. Habicht in Munich distrusted the Rintelen-Fey group, even though—according to this story—it was to pave the way for a Nazi régime; therefore Habicht jumped the gun on July 25 and therefore Fey, Rintelen, and company, not knowing whether the *Putsch* going on was their *Putsch* or not, behaved with such confusion.

Rintelen might have been acquitted except for the evidence of his Italian servant Ripoldi, who testified that his master in Rome had frequently consorted with alleged Nazi emissaries. This contributed an obscure, bizarre footnote to the whole affair. Ripoldi had previously been the valet of a friend of Rintelen's, the financier Camillio Castiglione. He admitted in court that Castiglione had persuaded him to telegraph the court from Milan about his knowledge of Rintelen's doings, and had paid for the telegram.

Castiglione was born in Trieste, the son of a rabbi; he made enormous profits during the war selling airplanes; after the war he was Europe's greatest speculator in foreign exchanges; in his great days he rebuilt the Josefstaedter Theater for Max Reinhardt, helped finance the Salzburg festival, and paid some of Mussolini's bills for the March on Rome. He had been a close friend of Rintelen's for many years. Then these two cronies, buccaneers both, must have fallen out. The bond of their mutual interests snapped. Castiglione put Rintelen behind the bars.

VINCENT SHEEAN Why he selected

The THIRTEEN BUS*

I am down here at the Officers' Training School of the Army Air Force, where I have been since May 30th. I don't have much time for writing paragraphs of comment, and even so I imagine by now you have gone to press. I hope you will forgive me for this and that "Thirteen Bus" can appear in your anthology without any comment at all except (I should like this) the date when it was written—i.e., in December after the Munich agreement.

Miami Beach, Fla.   VINCENT SHEEAN (CAPT. J. V. SHEEAN)
June 24th, 1942

THE district of Maida Vale, according to the English novels of twenty or more years ago, was inhabited by light ladies, aspiring playwrights and gentlemen who were likely at any moment to be arrested by the police. If this was ever so (and you can't always tell about English novels) it is no longer so. The region exposes an innocent face to whatever sun it can get in a London December: its wide streets and blank brick houses, sometimes with gardens and oftener without, appear to harbor a population of blameless citizens. But then we Americans are always being taken in by English literature: it is what they call our heritage. Millions of us who have never seen London feel the cold thrust of mystery down our necks at the mention of Baker Street; we hear the roll of the printing press when one street is named, the chink of coin when we read of another. If Maida Vale is, after all, no odder than any prosperous district in New York or Chicago, and gives shelter and leg room to an equal number of merchants, bankers, film stars and legislators, we are wrong to be disappointed. The fault lies partly in our gullible selves and partly with those English novels of the

---

* Written in December, 1938, three months after the Chamberlain-Hitler agreement in Munich, and having first appeared as the first chapter of *Not Peace but a Sword*, a record of observations of the capitals of Europe at a time during the progress of the Spanish Civil War.

days before and just after the war of 1914-18, which purported to tell us what life in London was like and misled us so badly that we are always craning our necks from the top of the bus to exclaim "So *that* is the Strand! So *that* is Pall Mall!" In years of casual visits to London I had never beheld Maida Vale: when I did it reminded me of Chicago. I might have written a letter of discovery to *The Times*, but didn't, for my only practical interest in Maida Vale was that somewhere near there was where you got the Thirteen Bus.

I heard about the Thirteen Bus from a sound authority.

"When I have relatives up from the provinces," the sound authority said, "I always take them for a nice ride on the Thirteen Bus. You go right through London and can do all your sight-seeing without getting off. It starts at Golders Green or Hendon or some such place, but you get on in the Abbey Road. I've tried them all, and the Thirteen Bus is best."

Well, I have tried it now, too, and am prepared to give a report. I can hardly do so without paying a fervent tribute to the London General Omnibus Company (and to the Traffic Combine of which it forms a part) for the solidity of its rolling stock: for the unfailing courtesy of its hired hands; and for the extreme latitude permitted in such matters as smoking and lolling about on the top deck. No General Omnibus Company in the world—indeed, no Traffic Combine—can do you better for fivepence.

II

Maida Vale is respectable upper-middle-class, with the wintry sun trickling down on well-fed people who are not in a great hurry to get anywhere. It blossoms, after a bit, into St. John's Wood, which is more elegant: there are some huge houses here, with walled gardens, and steps down which people come at night, they say, in garments white and glistering. The bus careens along; not many people seem to need it in these parts; it takes its corners with a kind of fleet, self-confident dignity, its balance ever sure, until we come to a stop to let an old lady with a dog descend. Regent's Park. That is where they have all the monkeys and elephants and Professor Julian Huxley (God bless 'im!). If you belong to the London Zoological Society you can go to the Zoo on Sunday, which is a private day; you can even do this if you know a man who knows a man who is a member, and it doesn't make the slightest difference to the animals, except that perhaps the ordinary days, being less crowded, are more restful. It is a very fine zoo, although they have spent a lot of their money on fish and snakes, creatures with which I at least do not commune easily. I once saw a python devour a live chicken there, in the Serpent House, while an avid crowd watched. It was a loathsome sight, I thought, and had the effect of causing my throat to distend so that I burst my collar and had to go home.

Baker Street. Now this is a really curious phenomenon: a street so huge, so crowded, so lined with shops and humming with the purposeful din of a lot of people going after what they want, suggests to most Americans one thing only, and that is Sherlock Holmes. For all I knew, it might have been a cavernous hollow place deserted of all living, the haunt of bats by night, a forgotten corner between yesterday and the day before: the place where Sherlock Holmes and Dr. Watson had "rooms." In that far-off period when I read and reread the chronicles of the great detective, I probably thought of it as a permanently darkened street. Such very peculiar things used to happen there, things that had no place in the ordinary light of day. Every ring at the door meant that somebody had been done to death in a mysterious manner; the postman brought nothing but clues; there were jewels in the gutter. And there it lies before us, straight, bright and noisy, for all the world like lower Fifth Avenue, a street which has forgotten its ghost. Along its cluttered pavement the posters of the newspapers blare out in red or black letters eight inches high:

TUNIS:
FRANCE SENDS
MORE TROOPS

But I don't really believe that anybody in this street cares much what happens to Tunis, no matter how many more troops France sends there. That woman in the red hat, for instance, making tracks into the hairdressers: what does she care? She is going to get a permanent wave (which she probably calls a "perm") and perhaps to get her nails done, so that she can keep her appointment at lunch with a feeling that she is looking her best and that forty-two isn't really so old, after all, if a woman takes care of herself. I don't see anybody buying the newspapers, in spite of the poster which the boy waves lackadaisically, now and again, to attract any interested eye. That man in a bowler hat with the envelopes under his arm: what does he care about Tunis? He knows that if he doesn't deliver such-and-such to so-and-so in the Marylebone Road by eleven o'clock he will lose his job, or at least get a sharp reprimand from Mr. 'Iggins. They don't any of them care about Tunis because they don't know where it is. They don't know that it is here, in London, in Baker Street, and that practically every place is the same place now. That is the extraordinary and almost unbeliev-able truth which will shake them out of the frame of their lives when it does come. Unfortunately it probably won't reach them at all until it dawns in red tracer bullets across the dingy sky, and then it may be just a little late to do them any good.

ROME:
ANTI-FRENCH
SCUFFLE

There you are, another one, and with no different results in the sale of newspapers, so far as I can see. Everybody is doing something of supreme interest to himself, of immediate, exact, practical interest, catching the bus, buying the book, hailing the cab, keeping the appoint-ment, running the errand: the whole street is alive with the needle points of concentrated selves, so many selves in purposive immediate activity that they are unaware of each other and of the desperate speed with which they approach their end.

Never mind. Here's another poster.

WEST END
THRU'
A KEYHOLE

That's better. I did actually see somebody buy that paper. It was a weekly paper the name of which I couldn't quite read from the top of the bus, but it must be a very fine paper. It must be rather like a num-ber of our papers in America, which attempt with some success to describe the private lives of the rich. I know enough about London newspapers to understand that the term "West End" is only used of the rich, the titled, or the notorious. No doubt that good housewife

who bought the paper is going to have herself a nice hot cup of tea at
the Corner House and rest her feet while she reads about how Lady
Mary Fiddlesticks is not really going to do this or that because she is
already doing something else. It is amazing how the Anglo-Saxons
will eat up that kind of stuff. You get hardly any of it in France or
elsewhere in Europe; but the English and the Americans like it very
much. Vast fortunes are built on it by clever newspaper proprietors.
It seems to me that there is a difference—slight, but true—between the
Americans and the English in respect of this appetite for scandal about
the rich. The Americans in these matters are much farther advanced
into the dream world than the English: such stories are not very real to
them. They devour scandal about all sorts of people without thinking
of them as people at all, but as mere characters in a drama contrived for
the general amusement. Your taxicab driver in New York will discuss
the persons in a celebrated divorce case with you, whether you like it
or not; it is all part of a show at which you and he are equally spectators. There is no cruelty in this: there is a deficient sense of reality, a
kind of fantastication of life which is created by the films, radio and
newspapers. In that region of half-belief it is as easy to accept an invasion from Mars as it is to accept any of the other stories that are
poured out in an immense and inconceivable stream of tittle-tattle. The
Englishman who buys a paper because its poster says "West End thru'
a Keyhole" is probably a little furtive about it; he loves to know all
he possibly can about Lady Mary Fiddlesticks, and will repeat it at the
earliest opportunity, but if he ever met the lady, or any of her friends,
he would pretend that he had never heard of her. The English are still
aware that these persons described in the papers are real; that is all.
Otherwise there isn't much difference: on both sides of the ocean the
press that reaches the largest number of people is the press that deals
most in this line of goods.

Meanwhile Tunis and the French troops and the anti-French scuffle
in Rome don't stand much of a chance. Not with this crowd in Baker
Street.

III

The Thirteen Bus turns from Baker Street (which has unaccountably called itself Orchard Street for the last small stretch) into Oxford

Street, at a corner massively held down by Selfridge's Stores. You
can, as is well known, buy anything there, and a very large number of
people seem to be doing so at the present moment. With Oxford Street
we reach a higher point in the crescendo of noise and confusion in
which the Thirteen Bus thunders on to its terminus. Here it is no
longer possible to watch any single person for more than a few steps:
these are the merest glimpses, not even of a whole person at a time, a
leg, an arm, an eye, a hat; the parts extrude from the mass and enter
it again; there is a sale on at Selfridge's. The Thirteen Bus, adding
its bulk to what was already there, jams in the thick of it and stops:
the traffic is blocked. Taxis, bicycles, buses, and even the resplendent
closed car with the superb old lady in it can move no more. The people
down in the street, as if aware of the temporary superiority of their
legs, walk with increased decorum. They are detached again, each
complete in himself, pursuing a definite aim with speed but dignity.
What would happen, I wonder, if I got off the bus now and went over
to that white-haired woman who is looking into the shopwindow and
said to her: "Madam, do you know anything about the Ebro?"

    She would probably call the police. If by any chance she did not,
and took the question for what it was, she would no doubt say: "The
Ebro? The Ebro? It's a river, isn't it? Somewhere in India, or is that
the Ganges? No, I've got it. It's a river in Spain. Is that right?"

    If I told her it was a river flowing down Oxford Street she would
be sure I was a lunatic. ("The most astonishing thing happened to me
today, my dear. I was standing looking into Selfridge's window when a
man came up to me and said the river Ebro was flowing down Oxford
Street. Fancy!")

    But if she said what was really in her mind, instead of trying to
guess where the river Ebro was, her reply would probably be something
like this:

    "I told Ellen yesterday that I wouldn't put up with those wretched
cretonne curtains any longer, and I won't. Three-and-six a yard. That
seems very expensive. I wonder if I went in and looked about— But
they always persuade one to buy something. Now if I could find something at about one-and-nine the yard, that would be the thing. I wonder
if I should go in and get it over with?"

    There she stands, protected by the Ebro, an isle in the Ebro, no less,
while the guns thunder on all sides of her and the upper air is filled

with the moaning of shells. She is very tidily dressed in gray, with
brown shoes and a fur, and there is the wing of a brown bird on her
hat. Presently she will go in and look at cretonne curtains and buy
none, but on further thought may go up to the third floor and poke
about among the toys to see if she can't find something for Sarah's
little boy, who will be five in a week or two. He is fond of all sorts
of mechanical gadgets, particularly airplanes.

IV

"This is the national program. . . ."

From Oxford Circus (which we reach through successive congela-
tions and degelations of traffic) there is a moment when passengers on
the top of the Thirteen Bus may, if they look sharp, get a view of the
British Broadcasting Company's building. It lies up there to your left,
beyond the Queen's Hall, and you can see its square white stone growing dirty in the London smoke. It is a tremendous building, a tremendous company, a tremendous transaction going on all the time
between the whole world and the minds of the people living in these
islands. Its organization is something of a curiosity: it is a corporation
not for profit, a monopoly not directly of the state, supported by the
licenses paid to the state by the owners of radio sets. The autonomous
corporation invented to deal with the new invention grew so rich on
the licensing fees that it has been able to spend more and more money
on programs and equipment; to build this vast building; and to contribute part of its annual surplus to various suitable enterprises. It has
its own orchestra or orchestras, its own companies of actors, singers,
and even (for television) dancers; it has its press, too. No advertising is
permitted on programs of the British Broadcasting Company. But these
advantages, formidable as they are, are outweighed by the one tremendous disadvantage: it is a semigovernmental monopoly. The air in
England is not free.

How often have we heard the pale voices of the B.B.C. young men
reciting their nightly translation of the events that change the world!—
heard them, and cursed. This was once when we lived for a while in
a village on the south coast and listened to the news at six forty-five
and nine and ten and sometimes at eleven-fifty. There was one young

man in particular who had the knack of making the most incontro-
vertible events sound like hypotheses emitted with caution at a sewing
bee.

"According to reports from the Franco-Spanish frontier," he would
say, "the Nationalists are approaching San-tan-daire."

This was a long time ago—two whole years. Last summer he used
to say:

"Republican sawces assert that the Republican offensive across the
river Ebro has been a complete success, maw than seven thousand
prisoners having been taken in three days. Nationalist sawces deny
this, and say that the Republican attack has been repulsed all along
the line."

Two years ago he had a lot of trouble over the word Gijon. He
wanted to pronounce it very Spanish, so that it came out of the radio
like the click of castanets, but it didn't quite work, and until you got
the hang of it you didn't know what he was talking about.

The voices don't matter so much; it is what they say. The low temperature, the pallor, the desuetude. There were certain plain facts in late
August and early September: facts which only had to be stated. Hitler's
maneuvers had the quality of direct menace. His intentions were clear.
He was going to dismember Czechoslovakia. The B.B.C. continued in
righteous unawareness of this fact during the time when I was hearing
it in England—and is, perhaps, still unaware. I had no secret source
of information, but I knew in August what was going to happen in
September, and made my plans accordingly. Facts plain enough to be
seen by an American journalist ought to have been plain enough to be
seen by the B.B.C. and by the government which whispers in its ear.
If they had been seen, clearly and in time, there would have been no
"crisis" of surprised horror and confusion: there would have been a
course decided upon with the full knowledge and approval of the
people and adhered to thereafter. In the political disaster of 1938, the
worst of modern times, the British Broadcasting Company did its bit.

So far as I know the air is not free in any country. In most countries of Europe, broadcasting is a monopoly of the state. In America
there is not only a Federal Commission which exercises some degree of
control, but there are innumerable small censorships created by the
advertisers' fear of antagonizing groups of listeners. These are evils;

but the B.B.C. has its own variety of evil, which derives from the ambiguity of its constitution and even more from the general ambiguity of the life around it. It is of the state and not of the state at the same time. It has a mighty instrument and is afraid to use it. When the world as we have known it lies all in ruins, those pale voices will still be murmuring into the void their careful alternatives, yes and no and yes and no, she loves me, she loves me not.

How could that woman in front of Selfridge's be expected to know where the Ebro is? She only hears about it from the B.B.C., and they make it sound very far away indeed—far away, and of no positive account, since nothing that happens there can be stated as a fact.

v

Once upon a time Regent Street curved grandly down to Piccadilly Circus between buildings of the Regency period; these are gone now, and what you see from the top of the bus is much the same as what you might see in Milwaukee. The crowds show the same urgency in getting in and out of shops, time presses, the road is long; they are all in a hurry. Even more do they press and churn in the great pit of Piccadilly Circus, where the lighted signs burn all day and the old woman with the stubby fingers sells apples in front of the Criterion. Piccadilly to the right there, broad and proud: that way to the hotels, gentlemen, to the Ritz, to the Berkeley, to the Park, to Mayfair: scented ladies, pâté de foie gras, next year's strawberries. The West End thru' a Keyhole. But the Thirteen Bus does not go that way; it wheels round firmly through the gyratory traffic and—with a glimpse of the bawds and gauds of Leicester Square—turns its beam to the West End and heads down the Haymarket.

This is the place where Tree built his wonderful theater—His Majesty's Theatre, it is called . . . dark and empty now, but it has had forty profitable years and more to come. . . .

There is nothing much to put in a London theater nowadays. The funny plays come from America or France, and there are to all intents and purposes no serious ones. Unless a manager is to run his theater on Shakespeare, Sheridan and Shaw—a thought which would drive any proper London manager to suicide—he has to take what comes, and mostly it is pretty bad. The last thing I saw in His Majesty's Theatre was an exceedingly pretentious production of an ornate and fancy play, Flecker's *Hassan*, many years ago. Since then it has not harbored anything that called for my money. Across the street, there, is the Haymarket Theatre. The last thing I saw there was *Ten Minute Alibi*. Well, that, anyhow, was a good thriller.

VI

Pall Mall, to the right is where the clubs are. (Not all of them, we say hastily, not all.) We don't see much of them from the top of the bus; in fact we are rapidly turning our backs to them as we wheel into Cockspur Street for Trafalgar Square. But we can hardly catch even a glimpse of those solemn gray exteriors, all Regency or early Victorian, without thinking of the extraordinary form of life they sequestrate and fertilize. The club would not be possible, I suppose, without the university; it is the university which trains Englishmen of the upper classes to believe that they must shelter themselves from their womenfolk in order to read a newspaper. Hence these huge, comfortable monasteries where you can eat a very bad lunch and drink magnificent wine with it, in the best English tradition, and sit over your coffee afterwards in a lounge where everybody talks in a discreet undertone, and all the papers published in London, daily and weekly, are to be seen if somebody else hasn't got what you want first. These are the political clubs, the clubs which date from the nineteenth century; the purely aristocratic clubs are further away, in St. James's, and do not come within the purview of the Thirteen Bus. There is an exception even to this rule: for that club up the way (next to the Athenaeum) is aristocratic enough, and nonpolitical, having been founded "for gentlemen who have made the Grand Tour."

The Grand Tour. . . .

Well, at that, the men in those clubs do have some idea of what is going on. They know exactly where Tunis is, and the Ebro, and Slovakia, and the Ukraine. They have at times an absolutely terrifying plenitude of information, combined with a set of opinions fully worked out and not susceptible of modification. Their information is of the sort you get in a *Times* supplement, import and export, balance of trade, alignment of political parties, architectural monuments, etc., etc. They don't actually know how the people feel about anything, but they don't want to. Their interest in the people is of a purely electoral or philanthropic nature; they want them to vote this way or that, and they are quite willing to contribute to funds to keep them from starving to death outright. They also support the "voluntary" hospital system of England, which, although very bad, is regarded with the utmost pride by a class which appreciates its own virtue before everything else. They take an unflagging interest in all public affairs, which to them are mere shoptalk; for they are the governing class of England.

Americans often do not know what the governing class of England is. Sometimes they think it is the aristocracy; sometimes they think it is the democracy (although not often); sometimes they think it is the rich. Such clues as I have been able to obtain lead me to think that the English governing class is recruited from the public schools and the universities, which is a purely economic selection only slightly mitigated by the system of university scholarships offered to promising students of the ordinary schools. But this economic selection (which is basic) is supplemented by an intricate machinery of social selection as well. A man may come of the most respectable family, pass all his examinations handsomely at Oxford or Cambridge, and still not get into the Foreign Office if he has the bad luck to offend in any one of a number of ways. He may be forced into the Treasury; or, if the Treasury will not have him, into the Colonial Office or the India Office or the Admiralty or the Home Office. When you see what did get into the Foreign Office, you marvel that anybody could ever have been refused for it; but they say people are refused all the time. One man I know had his eye on the Treasury all through Cambridge, and then landed in the Colonial Office, to his bitter disappointment. Some day he will no doubt be exercising the powers of empire over some godforsaken tribe of blacks which never will be able to understand why, at times, his eyes grow misty and his arm of justice falters; for how can the Senegambian know about Pall Mall and Whitehall?

It does seem a foolish way to govern, but it worked remarkably well during the great imperial period of which the present time is the dregs. The men who made the empire were, of course, seldom from the governing class: they were the traders, merchants and adventurers who came from all classes and expressed in their way the bursting vitality of a people too big for their island. The governing class came along afterwards and wielded the scepter. H. G. Wells once said that they had all been brought up by governesses and consequently had the minds of governesses, which may indeed be true; I never knew a governess. But it seems to me that their chief limitations come rather from this lifelong habit of secluding themselves in quiet rooms with deep carpets among other men exactly like themselves. It starts in school (without the quiet or the deep carpets), is fixed by the university, and continues throughout the lives of hundreds of men who might otherwise—in spite of the economic and social prejudices of their class—achieve a fairly comprehensive view of the material which is, after all, what they deal with, the existence of the population. They can tell you almost anything in the way of statistical, political, geographical, historical or ethnological information, but they don't seem to realize why it matters. To expect any collection of such men to solve a problem involving the passions of a people would be idiotic, you might say; and yet the Runciman mission was sent to Czechoslovakia.

All the English governing class is not in Pall Mall clubs, of course; nor does everybody in the clubs belong to the governing class. But all those men from the Foreign Office and the Home Office and the rest of it, with their parliamentary cousins, their womenfolk and their friends—the people who have the habit of their company—make up what can be called, fairly accurately, the governing class. It is a thing distinct from the aristocracy, although members of the aristocracy often belong to it; and it is certainly distinct from "society," an institution which exists in England (as elsewhere) for enjoyment or display. I think it has no exact counterpart in any other country, for it does not fit into an exact economic or social category. Like the B.B.C., it is and it is not an organ of the state. This ambiguity and lack of definition characterize so much of the structure here that foreigners are sometimes (like the bewildered French writer) inclined to put it all on to climate, and say that England as a whole lives in a fog.

But even if it were true, it is a fog from which all those gentlemen in the clubs in Pall Mall have emerged at some time or other. They have surveyed the foreigner in his habitat; they have made the Grand Tour.

VII

Cockspur Street is a brief interlude of shipping offices, with posters inviting the passer-by to visit India, Egypt, Ceylon, the South Seas; the bus makes no stop here, but plunges up the slight incline that leads to Trafalgar Square. Here, alongside the early-Victorian-neo-Grecian hideosity of the National Gallery, it comes to a determined stop, behind a line of other buses similarly at rest. The big square is in its ordinary bustling mood today, with ordinary traffic proceeding as usual, and the policemen in the observation post near the tube station have nothing much to observe. Sometimes, at least on Sundays, there are rousing political demonstrations here, and vigorous speeches are made to the reward of loud cheers. The crowd then, on occasion, takes its foot in its hand and goes to Downing Street—just below there, off Whitehall—and "demonstrates" in front of the Prime Minister's house, or the Foreign Office across from it, or even simply at the entrance to that little blind alley about which so much has been heard. The demonstrations usually consist of a few cheers, hisses and boos, a little noise, a little jostling. Nobody pays much attention to them. It is well understood in all ranks of society that only cranks, crackpots, people slightly off in the head, will take part in such assertions of disagreement with the governing class.

The big square is dominated by the statue of Nelson on its column one hundred and eighty-four feet and ten inches (184 ft. 10 in.) high. Now there was a man. He had a fine command of language, and although his political intelligence was rudimentary, he could say a plain thing or two when it was his will. It would be interesting to hear his opinion of the present British government. . . . He had hardly any external characteristic of what is called "an English gentleman" . . . The only thing is, the man was an authentic blazing hero. In that, the instinct of the English people has somehow driven through the fog and found a truth. He was brave, tender and honest, with a gift of inspiring devotion and with a genius for naval battle; but most of all he had the special thing, the single mind, the passion and fire of the antique hero, the thing Napoleon never possessed. It is a pity he is dead.

VIII

. . . The bus is off; we are for Charing Cross and the Strand now. Below us on the right is the broad straight street called Whitehall, lined with aging buildings in Portland stone, some of them good (at least one is). That, and mark it well, is the seat of administration of the British Empire. The Admiralty, the War Office, the Foreign Office, Scotland Yard—there they all are, and the little alley called Downing Street, alongside the Foreign Office, and God knows what else besides. These are the immense and nonetheless crowded offices in which all the men who lunch at the clubs in Pall Mall do their work, along with other men who don't belong to clubs, and others who are too grand to go to them. Cabinet ministers are two-a-penny down there, and the crowd which is so eager to watch almost any curiosity scarcely notices them as they come and go. Somehow, by means of an incalculable amount of writing on paper (some of it still done with pen and ink), the British Empire gets governed. A young man who has lunched too well at his club may possibly mislay a dispatch, as a result of which ten sentences of execution in India cannot be commuted in time and cause popular disorders which in turn cost many lives, but these are the accidents of the trade and can't be helped. Somewhere down there is also a vast Victorian Gothic building which shelters that celebrated debating society, governed by party caucus, called the House of Commons. The Thirteen Bus, showing unimpeachable judgment, passes up all that and, pausing for the necessities of traffic at the Charing Cross railroad station, dives recklessly into the Strand.

This, again, is not all that the novels and stories of some years ago might have led us to expect. The Strand was (or so they told us) something like New York's Broadway, lined with theaters and bright with lights. But time has changed all that. The theaters are mostly scattered about in side streets of the West End now, and there are not enough of them in the Strand to give it a special character. Small shops and nondescript nineteenth-century buildings with an infinity of tenants line the street; we read twenty different signs on the windows of one floor; there is a multiplication of business here, like the multiplication of traffic in the road. The Strand is so crowded because it is the main thoroughfare between the West End and the City of London: for centuries no other straight road was built between the two, which is one explanation of their extraordinary separateness. Downtown New York is separate from uptown New York, but it is neither unknown nor inaccessible; whereas there are millions of people who live for years in the West End of London without ever seeing the City. The Strand is choked with people going between the two, but the City remains a different world.

HITLER'S
THREAT TO
CATHOLICS

That is what the posters say here, in glaring red, but nobody seems to mind. Perhaps there are no Catholics in the Strand. Off there to the right there used to be the buildings called the Adelphi, a region all built by the four Adam brothers; on Adelphi Terrace there were flats overlooking the river, and some very distinguished literary gentlemen, among others, inhabited them. Shaw and Barrie lived there. The region is still vaguely called the Adelphi, but the Terrace is occupied now by a big new block of flats. Beyond it, the Savoy—the theater, the courtyard, the hotel: Gilbert and Sullivan, the Savoy Grill.

I have a great deal more to say for the Savoy Grill than for Gilbert and Sullivan; but since it is regarded as a high crime in all English-speaking countries to criticize these citizens of another era, I will be brief. Their operas were mostly produced at the Savoy Theatre, and constitute, to the present moment, the favorite humorous works of the gentlemen who eat lunch in Pall Mall and work in Whitehall. The ruling ideas of Gilbert and Sullivan—that everything is very funny, especially in foreign countries, and that everything will be all right if you laugh at it—have made an indelible impression upon the minds of the British governing class. They can all make jingles in the style of Gilbert, and do; they can quote him by the yard; they are even willing to endure the music (if you call Sir Arthur Sullivan's compositions music) so long as it is dominated by the arch and skittish rhymes of the master. These productions, as intensely English as a game of cricket, form an important part of the culture of an English gentleman. They form him, as the school and the university form him, and as Shakespeare never succeeded in forming him. It is in great part because of Gilbert and Sullivan that they worship "the sense of humor," which is such a peculiar invention that each one of them is free to suppose that each other one of them lacks it. It is chiefly to Gilbert that they owe their capacity for laughing at every human passion the moment it takes visible form or causes a deviation from their visible standards.

The best thing I know about W. S. Gilbert is that a man named Jim Lardner, while marching with the 15th Brigade to the Ebro, composed a ribald song to the rhythm of "Tit-willow."

The bus, meanwhile, has whisked us along through the Strand, past Somerset House (where you find out about births, deaths, marriages and wills) to the place where the street divides in the middle for the churches: St. Mary-le-Strand, St. Clement Danes. Like other old London churches, these have tablets and windows and such to inform you of the great men who worshiped there in the past. . . .

The Law Courts, another of these immense Victorian buildings in Gothic style, catches our eye (indeed) as we trundle on out of the Strand. The law—in England above all places—inspires us with a respect for its mysteries and a desire never to investigate them. It may be that there have been abuses, irregularities, monstrous inadaptabilities and archaisms, but we are content to accept the current belief that English law is the most equitable in the world, and the best administered, and the least unjust. If we had the desire to question it, the bus would allow us no time, for it parts the traffic like a boat on the water and swings us along to Temple Bar. Here, where a gateway once stood—a gateway where they exhibited the heads of criminals stuck on pikes, you remember; and where they had a pillory which was once occupied by poor old Daniel Defoe—the City of London begins. The City of London, the abode of the burghers in the old days, the home of finance, commerce and the press now, still with an immense and complicated system of privilege, retains all sorts of quaint practices to show its traditional autonomy. One of them is that here, at Temple Bar, the reigning sovereign on his state visits to the City must pause to be received by the Lord Mayor, and to receive from him (for the duration of the visit) the sword of the City of London. I have not inquired, but it seems probable that it is a sword made of cardboard.

And here, as the bus, ignoring such medievalism, pushes along, we enter Fleet Street.

IX

Every newspaper in the world has some kind of representation in Fleet Street, even if it is only through the press associations of the various countries. The great London daily papers have their presses on the side streets between here and the river; the principal ones (except *The Times*) are in or near Fleet Street itself. None of them, except the black-and-clear-glass palace of the *Daily Express*, strikes us as particularly noticeable architecturally. It is a street of higgledy-piggledy late nineteenth-century buildings, mostly, some high and some low, some imposing and some shabby, all dirty, all busy at nearly every hour of the day. The life of the place goes on in the street, in the pubs, in the eating places as much as in the offices themselves. Nearly every kind of human being is to be found hereabouts engaged somehow in the production or distribution of newspapers. There are elegant ladies and gentlemen of high degree employed to collect gossip about their friends and relations; there are millionaires who like to own newspapers because of the power it gives them, and there are millionaires who made their money out of the papers; there are innumerable varieties of journalists and editors, special writers and tipsters and hangers-on; there are the printers themselves, and there are thousands of workers in distribution.

But what is it that they write, print and distribute?

The inquiry could occupy us far longer than it will take for the Thirteen Bus to pass through the street and climb Ludgate Hill. They write, print and distribute newspapers of a wider range than can be found anywhere else in the world except New York. The worst American press is probably worse than the worst English; but the best American press, I think, better than the best English. That is, our best newspapers will suppress nothing and garble nothing in a moment of great crisis, so long as they are not directly subjected to an official censorship. By reason of its ownership or its relations with the government, the English press has no such independence. This has been shown very clearly in two recent crises which profoundly disturbed the whole country: the first was the abdication of Edward VIII, the second the triumph of Hitler in September, 1938. In the first of these instances the English press, having been silent as the grave about the whole business, suddenly began (on whose signal?) to thunder at the King because of his intention to marry, and by means of a crisis of the most sudden and trumped-up nature, forced an abdication. In that whole affair the press acted simply as an organ of the government of the day. Again in September, when very much graver matters were being decided, the press as a whole, seized by the panic fear of war, followed the lines of policy decided upon (or stumbled into) by the government of the day, and actually saluted Neville Chamberlain as the savior of the world's peace when he returned from Munich. Generations which will have to bear the frightful consequences of that unnecessary surrender may never understand, as they pore over the press of the months just past, how such things could be written, printed and read.

Along there on the left side of the street, as we whisked by, I caught sight of a white shaft let into the wall of the church of St. Dunstan-in-the-West. It was surmounted by a marble head, and the inscription beneath it said that it was a memorial to Northcliffe.

That, perhaps, would supply a clue to the relations of the press and government in England: a serious study, which should someday be possible, of the life of Alfred Harmsworth, Lord Northcliffe. H. G. Wells has given us some very illuminating pages on the subject in his autobiography. He taught some of the Harmsworth children (not Alfred) in school, and had seen, in those far-off days, the first copies of the school newspaper, written and printed by Alfred a year or so before. Decades later Wells came again into relations with Alfred Harmsworth when the *Daily Mail* had become a market for a writer's work, and through an association of some years he was able to get an idea not only of the tangle of publications over which Harmsworth was lord, but also of the curious unbalanced man, irresponsible, uninformed, violent and despotic, who wielded that immense power Northcliffe was, of course, a journalistic genius, in that he was always thinking of some new trick or gadget for catching the public's fancy and making money out of increased circulation and advertising; but that sort of genius can scarcely compensate for an ignorant and irresponsible use of colossal power. Wells tells us that the war-time cabinet, to keep Northcliffe and his younger rival, Beaverbrook, quiet, invented ministries for them; and there is a funny scene in the book, where Northcliffe, seated solemnly in a drawing room at Crewe House as minister of propaganda, says to Wells (in effect): "You are a believer in social revolution. We two are here. Isn't that social revolution enough for you?"

The government is quick to grant peerages to the owners of newspapers, quick to give them any sort of honor, distinction or privilege they may fancy, and to see that they have no cause to complain of the social or political system. Alfred Harmsworth at a smart London dinner party, surrounded by a gaggle of duchesses, could hardly have been expected to retain his independence of judgment, even if he had possessed the powers of intelligence or the education to make a sound judgment on any serious question. He was not, apparently, much taken in by the purely social aspects of his bewildering success, but its ramifications in political power were too much for him; he governed his realm by whim, by fantasy, held everything else of no account, and came to grief in the end because his mind could not stand the strain.

SHIPPING MAGNATE
FALLS TO
DEATH

That is what the new poster says, flourished by the boy down on the corner of Fleet Street and Ludgate Circus; it is just out, with the ink still wet, and covers over the anti-French scuffle in Rome and the new French troops in Tunis. The shipping magnate (if I bought the newspaper I might find out that he was a bookkeeper in a shipping firm) had apparently fallen or been pushed from a window, and it is possible to imagine fifty reasons why this event should have taken place, but not one of them fully explains why the event is more interesting than the anti-French scuffle in Rome or the new French troops in Tunis.

That is what they are interested in, there is no doubt: that is why most people buy most newspapers, to find out about the shipping magnate who falls to death, to see the West End thru' a Keyhole. The sober journals of opinion (so called) do not circulate widely, and the more unsober the journal the more people it finds to share its insobriety. Northcliffe was among the first to discover the depth and width of this phenomenon, and his monument is not *The Times* (which he did, indeed, own for a while toward the end, out of sheer vainglory) but the popular press of London. That, and a queer legend of Fleet Street, and a shaft of white stone at St. Dunstan-in-the-West.

x

We have passed the Temple without a word, for its gates are so lost in the turmoil of Fleet Street that they give no hint of the conventual precincts beyond. . . .

Up Ludgate Hill to St. Paul's, with its wonderful Dome that cannot be seen for the crowding buildings on every side: inside here are many architectural curiosities, Wren's own combination of Gothic and classical as modified by the taste of the court ladies and sycophants. There are also an excessive number of monuments to national idols of various kinds, Kitchener, Lord Leighton, Gordon, Wellington, Roberts, Sir Joshua Reynolds, Lord St. Vincent, Sir Arthur Sullivan, Dr. Johnson, Nelson (this is by Flaxman), Sir John Moore, Florence Nightingale and so on. Nelson was buried under the Dome of St. Paul's in a black marble sarcophagus originally ordered by Cardinal Wolsey for himself. All these facts we can verify if we get off the bus and go in; we can admire nave, aisle and dome, immense and beautiful, or we can count prebendaries and minor canons, depending on our frame of mind. In the present instance, time presses, for our main object of inquiry is the course of the Thirteen Bus, and we pursue it with hardly a pause for the cathedral, on into Cannon Street and the heart of the City of London.

The whole look of the people in the streets has changed now. They are mostly men and they are dressed in two varieties of uniform. One is young men in gray flannel trousers and tweed coats, the other is older men in black suits with bowler hats. I suspect a social and economic difference between the two as well, but I do not know what it is. The black uniform, the "City suit," is predominant here, and you see more bowler hats in five minutes than you would see in the West End of London in five years. They rush in and out of dirty nineteenth-century buildings where the names of a thousand businesses stare at you from grimy windows. The bus pokes its way hardily down the long slanting street, stops briefly at the railway station, and concludes its first exploration of Cannon Street by a halt at the corner of corners.

This is a place where Cannon Street crosses Queen Victoria Street, and it is the stop for the Bank of England. A few steps to the left, there, is a junction of streets: Cheapside, Cornhill, Lombard Street, Threadneedle Street, Princes Street and Queen Victoria Street. It is a very important corner, dominated by the huge new building of the Bank of England, by the Royal Exchange, the National Provincial Bank, and the Liverpool and London and Globe Assurance Company. The newsboy in front of the Liverpool and London and Globe Assurance Company is flourishing a poster which looks like an old friend:

HITLER'S
THREAT TO
CATHOLICS

Poland, Ukrainia, the Ebro? These people have far better fish to fry. The Bank of England is the agent of the government in everything connected with the national debt. (Ten thousand million pounds, twelve thousand million pounds, fourteen thousand million pounds— it rises and must rise, and there are many transactions.) The reserve of every bank in England consists of its account with the Bank of England. The Bank of England receives and registers transfers of stock. The Bank of England is the only bank in England which can issue paper money. It is thus guaranteed in exclusivity the control of the whole banking system, the fiduciary circulation (under the Treasury) and the operations of finance capital. Its Governor, Deputy Governor and twenty-four directors are more powerful than any other group of financial bigwigs in the world. Some consciousness of the immensity of this power and of its importance to all now living, dwellers in the Florida swamps or the plains of the Argentine, the Chinese coolie and the miner in Wales, animates the neat, anxious faces beneath the bowler hats as their owners post from one street to another in the rabbit warren of the City. The whole structure, the system, is centered here; this is the mainspring; no one of the thousands who work here and hereabouts can fail to know that the life of the whole world is profoundly influenced by the decisions taken in that great stone edifice across the way. That the decisions taken there are calculated to sustain and fortify at any price the system of which the Bank is the center, that such decisions will be ruthlessly enforced, and that in crucial matters no power alive can stand against the Bank, must be self-evident truths. Self-preservation is still the first law of nature, however often it may be misunderstood by the mood of alarm. The Bank must wield its unique power and all its complicated influences, tangible and intangible, for the preservation (and if possible the extension) of British capital imperialism, with increasing attention to the preservation of kindred capital systems in other countires even when their political structures are profoundly alien. This is the Vatican of capitalism, fully conscious of its mission, and all who bring gold are welcome.

Just off the street there is a suggestively placed sign:

INCOME TAX CONSULTANTS

Over there (we can't see it) behind Threadneedle Street is another institution, the Stock Exchange, which plays its own part in the control of events, but (unlike the Bank) most often half consciously or unconsciously. It is a speculative assembly not a deliberative one, governed simply by the motive of profit. Its four or five thousand members are generally not aware of doing anything to influence the world; indeed their most frequent complaint is that the world, by undue agitation, influences their Stock Exchange. To complain of this surface symptom is as far as they get. Many of them are men of merit who support the symphony orchestras, vote Conservative and play golf on Sunday. The church of St. Mary Woolnoth, at hand here, has a poster alongside its gloomy entrance advertising a performance of the "Deutsches Requiem" (known in England simply as "Brahms' Requiem"). There will be many City men, Bank and Exchange people who care enough about it to go and listen even on a Sunday. Some of them collect pictures, and all—so my acquaintance with them suggests—eat very well.

The corner is indeed a momentous one, for down on the right, off Queen Victoria Street, is *The Times* newspaper, an institution unique in its sensitiveness to the mood of the government class. It is scarcely a newspaper at all; it is rather a mirror in which the governing class, and indeed, to make it more specific, the governing clique, can admire themselves. It is an eminently satisfactory mirror because the picture it presents is always flattering under any circumstances. It also has the magic property of leading its devotees onward—few mirrors can predict and make their predictions come true and thereafter cause the accomplished fact to be gazed upon with ecstatic admiration. Yet this is what *The Times* newspaper accomplished in the autumn of 1938. It was *The Times* newspaper that first tipped us off to the impending vivisection of Czechoslovakia, in a leading article of unexampled slyness and perfidy (September 6, 1938). The governing class was not altogether pleased with that, and there was quite a row for a while, but as event followed event, and Mr. Neville Chamberlain took airplane after airplane, *The Times* newspaper upheld and carried him like a full Wagnerian orchestra under a shaky soprano, until the goal was reached at last, Hitler had been temporarily appeased by the offering of the flesh and blood of others, and *The Times* could proclaim, as it did on October 1, 1938, "A New Dawn," to the universal satisfaction of its readers.

And let it be clear: if you want to know how those people's minds work you must read *The Times* every day for a long while. It is absolutely indispensable. You must read it all, the dramatic criticisms, the reviews of books, the news from America, the news from India and the colonies, the news of Spain, China and the whole continent of Europe, the correspondence columns. Not even the smallest letter from a clergyman in the country who has heard the first cuckoo should be disregarded. The transaction between *The Times* and the mind of the British upper class is so continuous, intimate and hereditary that it is almost impossible to tell, under ordinary circumstances, which originates and which replies in the flow of communication between them. Yet at important periods, such as this last autumn, you can feel the slight tug of discreet leadership, in which *The Times* reveals (without at all displaying) its conscious direction. Once a crisis is past, *The Times* and its readers subside into their normal state of exchange, in which the editorial comment tells the reader exactly what he already thinks in words which seem to him exactly what he would have used if he could have thought of them: the correspondence columns are

filled with the usual debates over dates, places or quotations; conscience funds are started for the victims of the last crisis; and the upper
class is enabled again to contemplate its own virtue in the mirror which
The Times faithfully presents every morning at breakfast.

XI

Beyond that tremendous corner Cannon Street slopes to the river.
The preoccupied throngs in the street look the same as back there;
they wear the same City uniform; but we know as we draw near the
river, by the signs on the windows, that the nature of the businesses
has changed. We are getting into a region of maritime insurance,
shipping, import and export, all the things that have to do with the
sea and all the things that come out of it. The distance is small and
the pace is swift; we are in King William Street now; the Thirteen
Bus is nearing the end of its journey. On the right there already rises
the square gray monument of Fishmongers' Hall with its bold inscription: "All Worship Be to God." And here, with a shock of surprise,
we leave all the dirty buildings and the curious gloom of the City: we
are on London Bridge. There is air here; also space, a wintry, shifting,
pearly light, and the immense sweep of the Thames.

The river seems very big. It looks as if it emptied directly there,
below Tower Bridge, into the limitless ocean. Ocean-going steamers
can come up as far as London Bridge, through the Tower Bridge;
there is a steamer moored there now at the wharf, with a name in
strange lettering on its prow. It is called the Sibir, and comes from
Leningrad. The bus sweeps across London Bridge, through the region
of light and air, and plunges into the labyrinth on the other side very
briefly, for its terminus is the London Bridge Station.

Here I got off the bus and walked back to London Bridge. The
journey was over, and I had half an hour. I was trying to assemble
the bits of what I had seen from the Thirteen Bus. What had I omitted to note? There was Portman Square, for instance, which we had
passed through long ago, coming down Baker Street. I had taken no
note, and yet its trim iron railings, its protected verdure and proprietary
grass had struck me as we passed. The Wallace Collection, the National Gallery: works of art. I had no note of them. But it didn't mat-

ter much, with the Pool of London lying silver gray below there, the boat from Leningrad moored in it, and Billingsgate just over the way. The Port of London begins here, I was thinking: and this is the real origin of the whole business. Without the sea-borne traffic this city of egoism and indifference could never have filled its streets with millions of people and its pockets with gold. Was it all egoism and indifference?

Such accusations are no easier to make of the English (or even of the Londoners) than of any other collection of people. What it is possible to do is to observe the behavior of a nation in its institutions as they develop, in the men it elects to office or submits to be governed by, in the influences it permits to flow unchecked over its mind, in the high acts of its life. The behavior of England in 1938 (as the culmination of a process which has been going on at least since 1933 if not before) seems to me to indicate a mixture of bewildered weakness and courageous perfidy in the dominant characters of the state. The same might have been said of the years 1861-63, or of a number of other periods in which pressure from abroad was felt in England to an uncomfortable degree. Canning's day was a day of little light, and the parallel has occurred to many; Mr. Neville Chamberlain himself, in a correspondence in *The Times*, accepted the comparison with gratitude. But will it ever be possible now to call the New World in to redress the balance of the Old?

The river that flows beneath this bridge contains the water of the Ebro, and there is blood in it (some of it English blood). Austria, Czechoslovakia, China, Ethiopia, Spain: they are all around, as near as Billingsgate, as inexorable as the river's movement toward the sea. In the air over our heads you can hear the last breath of the dying, and the tread of the refugees sounds from London Bridge. So many betrayals have no precedent and no explanation. Hypocrisy, perfidy, egoism, all those accusing nouns of an individual flavor do not serve, since they attach themselves to single persons and do not reach to the mass phenomenon underneath. There must be some element of vital decay here—a governing class unsure of its tenure, a nation weary of acting as a nation, an economy and society shaken to their base. The mines and the cotton trade are dead and there is a blight over whole areas in the north. You can drive there through towns which gape empty to the moon. In the vacant valleys of the north (in a place like

Todmorden, for instance) you can feel with dismal certainty that life has departed from at least some members of the English body, and that it will never come back again under the system of things as they are. This has gone on for twenty years, and there is a whole new generation in some areas that has never found employment at all. The solvent part of the population never ceases complaining of the necessity of feeding (not well, but feeding) the part that cannot work. In such a state, what preoccupations can there be other than the desire to make money, and more money, and to keep it; to risk nothing; to scurry from task to immediate task, intent and troubled, with no thought for the world that crowds steadily in upon this would-be tight little island; to reach happiness in such economic security that, in the end, one's children may go to the public schools and the universities and eat their lunches in Pall Mall and work in Whitehall? From the top of the Thirteen Bus it looks like a whole population in blinkers. We know that there are millions who do not wear blinkers, who are aware of the interdependence of all peoples in the contemporary world, and who realize to the full that the frontiers of England and of the enduring ideas of England are still in foreign lands. These are to be found even in high places, among Tories of the tradition, among cabinet ministers and former cabinet ministers. Few men in public life can ever have spoken more courageously than Mr. Winston Churchill throughout the era of betrayals and surrenders. But it is not courage that is wanted here; it is not clear sight and plain speech; it is something to hide under, a cloud of words, a phrase that will do, anything at all to shut away the terrible reality for a little while longer. The word "appeasement" served as the wing for the ostrich; it made the dominant millions content with their animal comfort that cost half the world. Ethiopia, China, Czechoslovakia, Austria, Spain: to them will be added others before long: the time will come when even the New World cannot redress the balance of the Old, since England will not stir.

And indeed, why should it try? Why should the New World care, I ask, looking down at the crowded Port of London in the pearly winter light, for the freedom of the Old World's inhabitants, since those who have been its guardians for centuries are sunk in coma and decay? With France wavering into timorous reaction, half Fascism and half sheer cowardice, and with England thus covered and drugged by a single word, what is there worth saving in the Eastern Hemisphere?

There is still something: there is the mass of human life that speaks in our blood from ages past, there is the whole treasure of poetry and tradition, liberty and law, which we have taken from here, and there is the surviving life of the millions of ordinary people who are our brothers. These may not even be worth saving if their active possessors make no effort to save them; and yet when the time comes it will be very hard for us in the New World to look at the inevitable struggle with indifference, going busily about our immediate individual affairs as these people in the streets of London now do. Interest and emotion alike will propel us into action, and in all probability we shall save them again, as we did in 1918, even though we know very well that they have deserved their fate to the fullest. The dying empire will die just the same, but not, at least, under the heel of the foreigner. In its peaceful disintegration whole classes of the depressed, the comatose, will come to life again with the realization that the order of things on earth is not changeless. The crusts and layers will be broken and the fences taken down; the English may become a people again, as they were in the nineteenth century.

Now that, I say, leaning on the bridge, is looking very far ahead. At the moment what I can see is Billingsgate, the Pool of London, Tower Bridge, with the tidal river beyond broadening to the sea. The Ebro and Prague are far away; nobody has thought of them in these crowded streets; and here the bus has come along to take me back again.

When I left London Bridge I gave it a good test with both feet. It still seemed solid.

LILLIAN HELLMAN Why she selected

 ## The LITTLE WAR

These are pieces from a diary written on a long trip to Europe in 1937. This part is about Spain during the Civil War. I don't know whether they are my favorites. I don't even know whether I have favorite pieces of writing. I do know that I hope these people are alive, that they will live to see a better day.

Pleasantville, N. Y.   LILLIAN HELLMAN
June, 1942

Valencia, October 13, 1937

I WENT for a walk this morning and stopped at the flower market and bought a bunch of flowers and some green leaves I had never seen before. I went around the corner and down the street and felt good walking in the hot sunshine. Ahead of me was a cat and I don't think I paid any attention to what had happened until I saw the cat suddenly sit down in the middle of the street. While I stood there looking at him, I began to hear the sirens. A woman with a pushcart suddenly picked up a little girl, threw the girl in the cart, and wheeled it swiftly away. I think a few people began to run, but most people stopped, suddenly, and then moved on again more swiftly, and I knew afterwards, by the way my jaw felt, that I had been pressing my teeth together too hard. I turned, too, and began to walk, and told myself over and over again that as long as the sirens sounded the planes had not yet arrived. I went through a square, towards my hotel, and when I first heard the noise of the motors I didn't want to turn to see where they were. I thought: in that hotel room is a toothbrush, a clean night-gown, a cake of soap, an old coat and a box of lousy candy. Yet I am hurrying to it, it is where I am trying to go, it is the place where I have what belongs to me, it is home. And I knew, then, why even the poorest women in Valencia wanted to stay with what was theirs. It hasn't got anything to do with how much you have.

When I got to the corner of the hotel, the noise of the planes was close. I stopped at the corner and leaned against the wall. The planes were high in the east and flying fast. Next to me were two soldiers. One of them had a bunch of grapes in his hand. In a minute he said something to his friend and pointed in another direction. From the south four planes were flying towards us. They came up, swung around. The soldier with the grapes touched my arm and said, "They are ours. There go ours." Then he pulled off some grapes, wiped them clean on his coat, and handed them to me. He said, "Our planes are up. It will be all right, now." It wasn't all right. In the section around the port, three minutes later, the Italian bombers killed sixty-three people. But as we ate the grapes and smiled at each other, we didn't know that.

Valencia, October 17, 1937

I drove up to the base hospital at Benicasim with a German Catholic who was a fairly well known novelist until Hitler came in. He had been a Captain in the World War and had been badly injured in this, the "little war," when his car was bombed to pieces going up to the front lines. Driving fast towards Benicasim we talked about writers and writing and got excited and argued and had fun. We got to Benicasim at dinner time, and the Germans and the Americans were eating at one large table. Some of their wives were there with them and I thought what good looking people they all were and how generous they were with their food and cigarettes. (There wasn't much food and it was very bad.) Later that night, lying on a straw bed next to the wife of a Czech officer, I thought that these foreigners from everywhere were noble people. I had never used the word noble before, and it came hard, even to say it to myself. When the Spanish war was over, if they came out alive, or with enough arms and legs to seem alive, there would be no glory and no reward. They had come because they thought that if a man believed in democracy he ought to do something about it. That's all they would go home with,—wherever home would be. I prayed they would get what they wanted. Lying there, in bed, in the dark, praying, was like being a child again.

The next morning the American, Dr. Busch, the political commissioner and I went on a round of visits. In the third room we visited, there were two men. One was a Canadian. The other was a New York boy with the small, white face that is so common among poor people in New York. The Canadian had lost his left foot and didn't know it yet. The American boy was lying on his side, his face twitching with pain. He was so bad that I couldn't look at him and, as Busch went over to the bed to examine him, I moved towards the political commissioner, a fat little man, who had just recovered from a bad spine wound. The New York boy was crying hard and I said to the political commissioner, "What's the matter with him?" He said, "He was shot through the kidneys and through the thigh. The thigh wound is open." I said, "Can't he have some dope? Listen to him." The commissioner nodded, "Sure. Busch will give him something. But don't mind the kid too much: he's a hypochondriac."

A BLONDE LADY

On the Road to Madrid, October 22, 1937

Luis and I had known each other since seven o'clock in the morning. At three in the afternoon, coming down the long hot stretch of road to Aranjuez, we were tired of each other. We were tired, too, of the sun and the road and the warm, squashed grapes lying between us on the seat. I guess we had talked too much: of the war, of automobiles, of my passport, of the long, purplish plus-fours that he had bought from a hotel clerk in Valencia. I had admired them, had not admired his driving. He had liked my cigarettes, had not liked my English. He had said over and over again that I was the only American he couldn't understand. He said I talked like a Swede, which isn't true, but ever since early morning when he had officiously peered over the first road-guard's shoulder to look at my passport, he had made a determined mystery of me. He liked it that way.

We had talked of Brunette. Luis had been the chauffeur for General Alvarez. He said the General thought him brave and he thought the General brave, but the General, like all Spaniards except himself, knew nothing about automobiles and, therefore, could not appreciate good driving. That was very smart of the General who is around Concud now but who wouldn't be if Luis were still driving his car.

But by three o'clock we were too tired and hungry to talk any more. The mountain road was winding down and Luis dozed from time to

time. It is not a good idea to sleep on the Madrid-Valencia road, and
when we came too near an army truck, I shoved him with my elbow.
He came angrily to life, put his hand on the horn and kept it there.
The truck didn't move because there was no place to move to, and our
back wheels scraped the mountain fence as we speeded up to pass it.
We passed it and Luis twisted the wheel violently, ignored the next
curve to shout back at the truck, to explain to me for the twentieth
time that all Spaniards are brave soldiers and bad chauffeurs.

I stopped trembling. My head had hit the side of the car as we
careened.

"For God's sake," I said, "let me drive."

He said, "A woman couldn't drive this road."

We had been over this many times in the last eight hours and my
voice was sharp now.

I said, "I've been driving a car since I was fourteen years old."

He said, "All right. But the automobile change too much in all
that time."

"No," I said, "that isn't what I mean. I've been driving for eighteen
years, ——"

He nodded. "Sure. Sure. But the picture in the passport book look
more than any of that. You look forty-three, maybe fifty-three."

I must have laughed too long. I was tired of the side remarks about
my passport. When I stopped laughing, he looked at me.

"You need to eat."

I didn't want to eat. It had been hard to eat in the last few weeks.
I couldn't stand the smell of the rancid olive oil and I hadn't eaten
very much. Most of the time I had felt light and pleasant, but I guess
the bad part of hunger was setting in and I felt weak and irritable
now. Luis said I could do what I wanted, but he was going to find a
place to eat. I said there wasn't much to get from these people along
the road, they needed the little they had, and why didn't we wait
until we got to Madrid?

He looked at me. "If they have nothing, they will say it. If they
have something, they will give it. That is Spanish."

I knew what he meant so I didn't say anything. We rode on for a
long time without passing a house and then suddenly, as we came out

of the shadows of a hill, the inevitable church appeared, high and handsome above the mud.

Luis said, "Where there is a church that high, there are people that poor. They will give us something."

We wheeled off the road, went bouncing and rattling into the ruts of the little square around the church. This village was like all the rest, and I thought about the people who used to come to these places because they found the heavy laden mules, the silent, hungry children, the houses-before-Christ picturesque.

Nobody paid much attention to us except the kids and the dogs. They came to the car and stood looking at us. They didn't beg: they just looked. If we had anything, they thought, we might give them a little. Hot and aching I groaned my way out of the car and sat down suddenly on the running board. Luis was already across the street, eyeing the most likely house and, when a group of soldiers came out of a house and spoke to him, he disappeared. I sat there on the running board and stared at the deserted church. A little girl came along, leading a donkey towards a high hill facing me. I watched her and it was only when she was half way up the hill that I saw where bombs had been on another day. Two houses were gone, and the child turned her head away as she passed them. I patted a dog whose bones were out beyond his frame, and a very little boy, unaccountably fat, kept smiling at me and saying, "Salud." I said, "Salud, nino," but he said salud so many times that I stopped answering him. He was funny standing there, singing it, the way children will do with words. I must have put my head in my hands—I felt weak and dizzy—because a man came towards me from a basement hut across the square. His trousers were rolled and his feet were red with wine. He had a glass of wine in his hand and he pushed it at me and smiled. I was afraid that it would make me dizzier, but I didn't know how to say that, so I drank it. It was raw and fresh and it tasted good. Two women came out to watch me drink it and when Luis came back, looking foolish in his purple plus-fours and army cap, they ran back to get him a glass of wine.

Luis said, "All right. I told you. They got two eggs and they give potatoes for you. Come on."

We went up a flight of white-washed steps into a room with a fire-

place and a table. There were four women in the room. They all
bowed to me except the one who was sitting by the fireplace, frying
our eggs. She got up, wiped her hand, gave it to me. She was a fat,
jolly-looking, youngish woman with very bleached blonde hair.

I said to Luis, "Please tell her that I do not want any food. Say
that I thank her, but I'm not hungry and she must not waste the
egg——"

He looked at me so hard that I shut up. Anyway, she had understood me. Her English was heavy with that almost German accent
that Spaniards sometimes have.

She said, "We have enough for a stranger."

I went and sat down at the table, tired of myself. Luis sat down
with a bota of red wine and drank it through the funnel. Through the
drinking, he talked to the ladies. The country women looked at me,
shyly, and didn't answer him, but the bleached lady talked. She was
from Madrid. She had moved here to be safer. It wasn't much safer;
they had been bombed three times yesterday. She scooped the potatoes
from the pan and put the egg on top of them. She decorated the plate
with a small saffron flower. She gave it to me and I tried to thank her,
but she shook her head and stood close, watching me. Luis gulped his
egg and pointed to me.

"She is an American, she says."

She said to me, "An American. What work do you do?" I smiled
and shrugged my shoulders with that coyness you have before you say,
"I am a writer."

Before I could say it, Luis said, "She write. On the stage. Write,
write, write." The blonde lady understood, but he didn't believe it.
He took from his pocket a dirty piece of paper, pretended his finger
was a pencil, and made frantic movements on the paper. He did it for
so long that I sighed and the lady laughed.

"All right," he said, "laugh. It is true. I see it on her passport which
does not look so all right. Also, also," and he paused and turned to
the country women, "also she write in the moving pictures." He said
this again in Spanish: he didn't have to because nobody believed him.
So he said it again, angrily. Then he got up, made an ironic bow to the
silent women, and added Charlie Chaplin to what he was saying. I said
no, nothing about Chaplin, I hardly knew Mr. Chaplin, I only met ——

He sat down and looked at me. "All right. All I say was that you are cousin to Charlie." He hadn't. He had said I was Chaplin's sister. "They do not believe you write. They have not before met one who does. They are stupid. So I speak of Charlie and now they know." The bleached lady nodded admiringly.

She turned to me and pointed to the youngest of the country women. "I make two sausages for her child. But if you like small taste ——"

I said no, no, so hurriedly and with such excitement that she shrugged.

"They are clean. I make them for her *child*."

I said, "Of course. I didn't mean that, but I'm not hungry ——"

And stopped. I thought that if I stayed in this country for another few weeks I might lose the dancing school manners. "No, thank you." "No, really I couldn't take it." "No, I do not wish to deprive you." All the words that people of plenty say to other people of plenty. They aren't good words with poor people and they sound rude. If I stayed for a while I might learn to say simply, thank you, and take what I was given. I hoped I would learn that soon. I took some more potatoes, and I was glad because that pleased the blonde lady and she smiled, moved toward me, and stopped to look down at my hand.

She touched my hair. "You do something to it?"

"Yes," I said, "sometimes I have it bleached. At the roots."

"I know," she said, "that was my work in Madrid. What color is it that you were born with?"

I laughed. "I don't know. I've forgotten. Something like this, I guess, only not as blonde."

She laughed and said, "I know. It's like that with me, also." And then one of the country women said something to her, and she turned to look out of the window. I turned, too, and watched. A young woman was going up a hill carrying a heavy load of wood. It was the kind of wood you get from a house that has been bombed.

The bleached lady shook her finger. "I tell her every day. She should not be here. The bombs make her sick. It is bad to be frightened when a baby is coming. A doctor could tell you that."

Then, casually, she leaned over me again, parted my hair in several places, examined it, then patted it back in place and straightened up.

She said, "Soon you will need color there."

Luis looked at his watch, stretched himself, took a long drink of wine and got up from the table. He bowed to me. "All right, Miss Chaplin, we go." He looked at the women, bowed to me again. "All right, Miss Chaplin. If you are ready, Miss Chaplin."

The blonde lady said, "When you get to Madrid go to a shop called Maria's, on the Calle de la Cruz. It is not open now but there will be a paper on the door saying where Maria is. She is a cousin to me and she works good on the hair. Tell her I send you. Tell her I did not have the baby." She picked up the dishes and began to move away. Her face had stopped as a watch would stop and when it moved again, she did not turn towards me. "Tell her she must put soap in the bleach and do good job."

Four or five days later I tried to find Maria's. Maybe I had misunderstood the blonde lady or maybe the Calle de la Cruz had been bombed away.

EDNA FERBER Why she selected

NO ROOM at the INN

I have selected "No Room at the Inn" because it is beautifully and simply written; because it has meaning and purpose; and because it is plagiarized, in plot and in all its characters, from one of the most widely read books of all time.

Easton, Conn.   EDNA FERBER
May 16, 1942

"NOBODY" IS BORN IN NO MAN'S LAND

BY THE UNITED PRESS.

PRAGUE, OCT. 25.—*A baby born in the no man's land south of Brno, where 200 Jewish refugees have been living in a ditch between Germany and Czechoslovakia for two weeks, was named Niemand (nobody) today.*

SHE had made every stitch herself. Literally, every stitch, for the sewing was so fairylike that the eye scarcely could see it. Everything was new, too. She had been almost unreasonable about that, considering Joe's meager and uncertain wage and the frightening time that had come upon the world. Cousin Elisabeth had offered to give her some of the clothing that her baby had outgrown but Mary had refused, politely, to accept these.

"That is dear and good of you, 'Lisbeth," Mary had said. "I know it seems ungrateful, maybe, and even silly not to take them. It's hard to tell you how I feel. I want everything of his to be new. I want to make everything myself. Every little bit myself."

Cousin Elisabeth was more than twice as old as Mary. She understood everything. It was a great comfort to have Elisabeth so near, with her wisdom and her warm sympathy. "No, I don't think it's silly at all. I know just how you feel. I felt the same way when my John was coming." She laughed then, teasingly: "How does it happen you're so sure it's going to be a boy? You keep saying 'he' all the time."

Mary had gone calmly on with her sewing, one infinitesimal stitch after the other, her face serene. "I know. I know." She glanced up at her older cousin, fondly. "I only hope he'll be half as smart and good as your little John."

Elisabeth's eyes went to the crib where the infant lay asleep. "Well, if I say so myself, John certainly is smart for his age. But then"—hastily, for fear that she should seem too proud—"but, then, Zach and I are both kind of middle-aged. And they say the first child of middle-aged parents is likely to be unusually smart."

The eighteen-year-old Mary beamed at this. "Joe's middle-aged!" she boasted happily. Then she blushed the deep, flaming crimson of youth and innocence; for Joe's astonishment at the first news of the child's coming had been as great as her own. It was like a miracle wrought by some outside force.

Cousin Elisabeth had really made the match between the young girl and the man well on in years. People had thought it strange; but this Mary, for all her youth, had a wisdom and sedateness beyond her years, and an unexpected humor, too, quiet and strangely dry, such as one usually finds associated with long observation and experience. Joe was husband, father, brother to the girl. It was wonderful. They were well mated. And now, when life in this strange world had become so frightening, so brutal, so terrible, it was more than ever wonderful to have his strength and goodness and judgment as a shield and staff. She knew of younger men, hotheaded, who had been taken away in the night and never again heard from. Joe went quietly about his business. But each morning as he left her he said, "Stay at home until I come back this evening. Or, if you must do your marketing, take Elisabeth with you. I'll stop by and tell her to call for you. Don't go into the streets alone."

"I'll be all right," she said. "Nobody would hurt me." For here pregnant women were given special attention. The government wanted children for future armies.

"Not our children," Joe said bitterly.

So they lived quietly, quietly they obeyed the laws; they went nowhere. Two lower middle-class people. Dreadful, unspeakable things were happening; but such things did not happen to her and to her husband and to her unborn child. Everything would right itself. It must.

Her days were full. There were the two rooms to keep clean, the marketing, the cooking, the sewing. The marketing was a tiring task, for one had to run from shop to shop to get a bit of butter, an egg for Joe, a piece of meat however coarse and tough. Sometimes when she came back to the little flat in the narrow street and climbed the three flights of stairs, the beads of sweat stood on her lip and forehead and her breath came painfully, for all her youth. Still, it was glorious to be able at night to show Joe a pan of coffeecake or a meat ball, or even a pat of pretty good butter. On Friday she always tried her hardest to get a fowl, however skinny, or a bit of beef or lamb because Friday was the eve of the Sabbath. She rarely could manage it; but that made all the sweeter her triumph when she did come home, panting up the stairs, with her scrap of booty.

Mary kept her sewing in a wicker basket neatly covered over with a clean white cloth. The little pile grew and grew. Joe did not know that she had regularly gone without a midday meal in order to save even that penny or two for the boy's furnishings. Sometimes Joe would take the sewing from her busy hands and hold it up, an absurd fragment of cloth, a miniature garment that looked the smaller in contrast with his great, work-worn hand. He would laugh as he held it, dangling. It seemed so improbable that anything alive and sentient should be small enough to fit into this scrap of cloth. Then, in the midst of his laugh, he would grow serious. He would stare at her and she at him and they would listen, hushed, as for a dreaded and expected sound on the stairs.

Floors to scrub, pots and pans to scour, clothes to wash, food to cook, garments to sew. It was her life, it was for Joe, it was enough and brimming over. Hers was an enormous pride in keeping things in order, the pride of possession inherited from peasant ancestors. Self-respect.

The men swarmed up the stairway so swiftly that Mary and Joe had scarcely heard their heavy boots on the first landing before they were kicking at the door and banging it with their fists. Joe sprang to his feet and she stood up, one hand at her breast and in that hand a pink knitted hood, no bigger than a fist, that she was knitting. Then they were in the room; they filled the little clean room with their clamor and their oaths and their great brown-clad bodies. They hardly looked at Joe and Mary, they ransacked the cupboards, they pulled out the linen and the dishes, they trampled these. One of the men snatched the pink cap from her hand and held it up and then put it on its own big, round head, capering with a finger in his mouth.

"Stop that!" said one in charge. "We've no time for such foolishness." And snatched off the pink hood, and blew his nose into it, and threw it in a corner.

In the cupboard they came upon the little cakes. She had saved drippings, she had skimmed such bits of rare fat as came their way, she had used these to fashion shortening for four little cakes, each with a dab of dried plum on top. Joe had eaten two for his supper and there had been two left for his breakfast. She had said she did not want any. Cakes made her too fat. It was bad for the boy.

"Look!" yelled the man who had found these. "Cakes! These swine have cakes to eat, so many that they can leave them uneaten in the cakebox." He broke one between his fingers, sniffed it like a dog, then bolted it greedily.

"Enough of this!" yelled the man in authority. "Stop fooling and come on! You want to stay in this pigsty all night! There's a hundred more. Come on. Out!"

Then they saw Mary, big as she was, and they made a joke of this, and one of them poked her a little with his finger and still Joe did nothing; he was like a man standing asleep with his eyes wide open. Then they shoved them both from the room. As they went Mary made a gesture toward the basket in the corner—the basket that had been covered so neatly with the clean white cloth. Her hand was outstretched, her eyes were terrible. The little stitches so small that even she had scarcely been able to see them, once she had pricked them into the cloth.

The man who had stuffed the cakes into his mouth was now hurriedly wiping his soiled boots with a bit of soft white, kneeling by the overturned basket as he did so. He was very industrious and concentrated about it, as they were taught to be thorough about everything.

His tongue was out a little way between his strong yellow teeth and he rubbed away industriously. Then, at an impatient oath from the leader, he threw the piece of cloth into a corner with the rest of the muddied, trampled garments and hurried after so that he was there to help load them into the truck with the others huddled close.

Out of the truck and on the train they bumped along for hours—or it may have been days. Mary had no sense of time. Joe pillowed her head on his breast and she even slept a little, like a drugged thing, her long lashes meeting the black smudges under her eyes. There was no proper space for them all, they huddled on the floor and in the passages. Soon the scene was one of indescribable filth. Children cried, sometimes women screamed hysterically, oftenest they sat, men and women, staring into space. The train puffed briskly along with the businesslike efficiency characteristic of the country.

It was interesting to see these decent middle-class people reduced to dreadful squalor, to a sordidness unthought of in their lives. From time to time the women tried to straighten their clothing, to wash their bodies, but the cup of water here and there was needed for refreshment. Amidst these stenches and sounds, amidst the horror and degradation, Joe and Mary sat, part of the scene, yet apart from it. She had wakened curiously refreshed. It was as though a dream she had dreamed again and again, only to awake in horror, had really come to pass, and so, seeing it come true, she was better able to bear it, knowing the worst of it. Awake, she now laid his head in its turn on her breast and through exhaustion he slept, his eyes closed flutteringly but his face and his hands clenched even in sleep. Joe had aged before her eyes, overnight. A strong and robust man, of sturdy frame, he had withered; there were queer hollows in his temples and blue veins throbbed there in welts she never before had seen.

Big though she was with her burden, she tried to help women younger and older than she. She was, in fact, strangely full of strength and energy, as often is the case with pregnant women.

The train stopped, and they looked out, and there was nothing. It started again, and they came to the border of the next country. Men in uniform swarmed amongst them, stepping over them and even on them as if they were vermin. Then they talked together and alighted from the train, and the train backed until it came again to the open fields where there was nothing. Barren land, and no sign of habitation. It was nowhere. It was nothing. It was neither their country nor the adjoining country. It was no man's land.

They could not enter here, they could not turn back there. Out they went, shoved and pushed, between heaven and hell, into purgatory. Lost souls.

They stumbled out into the twilight. It was October, it was today. Nonsense, such things do not happen, this is a civilized world, they told themselves. Not like this, to wander until they dropped and died.

They walked forward together, the two hundred of them, dazedly but with absurd purposefulness, too, as if they were going somewhere. The children stumbled and cried and stumbled again. Shed, barn, shelter there was none. There was nothing.

And then that which Mary had expected began to take place. Her pains began, wave on wave. Her eyes grew enormous and her face grew very little and thin and old. Presently she could no longer walk with the rest. They came upon a little flock of sheep grazing in a spot left still green in the autumn, and near by were two sheepherders and a tiny donkey hardly bigger than a dog.

Joe went to the sheepherders, desperate. "My wife is ill. She is terribly ill. Let me take your donkey. There must be some place near by— an inn. Some place."

One of the shepherds, less oafish than the other, and older, said, "There's an inn but they won't take her."

"Here," said Joe, and held out a few poor coins that had been in his pocket. "Let her ride just a little way."

The fellow took the coins. "All right. A little way. I'm going home. It's suppertime. She can ride a little way."

So they hoisted her to the donkey's back and she crouched there, but presently it was her time, and she slipped off and they helped her to the ditch by the side of the road.

She was a little silly by now, what with agony and horror. "Get all the nice clean things, Joe. The linen things, they're in the box in the cupboard. And call Elisabeth. Put the kettle on to boil. No, not my best nightgown, that comes later, when everything is over and I am tidy again. Men don't know."

Her earth rocked and roared and faces were blurred and distorted and she was rent and tortured and she heard someone making strange noises like an animal in pain, and then there came merciful blackness.

When she awoke there were women bending over her, and they had built a fire from bits of wood and dried grass, and in some miraculous way there was warm water and strips of cloth and she felt and then saw the child by her side in the ditch and he was swaddled in decent wrappings. She was beyond the effort of questioning, but at the look in her eyes the woman bending over her said, "It's a boy. A fine boy." And she held him up. He waved his tiny arms and his hair was bright in the reflection of the fire behind him. But they crowded too close around her, and Joseph waved them away with one arm and slipped his other arm under her head and she looked up at him and even managed to smile.

As the crowd parted there was the sound of an automobile that came to a grinding halt. They were officials, you could see that easily enough, with their uniforms and their boots and their proud way of walking.

"Hr-r-rmph!" they said. "Here, all of you. Now then, what's all this! We had a hell of a time finding you, we never would have got here if we hadn't seen the light in the sky from your fire. Now, then, answer to roll call; we've got the names of all of you, so speak up or you'll wish you had."

They called the roll of the two hundred and each answered, some timidly, some scornfully, some weeping, some cringing, some courageously.

"Mary!" they called, "Mary."

She opened her eyes. "Mary," she said, in little more than a whisper.

"That must be the one," they said amongst themselves, the three. "That's the one had the kid just born." They came forward then and saw the woman Mary and the newborn babe in the ditch. "Yep, that's it. Born in a ditch to one of these damned Jews."

"Well, let's put it on the roll call. Might as well get it in now, before it grows up and tries to sneak out. What d'you call it? Heh, Mary?" He prodded her a little, not roughly, with the toe of his boot.

She opened her eyes again and smiled a little as she looked up at him and then at the boy in her arm. She smiled while her eyes were clouded with agony.

"Niemand," she whispered.

"What's that? Speak up! Can't hear you."

She concentrated all her energies, she formed her lips to make sound again, and licked them because they were quite dry, and said once more, "Niemand . . . Nobody."

One man wrote it down, but the first man stared as though he resented being joked with, a man of his position. But at the look in her eyes he decided that she had not been joking. He stared and stared at the boy, the firelight shining on his tiny face, making a sort of halo of his hair.

"Niemand, eh? That the best you can do for him! . . . Jesus! . . . Well, cheer up, he's a fine-looking boy. He might grow up to be quite a kid, at that."

KAY BOYLE Why she selected

THEY WEREN'T GOING TO DIE

The Senegalese in France have always had a very particular meaning for me. They were men to be cherished as symbol for what the Fascist mind must, obviously, name inferior. I began to write of them almost twenty years ago when I was living in Le Havre, when the mere sight of them walking down the bleak stone quays of that city in their broken shoes in the cold was as eloquent a vocabulary as any I could hear. I hated the sea and the stones of that coast and the sense of northern doom that was on them. It was only the Senegalese who brought a taste of something else to the city's streets; it was only their voices that brought an indolent music to the place's bitterness as they cried out in the lingo of the outcast over the bright, stiff starfish washed up on the shingles, or the pieces of bottle-glass lying blue as sapphires among the stones. I loved the sound of that music, and the look of racial and absolutely alien purity their faces bore.

A good many years after that I remember sitting with Alexander Berkman on the terrace of a little mountain-village hotel. It was the night of the Fourteenth of July, 1933, and we had driven up from Nice into the foothills for supper and the feel of air. The native part of the fête had come to an end as we sat there late into the evening, and those of the French who were not in bed were drinking quietly at the tables, with the paper and dèbris from the celebration lying in the one village street in the dark and in the square. All around was the profound mountain darkness and silence, and then after a little a single fire was lighted not far from us on the outskirts of the village. There were Senegalese military stationed in the forts high up on the Italian frontier who had come down to watch the fête, and now that the white men had withdrawn in weariness, their singing and dancing began.

The fire illuminated the blasted, rocky cavern of the roadway, and in this light they danced, at first slowly, and then with increasing impetus, the rhythm steadily and unappeasably quickening—their heads bowed, their arms hanging, their bare palms turned open, exposed and vulnerable, toward the central heart of fire that burned in the dust. Others of them were seated on the ground, beating the tom-toms, but it was the dancers' voices, rapt and tragic, that moaned the songs aloud. Neither the dance nor the song worked toward nor achieved conclusion; the music and movement merely paused for that instant which elapsed when the dancers and singers fell singly and at intervals in exhaustion to the ground and before the others sprang up from the sidelines to take up where they left off.

We got up to go when it was late, and the French drifted off from the café tables to bed. In window after window the lights were extinguished, but on the mountain's dark, vast stage the dancers danced on. Berkman said, "The articulators of faith never perish. It is only the spectators at a performance who accept to pass out of the benches and away." As we drove down the rocky, narrow road, the civilized slept while the Senegalese stamped the power and grief of their inscrutable triumph out across the darkened and abandoned theatre's boards.

I have tried to say this thing of Berkman's in my story about the Senegalese in France. I have wanted to make it clear that the Senegalese who are killed in the story remain the living performers in it, not writing of them in any feeling of pity. It was also from Berkman that I learned how viciously pity can alter the quality of one's tribute to the thing in which one believes.

Mt. Vernon, N. Y.   KAY BOYLE
June, 1942

T HEY were most of them rather tall men—tall, lanky black men with their heads carried high and with dignity on their smooth, straight necks. If you walked behind a group of them wandering idly down the road, you could hear their shy, giddy laughter and speech, and you saw at once that the uniform they wore had nothing to do with their bones or their gait. The tunics and trousers and boots had all been made for somebody else, for some other race of men, who knew when they came to a town what they wanted: a *bistro*, or a *tabac*, or paper and ink to write to somebody at home. They were never made for the softly hee-heeing, melodiously murmuring Senegalese, who went plucking the heads off daisies and nudging each other like schoolgirls as they ambled through the springtime evening toward the river and fields out of the direction of, and the setting for, war.

There was a general term for the Senegalese. Frenchmen, marking with colored pins on the wall map the drastic, sweeping line of the German descent through France, would put their fingers down south of Lyons and say, "Here's where we're pushing the *chair de canon* up." If the black men had heard it, they would not have known what it meant, or anyway that it was meant for them. But they wouldn't have heard it, because they would have been wandering off toward the river, the incongruous army boots heavy and dusty on their feet and daisies or the flowers of other weeds broken off and brushing switchlike in their hands. They knew they were going to kill people, maybe a lot of people. They hadn't walked down the hills of home, descending the paths with their hands in their fathers' or their uncles' or their male cousins' or their older brothers' hands, toward the colonial towns and military service for absolutely nothing. They had taken a long time learning which was the right and which was the left, and how to count up to forty-six or seven, and what the foreign commands meant. In a little while they knew they were going to start singing again and do the belly dance to the tom-toms. But one thing they weren't going to do: they certainly weren't going to die.

Twenty or more of them had been billeted in the Count's stable on his property south of the city, and the first evening the Count left them alone. In the morning he put on his London-cut gray tweed jacket and smoothed his oiled, thinning hair back and stepped down the driveway to look the Senegalese over in the sun. He was a big, well-manicured gentleman of fifty, with heavy shoulders and a corsetted *tour de taille* and pince-nez hanging on a ribbon. He stood in the stable door with the light behind him, and the baby lieutenant, whose family kept a good hotel on the waterfront at Cannes, was not quite certain how to address him or exactly what to say.

The Count said at once, "I gathered there was someone too young for it in command," and he snapped the pince-nez on the high, hard arch of the nose his ancestors had handed down from one generation to the next. "There's one of them got into the house," the Count said. "I saw the back of him making down the corridor as I came out."

The little lieutenant straightened up like a flash and settled his leather belt in a military way. "I'll have it taken care of at once, Monsieur," he said, but the Count wasn't finished with him yet. He took off his pince-nez and with the rim of one glass he tapped the lieutenant sharply on his khaki breast.

"I don't know what the Army's composed of this time or what kind of war you're running, young man," he said. "As far as I can see, there's no discipline, no order, not an ounce of stamina in the superiors." He drew up his heavy, stooping shoulders, sucked his waist in, as if for military bearing, and looked down on the young officer with his bleak, withering eye.

"I feel certain it won't happen again, Monsieur," the little officer said, but for all of that, it happened three times again that day.

It seemed there was nothing to be done with the tall, black, grinning fool who went sidling out of the loft no matter whom the lieutenant set to guard him, and went ambling back through the château's ancient, imported trees, and in through a window or a door, and down the ground-floor corridor to the place he liked so well. There they found him the first time when they searched the house, and there he was the second, and the third, not even taking the trouble to lock the door, as other people did when they entered this particular place. He was sitting on the window sill above the porcelain receptacle, his puttees unwound and his breeches drawn up high, and his bare black feet hung down in the water that was there for another use entirely. The servants said they could hear him laughing out loud all the way to the kitchen whenever he pulled the chain and the water flushed up across his shins. The third time the lieutenant opened the door, the black man was sitting there, smiling right across his face.

"What in the name of God do you think you're in France for?" the Count exploded before the lieutenant could clear his throat.

"Kill Boche," said the Senegalese, with his feet dabbling in the water. "Come kill Boche," he said, and he was reaching up to pull the

chain when the lieutenant took him by his tunic's neck and jerked him
of the sill.

The Count told the lieutenant that afternoon to get the blacks busy
on the soil. His gardeners had been mobilized and he had been making
out with a boy as best he could, but now he had had quite enough of
this military horseplay. The potato plants were waiting for the earth to
be hoed up compactly around them, so a half-dozen of the Senegalese
were set to that, stripped to the waist and bent like oarsmen under the
sun. Others were put to work the length of the strawberry beds, weed-
ing and raking out between the clumps of low, glossy leaves and the
just shedding strawberry flowers beneath the southern wall. The pear
trees had been trained to spread out like vines across the wall's hot
stones. On the other side the main road from Lyons led on around the
curve and dropped down the hill to the village. Whenever the Senegalese turned their heads that way, they could see over the top of the
wall, through the pear leaves, whatever happened to be passing by.

They could see the trees and the fields and the waters of the river
moving off beyond, and they leaned on the rake handles and the spade
handles, talking among themselves. They would strike at the ground a
little, and then they would pause again, giggling at each other. They
might have been merely waiting there. The Count came out after tea
and he saw them leaning in these long, loose attitudes of ease, their big
hands hanging from their idle wrists or clasped at rest on the rake handles and the spade handles and the hoes. There they had paused, like
children halted on the edge of Christmas Eve.

"What are you *canaille* waiting for?" the little lieutenant called out
as he hurried across the drive. He was beginning to play his part quite
well, although in a gentle way. The Senegalese shifted the instruments
in their hands, and moved their feet, and looked out toward the river.
"What are you waiting for to get on with the job?" the lieutenant
shouted out, and one of the black men lifted his hand, like a black lily
drooping from his wrist, and moved it toward the sky.

"Kill Boche," he said. "Waiting for the sun to go."

The Count looked around in mock bewilderment.

"But where is the Boche? There's no Boche here, as far as I can
see," he said. "Everything's very peaceful and quiet here. No Boche,

no kill," he said, and smiled around the vegetable garden at them. "Work," he said, and he made the gestures of spading, hoeing, raking before them on the air.

"Boche tomorrow, maybe Boche tonight," said the black man, and he lifted his hand again and moved it in casual indication from place to place. "Kill Boche there—there—there—there," he said, letting it fall from the wrist once toward the trees and once toward the wall and twice toward the road beyond it, and the Senegalese music of talk rose on their tongues again, then waned and died.

It was just before six that evening that the first motorcycle was heard coming down the road. The three Senegalese near the pear trees straightened up from the strawberry beds. They saw first the trees on the other side of the wall and then the surface of the road and at last the color of the solitary rider's jacket as he came leaning to the handlebars. They spoke the word or gave the sign in silence, and then raced back across the garden and the drive to where the guns were stacked in the stable yard, their legs reaching, their mouths splitting wide. They went so fast they were back in time for the second one; he dropped from his machine just where the brass studs began marking the curve, and the motorcycle ran of itself a little way down the hill before it hit a tree. The third had a sidecar with a machine gunner riding in it, but neither the driver on the leather saddle nor the gunner behind his curved glass shield had time to see the khaki turbans or the guns along the wall. The motorcycle did not make the turn this time but ran with the two dead men on its seats into the ditch and sputtered out there, and others coming along behind were thirty seconds too late to see. There they came, hastening down the road from Lyons, sidecar after sidecar, and as they came, the black men picked them off over the garden wall and jumped up and down on the strawberry plants on their naked feet in glee.

The seventh or eighth was a single rider again, and this time the warning was there, splattered out on the road before him. He lifted his head to the pear leaves on top of the wall, and braked so that the tires cried aloud, and swung the machine on its haunches, rearing and pawing the air. When he poured into speed and streamed back up the road, crouched flat to the bars, the black men's hearts stood still in pain. They waited there for a moment, and then they looked at each other, and they could no longer find the sounds of laughter or speech. It might have been just after six on Christmas Day, and the stockings emptied, the presents all opened, the candles on the tree put out. They hadn't quite got over it when the nimble little tank came down the road, its eyes, like those of a snail, fingering them out, or when the second tank came down behind it and a piece of the garden wall suddenly blew in.

The look of disappointment was on their faces still when the Count came out to have a look at them lying there. The machine gunners who had finished them off were removing smoked goggles just inside the gate. A German officer met the Count and chatted amiably with him as they walked out through the rose garden, which shielded the vegetable beds from the drive. There were the black men, foolish-looking and rather giddy even in death, lying among the strawberry flowers and the potato plants.

"The staff will be along almost at once," the German officer said in a rather heavy but easy French. "I'd like to get this cleaned up without delay. It's a charming place, really charming. Regrettable that it was necessary to touch the wall."

The Count put his pince-nez on with a hand that did not tremble, and the thought struck him with singular force: Gentlemen, actually well-bred men this time. He said aloud, "The bodies removed?" and he felt himself sickening, and turned the other way.

"Buried," said the German officer pleasantly. He had a kid glove, as scrupulously clean as if just lifted from the haberdasher's counter, on the hand with which he touched the Count's tweed. "I'm sorry to give you all this trouble," he said. "The staff will require most of the bedrooms, for the moment at least." Then he turned toward the black men again and gave his orders. "Right where they are," he said shortly. "Sniper's burial."

"Right there—there, you mean?" said the Count. He was thinking confusedly of the potato plants and the strawberry flowers, but he could not bring himself to turn and look at them again.

WILLIAM L. SHIRER Why he selected

HITLER at COMPIÈGNE

This little piece was dashed off as fast as I could type it on the afternoon of June 21, 1940. I was sitting on the stump of an old tree in a little clearing in Compiègne Forest. A few feet away was the dilapidated old *Wagon-Lit* car in which the 1918 Armistice had been dictated by Marshal Foch. Now on this bright June afternoon of 1940 Hitler had been sitting in the car dictating *his* Armistice.

I had been to Compiègne before. I had seen it when it was a great Allied shrine. And I had seen over the post-war years the Allied decline and the Nazi conquest. Here in the French forest on the June afternoon you saw the climax of all that. I guess I felt it rather deeply. My little piece sort of wrote itself. Like almost all that I've written in the past fifteen years, it was done for the hour. I had a broadcast to do, a deadline to meet, minutes and seconds to count. Later these notes found their way into a Berlin diary that was published. No one is more surprised than am I that words so hastily scribbled should outlive that memorable summer afternoon during which they were written.

Bronxville, N. Y.   WILLIAM L. SHIRER
June, 1942

Paris, June 21, 1940

On the exact spot in the little clearing in the Forest of Compiègne where at five a.m. on November 11, 1918 the armistice which ended the World War was signed, Adolf Hitler today handed *his* armistice terms to France. To make German revenge complete, the meeting of the German and French plenipotentiaries took place in Marshal Foch's private car, in which Foch laid down the armistice terms to Germany twenty-two years ago. Even the same table in the rickety old *Wagon-Lit* car was used. And through the windows we saw Hitler occupying the very seat on which Foch had sat at that table when he dictated the other armistice.

The humiliation of France, of the French, was complete. And yet in the preamble to the armistice terms Hitler told the French that he had not chosen this spot at Compiègne out of revenge; merely to right an old wrong. From the demeanour of the French delegates I gathered that they did not appreciate the difference.

The German terms we do not know yet. The preamble says the general basis for them is: (1) to prevent a resumption of the fighting; (2) to offer Germany complete guarantees for her continuation of the war against Britain; (3) to create the foundations for a peace, the basis of which is to be the reparation of an injustice inflicted upon Germany by force. The third point seems to mean: revenge for the defeat of 1918.

Kerker for NBC and I for CBS in a joint half-hour broadcast early this evening described today's amazing scene as best we could. It made, I think, a good broadcast.

The armistice negotiations began at three fifteen p.m. A warm June sun beat down on the great elm and pine trees, and cast pleasant shadows on the wooded avenues as Hitler, with the German pleni-potentiaries at his side, appeared. He alighted from his car in front of the French monument to Alsace-Lorraine which stands at the end of an avenue about two hundred yards from the clearing where the armistice car waits on exactly the same spot it occupied twenty-two years ago.

The Alsace-Lorraine statue, I noted, was covered with German war flags so that you could not see its sculptured work nor read its inscription. But I had seen it some years before—the large sword representing the sword of the Allies, and its point sticking into a large, limp eagle, representing the old Empire of the Kaiser. And the inscription under-neath in French saying: "TO THE HEROIC SOLDIERS OF FRANCE . . . DEFENDERS OF THE COUNTRY AND OF RIGHT . . . GLORIOUS LIBERATORS OF ALSACE-LOR-RAINE."

Through my glasses I saw the Führer stop, glance at the monument, observe the Reich flags with their big Swastikas in the centre. Then he strode slowly towards us, towards the little clearing in the woods. I observed his face. It was grave, solemn, yet brimming with revenge. There was also in it, as in his springy step, a note of the triumphant conqueror, the defier of the world. There was something else, difficult to describe, in his expression, a sort of scornful, inner joy at being present at this great reversal of fate—a reversal he himself had wrought.

Now he reaches the little opening in the woods. He pauses and looks slowly around. The clearing is in the form of a circle some two hundred yards in diameter and laid out like a park. Cypress trees line it all round—and behind them, the great elms and oaks of the forest. This has been one of France's national shrines for twenty-two years. From a discreet position on the perimeter of the circle we watch.

Hitler pauses, and gazes slowly around. In a group just behind him are the other German plenipotentiaries: Göring, grasping his field-marshal's baton in one hand. He wears the sky-blue uniform of the air force. All the Germans are in uniform. Hitler in a double-breasted grey uniform, with the Iron Cross hanging from his left breast pocket. Next to Göring are the two German army chiefs—General Keitel, chief of the Supreme Command, and General von Brauchitsch, commander-in-chief of the German army. Both are just approaching sixty, but look younger, especially Keitel, who has a dapper appearance with his cap slightly cocked on one side.

Then there is Dr. Raeder, Grand Admiral of the German Fleet, in his blue naval uniform and the invariable upturned collar which German naval officers usually wear. There are two non-military men in Hitler's suite—his Foreign Minister, Joachim von Ribbentrop, in the field-grey uniform of the Foreign Office; and Rudolf Hess, Hitler's deputy, in a grey party uniform.

The time is now three eighteen p.m. Hitler's personal flag is run up on a small standard in the centre of the opening.

Also in the centre is a great granite block which stands some three feet above the ground. Hitler, followed by the others, walks slowly over to it, steps up, and reads the inscription engraved in great high letters on that block. It says: "HERE ON THE ELEVENTH OF NOVEMBER 1918 SUCCUMBED THE CRIMINAL PRIDE OF THE GERMAN EMPIRE . . . VANQUISHED BY THE FREE PEOPLES WHICH IT TRIED TO ENSLAVE."

Hitler reads it and Göring reads it. They all read it, standing there in the June sun and the silence. I look for the expression on Hitler's face. I am but fifty yards from him and see him through my glasses as though he were directly in front of me. I have seen that face many times at the great moments of his life. But today! It is afire with scorn, anger, hate, revenge, triumph. He steps off the monument and con-- trives to make even this gesture a masterpiece of contempt. He glances back at it, contemptuous, angry—angry, you almost feel, because he cannot wipe out the awful, provoking lettering with one sweep of his high Prussian boot. He glances slowly around the clearing, and now, as his eyes meet ours, you grasp the depth of his hatred. But there is triumph there too—revengeful, triumphant hate. Suddenly, as though his face were not giving quite complete expression to his feelings, he throws his whole body into harmony with his mood. He swiftly snaps his hands on his hips, arches his shoulders, plants his feet wide apart. It is a magnificent gesture of defiance, of burning contempt for this place now and all that it has stood for in the twenty-two years since it witnessed the humbling of the German Empire.

Finally Hitler leads his party over to another granite stone, a smaller one fifty yards to one side. Here it was that the railroad car in which the German plenipotentiaries stayed during the 1918 armistice was placed—from November 8 to 11. Hitler merely glances at the inscription, which reads: "The German Plenipotentiaries." The stone itself, I notice, is set between a pair of rusty old railroad tracks, the ones on which the German car stood twenty-two years ago. Off to one side along the edge of the clearing is a large statue in white stone of Marchal Foch as he looked when he stepped out of the armistice car on the morning of November 11, 1918. Hitler skips it; does not appear to see it.

It is now three twenty-three p.m. and the Germans stride over to the armistice car. For a moment or two they stand in the sunlight outside the car, chatting. Then Hitler steps up into the car, followed by the others. We can see nicely through the car windows. Hitler takes the place occupied by Marshal Foch when the 1918 armistice terms were signed. The others spread themselves around him. Four chairs on the opposite side of the table from Hitler remain empty. The French have not yet appeared. But we do not wait long. Exactly at three thirty p.m. they alight from a car. They have flown up from Bordeaux to a near-by landing field. They too glance at the Alsace-Lorraine memorial, but it's a swift glance. Then they walk down the avenue flanked by three German officers. We see them now as they come into the sunlight of the clearing.

General Huntziger, wearing a bleached khaki uniform, Air General Bergeret and Vice-Admiral Le Luc, both in dark blue uniforms, and then, almost buried in the uniforms, M. Noël, French Ambassador to Poland. The German guard of honour, drawn up at the entrance to the clearing, snaps to attention for the French as they pass, but it does not present arms.

It is a grave hour in the life of France. The Frenchmen keep their eyes straight ahead. Their faces are solemn, drawn. They are the picture of tragic dignity.

They walk stiffly to the car, where they are met by two German officers, Lieutenant-General Tippelskirch, Quartermaster General, and Colonel Thomas, chief of the Führer's headquarters. The Germans salute. The French salute. The atmosphere is what Europeans call "correct." There are salutes, but no handshakes.

Now we get our picture through the dusty windows of that old *wagon-lit* car. Hitler and the other German leaders rise as the French enter the drawing-room. Hitler gives the Nazi salute, the arm raised. Ribbentrop and Hess do the same. I cannot see M. Noël to notice whether he salutes or not.

Hitler, as far as we can see through the windows, does not say a word to the French or to anybody else. He nods to General Keitel at his side. We see General Keitel adjusting his papers. Then he starts to read. He is reading the preamble to the German armistice terms. The French sit there with marble-like faces and listen intently. Hitler and Göring glance at the green table-top.

The reading of the preamble lasts but a few minutes. Hitler, we soon observe, has no intention of remaining very long, of listening to the reading of the armistice terms themselves. At three forty-two p.m., twelve minutes after the French arrive, we see Hitler stand up, salute stiffly, and then stride out of the drawing-room, followed by Göring, Brauchitsch, Raeder, Hess, and Ribbentrop. The French, like figures of stone, remain at the green-topped table. General Keitel remains with them. He starts to read them the detailed conditions of the armistice.

Hitler and his aides stride down the avenue towards the Alsace-Lorraine monument, where their cars are waiting. As they pass the guard of honour, the German band strikes up the two national anthems, *Deutschland, Deutschland über Alles* and the *Horst Wessel* song. The whole ceremony in which Hitler has reached a new pinnacle in his meteoric career and Germany avenged the 1918 defeat is over in a quarter of an hour.

June 22, 1940

As I finished speaking into the microphone, winding up the broadcast, a drop of rain fell on my forehead. Down the road, through the woods, I could see the refugees, slowly, tiredly, filing by—on weary feet, on bicycles, on carts, a few on trucks, an endless line. They were exhausted and dazed, those walking were footsore, and they did not know yet that an armistice had been signed and that the fighting would be over very soon now.

I walked out to the clearing. The sky was overcast and rain was coming on. An army of German engineers, shouting lustily, had already started to move the armistice car.

"Where to?" I asked.

"To Berlin," they said.

X
THE REALM OF BEING

ALLAN NEVINS Why he selected

IN DEFENCE OF HISTORY

Herewith a selection I would like to have placed in the anthology
. . . a complete essay, "In Defence of History," which I think will
appeal to anyone; it is not heavily written, and is allusive enough to be
entertaining. I select this because it presents in compact form some
of my ideas on the importance of history, the values it presents, the
way it should be written, and the way it should be read. It emphasizes
my feeling of the importance of the literary element in historical writing—an element grossly neglected by most American historians of
recent years.

New York, N. Y.   ALLAN NEVINS
June 23, 1942

E VERYONE recalls the majestic exordium of Webster's reply to
Hayne. "Mr. President," he began, "when the mariner has
tossed for many days in thick weather, and on an unknown sea, he
naturally avails himself of the first pause in the storm, the earliest
glance of the sun, to take his latitude and ascertain how far the
elements have driven him from his true course." In that sentence
Webster indicated one of the cardinal utilities of history. Mankind is
always more or less storm-driven; and history is the sextant and compass of states which, tossed by wind and current, would be lost in
confusion if they could not fix their position. It enables communities
to grasp their relationship with the past, and to chart on general lines
their immediate forward course. It does more. By giving peoples a
sense of continuity in all their efforts, and by chronicling immortal
worth, it confers upon them both a consciousness of their unity, and a
feeling of the importance of human achievement. History is more

than a mere guide to nations. It is first a creator of nations, and after that, their inspirer. Without it this world, a brilliant arena of human action canopied by fretted fire, would indeed become stale, flat, and unprofitable, a congregation of pestilent vapors.

By looking either at the past or the present we can see how vitally history serves its purpose as a womb or matrix of nations. The strongest element in the creation of any human organization of complex character and enduring strength is the establishment of common tradition by the narration of its history. Members of a religion may be knit together by their gospel, but even that must contain historic elements; while members of a nation are knit together above all else by a common history—by learning of their past. The Greek who thrilled over Thermopylae, the Roman exulting in the tale of Caesar's conquests and triumphs, the Briton reading of the assault on Badajoz, the American following the epic story of Western pioneering, all have responded to the same emotion. When Treitschke resolved to revive the national spirit of the Germans he began by writing their history; when Vienna wished to hinder the growth of patriotism among the Czechs it threw obstacles before the publication of Palacký's history of Bohemia. To give a people a new sense of their future we need first the historian who will give them a new sense of their past. The school text that told the story of Valley Forge, the rhetorical page of Bancroft, helped immeasurably to make America a nation. Communist Russia was welded together with the aid of a Communist version of history, and Fascist Italy and Nazi Germany by Fascist and Nazi histories. "Laws die, books never"—and the nation-builder may well say that he cares not who writes the laws of a country if he can write its history.

But if history is a maker of nations, her rôle as their inspirer is almost equally great. Clio was the first of the Muses; and while she began as minstrel and wonder-teller, she soon became instructress. It is in that part that she has chiefly impressed the modern world. "All learners, all inquiring minds of every order," writes Carlyle, "are gathered round her footstool, and reverently pondering her lessons as the true basis of wisdom." But there is more than wisdom in her inspiration. All thoughtful men tend in some degree to identify themselves with the figures and forces of history. They realize that each individual mind is one more incarnation of a universal mind. We can understand history only as we understand that it was wrought by men and women basically like ourselves; that what Shakespeare and Napoleon achieved, what Caesar Borgia and Ivan the Terrible perpetrated, what Hasdrubal and Gustavus Adolphus dared and endured, are illustrations of the powers, debasements, and fortitudes of our common human nature. This universal nature gives value to our lives, and from it we may select the best. The grandeur of history sheds a grandeur upon ourselves. In the largest accomplishments of the past we feel that we have a share. "We sympathize in the great moments of history, in the great discoveries, the great resistances, the great prosperities of men; because there law was enacted, the sea was searched, the land was found, or the blow was struck, *for us,* as we ourselves would have done in that place or applauded."[1]

Poetry, philosophy, drama, all have a dignity of their own; but it is inferior to the dignity of history, for each is dependent upon history for a great part of its materials. As the distillation of everything that humanity has suffered, dared, failed, and vanquished, history is indeed the deepest philosophy, the truest poetry. Seated at the roaring loom of time, for six thousand years man has woven a seamless garment. But that garment is invisible and intangible save where the dyes of written history fall upon it, and forever preserve it as a possession of generations to come. Call it a department of literature or knowledge as you will—it is both—the work of historians will be most read when men are roused to a sense of their own dignity; when great events wake them to their most serious and responsible temper. Two thousand years ago Lucian was writing: "From the beginning of the present excitements—the barbarian war, the Armenian disaster, the succession of victories—you cannot find a man but is writing history; nay, everyone you meet is a Thucydides, a Herodotus, a Xenophon." It was no accident that the convulsion of the World War fostered such an interest in history that for a time the number of books devoted to it in English exceeded the titles in fiction; that on the heels of that war when men groped for some guiding conception of the course of civilization, appeared the most-widely read volume of its kind in modern times, H. G. Wells's *Outline of History.*

[1] Emerson's *Works,* Concord Ed., II, 4.

II

Modern history, in spirit and method, is largely a product of the eighteenth century Enlightenment; and it was just as that Enlightenment began to merge in the Industrial Revolution that the United States was born. Various writers, such as Lord Morley in his *Voltaire,* have pointed out how great a part historical writing and reading played in the mature phases of the Enlightenment. The literate generation contemporary with the American and French Revolutions, in Western Europe and the United States, was steeped in history. When the eighteenth century ended no gentleman's library was complete without Thucydides, Livy, and Tacitus, and few cultivated men could not discuss the historical works of Voltaire, Hume, Gibbon, and Robertson. Henry Adams in his life of John Randolph of Roanoke speaks of the "literary standards of the day" to which Randolph's education conformed: "He read his Gibbon, Hume and Burke; knew English history . . ." Even at an earlier period three historical works— Raleigh's eloquent *History of the World,* Bishop Burnet's *History of the Reformation,* and above all, Fox's *Book of Martyrs,* had been widely diffused throughout the American colonies. The last-named was so frequent a companion to the Bible that it may be said to have transported history to the common body of readers. But these three books are all upon an inferior historical plane; and as the Enlightenment widened its appeal to the intellectual aristocracy of the time, it brought in more select works. The men who took the leadership of our young republic were well acquainted with the first great modern historical classics. Law was no doubt their primary study, but history maintained a place close beside it.

Thus it is that we find George Washington after the Revolution ordering from England a small library of historical works—Robertson's *Charles V* and *History of America*; Voltaire's *Charles XII* and Sully's *Memoirs*; lives of Peter the Great, Louis XV, and Gustavus Adolphus; and histories of Rome and Portugal.[2] Thus it is that we find John Adams, in discussing the qualifications of a Secretary of State, writing a little later: "He ought to be a Man of universal Reading

---

[2] Paul Leicester Ford, *The True George Washington,* pp. 203-204.

in Laws, Governments, History."[3] Thus it is, again, that we find Chancellor Kent confessing in his autobiography that in 1782, at Poughkeepsie, he varied his study of law by reading Smollett's and Rapin's histories of England. "The same year I procured Hume's *History*, and his profound reflections and admirable eloquence struck most deeply on my youthful mind." Alexander Hamilton's library included not only Greek and Roman historians, but well-thumbed sets of Gibbon, Hume, and Robertson. It is safe to say that few well-educated Americans, editors, theologians, and attorneys as well as politicians, failed at this time to regard history as a necessary discipline even if they did not take to it as a delight. Most of them would have agreed with Jefferson, himself a lover of Hume, Voltaire, Robertson, and later Hallam, in what he wrote of the proper nature of Virginia's educational law:

But of the views of this law none is more important, none more legitimate, than that of rendering the people the safe, as they are the ultimate, guardians of their own liberty. For this purpose the reading in the first stage, where *they* will receive their whole education, is proposed, as has been said, to be chiefly historical. History, by apprizing them of the past, will enable them to judge of the future; it will avail them of the experience of other times and other nations; it will qualify them as judges of the actions and designs of men; it will enable them to know ambition under every guise it may assume; and knowing it, to defeat its views.[4]

The spell which history exercised over the aristocratic and intellectual groups of America remained undiminished for a long generation. Hear young Charles Sumner, for example, writing a friend just after his graduation from Harvard in 1830. "I have marked out to myself a course of study which will fully occupy my time—namely, a course of mathematics, Juvenal, Tacitus, a course of modern history, Hallam's *Middle Ages* and *Constitutional History*, Roscoe's *Leo* and *Lorenzo*, and Robertson's *Charles V* . . ."[5] Even pioneer America felt that history befitted the leader, and after the log cabin campaign Webster spent a wearisome day deleting the names of Greek heroes

---

[3] *Statesman and friend: Correspondence of John Adams with Benjamin Waterhouse*, p. 57.

[4] *Notes on Virginia* (Jefferson's *Works*, Memorial Edition, II, 206, 207).

[5] E. L. Pierce, *Memoir and Letters of Charles Sumner*, I, 80-82.

and Roman consuls from William Henry Harrison's inaugural address.

But to fulfill its proper purpose in a country like the United States, history had to become democratized. That feat required a group of great talents, but it was performed. It is a salient fact of American literature, and one of the most creditable chapters in our cultural record, that from 1830 to 1870 history stood as one of the most popular literary forms—that it was continuously and strongly popular. Prescott's *Conquest of Mexico* sold 5,000 copies in four months in the United States, and then went through edition after edition; his *Conquest of Peru* sold 7,500 copies in England and America in the same brief period, then commencing a career that is still far from ended. The works of Bancroft and Motley, of Parkman and Irving, had equal or greater currency. Indeed, Irving's life of Washington, the ablest study of the Revolution made up to that time, was one of the great successes of American publishing prior to the Civil War. Even volumes which might have seemed destined to a slender public, such as Ticknor's dry *History of Spanish Literature*, reached a large fraction of the readers of the day. When it is recalled that meanwhile the histories of Macaulay and Carlyle were not merely brought out by authorized publishers, but pirated in huge cheap editions and scattered in myriads through the land, while translated histories like Rollin's sold widely, we can comprehend why the American mind retained a distinct historical bias during most of the century. We can understand why a philosopher like Fiske turned to history as the best medium for disseminating his ideas; why novelists like Mark Twain and Edward Eggleston wrote formal histories as well as fiction; and why in the greatest days of the *Atlantic, Century*, and *Harper's*, history occupied a prominent place in their tables of contents.

This popularity, beyond question, has been followed by a period of comparative deliquescence. Since Parkman published his last history in 1892, and Fiske in 1899, no writer can be named who has rivalled their appeal. Successful books there have been in large numbers. But the greatest of the latter-day historians in many respects, Henry Adams, complained that he was hardly read at all, and it took thirty years for his history of the United States from 1801 to 1817 to reach a second edition. While the work of John Bach McMaster and James Ford Rhodes, begun in the eighties, commanded a substantial sale, it never reached so large a fraction of the literate population as did Prescott and Motley. Since the World War the greatest successes in serious literature have been biographical, and the sale of extended histories—histories in sets—has declined to very slender proportions.

For both this broad appeal of history during the half-century 1835-85, and its comparative decline in popularity in the half-century 1885-1935, manifold reasons may be assigned. It is conventional to say that history in its era of ascendancy was highly literary in character, more literary than today. But this does not wholly express the difference. To be sure, Macaulay, Carlyle, and Froude, Prescott, Parkman, and Motley were masters of style whose literary gifts—that is, whose powers of description, exposition, and narration—amounted in four of the six to genius, and in the other two to very rare talent. It would be difficult to point to any British or American histories since 1885 of equally sustained literary power. But the subjects and methods of these writers had much to do with their "literary" excellence.

They belonged, like Gibbon and Robertson before them, to the great age of historical exploration. In their day the field of history lay spread before mankind like a huge half-completed map, full of mountain ranges, seas, and plains still to be traversed and measured. It appealed to the imagination, for it offered tasks of vast scope and rich color, and at every new turn held novelty and adventure. Gibbon was a veritable Columbus, who traveled across wider reaches than any predecessor, and showed the decline of one world and the rise of a new one. Macaulay in his history of the momentous transition from Stuart to Hanoverian England and the rise of a new democratic state and Parkman in his chronicle of the conflict which determined that North America should have a British and not a French civilization, were like Humboldt and Livingstone, mapping huge new territories. The readers of Prescott's story of the Spanish conquest of the New World experienced much the same emotions as those who followed the feats of Frémont and Stanley. They were the first who ever burst into that historical domain, and they saw a great panorama unrolled as from a mountain top. The period in which these historians wrote might well be called the age of wonder in history, and its special rapture can never be regained.

These eminent literary histories, moreover, appertained to a simpler age in another sense. It was an age in which men felt that they held more of the key to the universe than educated men can believe they hold today. To the Victorians in Britain and America all moral and scientific values seemed to be coming within grasp. The domain of physics was ruled by Newton. The globe was fast being conned and triangulated to its farthest corners. The doctrines of evolution and natural selection answered the chief riddles of biology, psychology, and sociology. Historians did not need to be writers of many ideas, for simple ideas—which were all that even Macaulay, Carlyle, and Prescott offered—sufficed. They did not need to integrate their histories with a complex set of sciences, for science seemed to have little complexity. In a simple, direct world simple, direct historians, writing in the temper of democratic, progressive, rationalist peoples, could be sure of understanding and acceptance. It was an acceptance all the more enthusiastic when they none too subtly flattered the preconceptions of their readers, as they usually did:—Macaulay with his Whig bias their democratic preconceptions; Motley, Froude, and Parkman their Protestant preconceptions; Carlyle their moral preconceptions and their worship of work and efficiency; Freeman and John Fiske their belief in the endless linear progress of man.

In one respect not so obvious the simplicity of the age tended to the popularization of history. In the United States and Europe the first three-fourths of the nineteenth century was primarily an age of political interests, while the period which followed it became—at least in intellectual circles—primarily an age of economic and sociological interests. If this statement sounds extreme, it is at least accurate to say that after the middle of the nineteenth century economic and sociological factors received increasing attention as compared with political topics. Now political history, which is comparatively easy to write and to read, appeals alike to the well-educated and the semi-educated. But history which gives due weight to both social and economic elements is, on the contrary, seldom appreciated save by the fully educated, and not a little of it is appreciated only by specialists. Particularly is this true so long as the social and economic elements in history are unskillfully and pedantically treated by writers who still lack finished models and well-settled rules, as till lately has been the fact. In short, it seemed easier in the midde of the nineteenth century to combine instruction with entertainment—it was easier—than in the middle of the twentieth century.

Most Americans, Britons, Frenchmen, and Germans in the age of Lincoln, Gladstone, Thiers, and Bismarck instinctively believed that the central focus of men's attention, in current affairs and historical study alike, should be the state, its fortunes and misfortunes. Hence it was that Macaulay's stirring portrayal of the evils of James II's reign, the crushing of Monmouth's rebellion, the rising tide of anger against real temporal and threatened ecclesiastical tyranny, the "glorious revolution" of 1688, the vicissitudes of William and Mary's reign, seemed admirable history to his own and the succeeding generation. Macaulay's fourth chapter, while social history of a rare kind, is a small part of the whole. Hence it is that Thierry's *Norman Conquest,* dealing with the English dissensions under Harold, with Stamford Bridge, with William's invasion, the battle of Hastings, and the ensuing conquests, confiscations, and administrative acts of the Conqueror, seemed perfect history to our forefathers. Today most men believe that the central focus of their attention should be *society,* not the state, and society is more complicated and formless than politics. Good history is correspondingly harder to write, and unless done with consummate art, harder to read.

It is sometimes said that history was more widely read a century ago than today because, good books being fewer, it encountered less competition. But in so far as the literature of books goes, this is not merely a dubious but a false assertion. The nineteenth century was a century of great novelists, great essayists, and great poets. Men of Macaulay's time did not turn to history because there was little else to read; they had Thackeray, Dickens, and Trollope; Tennyson, Browning, and Swinburne; De Quincey, Bagehot, and Arnold. Men of Parkman's day did not read him because of a paucity of American books; they had Howells, James, and Mark Twain; Longfellow, Lowell, and Whittier. The quarter in which history meets a really novel degree of competition in our day is the journalistic quarter—the field of current discussion.

Readers, like other consumers, demand a balanced diet; they will accept but so much poetry and so much prose, so much entertainment and so much wisdom. History, though by no means without entertaining values, is to be classified primarily as serious matter; and for serious matter men in the turmoil of today turn largely to the discussion of contemporaneous problems in newspapers, reviews, and books. To a far greater extent than in the more placid Victorian days they are prone to feel that history is a dead field, that it concerns itself with a lifeless past, and that for the purposes of earnest, living men it is often useless enough to deserve Henry Ford's epithet— "bunk." Particularly since the vast upheaval of the World War, they wish a discussion of current issues. Having read enough books and articles upon unemployment and corporation control, upon disarmament and neutrality, upon the Supreme Court and the Securties Commission, upon Nazi Germany and Communist Russia, to feel well informed, they turn for recreation to fiction, and for refreshment to essays and poetry. The present has become so exigent that the demands of the past seem tame and colorless.

This is of course a temporary attitude; but even if evanescent, it is unjust to history. The political present, the economic present, the sociological present, cannot be understood without knowledge of the past. The attitude is not wholly unjust to the latter-day race of historians. Most of them have failed to solve the problem of uniting human appeal with the new stuff of history; the problem of bringing insight, imagination, and eloquence to bear upon the more refractory materials that now go into their crucibles. But it is unjust to history as a whole. Who can understand Nazi Germany without knowing something of Germany of the Weimar Constitution, Germany of the Kaisers, and back of that the Germany of Jena and Leipzig? Who can understand Franklin D. Roosevelt's New Deal without studying Woodrow Wilson's New Freedom, the elder Roosevelt's New Nationalism, and back of that the democratic ideals of Lincoln, Jackson, and Jefferson? The more exigent the present day the more exigent also the past, for they are indissolubly united. But this necessity of studying the origins of present-day forces and tendencies in bygone times is far from being the only reason why history is essential even to the man who tries to fasten his eyes narrowly upon what is current and practical. A knowledge of history is needed, in addition, to throw the present into perspective. We can endure the current economic boom or depression better if we comprehend what preceded and followed 1837 and 1873. We can take a clearer view of Mussolini if we are familiar with the career of Napoleon III. It throws the course of the Japanese in China into better definition to know something of the time when the savage horsemen of Tamerlane rode across the roof of the world.

History has also suffered, by a natural paradox, from overproduction. The period in which it bore its greatest names was also a period in which it had many fewer small names, many fewer mediocre practitioners, than in late years. As a branch of literature it then demanded passports of talent from all entrants. It has tended too largely to become a mere branch of learning; and in that field the only passports are diligence and accuracy, which are too often synonymous with plodding dullness. The Artisans of history have multiplied beyond all proportion to the Artists. Far more historical works are printed, sold (or not sold), and put on library shelves, than when history was most read. A multitude of books, chiefly petty in scope and pettier in aim, stream from presses to be forgotten. The very size of the shallow stream, the brawling clamor it wakes in reviews, its brackish taste when sampled, repel many readers from history altogether. Nothing could do more for widespread historical reading than some reform by which fewer men would take up their pens, and these few would do so later in life, or at any rate not until intellectually mature and fully trained in their craft. Failing this, history would at least benefit by a more discriminating terminology. As a fairly clear line is drawn between poetry and verse (even Kipling modestly called his compositions by the latter name), so such a line might be drawn between history on one side, and chronicles, compilations, and monographs on the other. We could then speak of Parkman's histories, but, to select a writer long dead and of greater stature than most, of Hildreth's chronicles.

But most of all, history has suffered in recent years from confusion of aims and standards. It has passed through what John Richard Green and John Bach McMaster thought a mere age of transition into an age of utter revolution, and has not yet quite oriented itself. Of course all literary forms which possess any vitality manifest their constant changes of mode and temper. Poetry moves from a classical age to a romantic age; the novel is wrested from the realistic school by the naturalistic school. But history has been altered simultaneously and radically not only by this type of change, but by another of very different character.

It was inevitable that it, like other prose of the nineteenth century should alter from a romantic to a realistic mood, from the rich coloring and adventurous pace of Macaulay, Prescott, and Parkman to the sober tones of Mommsen, Freeman, and Henry Adams. Such a change was part of the spirit of the time. It kept pace with the change from Byron and Keats to Browning and Meredith. But history differs from pure literature in being closely interconnected not only with the spirit of the time, but with the whole body of the social sciences. When these underwent their tremendous expansion and development in the latter half of the nineteenth and early twentieth centuries, history had to expand, develop, and change with them. While the old history did not cease to be a true history, men perceived that it was only part of the truth. The new wine had to be poured into new bottles, and historians fell to quarreling as to their shape if they were not to break. Lovers of old traditions and standards even denied that men should attempt, in any greater degree than Von Ranke or Guizot, the analysis of economic institutions, the dissection of social structure. Enthusiasts for the application of social science to history simultaneously, and with equal folly, denied that politics, war, and diplomacy held any weighty place in history at all—that they were more than the spume and bubble on the river of human development. This lack of settled standards not only bewildered some writers of history, but encouraged many readers to underrate its importance. They asked "What is history?" and picking up the latest magazine, would not pause for an answer.

But out of confusion slowly emerges integration; little by little the new bottles are being shaped for the new wine. As the limitations of the old history are more charitably weighed and the limits of the new history more sharply appraised, it is being found that the truly sound specimens of both are not far apart. It is also being found that the best history is a combination of old and new. Henry Adams wrote history as political in character as Von Ranke, as much devoted to *Staatsrecht*; but the first six chapters of his greatest work are a social history (descriptive, not analytical, to be sure) of transcendent merit. William Roscoe Thayer's *Cavour* would be classified as a political history. But no sociological historian could be more thorough in displaying the vast and complex net work of forces, social, religious, and economic, local, national, and international, through whose warring confusion Cavour had to fight his way to his goals. Nor could any psychological historian do better in measuring the fluctuating tides of opinion, prejudice, and sentiment, and the fierce uneven growth of nationalist feeling in Italy. If we think of intellectual history, Henry Osborn Taylor's *Medieval Mind* unites sympathy with the scientific spirit in as notable a union, and with as vigorous a grasp, as anyone could demand; while in such a chapter as "The Spotted Actuality" he shows a very modern realism. These men are "old" historians, and yet they are new. Such active present-day historians as George Macaulay Trevelyan know how to combine the old standards of brilliant narrative, as in his Garibaldi volumes, with the new standards of scientific breadth, as in his Queen Anne volumes. The establishment of accepted norms is possible and will come. Meanwhile the confusion is at least a sign of healthy growth; and when it ends history will be the richer and stronger for it.

The history written in the future will necessarily be eclectic in the best sense. Because the full truth is the only real truth, history as a whole will make all possible use of science—of statistics, sociology, economics, psychology, geography—to present a complete and exact picture of the past. Because the state is usually the greatest common denominator of society, and is often its highest expression, history will never neglect political movements. Because even business cannot be interpreted solely by statistics of prices and profits—because ruined men weep and suddenly enriched men dance—the best historian will still look deep into the human heart. Because narrative power is indispensable to the highest kind of history, future historians will still tell romantic, heroic, and heart-rending stories, and still have their heroes, their villains, and their yet more interesting mixtures of the heroic and the villainous.

III

Meanwhile we possess the serried shelves of the great historians of the past, a department of letters as rich and noble as any other, and as deathless as the writings of the great poets or philosophers. Their work is not a dead record. Instead, it pulses with fire. Again and again great events have found a historian who knew how to paint with unfading colors, so that intervening time melts away between us and his scene. We are still moved by the sight of Nebuchadnezzar, his hair tangled on his shoulders, his uncombed beard hanging down his swart chest, his nails sharp as eagle's talons, returning sane at last to the gates of Babylon. We still thrill to the shout of Xenophon's Ten Thousand as, reaching the crest of their final hill, they at last descry the dark line of the Euxine Sea. We catch the crash of brazen impact, the crackling of flames, and the yells of rage and pain as Antony's five hundred ships close with the Octavian fleet, and then we see the purple sails of Cleopatra puff in the breeze as she signals the Egyptian vessels to flee with her. We watch Diocletian, leaving his huge palace at Spalato and driving to his massive amphitheatre, take the salute of two bands of doomed criminals before, rushing upon one another with sword and spear, they open the gladiatorial show. We see the thin English line at Crécy halting at Edward's sharp word, planting their pointed stakes in the mud, drawing bow to ear, and suddenly darkening the air with clothyard arrows that crumple the French host in front. And so the story marches down with its ever-widening sweep until we see Wolfe reciting the Elegy below Quebec, Pitt bidding his servant roll up the map of Europe, Lincoln sinking back unconscious in his arm-chair in Ford's theater, Bismarck presiding over the Congress of Berlin, the German tide rolling through Brussels in 1914; until, with a start, we face the events of only yesterday—Woodrow Wilson struggling to found a League of Nations, and Lenin founding a Communist state.

On these serried shelves there is fare for every taste and nutriment for every mind. There are perhaps lovers of rich and picturesque description who have never read Herodotus's pages telling how the Arabians collected frankincense from trees guarded by winged serpents, how the Scythians boiled meat without firewood, and how the Carthaginians carried on a dumb commerce with certain African tribes. There are perhaps lovers of tense and harrowing narrative who have never followed the chapter in which Thucydides relates how the Athenian expedition came to utter ruin before Syracuse. There are perhaps men who like a panoramic picture of a world-shaking struggle, yet who have never perused Livy's detailed and engrossing story of how Hannibal massed an army in Spain, marched it across the Alps, and bringing it into the plains of Italy, defeated one Roman army after another until he stood at the gates of the desperate capital. The potential readers of history who have missed these works are to be pitied. We could better lose a thousand current novels than any one of the three. Some men, again, may like a picture of a dark age painted in dark colors. If they wish to feed a taste for the sensational they need only turn to Tacitus. Himself an eye-witness of the reign of terror in the last three years of Domitian, he saw only the worst side of imperialism; and figuring Tiberius as another tyrant of the Domitian stripe, he has retold us every horrible tale of the emperor's misdeeds.

Those who prefer the quieter side of history, a study of works and days, may find it in a long shelf of works, from the portraiture of national life and manners in Xenophon's *Education of Cyrus* and in Tacitus's *Germania* down to Elie Halévy's masterly presentation of every aspect of British life in his *English People in 1815*, and Lamprecht's vivid and scholarly volumes on the cultural development of Germany. For those interested in the intellectual and spiritual history of mankind an equal treasury of material exists. They may begin with James H. Breasted's study of *The Dawn of Conscience*, describing the full emergence of a sense of social morals in Egypt five thousand years ago, with W. Robertson Smith's *Religion of the Semites*, and with Gilbert Murray and G. Lowes Dickinson on the history of the Greek mind and spirit; and from this they may come down to such historians of the modern mind as Taine, Lecky, Brandes, and Vernon Parrington. Some may prefer history of the highly analytical order, with ample introduction of statistical and sociological data; such history as we encounter in Leroy-Beaulieu on Russian economic changes, or in the works of J. B. and Barbara Hammond on

the town laborer and rural laborer in England. Some may like insti-
tutional history, which Maitland has shown may be made witty and
entertaining. Others, again, may like history written so closely around
some central figure, as in Parkman's *Frontenac and New France*, or
Mommsen's chapters upon Rome in Caesar's day, that it almost becomes biography. Every department of history spreads an ample feast
to those who will but seek it out.

No nation, it is pleasant to note in this connection, has done more
in the last fifty years to add to the amplitude and vitality of its own
historical record than the United States. Great single names, unless
license be taken to call Rhodes and Henry Adams great, are indeed
lacking. But for this deficiency our writers have largely atoned by a
wealth of monographic work, not a little of it brilliant, more of it
searching, and still more of it impressively thorough. It is seldom
realized, even by the well-read, how much remained to be done forty
years ago—what great areas of the American past stood untouched,
what other areas were like raw, new-broken, prairie. Our best historians, Prescott, Motley, and Parkman, had not turned to national
history at all; Bancroft had but reached the threshold of that field;
the history of the West, the period since the Civil War, the history
of business, of thought, and of institutions all remained to be written.
Theodore Roosevelt only forty years ago could speak of the great
inviting reaches that beckoned to authors.[6] They could paint anew
he declared, the labors of the colonists to plant civilization in the
Indian-haunted forests. They could describe almost for the first time
the backwoodsmen with their long rifles and light axes hewing their
way to the Mississippi; the endless march of white-topped wagons
across plain and mountain to the Pacific. "They will show how the
land which the pioneers won slowly and with incredible hardship was
filled in two generations by the overflow from the countries of western
and central Europe. The portentous growth of the cities will be shown,
and the change from a nation of farmers to a nation of business men
and artisans, and all the far-reaching consequences of the rise of the
new industrialism. The formation of a new ethnic type in this melting-
pot of the nations will be told. The hard materialism of our age will
appear, and also the strange capacity for lofty idealism which must be

---

[6] In *Works*, National Ed., XII, 23, 24: "History as Literature."

reckoned with by all who would understand the American character." Most of this has been done, and part of it with compelling interest. The remainder will rapidly be accomplished. The history written of and by Americans in the last generation not only illuminates our past, but suffuses a glow which more than anything else—more than the work of sociologists, economists, or political experts—lights up our immediate future. The American who ignores it has neglected the most vital part of his education.

Were history as nearly static as some branches of learning, it would be a drab affair; but it is alive in every sense. It is most of all alive in this, that it is constantly being reborn like a phoenix from its own ashes. As mankind lengthens its record, perspectives steadily change. The lenses through which we look at the past must be refocussed from generation to generation. What seemed wisdom to our fathers is often folly to us; what is intensely dramatic to our age may seem naïve or banal to the next. While the best history is perdurable, there is a sense in which every generation needs to have history rewritten anew for it; and in this fact lies much of the challenge and fascination which historical activity will always have to thoughtful men. The history written in any age insensibly bodies forth the form and spirit of that age; a succession of histories is a record of the stages through which thought and feeling have passed. History in its protean forms touches the realm of ideas at more points than any other study, and in the best of its forms it is compact as much of ideas as of fact. There was a profound and not merely superficial meaning in the last instructions Napoleon left for the King of Rome: "Let my son often read and reflect on history; this is the only true philosophy."[7]

PORTRAIT OF A PRESIDENT: ULYSSES S. GRANT

MEETINGS in the large, bright Cabinet Room (so used from Andrew Johnson to Theodore Roosevelt) on the second floor of the White House, above the East Room; meetings in the President's

[7] August Fournier, *Napoleon the First: A Biography,* one volume edition (1903), p. 743.

office on the same floor; meetings at official receptions and dinners; meetings at Fish's own house, to which Grant sometimes strolled for evening exercise—at all these Hamilton Fish continued his friendly scrutiny of the President.

Physically Grant was unimpressive. He was scarcely five feet eight inches tall, slightly stooped, and so retiring in manner, especially in a crowded room, that he gave an appearance of shyness. When the war ended he had been slender, weighing at most one hundred and forty pounds; now he was portly enough to fill out his shining broadcloth frock coat. His hair, brushed back from his forehead in a rough cowlick, was becoming grizzled, but his close-cropped beard and mustache were still a warm chestnut brown. His Cromwellian wart, just above the mustache on the right side, was becoming lost in lines engraved by time. A high, broad, squarish brow was the feature which first caught attention; a brow now corrugated by heavy horizontal wrinkles, which with the thoughtful droop of his left eye gave him a careworn and rather sad aspect. The eyes were arresting; not large, not widely-spaced, their steel-blue glint bespoke determination; yet they held a perplexed look. But his most striking features were his mouth and chin. The lips showed grim firmness, meeting closely in an almost horizontal line; the jaw was square, heavy, and in repose had a set rigidity that expressed his tenacity and force of character. Once during his Presidency he shaved his chin, revealing it as even longer, squarer, and grimmer than people supposed—the chin of a fighter. His voice was low-pitched but exceedingly musical, one of the clearest and most distinct imaginable, and so penetrating that it was heard at a surprising distance. In talking he was fond of two gestures; he stroked his chin with his left hand, or rhythmically raised and lowered his right, resting it at intervals on his knee. Despite his grim, careworn appearance, his nature was actually buoyant and optimistic. In social exchanges his eyes often lit up with a merry twinkle, and he would sometimes laugh heartily. Like Lincoln, he was essentially democratic; while sometimes silent, he was never brusque; he treated everyone, great or small, with courtesy; and though his acts might be autocratic, his speech and manners never were. It was possible for men who knew him well, as Fish soon did, to conceive a genuine affection for him; but no one knew him so well that he ceased to be a little of a puzzle

Little by little Fish made up his mind as to the President. Grant's was a contradictory personality, and facile generalizations upon him are to be avoided. His mind, though undisciplined by study and unbroadened by cultivation, was by no means always casual. It could be remarkably logical and purposeful. No one can read his military dispatches or his *Memoirs* without realizing that at times it possessed great precision and lucidity. But he labored under two heavy disabilities. One was the fruit of his training at West Point and in the Mexican and Civil Wars. Having acquired a military point of view, he clung to it tenaciously in a political environment. His subordinates he regarded as so many staff officers or field commanders; his policies were to be executed like campaigns; and while opposition was to be expected from the enemy, any exhibition of it from within his own camp was worse than insubordination—it was treason. "In military matters," as Jacob D. Cox long afterwards wrote, "the objective is usually a very definite one, and the end being clearly aimed at, the intervening steps arrange themselves when there is true courage and tenacity of purpose. In civil affairs there would be danger that such a rule would run into the pernicious maxim that the end justifies the means. A very different kind of knowledge, both of men and of affairs, is needed to conduct properly the civil business of the State." Not merely did Grant lack that knowledge—he was incapable of gaining it.

The other disability was in part inborn, and in part the result of the long years of reverses, miseries, and humiliations which had driven him in upon himself. He was destitute of the great gift which may be called the consultative talent. Not only was he naturally reticent; in intellectual fields he felt a bashful inferiority. Hence his reticence became an awkward self-constraint in the presence of men of superior reading, information, and knowledge of law, government, and the world in general. On meeting them he froze instantly, while they, awed in turn by his great reputation, found it almost impossible to break down the barrier. In time Fish, as we shall see, with his simplicity, kindliness, and strong good sense, did it. But even Attorney-General Hoar, whose geniality and wit conquered nearly everybody, could with difficulty reach Grant; while a stiffer man like Jacob D. Cox met impenetrable armor. Not so the coarser politicians. This quick-witted tribe, who had no more cultivation than Grant himself, who showed a flattering deference, who studied his peculiarities, found his ear open. They obtained easy access to him, and urged their schemes with skilful arguments and passionate intensity. Then, without waiting for a reply, they trusted to the slow effect of their words. Confederates tactfully seconded them by similar speeches. He had few advisers to point out sophistries; he was so devoid of subtlety that he seldom suspected any plausible fellow of guile. Frequently he would accept their view. Then, with ingrained Scotch persistence, with that indomitable will which had served the nation so magnificently before Vicksburg and Richmond, he clung to it to the end.

Fish and other Cabinet members slowly grasped the facts which Adam Badeau, Orville E. Babcock, and other clever men, long associated with Grant, had already perceived. Badeau, living in the same house with young Henry Adams, sketched the new President in caustic terms:

Loyal to Grant . . . he held that no man except himself and Rawlins understood the General. To him, Grant appeared as an intermittent energy, immensely powerful when awake, but passive and plastic in repose. He said that neither he nor the rest of the staff knew why Grant succeeded; they believed in him because of his successes. For stretches of time, his mind seemed torpid. Rawlins and others would systematically talk their ideas into it, for weeks, not directly, but by discussion among themselves in his presence. In the end, he would announce the ideas as his own, without seeming conscious of the discussion; and would give the orders to carry them out with all the energy that belonged to his nature. They could never measure his character or be sure when he would act. They could never follow a mental process in his thought. They were not sure that he did think.

Through his obtuseness, trustfulness, and responsiveness to flattery, Grant had little capacity for self-protection. He did not understand a fraud or "game" or plot. In legislation he responded to wirepullers and in administration to adventurers. His friends were soon condoning his errors on the ground that he was "only a blunt, simple soldier," or that he had "had his mind poisoned." He was also sadly crippled by his total ignorance of law, of which most Presidents have possessed at least a smattering. Fish noted this deficiency in many a Cabinet meeting. Gideon Welles had noted it before him, and had written in his diary of Grant's amazing lack of comprehension of the machinery or spirit of civil government as well. Ignorance of law helps to explain Grant's failure in Southern affairs, for example; essentially a failure to respect the Anglo-American tradition of the subordination of the military arm to the civil power. He was crippled, again, by his erratic memory, for Fish's diary shows that he kept forgetting facts of cardinal importance; and by his lack of system in work—Fish notes his confusion, his carelessness, and his failure to keep copies of important papers. And because harsh years of failure had made him keenly sensitive to criticism, he soon learned an intense distrust of reformers. A reformer is by definition a critic; they attacked him, while the "boys," the politicians, stood loyally by him—for their own ends. The very word reform became a red rag to him. But once he gave his friendship to any of the "boys," he gave it unreservedly. He had grown up in a chilly home, starved of affection by his mother; during his bleak years of poverty and failure he had come to crave admiration, comradeship, and loyalty inordinately; and he would go through fire for a man who, like his secretary Orville E. Babcock, seemed to offer them.

However intermittent was his mental energy, it will not do to underrate it. He was sometimes incredibly naïve—so naïve that in his travels he remarked seriously to a young woman that Venice would be a fine city if it were only drained. He could be incredibly awkward —so awkward that, retiring from a dining-room with the second Duke of Wellington, he broke a long silence by remarking, "They tell me, my Lord, that your father was also a military man." He displayed the same mastery of platitude that often convinced men of Grover Cleveland's dullness. But on occasion, as the Vicksburg campaign proved, he could think rapidly, independently (Sherman had condemned that plan of campaign), and effectively. Nor was he altogether inarticulate. "Few men," wrote Fish later, "had more powers of conversation and of narration than he when in the company of intimate friends. . . . His memory was minute and accurate to a degree. He was not fond of talking of the war, or of his battles; but when he could be led to the subject, he would carry it through, giving the incidents of a fight, stating minutely at the various stages of an engagement the location of each division or separate corps or regiment." In this statement we have the chief secret of the best book of military memoirs since Caesar. On occasion Grant showed a remarkable faculty of concentration. During the war no distraction—the roar of battle, the noise of talking and laughing officers in his tent, the coming and going of orderlies—could interrupt his work. He wrote some of his most important orders amid a wild uproar. Much of his writing both during and after the war would have done any man credit. Always rapid in composition, he used words of Anglo-Saxon derivation as much as possible, and eschewed adjectives; the result was correct in grammar and (with rare exceptions) spelling; above all, it was lucid and forcible.

Grant possessed a fund of humor, enjoyed good stories and told them well, and sometimes displayed a pretty stroke of wit. When asked if he had heard Sumner converse, he replied: "No, but I have heard him lecture." When told that Sumner did not believe in the Bible, he remarked, "No, he did not write it." Once he spoke of his plan for woman suffrage. "Why, Ulyss, you never told me about that," said Mrs. Grant. "Oh," said he, "I would give each married woman two votes; then both husband and wife would be represented at the polls, without there being any divided families on the subject of politics."

Abused as a man of coarse tastes, he actually possessed much innate refinement, and his delicacy of feeling for his wife might have put many a sophisticated gentleman to the blush. When she visited his camp during the war, Grant and she would sometimes be surprised sitting in a corner of his tent holding hands like bashful lovers; after Appomattox, when she suggested taking her unfortunate squint to a surgeon, he dryly replied that he wanted her to keep the eyes with which he had fallen in love. Nothing aroused his indignation more than marital infidelity, and he made it a bar to any appointment. He was squeamish about profanity, about ribald stories, about the sight of blood. One of the few occasions on which his staff saw him lose his temper was when he found a teamster beating a horse upon the head. He loved animals, and especially horses and dogs, for which he had the sentiment usual among Anglo-Saxons of outdoor training. While his "trotters" in Washington and at Long Branch were ridiculed as a piece of vulgar display, they actually gratified the simple feeling which had led him to say during the war that he would like to close his days breeding fine horses, while they gave him—as he once shrewdly remarked—something to talk about to politicians when he wanted to stop their talk about offices. His tastes at table were so Spartan that during the war he often made a meal upon a sliced cucumber and coffee; and he objected to dining out because he had to sit through a long list of courses, few of which he ate. His one vice, after he entered the White House, was tobacco. He reeked with it; his cigars were black, rank, and poisonous; he consumed them in huge quantities, more even than Edwin Booth.

But we must repeat that the key to his defects as a civil leader lay partly in his very virtues as a military commander. "A soldier's first duty is to learn to obey his commander; I shall expect my orders to be obeyed as exactly and instantly as if we were on the field of battle"— this first speech to his regiment at Springfield he might have applied to his Cabinet and other subordinates. "I propose to move directly upon your works"—thus he envisaged any policy, from the annexation of Santo Domingo to the handling of Reconstruction. We must re-emphasize the pathetically insuperable barrier between him and nearly all the best minds he might have used. John G. Nicolay thought him unapproachable. "Anyone could come into his presence; he had no forms or ceremonies; but only a few people could get at his thought. . . . I have seen a man talk to Grant listening in rigid irresponse till, in sheer self-defence, the visitor was forced to rise and flee from the President's terrible accusing silence." Add to this his vast ignorance of civil affairs, economics, and history; his tendency to look upon the Presidency as a reward, not a responsibility; his indefeasible loyalty to any rascal who merely showed loyalty in return; and not least, his lack of magnanimity, for despite the Appomattox legend, he bore grudges and was a vengeful hater—and we can understand, as Fish gradually did, how terribly he was handicapped in his task.

PAUL de KRUIF Why he selected

The PEOPLE'S DEATH-FIGHT

Dear Mr. Burnett:

Your question is an extremely difficult one, in view of the fact that I truly do not think my writing to be very good, and due further to the fact that I try my best to forget all past writing in order to keep my head clear for the work of the present and the future. At the same time I would be greatly honored to be reprinted in your book. I am making the following nomination of a sample of my work, not because it is best, but because of the good effect it has had in a very important sector of the fight for life. I wish that you would use the description of the Detroit fight against tuberculosis, Chapter Five, in my book, *Why Keep Them Alive?* You may use this letter as my comment.

Holland, Mich.

May 28, 1942

Sincerely yours,

PAUL DE KRUIF

THESE are the plain questions that I had to ask myself at the end of watching this people's death-fight in Detroit—

If I as a citizen, concerned to guard myself and my own from illness and death and interested to a reasonable extent in the well-being of my neighbors, were to wake up, to understand, to find out—

That there was rampant in my community a plague the microbe of which had been known for fifty years—

And that all microbe hunters and death-fighters worthy of these names understood precisely how the microbe of this illness sneaked out of a sick victim to fatally bite other people who were well—

And that the authorities we pay to guard us from death have a sure test to determine, to spot every single person in whom this germ is lurking—

And that expert doctors exist in every considerable community—not only Detroit—equipped with a magic eye that is able to peer inside any threatened victim of this illness and so tell whether the man or the microbe is on top in the struggle—

And that this magic eye can reveal the fire of this death in its earliest smoldering, so that other expert doctors, equipped with a marvelous treatment, can cure nearly one hundred per cent of sufferers if the sickness is attacked reasonably early—

And that this treatment can bring back to life and strength nearly half of all the unfortunates discovered in the death's far-advanced stages—

If I were to learn that in addition to these technical death-fighting weapons, there also existed an abundance of food, fresh air, and sunshine that would help people to recover still more quickly when the technical weapons were used upon their sickness—

If I were perfectly certain of the existence of all these things, wouldn't it be natural for me to ask what excuse there is for this plague existing any longer, at all?

If then, going about in the wasteland of miserable hutches and warrens that pass for homes for a large number of the citizens of Detroit, I would hear, as if in answer to my question, the screaming of babies and the moaning of children now dying from this same illness, that today in our country still kills more children of fifteen and under than any other contagion—

And if that would stoke up my curiosity good and plenty, so that I'd drop other work, forget pleasure, and go out to see the torture and cock my ears to listen to the gasping of thousands of those mortally stricken by this same death, that today still murders three times more young people of twenty and under, than all other contagions put together—

And if in our blighted America it could be brought about, as a sort of sacrificial festival, that I could stand before a grim, vast funeral pyre, a ceremonial burning of all of the annual victims of this same microbe, that still slaughters more citizens in their prime of life between fifteen and forty than any other sickness whatsoever—

Wouldn't I become inquisitive about the mystery of the continued existence of tuberculosis, as a chief cause of death?

Wouldn't I call it not a mystery but an infamy?

Shouldn't I—if worthy of the name of a man—tell everybody: *The murder must stop?*

II

It is natural for us to look for human villains at the bottom of a tragedy and scandal so horrid as this one. This is my tendency, I know, and for the guilty party I haven't far to seek. For the accessory-before-the-fact of this murder is none other than myself, as a citizen, as a stockholder in U. S. A., Incorporated. All of us, all citizens, all men and women of voting age are now responsible for the continuance of this TB murder. Tuberculosis in the past few years has become something more than a matter for scientists and doctors. If our men against death never discover another fact about it, we could help them make this white death as dead as the dodo-bird in twenty years' time. And without our cooperation they're helpless. It is now the whole people's death-fight. This curious democracy of death-fighting has suddenly become possible, in the last few years. It has come about by a clicking into place of a lot of science that was discovered, much of it, as long as fifty years ago—and the facts of this science needn't detain us now. Your man in the street, as well as the doctor, knows about tubercle bacilli, tuberculin tests, X-rays, and he's even beginning in a vague way to know about the actual cure of tuberculosis—by a curious surgery that in a simple yet fantastic manner relaxes, collapses, rests sick lungs, in that way giving them their one chance to heal.

Yet many of our most expert death-fighters themselves don't truly appreciate the TB-smashing power of this new scientific artillery. They haven't an inkling of what it could do, once its different parts were put together, and served by doctors, public health experts, microbe hunters, public health nurses—

And most important of all by the people, all of them, from school-kids onward.

III

You see it's no cheap and simple shot-in-the-arm sort of a cure-all that is now ready to rid us for good and all of the curse of consumption. And the mass of doctors as well as the majority of us plain folks are still living in a fool's paradise about the white death. We need a mental housecleaning of allegedly scientific but actually old-fogey notions of how to treat it and the real way to prevent it. We'll have to let a gale of facts blow those mistakes out of our heads before we can really begin to set our new wonderful death-fighting machine going to make a beginning of rubbing out tuberculosis for good and ever.

Before I found out about what went on in Detroit, my ignorance about what I'd do, if the TB microbe were to be found starting his evil excavations in my own lungs—was sublime. Why, if you just found out about it early, if you just caught it in time, so I thought, so I told everybody, why, it was nothing.

But what's early, in this sinister sickness? Why, when I first began coughing, began losing weight, began feeling tired for no reason, began having a little daily fever and sweating nights and when I began maybe to find a little blood in what I'd coughed up in the morning . . . Wouldn't that be plenty early?

I would then hurry to my doctor. He would tap my chest. He would frown judicially. He would gravely adjust his stethoscope, connecting it from various parts of my chest to his ears. With an air of expertness he'd listen to what he thought were the first vague whisperings coming from the secret gnawings of those TB bugs that were beginning to excavate down in there. At last he would look at me and shake his head. He would show a bright yet solemn cheerfulness. He would admonish me with a forced yet hearty hopefulness.

And if I were a well-to-do man, though such citizens it's true rarely do get tuberculosis, I would then hurry to a good sanatorium. Or if I were poor—which for nine hundred thousand consumptives would be much more likely—I'd promptly get myself put at the tail-end of the long waiting list of my state sanatorium and hope to hell I'd get in there before my trouble had changed from what the good doctor had called "early" to what everybody could see was far-advanced. I would wait, taking the rest cure at home, if I could afford to stop working or if my home was better than the pig-sty the majority of tuberculous folks now have for homes. I'd lie flat on my back, waiting for the waiting list of the sanatorium to catch up to me, and, lying there till my fever cooled, I would eat heartily of choice viands if the state of the exchequer would stand it, and I would breathe my sick lungs full of good fresh air, if I lived where the atmosphere wasn't heavy with automobile exhaust gas and the fetid exhalations of our modern city.

This until a short time ago would have been what I would have done for myself, and what I would have called excellent if a doctor had advised it for others. Till I got to Detroit I didn't realize, alas, that anything a doctor could hear through a stethoscope, anything he could confidently call tuberculosis, more likely than not meant that the wee TB murderers had already got a dangerous grip on me.

I didn't realize that the moment you have any *symptoms* typical of consumption, it's no longer early.

And neither do nine out of ten doctors realize that, either. It isn't what they were taught at the medical college nor in Osler.

And say I'd had those so-called early symptoms that were really late ones and say I'd gone worried to my doctor, and he'd put a stethoscope to my chest, and listened, and heard nothing—as often happens even when the sickness is raging inside you—and if he'd said to me, with a cheerful whack on the back: "Not a thing there. You're all right, Paul; don't worry!" I didn't realize that this might be the death of me.

It is this way today that thousands of people are being murdered because of the false witness of stethoscopes; are being sent back to false security; are being sent back to what turns out to be their doom.

This is only the beginning of the low-down I got from Detroit's TB-fighters. They showed me that, just as stethoscopes are utterly and absolutely useless in detecting early tuberculosis, so in the same way the famous cure by good food, fresh air, and simple rest in bed is the feeblest kind of defense against consumption, once it has progressed far enough to cause those real symptoms—*which are never early.*

Until those Detroit men against death explained these things to me I was ignorant of the fate of folks who had TB microbes showing in their sputum, with cavities in their lungs from which they were coughing up those bugs, who were advised to put their trust in the still generally prevalent rest-cure.

What chance has rest in bed alone to cure them?

Doctor Barnes of the Wallum Lake Sanatorium in Rhode Island, before the white death took him, found the answer. He assembled the records of the lengths of the lives of all of fourteen hundred people who came to his house of rest when the stage of their sickness had got to the point when you could be sure there were cavities, when the microscope proved they were throwing off TB microbes in their sputum.

These were the days, mind you, when the new surgical, lung-resting treatment was just beginning to be tried in America and what started Barnes on his grim tracking down of those records was his suspicion that rest in bed was not enough.

He had to make a bitter confession to himself that he had been fooled. He remembered the many he had seen who had come to him with hopes, how he believed he was justified in encouraging them, how they apparently, for a while, got better under the excellent rest-in-bed care at Wallum Lake. They grew fat, many of them; yes, they were much better now, thank you, they would be ready to go back home soon now.

Barnes followed the fate of all this fourteen hundred, each and every one, for five years from the time they'd come, certainly consumptive, to that sanatorium to be treated by bed-rest alone—

Five years. And ninety-five point four per cent were dead.

IV

It's to the credit of the grimness of Barnes that he had the nerve to look this failure of the rest-in-bed cure in the face, and then to publish it, and then, before he himself died from TB, to become a pioneer of the new, genuinely curative TB science, as well as a destroyer of that futile bed-rest treatment that is still the only way in which the threat to the lives of the enormous majority of consumptives is fought by our doctors.

So much for the feebleness of the effect of this rest-in-bed treatment when it is started at a time when those subvisible TB devils have got far enough along with their mischief to gnaw a hole, a cavity, even a tiny one, in a human lung. The Detroit death-fighters.

and especially Surgeon Pat O'Brien, now taught me what because of my lack of education I hadn't dreamed of—

That consumption's not a gradual, chronic sickness; that every case is a dire emergency; that it's an acute, a contagious, a quick, devastating sickness that is only chronic because it takes you such a long time to die from ravages that occur in the acute beginning of it!

It is now well known that, if a little brew, a soup, an extract of dead TB germs is shot into the skin of any human being's arm, and if there's a certain redness and swelling in response to it, that this means there's a nest of live TB germs lurking somewhere in that person's body. In one high school in Michigan, all the pupils were given this tuberculin test. All showing the telltale red spots on their arms were X-rayed. Seven of these kids, all feeling healthy, not one complaining of any symptom at all, seven showed the sinister shadows of cavities in their X-ray pictures, and the lab-test showed TB microbes teeming in their sputum and they were on their way to their own death unaware of their danger and, without anybody knowing it, they were spreading deadliness around them.

The X-ray's magic eye that really can spot the gnawings of the tubercle bacillus at the jump-off, in the first faint skirmish of the terrible battle, this is what has really made all mere physical examinations, all stethoscopes for listening for TB's first whisper, as obsolete as ox-teams now are for going fast across the country. This was the lesson I learned from Surgeon O'Brien, and from Detroit's roentgenologist, Evans, who showed me the ultimate marvel of the X-ray: that this magic eye actually knows more about the tuberculosis of any man or woman or child than their bodies show, by their symptoms, by their subtlest feelings. It is basic and of the highest importance that the X-ray can tell you you're threatened with death when you imagine yourself to be entirely healthy.

Just two years ago, in Detroit, one of these routine X-ray tests revealed the mild, smoldering type of childhood tuberculosis in a little Detroit public school girl. It was nothing to get het up about, particularly, and it only meant, the TB doctors knew, that this little girl should be watched sharply throughout her girlhood and young womanhood. What worried them—they are all a gang of death-detect-

ing hawkshaws—was where this little girl had come by this little
benign infection? So, in the routine of that magnificent TB-spotting
system, it is a scientific sherlocking in which Detroit is unequaled
anywhere in the whole world, this little girl's family was visited by a
health department nurse.

This nurse suggested that X-ray snapshots be taken of the lungs
of the little girl's entire family, and to this curious photography of
the insides of their chests the father and mother submitted with laughter, protesting, it was really too silly, they were sound as apples, this
was really carrying new-fangled science to the point of absurdity.

The X-ray films were developed, peered at, all right, excellent, all
negative, excepting—wait! What was this faint cloud, technically in
X-ray jargon Pat O'Brien called it just a little blush, what was this
tiny hazy spot, maybe it was nothing, but what was this blurring on
the picture just under the right collar-bone of the little girl's mother?
Maybe nothing? Yes, maybe. But would the mother come back right
away? They'd snap a more exact picture of that suspicious spot; they'd
make an X-ray stereoscopic snapshot. They knew that, yes, it might
be nothing, a waste of time, a needless fuss-budgeting maybe, and
calculated only to make a hypochondriac, a worrier, of that mother.
The stereoscope might show it was all nonsense to bother at all and
that spot might be nothing at all, only slightly suspicious, but then
you never—

"But" is the most ominous word in the English language.

The mother laughed. It was hooey. She consumptive? She'd never
been sick a day in her life. She could lick her weight in wildcats and
why all this alarm! So she didn't go back for new pictures.

So she was scornful on this first of February and on the morning
of March 15th the little girl's mother woke up with a salty taste in her
mouth that you couldn't kill with a drink of water and then saltier,
and then choking, gurgling, and then, hemorrhage—

Next day the ambulance took her to the Henry Ford Hospital and
this time she was too sick to mind an X-ray picture—that showed how
that little no-account spot under her right collar-bone had exploded,
had riddled her whole right lung, had spread over to the left one.

Next day she was dead.

v

Till I got to Detroit I never realized with what terrible speed the white death could get you nor what trifling, tiny beginnings of the sickness you can see by the X-ray's magic eye and maybe you think this is exceptional, sensational, and needlessly frightening. Maybe you'll say it's well known that the TB death rate has been cut nearly in half in the last thirty years and this is true. It is true more people have had a chance at sanatoriums as more and more of these were built in those strange days when there still was money, so that consumptive people weren't going about spitting, coughing, talking invisible billions of TB microbes out of their lungs. There were less spreaders and so gradually less people had it spread to them. While there still was money during the first thirty years of the twentieth century, while credit was ballooning, the average American family ate better and better, and lived less crowded together and began getting out in the air and sunshine and this somewhat average better life did things for the mass of the people that the TB bug does not relish.

All these things during those years were happily true and the inertia of their effect has brought it about that, in many places, the TB death rate is still going down, though it's no longer true everywhere. And this thirty years of down and down of the death rate has actually fooled millions into feeling that the white death is all but conquered and not only the mass have been fooled into this wrong notion, but even the head of our country entertains it. A short time ago I heard our President thanking us for the way the people had dug down into their pockets to help his infantile paralysis foundation and he said he hoped that pretty soon that plague would be subdued, the way TB's in our power now!

This is what the President thought, at the moment the white death is still chief killer of all dying between ages fifteen and forty; while it still murders three times more children and young people than all other contagions put together.

Of course there's less consumption now, anybody can see that, especially in the homes of the well-to-do and the bon-ton. But who maintains that there's now an increase in the numbers of the prosperous?

And isn't TB a poor man's sickness? And finally it is a fact that it is
on the up-grade, at this moment, in thirteen of our leading cities.
What then must we do?

VI

To ask that question is to answer it. All the science is here, the
material and men are available right now to wipe tuberculosis from
the face of the earth. If you want to see what the people of a community can do, by working together, to begin to bring into action some
of the power of the new science, against the worst of odds caused by
increasing poverty, in order to begin the rubbing out of the white
death, then the place to go is Detroit, in Wayne County, Michigan.

In the middle nineteen twenties when there still existed that mysterious thing called municipal credit, Detroit citizens provided their TB
death-fighters with magnificent hospitals and sanatoriums, with ample
beds, apparatus, and operating rooms. Here they could actively treat,
could actually cure, could close the cavities in the lungs of more and
more of the white sickness's victims. The Detroit death-fighters had
gone back to an ancient scientific fundamental—

That consumption is contagious—

That you'll never catch consumption unless from somebody who's
already got it—

Who has open cavities—

Who's coughing up TB microbes out of them.

Now these death-fighters knew, too, that even if they could spot
every last victim whose sick lungs were invisibly spraying this death
out of their open cavities, it would not be enough to put them in bed
in their beautiful hospitals. It would be inhuman, as well as imprac-
ticable, to shut all of our hundreds of thousands up, like lepers, away
from their dear ones and all the world, till they died forlorn, and so
were no longer a danger to the rest of us.

Detroit had the great good luck or the wisdom, I don't know which,
to pick out surgeons and doctors for leaders in their death-fight who
were American pioneers in this fundamental of all TB science—

That if you rest the sick lung itself, as well as the man or woman who owns that lung, the majority of all cases of tuberculosis *are curable*.

That if you splint such a sick lung, resting it, stopping or greatly easing its breathing, the cavities of many, almost the majority of even far-advanced consumptives are closable and capable of healing.

The neglect of these facts that are so hopeful and fundamental is a black page in American medical history, and today it is still true that the enormous majority of consumptives die without ever having had a chance for this lung rest treatment, and this is why tuberculosis is in no sense any longer a mere matter of science or of medical art but a people's death-fight.

You may be sure if our people as a mass really had it through their heads that this chance for life really existed for their sick dear ones, for themselves, they'd shout, in masses they'd ask the question: Why don't our doctors save us?

It is now more than forty years since Carlo Forlanini in Italy shot a little air into the chests of far-gone consumptives, air that put a cushion between their sick lungs and their chest walls. This way Forlanini collapsed their sick lungs, relaxed them, stopped their breathing, and began closing those deadly holes, those cavities which now for the first time had a chance to heal—

So that not a single TB microbe could escape from those holes, to get outside, to spread death to others.

You say if you collapse a lung how do you breathe without it, but that's easy; you see, nature's been generous with the amount of lungs she's given us, so that actually, to breathe enough to live, one-fifth of one lung is all that you need to keep you going! Of course, otherwise this collapse treatment, this splinting of a sick lung, or even both sick lungs as they now can do it, wouldn't have been possible. And it turned out to be a sad fact that there were many consumptives who couldn't be saved by these magical air injections. Their lungs refused to collapse because they were stuck tight to their chests with adhesions. But even for these unlucky ones hope came very soon, from German surgeons, who invented a terrific operation. These surgeons knew that at all costs the deadly cavities had got to be closed, so to rest the sick lungs of these doomed people, they began actually to de-rib them. They cut all the ribs completely away from consumptives' chests on the side they were sickest and the mortality from those awful operations would have scared off anybody but the tough North German that old Ludolph Brauer was, so that he kept at this dreadful business of snapping the ribs off the spines and the breastbones of people who were surely going to die anyway, and presently a number of these lived—cured of their incurable consumption.

But alas there were other people too sick to stand the shock of this super-heroic effort to save their lives by de-ribbing them, but great is science, great is the devotion of our death-fighters, and now in a little while there was hope even for these who were most forlorn. Again it was Germans. They made no-account nicks in these sick folks' necks. They cut the phrenic nerve that governs the up-and-down pumping of the automatic muscle, the diaphragm. That paralyzed it. So that it rose into the sick man's chest. So that it relaxed his lung. And gave his now closed cavities a chance for healing.

It was a most complicated surgical art. Not one of these operations was sure-fire in closing cavities; not one worked always; but each one by itself, or even in combination with one or both of the others, now gave surgeons a powerful armament against the damnable TB microbe—

So that many years ago a famous doctor could say about this lung-resting treatment—

"When one has had the experience of seeing Lazarus rise from the dead, the fact cannot be forgotten."

VII

Maybe it was because it took an enormous amount of judgment and surgical skill, maybe it was because it started in Europe and our doctors are very bad at reading foreign languages, maybe it was because it was so much easier to put consumptives to rest in bed and hope they'd get well, maybe for all of these reasons it was only fifteen* years ago that this new healing art began to get any notice in America. Even in Detroit, up till six years ago,† the neglect to use collapse treatment caused the death of thousands and thousands. And these dying ones, with open cavities spewing out billions of TB microbes, were in turn the cause of the death of scores of thousands of others and this is the

* About 1920.
† About 1929.

scandalous situation in most of the rest of our country today. But now in Detroit these ways of saving individual lives began to expand into an impossible, a fanatically ambitious, plan to prevent the white death for future millions, to wipe TB out of the city.

In Detroit, led by Surgeon E. J. O'Brien—Pat O'Brien to you—they were radical. They were absolutely against TB practice all over the rest of the world, against the practice even in Germany, in Italy, where the new art was invented. In almost all other hospitals it was the system of surgeons to try one or another of these collapse operations after rest in bed had failed to cure the sick one. But now in Detroit the TB fighters developed this philosophy—it was true science, no doubt of it—

If lung-rest can save so many who are far gone, who are riddled with the white sickness, why wait till they've arrived at this forlorn condition? Every single day any consumptive lives with his cavities open—he's spreading death around him. So, therefore—why not close all cavities in TB's first stage?

This philosophy to the point of obsession dominates Detroit's men against the white death.

In the darkened conference room of the Herman Kiefer Hospital it is good to watch this cohort of death-haters working. There are famous men there—a tuberculosis controller, an X-ray expert, a chest surgeon who has probably operated on more consumptives than any surgeon in the world today—and along with these, mixing among these leaders with the utmost democracy in that half-darkness you see the white-coated figures of young resident physicians, surgeons, and even interns with the ink still wet on their diplomas. What is most striking at this conference is that there is no human leader, no generalissimo directing this shadowy platoon of TB's enemies who are at this moment at their job of fighting death in this darkened chamber.

Here they pass on the treatment, predict the maybe sad, maybe happy fate of patient after patient, yet during all this time there's never a sick man before them. They make decisions meaning life or death. Yet there's no chief doctor to give the final yes or no. What dominates this scientific soviet is a parade of X-ray pictures. Only the telltale lights and shadows in these skeleton portraits of the insides of one after another after another of an array of consumptive's chests—these blurs and blotches of dark mixed with patches of light on the X-ray film—these alone are the dictators of all their great and small decisions.

In this darkened room you hear no heated argument. There's no bumbling stuffed-shirt, "Yes, doctor, but now, in my opinion, doctor," the kind of hooey it is customary to hear at the typical medical consultation. The deviltry of the TB microbe is visible, is plain to be seen on the films made by the X-ray's magic eye. That, and no other consideration dominates the smallest judgments of all of them. This morning I sat there in awe of it. Not of this cohort of doctors so strangely without ego. But in awe of the power of science. It was above human. Where in any other sickness had I ever seen such an intimate knowledge, such an exact not arguable knowing of a sufferer's chance for life or dying? It was as if these doctors were inside their patients' chests. It was unprecedented.

Now a young physician gets up in the darkness and with only his paper illuminated he reads the history of a woman whose X-ray portrait is on the frame before them.

She has had not the slightest symptom of tuberculosis. But here is a shadowy spot, a blush of what's without question the beginning of the sickness, the stage called *minimal*.

The young doctor points it out on the film. Then he recommends immediate operation on her phrenic nerve, to paralyze her diaphragm, to rest her still so extremely slightly sick lung.

They vote. Okay.

Here's the X-ray record of the sickness of a man whose cavities this simple phrenic operation has failed to close. Look here on the film. You can see it. There's no if or but about it. Artificial pneumothorax— the cushion of air between lung and chest—this is now recommended.

A vote. Okay. Next patient.

This is the portrait of a man absolutely given up to die. He has galloping consumption. The phrenic operation failed to check it. The air injections had helped—a little. Enough so the surgeon had said, yes, he'd take a Brodie, his condition had got back good enough so this fellow just might stand a thoracoplasty—the drastic operation of de-ribbing one side of him.

Today it's a celebration. It's time for congratulations all round. Look at his portrait as of this morning: cavities closed absolutely.

Tuberculosis arrested. Discharge with continued bed-rest recommended. They vote.

There was a beauty of precision about it that was entirely not human. There was a coldness about their working that in my ignorance I didn't dream could yet exist in any death-fighting and in that dark room I had a feeling of something eerie. I felt this wasn't today but five hundred years into the future.

It was a dreadful discipline for all of them.

Between the X-ray records of victory over sure death were sandwiched pictures of disaster. These accused all of our death-fighting cohort of their foolish optimism, of their ignorance, of the frailty of their judgment, teaching them how their deciding to do this or failing to do that had doomed that man or this woman to death.

I forgot about Michigan's, Pennsylvania's, all of America's forgotten children this morning. What made this altogether the most stirring morning I had ever spent in the front line trenches of the death-fight was this—

That they all were so selfless. That they were only out to close every last dangerous, death-spreading cavity in every sick lung of all the scores of thousands of consumptives in Detroit, in Wayne County. That, by their honest admitting of their own mistakes, resulting in death, they were giving more and more doomed ones a fighting chance for strength and life.

With no appearance of sentiment or maudlinity at all it seemed as if for all these white-coated figures life was the one thing that counted. They had to be cold as steel to save lives in the mass and it remained for fathers, mothers, wives, husbands, brothers and sisters to be as sentimental as they wanted to be in the bosom of the families of those saved.

VIII

It was hard to walk from one room to another in this house of hope without having them wreck another of my old notions about tuberculosis. You know how folks suffering from consumption looked in the old days; they used to have a sort of stoop-shouldered gauntness. You know how uncomfortable it is to walk through hospitals when you yourself are healthy; it's embarrassing showing yourself to the patients who in the overwhelming majority look down-at-the-heel and sick. But now here at the Herman Kiefer Hospital they took me into the basement room where they give the air injections for the pneumo-thorax collapse treatment; and here I watched a parade of those who in the old days, considering the stage of consumption in which they'd come to the hospital, would by now have been ready for the under-taker.

And now look at them. It was a bit ghostly to watch them; it gave me the shivers because I knew most of these people that I saw should long ago have been under the ground.

It was astounding because they all looked so unhospitalish. Among folks never tuberculous you'd have had a hard time finding a more husky lot of men or a more buxom gang of women than these here now, stripped to the waist, smiling, raising one arm and turning half away from the white-coated resident physician, standing by a simple gadget of bottles, manometers and rubber tubing.

All of these husky-looking people, months or even years ago, had experienced the one human feeling that is more wonderful than the sensation of strength and perfect well-being; they had all felt the flow of strength, the flood of mysterious new life that carries you back from what you know was the approach to the valley of death. They had all of them experienced this deepest of all human feelings at the time when the air injection of the pneumothorax had succeeded in collapsing their sick lung, resting it, gently sealing the walls of what had been their deadly, open cavities together, boxing up the TB microbes. So that their own bodies could now begin killing the deadly invaders.

Now here these folks had all come back to the Herman Kiefer for their routine refills of air that kept their sick lungs rested for this mys-terious process of healing that was as long as it was certain, once you'd closed their cavities. Here they came, in an hour off from the work they could now do again to earn their livings. They all smiled at the moment of the quick jab of the needle between their ribs, and while the air flowed into their chests, and afterward. . . . They knew well enough what had saved them.

Now there was something very simple, not very technical about

this, but what I now saw in the operating room upstairs at the Herman
Kiefer was terrific, futuristic, and again like what went on in that
darkened X-ray conference room, prophetic of a happier future for all
sick men, women, and children. What I now saw was unlike what I
knew surgery in general to be, because what went on here was so successful. I had sworn a surgeon's knife would never touch me, except
in some desperate last resort or accident, because I knew how often
those knives were used for a haphazard, hit-or-miss, bloody, and
too often deadly tinkering with human machinery.

This morning I stood close in back of what's probably the most
famous chest surgery team in the world, headed by a strange, devoted,
hard-boiled, human dynamo of a man who has probably done more
chest surgery on consumptives than any man living. Now the anesthetic. And it was great how you didn't get the feeling of a guess, a
stab in the dark at what was wrong inside these patients. It was the
magic eye of the X-ray that guided the hand that held the scalpel.
The master chest surgeon's hand was sure like a robot pilot on an
airliner. The master surgeon looked at the deep-breathing consumptive
before him. Then he looked across to the illuminated box framing the
skeleton picture of the patient's lungs and chest. Then he looked at
his assistants who were both of them broad-shouldered, narrow-waisted
young men who reminded you of a couple of middle-weight boxers.
Let's go, all right, let's get going, the surgeon growled through his
gauze mask—

That's what he kept saying at each machine-like step of the operation, let's go, all right, *let's* go, while he kept looking from the patient
back at the X-ray picture and it was exactly as if the patient's chest was
laid wide open right before his eyes.

That morning I saw them do ten operations. I saw them sweating
at the taut, terrible job of four successive operations of de-ribbing four
fargone consumptives, beginning with that sweeping slash of the knife
that lays open one whole side of the back of your patient's chest. It
takes a man to do it, and you even have to be something of a man to
see it. And it is particularly momentous because you know that no
patient undergoes it unless he is absolutely doomed to die. And there's
encouragement in it because when you see these four people the next
morning after their mutilation, they say no, doc, I haven't had much

of any pain. They whisper it, looking a little exhausted, yet comfortable, and only one of them complains that his arm on the operated
side, feels tired. . . . And what triumph in man's death-fight is more
stirring than the way they now here at the Herman Kiefer in Detroit
save the lives, return to strength and working, and abolish all danger
of spreading tuberculosis to others—of very nearly half of this forlorn
rearguard who a few years ago would have been surer than sure to die?

Now this morning the four thoracoplasties, the four de-ribbing
operations are over and the master surgeon and his two middle-weight
helpers slump down in the dressing room, taking deep drags on their
cigarets, till the surgeon says let's go, *let's* get going, and we walk
through the hall where there are six people on six tables on wheels
waiting for the little operation called the phrenic. It is a mass production of life-saving.

They are wheeled in one after another and under local anesthetic
they have little nicks made in their six necks and one operation is
hardly finished before another's begun so that you get mixed up—as
you try to keep track of it, watching—not sure which X-ray picture
over there in the frame corresponds to what patient, it goes so fast.
"Let's go," says the surgeon, "they're queer ones today; they've all got
their nerves in the wrong place; this is a slow day; c'mon, boys, *let's*
get going." And the six operations for the interruption of the phrenic
nerve that will paralyze the diaphragms of these six people to rest their
sick lungs take altogether less than half an hour!

It is excellent. The X-ray in this house of hope has shown many a
dangerous cavity, open on the way up to the operating room, shut tight
as a result of this phrenic operation on the way down to the patient's
room! It is often magical. It is the mildest of any of the lung-rest treat-
ments, really the least effective lung-rester of any of them, and by it the
chance of cure of many a consumptive has been increased enormously.
In that early, minimal stage of the sickness, when the patient doesn't
yet really know he's ill, when only the X-ray can spot the beginning of
the TB microbe's murder, the cures by this little phrenic operation are
close to one hundred out of every one hundred.

And out of a sample series of one hundred people in Detroit, in
Wayne County, whose consumption was already moderately or far

advanced, with open cavities, mind you, seventy-four of them were
alive, five years later.

They were either completely cured or on the way back to perfect
health. And is this a contrast to the story of the fourteen hundred,
who were followed for five years by Doctor Barnes of Wallum Lake,
that cohort of fourteen hundred of whom only a handful lived to tell
the story after their cure by rest in bed? Before the lung-rest operations were available.

IX

Of course at this Herman Kiefer Hospital they kept telling me,
kept making it very definite, that no matter what kind of collapse
treatment they gave sick lungs, the owner's sick body had to be rested,
too. It's the same—this way closed TB cavities heal—as the way a bone
broken in your leg heals—*slowly*. It's just like when you put the two
ends of a broken leg bone together, splinting them, resting them. Even
if the X-ray showed some mending in that leg bone in four weeks, it
would be silly to go running around that early. So in consumption,
only more so, only longer. When the first fundamental life-saving
step of closing the cavity has been taken, you've got the TB microbes
imprisoned, yes. But they're still alive. Then, by rest in bed, maybe a
year of it, but hardly more, this lung-mended man or woman's body
gets a chance to heal itself, to build unbreakable prison walls round
the murderous bacilli.

The army of the tuberculous folks of Detroit, of Wayne County,
of Michigan, are beginning to know this now, and to reach out their
hands for it. At the Herman Kiefer Hospital, at the Maybury Sanatorium in near-by Northville, and at the American Legion Hospital
at Battle Creek, Michigan, our death-fighters used to have to cajole and
harangue consumptives into trying the air injections.

Now it's more and more rare, for the far-advanced, the desperate
ones, on whom maybe the pneumothorax air injection or the phrenic
operation have failed, to refuse even that last resort, the terrific operation of thoracoplasty, of de-ribbing.

They've watched their pals in the hospitals and they know. They've
seen the up-surge of strength, the new life that follows when collapse

treatment, no matter what form of it, closes the cavities, the holes of death.

x

I've said that these Detroiters have set out on the job of rubbing out tuberculosis, of making it as little of a menace as smallpox is now, of sending the white death to join the dodo. It is clear that the science to do it is here, it is as sure as sunrise tomorrow. What then is their progress?

They have fought their fight in the face of the worst financial breakdown in Detroit's history. The human material they've had to work on has been drawn not from people who have enough to eat and enough to wear, but mainly from among those hundreds of thousands of victims of the insecurity that makes our civilization a pain in the neck and a mockery.

The TB fighters have had to try to hold their own against this white death that thrives in those very conditions that have become more and more acute since 1930, for this is the death that grows where there are no dollars.

It has been the job of these surgeons, TB controllers, X-ray experts, examining doctors, public health nurses, and Detroit's brilliant Health Commissioner, Henry Vaughan, to try to keep this poor-man's sickness from spreading among miserable, castoff industrial thousands, whose upkeep and maintenance is not industry's headache, who are half-starved and live jammed together without regard for the simple decencies of life in dingy flats and houses, who are deprived of warm clothing, of food rich in vitamins, of sunshine—of those elementary necessities of life that ought to be the right of every last man, woman and child, of those basic needs that are the prime enemies of tuberculosis—

And that could be here for everybody, that could be produced and distributed in limitless abundance—if only . . .

What then for these forgotten thousands, now easier and easier prey for the white death that's lurking to destroy them, what in spite of their obstacles have our Detroit TB fighters been able to do?

Seven years ago, the year the fundamental fight to close all cavities

of all consumptives got off to its start, twenty-six out of every hundred
patients left the Maybury Sanatorium in the woods in Northville, in
coffins.

By 1931 this rate of dying had fallen to ten.

At the end of 1933 it had fallen to the figure of six out of every
hundred.

Seven years ago only eight out of every one hundred consumptives
left those woods free really to live again, free to work again, with
their disease arrested, which technically means free for one year from
cavities in their lungs, from TB microbes in their sputum.

But then the systematic, fanatic, drastic closing of cavities began
at Maybury Sanatorium, just as I've described it at the Herman Kiefer.

By 1931, thirty-four out of every hundred patients were walking out
away from there with health and strength restored. By 1933, this
number had risen to thirty-seven of every hundred.

And that does not tell half the story—

Because many more, who were cured no doubt of it, couldn't be
let go, turned out into Detroit, into Michigan, into our America whose
system of life doesn't give folks the simple right to live. You see, the
death-fighters who'd cured these people couldn't let them go back into
our country's desolation. Letting them go back would only increase the
number of the jobless. They would then be free-floating jobless instead
of institutionalized ones. They would be walking the streets. They
would stand forlorn, looking in show-windows. They would be getting under prosperous folks' feet. They would be going back to the
world with their gift of marvelous new life to find out that in our
glorious land of the free, where all men are created equal, life is the
cheapest thing there is. They would have to face it that, in our limit-
lessly wealthy land by reason of its lack of dollars it would have been
better, more fitting, if the surgeons had let them die.

So you understand the statistics of 1933 don't tell the whole story.
Our death-fighters who had so skillfully, so kindly, so foolishly—working with the conviction that there is no wealth but life—saved these
people's lives, didn't dare to send these tuberculous back to the poverty
that would bring back their danger from the white death, as sure as
tomorrow's sunrise.

Who that ponders this can see anything here but our system's dis-integration?

So much for our sick ones into whom the TB microbe had already sunk its subvisible fangs. With these people no longer spreading this death round them, what effect has this mass-cure had on TB in Detroit's population?

What effect has it had on the children?

Surely it is all right to guard the children. The children are inno-cent. They are not to be blamed for arriving in this sick world. They have not yet had time to become the vagrants, the bums that their poverty-stricken workless parents are now alleged to be. Does anybody here object to Detroit's death-fighters keeping the TB death away from the children? If so, let him stand up and be counted!

In 1930, the magnificent mass tuberculin-testing done by the City Health Department on all Detroit's children of fifteen and under who were examined, showed that fifty-four out of every hundred harbored the TB microbe. Though not sick necessarily, the red spots on their arms in this tuberculin test showed that they were infected, endangered.

By 1933, this number had taken a tumble down to twenty-eight per hundred!

In the old days in Detroit the death rate of babies dying from tuberculous meningitis (it is disagreeable, you remember, to hear their screaming as they die) this death rate was one hundred and forty-seven per hundred thousand live births.

Now granting that it is embarrassing to our system to keep too many babies alive but admitting that this annoyance is counterbalanced to some extent by the lessened screaming and baby suffering—it is pleasant to report that by the end of 1933, this TB meningitis baby death rate had tumbled from one hundred and forty-seven down to forty-five point three per hundred thousand of all babies born alive!

During the so-called prosperous days from 1923 to 1928 there had been no decline in Detroit's general TB death rate, it hovering around this high figure of ninety-five per hundred thousand.

Then came those magnificent hospitals, with beds furnished for every last threatened tuberculous one who came there.

This was an advance; at least it would be so considered by those who deplore human agony. It abolished the cruel, the still enormous "waiting list" of TB sufferers that's a scandal over the rest of Michigan, and a disgrace over the rest of America, where scores of thousands are now dying because they have no place to go to be cured. But now here in Detroit were plenty of beds in magnificent hospitals; there was only one fly in the ointment and that was that there might come a day when the bonds issued to build them might embarrass the city's credit. But let's not cross such bridges before we get to them. What other way is there to attain the one wealth that is life? Our system demands that we go into debt to gain this wealth. Not a soul among Detroit's influential citizens then thought of this crazy enigma, so let's issue the bonds to build the hospitals, and here they are. And now the death-fighters begin their mass closing of death-dealing TB cavities—

And so now, while mass poverty sent the TB death rate *up* in thirteen of our principal cities—

In Detroit, where the people armed their death-fighters before the wreck of the economic order, the death rate has tumbled from ninety-five per hundred thousand down to sixty-six and is still on the down-grade as this is written.

Could it be driven down to zero? There is now not the faintest doubt that science can say yes, can promise it.

What then can Detroit's citizens do to hurry it up, to make it come true, to demonstrate to all the rest of the cities of the world, so that they will be ashamed and follow her example, so that all will rub out the white death for good and ever?

I will not myself give the answer. I will ask you to come to a con-ference table in Detroit, to listen while I ask that question of five famous men against death who are sitting here with me. This is not imaginary. It is the true record of an evening in 1934.

Round the table you see Dr. Henry Chadwick, the former TB con-troller of Detroit and now Health Commissioner of the State of Massachusetts. And there is Dr. Bruce Douglas, who is now the TB controller of Wayne County, and close by him is Dr. Henry Vaughan, Detroit's Commissioner of Health, and Pat O'Brien is there, this same Pat, the master chest surgeon who has probably closed more death-dealing, death-spreading cavities in the lungs of more consumptives than any other surgeon alive. And Theo Werle, Secretary of Michigan's

TB Association, citizen fighter of tuberculosis, makes up the fifth of this group of unquestioned competence against the white death.

I am a reporter. In a way I represent my State's, my Country's communication system. It's my job to give people the lowdown, and I now ask this distinguished gang of men against death a plain question—

What is lacking, what then do they need, in order to demonstrate in one great community that this white death, this now needless human misery, can be rubbed out for good and ever?

Their answer is unanimous.

They would undertake to reduce tuberculosis to a negligible sickness, a no longer serious menace, if they had just one thing—

If they had money.

Now, mind you, we must not be utopic about this business. We must not be humane. We must be economists in the great tradition of scarcity. We must admit that this is not the Garden of Eden, but that it is Detroit, Michigan, United States of America.

Remembering this then, and being as practical as any bondholder, tax-payer, mortgage-shark, or banker, and not putting any value at all on the relieving of human suffering and sorrow, and not making the preposterous assumption that the lives of men, women, and children are worth more than any engraved pieces of paper, but making our calculations on the basis of the bookkeeping of our present economic system—

Would it be good business, would it be economical, would it be sensible, would it be true to that greatest of all virtues, thrift, would it help our down-trodden tax-payers, if Detroit could see to it that these TB fighters had the wherewithal, exactly as much of it as they figure is necessary?

Their answer is clear. Their answer is ready.

Six years ago, out of twenty-eight hundred consumptives, cared for at public expense in Wayne County hospitals, not three hundred were discharged as recovered.

In the six years of the death-fighting saga of which I've told you, this change has happened—

At present, out of the twenty-five hundred consumptives left in these hospitals, more than nine hundred walk out, robust, back to independent life and working.

It costs three dollars a day to keep a consumptive in these hospitals. The yearly saving has already jumped to more than eight hundred thousand dollars. But wait. That's nothing.

If, by spending the money for the doctors, X-ray experts, public health nurses, the tuberculin, the syringes, the X-ray machines and the papers for records, you would do the absolutely scientifically possible, and really spot all the consumption that's early, that's now latent, hidden, undiscovered—

You would change the sad population of these hospitals completely around. Instead of there being, as there now are, eighty per cent of moderately and far-advanced consumptives there, and only twenty per cent of minimals, you could reverse those figures completely.

And if you did that, the following remarkable thing would happen—

The stay in hospital of consumptives would be cut from eighteen months as it now is, on the average—

To nine months! In nine months they'd be walking out, discharged, cured, recovered.

But how long would it take to do this, I asked Henry Vaughan, the Health Commissioner.

He wasn't long answering. This could be done in maybe five but, at the very outside, in ten years.

And how much would it cost?

To obtain the X-ray machines, the films, the doctors, the nurses, to set Detroit's already trained men against death into full steam ahead to do it—

Not more than two hundred thousand dollars a year would be needed.

In short, it would cost per year not more than one-hundred-and-seventy-fifth the price of one death-dealing modern battleship, to save all these lives.

But to hell with these lives.

All right. Then, this spending of two hundred thousand dollars a year to find the early cases so that they would only have to stay half as long as they now do, in these hospitals—

Would, within ten years, effect a saving of more than one million dollars per year of the tax-payers' money.

But for this saving of millions of money, our system cannot spend a few hundred thousand. So this is now what I saw, and understood clearly, that this decadent, alternately crashing and booming, but surely dying system that rules us, cannot even afford to be thrifty. I now saw the enemy. I saw that, while science is surging forward, this is the cause of our people's defeat, that there no longer can be enough pennies for the saving of the dollars which still transcend the lives of men, women, and children.

STUART CHASE Why he selected

The ECONOMY of ABUNDANCE

I have taken this selection with a few minor changes from a book published in 1934, under the same title. . . .

I do not know whether it is my best writing—the style strikes me as a bit ornate in 1942—but I think the book represents my economic philosophy more completely than any other I have written. I feel that the thesis is more important today than it was when I wrote it. This war promises to increase mechanical energy and the capacity to produce in this country to heights hitherto inconceivable. When it ends we shall have a productive machine capable of smothering us with goods. Engineers and technicians for the first time in our history have been given the green light for all-out production. Look at Mr. Ford's bomber plant at Willow Run. Money does not count much any longer; only men and materials count, and the techniques of abundance.

After the war shall we stifle this potential output, retreat to an economy of high prices and restricted output, and let the magnificent new plant rot? Or is there a people's revolution on, as Mr. Wallace says, a raging political demand to stop such nonsense, and to let the goods come through? The war may prove to be that long-sought catalyst which will explode old financial barriers and bring the age of abundance really into its own. At any rate, the technological imperatives, that I have described here, seem to be marching on.

Redding, Conn.   STUART CHASE
June 18, 1942

S UPPOSE that the thirteen million people living in the United States in 1830 had awakened on the morning of January 1, 1831, with forty times the physical energy they had gone to bed with the night before. An active picture meets the mind's eye, a very active picture. A lumberman can fell forty times as many trees in a week, a housewife sweep forty times as many square feet of floor; forty barns can be built in the time hitherto required for one—and forty chests, and forty chairs. Porters can transport forty times their accustomed load in a day; weavers can ply their shuttles forty times as fast—if the shuttles can brook the strain; and children can raise forty times their normal rumpus.

Assuming no increase in the invention of labor-saving devices— and where would be the point with such an exuberance of labor available—what might we logically expect in the way of economic changes? From an economy of scarcity, with barely enough to go around, the young republic would almost immediately enter an economy of abundance. The food supply could be increased, not fortyfold, due to the lack of tools and cleared land, but perhaps five-fold, in a remarkably short time; whereas to double it would probably provide a plethora for all. Every family could have a fine house, filled with fine handmade colonial furniture; every man could have a fine coat, one for every day in the week; and every woman a chest of linen as big as a box stall. . . . Fine horses and fine carriages, books, flat silver, tapestries, gardens, great public buildings, medical attention, education.

The new energy would get through to everybody. It would flower at once into goods for the ultimate consumer. Workshops must be enlarged, tools multiplied, new houses, roads, capitols, libraries, theaters, hospitals, built. In a fairly simple economy such as that of 1830, the standard of living for the whole community could not fail to mount enormously within a relatively short time.[1] Indeed, a very high standard in terms of the forthright and durable articles of the day could be achieved with only a fraction of the energy delivered. Rather than forty-fold, perhaps five-fold, or even less, would be enough to achieve

[1] 1830 was not a pure handicraft society. Prime movers were just coming in, but their frailty is demonstrated by the historic thirteen-mile race on August 25, 1830, in Baltimore, between Tom Thumb, the first locomotive built in the country, and a horse and carriage. The horse won.

the standard, so rapid and direct was the conversion into consumers' goods at that time. Hours of labor could be cut to two or three a day, and still the citizens would have to take to climbing mountains or organizing expeditions to the unknown west, or playing the most strenuous variety of games, or writing long epic poems, or painting miles of murals like Diego Rivera, or even dispensing with work animals, to spend their surplus vitality.

Today, in the United States, we have precisely this equivalent of energy per capita. It is not in our muscles, but in our delivered power resources. Observe that it is not a potential total of installed horsepower, but actual coal, oil and natural gas burned, and water turbines turned. If we counted *capacity* to deliver work, the ratio would be greater than forty-fold. The average working hours for all central power stations in 1933 were only 2800 a year, or about 32 percent of capacity. The energy we are considering is given, and has been used, every foot-pound of it. Yet the average standard of living, while including more commodities and services than that of 1830, is still below the margin of health and decency; millions are acutely undernourished, miserably housed, deplorably clothed, while economic insecurity clutches at almost every heart.

Energy, the capacity to do work, is here, a living, demonstrable reality, but it has not got through to the wayfaring man as expressed in his standard of living; the essential work has not been done. Even in 1929, with an average wage of only $1300, it obviously had not been done. The furnaces roar, the turbines whirl, the compression chambers stiffen to the shock of the explosion, but life is a more uncertain business than it was a century ago, and that happiness which Mr. Jefferson bade us pursue is as remote as when he wrote the Declaration of Independence.

The capacity to produce goods, furthermore, is not measured by raw energy alone. Also important is the skill of the mechanism which takes the energy and shapes the product. To use a homely illustration: I can mow about an acre of pasture in a ten-hour day. My neighbor, a farmer all his life, can mow two acres in an equal time, with a smaller expenditure of energy. His muscles are trained to the scythe, where mine are not. Similarly, in the field of mechanical operations, engineers have devised increasingly skilful methods of utilizing a given quantity of energy. For the twenty years from 1909 to 1929, for example, engineers have computed an increase of 66 percent in kilowatt hours secured from every ton of coal used for the generation of electric power, and a 47 percent increase in railroad naulage per ton of fuel burned.

But multiplying energy, however efficient its application, cannot proportionately multiply standards of living in industrial societies. Such societies are subject to extreme specialization, and great quantities of energy are required to link the specialized processes together, especially in the form of transportation. The United States has been justly called an "experiment in transportation." Whereas in 1830, the forges of Connecticut obtained iron ore almost in their backyards, and delivered horseshoes and hinges to the man across the street, the steel mills of the 1930's haul iron ore by boat and rail from northern Minnesota, coke from Pennsylvania, manganese from Russia, and sell rails, girders, sheet steel and tin plate from Florida to Oregon. It takes energy to mine these raw materials—including the coal which is potential energy itself—to fabricate them in scores of interlocking processes, and to haul both the partly finished, and the completed article, all about the map.

So in the best ordered of societies devoted to technology, output for the consumer could not increase so rapidly as total energy. A philosopher would, however, expect to see living standards increase directly with energy delivered, but at a somewhat slower rate. Swinging his dispassionate eye upon the United States of America, he finds a forty-fold increase in energy per capita and a standard of living which, in terms of material wellbeing, is still deplorably low.

How great is the unavoidable loss due to specialization and to absorption in the process of transforming raw energy into useful heat and work? Even if we assume that this fraction is as large as 75 percent, which would seem generous, a forty-fold increase in energy would result in a ten-fold increase in living standards. But the actual increase in material well-being of 1930 over 1830 is probably not more than two-fold. Ninety-five percent of our energy is doing us no good.

Something is wrong here; something very wrong indeed. The "experiment in transportation" could never account for such a difference. Where has the balance of delivered energy gone? This is no academic question. Somebody has robbed us of that which is more vital than gold.

It is not difficult to analyze where the vanished energy has gone, leaving aside the technical factor of conversion loss. Some of it has gone into uneconomic building—unoccupied skyscrapers, surplus widget factories, and the like. Some has gone into wasteful crosshauling of raw materials and finished products back and forth across the country. Some has gone into maintaining great cities, where it has been calculated that more than 30 percent of all delivered energy has to be used for services that offset congestion. Much energy has gone into anti-conservation practices—like developing and irrigating submarginal farmland, cutting forests beyond prudent needs—and then into necessary conservation measures to cure the resulting erosion, forest fires, and other devastation. A great deal has been lost through competitive establishments that duplicate each others' facilities on a large scale, and a great deal through style changes, which may render worthless the output of weeks or months of operation.

Too much energy has gone into a monumental obsolescence rate —building and tearing down plants, houses, machines—some of it owing to shoddy construction and some to sales pressure; and far too much into overproduced goods which are destroyed or allowed to spoil. A great deal of our energy has gone into producing goods for export, for which no equivalent imports were exchanged. It is a favorite pastime of generous Uncle Sam, making goods for foreigners, but taking no goods from foreigners. The spirit, of course, is charming, but gifts on this scale require large blocs of energy. Finally, one of the greatest consumers of the new mechanical energy is probably the pleasure motorist, and the energy burned up in his engines is obviously not all waste. Some of it comes under the head of death and destruction, some under escape from intolerable cities, intolerable homes and intolerable monotony, some under the head of putting one's neighbor's eye out, and some under the head of genuine pleasure and use. What the various proportions may be, no sensible statistician would dare to compute.

All these outlets give us a reasonably complete story of where energy has been dissipated, and why so little gets through to the ultimate consumer. It is perfectly obvious that his wants and desires have never been central in the picture. The plant has been built with other ends in view; a crazy patchwork, magnificent in bulk, superb in some of its detail, but not designed for securing the most for the least.

Riding through North Carolina one day, I saw a bright blue motor car, resplendent with chromium fittings, in the yard of a dilapidated shack constructed of rough logs and plastered with red mud. The car and the hut belonged to the same share cropper. It struck me as a not unreasonable summary of the net gain in living standards since 1830. Measured in tonnage and variety, the wayfaring man has undoubtedly improved his position, but in fundamental wellbeing, I hold to the conviction that doubling the standard is a fair estimate.

These immense new powers have run to immense new wastes. Our very junk piles would have ransomed a king in the middle ages, with their stores of metal and findings. The state of New York undoubtedly contains more fabricated "wealth" than did all Europe in 1400 A.D. But, for all its due capitalization, it is not wealth in terms of human use and enjoyment. It is largely misplaced energy crystallized in stone and steel. The United States was a poor country in 1830 and is a poor country today in terms of the human calculus.

The Economy of Abundance is self defined. It means an economic condition where an abundance of material goods can be produced for the entire population of a given community, a condition never obtaining anywhere until within the last few years.

Behind this obvious definition, however, lurk a series of more subtle connotations. The smooth optimism of the phrase is seriously disturbed when, for instance, we set technological abundance into a background of prevailing financial habits. These habits were laid down in an Economy of Scarcity, and clash bitterly with the facts of plenty. Abundance is not alone a promise to mankind, it is a savage threat to the real or supposed interests of special and powerful groups of men everywhere.

What has been the major economic plague of the past ten years? The plague has been too much wheat to be profitably sold, and not enough bread; too much cotton and not enough clothes; too many bricks and not enough houses; too much drudgery and not enough jobs; too much goods and not enough purchasing power. The paradox of plenty is what has chiefly plagued us. Surplus, surplus everywhere, and often too little to eat. In these circumstances, corporate groups have moved heaven and earth to hold prices up by keeping production down, by sabotaging Abundance. The methods they have used are all too familiar—monopolies, mergers, holding companies, price-fixing agreements, international cartels, trade associations punishing "chiselers," suppression of new inventions, even trade union restrictions on output. The facts of technological plenty will not fit into the financial machinery of an age of scarcity.

The Economy of Abundance is not a mystical force, not a genie from a bottle, despite the fact that its pressures catch us unaware. It is:

A group of buildings, mines, farms, vibrant with machines, and connected by lines of energy and transportation; founded upon

A series of scientific laws, proliferating into specific processes and inventions, and

A set of human habits.

The latter may be further divided into the habits of the scientists and technicians who control and develop the physical processes, and the habits of laymen, connoting everybody else living within the high energy orbit.

Assuming that the abundance pattern will prevail, what are the terms upon which it will function? Obviously in the mêlée of transition it can function only by fits and starts. From the foregoing analysis, it is possible concretely to specify the terms. An abundance economy demands:

1. Capacity operation of its plant, or something near capacity, on the balanced load principle.

2. An unhampered flow of goods to consumers, involving the right to a minimum standard of living, regardless of work performed—*if no work is available*. Distribution must replace exchange. This imperative is practical, not idealistic, arising from the necessity of keeping the plant in operation. It is also likely to become a mass political demand.

3. The elimination of waste, restriction and private monopoly, as methods of maintaining prices.

4. The conservation of natural resources to the degree which, consistent with existing technical knowledge, will maintain adequate supplies of raw materials for the calculable future. Neglect of this imperative may cripple the whole productive mechanism through the failure of one resource—say copper, or oil.

5. The employment of a decreasing number of man-hours in industrial production.

6. The encouragement of research, new invention, and a fairly high obsolescence rate for plant and processes. No more suppressed inventions; no corporate patent monopolies.

7. The capital goods sector to grow only as technological improvement, mass purchasing power, or mass demand requires it. No reliance on this sector, as heretofore, as an automatic distributor of purchasing power.

8. A one-to-one relationship between the growth of physical production and the growth of the interest burden on total debt.

9. A sharp distinction between use property and industrial fixed assets. The latter should be socially controlled in that the units are no longer independent enterprises, but interlock one with another.

10. Economic decentralization; the end of Megalopolis, because it is too wasteful a unit to support. The liquidation of the distinction between city man and country man.

11. The industrialization of most agricultural staples, on a quantity production basis, and a declining number of man-hours in farming.

12. Shorter working hours for all.

13. A wide extension of social services and public works to absorb those inevitably to be displaced from industry, agriculture and the parasitic trades.

14. The continuation of industrial specialization—though decentralization may be expected to modify the trend somewhat.

15. No narrow economic nationalism. The plant still demands essential raw materials on a reasonable exchange basis from various parts of the world, but this demand is lessening with the development of synthetics.

16. Revised and simplified political forms. The revision of outworn political boundaries—for instance, many county subdivisions.

17. Centralization of government; the overhead planning and con-

trol of economic activity. In North America, such planning to satisfy technology should be continental rather than national. In Europe, technology will not tolerate national boundaries indefinitely. A working control over industry is indicated, if the plant is to be efficiently operated. Technical performance cannot be subject to popular vote, but the administrative group and broad policy should be more responsive than at present to the people's wishes.

18. Finally, and exceedingly important, Abundance demands no compromise. It will not operate at half speed. It will not allow retreat to an earlier level and stabilization there. Pharaoh did not tell the Nile what to do; the Nile told Pharaoh what to do. The industrial discipline must be accepted—all of it—or it must be renounced. The only retreat is back one hundred years to the Economy of Scarcity.

Such, substantially, are the terms upon which the Economy of Abundance will function; such the mold to which new social habits, new institutions, must conform. This is the way, and I think the only way, that a high energy culture will function in the long run. Some of the imperatives may be subject to modification in detail; other imperatives may arise; but the basic mold is set. This is the direction in which Mr. Roosevelt is now being forced. Underneath political smoke-screens, and the alarms of stagecoach champions, those of us who have eyes to see can detect the glacier advancing into Sweden, England, Italy, South America, Canada, Australasia. In Russia the march is luminous.

Do these terms violate human nature; are they inconsistent with normal behavior? Already many have been incorporated into our daily lives. What they do violate is a set of institutions largely developed in the eighteenth century, which in turn displaced an earlier cultural complex based on feudalism, which in turn displaced its predecessor, and so on back to Mesopotamia. Men talk as though the gold standard had been laid down by God, side by side with the law of gravitation. The universal gold standard is not so old as Mr. Roosevelt.

It is not to be gainsaid that these terms carry implications of substantial moral shock to many persons, especially to large owners of property hitherto vendible. The terms are now being bitterly fought, and will continue to be for years to come. Habit complexes do not change over night. If it requires at least a decade to modify the psychology of stolid Russian peasants, it may require twice as long to modify the psychology of Wall Street.

Technological imperative is impersonal, amoral and non-ethical. Like the Nile, it sets the boundaries within which a given culture must operate. The terms imposed by the machine age were onerous to the point of often violating human nature; the terms of the power age are more generous. Fortunate and perhaps fortuitous is the fact that the modern imperative is straight in the direction of an economic system based on serviceability. Machines do not care whom they serve, but they refuse to operate without a high volume of output; they care nothing about human leisure, but the laws of their spinning are inconsistent with the clumsy interference of the human hand. They will not tolerate the wastes and barriers of what Veblen used to call "vendibility."

There the imperatives are, for us to take or to leave. Can we adjust to them? No one can now know whether adjustment is possible; he can only be sure of the negative: that if adjustment is not made, high energy cultures will presently stand liquidated. He can further be reasonably sure that the liquidation will not be orderly and planned, but cataclysmic. Western man, failing adjustment, will be hurled back, bloodily and painfully, to a low energy, unspecialized economy.

The timid, with the bold, will do better to push on. If we must die, let it be in the front line. The chances of dying, furthermore, are to my mind appreciably less than of capturing the line. What kind of society would fit these imperatives; would it be bleak and rigorous beyond bearing? I think it would be less bleak than that which we lived through in the later stages of capitalism. If we have been able to adjust to the years 1914 to 1918, and 1930 to 1934 (and I might add, 1940 to 1943), a philosopher might say that we can adjust to anything.

The broad outlines of the future society stand clear in the list of imperatives. Political and economic boundaries will have to widen, not imperialistically but to accord with technological unities. Thus, the United States and Canada will fall into one regional frame; similarly most of Europe. Economically supreme over these frames should sit an industrial general staff to direct the smooth technical operation of all the major sources of raw material and supply. Political democracy will have little to say about the technical detail of economic matters; democracy in consumption will make enormous strides as standards of living are levelled upward; industrial individualism—anarchy is a better term—in the sense of each business man for himself, each corporation for itself, must be disallowed. The principles of insurance, savings, investment, will be greatly modified in favor of a collective guarantee of adequate living standards. The margin between the relatively rich and the relatively poor will shrink enormously; conspicuous consumption and its emulation will tend to pass. The margin in the United States in 1929 between the richest family ($12,000,000 income), and the poorest family ($300 income), was 40,000 to one. I doubt if in the projected society the margin can much exceed ten to one.

Use property will be extended and protected, but there will probably be an increase in the rental of such property from great service companies.

Income-producing property which one does not use may eventually pass out of individual possession. Title will vest in the community. It will include the bulk of land, mineral deposits, forest stands, public utilities, and most of the producing and distributing plant. Banking, credit and the issue of money will be a strict government function. The interest rate will approximate zero.

Work will be carefully allocated. Perhaps young people will be drafted to perform certain tasks for a year or more. In that work is a fundamental instinct, while jobs under integrated power age conditions will be at a minimum, we may see a surprising reversal of the public attitude toward labor. Rather than being envious of the idle, citizens may become envious of those who secure an opportunity to work. Allotments might be at a premium. A great deal of thought and experiment will have to be devoted to obtaining compensation for the instinct of workmanship in the expanded leisure of that society. One would look for a revival of handicrafts on a large scale, not for sale but for amusement, gifts, and exchange.

While industrial and agricultural labor will steadily decline, we may expect a great increase in service occupations, especially doctors, dentists, nurses, hospital attendants, teachers, research workers, technicians, librarians, artists, authors, public administrators, and so on.

A society such as this would not violate the eighteen imperatives. Within it, invention and technology could continue to expand, and mass production would function to a mass demand. I fail to see, furthermore, how it would violate human nature. It holds no terrors for me, in contemplation. It would be irksome for a time, in that it was different; but a retreat to stagecoach days would be even more irksome. I conclude, accordingly, that adjustment to such a society is not beyond human possibility. The administrative task is admittedly very great. Jobs hardly smaller were done in the first World War, however, and are being done today.

The eighteen imperatives must govern the platform of any political advance. Communists, technocrats, Republicans, Democrats, liberals, constitutionalists, what you will, who campaign for ends *that are not in line* with these imperatives are wasting their time and effort. Any political program now before any people anywhere, can be quickly judged by this acid test. Hitler is obviously working *against* the imperatives when he proscribed machines, hailed back-to-the-land movements, and breaking up industrial combines, the stultification of the scientific spirit. Indeed, his whole attitude up to 1934 has been more medieval than modern. Such policies are doomed in advance; they cannot prevail. Russia is working against the imperatives when she tries to teach Marxian physics and Marxian chemistry. President Roosevelt is working against them when he plows under cotton, puts a premium on the destruction of wheat, and tries to bolster up the debt edifice with loans from the Reconstruction Finance Corporation. These are pure scarcity techniques. Mussolini is working against the imperatives when he seeks to make Italy completely self-sufficient.

We can know by this test what is a through road and what is a blind alley. We could come close to formulating a party platform direct from the imperatives. Granted that a statesman made it his own, or that a group of new leaders espoused it, would citizens understand and would they follow? How strong would be the opposition?

These considerations are profound. Politics, too, has a kind of technology. I shall have to leave it to politicians and sociologists, with a solemn warning: They must apply their technique as means to an end in which technological imperatives are dominant. If they create imperatives of their own, beautiful as may be the method for leading the masses, the end of that leading will be down a steep place into the sea.

DONALD CULROSS PEATTIE

 Why he selected The HOURS

I do not know what, if any, of my writings deserve a place in this anthology, but the editor did not ask for such a judgment. He asked me to select some "favorite" passages. Those that I have taken from *A Book of Hours* are probably favorites only with the author, since his book, however charitably treated by reviewers, never achieved great popular success. Perhaps the blessed people who actually come into a bookstore and buy a book (as distinguished from borrowers and readers of magazine digests) showed discrimination in passing this one up. But it was and is a very personal expression of my self. In a general way it is my most natural voice, my own way of seeing daily things and of thinking and feeling about them in private.

A Book of Hours contains an essay for every hour in the twenty-four, each bearing the title of its hour; none depends on another for continuity of meaning, which was another reason for my choice of four of them for this anthology. I would like to remark that the book was written in times of peace. No application to the burning issues and dread and glorious problems of these days can be found there. But through peace or war, the great wheel of time turns eternally through light and dark.

Santa Barbara, Cal.   DONALD CULROSS PEATTIE
July 9, 1942

FIVE *ANTE MERIDIAN*

ITS enormous bulk forever heaving out of nether darkness, the earth is turning toward the sun. The leaf, the flower, the thought, the granite back of the continent, the systolic and diastolic oceans, face another day. Light will act upon each one of them, and cannot leave any of them unchanged. At the least it must take youth from all of them save the ocean—from the ocean it takes the clouds, in the perpetual convection of water.

A thousand miles an hour, day flies the Atlantic. It finds the tossing lightship, and picks up the white signal numbers on its gray flanks. It gives back to lonely driftwood, prophetic of land, and to sargassos of red kelp floating lazy and succulent, their existent shapes. It eats out darkness, leaving only the etched lines of the spars and masts of the fishing fleet. Meeting shore, it runs a finger of cold shine down marginal sand. Now the sea marsh grasses, stiff with the brine in their veins, shake light from their swords, spilling it toward the turf of rush and samphire in long runnels from the gutters of the blades. It smiles wanly on the crooked tidal creeks in their ebb, where the clapper rails prod in the black mud with sensitive bills.

Light finds the great port. It smites glory from the boast of the empty towers, striking on stone and steel and glass, that catch the day while the bottom of the street is still in night. The first busses plunge out from their flocking places in the old square with the arch in it. They climb the midtown hill with a groaning of gears that echoes in the stone hall of the avenue; they charge up the pavement that is glazed with the first watery blur, and, still empty, sweep past the closed museums.

For the moment the hive is cleanly. The day is babe innocent. Not a coin has clinked, not an armpit poured sweat, not a harlot has combed her hair, not a newspaper been read, not a scale been fiddled, not a scheme hatched.

Now here the star called sun is risen, first a red crescent, then an opening eye, then half a sphere, and at the last, quitting the horizon, it gives the illusion of clearing earthly contact with a discernible bound. Light, direct and ruddy, sweeps down the tree boles of the coastal forests. Five minutes later the miracle is repeated inland, preceded forever by the dawn breeze that finds out trembling aspens and cottonwoods and clatters by in them, running in no other trees.

Everywhere there is a secret withdrawal, a folding up and a putting away of nocturnal things. The children of darkness take themselves off to hideout, bed, and home. The moth goes to the under side of the leaf and, spreading serene gray wings, becomes invisible shadow. The nightcrawlers pour away, visceral-colored and cleanly, into the sod, cunningly plugging their burrows behind them with old leafage. Down every little pit of darkness in bark and stone and earth vanish the darkling-beetles, the rove-beetles, the clean wood roaches. The toad immobilizes at the stump base, the color and the lumpy moist texture of the loam itself. In the hollow of old orchards, the dew is a chill gray lake not yet diamonded and rubied.

Out of the pit files the night shift of the miners with empty pails. Women in gray wait for them, with arms still hugging only themselves and their fear.

Westward, the mirror of Ontario picks up the reflection of the zenith streamers, then almond Erie catches the gleam like humor in a long eye, then woman Huron, with its bays like arms flung open, then the pure pendant drop of Michigan, and last Superior, high and deep and ocean-cold. The wakened gulls sweep off the beaches of the fresh seas; the five mirror surfaces, curved liquids with the curvature of earth, come alight, change from shoreless cave lakes to open blue water combed with the long even summer swell.

The planet spins on, plunging Asia into night, giving back to every prairie grass blade the American day. Farther on, in mining towns that lie in canyon darkness, windows are lit where the next shift gulps hot coffee before going down. Above them, at ten thousand feet, the Rockies pick up the fierce astronomical signals of the sun, and flash rose and blue relays from their toppling glaciers. We give back soft answers here. under our envelope of moist and dusty atmosphere. In beauty are daily things begun and finished upon earth, not harshly and forever, as it is in heaven.

MERIDIAN

NOON stands over head, and from frontier to frontier the whistles salute it. So the cock is supposed to blow his horn for midnight. But I know of no other animal than man who makes anything of noon or does it homage. We blast the zenith air; suddenly, in the cities, the offices empty, and out of them the noon-flies swarm. White faces by the indistinguishable thousand show themselves to the sun's yellow face.

Looking down upon the human nest, a naturalist on Venus might suppose that its members responded simultaneously to the immense phototropism of high noon—the pull of light. Rather are they abroad in search of that elusive restaurant where one may fare better for a few cents less. The bright-winged ones skim the streets looking for it, the girls clothed in all their salaries, eager with their inexhaustible appetite for light sweet food and light sweet living. The men and boys go hunting for it, driven by a hunger that is nerve hunger; little they eat will go to muscle.

And there are other cravings; the public libraries at noon fill up. When I was a young twelve-dollar-a-week noon-fly, and no bought cooking could tempt me, I used sometimes to devour a book instead. I remember the beautiful girl, of the Galician Jewish type, who came there every noon and wrestled with the staggering city directory. Most people, if they cannot find a name in the telephone book, give up their man as lost. Only the lost themselves sometimes learn that every adult among seven millions is listed in the enormous volumes, his name and residence and occupation, if any. The history of all our ephemerid lives is there, and, if you go from volume to volume, you may trace the nomadism of each family, from one of our island wadis to the next, the gradual dispersal of its children, the deceases of the patriarchs, the giving in marriage of the daughters. For whom was this Ruth searching? Father, brother, lover—I never learned, and she never found him, not at least in my city noons.

One o'clock is the executive's hour. There are rich menus in it, and there is leisure. Noon belongs to the people, and the food is such as they can pay for and consume in half an hour. Your noon-fly, presumably, is not of enough importance to need time for more than the endless fight against starvation.

But I wanted to mark the meridian with prayer in some form. I used to see people slipping into the cathedral, and out of envy I followed them. But there was nothing inside except a rose-water twilight. I knelt—I have no hesitancy about kneeling anywhere; it is one of the body's natural attitudes, the way to embrace a standing child or to drink from a spring—but no prayers came.

For a year I had been hiding books on ornithology and plants in my office desk. When spring came I threw up my princely job, at a time when a million returned soldiers were hunting for jobs, and went south. The heaviest part of my baggage was my books, and a hand lens and a pair of field glasses with a scratch in the left eye piece.

As I remember those Blue Ridge weeks they seem to me now to

have been all noon. I remember that hour for its sheer sumptuousness, its excess of something good. The setting out and the coming back have faded from my memory. Only the noons are vivid because in them I was, myself, inactive. What I collected then that was green and growing was my thoughts.

The best place for noons is on a high rock, and the best attitude for them is the position that lichens assume. On your back, with your hand flung on your brow, you are in a posture of prayer. On your lips you take the communion of vertical light; it stains, as all wines do. So my hand became brown, and I learned a little and did a world of listening and seeing.

There was a valley bell, a very large and old one, that rang news of dinner—golden chicken, and spoon bread, and buttermilk from the spring-house, and soft hill water in the thick tumblers with the horse-shoe mark pressed in their bottoms. The noon train, on the other side of the mountain, whistled salute to the zenith hour and from the farm between the brooks came up the sound of cocks blowing.

That was the hour when bushes tucked shade beneath them, like skirts, and nothing escaped the good tyranny of light. You would have had to be a raccoon with a hollow tree at your command, or a beetle under a rock, to find total shadow at that hour. It was, indeed, the hour of the lizards, who shared the rock with me, of the golden wasp who shared the sweets of my luncheon, fanning the mica dust with the propeller breeze of its wings as it hovered, treading air. It was the hour, too, of the buzzard, who shared space and height with me, per-forming that feat of birds, a sudden upshooting ascent without a wing-stroke. There is no secret in it, of course; they ride to heaven on the strength of the upward column of air from the sun-baked valley floor. First grow your cambering wings, and you may do the same.

Country noons are prodigal of time and economical of shadow. They invite to the sort of contemplating that is done with the head between the knees, with a good view of a single ant, and in the hearing of a brook.

Contemplation is an art not suddenly to be begun. It takes more time to arrive at it than it does to perform it like a prayer. I am not propounding a literary whimsy; I am talking about the way, it seems to me, that a man may look into himself by staring into the crystal of the world. This is the only safe introspection; the examining of the conscience by night has a great deal too much of the torchlit dungeon and the rack in it. It makes fanatics, and fanatics make life intolerable. Night is a season for music, for love play, for feasting, drinking, dancing, for that blent life of the senses and imagination. These are the ingredients of romance. And night is to lie with. There is no true light in it by which to judge life's colors.

I dare the cynic to try his thoughts out in the noon sunshine that is without shadow. How hard then it is to lock your door, to make a wax image of your fellow man and stick pins in it or melt it! Such stuff is night work. Under noon it is more likely you who will melt, upon your rock, while in the clearing, in the valley below you, man swings his ax—a sun-twinkle and a padded blow—and man's wife, with the sun on her smooth hair and bare arms, walks out to bring him something: a meal in a pail, a kiss, a bit of news about a sick child or a child coming.

EIGHT *POST MERIDIAN*

LAST light fingers the tops of trees, stands them forth in a bathed glory, their heads in day, their long limbs and low boughs already in upwelling shadow. The birds now, you will have noticed, find the tree tops; they like a dead tree best, and they sit in rows upon the spindling twigs and face the spectacle of sunset like an audience. Rough-winged swallows, martins, grackles, and robins, I find, do this. Not one of them that turns his rump upon the lord of day; tranquilly they take the afterglow upon their breasts. The restless tribe—the swallows—wheel off in little erratic companies, describing a few banked spirals of joy, to return and edge along the perch and look again. The robin (a singer we have come to underestimate from a deafening familiarity with his lays) will lift up his beak and sing the sun a confident farewell. He has the gifts of the thrush family in his blood, and it is, it seems to me, the finest family of singers in all the temperate world.

Now we would say that the birds were at their reverences, and we would call the robin's slow-delivered syllables a hymn, were we not so certain that no other animal than ourselves has soul or eyes for beauty. This prejudice, I think, is something we have been taught and are afraid to deny. It is not what simple observation suggests to us. In our innocence we once supposed that birds sang when they were happy, like peasants in a Sicilian vineyard. It is true, no doubt, that the singing bird with his voice proclaims his territorial rights, and commands his mate to him. But the voice of a human lover is employed to the same end. A bird in song is, if you like, a creature actuated by instinctive, reflex and tropic conditions so that almost without will he sings because he must. To sing because one must—how pure a motive that were! Should human artists obey no other impulse, would art suffer?

The robin sings the sun down, tropic to light as a moth to candle flame. But there's the wood thrush, now, just beginning his song, and he addresses not the sunset but the forest. His voice floats out of the distant chancel like a religious chorister's. It drifts to us through the naves, without haste in the delivery. The notes, spinning one after another through the green clerestories, reach us without the clashing of an echo, for no vault shuts heaven away.

Hear my LAY? The first musical sentence asks the wood for its attention.

We hear your lay. The second line is a response, with the final syllable lowered and affirmative.

Now the singer delivers a long musical sentence, a testament of faith:

True to you, truly DEAR!

Each note shines forth with the chilled beauty of far-off stars, like Mercury, Venus and Jupiter all in the afterglow, sib to each other, part of one perfect creation, but disparate, spaced at visibly different depths in the deepening violet of the sky. Now the voice rises to a triumphant assertion:

Dear to ME!

And at the last, sustained but descending, perfectly rounding to the period of the cinquaine, the voice lowered without attempt at climax:

True to—

      —you.

There falls a rest, perfectly measured and identical with every other interval, the musical value of silence understood as well as if the singer were a conscious composer.

I am under the impression that when he is interrupted in the midst of his melody the thrush does not forget where he left off, but takes up the syllable following the last utterance. We shall not be the ones to interrupt him. We have leisure to listen because we take it as a priority of claim on our attention, to listen until the last note has ceased in the Gothic twilight, has run, a widening ripple of sound, unhurried, to the mile-off shore that is the auditory horizon. Like every religious singer, the wood thrush simply falls silent, and silent is the sevenfold amen of the leaves. He takes no bow and expects no applause. And the audience arises without speech and walks quietly out of the woods.

The first stars prick through, Venus serenely glittering. A star named for its limpid beauty. But she is no naked Aphrodite. She is forever wrapped in impenetrable clouds, unknown in depth, her seas, it may be, still suspended as vapor over the solid core on which we may not gaze.

Between the orbit of Venus in her stage of evolution that we have passed, and that of Mars, a planet that has perhaps lost its seas and clouds so that we actually gaze on its desertic surfaces, spins Earth, miraculously adapted to life.

That adaptation has been called the fitness of the environment, and the fitness of life to the environment is something so perfect that we are driven to conclude that the two mutual adaptations are in essence viewpoints of the same thing. Call this duality accident or design; it totals the same, so somewhere in the staggering mathematics of cosmos you get the equation of life. Once you have it, the number of possible permutations marches autonomously on. Out of the hells of the sun, the needful and terrible emptiness of the spaces, comes all we know,— the infinite individuality of every leaf in the wood, the holy beauty of the thrush's song, the sensitive ear of the listener.

Little earth, voice of bird, mind of man, these were not foreseen or foreseeable at creation as an astronomer thinks of the origin of things. Yet they must have been implied, and were perhaps inevitable, in the first premises of Nature.

TWO *ANTE MERIDIAN*

N OW is that hour that, in a gloomy view of Deity, has been
called God's. For it has been said by generations of old wives,
even by nurses and by doctors of an era past, that at this moment the
soul most easily quits the body, the body having within it metabolic
tides. This is the ebb, then, if we believe with some; this is the cesura,
the pause, the invisible suture where the closed circle of life was
welded in the fires of creation. Here the chain of the body breaks, at
its weakest line of stress, and the spirit steps down into the chill Styx.
Or it wakes to perpetual morning, if you prefer. In either event, it
quits the known; it comes not back. The weary, the dusty, the tormented escape. But the young and the fair, the precious and the
tender, are driven out of their fleshly habitation, evicted from life to
mysterious destiny, most ruthless at this nadir hour.

I believe I am right when I assert that hospital statistics do not
bear out this supposition. There is no one hour of the twenty-four at
which most souls slip away. In these matters, as in others, death is
impartial. It recruits by conscription, and its ranks are never filled.
The wise, perhaps, are submissive, but, submissive or rebellious, we
are propelled by a great hand against our naked shoulder.

The body, of course, cries out: But not my life! The heart that
loves cries: But not their lives! I am as vainly passionate here as any
other; I find, upon self-searching, that I cannot honestly believe that
all lives are equally precious. Who shall be the judge? I do not know,
but I say, beware of the man who affects to tell you. Beware of the
war-lords. Beware even of him who proclaims that God is the inscrutable judge who, if He slays the young and innocent, and lets the
evil flourish, knows best and will act in His time. That is jungle-
thinking, and every bone in me refuses it, hymn, cant, and voodoo.
Thank you, I shall fight for the child's breath. Civilized, I may tolerate
the Martian monster sitting astride the tank—though it is an open
question whether civilization dare tolerate him—for I have not much
violence in my blood. I have faith in science. I believe in the reality of
ethics. I have beheld beauty.

And you believe on these things. You imply your act of a modern's faith when you call the doctor, when you accept the certainty of the astronomer's calculation of the date of an eclipse, when you lie down to sleep in the assurance that those to whom you have given your trust are not wolves who will kill you in the night and put their mouths to your throat. The whole fabric of human life—with whose order and pattern no other animal life is momentarily comparable—is based upon these positive assumptions. The healthy soul is not passive, and man is not a fallen angel. But he may just possibly be on the evolutionary road toward angelic transmutation.

For he can hear the long trumpets; he lifts his head to listen. He beholds a few who stand out far ahead; the best of the rest follow, stumbling, by their lights. Defiance of death is but the most dramatic of heroisms. Every tolerant mind is heroic. All strenuous thinking is heroism; hourly and daily people less fortunate than I live more manfully than I, with less of self-pity and self-conceit. They accumulate the real wealth of the world, not for themselves but for the hive, the golden store of life's goodness.

So man, who comes out of darkness, goes not into it; only the individual body rightly travels on that road. He goes toward the open, the great free steppes—a spirit mounted upon stallion body, a tireless rider who swings from steed to steed.

JOSEPH HERGESHEIMER Why he

selected From an OLD HOUSE

I have sent you part of an autobiographical work, *From an Old House,* since, more than any other passage I could find, it superficially resembles fact. The truth is that books have no relation to actuality whatever; confined to a single plane, a horizontal order, of words and ideas they are unable even to hint at the simultaneous and irrational dimensions of life. For example poetry and quantitative chemistry alike can only associate arbitrary symbols with the recurrence of observed effects.

A house of fieldstone, however, is a reality and I was, once, younger. Those at least, avoiding dialectical philosophy, are facts. It is equally plain that, like Dorothy Wordsworth's *Alfoxden Journal, From an Old House* was an ingenuous performance. Its sale was, simply, fortunate. We were sustained for quite a while by that web of shadowy words. I had set out to describe, perhaps justify to myself, a dwelling made beautiful with literally my last dollar; I was addressed to permanent things, oak and masonry and wrought iron; but all I wrote about was the impermanence of life.

In a flash the winter succeeded autumn with the snow's light reflected from whitewashed walls and my pages; the frogs, the knee-deeps, piped in the water meadow and the scent of lilacs was too heavy for sleep; the locust came and pollinated heat; in a flash the harvest moon, autumn, returned to the apple tree.

I had, of course, provided myself with a milestone that already, if only a step, lay behind me. I was looking back on a fabric metaphorically finished within the hour. The years of passage had ended for a young man driving the Monterey stage down the Virginia mountainside to Travellers' Repose. That was earlier by twenty-five years than my book about the Dower House. An indolence of peace and plenty in Europe had followed: the Parisian elegance of great painters at Foyot's; Rolle and the green lawns Gibbon knew unchanged beside Lake Geneva; canticles in the Gregorian mode on Murano and the Ragazza diligence for a pedestrian's bag across the Venetian plain to the Dolomites and Innsbruck; the March beer at Munich and waters at Carlsbad where highborn English boys gambled away thousands of goldpieces and the Russians tens of thousands; the Göteborg Canal and yachts off Cowes with the young ladies racing in velvet basques through the salt spray.

All that, when I wrote *From an Old House*, was over; the democracy of gin, moving pictures and the automobile had prevailed; but I was on a byway leading back into the past. Only a premonition of this troubled me in 1925; at most I had been put in my place, admonished, by a habitation that made nothing of seven generations harder than mine; yet, as I tried to show, the imminence like dusk was a Lydian prelude to the night's long seclusion.

West Chester, Pa.   JOSEPH HERGESHEIMER
August 7, 1942

I REMEMBER without affection an early furnace in the Dower House, one of the first built for steam; at regular intervals a dry smell of scorching would inform us that once again we had neglected to keep the boiler supplied with water. This, we believed, might at any moment result in an explosion that would blow us, the stone walls, into nothingness; and I'd hurry down to repair the mistake with a sensation of heroism slightly contaminated by fear. The explosion, of course, never happened; but why we didn't crack the boiler, flooding it with cold water at the worst possible times, I can't imagine.

It was set in a pit, too deep for a comfortable step, and for ten years we endured a small block of wood with a habit of turning under our feet. It did this when anyone was in a hurry or carrying a shovelful of coal. With practice I was able to stand on the board laid over a floor of earth and pitch the coal directly into the furnace door; but the opening was hardly wider than the shovel; the least error would send a clatter of coal into the pit and against the wall. Then I'd have to stoop, a lamp in one hand, and pick the coal up singly. Perhaps I'd be dressed for dinner and Dorothy with a hired car waiting not altogether patient.

Something obstinate in my character forced me to recover every black greasy lump, and bitterly, one by one, throw them into the fire. Or I might be late dressing, and Dorothy, in her perishable dinner clothes, would go down to the furnace, and I'd hear the faint scrape of the shovel on the uneven wooden flooring of the coal bin. She would come up with her skirts under her elbows, her hair and temper disarranged and coal dust on her shoulders.

I knew all her dresses then—we discussed them for weeks before they were bought and consulted for a year about their minor changes. A dinner dress was a thing of unique importance; and, in the closet, it was covered by a sheet. Slippers did their full duty. I owned a formal evening coat out of the remote past; but it had been made smaller after my long illness in Italy; and I was reaching a state where it could only, with safety, be stood up in; the frock coat of my wedding was long ago impossible.

Now, after Dorothy came back from New York, and we were going to a party, she seemed almost strange in a new and unfamiliar dress. There was no trace in her bearing or appearance of the difficult years, sixteen of them, that had made up our life together. Her spirit was more vigorous, her grace more flexible, than when I had first seen her. Either the greater superficiality or superior depth of women kept them comparatively free from the marks with which time and struggle disfigured men. There was a costume she wore to dances in fancy dress, blue denim with exposed ruffled pantalets and a red wig with curls, and in it she seemed part of another and younger generation than mine.

I had stopped going to such parties—damn it, somewhere I had lost the most of my gaiety—and often, just before she left, we'd sit in the dining room over tall glasses filled with ice and a bottle of champagne . . . preferable to the gin she would later be offered. I would regard her in a surprise touched with consternation, she was so—so contemporary, so much at home in a present set to music that exasperated rather than soothed me. In a word I had placed myself—I expected music to be soothing.

Quaint survival of a period suspended on the lyrical waltzes of

Johann Strauss! The lines of the popular songs of my youth would now
be disdained by children; those I heard in the night clubs of New
York startled a not inconsiderable experience. I wasn't, I hoped,
censorious; I have explained that I didn't want to correct the present;
no, my adaptability to change was over. I was like a clock that had
stopped at an hour never again to return, or a marked date on a
calendar of the year before last. Suddenly, without warning, my elas-
ticity had departed just as, after the term of use, it left rubber.

I went to parties where dancing wasn't indispensable, and, for
a while, sufficiently enjoyed them; but I soon got tired—midnight had
the aspect of a purely hypothetical period, never reached. I couldn't
attach myself to new people, to a fresh charm. It was all forced: I'd
tell myself that a woman I had seen for the first time was utterly engaging; I would proceed—mechanically where there had once been
fervour—with a suggestion of later engagements; and then, riding
home, her image would fade like a scene overtaken by night. My mind
held the stamp of other, earlier faces, the inflections of different voices.
I fought against this, denied it, but it was useless. With the door of
my room closed, in the cool relinquishment of bed and a book to be
read or dropped, the truth would invade me—silence had become
more valuable than sound, rest more grateful than any activity.

That was especially true after a measurably young dinner in my
own house where there was no escape from the lateness of a successful
occasion. The victrola relentlessly ground out a dislocated music with,
the rugs pushed aside, dancers keeping up and up their improbable
rhythms. The mere laughter seemed incredible, shattering, in force;
everyone but me was capable of simply inexhaustible pleasure. When,
finally, they were gone I'd put the house in order, lay the rugs, and
gathering the glasses carry them to the pantry. The servants would
have long since departed for West Chester. I would empty ash trays
and conduct the dogs to where, on old shawls, they slept in the
kitchen.

They went very willingly now, for they were old too; their wheaten
muzzles were grey. The quiet, the tranquillity, of the Dower House
would surge back, stopping the sounds whirling in my head as though
my brain had become the victrola; opened doors, in winter, would
let in a bath of cold; and subconsciously I'd listen for the slow loud

ticking of the clock that used to hang on the kitchen wall. Even if it had still been there the pantry doors must have deadened the sound; it belonged to an era before the pantry, when the noises of the kitchen were almost equally shared by the dining room and beyond.

No matter who had been present it was an enormous relief to have them gone, to be alone, silent. This had become true in the face of the fact that I liked the people who made up our life; particularly the men. I welcomed them happily, and it wasn't my fondness but vitality that often sank before they went. I had been, as a child, very much alone; and I suppose the mental habit this bred was, the energy of youth departed, coming back. I had begun to regard a great many things in a way that even I recognized was old-fashioned, the fashion of the time of my malleability. A trait not discouraged by a growing habit of looking into the past for the subjects of my novels.

Yes, in her red wig Dorothy was triumphantly alive; she was a part, a note, of the music of today. There were phases of her life in which I had no place. Yet I was supported by a feeling that my present condition was better than the one it had followed. I was, for one thing, freer; but not, of course, free. I didn't long for a complete escape from the flesh; I wanted pleasure to be at once unrestrained and moderate; to close, when I was tired, with the neatness of a book. Old age, death, I saw, were not, after all, insuperable. With the thinning of the flame there was a lessening of the oil; the lamp, normally, cooled gradually to its extinction. Death was only a moment, a breath, on the lowered wick.

I didn't, however, solitary in my room dwell on that, but on the night that flooding the opened windows made the room one with its own profound immensity. At times it was brilliant with stars, again luminous with moonlight, or a gale would sweep across the north wall. Dorothy hated wind, it made her immeasurably wretched, but I liked to hear it beating against the solid fieldstone of the Dower House; the noise, perhaps, would sink to a stillness deepened by the soft flutter of snow all night against the panes.

In the morning Dorothy, who had been on the sleeping porch, would relate that her blankets were white and ask me to feel how cold her nose was. Her cheeks would be brilliant with colour and she'd want to dance . . . all day and through the next night. It wasn't unheard of for me to be annoyed by her mere exuberance. And for that, I began to think, for her activity of spirit, the red wig was a symbol. When she took it out of its box for a recurling at the hairdresser's, when Martha starched the pantalets, I knew that her unspent youngness was in the ascendancy; I prepared to hear the victrola as she got ready; and went for the bottle of champagne . . . it was so much better than the current gin; lighter and talisman of a more amber mood.

JOHN DEWEY Why he selected

DEMOCRACY and AMERICA

It happens that I have been engaged recently in making a study of the outgivings of Adolf Hitler—not only *Mein Kampf* but the many speeches he made before and after coming to power. As I now write a few words in connection with this reprint of what I wrote a few years ago, the net conclusion which stays with me from my reading is closely connected with what is said in what follows. Hitler fatally misunderstood the significance, the moving spirit, and the force of American democracy. He did so because he did not have the slightest insight into its moral aspects and moral foundation.

He thought democracy was necessarily weak because he identified it with the mechanics of voting and the quantitative aspect of majority rule; with the degenerate and futile parliamentarianism he has witnessed in Vienna; with the most divisive, and therefore the weakest aspect of finance capitalism.

Because of the necessities of his own campaign for power, he realized that to be strong a people must be united. He never realized the moral principle embodied in what is strong and enduring in American democracy: That this unity is toughest and strongest when it is the work of a continuously recreated voluntary consent, which in turn is the product of continual communication, conference, consultation, contact; of the free give-and-take of free beings. He thought it had to be the product of force and the kind of propaganda that is possible only by suppression of all free speech, free publication, free assembly, and free education. Whether or not he judged his own people correctly in this matter, his views and his practice rest upon the lowest kind of estimate of the capacities of human nature. The moral source of his final defeat will be just this total lack of faith. As far as democracy lives up to its faith in the potentialities of human beings, by means of putting into practical operation the democratic moral means by which these capacities may be realized, American democracy will do more than aid in winning the war. It will also play a significant role in an even more severe test and task, that of winning the peace. For the foundation of a pacified and unified Europe is the discovery by European peoples of the true nature of the democratic ideal and of the democratic methods by which alone the ideal can be made effective.

New York, N. Y.   JOHN DEWEY
June 29, 1942

I MAKE no apology for linking what is said in this with the name of Thomas Jefferson. For he was the first modern to state in human terms the principles of democracy. Were I to make an apology, it would be that in the past I have concerned myself unduly, if a comparison has to be made, with the English writers who have attempted to state the ideals of self-governing communities and the methods appropriate to their realization. If I now prefer to refer to Jefferson it is not, I hope, because of American provincialism, even though I believe that only one who was attached to American soil and who took a consciously alert part in the struggles of the country to attain its independence, could possibly have stated as thoroughly and intimately as did Jefferson the aims embodied in the American tradition: "the definitions and axioms of a free government," as Lincoln called them. Nor is the chief reason for going to him, rather than to Locke or Bentham or Mill, his greater sobriety of judgment due to that constant tempering of theory with practical experience which also kept his democratic doctrine within human bounds.

The chief reason is that Jefferson's formulation is moral through and through: in its foundations, its methods, its ends. The heart of his faith is expressed in his words "Nothing is unchangeable but inherent and inalienable rights of man." The words in which he stated the moral basis of free institutions have gone out of vogue. We repeat the opening words of the Declaration of Independence, but unless we translate them they are couched in a language that, even when it comes readily to our tongue, does not penetrate today to the brain.

He wrote: "These truths are self-evident: that all men are created equal; that they are endowed by their Creator with inherent and unalienable rights; that among these are life, liberty and the pursuit of happiness." Today we are wary of anything purporting to be self-evident truths; we are not given to associating politics with the plans of the Creator; the doctrine of natural rights which governed his style of expression has been weakened by historic and philosophic criticism.

To put ourselves in touch with Jefferson's position we have therefore to translate the word "natural" into *moral*. Jefferson was under the influence of the Deism of his time. Nature and the plans of a benevolent and wise Creator were never far apart in his reflections. But his fundamental beliefs remain unchanged in substance if we forget all special associations with the word *Nature* and speak instead of ideal aims and values to be realized—aims which, although ideal, are not located in the clouds but are backed by something deep and indestructible in the needs and demands of humankind.

Were I to try to connect in any detail what I have to say with the details of Jefferson's speeches and letters—he wrote no theoretical treatises—I should probably seem to be engaged in a partisan undertaking; I should at times be compelled to indulge in verbal exegesis so as to attribute to him ideas not present in his mind. Nevertheless, there are three points contained in what has to be said about American democracy that I shall here explicitly connect with his name. In the first place, in the quotation made, it was the *ends* of democracy, the rights of *man*—not of men in the plural—which are unchangeable. It was not the forms and mechanisms through which inherent moral claims are realized that are to persist without change. Professed Jeffersonians have often not even followed the words of the one whose disciples they say they are, much less his spirit. For he said: "I know that laws and institutions must go hand in hand with the progress of the human mind. . . . As new discoveries are made, new truths disclosed, and manners and opinions change with the change of circumstances, institutions must change also and keep pace with the times. We might as well require a man to wear the coat which fitted him when a boy, as civilized society to remain ever under the regime of their barbarous ancestors."

Because of the last sentence his idea might be interpreted to be a

justification of the particular change in government he was champion-
ing against earlier institutions. But he goes on to say: "Each generation has a right to choose for itself the form of government it believes
the most promotive of its own happiness." Hence he also said: "The
idea that institutions established for the use of a nation cannot be
touched or modified, even to make them answer their end . . . may
perhaps be a salutary provision against the abuses of a monarch, but
is most absurd against the nation itself." "A generation holds all the
rights and powers their predecessors once held and may change their
laws and institutions to suit themselves." He engaged in certain calculations based on Buffon, more ingenious than convincing, to settle
upon a period of eighteen years and eight months that fixed the natural span of the life of a generation; thereby indicating the frequency
with which it is desirable to overhaul "laws and institutions" to bring
them into accord with "new discoveries, new truths, change of manners and opinions." The word *culture* is not used; Jefferson's statement would have been weakened by its use. But it is not only professed followers of Jefferson who have failed to act upon his teaching.
It is true of all of us so far as we have set undue store by established
mechanisms. The most flagrantly obvious violation of Jefferson's democratic point of view is found in the idolatry of the Constitution as it
stands that has been sedulously cultivated. But it goes beyond this
instance. As believers in democracy we have not only the right but the
duty to question existing mechanisms of, say, suffrage and to inquire
whether some functional organization would not serve to formulate
and manifest public opinion better than the existing methods. It is not
irrelevant to the point that a score of passages could be cited in which
Jefferson refers to the American Government as an *experiment*.

The second point of which I would speak is closely bound up
with an issue which has become controversial and partisan, namely,
states rights versus federal power. There is no question of where
Jefferson stood on that issue, nor as to his fear in general of govern-
mental encroachment on liberty—inevitable in his case, since it was the
cause of the Rebellion against British domination and was also the
ground of his struggle against Hamiltonianism. But any one who stops
with this particular aspect of Jefferson's doctrine misses an underlying
principle of utmost importance. For while he stood for state action as

a barrier against excessive power at Washington, and while on the *practical side* his concern with it was most direct, in his theoretical writings chief importance is attached to local self-governing units on something like the New England town-meeting plan. His project for general political organization on the basis of small units, small enough so that all its members could have direct communication with one another and take care of all community affairs was never acted upon. It never received much attention in the press of immediate practical problems.

But without forcing the significance of this plan, we may find in it an indication of one of the most serious of present problems regarding democracy. I spoke earlier of the way in which individuals at present find themselves in the grip of immense forces whose workings and consequences they have no power of affecting. The situation calls emphatic attention to the need for face-to-face associations, whose interactions with one another may offset if not control the dread impersonality of the sweep of present forces. There is a difference between a society, in the sense of an association and a community. Electrons, atoms and molecules are in association with one another. Nothing exists in isolation anywhere throughout nature. Natural associations are conditions for the existence of a community, but a community adds the function of communication in which emotions and ideas are shared as well as joint undertakings engaged in. Economic forces have immensely widened the scope of associational activities. But it has done so largely at the expense of the intimacy and directness of communal group interests and activities. The American habit of "joining" is a tribute to the reality of the problem but has not gone far in solving it. The power of the rabblerouser, especially in the totalitarian direction, is mainly due to his power to create a factitious sense of direct union and communal solidarity—if only by arousing the emotion of common intolerance and hate.

I venture to quote words written some years ago: "Evils which are uncritically and indiscriminately laid at the door of industrialism and democracy might, with greater intelligence, be referred to the dislocation and unsettlement of local communities. Vital and thorough attachments are bred only in the intimacy of an intercourse which is of necessity restricted in range. . . . Is it possible to restore the reality of the less communal organizations and to penetrate and saturate their members with a sense of local community life? . . . Democracy must begin at home, and its home is the neighborly community."* On account of the vast extension of the field of association, produced by elimination of distance and lengthening of temporal spans, it is obvious that social agencies, political and non-political, cannot be confined to localities. But the problem of harmonious adjustment between extensive activities, precluding direct contacts, and the intensive activities of community intercourse is a pressing one for democracy. It involves even more than apprenticeship in the practical processes of self-government, important as that is, which Jefferson had in mind. It involves development of local agencies of communication and cooperation, creating stable loyal attachments, to militate against the centrifugal forces of present culture, while at the same time they are of a kind to respond flexibly to the demands of the larger unseen and indefinite public. To a very considerable extent, groups having a functional basis will probably have to replace those based on physical contiguity. In the family both factors combine.

The third point of which I would make express mention as to Jefferson and democracy has to do with his ideas about property. It would be absurd to hold that his personal views were "radical" beyond fear of concentrated wealth and a positive desire for general distribution of wealth without great extremes in either direction. However, it is sometimes suggested that his phrase "pursuit of happiness" stood for economic activity, so that life, liberty, and property were the rights he thought organized society should maintain. But just here is where he broke most completely with Locke. In connection with property, especially property in land, he makes his most positive statements about the inability of any generation to bind its successors. Jefferson held that property rights are created by the "social pact" instead of representing inherent individual moral claims which government is morally bound to maintain.

The right to pursue happiness stood with Jefferson for nothing less than the claim of every human being to choose his own career and to act upon his own choice and judgment free from restraints and constraints imposed by the arbitrary will of other human beings—

* *The Public and its Problems,* pp. 212-13.

whether these others are officials of government, of whom Jefferson was especially afraid, or are persons whose command of capital and control of the opportunities for engaging in useful work limits the ability of others to "pursue happiness." The Jeffersonian principle of equality of rights without special favor to any one justifies giving supremacy to personal rights when they come into conflict with property rights. While his views are properly enough cited against ill-considered attacks upon the economic relations that exist at a given time, it is sheer perversion to hold that there is anything in Jefferson democracy that forbids political action to bring about equalization of economic conditions in order that the equal right of all to free choice and free action be maintained.

I have referred with some particularity to Jefferson's ideas upon special points because of the proof they afford that the source of the American democratic tradition is moral—not technical, abstract, narrowly political nor materially utilitarian. It is moral because based on faith in the ability of human nature to achieve freedom for individuals accompanied with respect and regard for other persons and with social stability built on cohesion instead of coercion. Since the tradition is a moral one, attacks upon it, however they are made, wherever they come from, from within or from without, involve moral issues and can be settled only upon moral grounds. In as far as the democratic ideal has undergone eclipse among us, the obscuration is moral in source and effect. The dimming is both a product and a manifestation of the confusion that accompanies transition from an old order to a new one for the arrival of the latter was heralded only as conditions plunged it into an economic regime so novel that there was no adequate preparation for it and which dislocated the established relations of persons with one another.

Nothing is gained by attempts to minimize the novelty of the democratic order, nor the scope of the change it requires in old and long cherished traditions. We have not even as yet a common and accepted vocabulary in which to set forth the order of moral values involved in realization of democracy. The language of Natural Law was once all but universal in educated Christendom. The conditions which gave it force disappeared. Then there was an appeal to natural rights, supposed by some to center in isolated individuals although not in the original American formulation. At present, appeal to the individual is dulled by our inability to locate the individual with any assurance. While we are compelled to note that his freedom can be maintained only through the working together toward a single end of a large number of different and complex factors, we do not know how to coordinate them on the basis of voluntary purpose.

The intimate association that was held to exist between individualism and business activity for private profit gave, on one side, a distorted meaning to individualism. Then the weakening, even among persons who nominally retain older theological beliefs, of the imaginative ideas and emotions connected with the sanctity of the individual, disturbed democratic individualism on the positive moral side. The moving energy once associated with things called spiritual has lessened; we use the word *ideal* reluctantly, and have difficulty in giving the word *moral* much force beyond, say, a limited field of mutually kindly relations among individuals. That such a syllogism as the following once had a vital meaning to a man of affairs like Jefferson today seems almost incredible: "Man was created for social intercourse, but social intercourse cannot be maintained without a sense of justice; then man must have been created with a sense of justice."

Even if we have an abiding faith in democracy, we are not likely to express it as Jefferson expressed his faith: "I have no fear but that the result of our experiment will be that men may be trusted to govern themselves without a master. Could the contrary of this be proved, I should conclude either there is no God or that he is a malevolent being." The belief of Jefferson that the sole legitimate object of government among men "is to secure the greatest degree of happiness possible to the general mass of those associated under it" was connected with his belief that Nature—or God—benevolent in intent, had created men for happiness on condition they attained knowledge of natural order and observed the demands of that knowledge in their actions. The obsolescence of the language for many persons makes it the more imperative for all who would maintain and advance the ideals of democracy to face the issue of the moral ground of political institutions and the moral principles by which men acting together may attain freedom of individuals which will amount to fraternal associations with one another. The weaker our faith in Nature, in its laws and rights and its benevolent intentions for human welfare, the more urgent is the need for a faith based on ideas that are now intellectually credible and that are consonant with present economic conditions, which will inspire and direct action with something of the ardor once attached to things religious.

Human power over the physical energies of nature has immensely increased. In moral ideal, power of man over physical nature should be employed to reduce, to eliminate progressively, the power of man over man. By what means shall we prevent its use to effect new, more subtle, more powerful agencies of subjection of men to other men? Both the issue of war or peace between nations, and the future of economic relations for years and generations to come in contribution either to human freedom or human subjection are involved. An increase of power undreamed of a century ago, one to whose further increase no limits can be put as long as scientific inquiry goes on, is an established fact. The thing still uncertain is what we are going to do with it. That it is power signifies of itself it is electrical, thermic, chemical. What will be done with it is a moral issue.

Physical interdependence has increased beyond anything that could have been foreseen. Division of labor in industry was anticipated and was looked forward to with satisfaction. But it is relatively the least weighty phase of the present situation. The career of individuals, their lives and security as well as prosperity is now affected by events on the other side of the world. The forces back of these events he cannot touch or influence—save perhaps by joining in a war of nations against nations. For we seem to live in a world in which nations try to deal with the problems created by the new situation by drawing more and more into themselves, by more and more extreme assertions of independent nationalist sovereignty, while everything they do in the direction of autarchy leads to ever closer mixture with other nations—but in war.

War under existing conditions compels nations, even those professedly the most democratic, to turn authoritarian and totalitarian as the World War of 1914-18 resulted in Fascist totalitarianism in nondemocratic Italy and Germany and in Bolshevist totalitarianism in nondemocratic Russia, and promoted political, economic and intellectual reaction in this country. The necessity of transforming physical inter-dependence into moral—into human—interdependence is part of the democratic problem: and yet war is said even now to be the path of salvation for democratic countries!

Individuals can find the security and protection that are pre-requisites for freedom only in association with others—and then the organization these associations take on, as a measure of securing their efficiency, limits the freedom of those who have entered into them. The importance of organization has increased so much in the last hundred years that the word is now quite commonly used as a synonym for association and society. Since at the very best organization is but the mechanism through which association operates, the identification is evidence of the extent in which a servant has become a master; in which means have usurped the place of the end for which they are called into existence. The predicament is that individuality demands association to develop and sustain it and association requires arrange-ment and coordination of its elements, or organization—since other-wise it is formless and void of power. But we have now a kind of molluscan organization, soft individuals within and a hard constric-tive shell without. Individuals voluntarily enter associations which have become practically nothing but organizations; and then conditions under which they act take control of what they do whether they want it or not.

Persons acutely aware of the dangers of regimentation when it is imposed by government remain oblivious of the millions of persons whose behavior is regimented by an economic system through whose intervention alone they obtain a livelihood. The contradiction is the more striking because the new organizations were for the most part created in the name of freedom, and, at least at the outset, by exercise of voluntary choice. But the kind of working-together which has re-sulted is too much like that of the parts of a machine to represent a co-operation which expresses freedom and also contributes to it. No small part of the democratic problem is to achieve associations whose ordering of parts provides the strength that comes from stability, while they promote flexibility of response to change.

Lastly, in this brief survey, there is the problem of the relation of human nature and physical nature. The ancient world solved the problem, in abstract philosophical theory, by endowing all nature, in its cosmic scope, with the moral qualities of the highest and most ideal worth in humanity. The theology and rites of the Church gave this abstract theory direct significance in the lives of the peoples of the western world. For it provided practical agencies by means of which the operation of the power creating and maintaining the universe were supposed to come to the support of individuals in this world and the next. The rise of physical science rendered an ever increasing number of men skeptical of the intellectual foundation provided by the old theory. The unsettlement, going by the name of the conflict of science and religion, proves the existence of the division in the foundations upon which our culture rests, between ideas in the form of knowledge and ideas that are emotional and imaginative and that directly actuate conduct.

This disturbance on the moral side has been enormously aggravated by those who are remote from the unsettlement due to intellectual causes. It comes home to everyone by the effects of the practical application of the new physical science. For all the physical features of the present regime of production and distribution of goods and services are products of the new physical science, while the distinctively *human* consequences of science are still determined by habits and beliefs established before its origin. That democracy should not as yet have succeeded in healing the breach is no cause for discouragement: provided there is effected a union of human possibilities and ideals with the spirit and methods of science on one side and with the workings of the economic system on the other side. For a considerable period laissez-faire individualism prevented the problem from being even seen. It treated the new economic movement as if it were simply an expression of forces that were fundamental in the human constitution but were only recently released for free operation. It failed to see that the great expansion which was occurring was in fact due to release of *physical* energies; that as far as human action and human freedom is concerned, a problem, not a solution, was thereby instituted: the problem, namely, of management and direction of the new physical energies so they would contribute to realization of human possibilities.

The reaction that was created by the inevitable collapse of a movement that failed so disastrously in grasp of the problem has had diverse results, the diversity of which is part of the present confused state of our lives. Production of the material means of a secure and free life has been indefinitely increased and at an accelerated rate. It is not surprising that there is a large group which attributes the gains which have accrued, actually and potentially, to the economic regime under which they have occurred—instead of to the scientific knowledge which is the source of physical control of natural energies. The group is large. It is composed not only of the immediate beneficiaries of the system but also of the much larger number who hope that they, or at least their children, are to have full share in its benefits. Because of the opportunities furnished by free land, large unused natural resources and the absence of fixed class differences (which survive in European countries in spite of legal abolition of feudalism), this group is particularly large in this country. It is represented by those who point to the higher standard of living in this country and by those who have responded to the greater opportunities for advancement this country has afforded to them. In short, this group in both categories of its constituents, is impressed by actual gains that have come about. They have a kind of blind and touching faith that improvement is going to continue in some more or less automatic way until it includes them and their offspring.

Then there is a much smaller group who are as sensitive, perhaps more so, to the immense possibilities represented by the physical means now potentially at our command, but who are acutely aware of our failure to realize them; who see instead the miseries, cruelties, oppressions and frustrations which exist. The weakness of this group has been that it has also failed to realize the involvement of the new scientific method in producing the existing state of affairs, and the need for its further extensive and unremitting application to determine analytically—in detail—the causes of present ills, and to project means for their elimination. In social affairs, the wholesale mental attitude that has been referred to persists with little change. It leads to formation of ambitious and sweeping beliefs and policies. The human *ideal* is indeed comprehensive. As a standpoint from which to view existing conditions and judge the direction change should take, it cannot be too inclusive. But the problem of production of change is one of infinite attention to means; and means can be determined only by definite analysis of the conditions of each problem as it presents itself. Health is a comprehensive, a "sweeping" ideal. But progress toward it has been made in the degree in which recourse to panaceas has been abandoned and inquiry has been directed to determinate disturbances and means for dealing with them. The group is represented at its extreme by those who believe there is a necessary historical law which governs the course of events so that all that is needed is deliberate acting in accord with it. The law by which class conflict produces by its own dialectic its complete opposite becomes then the supreme and sole regulator for determining policies and methods of action.

That more adequate knowledge of human nature is demanded if the release of physical powers is to serve human ends is undeniable. But it is a mistake to suppose that this knowledge of itself enables us to control human energies as physical science has enabled us to control physical energies. It suffers from the fallacy into which those have fallen who have supposed that physical energies put at our disposal by science are sure to produce human progress and prosperity. A more adequate science of human nature might conceivably only multiply the agencies by which some human beings manipulate other human beings for their own advantage. Failure to take account of the moral phase of the problem, the question of values and ends, marks, although from the opposite pole, a relapse into the fallacy of the theorists of a century ago who assumed that "free"—that is to say, politically unrestrained— manifestation of human wants and impulses would tend to bring about social prosperity, progress, and harmony. It is a counterpart fallacy to the Marxist notion that there is an economic or "materialistic" dialectic of history by which a certain desirable (and in that sense moral) end will be brought about with no intervention of choice of values and effort to realize them. As I wrote some years ago, "the assimilation of human science to physical science represents only another form of abso- lutistic logic, a kind of physical absolutism."

Social events will continue, in any case, to be products of interaction of human nature with cultural conditions. Hence the primary and fundamental question will always be what sort of social results we supremely want. Improved science of human nature would put at our disposal means, now lacking, for defining the problem and working effectively for its solution. But save as it should reinforce respect for the morale of science, and thereby extend and deepen the incorporation of the attitudes which form the method of science into the disposition of individuals, it might add a complication similar to that introduced by improved physical science. Anything that obscures the fundamentally moral nature of the social problem is harmful, no matter whether it proceeds from the side of physical or of psychological theory. Any doctrine that eliminates or even obscures the function of choice of values and enlistment of desires and emotions in behalf of those chosen weakens personal responsibility for judgment and for action. It thus helps create the attitudes that welcome and support the totalitarian state.

I have stated in bare outline some of the outstanding phases of the problem of culture in the service of democratic freedom. Difficulties and obstacles have been emphasized. This emphasis is a result of the fact that a problem is presented. Emphasis upon the problem is due to belief that many weaknesses which events have disclosed are connected with failure to see the immensity of the task involved in setting mankind upon the democratic road. That with a background of millennia of non-democratic societies behind them, the earlier advocates of democracy tremendously simplified the issue is natural. For a time the simplification was an undoubted asset. Too long continued it became a liability.

Recognition of the scope and depth of the problem is neither depressing nor discouraging when the democratic movement is placed in historic perspective. The ideas by which it formulated itself have a long history behind them. We can trace their source in Hellenic humanism and in Christian beliefs; and we can also find recurrent efforts to realize this or that special aspect of these ideas in some special struggle against a particular form of oppression. By proper selection and arrangement, we can even make out a case for the idea that all past history has been a movement at first unconscious and then conscious, to attain freedom. A more sober view of history discloses that it took a very fortunate conjunction of events to bring about the rapid spread and seemingly complete victory of democracy during the nineteenth century. The conclusion to be drawn is not the depressing one that it is now in danger of destruction because of an unfavorable conjunction of events. The conclusion is that what was won in a more or less external and accidental manner must now be achieved and sustained by deliberate and intelligent endeavor.

The contrast thus suggested calls attention to the fact that underlying persistent attitudes of human beings were formed by traditions, customs, institutions, which existed when there was no democracy— when in fact democratic ideas and aspirations tended to be strangled at birth. Persistence of these basic dispositions accounts, on one side, for the sudden attack upon democracy; it is a reversion to old emotional and intellectual habits; or rather it is not so much a reversion as it is a manifestation of attitudes that have been there all the time but have been more or less covered up. Their persistence also explains the depth and range of the present problem. The struggle for democracy has to be maintained on as many fronts as culture has aspects: political, economic, international, educational, scientific and artistic, religious. The fact that we now have to accomplish of set purpose what in an earlier period was more or less a gift of grace renders the problem a moral one to be worked out on moral grounds.

Part of the fortunate conjunction of circumstances with respect to us who live here in the United States consists, as has been indicated, of the fact that our forefathers found themselves in a new land. The shock of physical dislocation effected a very considerable modification of old attitudes. Habits of thought and feeling which were the products of long centuries of acculturation were loosened. Less entrenched dispositions dropped off. The task of forming new institutions was thereby rendered immensely easier. The readjustment thus effected has been a chief factor in creating a general attitude of adaptability that has enabled us, save for the Civil War, to meet change with a minimum of external conflict and, in spite of an heritage of violence, with good nature. It is because of such consequences that the geographical New World may become a New World in a human sense. But, all the more on this account, the situation is such that most of the things about which we have been complacent and self-congratulatory now have to be won by thought and effort, instead of being results of evolution of a manifest destiny.

In the present state of affairs, a conflict of the moral Old and New Worlds is the essence of the struggle for democracy. It is not a question for us of isolationism, although the physical factors which make possible physical isolation from the warring ambitions of Europe are a factor to be cherished in an emergency. The conflict is not one waged with arms, although the question whether we again take up arms on European battlefields for ends that are foreign to the ends to which this country is dedicated will have weight in deciding whether we win or lose our own battle on our own ground. It is possible to stay out for reasons that have nothing to do with the maintenance of democracy, and a good deal to do with pecuniary profit, just as it is possible to be deluded into participation in the name of fighting for democracy.

The conflict as it concerns the democracy to which our history commits us is *within* our own institutions and attitudes. It can be won only by extending the application of democratic methods, methods of consultation, persuasion, negotiation, communication, co-operative intelligence, in the task of making our own politics, industry, education, our culture generally, a servant and an evolving manifestation of democratic ideas. Resort to military force is a first sure sign that we are giving up the struggle for the democratic way of life, and that the Old World has conquered morally as well as geographically—succeeding in imposing upon us its ideals and methods.

If there is one conclusion to which human experience unmistakably points it is that democratic ends demand democratic methods for their realization. Authoritarian methods now offer themselves to us in new guises. They come to us claiming to serve the ultimate ends of freedom and equity in a classless society. Or they recommend adoption of a totalitarian regime in order to fight totalitarianism. In whatever form they offer themselves, they owe their seductive power to their claim to serve ideal ends. Our first defense is to realize that democracy can be served only by the slow day by day adoption and contagious diffusion in every phase of our common life of methods that are identical with the ends to be reached and that resource to monistic, wholesale, absolutist procedures is a betrayal of human freedom no matter in what guise it presents itself. An American democracy can serve the world only as it demonstrates in the conduct of its own life the efficacy of plural, partial, and experimental methods in securing and maintaining an ever-increasing release of the powers of human nature, in service of a freedom which is co-operative and a co-operation which is voluntary.

We have no right to appeal to time to justify complacency about the ultimate result. We have every right to point to the long non-democratic and anti-democratic course of human history and to the recentness of democracy in order to enforce the immensity of the task confronting us. The very novelty of the experiment explains the impossibility of restricting the problem to any one element, aspect, or phase of our common everyday life. We have every right to appeal to the long and slow process of time to protect ourselves from the pessimism that comes from taking a short-span temporal view of events —under one condition. We must know that the dependence of ends upon means is such that the only *ultimate* result is the result that is attained today, tomorrow, the next day, and day after day, in the succession of years and generations. Only thus can we be sure that we face our problems in detail one by one as they arise, with all the resources provided by collective intelligence operating in co-operative action. At the end as at the beginning the democratic method is as fundamentally simple and as immensely difficult as is the energetic, unflagging, unceasing creation of an ever-present new road upon which we can walk together.

CARL SANDBURG Why he selected

... The PEOPLE, YES

I would suggest including in the anthology the last section of my book, *The People, Yes,* the part beginning, "The people will live on . . ." and ending ". . . Where to? What next?"

I like this piece because it is my favorite for reading to audiences; some spots don't work out in it—just like the people. It has a hope to it that if any man lacks these days he is going to have pretty rough going of it in the future.

New York, N. Y.
February, 1942

CARL SANDBURG

The people will live on.
The learning and blundering people will live on.
They will be tricked and sold and again sold
And go back to the nourishing earth for rootholds,
The people so peculiar in renewal and comeback,
You can't laugh off their capacity to take it.
The mammoth rests between his cyclonic dramas.

The people so often sleepy, weary, enigmatic,
is a vast huddle with many units saying:
"I earn my living.
I make enough to get by
and it takes all my time.
If I had more time
I could do more for myself
and maybe for others.
I could read and study
and talk things over
and find out about things.
It takes time.
I wish I had the time."

The people is a tragic and comic two-face:
hero and hoodlum: phantom and gorilla twisting to moan with a gargoyle mouth: "They
buy and sell me . . . it's a game . . .
sometime I'll break loose . . ."

   Once having marched
Over the margins of animal necessity,
Over the grim line of sheer subsistence
   Then man came
To the deeper rituals of his bones,
To the lights lighter than any bones,
To the time for thinking things over,
To the dance, the song, the story,
Or the hours given over to dreaming,
   Once having so marched.

Between the finite limitations of the five senses
and the endless yearnings of man for the beyond
the people hold to the humdrum bidding of work and food
while reaching out when it comes their way
for lights beyond the prison of the five senses,
for keepsakes lasting beyond any hunger or death.
   This reaching is alive.
The panderers and liars have violated and smutted it.
   Yet this reaching is alive yet
   for lights and keepsakes.

   The people know the salt of the sea
   and the strength of the winds
   lashing the corners of the earth.
   The people take the earth
   as a tomb of rest and a cradle of hope.
   Who else speaks for the Family of Man?
   They are in tune and step
   with constellations of universal law.

The people is a polychrome,
a spectrum and a prism
held in a moving monolith,
a console organ of changing themes,
a clavilux of color poems
wherein the sea offers fog
and the fog moves off in rain
and the labrador sunset shortens
to a nocturne of clear stars
serene over the shot spray
of northern lights.

The steel mill sky is alive.
The fire breaks white and zigzag
shot on a gun-metal gloaming.
Man is a long time coming.
Man will yet win.
Brother may yet line up with brother:

This old anvil laughs at many broken hammers.
    There are men who can't be bought.
    The fireborn are at home in fire.
    The stars make no noise.
    You can't hinder the wind from blowing.
    Time is a great teacher.
    Who can live without hope?

In the darkness with a great bundle of grief
    the people march.
In the night, and overhead a shovel of stars for
    keeps, the people march:
                        "Where to? what next?"

Biographies and Bibliographies

THE following biographies and bibliographies have been carefully compiled from the best available sources, and have been checked personally by each author. While every effort has been taken to make them complete in every detail, where authors have themselves requested that some of their earliest books be excluded from the bibliographies as juvenilia and others have requested the exclusion of pamphlets, textbooks, etc., these requests, since this is primarily an authors' book, have been complied with.

An asterisk before the title of a book indicates that the author has selected from that book material printed in *This Is My Best*. Where no asterisk appears, the material has never before appeared in book form. Unless otherwise specified the location of publishing houses mentioned in the bibliographies is New York City.

THE EDITOR

LOUIS ADAMIC, an immigrant American, was born in a village in Carniola, a Slovenian section of the Austro-Hungarian Empire, on March 23, 1899. He was a student in the *Gymnasium* at Ljubljana from 1910 to 1913, and received an honorary Litt.D. from Temple University in 1941. He came to the United States in 1913, and was naturalized in 1918, after serving in the United States army during the First World War.

Mr. Adamic has received numerous awards, including a Guggenheim Fellowship in 1932, a Rockefeller Foundation grant in 1937, and Carnegie grants in 1939, 1940, and 1941, and a $1000 John Anisfield award for his book *From Many Lands* in 1940.

His books have concerned his life as an immigrant (*Laughing in the Jungle*), his observations during a trip to his native land in *The Native's Return*; he has written two novels, a travel-history volume (*The House in Antigua*), and a great deal of book material on the social scene in America. Mr. Adamic is at present advisory editor of *Common Ground*, a quarterly magazine he founded, which is published by the Common Council for American Unity, part of whose program it is "to help create among the American people the unity and mutual understanding resulting from a common citizenship . . . to further an appreciation of what each group has con-

tributed to America . . . to overcome intolerance and discrimination because of foreign birth, descent, race, or nationality . . . to help the foreign-born and their children solve their special problems of adjustment."

Mr. Adamic was married to Stella Sanders in 1931, and lives on his farm in the Delaware Valley, in New Jersey.

Robinson Jeffers: A Portrait, University of Washington Press, Seattle, 1929

Dynamite: The Story of Class Violence in America, Viking Press, 1931

Laughing in the Jungle: The Autobiography of an Immigrant in America, Harpers, 1932

The Native's Return (autobiography), Harpers, 1934

Grandsons: A Story of American Lives (novel), Harpers, 1935

Lucas, King of the Balucas (short story), A. Whipple, Los Angeles, 1935

The Cradle of Life: The Story of One Man's Beginnings (novel), Harpers, 1936

The House in Antigua: A Restoration (travel, people, and places in Guatemala), Harpers, 1937

*My America, 1928-1938 (autobiography and social survey), Harpers, 1938

From Many Lands (stories of immigrant lives), Harpers, 1940

Two-Way Passage (analysis of the United States), Harpers, 1941

JAMES TRUSLOW ADAMS, historian and publicist, is a native of Brooklyn, New York, and was born on October 18, 1878. He married Kathryn M. Seely on January 18, 1927. A man of action as well as reflection, he has engaged in a varied range of important work. He received his A.B. from Brooklyn Polytechnic Institute in 1898 and his A.M. from Yale in 1900.

Mr. Adams was a partner in a New York Stock Exchange firm until 1912, secretary of the Jamestown & Chautauqua Railway, treasurer and director of the Rock Plaster Co., and vice-president and director of The First National Bank of Summit, N. J. He retired from business and worked with the Colonel House Commission to prepare data for the Peace Conference for five months early in the First World War. He resigned for more active service in the army, became a captain, and did special work preparing handbooks for officers in the field in the Russian and Siberian expeditions as a member of the Intelligence Division of the General Staff. He served at the Peace Conference in Paris, having charge of confidential maps for new boundaries and acting as liaison officer between the American and British Peace Delegations and the French *Service Géographique.*

On his discharge from the army he began serious writing, and with *The Founding of New England* he won the 1922 Pulitzer Prize for the best book on the history of the United States for the previous year. He was editor-in-chief of the *Dictionary of American History* (6 vol.) in 1940, and has contributed to the *Encyclopaedia Britannica,* the *Dictionary of American Biography,* and for ten years was a member of the advisory council of the *Yale Review.* He is an elector of the Hall of Fame and was a member of the Pulitzer jury from 1924 to 1932. He continues business interests and is a trustee of the Bridgeport-People's Savings Bank of Bridgeport, Conn., the second largest bank in that State. He is also Chancellor and Treasurer of the American Academy of Arts and Letters, a Fellow of the Royal Society of Literature in London, and an honorary Fellow or member of many learned societies.

Memorials of Old Bridgehampton, privately printed, Bridgehampton, N. Y., 1916
History of the Town of Southampton, privately printed, Bridgehampton, N. Y., 1918

The Founding of New England, Atlantic Monthly Press, Boston, 1921
Revolutionary New England, Atlantic Monthly Press, Boston, 1923
New England in the Republic, Little, Brown, Boston, 1926
Provincial Society (1690-1763), Macmillan, 1927
Hamiltonian Principles, Little, Brown, Boston, 1928
Jeffersonian Principles, Little, Brown, Boston, 1928
Our Business Civilization, Boni, 1929
The Adams Family, Little, Brown, Boston, 1930
The Tempo of Modern Life, Boni, 1931
**The Epic of America,* Little, Brown, Boston, 1931
The March of Democracy, two volumes, Scribners, 1932-33
Henry Adams, Boni, 1933
America's Tragedy, Scribners, 1933
The Record of America (with C. G. VANNEST), Scribners, 1935
The Living Jefferson, Scribners, 1936
Building the British Empire, Scribners, 1938
Empire on the Seven Seas, Scribners, 1940

GEORGE ADE was born in Kentland, Indiana, on February 9, 1866. He has acutely examined the language and foibles of the average American, beginning with his notable *Fables in Slang* in 1889. As satirist and humorist he followed with several other books about "people you know" and became known as a playwright, beginning with *The Sultan of Sulu* in 1903 and continuing with many plays until 1914.

He received his B.S. from Purdue in 1887, L.H.D. in 1926, and LL.D. from the University of Indiana in 1927. He is unmarried. He was in newspaper work in Indiana and Chicago until 1900, served as a delegate to the Republican National Convention in 1908, and as trustee of Purdue University from 1908 to 1915. In 1924 he promoted the Ross-Ade Stadium at Purdue. He is a member of the National Institute of Arts and Letters, and lives in Brook, Indiana.

Artie (sketches), Stone, Chicago, 1896
Pink Marsh (sketches), Stone, Chicago, 1897
Doc Horne (sketches), Stone, Chicago, 1899
Fables in Slang (short stories), Stone, Chicago, 1900
More Fables, Stone, Chicago, 1900
Forty Modern Fables, Russell, 1901
The Girl Proposition (fables), Russell, 1902
People You Know (sketches), Harpers, 1903

Handsome Cyril, Baudarlog Press, Phoenix, Ariz., 1903

Clarence Allen, Baudarlog Press, Phoenix, Ariz., 1903

Rollo Johnson, Baudarlog Press, Phoenix, Ariz., 1903

In Babel, McClure, 1903

The Sultan of Sulu (play), Harpers, 1903

Breaking into Society (fables), Harpers, 1904

True Bills (fables), Harpers, 1904

In Pastures New (travel stories), McClure, Phillips, 1906

The Slim Princess (novel), Bobbs-Merrill, Indianapolis, 1907

Knocking the Neighbors (fables), Doubleday, Page, Garden City, N. Y., 1912

Ade's Fables, Doubleday, Page, Garden City, N. Y., 1914

Hand-Made Fables, Doubleday, Page, Garden City, N. Y., 1920

Stay with Me Flagons, Lotus Club, 1922

*Single Blessedness (collected articles), Doubleday, Page, Garden City, N. Y., 1922

Marse Covington (play), French, 1923

Nettie (play), French, 1923

Speaking to Father (play), French, 1923

The Mayor and the Manicure (play), French, 1923

Just Out of College (play), French, 1924

Father and the Boys (play), French, 1924

The College Widow (play), French, 1924

The County Chairman (play), French, 1924

Bang! Bang! (stories), Sears, 1928

The Old-Time Saloon (sketches), Long & Smith, 1931

Thirty Fables in Slang, Arrow Editions, 1933

One Afternoon with Mark Twain (article), Argus Books, 1939

CONRAD AIKEN, poet and novelist, was born in Savannah, Georgia, on August 5, 1889, and was graduated from Harvard in 1911. In 1912 he married Jessie McDonald, and by her is the father of three children. He has lived in Boston, Rome, in Sussex on the English Channel, and on Cape Cod.

Mr. Aiken has written three volumes of short stories, and four novels, in which the interest is mainly psychological, if not psychoanalytical; a book of criticism, *Scepticisms*; and in his introduction to a selection of Emily Dickinson's poems in 1924 he reawakened attention to her poetry. He was from 1917 to 1919 contributing editor to *The Dial*, and from 1933 to 1936 the London correspondent of *The New Yorker* over the pseudonym of Samuel Jeake, Jr.

In 1930 Mr. Aiken was awarded the Pulitzer Prize for his *Selected Poems.* He now lives with his third wife, Mary Hoover Aiken, in Brewster, Massachusetts.

Earth Triumphant, and Other Tales, Macmillan, 1914

Turns and Movies (poetry), Houghton Mifflin, Boston, 1916

The Jig of Forslin (poetry), Four Seas, Boston, 1916

Nocturne of Remembered Spring (poetry), Four Seas, Boston, 1917

The Charnel Rose (poetry), Four Seas, Boston, 1918

Scepticism—Notes on Contemporary Poetry, Knopf, 1919

The House of Dust (poetry), Four Seas, Boston, 1920

Punch, the Immortal Liar (poetry), Knopf, 1921

Priapus and the Pool (poetry), Dunster House, Cambridge, Mass., 1922

Modern American Poets (anthology), Secker, London, 1922

The Pilgrimage of Festus (poetry), Knopf, 1923

Priapus and the Pool, and Other Poems, Liveright, 1925

*Bring! Bring!, and Other Stories, Liveright, 1925

Blue Voyage (novel), Scribners, 1927

Costumes by Eros (short stories), Scribners, 1928

Prelude (poetry), Equinox Cooperative Press, 1929

Selected Poems, Scribners, 1929

American Poetry, 1671-1928 (anthology), Modern Library, 1929

John Deth, and Other Poems, Scribners, 1930

Gehenna (short story), Random House, 1930

The Coming Forth by Day of Osiris Jones (poetry), Scribners, 1931

Preludes for Memnon (poetry), Scribners, 1931

Great Circle (novel), Scribners, 1933

And in the Hanging Gardens (poetry), privately printed, 1933

Among the Lost People (short stories), Scribners, 1934

Landscape West of Eden (poetry), Scribners, 1935

King Coffin (novel), Scribners, 1935

Time in the Rock (poetry), Scribners, 1936

A Heart for the Gods of Mexico (novel), Secker, London, 1939

The Conversation (novel), Duell, Sloan & Pearce, 1940

And in the Human Heart (poetry), Duell, Sloan & Pearce, 1940

MAXWELL ANDERSON, playwright and poet, was born in Atlantic, Pennsylvania, on December 15, 1888, the son of a minister. He spent his boyhood in Pennsylvania, Ohio, and Iowa, and went in 1907 to North Dakota, from whose state university he was graduated in 1911. He married Margaret Haskett in 1911, received his M.A. from Stanford in 1914, taught school for several years in California and North Dakota, and finally entered on a career of journalism, at first in San Francisco and after 1918 in New York, where he worked as an editorial writer for the *New Republic*, *Evening Globe*, and *Morning World* until 1924.

Mr. Anderson wrote his first play, *White Desert*, in 1923, and followed it the next year with the immensely successful *What Price Glory?*, written in collaboration with Laurence Stallings. In 1933 he was awarded the Pulitzer Prize for his *Both Your Houses*, a satire of political corruption in Congress, and both *Winterset* and *High Tor* won the Critics' Prize.

He was married for the second time in 1933 to Gertrude Maynard, and is the father of four children. He lives now at New City, Rockland County, New York.

You Who Have Dreams, Simon & Schuster, 1925
Three American Plays, Harcourt, Brace, 1926
Saturday's Children, Longmans, Green, 1927
Gods of the Lightning, and *Outside Looking In* (former with HAROLD HICKERSON), Longmans, Green, 1928
Elizabeth the Queen (verse play), Longmans, Green, 1930
Night over Taos (verse play), French, 1932
Both Your Houses, French, 1933
Mary of Scotland (verse play), Doubleday, Doran, 1934
Valley Forge (verse play), Dodd, Mead, 1934
*Winterset (verse play), Anderson House, Washington, 1936
The Masque of Kings (verse play), Anderson House, Washington, 1936
The Wingless Victory (verse play), Anderson House, Washington, 1936
High Tor (verse play), Anderson House, Washington, 1937
The Star-Wagon, Anderson House, Washington, 1937
Knickerbocker Holiday (musical comedy, music by KURT WEILL), Anderson House, Washington, 1938
The Feast of Ortolans (radio play), Dramatists Play Service, 1938
The Essence of Tragedy (essays), Anderson House, Washington, 1939

Key Largo (verse play), Anderson House, Washington, 1940
Eleven Verse Plays, Harcourt, Brace, 1940
Second Overture, Dramatists Play Service, 1940
Journey to Jerusalem, Anderson House, Washington, 1940
Candle in the Wind, Anderson House, Washington, 1941
The Eve of St. Mark, Anderson House, Washington, 1942

Unless there is indication to the contrary, all of Mr. Andersons's works are prose drama.

LUDWIG BEMELMANS, painter and writer, was born in Meran, Tirol, on April 27, 1898. He was educated at the *Koenigliche Realschule* at Regensburg and Rothenburg, in Germany, and married Madeline Freund in 1935. He has one daughter, Barbara.

Mr. Bemelmans came to the United States in 1914 and was naturalized in 1918, after serving with the army, the record of which experience he set down in *My War with the United States* (1937). His first fiction (with drawings of his own) appeared in the magazine *Story*, and subsequently he has had a widespread audience for his articles, short stories, biographical bits, and art work in *The New Yorker*, *Vogue*, *Town and Country*, *Stage*, etc.

Hansi (juvenile), Viking Press, 1934
The Golden Basket (juvenile), Viking Press, 1936
Castle Number Nine (juvenile), Viking Press, 1937
My War with the United States (autobiography), Viking Press, 1937
Quito Express (travel), Viking Press, 1938
Life Class (autobiography), Viking Press, 1938
Madeline (juvenile), Simon & Schuster, 1939
*Small Beer (short stories), Viking Press, 1939
Fifi (juvenile), Simon & Schuster, 1940
The Donkey Inside (travel), Viking Press, 1941
Hotel Splendide (fiction), Viking Press, 1941
I Love You, I Love You, I Love You (fiction), Viking Press, 1942
Rosebud (juvenile), Random House, 1942

ROBERT BENCHLEY was born in Worcester, Massachusetts, on September 15, 1889. After his graduation from Harvard in 1912 he married Gertrude Darling, and is now the father of two sons. Before beginning his career as humorist and dramatic critic he was with the advertising department of the Curtis Publishing Co., and later did industrial personnel work in Boston. In 1914 he became associate editor of the New York *Tribune* Sunday magazine section, and in 1917 was editor of the New York *Tribune Graphic.*

Mr. Benchley was managing editor of *Vanity Fair* for two years, dramatic editor of the old *Life Magazine* from 1920 to 1929, and of *The New Yorker* from 1929 to 1940. Recently he has been appearing in and writing dialogue for motion pictures in Hollywood.

Of All Things!, Holt, 1921
Love Conquers All, Holt, 1922
Pluck and Luck, Holt, 1925
The Early Worm, Holt, 1927
20,000 Leagues Under the Sea, or David Copperfield, Holt, 1928
The Bridges of Binding, Harrison & Smith, Minneapolis, 1928
*The Treasurer's Report, Harpers, 1930
No Poems, Harpers, 1932
From Bed to Worse, Harpers, 1934
Why Does Nobody Collect Me?, Prairie Press, Muscatine, Iowa, 1935
My Ten Years in a Quandary, Harpers, 1936
After 1903—What?, Harpers, 1938
Inside Benchley, Harpers, 1942

All of Mr. Benchley's works are humorous sketches.

STEPHEN VINCENT BENÉT, who is the brother of William Rose Benét, was born in Bethlehem, Pennsylvania, on July 22, 1898. His family name is Minorcan, and the family came to Florida from the island of Minorca in 1778. Before he had graduated from Yale in 1919 he had two volumes of verse to his credit, and shortly after he received his M.A. from Yale in 1920 he published his first novel, a college story. But his cardinal interest lay in poetry, and throughout the 20's one can trace in his published verse his growing interest in the American scene.

Mr. Benét reached his full power in *John Brown's Body,* a long narrative poem of the Civil War for which he was awarded the 1929 Pulitzer Prize and a Guggenheim Fellowship, on which he spent two years in France with his wife, Rosemary Carr Benét. He was married in 1921, and has three children. Since then he has lived principally in France, New York City, Rhode Island, and Connecticut.

The Selected Work of Stephen Vincent Benét in prose and poetry, is a recent Book-of-the-Month. Mr. Benét has recently been writing radio plays for the Office of Facts and Figures and for the Council For Democracy.

Five Men and Pompey (poetry), Four Seas, Boston, 1915
The Drug-Shop (poetry), privately printed, New Haven, Conn., 1917
Young Adventure (poetry), Yale University Press, New Haven, Conn., 1918
Heavens and Earth (poetry), Holt, 1920
The Beginning of Wisdom (novel), Holt, 1921
Young People's Pride (novel), Holt, 1922
Ballad of William Sycamore (poetry), Brickrow Bookshop, 1923
Jean Huguenot (novel), Holt, 1923
King David (poetry), Holt, 1923
Tiger Joy (poetry), Doran, 1925
Spanish Bayonet (novel), Doran, 1926
John Brown's Body (narrative poem), Doubleday, Doran, Garden City, N. Y., 1928
The Barefoot Saint (story), Doubleday, Doran, Garden City, N. Y., 1929
The Litter of the Rose Leaves (story), Random House, 1930
Ballads and Poems, Doubleday, Doran, Garden City, N. Y., 1931
A Book of Americans (poetry; with ROSEMARY CARR BENÉT), Farrar & Rinehart, 1933
James Shore's Daughter (novel), Doubleday, Doran, Garden City, N. Y., 1934
Burning City (poetry), Farrar & Rinehart, 1936
The Magic of Poetry and the Poet's Art (essay), Compton's Encyclopedia, Chicago, 1936
*The Devil and Daniel Webster (story), Countryman Press, Weston, Vt., 1937
The Headless Horseman (libretto), Schirmer, Boston, 1937
Thirteen O'clock (short stories), Farrar & Rinehart, 1937
Johnny Pie and the Fool-Killer (story), Countryman Press, Weston, Vt., 1938
My Favorite Fiction Character (pamphlet), privately printed, Ysletta, 1938
The Devil and Daniel Webster (libretto from the story), Farrar & Rinehart, 1939
Ballad of the Duke's Mercy (poem), House of Books, 1939
Nightmare at Noon (poetry), Farrar & Rinehart, 1940
Zero Hour (symposium; with others), Farrar & Rinehart, 1940
We Stand United (pamphlet), Council for Democracy, 1940
Tuesday, November 5th, 1940 (poem), House of Books, 1941
Listen to the People (poem), Council for Democracy, 1941

A Summons to the Free (essays), Farrar &
Rinehart, 1941
Selected Works of Stephen Vincent Benét, two
volumes, Farrar & Rinehart, 1942
They Burned the Books (radio play), Farrar
& Rinehart, 1942
Dear Adolph (radio plays), Farrar & Rine-
hart, 1942

WILLIAM ROSE BENÉT was born February 2,
1886, at Fort Hamilton in New York Harbor
of a family which had been military for generations. He was graduated from the Sheffield
Scientific School at Yale in 1907. After a period
spent in California with his family, he got a
job on *The Century Magazine*. He was a
reader from 1911 to 1914, and from 1914 to
1917 assistant editor. During this time he
married Teresa Frances Thompson, sister of
the novelist, Kathleen Norris, and became the
father of three children.

During the first World War, Mr. Benét
was commissioned a second lieutenant in the
Air Service (non-flying). An advertising job
and a position as assistant editor of *The
Nation's Business* followed; and in 1920 he
helped found *The Literary Review* of the
New York *Evening Post*, of which he was
associate editor until 1923. At that time Henry
Seidel Canby reorganized the Review as *The
Saturday Review of Literature* and established
it independently. All the old staff transferred
to the new venture, of which Mr. Benét
remained an associate editor. Of recent years
his status has changed to that of contributing
editor. In 1929-30 he was also editor of the
publishing firm of Brewer and Warren.

William Rose Benét is best known for
his poetry. *The Dust Which Is God* received the Pulitzer Prize for poetry in 1942.
His other works include a novel, essays, children's books, and he has compiled and edited
several distinguished anthologies. Being the
literary executor of his second wife, Elinor
Wylie, he collected and wrote the foreword to
her *Collected Poems*, and, in her *Collected
Prose*, wrote the preface to the "Fugitive
Prose" section. Mr. Benét's third wife was
Lora Baxter, the actress, now wife of Bretaigne
Windust, theatrical director. His fourth wife
is Marjorie Flack, writer and illustrator of
children's books. They live in New York City.

Merchants from Cathay, Century, 1913
The Falconer of God, and Other Poems, Century, 1914
The East I Know (translation from the French;
with TERESA FRANCES BENÉT), Yale University Press, New Haven, Conn., 1914

The Great White Wall, Yale University Press,
New Haven, Conn., 1916
The Burglar of the Zodiac, and Other Poems,
Yale University Press, New Haven, Conn.,
1918
Perpetual Light: A Memorial, Yale Univer-
sity Press, New Haven, Conn., 1919
Moons of Grandeur, Doran, 1920
Saturday Papers (essay on literature; with
HENRY SEIDEL CANBY and AMY LOVE-
MAN), Macmillan, 1921
The First Person Singular (novel), Doran,
1922
Poems for Youth (anthology), Dutton &
Company, 1925
The Flying King of Kurio (juvenile), Doran,
1926
Wild Goslings (essays), Doran, 1927
Man Possessed (selected poetry), Doran, 1927
Sagacity, Random House, 1929
Twentieth-Century Poetry (anthology; with
HENRY SEIDEL CANBY and JOHN DRINK-
WATER), Houghton Mifflin, Boston, 1929
Adventures in English Literature (anthology
text book; with others), Harcourt, Brace,
1931
*Collected Poems and Collected Prose of Elinor
Wylie* (editor), Knopf, 1932
Rip Tide (novel in verse), Duffield & Green,
1932
Starry Harness, Duffield & Green, 1933
Fifty Poets (anthology), Duffield & Green,
1933
Reviewing Ten Years ("a personal record of
The Saturday Review of Literature"),
Saturday Review Publishers, 1933
The Prose and Poetry of Elinor Wylie (essay),
Wheaton College Press, Norton, Mass.,
1934
The Pocket University (guide to daily read-
ing; editor), Doubleday, Doran, Garden
City, N. Y., 1934
Emblems and Electra (drawings by W. A.
DWIGGINS), Mergenthaler Linotype Co.,
Brooklyn, N. Y., 1935
Golden Fleece, Dodd, Mead, 1935
Harlem, and Other Poems, Methuen, London,
1935
From Robert & Elizabeth Browning (corre-
spondence), Murray, London, 1936
Mother Goose (a new collection; illustrations
by ROGER DuVOISIN), Heritage Press,
1936
The Oxford Anthology of American Literature
(anthology; with NORMAN HOLMES PEAR-
SON), Oxford University Press, 1938
Poems for Modern Youth (anthology; with
ADOLPH GILLIS), Houghton Mifflin, Bos-
ton, 1938
With Wings as Eagles, Dodd, Mead, 1940

Adolphus or The Adopted Dolphin and the Pirate's Daughter (juvenile verses; pictures by MARJORIE FLACK), Houghton Mifflin, Boston, 1941

The Dust Which Is God (semi-autobiographical novel in verse), Dodd, Mead, 1941

Unless otherwise indicated, Mr. Benét's works are poetry.

KAY BOYLE, short-story writer and novelist, has lived a great deal of her life in France. She was born in St. Paul, Minnesota, on February 19, 1903, and spent her youth in Philadelphia, Atlantic City, Cincinnati, and Europe. In 1923 she was married to Richard Brault, from whom she was later divorced, and in 1931 she married Laurence Vail. She is the mother of four children.

Miss Boyle's first book of short stories, entitled *Short Stories*, appeared in Paris in 1928. Since then she has published three collections of short stories, six novels, an allegorical tale, *The Youngest Camel* (1939), and a volume of poetry, *A Glad Day* (1938).

She was awarded a Guggenheim Fellowship in 1934 and the O. Henry Memorial Prize in 1936 and 1941. She lives now in Mount Vernon, New York.

Short Stories, Black Sun Press, Paris, 1928
Wedding Day (short stories), Smith & Haas, 1930
Plagued by the Nightingale (novel), Smith & Haas, 1931
Year Before Last (novel), Smith & Haas, 1932
The First Lover (short stories), Cape & Smith, 1933
Gentlemen, I Address You Privately (novel), Smith & Haas, 1933
My Next Bride (novel), Harcourt, Brace, 1934
The White Horses of Vienna (short stories), Harcourt, Brace, 1936
Death of a Man (novel), Harcourt, Brace, 1936
Monday Night (novel), Harcourt, Brace, 1938
A Glad Day (poetry), New Directions, Norfolk, Conn., 1938
The Youngest Camel (allegorical tale), Little, Brown, Boston, 1939
The Crazy Hunter (three short novels), Harcourt, Brace, 1940

LOUIS BROMFIELD represents the curious anomaly of a novelist who achieved his perspective on American life by residence abroad. He was born in Mansfield, Ohio, on December 27, 1896, but his tendency has been steadily eastward: he received his education at Cornell

and Columbia Universities, and in 1917 went to France as an ambulance driver for the French army, for which he was awarded the Croix de Guerre.

Returning to New York City he did newspaper work for several years, and in 1924, after having written four unpublished novels, he wrote *The Green Bay Tree*, which met with immediate success. *Early Autumn*, with its setting in New England (and the work of his of which he has said he is least fond) was the Pulitzer Prize novel for 1927. He has also been made a member of the Legion of Honor by the French government for his literary work.

From 1923 to 1939 Mr. Bromfield lived near Paris with his wife, Mary Wood Bromfield, whom he married in 1921. He now lives on his farm in Lucas, Ohio, which is run co-operatively.

The Green Bay Tree, Stokes, 1924
Possession, Stokes, 1925
Early Autumn, Stokes, 1926
A Good Woman, Stokes, 1927
The Scarlet Woman (short story), McClure's Magazine, 1927
The Strange Case of Miss Annie Spragg, Stokes, 1928
Awake and Rebearse, Stokes, 1929
Twenty-Four Hours, Stokes, 1930
Tabloid News, Random House, 1931
A Modern Hero, Stokes, 1932
The Farm, Harpers, 1933
Here Today and Gone Tomorrow, Harpers, 1934
The Man Who Had Everything, Harpers, 1935
The Rains Came, Harpers, 1937
It Takes All Kinds, Harpers, 1939
England, A Dying Oligarchy (pamphlet), Harpers, 1939
Night in Bombay, Harpers, 1940
Wild Is the River, Harpers, 1941
Until the Day Break, Harpers, 1942

Unless otherwise designated, all of Mr. Bromfield's works are novels.

VAN WYCK BROOKS, one of America's most respected critics, was born in Plainfield, New Jersey, on February 16, 1886. After his graduation from Harvard in 1908 he joined the editorial staff of Doubleday, Page & Co. In 1911 he married Eleanor Kenyon Stimson.

Mr. Brooks, in his career, has kept in close touch with the literary life of America. His first book, *The Wine of the Puritans* (1909), was recognized as a brilliant study, and it was followed by the author's appointment as an instructor at Leland Stanford University (1911-1913). After this he taught for a year in England. From 1915 to 1918 he was connected with the Century Co., and in 1920 he became associate editor of *The Freeman*.

The 1923 *Dial* prize of $2000 was awarded to Mr. Brooks in recognition of his having created a new point of view in criticism in this country. In 1927 he helped Alfred Kreymborg, Lewis Mumford, and Paul Rosenfeld, to found *The American Caravan*. Poor health obliged him to resign, however, after the first edition of this annual. He edited Randolph Bourne's *The History of a Literary Radical* (1920) and has done several translations.

In 1937 he was awarded the Pulitzer Prize for his *The Flowering of New England*, the first of a projected series of volumes sketching the literary history of the United States.

He now lives in Westport, Connecticut.

The Wine of the Puritans, Kennerley, 1909
The Malady of the Ideal, Fifield, London, 1913
John Addington Symonds, Kennerley, 1914
The World of H. G. Wells, Kennerley, 1915
America's Coming of Age, Huebsch, 1915
Letters and Leadership, Huebsch, 1918
The Ordeal of Mark Twain, Dutton, 1920
The Pilgrimage of Henry James, Dutton, 1925
Emerson and Others, Dutton, 1927
The Life of Emerson, Dutton, 1932
Sketches in Criticism, Dutton, 1932
Three Essays on America, Dutton, 1934
The Flowering of New England (1815-1865), Dutton, 1936
*New England: Indian Summer (1865-1915), Dutton, 1940
On Literature Today, Dutton, 1941
Opinions of Oliver Allston, Dutton, 1941

PEARL BUCK, winner of both the Nobel and the Pulitzer Prizes, has spent a great deal of her life in the China of which she writes so eloquently. She was born in Hillsboro, West Virginia, on June 26, 1892, but when she was a few months old she was taken to China, where her parents were missionaries. She remained there until she returned to America to enter Randolph-Macon College, and after being graduated in 1914, she returned to China. She came to America again in 1925, for one year, to study at Cornell for her master's degree. For a number of years she taught English at Southeastern University and Chung Yang University, both of Nanking.

Her first book was published in 1930, and *The Good Earth*, which was awarded the Pulitzer Prize, appeared in 1931. In 1938 she received the Nobel Prize in literature, for the body of her work.

She came to the United States in 1934, and makes her home in the countryside of Pennsylvania.

East Wind: West Wind (novel), Day, 1930
The Good Earth (novel), Day, 1931
The Young Revolutionist (short novel), Day, 1932
Sons (novel), Day, 1932
East and West and the Novel (lectures), College of Chinese Studies, Peiping, China, 1932
Is There a Case for Foreign Missions? (pamphlet), Day, 1932
The First Wife, and Other Stories, Day, 1933
All Men Are Brothers (translation from the Chinese), Day, 1933
The Mother (novel), Day, 1934
A House Divided (novel), Day, 1935
The Exile (biography), Day, 1936
Fighting Angel (biography), Day, 1936
This Proud Heart (novel), Day, 1938
The Patriot (novel), Day, 1939
The Chinese Novel (lecture), Day, 1939
Other Gods (novel), Day, 1940
Stories for Little Children, Day, 1940
*Today and Forever (short stories), Day, 1941
Of Men and Women (essays), Day, 1941
Dragon Seed (novel), Day, 1942
American Unity and Asia (essays and lectures), Day, 1942

JAMES BRANCH CABELL was born in Richmond, Virginia, on April 14, 1879, of a family which has lived in Virginia since colonial days. He was graduated from William and Mary in 1898, where as an undergraduate he taught French and Greek for two years. His first position was on the *Richmond Times*. The following year he went to New York and reported on the *New York Herald* from 1899 to 1901, when he returned to Richmond and worked on the *News*. He spent the period from 1902 to 1910 in writing, and his first magazine stories and books appeared in these years.

Mr. Cabell worked in the coal mines of West Virginia from 1911 to 1913, and upon his return to Virginia interested himself in genealogical and historical research and in his writing. He was editor of *The Reviewer* in 1921 and of the *American Spectator* from 1932 to 1935.

In 1913 he was married to Priscilla Bradley; they have one son, and live in Richmond.

Most of Mr. Cabell's books belong to a series which is referred to collectively as the *Biography of Manuel*. It is the history of an imaginary but perfectly constructed medieval country, Poictesme, which Mr. Cabell sees so minutely in his mind that he has drawn maps of it. In 1930, with the publication of *Townsend of Lichfield*, the Dom Manuel biography was complete, and since then Mr. Cabell has signed his books simply as Branch Cabell.

The Eagle's Shadow, Doubleday, Page, 1904
The Line of Love (short stories), Harpers, 1905
Gallantry (short stories), Harpers, 1907
Branchiana, a Record of the Branch Family in Virginia (genealogy), privately printed, 1907
Chivalry (short stories), Harpers, 1909
The Cords of Vanity, Doubleday, Page, 1909
Branch of Abingdon, a Record of the Branch Family in England (genealogy), privately printed, 1911
The Soul of Melicent, Stokes, 1913
The Rivet in Grandfather's Neck, McBride, 1915
The Majors and Their Marriages (genealogy), privately printed, 1915
The Certain Hour (short stories), McBride, 1916
From the Hidden Way (poetry), McBride, 1916
The Cream of the Jest, McBride, 1917
Beyond Life (criticism), McBride, 1919
Jurgen, McBride, 1919
The Judging of Jurgen (criticism), Bookfellows, Chicago, 1920
Domnei (reissue of *The Soul of Melicent*), McBride, 1920
Figures of Earth, McBride, 1921
The Jewel Merchants (one-act play), McBride, 1921
Joseph Hergesheimer (criticism), Bookfellows, Chicago, 1921
Taboo (criticism), McBride, 1921
The Lineage of Lichfield (criticism), McBride, 1922
The High Place, McBride, 1923
Straws and Prayer-Books (criticism), McBride, 1924
The Silver Stallion, McBride, 1926
The Music from Behind the Moon, Day, 1926
Something About Eve, McBride, 1927
Ballads from the Hidden Way (reprinted poetry, with introduction), Random House, 1928
The White Robe, McBride, 1928

The Way of Ecben, McBride, 1929
Sonnets from Antan (poetry), Fountain Press, 1929
Townsend of Lichfield (miscellanies), McBride, 1930
The Works of James Branch Cabell, eighteen volumes, McBride, 1927-1930
Between Dawn and Sunrise (selections), McBride, 1930
Some of Us (criticism), McBride, 1930
Autographed Cabell (autographed editions of previous works), nine volumes, McBride, 1932
These Restless Heads (autobiography), McBride, 1932
Special Delivery (series of letters), McBride, 1933
Smirt, McBride, 1934
Ladies and Gentlemen (series of letters), McBride, 1934
Smith, McBride, 1935
Preface to the Past (collected prefaces to *The Works*), McBride, 1936
Smire, Doubleday, Doran, Garden City, N. Y., 1937
The Nightmare Has Triplets (criticism), Doubleday, Doran, Garden City, N. Y., 1937
Of Ellen Glasgow, an Inscribed Portrait (with ELLEN GLASGOW), privately printed, 1938
The King Was in His Counting House, Farrar & Rinehart, 1938
Hamlet Had an Uncle, Farrar & Rinehart, 1940
The First Gentleman of America, Farrar & Rinehart, 1942

All of Mr. Cabell's works, unless otherwise specified, are novels.

ERSKINE CALDWELL was born in White Oak, Georgia, on December 17, 1902. He was educated in Erskine College, the University of Virginia, and the University of Pennsylvania. He has been twice married and has three children by his first wife, Helen Lannigan. His second wife, Margaret Bourke-White, whom he married in 1939, is his picture collaborator on several books about the American scene and one on Europe. He has worked as a cotton picker, stagehand, professional football player, newspaper reporter, book reviewer, lecturer, editor, and screen writer and was war correspondent for *PM* and Columbia Broadcasting System in Russia in 1941. Novels and volumes of short stories have been published abroad in following translations: French, German, Italian, Czech, Norwegian, Swedish, Danish, Russian, Georgian, Ukrainian, Japanese, Chinese, Spanish, and Portuguese. He lives now in the country near Darien, Connecticut.

"Country Full of Swedes" received the *Yale Review* $1000 Award for fiction in 1933. Many of his books concern poor whites of the South, and his novel *Tobacco Road*, dramatized by Jack Kirkland, brought to Broadway the plight of these people in a play which had a longer run on Broadway than any other play in history. His short stories, a form in which he is ranked among the leading practitioners in America, have been collected in the volume *Jackpot*.

The Bastard (novelette), Heron Press, 1929
Poor Fool (novelette), Rariora Press, 1930
American Earth (short stories), Scribners, 1931
Mama's Little Girl, privately printed, Mount Vernon, Me., 1932
Tobacco Road (novel), Scribners, 1932
God's Little Acre (novel), Viking Press, 1933
We Are the Living (short stories), Viking Press, 1933
A Message for Genevieve, privately printed, Mount Vernon, Me., 1933
Journeyman (novel), Viking Press, 1935
Kneel to the Rising Sun (short stories), Viking Press, 1935
Tenant Farmer (pamphlet), Phalanx Press, 1935
Some American People (vignettes), McBride, 1935
The Sacrilege of Alan Kent (novelette), Falmouth Book House, Portland, Me., 1936
You Have Seen Their Faces (documentary; with MARGARET BOURKE-WHITE), Viking Press, 1937
Southways (short stories), Duell, Sloan & Pearce, 1938
North of the Danube (documentary; with MARGARET BOURKE-WHITE), Duell, Sloan & Pearce, 1939
Trouble in July (novel), Duell, Sloan & Pearce, 1940
Jackpot (complete short stories), Duell, Sloan & Pearce, 1940
Say! Is This the U.S.A.? (documentary; with MARGARET BOURKE-WHITE), Duell, Sloan & Pearce, 1941
All-Out on the Road to Smolensk (autobiography), Duell, Sloan & Pearce, 1942

MORLEY CALLAGHAN is of Irish descent. He was born in Toronto, Canada, in 1903, and was graduated from St. Michael's College of the University of Toronto. After graduation he was a reporter on the Toronto *Daily Star*, and later the proprietor of a lending library

in his native city. He was graduated from the law school there and has become a member of the Canadian bar.

Mr. Callaghan was encouraged in his writing career by Ernest Hemingway and Ezra Pound, both of whom were instrumental in having his early stories published. His first novel, *Strange Fugitive*, was published in 1928. Since then he has written five more novels and three collections of short stories.

He was married in 1929 to Loretto Dee, and has two children. He lives in Toronto, Canada.

Strange Fugitive (novel), Scribners, 1928
A Native Argosy (short stories), Scribners, 1929
It's Never Over (novel), Scribners, 1930
No Man's Meat (short stories), E. W. Titus, Paris, 1931
A Broken Journey (novel), Scribners, 1932
Such Is My Beloved (novel), Scribners, 1934
They Shall Inherit the Earth (novel), Random House, 1935
Now That April's Here (short stories), Random House, 1936
More Joy in Heaven (novel), Random House, 1937

HENRY SEIDEL CANBY has said of himself that he is "a Quaker by inherited temperament, an Epicurean by taste and desire." He was born in Wilmington, Delaware, on September 6, 1878, attended Friend's School there, received his Ph.B. from Yale in 1899 and his Ph.D. in 1905. Two years later he married Marion P. Gause, and is now the father of three children.

Dr. Canby's life has been intimately associated with Yale University. From 1900 to the present time he has held a position there in the English department, successively as assistant, instructor, assistant professor, adviser in literary composition, and lecturer with professorial rank. In 1911 when the *Yale Review* was founded Dr. Canby was appointed assistant editor, and held this position until 1920, when he was asked to edit the *Literary Review* of the New York *Evening Post* at its inception.

In 1924 Dr. Canby and his editorial staff on the *Literary Review*, including Christopher Morley and William Rose Benét, organized *The Saturday Review of Literature*, of which Dr. Canby was editor-in-chief until 1936; he has remained on the editorial board. He has been chairman of the board of judges for the Book-of-the-Month Club since 1926.

Dr. Canby's many volumes of criticism,

literary history, and biography have influenced American letters.

The Short Story (critical and historical essay), Yale University Press, New Haven, Conn., 1902
The Short Story in English (history), Holt, 1909
College Sons and College Fathers (studies of the American college), Harpers, 1915
Education by Violence (essays on the First World War), Macmillan, 1919
Our House (novel), Macmillan, 1919
Everyday Americans (essays on American life), Century, 1920
Definitions (critical essays), Harcourt, Brace, 1922
Definitions, Second Series (critical essays), Harcourt, Brace, 1924
Better Writing (advice on how to write), Harcourt, Brace, 1926
American Estimates (critical studies), Harcourt, Brace, 1929
Classic Americans (critical and historical study), Harcourt, Brace, 1931
*The Age of Confidence (period history, semi-autobiographical), Farrar & Rinehart, 1934
Alma Mater—The Gothic Age of the American College (period history, semi-autobiographical), Farrar & Rinehart, 1936
Seven Years' Harvest (critical studies), Farrar & Rinehart, 1936
Thoreau: a Biography, Houghton Mifflin, Boston, 1939
The Brandywine (regional history), Farrar & Rinehart, 1941
A Life of Walt Whitman (in preparation)

Mr. Canby is also the author of a number of textbooks in English composition.

WILLA CATHER was born on a farm near Winchester, Virginia, on December 7, 1876, of an old Virginia family. At the age of eight she was taken to Nebraska, where her father settled on a ranch near Red Cloud; and she has said that her first two years in the West were, to her as a writer, the most important years of her life.

After graduation from the University of Nebraska in 1895 she returned East, joining the staff of the Pittsburgh *Daily Leader* as telegraph editor and dramatic critic. In 1901 she gave up this position to become head of the English department of the Allegheny High School, and in 1906 she went to New York to join the staff of *McClure's Magazine*. Two years later she was made managing editor. In 1911 she resigned her position and

turned to creative writing, which has been her occupation ever since. She is the author of short stories, verse, essays, and many distinguished novels. *One of Ours* was the Pulitzer Prize novel for 1922.

April Twilights (poetry), Badger, Boston, 1903 (enlarged 1923)
The Troll Garden (short stories), McClure, Phillips, 1905
Alexander's Bridge (novel), Houghton Mifflin, Boston, 1912
O Pioneers! (novel), Houghton Mifflin, Boston, 1913
The Song of the Lark (novel), Houghton Mifflin, Boston, 1915
My Antonia (novel), Houghton Mifflin, Boston, 1918
Youth and the Bright Medusa (short stories), Knopf, 1920
One of Ours (novel), Knopf, 1922
A Lost Lady (novel), Knopf, 1923
The Professor's House (novel), Knopf, 1925
My Mortal Enemy (novel), Knopf, 1926
Death Comes for the Archbishop (novel), Knopf, 1927
The Fear That Walks by Noonday (short story), Phoenix Book Shop, 1931
Shadows on the Rock (novel), Knopf, 1931
*Obscure Destinies (short stories), Knopf, 1932
December Night (scene from *Death Comes for the Archbishop*), Knopf, 1933
Lucy Gayheart (novel), Knopf, 1935
Not Under Forty (essays), Knopf, 1936
The Novels and Stories of Willa Cather, twelve volumes, Houghton Mifflin, Boston, 1937-1938
Sapphira and the Slave Girl (novel), Knopf, 1940

MARY ELLEN CHASE, author and educator, was born at Blue Hill, Maine, on February 24, 1887, and her most prominent novels deal with the New England scene in which she was reared. She received her B.A. from the University of Maine in 1909 and her Ph.D. in 1922 from the University of Minnesota, where she remained as instructor and assistant professor of English until 1926. Since then she has been professor of English at Smith College. She holds honorary degrees from the University of Maine, from Bowdoin, and from Colby College.

Mary Christmas (novella), Atlantic Monthly Press, Boston, 1926
Uplands (novel), Atlantic Monthly Press, Boston, 1927

Thomas Hardy from Serial to Novel, University of Minnesota Press, 1927
The Golden Asse, and Other Essays, Holt, 1929
Constructive Theme Writing, Holt, 1929
The Silver Shell (juvenile), Holt, 1930
*A Goodly Heritage (autobiography), Holt, 1932
Mary Peters (novel), Macmillan, 1934
Silas Crockett (novel), Macmillan, 1935
This England (essays), Macmillan, 1936
Dawn in Lyonesse (novel), Macmillan, 1938
A Goodly Fellowship (autobiography), Macmillan, 1939
Windswept (novel), Macmillan, 1941

Some of Miss Chase's early works have been omitted on her own request.

STUART CHASE, author of a distinguished list of social and economic studies, was born in Somersworth, New Hampshire, on March 8, 1888. He studied for two years at the Massachusetts Institute of Technology, and was graduated from Harvard *cum laude* in 1910. In 1914 he married Margaret Hatfield, by whom he is the father of two children.

Until 1917 he was a partner in the firm of Harvey S. Chase & Co., certified public accountants; then he began a career of public service, investigating the meat industry under the Federal Trade Commission and the Food Administration from 1917 to 1921, and with the Labor Bureau, Inc., from 1922 to 1939. He has acted as consultant at various times for the Securities and Exchange Commission, the National Resources Board, the Tennessee Valley Authority, and other government agencies.

He lives now in Connecticut with his second wife, Marian Tyler, and does his writing there in the intervals between lecturing and investigating trips.

The Tragedy of Waste, Macmillan, 1925
Your Money's Worth (with F. J. SCHLINK), Macmillan, 1927
Men and Machines, Macmillan, 1929
Prosperity—Fact or Myth?, Boni, 1930
The Nemesis of American Business, Macmillan, 1931
Mexico, a Study of Two Americas (with MARIAN TYLER), Macmillan, 1931
A New Deal, Macmillan, 1932
*The Economy of Abundance, Macmillan, 1934
Government in Business, Macmillan, 1935
Rich Land, Poor Land, McGraw-Hill, 1936
The Tyranny of Words, Harcourt, Brace, 1938

The New Western Front (with MARIAN TYLER), Harcourt, Brace, 1939
Idle Money, Idle Men, Harcourt, Brace, 1940
A Primer of Economics, Random House, 1941
The Road We Are Travelling, Twentieth Century Fund, 1942
Goals for America, Twentieth Century Fund, 1942

IRVIN S. COBB, journalist and humorist, has managed to combine his two callings during most of his life. He was born in Paducah, Kentucky, on June 23, 1876. "In my youth," he says, "I was the Younger Bohemian Set of Paducah." He began his journalistic career in his home town, becoming editor of the Paducah *News* when he was nineteen, and married Laura Baker of Savannah, Georgia, in 1900.

It was she who persuaded him to go to New York City, where, after a good many hardships, he became established on the staffs of several New York newspapers, including the *Evening Sun, Evening World,* and *Sunday World,* as humor editor, staff humorist, or feature writer. In 1905 he covered the Russo-Japanese Peace Conference at Portsmouth, New Hampshire, and during the First World War he represented *The Saturday Evening Post* as war correspondent in Europe.

Mr. Cobb was winner of the O. Henry Award for the best short story published in 1922. In the thirties he was starred in several moving pictures, and has written numerous stories for screen use.

Back Home, Doran, 1912
Cobb's Anatomy, Doran, 1912
The Escape of Mr. Trimm, Doran, 1913
Cobb's Bill of Fare, Doran, 1913
Roughing It De Luxe, Doran, 1914
Europe Revised, Doran, 1914
Paths of Glory, Doran, 1915
*Speaking of Operations—, Doran, 1915
Old Judge Priest, Doran, 1915
Fibble, D.D., Doran, 1916
Local Color, Doran, 1916
Speaking of Prussians—, Doran, 1917
Those Times and These, Doran, 1917
The Glory of the Coming, Doran, 1918
The Thunders of Silence, Doran, 1918
The Life of the Party, Doran, 1919
From Place to Place, Doran, 1919
Eating in Two or Three Languages, Doran, 1920
Oh Well, You Know How Women Are!, Doran, 1920
The Abandoned Farmers, Doran, 1920
A Plea for Old Cap Collier, Doran, 1921

One Third Off, Doran, 1921
Jeff Poindexter, Doran, 1922
Sundry Accounts, Doran, 1922
Stickfuls, Doran, 1923
Snake Doctor, Doran, 1923
A Laugh a Day, Doran, 1923
Goin' on Fourteen, Doran, 1924
North Carolina (history), Doran, **1924**
New York (history), Doran, 1924
Maine (history), Doran, 1924
Kentucky (history), Doran, 1924
Kansas (history), Doran, 1924
Indiana (history), Doran, 1924
"Here Comes the Bride—," Doran, 1925
Many Laughs for Many Days, Doran, 1925
Alias Ben Alibi, Doran, 1925
On an Island That Cost Twenty-Four Dollars, Doran, 1926
Some United States (history), Doran, 1926
Prose & Cons., Doran, 1926
Chivalry Peak, Doran, 1927
Ladies and Gentlemen, Doran, 1927
All Aboard, Cosmopolitan Book, 1928
This Man's World, Cosmopolitan Book, 1929
Irvin Cobb at His Best (collection of previous books), Doubleday, Doran, 1929
Red Likker, Cosmopolitan Book, 1929
To Be Taken Before Sailing, Cosmopolitan Book, 1930
Both Sides of the Street, Cosmopolitan Book, 1930
Incredible Truth, Cosmopolitan Book, 1931
Down Yonder with Judge Priest and Irvin S. Cobb, Ray Long & Richard R. Smith, 1932
One Way to Stop a Panic, McBride, 1933
Murder Day by Day, Bobbs-Merrill, Indianapolis, 1933
Faith, Hope, and Charity, Bobbs-Merrill, Indianapolis, 1934
Judge Priest Turns Detective, Bobbs-Merrill, Indianapolis, 1937
Azam, Rand McNally, Chicago, 1937
Four Useful Pups, Rand McNally, Chicago, 1940
Favorite Humorous Stories, Blue Ribbon Books, 1940
Exit Laughing (autobiography), Bobbs-Merrill, Indianapolis, 1941
Glory, Glory, Hallelujah! (chapter from the autobiography), Bobbs-Merrill, Indianapolis, 1941

All of Mr. Cobb's works not otherwise specified are humorous sketches.

ROBERT P. TRISTRAM COFFIN was born in Brunswick, Maine, on March 18, 1892, and many of his writings are intimately associated with the state of his birth. After his graduation from Bowdoin in 1915 he was elected Rhodes Scholar from Maine, and spent two years at Trinity College, Oxford. In 1918 he married Ruth Neal Phillip, and is now the father of four children.

From 1921 to 1934 he was professor of English at Wells College, and since 1934 has been professor of English at Bowdoin. In 1936 his *Strange Holiness* was awarded the Pulitzer Prize for poetry.

Christchurch (poetry), Seltzer, 1924
Book of Crowns and Cottages (essays), Yale University Press, New Haven, 1925
Dew and Bronze (poetry), Boni, 1927
Golden Falcon (poetry), Macmillan, 1929
A Book of Seventeenth-Century Prose (anthology), Harcourt, Brace, 1929
An Attic Room (essays), Doubleday, Doran, 1929
Laud, Storm Center of Stuart England (biography), Coward-McCann, 1930
The Dukes of Buckingham (biography), Coward-McCann, 1931
Portrait of an American (biography), Macmillan, 1931
The Yoke of Thunder (poetry), Macmillan, 1932
Ballads of Square-Toed Americans, Macmillan, 1933
*Lost Paradise (novel), Macmillan, 1934
Strange Holiness (poetry), Macmillan, 1935
Red Sky in the Morning (novel), Macmillan, 1935
John Dawn (novel), Macmillan, 1936
Saltwater Farm (poetry), Macmillan, 1937
**Kennebec: Cradle of Americans* (regional history), Farrar & Rinehart, 1937
Maine, a State of Grace (lecture), University of Maine Press, Orono, Me., 1937
New Poetry of New England: Frost and Robinson (lectures), Johns Hopkins Press, Homewood, Baltimore, 1938
Maine Ballads, Macmillan, 1938
*Collected Poems, Macmillan, 1939
Captain Abby and Captain John (novel), Macmillan, 1939
Thomas-Thomas-Ancil-Thomas (novel), Macmillan, 1941
Christmas in Maine (short story), Doubleday, Doran, 1941
**There Will Be Bread and Love* (poetry), Macmillan, 1942
The Substance That Is Poetry (essays), Macmillan, 1942
Book of Uncles (character sketches) Macmillan, 1942

E. E. CUMMINGS is distinguished both as a writer and as a painter. He was born in Cambridge, Massachusetts, on October 14, 1894, the son of a Harvard teacher, who later became prominent as a public lecturer and minister of South Congregational Church in Boston. E. E. Cummings received his A.B. from Harvard in 1915 and his M.A. the following year. During the First World War he served with an American ambulance corps in France, and in 1917 was confined for several months in a French detention camp as a suspicious character. This experience was literally described in *The Enormous Room*, which was published in 1922.

After the War he lived in Paris, gradually securing recognition both as a writer and as a painter. He has contributed to the *Dial* and other magazines, and has exhibited paintings with the Society of Independent Artists and the Salons of America. In 1925 he was given the *Dial* award for distinguished service to American literature.

In 1930 he spent three months in Soviet Russia, keeping a diary which was later published as *Eimi*. He has also published a play (produced at the Provincetown Playhouse, New York), a ballet-scenario based on *Uncle Tom's Cabin*, a book of satire, and a book of drawings and paintings.

Mr. Cummings's poetry depends for its effectiveness not only on his use of language but on his startling typographical innovations.

Eight Harvard Poets (poetry; with others), Gomme, 1917
The Enormous Room (prose), Boni & Liveright, 1922
Tulips and Chimneys, Seltzer, 1923 (enlarged 1937)
&, privately printed, 1925
XLI Poems, Dial Press, 1925
Is 5, Boni & Liveright, 1926
Him (play), Boni & Liveright, 1927
Christmas Tree, privately printed, 1928
By E. E. Cummings (prose), Covici, Friede, 1930
Viva, Liveright, 1931
CIOPW (drawings and paintings), Covici, Friede, 1931
Eimi (prose), Covici, Friede, 1933
The Red Front (translation from LOUIS ARAGON), Contempo Publications, Chapel Hill, N. C., 1933
No Thanks, Golden Eagle Press, Mt. Vernon, N. Y., 1935
Tom (prose), Arrow editions, 1935
1/20, R. Roughton, London, 1937
Collected Poems, Harcourt, Brace, 1938
Fifty Poems, Duell, Sloan, & Pearce, 1940

Unless otherwise indicated, Mr. Cummings's works are poetry.

PAUL DE KRUIF, author of many popular books on scientific subjects, was born in Zeeland, Michigan, on March 2, 1890, received his B.S. from the University of Michigan in 1912 and his Ph.D. in 1916, and was assistant professor of bacteriology there from 1915 to 1920. From 1920 to 1922 he was bacteriologist for the Rockefeller Institute, and from 1925 to 1940 was a science reporter for the Curtis Publishing Company. Since 1940 he has been a science reporter for *The Reader's Digest*. During the First World War he served as a lieutenant and later as a captain in the Sanitary Corps of the U. S. Army.

Dr. de Kruif collaborated with Sinclair Lewis on the novel *Arrowsmith* and with Sidney Howard on the play *Yellow Jack*. He was married in 1922 to Rhea Barbarin, and lives in Holland, Michigan.

Our Medicine Men, Century, 1922
Microbe Hunters, Harcourt, Brace, 1926
Hunger Fighters, Harcourt, Brace, 1928
Seven Iron Men, Harcourt, Brace, 1929
Men Against Death, Harcourt, Brace, 1932
*Why Keep Them Alive? (with Mrs. DE KRUIF), Harcourt, Brace, 1936
The Fight for Life, Harcourt, Brace, 1938
Health Is Wealth, Harcourt, Brace, 1940

BERNARD DE VOTO was born in Ogden, Utah, on January 11, 1897, of a family with a pioneering background. His father was of Italian descent, and his mother came of a Mormon family. He attended the University of Utah in 1915, transferred to Harvard and was graduated from there in 1920 "as of" 1918, having served during the First World War as a lieutenant in the infantry. He taught for a year in a junior high school, and from 1922 to 1927 was an instructor and assistant professor of English at Northwestern University in Evanston, Illinois.

Mr. DeVoto returned to Harvard in 1929, where he remained until 1935, first as instructor and tutor, later as lecturer in English literature. For two years during this period he edited the *Harvard Graduates' Magazine*, and from 1936 to 1938 he was editor of *The Saturday Review of Literature*. Since 1935 he has been the editor of "The Easy Chair" department of *Harper's*.

Mark Twain's America, which appeared in 1932, established Mr. DeVoto as one of America's foremost critics. He has published many other volumes, including critical and historical essays and four novels.

He was married in 1923 to Avis MacVicar,

and is the father of two sons. He lives in Cambridge, Massachusetts.

The Crooked Mile (novel), Minton, Balch, 1924
The Taming of the Frontier (history; with others), Minton, Balch, 1925
The Chariot of Fire (novel), Macmillan, 1926
The Writer's Handbook (textbook; with others), Macmillan, 1927
The House of Sun-Goes-Down (novel), Macmillan, 1928
**Mark Twain's America* (biography and criticism), Little, Brown, Boston, 1932
We Accept with Pleasure (novel), Little, Brown, Boston, 1934
Forays and Rebuttals (critical essays), Little, Brown, Boston, 1936
Minority Report (critical essays), Little, Brown, Boston, 1940
Mark Twain in Eruption (uncollected manuscripts, edited with introduction), Harpers, 1940
Mark Twain at Work (biography), Harvard University Press, Cambridge, Mass., 1942
The Year of Decision: 1846 (historical study), Little, Brown, Boston, to be published 1943

JOHN DEWEY, educator and philosopher, leading exponent of the pragmatic school since the death of William James, was born in Burlington, Vermont, on October 20, 1859. He received his A.B. from the University of Vermont in 1879 and his Ph.D. from Johns Hopkins University in 1884.

His long and distinguished academic career took him first to the University of Michigan, where he was assistant professor of philosophy until 1888; thereafter he was chairman of the Philosophy Department until 1894. From that year until 1904 he was head of the combined departments of Psychology, Philosophy and Education at the University of Chicago; in connection with the latter department, he founded one of the first experimental schools in the country, developing educational ideas which, through his writings, have had manifold influence in this and in foreign countries, notably China and Turkey. Since 1904 he has been a professor of philosophy at Columbia, becoming "emeritus" in 1931.

He has called his own philosophy "empirical naturalism." His special theory of knowledge, which he has developed on a basis of thoroughgoing naturalism, he has called "instrumentalism," since it treats intelligence and experimental science as the sole dependable agencies for promotion and realization of values esthetic, economic, political and moral in all phases of human life. He has insisted especially upon the function of intelligence, backed by scientific knowledge, in formation of new ends and new types of value. In consequence, his philosophy is often known as "experimentalism."

He married Alice Chipman in 1886 and is the father of five children. He lives now in Manhattan.

Psychology, Harpers, 1886
Leibnitz, Griggs, Chicago, 1888
Outlines of a Critical Theory of Ethics, Register Publishing Co., Ann Arbor, Mich., 1891
A Study of Ethics, Register Publishing Co., Ann Arbor, Mich., 1894
School and Society, University of Chicago Press, Chicago, 1899
Studies in Logical Theory, University of Chicago Press, Chicago, 1903
How We Think, Heath, 1909
The Influence of Darwin on Philosophy, and Other Essays, Holt, 1910
German Philosophy and Politics, Holt, 1915
Essays in Experimental Logic, University of Chicago Press, Chicago, 1916
Democracy and Education, Macmillan, 1916
Reconstruction in Philosophy, Holt, 1920
Human Nature and Conduct, Holt, 1922
Experience and Nature, Open Court, Chicago, 1925
The Public and Its Problems, Holt, 1927
The Philosophy of John Dewey (selections), Holt, 1928
The Quest for Certainty, Minton, Balch, 1929
Characters and Events (essays), Holt, 1929
Experience and Nature, Norton, 1929
Impressions of Soviet Russia and the Revolutionary World, Mexico—China—Turkey, New Republic, 1929
The Sources of a Science of Education (lecture), Liveright, 1929
Construction and Criticism (lecture), Columbia University Press, 1930
Individualism, Old and New, Minton, Balch, New York, 1930
The Way Out of Educational Confusion (lecture), Harvard University Press, Boston, 1931
Philosophy and Civilization, Minton, Balch, 1931
Art as Experience, Minton, Balch, 1934
A Common Faith, Yale University Press, New Haven, 1934
Liberalism and Social Action, Putnam, 1935
Logic, the Theory of Inquiry, Holt, 1938
Experience and Education (lecture), Macmillan, 1938
**Freedom and Culture,* Putnam, 1939

Intelligence in the Modern World (selections; edited by JOSEPH RATNER), Modern Library, 1939

Theory of Valuation, University of Chicago Press, 1939

The Living Thoughts of Thomas Jefferson (selections, with essay), Longmans, Green, 1940

Education Today, Putnam, 1940

A Bibliography of John Dewey, 1882-1939, by MILTON HALSEY THOMAS, with an introduction by HERBERT W. SCHNEIDER, Columbia University Press, 1939

JOHN DOS PASSOS has combined in his writing a keen social consciousness and sympathy for the victims of injustice. He was born in Chicago on January 14, 1896. After his graduation from Harvard he went to Spain to study architecture, but he soon entered the World War as a member of the French ambulance service, later joining the U. S. medical corps. His experiences during this period furnished the material for his first book, *One Man's Initiation—1917,* a semi-autobiographical novel about an ambulance driver.

On his return to the United States Mr. Dos Passos married Katherine Smith. He has lived in Chicago, New York, Washington, Cambridge, London, Brussels, Madrid, and Paris. In 1930 he published *The 42nd Parallel,* the first novel in his *U.S.A.* trilogy (collected 1937), which also includes *1919* and *The Big Money.* These novels tell the story of the first three decades of the 20th century in a wide panorama of American life and are outstanding especially for their experiments in form.

Aside from his other novels Mr. Dos Passos has published volumes of poetry, essays, travel, and plays.

One Man's Initiation—1917 (novel), Allen & Unwin, London, 1920

Three Soldiers (novel), Doran, 1921

A Pushcart at the Curb (poetry), Doran, 1922

Rosinante to the Road Again (essays), Doran, 1922

Streets of Night (novel), Doran, 1923

Manhattan Transfer (novel), Harpers, 1925

The Garbage Man (play), Harpers, 1926

Orient Express (travel diary), Harpers, 1927

Airways, Inc. (play), Macaulay, 1928

The 42nd Parallel (novel), Harpers, 1930

1919 (novel), Harcourt, Brace, 1932

In All Countries (travel), Harcourt, Brace, 1934

Three Plays, Harcourt, Brace, 1934

The Big Money (novel), Harcourt, Brace, 1936

U.S.A. (trilogy), Harcourt, Brace, 1937

Journeys Between Wars (travel and current history), Harcourt, Brace, 1938

*Adventures of a Young Man (novel), Harcourt, Brace, 1939

The Living Thoughts of Tom Paine (selections, with essay), Longmans, Green, 1940

The Ground We Stand On (political essays), Harcourt, Brace, 1941

THEODORE DREISER was born at Terre Haute, Indiana, on August 27, 1871. His father, whom he has described as an intensely religious man, was of peasant German origin who settled in the Middle West, and his mother was born in Bethlehem, Pa., of older Menonite German-American stock. After attending the public schools of Warsaw, Indiana, he worked in Chicago for two years (at five dollars a week) and then enrolled in Indiana University, but after a year was forced to leave because of economic pressure.

After several years of work as a clerk and as a collector for a furniture company, Mr. Dreiser achieved in 1892 his ambition to do newspaper work. His newspaper career, which began on the Chicago *Daily Globe,* took him to St. Louis and later to New York, and lasted until 1907, when he became editor-in-chief of the Butterick Publications, including *The Delineator.* He held this position until 1910.

In the meantime his *Sister Carrie* had been published in 1900, and was immediately suppressed. All of his books, which express his naturalistic concept of American society and his consciousness of the tragedy of life, have aroused controversy, even indignation. His *An American Tragedy,* which appeared in 1925, was brought into the Boston courts and is still banned there, although a number of colleges have it on their reading lists for students.

In 1910 Mr. Dreiser gave up journalism to devote himself exclusively to creative writing. He visited Russia in 1927, and returned with a hopeful belief in socialism, to which he gave expression in his *Dreiser Looks at Russia* (1928) and which contrasts sharply with his former naturalism.

He lives now in Hollywood, California.

Sister Carrie (novel), Doubleday, Page, Garden City, N. Y., 1900

Jennie Gerhardt (novel), Harpers, 1911

The Financier (novel), Harpers, 1912

A Traveller at Forty (autobiography), Century, 1913

The Titan (novel), Lane, 1914
The Genius (novel), 1915
Plays of the Natural and Supernatural, Lane, 1916
A Hoosier Holiday (autobiography), Lane, 1916
Life, Art and America (pamphlet), The Seven Arts, 1917
Free, and Other Stories, Boni & Liveright, 1918
The Hand of the Potter (drama), Boni, 1918
Twelve Men (character studies), Boni, 1920
Hey Rub-a-Dub-Dub (essays), Boni, 1920
A Book about Myself (autobiography), Liveright, 1922
The Color of a Great City (vignettes), Boni & Liveright, 1923
An American Tragedy (novel), two volumes, Liveright, 1925
Moods, Cadenced and Declaimed (poetry), Liveright, 1926 (enlarged 1928)
Chains (short stories), Liveright, 1927
Carnegie Works at Pittsburgh (article), privately printed, Chelsea, N. Y., 1927
Dreiser Looks at Russia, Liveright, 1928
A Gallery of Women (short stories), two volumes, Liveright, 1929
The Aspirant (poetry), Random House, 1929
My City (vignettes), Liveright, 1929
Epitaph (poem), Liveright, 1930
Fine Furniture (essay), Random House, 1930
Dawn (autobiography), Liveright, 1931
Tragic America (social criticism), Liveright, 1931
The Living Thoughts of Thoreau (selections, with essays), Longmans, Green, 1940
America Is Worth Saving (current events), Modern Age, 1941

IRWIN EDMAN, author, educator, and critic, has remained in close touch with Columbia University all his life. He was born in New York City on November 28, 1896, received his B.A. from Columbia in 1917 and his Ph.D. in 1920. He began as a lecturer on philosophy at Columbia in 1918, was made an instructor in 1920, an assistant professor in 1925, an associate professor in 1931, and has been a full professor of philosophy since 1935. He was also the Henry Ward Beecher lecturer at Amherst College in 1935, and lecturer at the University of California in the summer of 1939.

Mr. Edman's works include poetry, history of philosophy, and philosophical criticism. He has edited the works of Plato and Santayana, has contributed articles to many magazines, including *The Nation, Harper's, The Journal of Philosophy, The New Yorker,* and

The Saturday Review of Literature, and is a member of the editorial board of the *American Scholar.*

Mr. Edman is unmarried, and lives in New York City.

Human Traits and Their Social Significance, Houghton Mifflin, Boston, 1920
Richard Kane Looks at Life (imaginary portrait), Houghton Mifflin, Boston, 1926
Poems, Simon & Schuster, 1925
The World, the Arts and the Artists (aesthetics), Norton, 1928
Adam, the Baby, and the Man from Mars (collected essays), Houghton Mifflin, Boston, 1929
The Contemporary and His Soul, Viking Press, 1931
Living Philosophies (a symposium), Simon & Schuster, 1931
The Mind of Paul (religion), Holt, 1935
Four Ways of Philosophy, Holt, 1937
Philosopher's Holiday (memoirs), Viking Press, 1938
Candle in the Dark: A Postscript to Despair (moral essay), Viking Press, 1939
Arts and the Man (aesthetics), Norton, 1939
Fountainheads of Freedom: The Growth of the Democratic Idea (with H. W. SCHNEIDER), Reynal & Hitchcock, 1941
Landmarks in Philosophy (with H. W. SCHNEIDER), Reynal & Hitchcock, 1941

JAMES T. FARRELL, novelist and short-story writer, was born in Chicago on February 27, 1904. His early experiences as a baseball enthusiast and pupil of Catholic schools on Chicago's South Side afforded him much of the material for his Studs Lonigan trilogy. He attended the University of Chicago for three years, and later worked as a clerk, salesman, filling station attendant, and newspaper reporter.

In 1932 his *Young Lonigan* attracted wide attention. It has been followed by many novels and short stories, all of them reflecting Mr. Farrell's interest in the common facts of modern American life. In 1936 he was awarded a Guggenheim Fellowship in creative writing, and in 1937, in recognition of the Studs Lonigan trilogy, the Book-of-the-Month Club gave to Mr. Farrell a $2500 award, "to recognize the strong and vigorous sincerity with which he represents an underprivileged section of American life."

Mr. Farrell lives now with his second wife, Hortense Alden Farrell, and their young son in New York City.

Young Lonigan, Vanguard Press, 1932

Gas-House McGinty, Vanguard Press, 1933
The Young Manhood of Studs Lonigan, Vanguard Press, 1934
Calico Shoes (short stories), Vanguard Press, 1934
Judgment Day, Vanguard Press, 1935
*Guillotine Party and Other Stories, Vanguard Press, 1935
Studs Lonigan, a Trilogy (three volumes in one), Vanguard Press, 1935
A Note on Literary Criticism (essay), Vanguard Press, 1936
A World I Never Made, Vanguard Press, 1936
Can All This Grandeur Perish? and Other Stories, Vanguard Press, 1937
The Short Stories of James Thomas Farrell, Vanguard Press, 1937
Fellow Countrymen (collected stories), Constable, London, 1937
No Star Is Lost, Vanguard Press, 1938
Tommy Gallagher's Crusade, Vanguard Press, 1939
Father and Son, Vanguard Press, 1940
Ellen Rogers, Vanguard Press, 1941
$1000 a Week, Vanguard Press, 1942

All of Mr. Farrell's works, unless otherwise indicated, are novels.

WILLIAM FAULKNER has been compared to Dostoevsky for the intensity of his interest in the psychological aspects of humanity. He was born in New Albany, Mississippi, on September 25, 1897, and attended school in Oxford, Mississippi. His studies at the state University were interrupted when he went to France to serve with the British Royal Air Force in the First World War, where he was wounded in a crash.

On his return to this country he served as a postmaster for two years in Mississippi, and then went to New Orleans, where he became friendly with Sherwood Anderson while working on his first novel, *Soldier's Pay,* and writing occasional sketches for the magazine section of the New Orleans Sunday *Times-Picayune.*

In 1929 Mr. Faulkner was married to Estelle Franklin. He is a particular enemy of crowds and cities, and lives in the small town of Oxford, Mississippi.

The Marble Faun (poetry), Four Seas, Boston, 1924
Soldier's Pay (novel), Boni & Liveright, 1926
Mosquitoes (novel), Boni & Liveright, 1927
Sartoris (novel), Harcourt, Brace, 1929
The Sound and the Fury (novel), Smith & Haas, 1929
As I Lay Dying (novel), Smith & Haas, 1930
Sanctuary (novel), Smith & Haas, 1931

Idyll in the Desert (short story), Random House, 1931
*These Thirteen (short stories), Smith & Haas, 1931
Light in August (novel), Smith & Haas, 1931
Miss Zylphia Gant (short stories), Book Club of Texas, Dallas, 1932
Salgamundi (essays and poems), Casanova Press, Milwaukee, 1932
This Earth (poem), Equinox Cooperative Press, 1932
A Green Bough (poetry), Smith & Haas, 1933
Dr. Martino, and Other Stories, Smith & Haas, 1934
Pylon (novel), Smith & Haas, 1935
Absalom, Absalom! (novel), Random House, 1936
The Unvanquished (short stories), Random House, 1938
The Wild Palms (novel), Random House, 1939
The Hamlet (novel), Random House, 1940
Go Down Moses and Other Stories, Random House, 1942

EDNA FERBER was born in Kalamazoo, Michigan. Her mother was born in Milwaukee, Wisconsin, and her father was a Hungarian who came to the United States when a lad of fifteen. Her childhood was spent in Iowa and Wisconsin. After graduation from high school at the age of seventeen she got a newspaper reporting job at three dollars a week on the Appleton, Wisconsin, *Crescent.* This was followed by three years as reporter and feature writer on the Milwaukee *Journal.* Her first fiction story was published in *Everybody's* and her first novel, *Dawn O'Hara,* appeared in 1911.

Her best-known novels are *So Big, Show Boat, Cimarron, American Beauty, Saratoga Trunk,* and *Come and Get It.* In 1939 there was published an autobiographical book entitled *A Peculiar Treasure,* written in protest against the bigotry and intolerance which was seeping into the United States through Hitlerian channels.

Aside from her many novels and short stories Miss Ferber has written several plays of distinction, usually in collaboration with George S. Kaufman. They include *The Royal Family, Dinner at Eight,* and *Stage Door. Show Boat,* with music by Jerome Kern, was adapted from her novel and produced as a musical comedy by the late Florenz Ziegfeld. It was one of the outstanding successes of the American theatre.

Miss Ferber, who lived for many years in New York, has now made her home in Connecticut.

Dawn O'Hara (novel), Stokes, 1911

Buttered Side Down (short stories), Stokes, 1912

Roast Beef, Medium (short stories), Stokes, 1913

Personality Plus (short stories), Stokes, 1914

Emma McChesney and Co. (short stories), Stokes, 1915

Fanny Herself (novel), Stokes, 1917

Cheerful by Request (short stories), Doubleday, Doran, Garden City, N. Y., 1918

Half Portions (short stories), Doubleday, Doran, Garden City, N. Y., 1920

$1200 a Year (play; with NEWMAN LEVY), Doubleday, Doran, Garden City, N. Y., 1920

The Girls (novel), Doubleday, Doran, Garden City, N. Y., 1921

Gigolo (short stories), Doubleday, Doran, Garden City, N. Y., 1922

So Big (novel), Doubleday, Doran, Garden City, N. Y., 1924

Minick (play; with GEORGE S. KAUFMAN), Doubleday, Doran, Garden City, N. Y., 1924

The Eldest (play), Doubleday, Doran, Garden City, N. Y., 1925

Show Boat (novel), Doubleday, Doran, Garden City, N. Y., 1926

Mother Knows Best (short stories), Doubleday, Doran, Garden City, N. Y., 1927

The Royal Family (play; with GEORGE S. KAUFMAN), Doubleday, Doran, Garden City, N. Y., 1928

Cimarron (novel), Doubleday, Doran, Garden City, N. Y., 1930

American Beauty (novel), Doubleday, Doran, Garden City, N. Y., 1931

Dinner at Eight (play; with GEORGE S. KAUFMAN), Doubleday, Doran, Garden City, N. Y., 1932

They Brought Their Women (short stories), Doubleday, Doran, Garden City, N. Y., 1933

Come and Get It (novel), Doubleday, Doran, Garden City, N. Y., 1935

Stage Door (play; with GEORGE S. KAUFMAN), Doubleday, Doran, Garden City, N. Y., 1936

Nobody's in Town (two novelettes), Doubleday, Doran, Garden City, N. Y., 1938

A Peculiar Teasure (autobiography), Doubleday, Doran, Garden City, N. Y., 1939

No Room at the Inn (story), Doubleday, Doran, Garden City, N. Y., 1941

Saratoga Trunk (novel), Doubleday, Doran, Garden City, N. Y., 1941

The Land Is Bright (play; with GEORGE S. KAUFMAN), Doubleday, Doran, Garden City, N. Y., 1941

DOROTHY CANFIELD FISHER, known to readers of her novels and short stories as Dorothy Canfield, was born February 17, 1879. Her family had lived, since the founding of the town in 1764, in Arlington, Vermont, where Mrs. Fisher has her home. For twenty years, during her childhood and youth, her father was on the faculty of one and another State University. Her education was received alternately in France, in the middle-western towns where her father's profession took the family, and in New York, where for a decade her father was Librarian of Columbia University. In 1907 she married John Redwood Fisher of New York and Philadelphia, and since then has divided her time between France and Vermont. Three years of War work were done by the Fishers in France between 1915 and 1918, Mr. Fisher having served during those years in the American Ambulance Field Service.

Most of Mrs. Fisher's novels deal with the problems of the adjustment to life, especially to family life under modern conditions, by modern women of intelligence and vitality.

Corneille and Racine in England, Macmillan, 1904

English Rhetoric and Composition (with G. R. CARPENTER), Macmillan, 1906

What Shall We Do Now? (with others), Stokes, 1906

Gunhild (novel), Holt, 1907

The Squirrel Cage (novel), Holt, 1912

The Montessori Mother (book on child training), Holt, 1913

Mothers and Children (book on child training), Holt, 1914

Hillsboro People (short stories), Holt, 1915

The Bent Twig (novel), Holt, 1915

The Real Motive (short stories), Holt, 1916

Fellow Captains (prose and poetry; with SARAH N. CLEGHORN), Holt, 1916

Understood Betsy (juvenile), Holt, 1917

Home Fires in France (short stories), Holt, 1918

The Day of Glory (novel), Holt, 1919

The Brimming Cup (novel), Harcourt, Brace, 1921

Rough Hewn (novel), Harcourt, Brace, 1922

Raw Material (sketches), Harcourt, Brace, 1923

The Home-Maker (novel), Harcourt, Brace, 1924

Made-to-Order Stories, Harcourt, Brace, 1925

Her Son's Wife (novel), Harcourt, Brace, 1926

Why Stop Learning? (book on adult education), Harcourt, Brace, 1927

Self-Reliance (child psychology), Harcourt, Brace, 1929

The Deepening Stream (novel), Harcourt, Brace, 1930
Learn or Perish (lecture), Liveright, 1930
Basque People (short stories), Harcourt, Brace, 1931
Bonfire (novel), Harcourt, Brace, 1933
Tourists Accommodated (drama), Harcourt, Brace, 1934
Fables for Parents (short stories), Harcourt, Brace, 1937
*Seasoned Timber (novel), Harcourt, Brace, 1939
Election of Academy Hill (story), Harcourt, Brace, 1939
Tell Me a Story (stories for children), University Publishing Co., Lincoln, Neb., 1940
Nothing Ever Happens (stories; with SARAH N. CLEGHORN), Beacon Press, Boston, 1940

ROBERT FROST, on whose stature as a poet no words need be wasted, was born in San Francisco on March 26, 1875. It was an accident of circumstance that he was born in the West: his family was of New England, and at the age of ten he returned to the New England farm country with which his poetry is identified.

He entered Dartmouth College in 1892 but so disliked academic life that he left after a few months and took a job in a mill. A later attendance at Harvard terminated also in his leaving to take up various occupations, including shoemaking, editing a country newspaper, teaching, and farming. Tiring of these, he left for England in 1912, taking with him his wife, Eleanor White Frost, whom he had married in 1895, and his four children.

His first book of verse, *A Boy's Will*, was published in England in 1913. Returning to America in 1915, he taught for four years at Amherst College, and from 1921 to 1923 he was "poet in residence" at the University of Michigan. Since then his teaching career has taken him to many institutions, including Amherst, Harvard, Yale, and Middlebury.

Mr. Frost received the Loines Prize for Poetry in 1931, the Mark Twain Medal in 1937, and awards from the National Institute of Arts and Letters and the Poetry Society of America. And he has had the unique distinction of receiving three Pulitzer Prizes for poetry, in 1924, 1931, and 1937.

A Boy's Will, Nutt, London, 1913
North of Boston, Nutt, London, 1914
Mountain Interval, Holt, 1916
New Hampshire, Holt, 1923

Selected Poems, Holt, 1923 (enlarged 1928, 1934, and by Cape, London, in 1936)
West-Running Brook, Holt, 1928
A Way Out, Harbor Press, 1929
The Cow's in the Corn (verse play), Slide Mountain Press, Gaylordsville, Vt., 1929
The Lovely Shall be Choosers, Random House, 1929
Collected Poems, Holt, New York, 1930
Two Letters Written on His Undergraduate Days at Dartmouth College in 1892 (pamphlet), Printer's Devil Press, Hanover, N. H., 1931
The Lone Striker, Knopf, New York, 1933
Gold Hesperidee, Bibliophile Press, Cortland, N. Y., 1935
Three Poems, Daniel Oliver Associates, Hanover, N. H., 1935
From Snow to Snow, Holt, 1936
A Further Range, Holt, 1936
*Collected Poems, 1939, Holt, 1939
*A Witness Tree, Holt, 1942

All of Mr. Frost's works, unless otherwise indicated are poetry.

WOLCOTT GIBBS, writer and critic, was born in New York City on March 15, 1902. After studying at the Hill School in Pottstown, Pennsylvania, he reported on various newspapers from 1922 to 1927. In 1927 began his association with *The New Yorker*, which has continued until the present day: from 1928 to 1937 he was associate editor; he has been an editorial writer since 1937 and drama critic since 1940.

Mr. Gibbs was married in 1933 to Elinor Sherwin, and has a son and a daughter. He lives in New York City.

Bed of Neuroses (humorous essays), Dodd, Mead, 1937

ELLEN GLASGOW has declared that she was born a novelist, and she has used her talent to break away from the sentimentality and romanticism of the traditional novel of the South, protesting always against the old system of chivalry in which a woman's education "was designed to paralyze her reasoning faculties." She was born in Richmond, Virginia, on April 22, 1874, of an aristocratic Southern family, and was educated privately.

Her first novel, *The Descendant*, was published anonymously in 1897; her third, *The Voice of the People*, which appeared in 1900, was the first of a series in which she has recorded much of the social history and political atmosphere of Virginia from the 1850's to the present. In 1940 she received from the American Academy of Arts and Letters the quinquennial Howells medal for "eminence in creative literature as shown in the novel"; and in the same year she received *The Saturday Review of Literature* special award for distinguished service to American literature. *In This Our Life*, her latest work, was the 1942 Pulitzer Prize novel.

Since 1924 Miss Glasgow has been president of the Richmond Society for the Prevention of Cruelty to Animals. She is unmarried, and lives in the city of her birth.

The Descendant, Harpers, 1897
Phases of an Inferior Planet, Harpers, 1898
The Voice of the People, Doubleday, Page, 1900
The Freeman and Other Poems, Doubleday, Page, 1902
The Battle-Ground, Doubleday, Page, 1902
The Deliverance, Doubleday, Page, 1904
The Wheel of Life, Doubleday, Page, 1906
The Ancient Law, Doubleday, Page, 1908
The Romance of a Plain Man, Doubleday, Page, 1909
The Miller of Old Church, Doubleday, Page, Garden City, N. Y., 1911
Virginia, Doubleday, Page, Garden City, N. Y., 1913
Life and Gabriella, Doubleday, Page, Garden City, N. Y., 1916
The Builders, Doubleday, Page, Garden City, N. Y., 1919
One Man in His Time, Doubleday, Page, Garden City, N. Y., 1922
The Shadowy Third and Other Stories, Doubleday, Page, Garden City, 1923
Barren Ground, Doubleday, Page, Garden City, N. Y., 1925
The Romantic Comedians, Doubleday, Page, Garden City, N. Y., 1926
They Stooped to Folly, Doubleday, Doran, 1929
The Sheltered Life, Doubleday, Doran, 1932
The Old Dominion Edition of the Works of Ellen Glasgow, eight volumes, Doubleday, Doran, 1930-1932
Vein of Iron, Harcourt, Brace, 1935
The Virginia Edition of the Works of Ellen Glasgow, twelve volumes, Scribners, 1938
In This Our Life, Harcourt, Brace, 1941

All of Miss Glasgow's work, unless otherwise indicated, are novels.

JOHN GUNTHER is internationally known not only as a reporter of events but as a reporter of entire continents since the publication of his three famous "inside" volumes, *Inside Europe, Inside Asia,* and *Inside Latin America.*

He was born in Chicago August 30, 1901, and began his literary life at four as a bookworm; at six he was particularly fond of the *Iliad,* which he knows by heart; and at eleven he had written his own personal digest of Ridpath's *Universal History.*

He went to college in Chicago, hoping to be a chemist, but in 1924 he joined the Chicago *Daily News* and has been a writer of either fact or fiction ever since. He has worked in every country in Europe and he went around the world in connection with *Inside Asia.* For the Latin American book he flew 18,000 miles and covered twenty countries as well as Puerto Rico and Trinidad on a five and one-half month fact-gathering job. His three "inside" books have sold well over a million copies and he has done considerable lecturing and radio commentating. His first four books were novels.

Frances Gunther, whom he married in 1927, has also worked as a foreign correspondent in Europe and they have a son, John, aged 12, who attends school at Riverdale with the sons of three other former foreign correspondents—Jay Allen, Dorothy Thompson, and M. W. Fodor.

Mr. Gunther lives in New York City when he is not on the wing somewhere.

The Red Pavilion (novel), Harpers, 1926
Eden for One (novel), Harpers, 1927
The Golden Fleece (novel), Harpers, 1929
The Bright Nemesis (novel), Bobbs-Merrill, Indianapolis, 1932
Inside Europe (current history), Harpers, 1936
Inside Asia (current history), Harpers, 1939
The High Cost of Hitler (broadcasts), Hamilton, London, 1939
Inside Latin America (current history), Harpers, 1941

"H. D." is the pen name of Hilda Doolittle. She was born in Bethlehem, Pennsylvania, on September 10, 1886, where her father was professor of mathematics and astronomy at Lehigh University. She attended school in Bethlehem and Philadelphia, and entered Bryn Mawr College in 1905, but after two years continued her classical studies privately.

In 1911 she went to Europe for a short visit to Italy, France, and England, but in London she met Ezra Pound, whom she had known previously in Pennsylvania, became interested in the current literary movements, and decided to stay. She was one of the first Imagists, and in her later and more varied range of expression has consistently remained one. Pound used his influence to get her work published in *Poetry Magazine*, which two years later awarded her the Guarantors Prize and in 1938 the Helen Haire Levinson Prize. Her first book, *Sea Garden*, was published in England in 1916.

"H. D." was married to Richard Aldington, the British Imagist poet, in 1913; during the First World War she took his place as editor of *The Egoist*. Since then she has visited her native country twice, once in 1920 and again in 1936; her permanent home is in England.

Choruses from Iphigeneia in Aulis (translation), Ballantyne Press, London, 1915
Sea Garden (poetry), Houghton Mifflin, Boston, 1916
The Tribute and Circe (two poems), privately printed, London, 1917
Choruses from the Iphigeneia in Aulis and the Hippolytus of Euripides (translation), Egoist, Ltd., London, 1919
Hymen (poetry), Holt, and Egoist Press, London, 1921
Heliodora and Other Poems (poetry), Houghton Mifflin, Boston, 1924
*Collected Poems of H. D., Boni & Liveright, 1925
The Pamphlet Poets: H. D., Simon & Schuster, 1926
Palimpsest (story), Houghton Mifflin, Boston, 1926
Hippolytus Temporizes (verse play), Houghton Mifflin, Boston, 1927
Hedylus (story), Houghton Mifflin, Boston, 1928
Red Roses for Bronze (poetry), Houghton Mifflin, Boston, 1931
The Hedgehog (story), Brendin Publishing Co., London, 1936
Euripides Ion (translation, with notes), Houghton Mifflin, Boston, 1937

LILLIAN HELLMAN, who within a very few years has risen to eminence as a playwright, was born in New Orleans on June 20, 1905, and was educated at New York University and Columbia. Her first position was with Horace Liveright, the publishing house. She has been a writer since 1925, and since 1935 has also done movie scenarios. Her dramatizations for the screen include *The Dark Angel*, *These Three*, *Dead End*, and her own *The Little Foxes*.

Miss Hellman was married in 1925 to Arthur Kober, the author, and divorced from him in 1932. She lives now in Pleasantville, New York, on her own farm.

The Children's Hour, Knopf, 1935.
Days to Come, Knopf, 1937
The Little Foxes, Random House, 1939
Watch on the Rhine, Random House, 1941

All of Miss Hellman's works are plays.

ERNEST HEMINGWAY, the son of a doctor, was born in Oak Park, Illinois, on July 21, 1898. While attending school he made frequent hunting and fishing expeditions in northern Michigan, and these early experiences are reflected in the vigor of his writing.

After working as a reporter in Kansas City, he joined a volunteer ambulance unit in France during the First World War, and later transferred to the Italian Arditi where he saw front-line action and was seriously wounded. The Italian Government decorated him with two of the highest medals of the country.

At the close of the war, Mr. Hemingway reentered newspaper work as a foreign correspondent, in which capacity he reported battles in the Near East. He then settled in Paris as a member of the expatriate group which included Ezra Pound and Gertrude Stein, and within a short time had begun to exercise a tremendous influence in American letters. He became the leading spokesman for the "lost generation," expressing the loss of faith and hope which succeeded the War and urging a return to primal emotions.

Since 1927 his restless vitality, expressed in skiing, fishing, and hunting have led him on journeys throughout the world. He covered the Spanish Civil War for the North American Newspaper Alliance.

Three Stories and Ten Poems, Contact Publishing Co., Paris, 1923
In Our Time (short stories), Three Mountains Press, Paris, 1924
In Our Time (short stories), Boni & Liveright, 1925 (revised and enlarged by Scribners, 1930)
The Torrents of Spring (novel), Scribners, 1926
The Sun Also Rises (novel), Scribners, 1926
Today Is Friday (play), As Stable Press, Englewood, N. J., 1926
Men Without Women (short stories), Scribners, 1927
A Farewell to Arms (novel), Scribners, 1929
Death in the Afternoon (book on bull fighting), Scribners, 1932

God Rest You Merry Gentlemen (short story), House of Books, 1933
Winner Take Nothing (short stories), Scribners, 1933
The Green Hills of Africa (travel), Scribners, 1935
Gattorno (pictures and commentary), Ucar, Garcia, Havana, 1935
To Have and Have Not (novel), Scribners, 1937
*The Fifth Column and the First Forty-Nine Stories, Scribners, 1938
Spanish Earth (commentary and narrative for film), J. B. Savage, Cleveland, 1938
The Spanish War (collected newspaper articles), Fact Publishing Co., London, 1938
The Fifth Column (play), Scribners, 1940
For Whom the Bell Tolls (novel), Scribners, 1940

JOSEPH HERGESHEIMER was born in Philadelphia on February 15, 1880, of Pennsylvania Dutch and Scots parents. He went to a Quaker school in his native city and at seventeen entered the Pennsylvania Academy of Fine Arts; but after further study and painting in Italy he turned to literature. His first novel, *The Lay Anthony,* appeared in 1914, and was followed by many others. Mr. Hergesheimer has also published collections of short stories, a biography of General Sheridan, and three autobiographical works: *San Cristóbal de la Habana, From an Old House,* and *The Presbyterian Child.*

He was married in 1907 to Dorothy Hemphill and lives at The Dower House, West Chester, Pennsylvania.

The Lay Anthony, Knopf, 1914
Mountain Blood, Knopf, 1915
The Three Black Pennys, Knopf, 1917
Gold and Iron (three novelettes), Knopf, 1918
Hugh Walpole: An Appreciation (literary criticism), 1919
Java Head, Knopf, 1919
The Happy End (short stories), Knopf, 1919
Linda Condon, Knopf, 1919
San Cristóbal de la Habana (autobiography), Knopf, 1920
Cytherea, Knopf, 1922
The Bright Shawl, Knopf, 1922
The Presbyterian Child (autobiography), Knopf, 1923
Merry Dale (short story), 1924
Balisand, Knopf, 1924
From an Old House (autobiography), Knopf, 1925
Tampico, Knopf, 1926
Quiet Cities (short stories), Knopf, 1928

Swords and Roses (history), Knopf, 1929
Triall by Armes (short story), Mathews & Marot, London, 1929
The Party Dress, Knopf, 1930
The Limestone Tree, Knopf, 1931
Sheridan (biography), Houghton Mifflin, Boston, 1931
Berlin (travel), Knopf, 1932
Love in the United States and The Big Shot (two short stories), Benn, London, 1932
Tropical Winter (short stories), Knopf, 1933
The Foolscap Rose, Knopf, 1934

Unless otherwise indicated, Mr. Hergesheimer's works are novels.

LANGSTON HUGHES, the Negro poet, has had an adventurous career. He was born on February 1, 1902, in Joplin, Missouri, where his father was a lawyer. He graduated from high school in Cleveland, Ohio, in 1920, spent a year teaching English in a business academy in Mexico, entered Columbia University in 1921 but left after one year to go to sea. His wanderings lasted three years, and took him to Africa, France, and Italy.

In 1925 Mr. Hughes was awarded first prize in poetry in a contest conducted for Negro writers by the magazine *Opportunity.* His first book of poems, *The Weary Blues,* was published the following year. He received a Guggenheim Fellowship for creative writing in 1935 and the Rosenwald Fellowship in 1941. Besides his books, Mr. Hughes has written for radio, screen, and stage, his play, *Mulatto,* having had the longest run on Broadway of any dramatic work yet written by a Negro.

The Weary Blues, Knopf, 1926
Fine Clothes to the Jew, Knopf, 1927
Not Without Laughter (novel), Knopf, 1930
Dear Lovely Death, Troutbeck Press, Amenia, N. Y., 1931
The Negro Mother, Golden Stair Press, 1931
Popo and Fifina (children's story of Haiti; with ARNA BONTEMPS), Macmillan, 1932
The Dream Keeper, Knopf, 1932
Scottsboro Limited (poems and verse play), Golden Stair Press, 1932
The Ways of White Folks (short stories), Knopf, 1934
The Big Sea (autobiography), Knopf, 1940
Shakespeare in Harlem, Knopf, 1942

Mr. Hughes's works, unless otherwise specified, are poetry.

ROBINSON JEFFERS has said that during his college years he was "not deeply interested in anything but poetry." He adds that poetry runs pretty thin under such a limitation, and he had passed thirty before he wrote anything worth reading. He was born in Pittsburgh, Pennsylvania, on January 10, 1887, the son of a scholar. His ancestry, he says, was "all pre-revolutionary American, except paternal grandfather from North Ireland." He went to school in Europe, and on his return to this country was graduated from Occidental College, Los Angeles, at the age of eighteen. Subsequently he spent what he calls "desultory years" at the University of Zurich and the University of Southern California Medical School.

Mr. Jeffers married Una Call Kuster in 1913, and settled in Carmel, California, building his own house of sea boulders. In 1916 he became the father of twin sons, Garth and Donnan.

His first volume of poetry to attract wide attention was *Tamar and Other Poems*, published in 1924. Through this and his subsequent works he has earned the title of the poet of tragic terror. His poetry is characterized by emotional violence and an intense revulsion from society. "Cut humanity out of my being," he has written, "that is the wound that festers."

Flagons and Apples, Grafton Press, Los Angeles, 1912
Californians, Macmillan, 1916
*Tamar and Other Poems, Peter Boyle, 1924
Roan Stallion, Tamar, and Other Poems, Boni & Liveright, 1925
The Women at Point Sur, Liveright, 1927
Poems, Book Club of California, San Francisco, 1928
Cawdor, and Other Poems, Liveright, 1928
Dear Judas, and Other Poems, Liveright, 1929
Descent to the Dead, Random House, 1931
Thurso's Landing, and Other Poems, Liveright, 1932
Give Your Heart to the Hawks, and Other Poems, Random House, 1933
Solstice, and Other Poems, Random House, 1935
Such Counsels You Gave to Me, and Other Poems, Random House, 1937
Selected Poetry, Random House, 1938
Be Angry at the Sun, Random House, 1941

All of Mr. Jeffers's work is poetry. A large number of limited editions have been omitted from the bibliography on his own request.

Joseph Wood Krutch, essayist and critic, was born in Knoxville, Tennessee, on November 25, 1893, and received his B.A. from the University of Tennessee in 1915. During the First World War he served in the Psychological Corps of the American army, and in 1919-1920 he traveled abroad on a Columbia University fellowship. In 1923 he received his Ph.D. from that university, after teaching English there and at the Polytechnic Institute of Brooklyn.

Dr. Krutch's editorial career began in 1924 when he joined the staff of *The Nation* as dramatic critic and associate editor. He was a member of the board of editors from 1932 to 1937, and has been dramatic critic since 1937. In the meantime he continued his teaching career as special lecturer with the rank of professor at Vassar College, as associate professor in the School of Journalism of Columbia, and as lecturer at the New School for Social Research. Since 1937 he has been a professor of English at Columbia. In 1930 a Guggenheim Fellowship enabled him to spend six months abroad writing an essay on aesthetics.

Dr. Krutch was married in 1923 to Marcelle Leguia, a Frenchwoman. He lives in New York City.

Comedy and Conscience after the Restoration, Columbia University Press, 1924
Edgar Allen Poe: A Study in Genius, Knopf, 1926
The Modern Temper: A Study and a Confession, Harcourt, Brace, 1929
*Five Masters: A Study in the Mutations of the Novel, Smith & Haas, 1930
Experience and Art: Some Aspects of the Aesthetics of Literature, Smith & Haas, 1932
Was Europe a Success?, Farrar & Rinehart, 1934
The American Drama Since 1918, Random House, 1939

Stephen Leacock, a citizen of Canada, has led a double life: on the one hand he is head of the department of political science and economics at McGill University in Montreal; on the other he has achieved an international reputation for his books of humorous stories and essays. He was born in Swanmoor, Hanto, England, on December 30, 1869, but moved at an early age to Canada (in 1876). In 1891 he received his B.A. from the University of Toronto and in 1903 his Ph.D. from the University of Chicago.

Since 1901 Mr. Leacock has been associated with McGill University in the department of political science and economics, and from 1908 until his retirement in 1936 he was head of the department of economics. His published works range from such treatises as *Elements of Political Science* (1905) and *The*

Unsolved Riddle of Social Justice (1920) through biographies of Dickens and Clemens to his many volumes of humor, which combine gay absurdities with penetrating criticism of contemporary society.

Adventures of the Far North (chronicle), Glasgow, Brooks, Toronto, 1904

The Dawn of Canadian History (chronicle), Glasgow, Brooks, Toronto, 1904

The Mariner of St. Malo (chronicle), Glasgow, Brooks, Toronto, 1904

Elements of Political Science (treatise), Houghton Mifflin, Boston, 1906

Baldwin Lafontaine, Hincks: Responsible Government (treatise), Morang, Toronto, 1907

Literary Lapses, Lane, 1911

Nonsense Novels, Lane, 1911

Sunshine Sketches of a Little Town, Lane, 1912

Behind the Beyond, Lane, 1913

Arcadian Adventures with the Idle Rich, Lane, 1914.

Moonbeams from the Larger Lunacy, Lane, 1915

Essays and Literary Studies (essays), Lane, 1916

Further Foolishness, Lane, 1916

Marionettes' Calendar, Lane, 1916

Frenzied Fiction, Lane, 1918

Hohenzollerns in America, Lane, 1919

The Unsolved Riddle of Social Justice (social study), Lane, 1920

Short Circuits, Lane, 1920

Winsome Winnie, Lane, 1920

My Discovery of England, Dodd, Mead, 1922

Over the Footlights, Dodd, Mead, 1923

College Days, Dodd, Mead, 1923

The Garden of Folly, Dodd, Mead, 1924

Winnowed Wisdom, Dodd, Mead, 1926

The Iron Man and the Tin Woman, Dodd, Mead, 1929

Laugh with Leacock (selected works), Dodd, Mead, 1930

The Leacock Book (selections), Lane, 1930

Economic Prosperity in the British Empire (treatise), Macmillan, Toronto, 1930

Further Foolishness, Lane, London, 1931

Wet Wit and Dry Humour, Dodd, Mead, 1931

Afternoons in Utopia, Dodd, Mead, 1932

Back to Prosperity (treatise), Macmillan, Toronto, 1932

College Days, Dodd, Mead, 1932

Dry Pickwick and Other Incongruities, Lane, London, 1932

Mark Twain (biography), Davies, London, 1932

Stephen Leacock's Plan (pamphlet), Macmillan, Toronto, 1933

Charles Dickens, His Life and Work (biography), Doubleday, Doran, 1934

Lincoln Frees the Slaves (history), Putnam, 1934

The Perfect Salesman, McBride, 1934

The Pursuit of Knowledge (treatise on education), Liveright, 1934

Humor: Its Theory and Technique (study of humor), Dodd, Mead, 1935

Funny Pieces, Dodd, Mead, 1936

The Gathering Financial Crisis in Canada (treatise), Macmillan, Toronto, 1936

The Greatest Pages of American Humor (anthology), Doubleday, Doran, 1936

Hellements of Hickonomics (humorous verse), Dodd, Mead, 1936

How Are My Lectures and Stories, Dodd, Mead, 1937

My Discovery of the West (a description), Hale, Cushman, & Flint, Boston, 1937

Humor and Humanity (treatise), Holt, 1938

Model Memoirs, Dodd, Mead, 1938

Too Much College, Dodd, Mead, 1939

All Right, Mr. Roosevelt (pamphlet), Farrar & Rinehart, 1939

The British Empire: Its Structure, Its Unity, Its Strength (treatise), Dodd, Mead, 1940

Stephen Leacock's Laugh Parade, Dodd, Mead, 1940

*My Remarkable Uncle, Dodd, Mead, 1942

Our Heritage of Liberty (historical study), Dodd, Mead, 1942

Canada (history), Gazette Co., Montreal, 1942

How to Write (humorous essay), Dodd, Mead, 1942

All of Mr. Leacock's works, unless otherwise specified, are books of humorous stories and essays.

SINCLAIR LEWIS, the first American author to be awarded the Nobel Prize for distinction in world literature, was born in Sauk Centre, Minnesota, on February 7, 1885, the son of a doctor. His boyhood was typically middlewestern, but he insisted on attending Yale University, and came East in 1903. His college career was interrupted for a year in 1906-7, when he spent a couple of months in Upton Sinclair's Helicon Hall, the co-operative colony at Englewood, New Jersey, wandered down to the Panama Canal by steerage and vainly tried to find a job there, lived on the East Side of New York trying to freelance, and for a few months was assistant editor of *Translantic Tales,* a magazine of translations.

After graduation from Yale, in 1908, he worked on newspapers in Iowa and San Francisco, on the Associated Press in the latter, and on a magazine for the deaf in Washington, D. C., and finally found a measure of security as editor for the publishers Frederick A. Stokes and then George H. Doran. In 1914 he married Grace Hegger, and became in 1917 the father of Wells Lewis, who since then has served in the army and himself written a novel.

He left his job at the Doran Company in 1915, for freelancing, and in 1920 achieved recognition with *Main Street*, his seventh novel. This was followed in 1922 by *Babbitt*, a satirical portrayal of an American business-man, and in 1925 by *Arrowsmith*, chronicling a man of science. It was awarded the Pulitzer Prize, which Mr. Lewis refused as a protest against the restrictive terms of the award.

In 1928 Mr. Lewis was divorced from his first wife and married Dorothy Thompson, the political commentator; in 1930 they had a son. And in 1930 Mr. Lewis received the Nobel Prize. In his speech of acceptance he devoted himself to an attack on the American Academy of Arts and Letters (of which he is now a member) for its conventional standards of taste and morals.

Aside from his novels, Mr. Lewis has writ-ten several plays, including *Hobohemia*, and the dramatization of his own novel *It Can't Happen Here*, which shows a shift from the social analysis of most of his novels to a more immediate political concern with the danger of Fascism in this country. *Jayhawker*, a play which he wrote with Lloyd Lewis, deals with Abolitionist days and *Angela Is Twenty-Two*, in which Mr. Lewis himself appeared, is a comedy of May and December.

Mr. Lewis now divides his time between Minnesota, New York, New England, and California.

Hike and the Aeroplane (boys' story), Stokes, 1912
Our Mr. Wrenn, Harpers, 1914
The Trail of the Hawk, Harpers, 1915
The Job, Harpers, 1917
The Innocents, Harpers, 1917
Free Air, Harcourt, Brace, 1919
Main Street, Harcourt, Brace, 1920
Babbitt, Harcourt, Brace, 1922
Arrowsmith, Harcourt, Brace, 1925
Mantrap, Harcourt, Brace, 1926
John Dos Passos' Manhattan Transfer (Criti-cism), Harpers, 1926
Elmer Gantry, Harcourt, Brace, 1927
The Man Who Knew Coolidge, Harcourt, Brace, 1928
Dodsworth, Harcourt, Brace, 1929
Cheap and Contented Labor (tract), Women's Trade Union League, Philadelphia, 1930
Addresses by Eric Axel Karlfeldt and Sinclair Lewis (speech), Harcourt, Brace, 1930
Launcelot (poem), Harvey Taylor, 1932

Sinclair Lewis on The Valley of the Moon, Harvey Taylor, 1932
Ann Vickers, Doubleday, Doran, Garden City, N. Y., 1933
Work of Art, Doubleday, Doran, Garden City, N. Y., 1934
It Can't Happen Here, Doubleday, Doran, Garden City, N. Y., 1935
Selected Short Stories, Doubleday, Doran, Gar-den City, N. Y., 1935
Jayhawker (drama; with LLOYD LEWIS), Doubleday, Doran, Garden City, N. Y., 1935
Prodigal Parents, Doubleday, Doran, Garden City, N. Y., 1938
It Can't Happen Here (a play from the novel), Dramatists Play Service, 1938
Bethel Merriday, Doubleday, Doran, 1940

All of Mr. Lewis's works unless otherwise speci-fied are novels.

ARCHIBALD MACLEISH was born on May 7, 1892, in Glencoe, Illinois, near Lake Michi-gan. He was graduated from Yale in 1915 and received his LL.B. from Harvard in 1919, but in the meantime had married Ada Hitch-cock in 1916 and had seen action in France in the first World War, entering the army as a private and leaving it a captain. Since then, Mr. MacLeish has become the father of three children and the recipient of honorary degrees from many universities.

After practicing law for three years, Mr. MacLeish began his poetic career in 1923 when he went to France, where he remained until 1928. His poetry of this period expressed the individual's hopelessness in the face of post-war chaos and was subjective in character.

On his return to the United States his poetry began to show a growing awareness of his national and cultural heritage, and with *Conquistador*, an epic of the conquest of Mexico, he won the 1933 Pulitzer Prize for poetry. Since then he has turned his atten-tion more and more to the immediate social issues of the American scene and to the prob-lems facing American democracy in the modern world. His interest in these matters has ex-pressed itself primarily in verse plays, sev-eral of them written specifically for radio presentation.

Mr. MacLeish was one of the editors of *Fortune* from its beginning to 1938. He set up the Nieman Fellowships in Journalism at the Harvard School of Journalism. In 1939 he was appointed Librarian of Congress, a posi-tion he still holds, and from October, 1941 to June, 1942, he served, in addition, as Director of the United States Office of Facts and Figures.

Songs for a Summer Day, Yale University Press, New Haven, Conn., 1915

Tower of Ivory, Yale University Press, New Haven, Conn., 1917

The Happy Marriage, Houghton Mifflin, Boston, 1924

The Pot of Earth, Houghton Mifflin, Boston, 1925

Nobodaddy (drama), Dunster House, Boston, 1926

Streets in the Moon, Houghton Mifflin, Boston, 1926

The Hamlet of A. MacLeish, Houghton Mifflin, Boston, 1928

Einstein, Black Sun Press, Paris, 1929

New Found Land, Black Sun Press, Paris, 1930

Before March, Knopf, 1932

Conquistador, Houghton Mifflin, Boston, 1932

Frescoes for Mr. Rockefeller's City, Day, 1933

Selected Poems of Archibald MacLeish, 1924-1933, Houghton Mifflin, Boston, 1933

Panic (drama), Houghton Mifflin, Boston, 1935

Public Speech, Farrar & Rinehart, 1936

The Fall of the City (verse play for radio), Farrar & Rinehart, 1937

Land of the Free, Harcourt, Brace, 1938

Air Raid (verse play for radio), Harcourt, Brace, 1938

**America Was Promises*, Duell, Sloan, & Pearce, 1939

The Irresponsibles, Duell, Sloan, & Pearce, 1940

The States Talking (pamphlet), Free Company, 1941

The American Cause (essay), Duell, Sloan, & Pearce, 1941

Prophets of Doom (lecture), University of Pennsylvania Press, Philadelphia, 1941

A Time to Speak (selected prose), Houghton Mifflin, Boston, 1941

Unless otherwise indicated, Mr. MacLeish's works are poetry.

JOHN P. MARQUAND was born in Wilmington, Delaware, on November 10, 1893, and received his A.B. from Harvard in 1915. After two years as assistant managing editor of the Boston *Transcript*, he saw action on the front as a first lieutenant in the Field Artillery, and returned in 1919 to resume his newspaper career, this time with the New York *Herald Tribune*. He married Christina Sedgwick in 1922, and was remarried in 1937 to Adelaide Hooker; he is now the father of three children.

Mr. Marquand has led a literary double life, writing on the one hand popular detective stories centering around the character of Mr. Moto and on the other hand a number of searching novels with their setting in New England. His *The Late George Apley*, a novel in the form of a memoir satirizing the life of a Boston Brahmin, was awarded the 1938 Pulitzer Prize.

The Unspeakable Gentleman, Scribners, 1922

Four of a Kind, Scribners, 1923

The Black Cargo, Scribners, 1925

Lord Timothy Dexter, Minton, Balch, 1925

Warning Hill, Little, Brown, Boston, 1930

Haven's End, Little, Brown, Boston, 1933

Ming Yellow, Little, Brown, Boston, 1935

No Hero, Little, Brown, Boston, 1935

Thank You, Mr. Moto, Little, Brown, Boston, 1936

**The Late George Apley*, Little, Brown, Boston, 1937

Think Fast, Mr. Moto, Little, Brown, Boston, 1937

Mr. Moto Is So Sorry, Little, Brown, Boston, 1938

Wickford Point, Little, Brown, Boston, 1939

Mr. Moto Takes a Hand, Robert Hale, London, 1940

Don't Ask Questions, Robert Hale, London, 1941

H. M. Pulham, Esq., Little, Brown, Boston, 1941

All of Mr. Marquand's works are novels.

EDGAR LEE MASTERS was born at Garnett, Kansas, on August 23, 1869, the son of a lawyer. When he was eleven his family moved from Petersburg to Lewistown, Illinois, where he attended high school. After four years of work on the local weekly, during which time he contributed stories and poems to various magazines, he entered Knox College, Illinois, where he remained for a year. Returning to Lewistown, he studied law, was admitted to the bar in 1891, and for a year was in partnership with his father. Then he went to Chicago, where he opened a law office, and until 1922 he was engaged in the legal profession.

Mr. Masters achieved first fame with his *Spoon River Anthology* in 1915. Since then he has published many volumes, including poetry, drama, novels, and biography.

A Book of Verses, Way & Williams, Chicago, 1898

Maximilian (blank verse drama), Badger, Boston, 1902

The New Star Chamber, and Other Essays, Hammersmark Publishing Co., Chicago, 1904

Blood of the Prophets (poetry), Hammersmark Publishing Co., Chicago, 1905

Althea (play), Rooks Press, Chicago, 1907

The Trifler (play), Rooks Press, Chicago, 1908

Songs and Sonnets, Rooks Press, Chicago, 1910

Eileen (play), Rooks Press, Chicago, 1910

The Leaves of the Tree (play), Rooks Press, Chicago, 1910

The Locket (play), Rooks Press, Chicago, 1910

The Bread of Idleness (play), Rooks Press, Chicago, 1911

Spoon River Anthology (poetry), Macmillan, 1915

Songs and Satires (poetry), Macmillan, 1916

The Great Valley (poetry), Macmillan, 1916

*Toward the Gulf (poetry), Macmillan, 1918

Starved Rock (poetry), Macmillan, 1919

Mitch Miller (novel), Macmillan, 1920

Domesday Book (poetry), Macmillan, 1920

The Open Sea (poetry), Macmillan, 1921

Children of the Market Place (novel), Macmillan, 1922

Skeeters Kirby (novel), Macmillan, 1923

The Nuptial Flight (novel), Liveright, 1923

Mirage (novel), Liveright, 1924

The New Spoon River (poetry), Liveright, 1924

Selected Poems, Macmillan, 1925

Lee, a Dramatic Poem, Macmillan, 1926

Kit O'Brien (novel), Liveright, 1927

Jack Kelso (dramatic poem), Appleton, 1928

The Fate of the Jury (poetry), Appleton, 1929

Gettysburg, Manila, Acoma (poetry), Liveright, 1930

Lichee Nuts (poetry), Liveright, 1930

Lincoln the Man (biography), Dodd, Mead, 1931

Godbey (dramatic poem), Dodd, Mead, 1931

The Serpent in the Wilderness (poetry), Dick, 1933

The Tale of Chicago (history), Putnam, 1933

Dramatic Duologues (plays), French, 1934

Richmond (dramatic poem), French, 1934

Invisible Landscapes (poetry), Macmillan, 1935

Vachel Lindsay (biography), Scribners, 1935

Poems of People, Appleton-Century, 1936

The Golden Fleece of California (poetry), Countryman Press, Weston, Vt., 1936

Across Spoon River (autobiography), Farrar & Rinehart, 1936

Walt Whitman (biography), Scribners, 1937

The New World (poetry), Appleton-Century, 1937

The Tide of Time (novel), Farrar & Rinehart, 1937

Mark Twain (biography), Scribners, 1938

More People (poetry), Appleton-Century, 1939

The Living Thoughts of Emerson (selections, with essay), Longmans, Green, 1940

Illinois Poems, Press of James A. Decker, Prairie City, Ill., 1941

The Sangamon (regional history), Farrar & Rinehart, 1942

Along the Illinois (poetry), Decker, Prairie City, Ill., 1942

"Spoon River Anthology" has been translated into Swedish by Bertel Gripenberg (Holger Schildts Forlag, Helsingfors, 1927), into Danish by Ova Brusendorf (Jespersen Og Forlag, Copenhagen, 1935), into Dutch (Bij De Boekengilde, Antwerp), Into Japanese by Gan Yamaoka (Tokio, 1931), and into Norwegian.
"The Nuptial Flight was translated into German by Anna Nusbaum, with an introduction by Upton Sinclair (F. G. Speidelsch, Vienna and Leipzig, 1929).

H. L. MENCKEN, journalist, critic, and essayist, was born in Baltimore, Maryland, on September 12, 1880. His German grandfather had come to the United States in 1848 and had founded a tobacco business, which Mr. Mencken's father wished him to carry on; but he was determined to become a journalist, and after his schooling at the Baltimore Polytechnic he became a reporter on the Baltimore *Morning Herald*. By 1903, when he was only twenty-three years old, he was city editor. In this year also he published his first book, *Ventures into Verse*.

Mr. Mencken was editor of the *Evening Herald* in 1905 and 1906, on the staff of the Baltimore *Sun* from 1906 until 1941. During 1917 he was war correspondent for the *Sun* in Germany. Meanwhile he had become literary critic for *The Smart Set*, and from 1914 on he was co-editor of the magazine with George Jean Nathan. In 1924 he founded with Nathan *The American Mercury*, of which he was sole editor from 1925 to 1933.

In 1930 he married Sara Haardt, the author, who died in 1935. He lives in Baltimore.

Ventures into Verse, Marshall, Beek, & Gordon, 1903

George Bernard Shaw—His Plays, Luce, Boston, 1905

The Philosophy of Friedrich Nietzsche, Luce, Boston, 1908

Men Versus the Man (with R. R. LaMonte), Holt, 1910

The Artist (drama), Luce, Boston, 1912

Europe After 8:15 (travelogue; with George Jean Nathan and W. H. Wright), Lane, 1914

A Book of Burlesques (sketches), Knopf, 1916

A Little Book in C Major (epigrams), Knopf, 1916

A Book of Prefaces (essays), Knopf, 1917

In Defense of Women, Knopf, 1918

Damn—A Book of Calumny (essays), Knopf, 1918

The American Language (philology), Knopf, 1919

Prejudices (essays), Knopf
—*First Series*, 1919
—*Second Series*, 1920
—*Third Series*, 1922
—*Fourth Series*, 1924
—*Fifth Series*, 1926
—*Sixth Series*, 1927
The American Credo (essays; with GEORGE JEAN NATHAN), Knopf, 1920
Heliogabalus (drama; with GEORGE JEAN NATHAN), Knopf, 1920
Notes on Democracy, Knopf, 1926
James Branch Cabell, McBride, 1927
Selected Prejudices (essays), Knopf, 1927
Menckeniana, a Schimpflexikon (comments on H. L. MENCKEN), Knopf, 1928
Treatise on the Gods, Knopf, 1930
Lo, the Poor Bookseller (pamphlet), Stanley Rose, Hollywood, Cal., 1930
Making a President, Knopf, 1932
Treatise on Right and Wrong, Knopf, 1934
Happy Days, 1880-1892 (autobiography), Knopf, 1940
**Newspaper Days, 1899-1906* (autobiography), Knopf, 1941
A New Dictionary of Quotations, Knopf, 1942

EDNA ST. VINCENT MILLAY has been a poet since childhood: before she reached high school her verses were published in *St. Nicholas*. She was born in Rockland, Maine, on February 22, 1892, and spent her early years in New England. At the age of nineteen, while still a schoolgirl, she wrote her first long poem, "Renascence," which won for her nation-wide fame and admiration.

After a brief period at Barnard College Miss Millay went to Vassar, where she won the cup awarded in the Intercollegiate Poetry Contest and from which she was graduated in 1917. Her first volume of poetry, *Renascence and Other Poems*, was published the same year. After graduation she moved to New York, wrote and acted for the Provincetown Players, and took part in productions of the Theatre Guild; and to support herself she published short stories over the pseudonym "Nancy Boyd." She wrote and published poetry and experimented in poetic plays, of which she published three in 1921. In 1925 the Metropolitan Opera Association commissioned her to write the book for an opera, the music to be written by Deems Taylor; and *The King's Henchman*, produced in 1927, was perhaps the most successful American opera given in New York to that date.

In 1920 *Poetry* gave Miss Millay a cash prize, and in 1931 it awarded her the Helen Haire Levinson Prize. *The Harp-Weaver and*

Other Poems received the 1923 Pulitzer Prize for poetry.

In the same year she married Eugen Jan Boissevain, and not long after they moved from Greenwich Village to a farm in the Berkshires. Recently they have bought an island off the Maine coast.

Renascence and Other Poems, Kennerley, 1917
Possession, a Sonnet, privately printed, 1918
A Few Figs from Thistles, Shay, 1920 (enlarged 1920, 1921)
Aria da Capo (play), Harpers, 1920
Second April, Kennerley, 1921
The Lamp and the Bell (poetic drama), Harpers, 1921
Two Slatterns and a King (poetic drama), Stewart, Kidd, Cincinnati, 1921
The Ballad of the Harp-Weaver, Shay, 1922
The Harp-Weaver and Other Poems, Harpers, 1923
Poems, Harpers, 1923
Renascence, Fredrick & Bertha Goudy, 1924
Distressing Dialogues (humor), Harpers, 1924
The King's Henchman (libretto), 1926 (complete edition without music)
Three Plays, Harpers, 1926
The Pamphlet Poets: Edna St. Vincent Millay, Simon & Schuster, 1927
The Buck in the Snow & Other Poems, Harpers, 1928
Edna St. Vincent Millay's Poems Selected for Young People, Harpers, 1929
Fatal Interview, Harpers, 1931
The Princess Marries the Page (poetic drama), Harpers, 1932
Wine from These Grapes, Harpers, 1934
Epitaph for the Race of Man (Vol. 2 of the limited edition of *Wine from These Grapes*), Harpers, 1934
Vacation Song, Harpers, 1936
Flowers of Evil (translation from the French of Baudelaire; with George Dillon), Harpers, 1936
Conversation at Midnight, Harpers, 1937
Huntsman, What Quarry?, Harpers, 1939
Make Bright the Arrows, Harpers, 1940
There Are No Islands Any More, Harpers, 1940
**Collected Sonnets*, Harpers, 1941

Unless otherwise indicated, all Miss Millay's works are poetry. Not included in the bibliography are the large number of her verses which have been set to music and published as sheet music.

MARIANNE MOORE has been described by Alfred Kreymborg as "an astonishing person with Titian hair, a brilliant complexion and a mellifluous flow of polysyllables which held every man in awe"; and she has said of her writing that "it is my one principle that nothing is too much trouble." She was born in St. Louis on November 15, 1887, and was graduated from Bryn Mawr College in 1909. After a year of study at a commercial college she taught commercial subjects for four years at the Carlisle United States Indian School.

From 1921 to 1925 Miss Moore was an assistant in the New York Public Library. In 1921 poems of hers had been collected by a group of her friends and published under the title *Poems*, without, however, the knowledge of the author, and in 1924 she published *Observations*. On the basis of these two volumes she received the *Dial* award for 1924, and from 1925 to 1929 she was acting editor of this periodical.

Other honors have included the Helen Haire Levinson Prize (1933), the Ernest Hartsock Memorial Prize (1935), and the Shelley Memorial Award for 1940.

Miss Moore lives in Brooklyn, New York.

Poems, Egoist Press, London, 1921
Observations, Dial Press, 1924
Selected Poems, Macmillan, 1935
The Pangolin, and Other Verse, Brendin Publishing Co., London, 1936
*What Are Years?, Macmillan, 1941

All of Miss Moore's work is verse.

CHRISTOPHER MORLEY was born in Haverford, Pennsylvania, on May 5, 1890 and spent his teens in Baltimore. He was graduated from Haverford College in 1910, and the same year was awarded a Rhodes Scholarship, and went to New College, Oxford.

Returning to the United States in 1913, Mr. Morley was first on the editorial staff of Doubleday, Page, & Co., later of *The Ladies' Home Journal*, the Philadelphia *Public Ledger*, and the New York *Evening Post*. From 1924 to 1940 he was on the staff of *The Saturday Review of Literature*, of which he was one of the founders. In 1928, Mr. Morley helped organize a company at the Old Rialto Theatre in Hoboken, which revived some old melodramas and produced some of Mr. Morley's own plays. He was editor-in-chief of the new edition of Bartlett's *Familiar Quotations* (1937) and has been one of the judges of the Book-of-the-Month Club since its beginning in 1926.

Christopher Morley, asked for full details of his many writings, said he is both too modest and too patriotic to traverse the shortage of valuable paper. He referred us to Alfred P. Lee, *Bibliography of Christopher Morley*,

published in 1935 by the J. B. Lippincott Co., of Philadelphia, which collates all this material in full to that date.

Mr. Morley wrote: "I suggest that you confine your memorandum to the following. In twenty-five years I have written a dozen works of fiction, a dozen collections of short pieces which have been labelled *essays*, though I never thought of them as such, half a dozen small books of verse in differing moods, and I suppose a dozen or so other volumes of various sorts, *viz.*, travel pieces, plays, theology, autobiography, and stories for children. You might leave it at that. If anyone wished to investigate, a bookseller or librarian can help. If he wished my own testimony on the matter I would suggest he try *Where the Blue Begins*, *Thunder on the Left*, *The Romany Stain*, *John Mistletoe*, *The Trojan Horse*, and *Kitty Foyle*, and convince himself they could not all have been written by the same person."

Of Mr. Morley's selections for this anthology, "Nightpiece to Herrick" and "Hampstead Coach" have never appeared in books. "A Song for Eros" is reprinted from *The Trojan Horse*, and "Dogwood Tree" from *John Mistletoe*.

OGDEN NASH was born on August 16, 1902, in Rye, New York. He attended the St. George's School in Newport, Rhode Island, and Harvard (1920-1921). His light verse has appeared in *The New Yorker*, *The Saturday Evening Post*, and many other magazines. In it nonsense, wit, and satire appear in varying degrees, and most of it is notable for eccentricities of meter, including line-lengths ranging from two syllables to sixty-two, and for studied and startling inaccuracies of rhyme.

Mr. Nash, who married Frances Rider Leonard in 1931, is the father of two children and lives in Baltimore.

The Cricket of Carador (juvenile; with JOSEPH ALGER), Doubleday, Page, Garden City, N. Y., 1925
Born in a Beer Garden (sketches; with others), Rudge, 1930
Free Wheeling, Simon & Schuster, 1931
Hard Lines, Simon & Schuster, 1931
Happy Days, Simon & Schuster, 1933
Four Prominent So and So's (song; music by Robert Armbruster, illustrations by Soglow), Simon & Schuster, 1934
The Primrose Path, Simon & Schuster, 1935
The Bad Parents' Garden of Verse, Simon & Schuster, 1936
Boy Voyage (folder), Doubleday Doran Book Shops, 1936

I'm a Stranger Here Myself, Little, Brown, Boston, 1938
*The Face Is Familiar (selected poems), Little, Brown, Boston, 1940

GEORGE JEAN NATHAN, dramatic critic and author, was born in Fort Wayne, Indiana, on February 14, 1882, and received his A.B. from Cornell in 1904. His career in journalism began in 1905 on the James Gordon Bennett New York *Herald*. In 1908 began his famous association with *The Smart Set*, of which he was dramatic critic until 1923 and co-editor with H. L. Mencken from 1914 to 1923. *The American Mercury* was founded by Mencken and Nathan in 1924; Mr. Nathan was co-editor until 1925, and from 1925 to 1930 he was contributing editor and dramatic critic. In 1932 he was one of the founders and editors of *The American Spectator*.

Since then Mr. Nathan has been associated with many magazines as dramatic critic, including *Vanity Fair, The Saturday Review of Literature, Esquire, Scribner's, Newsweek, Liberty,* the new *American Mercury*, etc. He is the authority on the American theatre and drama for the *Encyclopaedia Britannica* and the *Britannica Book of the Year*. He is a bachelor by conviction, and lives in New York City.

Europe After 8:15 (travelogue; with H. L. MENCKEN and W. H. WRIGHT), Lane, 1914
Another Book on the Theatre, Huebsch, 1915
Bottoms Up (sketches), Goodman, 1917
Mr. George Jean Nathan Presents, Knopf, 1917
A Book Without a Title (sketches), Goodman, 1918
The Popular Theatre, Knopf, 1918
Comedians All, Knopf, 1919
The American Credo (philosophical humor; with H. L. MENCKEN), Knopf, 1920
Heliogabalus (drama; with H. L. MENCKEN), Knopf, 1920
The Theatre, the Drama, the Girls, Knopf, 1921
*The Critic and the Drama, Knopf, 1922
The World in Falseface, Knopf, 1923
Materia Critica, Knopf, 1924
The Autobiography of an Attitude, Knopf, 1925
The House of Satan, Knopf, 1926
The New American Credo (philosophical humor), Knopf, 1927
The Land of the Pilgrims' Pride (Essays and criticism), Knopf, 1927
Art of the Night, Knopf, 1928
Monks Are Monks (fiction), Knopf, 1929

Testament of a Critic, Knopf, 1931
The Intimate Notebooks of George Jean Nathan (biography and criticism), Knopf, 1932
Since Ibsen (history of the popular theatre since 1900), Knopf, 1933
Passing Judgments, Knopf, 1935
The Theatre of the Moment, Knopf, 1936
The Avon Flows (rearrangements of Shakespeare), Random House, 1937
The Morning After the First Night, Knopf, 1938
Encyclopaedia of the Theatre, Knopf, 1940
The Bachelor Life (essays), Reynal & Hitchcock, 1941
The Entertainment of a Nation (criticism and Essays), Knopf, 1942

All of Mr. Nathan's works, unless otherwise specified, are dramatic criticism.

ROBERT NATHAN was born in New York City on January 2, 1894, and was educated in schools here and in Switzerland, including Exeter Academy and Harvard. He has been married four times, the last time in 1940 to Janet McMillan.

Mr. Nathan is gifted not only as a writer but also as an artist and a musician. He has composed some music, and a great deal of his musical feeling is to be found in his prose and poetry, which is distinguished primarily for its tone of delicate satirical phantasy.

He was a vice president of the National Institute of Arts and Letters from 1938 to 1941, and has been President of the P.E.N. since 1940. His home is in New York, and he spends his summers in Truro, Massachusetts.

Peter Kindred, Duffield, 1919
Autumn, McBride, 1921
Youth Grows Old (poetry), McBride, 1922
The Puppet Master, McBride, 1923
Jonah, McBride, 1925
The Fiddler in Barly, McBride, 1926
The Woodcutter's House, Bobbs-Merrill, Indianapolis, 1927
The Bishop's Wife, Bobbs-Merrill, Indianapolis, 1928
A Cedar Box (poetry), Bobbs-Merrill, Indianapolis, 1929
There Is Another Heaven, Bobbs-Merrill, Indianapolis, 1929
The Orchid, Bobbs-Merrill, Indianapolis, 1931
*One More Spring, Knopf, 1933
Road of Ages, Knopf, 1935
Selected Poems, Knopf, 1936
The Enchanted Voyage, Knopf, 1936
Winter in April, Knopf, 1938

The Barly Fields (collection of five earlier novels), Knopf, 1938
Journey of Tapiola (story), Knopf, 1938
Portrait of Jennie, Knopf, 1940
The Concert (short story), House of Books, 1940
A Winter Tide, Knopf, 1940
They Went On Together, Knopf, 1941
Tapiola's Brave Regiment, Knopf, 1941
The Sea-Gull Cry, Knopf, 1942

All of Mr. Nathan's works, unless otherwise indicated, are novels.

ALLAN NEVINS, journalist, educator, and historian, twice winner of the Pulitzer Prize for biography, was born in Camp Point, Illinois, on May 20, 1890. He received his A.B. from the University of Illinois in 1912, and was an instructor of English there during the next year while working on his A.M., which he received in 1913. For ten years thereafter he was an editorial writer for the New York *Evening Post* and *The Nation*. In 1924 and 1925 he was literary editor of the New York *Sun*, and then was one of the editors of the New York *World*, until its death in 1931.

While still an active journalist Mr. Nevins took up teaching; in 1927 and 1928 he was professor of American history at Cornell, and from 1928 until the present time has been at Columbia, where he is now De Witt Clinton Professor of History. He was Harmsworth Professor of American history at Oxford in 1940-41.

Mr. Nevins has published many stimulating works of history and biography, has edited the diaries of Philip Hone, John Quincy Adams, and Polk, and the letters of Grover Cleveland and Brand Whitlock. His *Grover Cleveland—A Study in Courage* and *Hamilton Fish—The Inner History of the Grant Administration* were awarded the Pulitzer Prize for biography in 1933 and 1940.

He was married in 1916 to Mary Richardson and is the father of two children. He lives in Bronxville, New York.

The Life of Robert Rogers, Caxton Club, Chicago, 1914
Illinois, Oxford University Press, 1917
The Evening Post—A Century of Journalism, Boni & Liveright, 1922
American Social History Recorded by British Travelers, Holt, 1923
The American States During and After the Revolution, Macmillan, 1924
The Emergence of Modern America, Macmillan, 1927

Frémont, the West's Greatest Adventurer, Harpers, 1927
American Press Opinion, Washington to Coolidge (anthology), Heath, 1928
Henry White—Thirty Years of American Diplomacy, Harpers, 1930
Grover Cleveland—A Study in Courage, Dodd, Mead, 1932
Abram S. Hewitt, with Some Account of Peter Cooper, Harpers, 1935
Hamilton Fish—The Inner History of the Grant Administration, Dodd, Mead, 1936
**The Gateway to History* (historiography), Appleton-Century, 1938
Frémont, Pathmarker of the West (revision and enlargement of *Frémont, the West's Greatest Adventurer*), Appleton-Century, 1939
John D. Rockefeller: the Heroic Age of American Enterprise, two volumes, Scribners, 1940
This Is England Today, Scribners, 1941
America in World Affairs, Oxford University Press, 1942

CLIFFORD ODETS is generally recognized as one of America's most gifted playwrights. He was born on July 18, 1906, in Philadelphia, where his father was a printer. His family moved to New York when he was two years old; he was raised in New York. At the age of fifteen he left school to become an actor, played five years of stock, announced and performed on the radio, acted with the Theatre Guild in 1928-9, and in 1930 became a founding member of The Group Theatre. While acting in this company he wrote the play produced in 1935 as *Awake and Sing!* The success of this play and of his *Waiting for Lefty*, which won the Yale Drama Prize for 1935, and in which Mr. Odets played, transformed a surprised young actor to a successful playwright. Mr. Odets has since produced a new play almost every year and has written several movie scripts in Hollywood.

Awake and Sing!, Random House, 1935
Three Plays: Awake and Sing!; Waiting for Lefty; Till the Day I Die, Random House, 1935
Waiting for Lefty, and Till the Day I Die: Two Plays, Random House, 1935
Paradise Lost, Random House, 1936
Golden Boy, Random House, 1937
Rocket to the Moon, Random House, 1939
**Six Plays of Clifford Odets*, Random House (Modern Library), 1939
Night Music, Random House, 1940
Clash by Night, Random House, 1941

Mr. Odets's works are plays.

EUGENE O'NEILL, playwright and winner of
the Nobel Prize for Literature in 1936, has
had an intensely vivid and varied career. Born
in an hotel on what is now Times Square in
New York on October 16, 1888, a son of the
famous romantic actor, James O'Neill, he has
been in intimate touch with the theatre since
earliest childhood.

A college career at Princeton ended after
one year. He then worked in a small mail-
order house in New York for a year and a
half. In 1909 he went on a gold-prospecting
trip to Honduras, where he found no gold but
contracted malaria. He returned to this country, and after a short period as assistant manager of "The White Sister," in which his
father was one of the stars, he sailed on a
Norwegian barque to Buenos Aires, where he
worked for short periods with the Westing-
house Electrical Co., Swift Packing Co., and
Singer Sewing Machine Co. Then he went to
sea again as ordinary seaman on a British
tramp steamer, and later as an able bodied
seaman on trans-Atlantic American Line ships.
His ambition at this time, as he says, was "to
be a Jack London 'he-man' sailor."

In 1912, he acted for part of a season with
his father, and later worked as a reporter on
a New London, Connecticut, newspaper. At the
end of that year he suffered a physical breakdown and was forced to go to a tuberculosis
sanatorium for six months. This period of rest
cure he acknowledges as a turning point of his
life: it was then, he has said, that he first
began "thinking it over," and a few months
after he left the sanatorium he wrote his first
play. In 1914-15 he studied the technique of
playwrighting for one year in Baker's famous
"47 Workshop" at Harvard. In 1916 he joined
the Provincetown Players, and for many years
it was this group which gave him his chance
to be heard in the theatre, and produced almost all of his work.

Recognition as the foremost American playwright came in 1920 with the Pulitzer Prize
for his *Beyond the Horizon.* Since then he has
been awarded the Pulitzer Prize twice, in 1922
for *Anna Christie* and in 1928 for *Strange
Interlude.*

One detects two main types in Mr. O'Neill's
dramatic works; naturalistic studies of tragic
frustration, and brilliant experiments in symbolic expressionism. He has always been an experimenter in forms, and his influence in bringing about the birth of a vital American theatre
has been enormous.

Thirst, and Other One-Act Plays, Badger,
Boston, 1914
Before Breakfast, Frank Shay, 1916

*The Moon of the Caribbees, and Other One-Act
Plays of the Sea,* Liveright, 1919
Gold, Liveright, 1920
Beyond the Horizon, Liveright, 1921
The Emperor Jones; Diff'rent; The Straw,
Liveright, 1921
*The Hairy Ape; Anna Christie; The First
Man,* Liveright, 1922
All God's Chillun Got Wings; Welded, Live-
right, 1924
Complete Works, two volumes, Boni & Live-
right, 1924
Desire Under the Elms, Liveright, 1925
*The Great God Brown; The Fountain; The
Moon of the Caribbees, and Other Plays,*
Liveright, 1926
Lazarus Laughed, Liveright, 1927
Marco Millions, Liveright, 1927
Strange Interlude, Liveright, 1928
Dynamo, Liveright, 1929
Mourning Becomes Electra, Liveright, 1931
Nine Plays, Random House, 1932
Ah, Wilderness!, Random House, 1934
Days Without End, Random House, 1934
Plays, three volumes, Random House, 1941

All of Mr. O'Neill's works are plays.

DOROTHY PARKER was born in West End,
New Jersey, on August 22, 1893, and attended
school in Morristown, New Jersey, and in
New York City (where the only thing she
learned, as she says, was that if you spit on
a pencil eraser it will erase ink).

Mrs. Parker was on the editorial staff of
Vogue in 1916 and 1917, and from 1917 to
1920 she was dramatic critic for *Vanity Fair.*
In 1927 she became book reviewer for *The
New Yorker,* but since 1920 has devoted her-
self mainly to free-lance writing.

She married Edwin Pond Parker II in 1917,
and was divorced from him in 1928. She is
now married to Alan Campbell, the actor, in
collaboration with whom she has written
numerous motion-picture scenarios. During the
Spanish Civil War she was a correspondent in
Spain. Her story, *Big Blonde,* won the O.
Henry Memorial Prize in 1929.

Men I'm Not Married To (humorous sketch),
Doubleday, Page, Garden City, N. Y.,
1922
Enough Rope (poetry), Liveright, 1926 (en-
larged 1934)
Sunset Gun (poetry), Liveright, 1928 (en-
larged 1934)
Close Harmony (play; with ELMER RICE),
French, 1929
Laments for the Living (short stories), Viking
Press, 1930

Death and Taxes (poetry), Viking Press, 1931
After Such Pleasures (short stories), Viking Press, 1933
Not So Deep as a Well (collected poems), Viking Press, 1936
Here Lies (collected short stories), Viking Press, 1939

DONALD CULROSS PEATTIE, poet and naturalist, was born June 21, 1898 in Chicago, although much of his childhood was passed in the North Carolina mountains where nature first made on him its deep impression. He was graduated in 1922 from Harvard, where he was trained as a botanist and won the Witter Bynner poetry prize. Entering the Department of Agriculture, he served three years as botanist, and then decided to become a nature writer. His first work appeared in a column in the Washington *Star*. These sketches, written from his home in northern Virginia, were the forerunners of *An Almanac for Moderns*, the book that brought him his first success and was awarded the first gold medal of the Limited Editions Club, as the recent American work most likely to become a classic.

Mr. Peattie's writings have included not only scholarly scientific studies, but biography, autobiography, history, essays, conservation appeals, and other journalism, as well as novels and juveniles. He still continues the brief, reflective nature sketch with which his career first began, in *The Nature of Things*, one of the regular features of the *Audubon Magazine*.

Mr. Peattie is married to Louise Redfield Peattie, the novelist. They have three children and live in Santa Barbara, California.

Cargoes and Harvests (popularization of economic botany), Appleton, 1926
Bounty of Earth (nature essay; with his wife), Appleton, 1926
Up Country (novel; with his wife), Appleton, 1927
Down Wind (animal stories; with his wife), Appleton, 1929
Flora of the Indiana Dunes, Field Museum of Natural History, Chicago, 1930
Vence, the Story of a Provençal Town, privately printed, Nice, France, 1930
Port of Call (novel), Century, 1932
Sons of the Martian (novel), Longmans, Green, 1932
Flora of the Tryon Region of North and South Carolina, six parts, Elisha Mitchell Scientific Journal, Chapel Hall, N. C., 1928-32
The Natural History of Pearson's Falls, printed for the Garden Club of Tryon, N. C., 1933
The Bright Lexicon (novel), Putnam, 1934

Trees of North America, Whitman Publishing Co., Racine, Wis., 1934
An Almanac for Moderns (nature essays), Putnam, 1935
Singing in the Wilderness: A Salute to John James Audubon, Putnam, 1935
The Happy Kingdom (Riviera travel, history, nature, autobiography; with his wife), Blackie & Sons, Glasgow, Scotland, 1935
Green Laurels (biography), Simon & Schuster, 1936
Old-Fashioned Garden Flowers, Field Museum of Natural History, Chicago, 1936
*A Book of Hours (essays), Putnam, 1937
A Child's Story of the World (juvenile), Simon & Schuster, 1937
A Prairie Grove (ecological novel), Simon & Schuster, 1938
This Is Living (photographic nature anthology with essays; with GORDON AYMAR), Dodd, Mead, 1938
A Gathering of Birds (anthology), Dodd, Mead, 1939
Flowering Earth (popularization of botany), Putnam, 1939
The Road of a Naturalist (autobiography), Houghton Mifflin, Boston, 1941
Forward the Nation (tribute to Lewis and Clark and their Indian woman guide, Sacajawea), Putnam, 1942

S. J. PERELMAN was born in Brooklyn on February 1, 1904, and graduated from Brown University in 1925. For four years thereafter he was an artist and writer for *Judge,* and later for *College Humor.* Since 1930 he has been writing for motion pictures and the theater. He has written a number of sketches for various revues, as well as two plays with his wife, *All Good Americans* (1934) and *The Night Before Christmas* (1940). Since 1934 he has contributed regularly to *The New Yorker.*

Mr. Perelman was married in 1929 to Laura West, and is the father of two children. He lives in Bucks County, Pennsylvania.

Dawn Ginsbergh's Revenge (essays), Liveright, 1929
Parlor, Bedlam, and Bath (novel), Liveright, 1930
Strictly from Hunger (essays), Random House, 1937
Look Who's Talking! (essays), Random House, 1940

KATHERINE ANNE PORTER was born in Indian Creek, Texas, on May 15, 1894, and was educated in various private schools. Since 1920 she has lived in New York or abroad, in Europe and Mexico. In 1931 and 1938 she was awarded a Guggenheim Fellowship for creative writing abroad, and in 1937 she received a Book-of-the-Month Club $2500 award "in recognition of the precise and delicate art of her short stories of American and Mexican life." In 1940 she was awarded the first annual Gold Medal for literature by the Society for the libraries of New York University for her *Pale Horse, Pale Rider*. She was married in 1938 to Albert Russell Erskine, Jr. This marriage was dissolved in June, 1942. She lives now in Saratoga Springs, New York. She recently translated *The Itching Parrot*, a Mexican novel of the last century, from the Spanish, and her first novel, *No Safe Harbor*, is scheduled to appear in 1942.

Flowering Judas (short stories), Harcourt, Brace, 1930 (augmented 1935)

Katherine Anne Porter's French Song Book (collection of songs), Harrison, Paris, 1933

Hacienda (short story), Harrison of Paris, 1934

Noon Wine (novella), Schumann's, Detroit, 1937

Pale Horse, Pale Rider (three novellas), Harcourt, Brace, 1939

No Safe Harbor (novel), Harcourt, Brace, 1942

The Itching Parrot (translation from the Spanish, with preface), Doubleday, Doran, 1942

The Leaning Tower (short stories), Harcourt, Brace, to be published 1943

MARJORIE KINNAN RAWLINGS has said that in 1928 she "deliberately cut her civilized ties . . . and migrated to the firmly intrenched outpost of the vanishing frontier," the hummock country of Florida that forms the setting for her fiction. She was born in Washington, D. C., on August 8, 1896, and received her A.B. from the University of Wisconsin in 1918. After doing War publicity work she became a newspaper writer for the Rochester *Journal* of Rochester, New York, and later wrote syndicated verse for United Features.

Since 1931 Mrs. Rawlings has been writing fiction. In 1933 she received the O. Henry Memorial Award, and her *The Yearling*, the story of a young boy's love for his pet fawn, was awarded the Pulitzer Prize in 1939.

She married Charles Rawlings in 1919, and was divorced from him in 1933. In 1941 she

was remarried to Norton Baskin; they live in Hawthorn, Florida.

South Moon Under (novel), Scribners, 1933
Golden Apples (novel), Scribners, 1935
The Yearling (novel), Scribners, 1938
When the Whippoorwill— (short stories), Scribners, 1940
Cross Creek (autobiography), Scribners, 1942

AGNES REPPLIER, the essayist, was born of French and German parentage in Philadelphia on April 1, 1858, and received her education from French nuns at the Sacred Heart Convent of Torresdale, Pennsylvania, where she was taught to speak French. Her literary career began with the writing of short stories, some of which she sold to *The Catholic World*, but she turned soon to essays, and it is as an essayist that she is best known.

Miss Repplier's devotion to France, is only equalled by her love of England. Her published books include many volumes of familiar and critical essays, biography, and one autobiographical work. She has received honorary degrees from several universities, and was one of the first four women honored by the Nation Institute of Arts and Letters.

Miss Repplier lives in retirement now in the city of her birth.

Books and Men (essays), Houghton Mifflin, Boston, 1888
Points of View (essays), Houghton Mifflin, Boston, 1891
Essays in Miniature, Houghton Mifflin, Boston, 1892
Essays in Idleness, Houghton Mifflin, Boston, 1893
In the Dozy Hours (essays), Houghton Mifflin, Boston, 1894
Varia (essays), Houghton Mifflin, Boston, 1897
Philadelphia: The Place and the People, Macmillan, N. Y., 1898
The Fireside Sphinx (History of the cat), Houghton Mifflin, Boston, 1901
Compromises (essays), Houghton Mifflin, Boston, 1904
In Our Convent Days (autobiography), Houghton Mifflin, 1905
A Happy Half-Century (essays), Houghton Mifflin, Boston, 1908
Americans and Others (essays), Houghton Mifflin, Boston, 1912
Counter-Currents (essays), Houghton, Mifflin, Boston, 1916
J. William White, M.D. (biography), Houghton Mifflin, Boston, 1919

Points of Friction (essays), Houghton Mifflin, Boston, 1920

Under Dispute (essays), Houghton Mifflin, Boston, 1924

The Promise of the Bell (pamphlet), Houghton Mifflin, Boston, 1924

Père Marquette (biography), Doubleday, Doran, Garden City, N. Y., 1929

Mère Marie of the Ursulines (biography), Doubleday, Doran, 1931

Times and Tendencies (essays), Houghton Mifflin, Boston, 1931

To Think of Tea! (a history of tea), Houghton Mifflin, Boston, 1932

Junipero Serra (biography), Doubleday, Doran, Garden City, N. Y., 1933

Agnes Irwin (biography), Doubleday, Doran, Garden City, N. Y., 1934

In Pursuit of Laughter (essays), Houghton Mifflin, Boston, 1936

*Eight Decades (autobiographical sketch and essays), Houghton Mifflin, Boston, 1937

ELMER RICE was born in New York City on September 28, 1892, and attended New York Law School at night while he worked as office boy and later as managing clerk in a downtown law office. In 1913 he was admitted to the bar, but gave up his practice suddenly to write plays.

His first play, *On Trial*, was accepted at once and presented in 1914. It employed for the first time on the stage the familiar film device of the "cutback" or "flashback," reversing chronology in the order of the scenes. Thereafter he was one of the organizers of the Morningside Players, served as dramatic director for the University Settlement in New York, as chairman of the Inter-Settlement Dramatic Society and, many years later, as regional director of the New York Federal Theatre Project.

His *Street Scene*, which had been rejected by nearly every theatrical manager in New York, ran for 601 performances on Broadway and was awarded the Pulitzer Prize for 1929.

In 1938, Mr. Rice, together with Maxwell Anderson, S. N. Behrman, Robert E. Sherwood and the late Sidney Howard, formed the Playwrights' Producing Company. Since 1939 he has been President of the Dramatists' Guild of the Authors' League of America. He is a member of the Board of Directors of the American Civil Liberties Union, of the Council of the League of British Dramatists, of the National Panel of the American Arbitration Association and of the National Institute of Arts and Letters.

Mr. Rice married Betty Field in 1942. He has two children by a former marriage. He lives in Stamford, Connecticut.

On Trial, French, 1914

The Morningside Plays, Frank Shay, 1917

*The Adding Machine, Doubleday, Page, 1923

The Passing of Chow-Chow, French, 1925

Wake Up, Jonathan (with HATCHER HUGHES), French, 1928

Close Harmony (with DOROTHY PARKER), French, 1929

Cock Robin (with PHILIP BARRY), French, 1929

Street Scene, French, 1929

The Subway, French, 1929

See Naples and Die, French, 1930

A Voyage to Purilia (novel), Cosmopolitan Book Corp., 1930

Counsellor-at-Law, French, 1931

The Left Bank, French, 1931

The House in Blind Alley, French, 1932

Plays of Elmer Rice (four plays), Gollancz, London, 1933

We, the People, Coward-McCann, 1933

The Home of the Free, French, 1934

Judgment Day, Coward-McCann, 1934

Three Plays Without Words, French, 1934

Other Plays, and Not for Children (four plays), Gollancz, London, 1935

Two Plays, Coward-McCann, 1935

Imperial City (novel), Coward-McCann, 1937

Black Sheep, Dramatists Play Service, 1938

American Landscape, Coward-McCann, 1939

Two on an Island, Coward-McCann, 1940

Flight to the West, Coward-McCann, 1941

All of Mr. Rice's works, unless otherwise specified, are plays.

CONRAD RICHTER was born in Pine Grove, Pennsylvania, on October 13, 1890, of a family which, several generations previously, had helped settle the town. His father was a preacher, and during his youth Conrad Richter lived in many small towns in Pennsylvania. After his education in high school and preparatory school he was busy at a varied number of jobs: he was a private secretary, drove a wagon, worked in a machine shop, was a bank clerk and a farmer, had his own small timber business, and investigated the silver and lead mines of Idaho. He was a country reporter for Philadelphia papers, and later a reporter for newspapers in Johnstown and Pittsburgh. During these jobs Mr. Richter traveled extensively throughout the country, especially in the West, for which he has a particular fondness.

In 1915 he set up business as a small publisher, married Harvena Achenbach, by whom he has one daughter, and started writing in earnest. His first book, *Early Americana,* is a collection of short stories which appeared in 1936; since then he has published three novels. He lives part of the time in the East and part in the West, especially New Mexico.

Early Americana (short stories), Knopf, 1936
The Sea of Grass (short novel), Knopf, 1937
The Trees (novel), Knopf, 1940
Tacey Cromwell (novel), Knopf, 1942

MURIEL RUKEYSER was born in New York City on December 15, 1913, went to school there, and after two years at Vassar began to work on magazines, in the theatre, and in stores and offices while she was writing the poems of her first book. During these years she was for its short lifetime associate editor of *Housatonic,* a small magazine published in Connecticut one summer; and later associate editor of *New Theatre,* and more recently of *Decision.*

With some time spent in Spain and England, Mexico and California, most of Muriel Rukeyser's work has been done in New York and on the East coast. She has written text for photographs, and worked with documentary films from *Stop Japan* (1936) to *A Place to Live* (1941), but her poems are the main line of any concern in work, and she feels that the other various activities feed back into the poems. She says of her film work that it is "the best 'exercise' I know for the kind of poems I mean to write."

Theory of Flight was published in the Yale Series of Younger Poets in 1935. Since then she has published four other books of poetry, delivered a series of lectures on poetry and communication—"The Usable Truth"—and written a biography of Willard Gibbs. In 1942 her creative writing was honored with a $1000 award by the American Academy of Arts and Letters and the National Institute of Arts and Letters.

Miss Rukeyser is not married. She lives in New York City.

Theory of Flight (poetry), Yale University Press, New Haven, Conn., 1935
U. S. 1 (poetry), Viking Press, 1938
A Turning Wind (poetry), Viking Press, 1939
The Soul and Body of John Brown (etchings and poem), Ripper & Ault, 1941
Wake Island (poem), Doubleday, Doran, 1942
Willard Gibbs (biography), Doubleday, Doran, 1942

CARL SANDBURG has been called the folk singer of America, "who comes out of the

prairie soil, who can hand back to the people a creation that has scraps of their own insight, humor, and imagination." He was born in Galesburg, Illinois, on January 6, 1878. His parents were Swedish immigrants, and his family name was Johnson until his father had it changed to Sandburg to avoid confusion with the many other Johnsons in the town.

He left school at the age of thirteen to do odd jobs such as driving a milk wagon, helping out in a barber shop, shifting scenery, truck driving, dish washing, house painting, and carpentering. In 1898 he enlisted with the Sixth Illinois Volunteers and saw active service in Puerto Rico as a soldier in the Spanish-American War. On his return he worked his way through Lombard College in Galesburg, and after graduation in 1902 became an advertising writer, journalist, and organizer for the Social-Democratic Party in Wisconsin. He was secretary to the Socialist mayor of Milwaukee from 1910 to 1912.

Mr. Sandburg then entered journalism with a position as associate editor of *System,* a magazine published in Chicago. In 1917 he joined the staff of the Chicago *Daily News,* and in 1918 he visited Norway and Sweden as correspondent for the Newspaper Enterprise Association. Upon his return he became associated with the *Daily News* in the capacity of editorial writer.

His earliest poems were privately printed in 1904. It was in 1914 that he won his first literary award, the Levinson Prize. Since then his reputation has become international. *Cornhuskers,* a book of verse, shared the prize of the Poetry Society of America in 1918, and his *Abraham Lincoln: The War Years,* the second part of his six-volume biography of Lincoln, was awarded the Pulitzer Prize in 1940.

Mr. Sandburg has traveled throughout America, collecting and singing native ballads and folk songs, which he has published in book form as *The American Songbag* (1927). He is a master interpreter of his own verse, in recitation or song.

Mr. Sandburg was married in 1908 to Lillian Steichen, and is the father of three daughters. He lives in Harbert, Michigan.

In Reckless Ecstasy, privately printed, Galesburg, Ill., 1904
Chicago Poems, Holt, 1916
Cornhuskers (poetry), Holt, 1918
The Chicago Race Riots (history), Harcourt, Brace & Howe, 1919
Smoke and Steel (poetry), Harcourt, Brace & Howe, 1920. Reprinted with the next title by Harcourt, Brace, in 1938. Reprinted

with the next title and *Good Morning, America* by Harcourt, Brace, in 1942

Slabs of the Sunburnt West (poetry), Harcourt, Brace, 1922. Reprinted with *Smoke and Steel* by Harcourt, Brace, in 1938. Reprinted with *Smoke and Steel* and *Good Morning, America* by Harcourt, Brace, in 1942

Rootabaga Stories (juvenile), Harcourt, Brace, 1922. Reprinted with the next title in 1936

Rootabaga Pigeons (juvenile), Harcourt, Brace, 1923. Reprinted with *Rootabaga Stories* in 1936

Selected Poems (edited by REBECCA WEST), Harcourt, Brace, 1926

Abraham Lincoln: The Prairie Years (biography), two volumes, Harcourt, Brace, 1926

The American Songbag (anthology of folk songs), Harcourt, Brace, 1927

Good Morning, America (poetry), Harcourt, Brace, 1928. Reprinted with *Smoke and Steel* and *Slabs of the Sunburnt West* by Harcourt, Brace, in 1942

Abe Lincoln Grows Up (selection for young folks from *Abraham Lincoln: The Prairie Years*), Harcourt, Brace, 1928

Rootabaga Country (selections from *Rootabaga Stories* and *Rootabaga Pigeons*), Harcourt, Brace, 1929

Steichen, the Photographer (biography), Harcourt, Brace, 1929

Potoato Face (juvenile), Harcourt, Brace, 1930

Early Moon (selected poems, especially for children), Harcourt, Brace, 1930

Mary Lincoln, Wife and Widow (biography; Part II by Paul Angle), Harcourt, Brace, 1932

. . . The People, Yes (poetry), Harcourt, Brace, 1936

Lincoln and Whitman Miscellany, Holiday Press, Chicago, 1938

Abraham Lincoln: The War Years (biography), four volumes, Harcourt, Brace, 1939

Storm Over the Land: A Profile of the Civil War, Harcourt, Brace, 1942

WILLIAM SAROYAN began his writing career in February, 1934, with a short story published in *Story*. He was born in Fresno, California, on August 31, 1908, and went to the public schools there until he was 15. He has drawn extensively on his life in Fresno for short stories and plays.

In 1935 after the success of his first book, *The Daring Young Man on the Flying Trapeze*, he traveled in Russia and Armenia and since then has gone back and forth between New York and Hollywood or Hollywood and San Francisco, his home since he was 17. He has

done several original radio presentations, and won the Pulitzer Prize in 1940 for his play, *The Time of Your Life*, but refused it on the basis that an artist should not be condescended to by prize committees. He has done many other plays and his *The Beautiful People* (1941) won honors from the New York Drama Critics Circle.

He writes rapidly but only when he feels like writing and then, he has said, "I write swiftly and easily and without any of the agony which is supposed to accompany the activity of writing, seldom spending more than one to three hours on a short story."

The Daring Young Man on the Flying Trapeze (short stories), Random House, 1934

A Christmas Psalm, 1935 (poetry), Crelber, Lilienthal, San Francisco, 1935

Inhale and Exhale (short stories), Random House, 1936

Three Times Three (short stories), Conference Press, Los Angeles, 1936

Those Who Write Them and Those Who Collect Them (pamphlet), Black Archer Press, Chicago, 1936

Little Children (short stories), Harcourt, Brace, 1937

The Gay and Melancholy Flux (short stories), Faber & Faber, London, 1937

Love, Here Is My Hat (short stories), Modern Age, 1938

A Native American (short story), Fields, San Francisco, 1938

The Trouble with Tigers (short stories), Harcourt, Brace, 1938

My Heart's in the Highlands (play), Harcourt, Brace, 1939

Peace, It's Wonderful (short stories), Modern Age, 1939

The Hungerers (play), French, 1939

The Time of Your Life (play and essays), Harcourt, Brace, 1939

My Name Is Aram (short stories), Harcourt, Brace, 1940

The State of the Nation (essays; with others), Little Man Press, Cincinnati, 1940

The Ping-Pong Game (play), French, 1940

Subway Circus (play), French, 1940

Three Plays, Harcourt, Brace, 1940

A Special Announcement (radio sketch), House of Books, 1940

Saroyan's Fables, Harcourt, Brace, 1941

Insurance Salesman, and Other Stories, Faber & Faber, London, 1941

Love's Old Sweet Song (play), French, 1941

Curtain Preface (pamphlet), Community Playhouse, Pasadena, Cal., 1941

The People with Light Coming Out of Them (pamphlet), Free Company, 1941

The Beautiful People (three plays), Harcourt, Brace, 1941

Harlem (text; pictures by ALBERT HIRSCHFELD), Hyperion Press, 1941

*Razzle-Dazzle, Harcourt, Brace, 1942

VINCENT SHEEAN was born in Pana, Illinois, on December 5, 1899, and was educated at the University of Chicago. During his career as foreign correspondent, at first for the Chicago *Tribune* and later for news syndicates, he reported the Fascist march on Rome, the French and Spanish wars on the Rif tribes, the overthrow of the Hankow government in China, and the Palestine riots of 1929. In *Personal History* (1935) he records the development of his mind through these experiences of the post-war decades, and *Not Peace But a Sword*, published in 1939, is a survey of European conditions in that year. Mr. Sheean has also written five novels, a book of short stories, and a play.

In 1935 he married Diana, daughter of Sir Johnston and Lady Forbes-Robertson, and is the father of two daughters. He is now a captain in the Army Air Force.

An American Among the Riffi (current history), Harcourt, Brace, 1926

The Anatomy of Virtue (novel), Harcourt, Brace, 1927

The New Persia (current history), Harcourt Brace, 1927

Gog and Magog (novel), Harcourt, Brace, 1930

The Tide (novel), Doubleday, Doran, 1933

Personal History (autobiography), Doubleday, Doran, 1935

Sanfelice (novel), Doubleday, Doran, 1936

The Pieces of a Fan (short stories), Doubleday, Doran, 1937

A Day of Battle (novel), Doubleday, Doran, 1938

**Not Peace But a Sword* (history), Doubleday, Doran, 1939

Bird of the Wilderness (novel), Random House, 1941

ROBERT E. SHERWOOD, three times winner of the Pulitzer Prize for drama, was born in New Rochelle, New York, on April 4, 1896, and educated at Harvard University. He interrupted his college career to enlist with the Black Watch of the Canadian Expeditionary Force in 1917, and saw service overseas.

Returning to New York in 1919, he was first the dramatic editor of *Vanity Fair*, then associate Editor of *Life*, and from 1924 to 1928 editor.

Since his first play, *The Road to Rome,* which he wrote in 1927, Mr. Sherwood has devoted the greater part of his energies to the stage. *Idiot's Delight, Able Lincoln in Illinois,* and *There Shall Be No Night* were all awarded Pulitzer Prizes.

Mr. Sherwood has also written one novel, *The Virtuous Knight* (1931). He is doing war work now with the office of War Information, and lives with his second wife, Madeline Hurlock Sherwood, in New York City.

The Road to Rome, Scribners, 1927
The Queen's Husband, Scribners, 1928
Waterloo Bridge, Scribners, 1930
This is New York, Scribners, 1931
The Virtuous Knight (novel), Scribners, 1931
Reunion in Vienna, Scribners, 1932
Unending Crusade, Heinemann, London, 1932
The Petrified Forest, Scribners, 1935
Idiot's Delight, Scribners, 1937
**Abe Lincoln in Illinois,* Scribners, 1939
There Shall Be No Night, Scribners, 1940

All of Mr. Sherwood's works are drama.

WILLIAM SHIRER was born in Chicago, on February 23, 1904, and received his early schooling in Cedar Rapids, Iowa. After graduating from Coe College and working for a time on Cedar Rapids newspapers, he went to New York to continue journalism, but his next job did not materialize until he reached Paris in 1925. After a year on the Paris edition of the *Chicago Tribune*, he joined the European staff of the paper and was chief of the *Chicago Tribune's* Central European bureau from 1929 to 1932 with headquarters in Vienna.

After a year in India and another loafing on the Catalan coast, he went to Berlin in 1934 as correspondent for the Universal Service. In 1937 he joined the Columbia Broadcasting System and had perhaps the largest audience of listeners of any European radio correspondent. Back in America now, he is a news commentator on the Columbia Broadcasting System and lives in Bronxville, near New York City.

In Vienna he married Therese Stibernitz and has two daughters, Elena, five, and Linda, born in 1941.

His day-by-day notes as foreign correspondent in Berlin from 1934 to 1941, published as *Berlin Diary*, is his first book. It had the largest reading audience of any American journalist's book of the Second World War.

*Berlin Diary (journal, 1934-1941), Knopf, 1941

UPTON SINCLAIR was born in Baltimore, Maryland, on September 20, 1878. His book about the Chicago stockyards, *The Jungle,* has been compared with *Uncle Tom's Cabin* and some of the novels of Charles Dickens for its influence on legislation and its help in improving the conditions of the poor.

Mr. Sinclair worked his way through the College of the City of New York by writing dime novels, and received his A.B. in 1897. He did post-graduate work at Columbia for four years. In 1906 he participated in the government investigation of the Chicago stockyards, and after publication of *The Jungle* he founded the Helicon Home Colony in Englewood, New Jersey, an experiment in practical Socialism in which Sinclair Lewis also took part.

He has said that the three men who shaped his thought were Jesus, Hamlet, and Shelley, and that he has "written exclusively in the cause of human welfare." All of his books have had as their purpose the elimination of social ills.

It was his interest in the welfare of society also which lay behind his entrance into politics on the Socialist ticket. He was the Socialist candidate for Congress from New Jersey in 1906, from California in 1920, and for the United States Senate in 1922. He was the Socialist candidate for the governorship of California in 1926 and 1930, and the Democratic candidate in 1934. At the start of the last campaign he founded the famous EPIC league —"End Poverty in California." He was also the founder of the American Civil Liberties Union, Southern California branch.

In 1913 Mr. Sinclair married Mary Craig Kimbrough, the poet. He lives now in Pasadena, California, where he publishes many of his own writings.

Springtime and Harvest (novel), publisher unknown, 1901

King Midas (reissue of *Springtime and Harvest*), Funk & Wagnalls, 1901

†*The Journal of Arthur Stirling* (novel), Appleton, 1903

Prince Hagen, a Phantasy (novel), Page, Boston, 1903

†*Manassas* (novel), Macmillan, 1904

Our Bourgeois Literature: The Reason and the Remedy (pamphlet), Kerr, Chicago, 1905

A Captain of Industry (novel), Haldeman-Julius, Girard, Kans., 1906

††*The Jungle* (novel), Doubleday, Page, Garden City, N. Y., 1906

What Life Means to Me (autobiography; pamphlet), Kerr, Chicago, 1906

A Home Colony (prospectus), Helicon Home Colony, Englewood, N. J., 1906

The Industrial Republic (social study), Doubleday, Page, Garden City, N. Y., 1907

The Helicon Home Colony (prospectus), Helicon Home Colony, Englewood, N. J., 1907

The Overman (short story), Doubleday, Page, Garden City, N. Y., 1907

†*The Metropolis* (novel), Moffat Yard, Boston, 1908

†*The Moneychangers* (novel), Dodge, New York, 1908

Good Health and How We Won It (health study; with MICHAEL WILLIAMS), Stokes, 1909

††*Prince Hagen* (play), 1909

†*Samuel the Seeker* (novel), Dodge, New York, 1910

†*Love's Pilgrimage* (novel), Kennerley, 1911

†*The Fasting Cure* (health study), Kennerley, 1911

Plays of Protest, Kennerley, 1912

†*Damaged Goods* (novel), Winston, Philadelphia, 1913

†*Sylvia* (novel), Winston, Philadelphia, 1913

†*Sylvia's Marriage* (novel), Winston, Philadelphia, 1914

Sinclair-Astor Letters (correspondence), National Civic Federation, 1914

†*The Cry for Justice* (anthology of the literature of social protest), Winston, Philadelphia, 1915

†*King Coal* (novel), Macmillan, New York, 1917

The Price I Paid (pamphlet), Sinclair, Pasadena, Cal., 1917

The Profits of Religion (economic study of the church), Sinclair, Pasadena, Cal., 1918

The Brass Check (study of American journalism), Sinclair, Pasadena, Cal., 1919

†*Jimmie Higgins* (novel), Boni & Liveright, New York, 1919

100%: The Story of a Patriot (novel), Pasadena, Cal., 1920

National News (pamphlet), Sinclair, Pasadena, Cal., 1920

The Book of Life, Mind, and Body (study in the conduct of life), Macmillan, 1921 (Part I), Sinclair, Pasadena, Cal., 1922 (Part II)

The Associated Press and Labor (seven chapters from *The Brass Check*), Sinclair, Pasadena, Cal., 1921

The Crimes of the "Times" (pamphlet), Sinclair, Pasadena, Cal., 1921

McNeal-Sinclair Debate on Socialism (pamphlet), Haldeman-Julius, Girard, Kans., 1921

They Call Me Carpenter (novel), Sinclair, Pasadena, Cal., 1922

Hell (verse drama and photoplay), Sinclair, Pasadena, Cal., 1923

The Goose-Step (study of American education), Sinclair, Pasadena, Cal., 1923

To the Chief of Police of Los Angeles (pamphlet), Sinclair, Pasadena, Cal., 1923

The Millennium (novel), three pamphlets, Sinclair, Pasadena, Cal., 1924

The Pot Boiler (play), Haldeman-Julius, Girard Kans., 1924

The Naturewoman (play), Haldeman-Julius, Girard, Kans., 1924

Singing Jailbirds (play), Sinclair, Pasadena, Cal., 1924

My Life and Diet (health study), Sinclair, Pasadena, Cal., 1924

The Goslings (study of the American schools), Sinclair, Pasadena, Cal., 1924

Mammonart (social study), Sinclair, Pasadena, Cal., 1925

Bill Porter (play), Sinclair, Pasadena, Cal., 1925

What's the Use of Books? (pamphlet), Vanguard Press, 1926

Letters to Judd, an American Workingman (pamphlet), Sinclair, Pasadena, Cal., 1926

The Spokesman's Secretary (fiction), Sinclair, Pasadena, Cal., 1926

†*Oil!* (novel), Boni, New York, 1927

†*Money Writes!* (social study), Boni, New York, 1927

†*Boston* (novel), two volumes, Boni, New York, 1928

Oil! (a play from the novel), Sinclair, Pasadena, Cal., 1929

†*Mountain City* (novel), Boni, New York, 1930

†*Mental Radio* (study in telepathy), Boni, New York, 1930

Books of Upton Sinclair in Translations and Foreign Editions (bibliography), Sinclair, Pasadena, Cal., 1930 (enlarged, 1938)

†*Roman Holiday* (novel), Farrar & Rinehart, New York, 1931

†*The Wet Parade* (novel), Farrar & Rinehart, New York, 1931

Socialism and Culture (pamphlet), Haldeman-Julius, Girard, Kans., 1931

Books of Upton Sinclair in Russia (pamphlet), Sinclair, Pasadena, Cal., 1931

†*American Outpost* (reminiscences), Farrar & Rinehart, New York, 1932

I, Governor of California: And How I Ended Poverty (political pamphlet), Farrar & Rinehart, New York, 1933

Upton Sinclair Presents William Fox (biography), Sinclair, Pasadena, Cal., 1933

††*The Way Out: What Lies Ahead for America* (political and social study), Farrar & Rinehart, New York, 1933

EPIC Answers: How to End Poverty in California (political pamphlet), Sinclair, Pasadena, Cal., 1934

††*The EPIC Plan for California* (political pamphlet), Farrar & Rinehart, New York, 1934

The Lie Factory Starts (political pamphlet), Sinclair, Pasadena, Cal., 1934

Immediate EPIC: The Final Statement of the Plan (political pamphlet), Sinclair, Pasadena, Cal., 1934

†*An Upton Sinclair Anthology* (selected works, compiled by I. O. Evans), Farrar & Rinehart, New York, 1934

Depression Island (play), Sinclair, Pasadena, Cal., 1935

I, Candidate for Governor: And How I Got Licked (political pamphlet), Sinclair, Pasadena, Cal., 1935

We, People of America: And How We Ended Poverty (political pamphlet), Sinclair, Pasadena, Cal., 1935

†*Co-Op* (novel), Farrar & Rinehart, New York, 1936

†*What God Means to Me* (study of religion), Farrar & Rinehart, New York, 1936

†*The Gnomobile* (juvenile), Farrar & Rinehart, New York, 1936

Wally for Queen! (play), Sinclair, Pasadena, Cal., 1936

The Flivver King (pamphlet novel), Sinclair, Pasadena, Cal., 1937

No Pasarán! (pamphlet novel), Sinclair, Pasadena, Cal., 1937

†*Our Lady* (novel), Rodale Press, Emmaus, Pa., 1938

†*Little Steel* (novel), Farrar & Rinehart, New York, 1938

Terror in Russia? Two Views by Upton Sinclair and Eugene Lyons (political study), Richard R. Smith, New York, 1938

What Can Be Done About America's Economic Troubles? (pamphlet), Sinclair, Pasadena, Cal., 1939

Your Million Dollars (pamphlet), Sinclair, Pasadena, Cal., 1939

†*Marie Antoinette* (play), Vanguard Press, New York, 1939

Expect No Peace (pamphlet of essays), Sinclair, Pasadena,, Cal., 1939

Telling the World (previously published essays), Laurie, London, 1940

World's End (novel), Viking Press, New York, 1940

Between Two Worlds (novel), Viking Press, New York, 1941

Peace or War in America (debate with PHILIP LAFOLLETTE), Sinclair, Pasadena, Cal., 1941

Dragon's Teeth (novel), Viking Press, 1942

Wide Is the Gate (novel), Viking Press, to be published 1943

One dagger (†) before a title in the above bibliography indicates that Mr. Sinclair published his own edition at some time later than the other publisher mentioned.

Two daggers (††) before a title indicate that Mr. Sinclair published his own edition at the same time as the other publisher.

During the years 1897 to 1900 Mr. Sinclair paid his way as a graduate student at Columbia University by writing what in those days were termed half-dime novels. These works did not appear under his name, and he insists that they are altogether without merit. They are omitted from the bibliography on his own request.

CORNELIA OTIS SKINNER is the daughter of the late Otis Skinner, the actor, and from him she received much of her training for the stage. She was born in Chicago on May 30, 1901, educated in New York City and a member of the class of 1922 of Bryn Mawr College. Later she attended the Sorbonne, and studied for the stage with the *Sociétaires de la Comédie Française* and at the School of Jacques Copeau. She was married to Alden Blodget in 1928.

Miss Skinner is known as an actress, writer, and monologuist. She has appeared in many plays, and has written and produced several original sketches, including "The Wives of Henry VIII," "The Empress Eugenie," and "Mansion on the Hudson." She also dramatized, produced, and acted in the complete mono-drama *Edna His Wife*, which she presented in America and London, and has contributed articles and verse to many magazines.

Miss Skinner wrote the play, "Captain Fury," which was produced in December, 1925. She lives now in New York City.

Tiny Garments (sketches), Farrar & Rinehart, 1932
Excuse It, Please! (sketches), Dodd, Mead, 1936
Dithers and Jitters (sketches), Dodd, Mead, 1938
**Soap Behind the Ears* (sketches), Dodd, Mead, 1941

JOHN STEINBECK, whose *Grapes of Wrath* is one of the great books in American literature for its awakening of the public to an awareness of a social problem, is of mixed German and Irish stock. His father's family pioneered in the Big Sur region of California, where John was born on February 27, 1902. His early education was conventional, although, after being graduated from Salinas High School, he enrolled at Stanford University, where his attendance was irregular and extended over a

period of eight years. He never received a degree.

Coming to New York as a young man he found a job as reporter on one of the Metropolitan newspapers, but his friends say that he was fired because he was unable to write his stories without infusing them with the sympathy with underprivilege which has since distinguished most of his writing. For a while he worked as a bricklayer during the erection of Madison Square Garden, and later as a chemist and a painter's apprentice. Then he returned to his home in California to write his novels. Mr. Steinbeck married Carol Henning in 1930.

The Grapes of Wrath was awarded the Pulitzer Prize for 1940

Cup of Gold (fictionalized biography), McBride, 1929
The Pastures of Heaven (short stories), Brewer, Warren, & Putnam, 1932
To a God Unknown (novel), Ballou, 1933
Tortilla Flat (novel), Covici Friede, 1935
In Dubious Battle (novel), Covici Friede, 1936
Nothing So Monstrous (story), privately printed, 1936
Saint Katy the Virgin (short story), Covici Friede, 1936
The Red Pony (short story), Covici Friede, 1937
Of Mice and Men (novel), Covici Friede, 1937
*The Long Valley (short stories), Viking, 1938
Their Blood Is Strong (pamphlet), Simon J. Lubin Society of California, San Francisco, 1938
The Grapes of Wrath (novel), Viking, 1939
Steinbeck Replies (pamphlet), Friends of Democracy, 1940
The Forgotten Village (documentary narrative), Viking, 1941
Sea of Cortez (travel; with E. F. RICKETTS), Viking, 1941
The Moon Is Down (novel), Viking, 1942

WALLACE STEVENS has distinguished himself both in business and in poetry. He was born in Reading, Pennsylvania, on October 2, 1879, studied at Harvard and the New York Law School, and was admitted to the New York bar in 1904. Since 1916 he has been associated with the Hartford Accident and Indemnity Company of Hartford, Connecticut, and since 1934 has been vice president.

Mr. Stevens's poetry was first collected in the volume *Harmonium* in 1923; three further volumes have followed. He is married, and the father of a daughter. His home is in Hartford, Connecticut.

Harmonium, Knopf, 1924 (enlarged 1931)
Ideas of Order, Alcestis Press, 1935 (enlarged by Knopf, 1936)
Owl's Clover, Alcestis Press, 1936
The Man with the Blue Guitar, Knopf, 1937
Parts of a World, Knopf, 1942
Notes Toward a Supreme Fiction, Cummington Press, Cummington, Vt., 1942

Mr. Stevens's works are poetry.

JESSE STUART was born in W-Hollow near Riverton, Kentucky, on August 8, 1907. He attended Lincoln Memorial University, from which he received his A.B. in 1929; in 1931-1932 he was a student at Vanderbilt University. He was awarded a Guggenheim Fellowship for foreign travel in 1937, and has taught school, but his real occupation, aside from his writing, is work on his own farm in Kentucky.

His first published book was a volume of seven hundred sonnets, *Man with a Bull-Tongue Plow* (1934), dealing with the land and people of his state. It was hailed as indigenous poetry close to the traditions of his native mountains. Since then he has written two books of short stories, an autobiography, and a novel.

Mr. Stuart was married in 1939 to Naomi Deane Norris. They live on their own farm in W-Hollow near Riverton, Kentucky.

Man with a Bull-Tongue Plow (poetry), Dutton, 1934
Head o' W-Hollow (short stories), Dutton, 1936
Beyond Dark Hills (autobiography), Dutton, 1938
Trees of Heaven (novel), Dutton, 1940
Men of the Mountains (short stories), Dutton, 1941

FRANK SULLIVAN was born in Saratoga Springs, New York, on September 22, 1892, and received his A.B. from Cornell University in 1914. He began newspaper work at Saratoga in 1910, just after graduation from high school, and later conducted a column in the New York *World.* During the First World War he served as a lieutenant in the infantry.

Mr. Sullivan is a regular contributor to such magazines as *The New Yorker,* and to the newspaper *PM.* His published works are

for the most part books of humorous sketches. He is unmarried, and lives in Saratoga Springs.

The Life and Times of Matha Hepplethwaite, Liveright, 1926
The Adventures of an Oaf (fantasy; with HERB ROTH), Macy-Masius, 1927
Innocent Bystanding, Liveright, 1928
Broccoli and Old Lace, Liveright, 1931
In One Ear . . . , Viking Press, 1933
A Pearl in Every Oyster, Little, Brown, Boston, 1938
Sullivan at Bay, Dent & Sons, London, 1939

Unless otherwise indicated Mr. Sullivan's works are humorous sketches.

BOOTH TARKINGTON has twice been awarded the Pulitzer Prize, for *The Magnificent Ambersons* in 1919 and for *Alice Adams* in 1922. He was born in Indianapolis, Indiana, on July 29, 1869, the son of a lawyer and Civil War soldier. He received his education at Phillips Exeter Academy, Purdue University, and Princeton. His early ambition was to be a painter. His first published novel is *The Gentleman from Indiana* (1899).

In 1902 Mr. Tarkington was married to Louisa Fletcher of Indianapolis; in 1912 to Susanah Robinson of Dayton, Ohio. In 1902-1903 he served in the Indiana Legislature, where he was an insurgent against his own party's machine.

He is best known as a novelist, but has also written many successful plays, short stories, and essays. For many years he has spent his winters in Indianapolis and his summers at Kennebunkport, Maine.

The Gentleman from Indiana, Doubleday, McClure, 1899
Monsieur Beaucaire, Doubleday, McClure, 1900
The Two Vanrevels, McClure, Phillips, 1902
Cherry, Harpers, 1903
In the Arena, McClure, Phillips, 1905
The Conquest of Canaan, Harpers, 1905
The Beautiful Lady, McClure, Phillips, 1905
His Own People, Doubleday, Page, Garden City, N. Y., 1907
The Guardian (play), 1907
The Guest of Quesnay, McClure, 1908
The Man from Home (play; with HARRY LEON WILSON), Doubleday, Page, Garden City, N. Y., 1908
Beasley's Christmas Party, Harpers, 1909
Beauty and the Jacobin (play), Harpers, 1912
The Flirt, Doubleday, Page, Garden City, N. Y., 1913
Penrod, Doubleday, Page, Garden City, N. Y., 1914

The Turmoil, Harpers, 1915

The Spring Concert (pamphlet), Ridgeway, 1916

Penrod and Sam, Doubleday, Page, Garden City, N. Y., 1916

Seventeen, Harpers, 1917

The Magnificent Ambersons, Doubleday Page, Garden City, N. Y., 1918

Ramsey Milholland, Doubleday Page, Garden City, N. Y., 1919

The Gibson Upright (play; with HARRY LEON WILSON), Eastman Kodak Co., Rochester, N. Y., 1919

The Works of Booth Tarkington, fourteen volumes, Doubleday, Page, Garden City, N. Y., 1918-1919

The Country Cousin (play; with JULIAN STREET), French, 1921

The Intimate Strangers (play), French, 1921

Clarence (play), French, 1921

Alice Adams, Doubleday, Page, Garden City, N. Y., 1921

Harlequin and Columbine, Doubleday, Page, Garden City, N. Y., 1921

Gentle Julia, Doubleday, Page, Garden City, N. Y., 1922

The Wren (play), French, 1922

The Midlander, Doubleday, Page, Garden City, N. Y., 1923

The Fascinating Stranger, and Other Stories, Doubleday, Page, Garden City, N. Y., 1923

The Ghost Story (play), Stewart Kidd, Cincinnati, 1923

The Trysting Place (play), Stewart Kidd, Cincinnati, 1923

Tweedles (play; with HARRY LEON WILSON), French, 1924

The Collector's Whatnot (manual for antique collectors; with others), Houghton Mifflin, Boston, 1923

Women, Doubleday, Page, Garden City, N. Y., 1925

Bimbo, the Pirate (play), Appleton, 1926

Looking Forward and Others (essays), Doubleday, Page, Garden City, N. Y., 1926

Growth (trilogy: *The Magnificent Ambersons*, *The Midlander*, *The Turmoil*), Doubleday, Page, Garden City, N. Y., 1927

The Plutocrat, Doubleday, Page, Garden City, N. Y., 1927

The Travelers (play), Appleton, 1927

Station YYYY (play), Appleton, 1927

Claire Ambler, Doubleday, Doran, 1928

The World Does Move (reminiscences), Doubleday, Doran, 1928

Young Mrs. Greeley, Doubleday, Doran, 1929

Penrod Jashber, Doubleday, Doran, 1929

How's Your Health? (play; with HARRY LEON WILSON), French, 1930

Mirthful Haven, Doubleday, Doran, 1930

Penrod, His Complete Story (the three Penrod books), Doubleday, Doran, 1931

Mary's Neck, Doubleday, Doran, 1932

Wanton Mally, Doubleday, Doran, 1932

Presenting Lily Mars, Doubleday, Doran, 1933

Little Orvie, Doubleday, Doran, 1934

Mr. Antonio (play), French, 1934

The Help Each Other Club (play), Appleton-Century, 1934

**Mr. White, The Red Barn, Hell, and Bridewater* (short stories), Doubleday, Doran, 1935

The Lorenzo Bunch, Doubleday, Doran, 1936

Rumbin Galleries, Doubleday, Doran, 1937

Some Old Portraits (essays), Doubleday, Doran, 1939

The Heritage of Hatcher Ide, Doubleday, Doran, 1941

The Fighting Littles, Doubleday, Doran, 1941

All of Mr. Tarkington's works, unless otherwise specified, are novels.

JAMES THURBER is known as a writer, cartoonist, and playwright. He was born in Columbus, Ohio, on December 8, 1894, and studied at Ohio State University. After two years as a code clerk in the United States State Department he began journalistic work. From 1920 to 1924 he was a reporter for the Columbus *Dispatch*, and then for two years with the Chicago *Tribune* in Paris. In 1926 he became a member of the staff of the New York *Evening Post*, and since 1927 he has been a regular contributor of both writing and drawings to *The New Yorker*.

Mr. Thurber collaborated with Elliott Nugent on *The Male Animal* in 1940, a comedy which enjoyed a successful run on Broadway and was made into a movie.

Is Sex Necessary? (with E. B. WHITE), Harpers, 1929

The Owl in the Attic and Other Perplexities, Harpers, 1931

The Seal in the Bedroom and Other Predicaments, Harpers, 1932

**My Life and Hard Times*, Harpers, 1933

The Middle Aged Man on the Flying Trapeze, Harpers, 1935

Let Your Mind Alone!, Harpers, 1937

The Cream of Thurber (selections), Hamilton, London, 1939

The Last Flower, Harpers, 1939

Fables for Our Time, Harpers, 1940

The Male Animal (play; with ELLIOTT NUGENT), Random House, 1940

Unless otherwise noted, Mr. Thurber's works are collections of humorous stories and sketches.

LOUIS UNTERMEYER is one of the rare men who have been successful both in business and in the arts. He was born in New York City on October 1, 1885, where he lived, except for brief intervals, until 1923. He attended the De Witt Clinton High School, but a failure to comprehend geometry prevented him from graduating. His early ambition was to be a composer, and at sixteen he appeared as a semi-professional pianist. At seventeen he entered his father's jewelry business, and became vice-president before he resigned in 1923 to devote himself entirely to literature. He was one of the founders and a contributing editor to *The Liberator* and *The Seven Arts*; from 1934 to 1937 he was poetry editor of *The American Mercury*. He has lectured, chiefly on American culture, at many colleges, and was "poet in residence" at the University of Michigan in 1939-1940. He is a member of the faculty at the annual Writers' Conference at Bread Loaf, Vermont.

Mr. Untermeyer's work is divided into four kinds: his poetry, his parodies, his translations, and his critical prose. He is also known as the compiler of many anthologies of poetry.

Mr. Untermeyer's first wife was Jean Starr, the poet; his second was Virginia Moore; in 1933 he married exJudge Esther Antin, his third wife. He is the father of three children. In 1928 he achieved his life-long desire, acquiring a farm, a trout stream, and half a mountain of sugar maples in the Adirondacks.

The Younger Quire (parodies), Moods Publishing Company, 1910
First Love (poetry), Sherman, French, Boston, 1911
Challenge (poetry), Century, 1914
"—and Other Poets" (parodies), Holt, 1916
Poems of Heinrich Heine (translations), Holt, 1917
These Times (poetry), Holt, 1917
Including Horace (translations and parodies), Harcourt, Brace, 1919
Modern American Verse (anthology), Harcourt, Brace, 1919
Modern British Poetry (anthology), Harcourt, Brace, 1920 (revised and enlarged 1925, 1930, 1936, 1942)
The New Adam (poetry), Harcourt, Brace, 1920
A Miscellany of American Poetry (biennial anthology, 1920-1927), Harcourt, Brace, N. Y. C.
Modern American Poetry (anthology), Harcourt, Brace, 1921 (revised and enlarged 1925, 1930, 1936, 1942)

Heavens: a Book of Burlesques, Harcourt, Brace, 1922
Roast Leviathan (poetry), Harcourt, Brace, 1923
This Singing World (anthology), Harcourt, Brace, 1923
American Poetry Since 1900 (critical essays), Holt, 1923
Mass-Man (translation of Toller's *Massenmensch*), Doubleday, Doran, 1924
The Fat and the Cat (short stories freely adapted from the Swiss), Harcourt, Brace, 1925
Collected Parodies, Harcourt, Brace, 1926
This Singing World for Younger Children (with notes), Harcourt, Brace, 1926
The Forms of Poetry (a "pocket dictionary of verse"), Harcourt, Brace, 1926
Yesterday and Today (a "comparative" anthology), Harcourt, Brace, 1927
Burning Bush (poetry), Harcourt, Brace, 1928
Moses (novel), Harcourt, Brace, 1928
New Songs for New Voices (lyrics and music; with David and Clara Mannes), Harcourt, Brace, 1928
Blue Rhine—Black Forest (travel book), Harcourt, Brace, 1930
American Poetry: From Its Beginnings to Whitman (anthology), Harcourt, Brace, 1931
Food and Drink (poetry), Harcourt, Brace, 1932
The Book of Living Verse (anthology), Harcourt, Brace, 1932
The Donkey of God (children's travel book), Harcourt, Brace, 1932
Chip—My Life and Times (animal story), Harcourt, Brace, 1933
Poetry—Its Appreciation and Enjoyment (essays; with H. Carter Davidson), Harcourt, Brace, 1934
The Last Pirate (tales from Gilbert and Sullivan operettas), Harcourt, Brace, 1934
Selected Poems and Parodies, Harcourt, Brace, 1935
Rainbow in the Sky (anthology for children), Harcourt, Brace, 1935
Heinrich Heine—Paradox and Poet (biography and translations), two volumes, Harcourt, Brace, 1937
Doorways to Poetry (treatise and textbook), Harcourt, Brace, 1937
Play in Poetry (critical essays), Harcourt, Brace, 1938
From Another World (autobiography), Harcourt, Brace, 1939
Stars to Steer By (anthology), Harcourt, Brace, 1941
A Treasury of Great Poems (anthology and biography), Simon & Schuster, 1942

CARL VAN DOREN has had an active and vigorous career as teacher, editor, and writer. He was born in Hope, Illinois, on September 10, 1885, received his A.B. degree from the University of Illinois in 1907 and taught there for a year as assistant in rhetoric. After receiving his Ph.D. from Columbia in 1911 he was a member of the English department till 1916 and part-time lecturer till 1930. He was headmaster of the Brearley School in New York City from 1916 to 1919.

Mr. Van Doren was literary editor of *The Nation* from 1919 to 1922 and of *The Century Magazine* from 1922 to 1925, editor-in-chief of the Literary Guild from 1926 through 1934, and chairman of the editorial committee of the Readers Club from 1941. He was also managing editor of *The Cambridge History of American Literature* (published 1917-21).

His works include biographies (primarily), histories of literature, critical studies, anthologies, a novel (*The Ninth Wave*, 1926), a collection of short stories (*Other Provinces*, 1925), and an autobiography (*Three Worlds*, 1936). In 1939 his *Benjamin Franklin* was awarded the Pulitzer Prize for biography.

Mr. Van Doren lives with his second wife, Jean Wright Van Doren, in New York City.

The Life of Thomas Love Peacock, Dutton, 1911
The American Novel, Macmillan, 1921 (revised 1940)
Contemporary American Novelists: 1900-1920, Macmillan, 1922
The Roving Critic, Knopf, 1923
Many Minds (critical studies), Knopf, 1924
Other Provinces (short stories), Knopf, 1925
James Branch Cabell, McBride, 1924 (revised 1932)
American and British Literature Since 1890 (with MARK VAN DOREN), Appleton-Century, 1925 revised 1939)
The Ninth Wave (novel), Harcourt, Brace, 1926
Swift (biography), Viking Press, 1930
American Literature: An Introduction, U. S. Library Association, Los Angeles, 1933
Sinclair Lewis, Doubleday, Doran, 1933
Modern American Prose (anthology), Harcourt, Brace, 1934
An Anthology of World Prose, Reynal & Hitchcock, 1935
What Is American Literature? (reissue of *American Literature: An Introduction*), Morrow, 1935
The Borzoi Reader (anthology), Knopf, 1936
Three Worlds (autobiography), Harpers, 1936
Benjamin Franklin, Viking Press, 1938

An Illinois Boyhood (first part of *Three Worlds*), Viking Press, 1939
Secret History of the American Revolution, Viking Press, 1941

MARK VAN DOREN is nine years younger than his brother Carl Van Doren. He was born in Hope, Illinois, on June 13, 1894, and lived there for six years before moving to Urbana, where he received his A.B. from the University of Illinois in 1914, and his A.M. the following year. Further study was interrupted by the First World War, during which he served in the infantry. He received his Ph.D. in English from Columbia in 1920, and remained in the English department there as an instructor. In 1924 he was made assistant professor, in 1935 associate professor and in 1942 professor.

Mr. Van Doren was literary editor of *The Nation* from 1924 to 1928, and motion picture critic for that journal from 1935 to 1938. He began his literary career as a critic with his *Henry David Thoreau—A Critical Study* in 1916, following it by *The Poetry of John Dryden* in 1920, *Shakespeare* in 1939, and *The Private Reader* in 1942. Since then he has been interested mainly in poetry; his *Collected Poems* was awarded the Pulitzer Prize in 1940. He is known also as the chairman of the radio program, "Invitation to Learning," and as the editor of several anthologies. He has published two novels, *The Transients* and *Windless Cabins*.

Mr. Van Doren was married in 1922 to the novelist Dorothy Graffe, and has two sons. He lives in New York City.

Henry David Thoreau—A Critical Study, Houghton Mifflin, Boston, 1916
The Poetry of John Dryden, Harcourt, Brace, 1920
Spring Thunder, and Other Poems, Seltzer, 1924
American and British Literature Since 1890 (with CARL VAN DOREN), Century, 1925 revised 1939)
7 p.m., and Other Poems, Boni, 1926
Edward Arlington Robinson, Literary Guild, 1927
An American Bookshelf (anthology), five volumes, Macy & Masius, 1927-1928
Now the Sky, and Other Poems, Boni, 1928
An Anthology of World Poetry, Boni, 1928 (revised, Reynal & Hitchcock, 1936)
An Autobiography of America (compilation of American autobiographical documents), Boni, 1929

*Correspondence of Aaron Burr and His Daugh-
ter Theodosia* (compilation of letters, with
preface), Covici, Friede, 1929
Dick and Tom (juvenile), Macmillan, 1931
Jonathan Gentry (narrative poem), Boni, 1931
Dick and Tom in Town (juvenile), Mac-
millan, 1932
American Poets, 1630-1930 (anthology), Lit-
tle, Brown, Boston, 1932
The Oxford Book of American Prose (an-
thology), Oxford University Press, 1932
The Transients (novel), Morrow, 1935
A Winter Diary, and Other Poems, Mac-
millan, 1935, Holt, 1938
The Last Look, and Other Poems, Holt, 1937
Studies in Metaphysical Poetry (essay and bib-
liography; with THEODORE SPENCER), Co-
lumbia University Press, 1939
*Collected Poems, 1922-1938, Holt, 1939
Shakespeare, Holt, 1939
Windless Cabins (novel), Holt, 1940
The Transparent Tree (juvenile), Holt, 1940
Invitation to Learning (transcripts of radio
broadcasts; with others), Random House,
1941
The Mayfield Deer (narrative poem), Holt,
1941
The Private Reader (critical essays and re-
views), Holt, 1942
Our Lady Peace and Other War Poems, New
Directions, Norfolk, Conn., 1942
The New Invitation to Learning (transcripts of
radio broadcasts; with others), Random
House, 1942

HENDRIK WILLEM VAN LOON, who was born
on Jan. 14, 1882, in Rotterdam, Holland,
and is six feet three when he stands erect,
has written and illustrated 37 books (which
in turn have appeared in 158 editions in 21
languages) ; he has spent three years of his
life on the ocean, going places; he has a
reading knowledge of most European languages (as part of his trade) but says he
would not undertake to lecture in more than
five of them; he has done political cartooning
for quite a large number of magazines and
is forever finding books for which, at one
time or another, he wrote an introduction; he
enjoys a prominent place on Herr Hitler's
black list; he has a couple of knighthoods
(but has never specialized in honorary degrees) ; he was torpedoed only once in his
life but bombed, machine-gunned and shelled
innumerable times (while studying the practical side of war) and as he has always been
much too busy, he says, to (1) make money
(2) reduce. As a result he now weighs

269 pounds and is obliged to work as hard as
ever before to make both ends meet.

Those ends include two sons, one daughter-in-law, three male grand-children and
three dogs, a cat and a canary. Also the
larger number of those foreign writers who,
less fortunate than he, put off coming to
America until it was almost too late.

As Dr. van Loon never has employed a
clipping bureau, refuses to open packages
when they seem to hold copies of anything
resembling photographs, and as all the original
documents about his early life were destroyed
when the Germans burned down the cities of
Rotterdam and Middleburg, his biographer
will experience considerable difficulty when
the time shall have come to reconstruct the
existence of a man whose works within the
realm of history and geography have been as
off the beaten track as those of Lewis Carroll
were within the field of humor.

The author admits of only one ambition—
that he may be remembered as that disciple
of Erasmus and Spinoza who devoted all his
time to the propagation of the faith of Mutual
Goodwill and Tolerance. The list of his published works clearly shows this tendency in
his writing.

The Fall of the Dutch Republic, Houghton
Mifflin, Boston, 1913
The Rise of the Dutch Kingdom, Doubleday,
Page, Garden City, N. Y., 1915
The Golden Book of the Dutch Navigators,
Century, 1916
A Short History of Discovery, McKay, Phila-
delphia, 1917
Ancient Man, Boni & Liveright, 1920
The Story of Mankind, Boni & Liveright,
1921
The Story of the Bible, Boni & Liveright, 1923
The Story of Wilbur the Hat ("spiritual phi-
losophy for children"), Boni & Liveright,
1925
Tolerance (history of the growth of tolerance),
Boni & Liveright, 1925
America (history), Boni & Liveright, 1927
Adriaen Block (biography), Block Hall, 1928
The Life and Times of Pieter Stuyvesant, Holt,
1928
Man the Miracle Maker, Liveright, 1928
Rembrandt van Rijn (fictionalized biography),
Liveright, 1930
Van Loon's Geography, Simon & Schuster,
1932
To Have or to Be—Take Your Choice (phi-
losophy), Day, 1932
An Elephant up a Tree (juvenile), Simon &
Schuster, 1933

An Indiscreet Itinerary (travel), Harcourt, Brace, 1933

A World Divided Is a World Lost (philosophy), Cosmos Publishing Co., 1935

Ships and How They Sailed the Seven Seas, Simon & Schuster, 1935

Around the World with the Alphabet (juvenile), Simon & Schuster, 1935

Air-Storming (radio talks), Harcourt, Brace, 1935

The Songs We Sing (collection of songs, with music), Simon & Schuster, 1936

*The Arts (history of art), Simon & Schuster, 1937

Christmas Carols (collection, with music), Simon & Schuster, 1937

Observations on the Mystery of Print and the Life of Johann Gutenberg, Book Manufacturers Institute, 1938

Our Battle (polemic), Simon & Schuster, 1938

Folk Songs of Many Lands (collection; with GRACE CASTAGNETTA), Simon & Schuster, 1938

How to Look at Pictures (essay), Simon & Schuster, 1938

The Last of the Troubadours, Carl Michael Bellman, 1740-1795 (with GRACE CASTAGNETTA), Simon & Schuster, 1939

Songs America Sings (collection; with GRACE CASTAGNETTA), Simon & Schuster, 1939

The Story of the Pacific, Simon & Schuster, 1940

Invasion (fiction), Harcourt, Brace, 1940

The Life and Times of Johann Sebastian Bach, Simon & Schuster, 1940

The Story of Rabelais and Voltaire, Bantam Publications, Los Angeles, 1940

Van Loon's Lives (biography), Simon & Schuster), 1942

PIERRE VAN PAASSEN was born in Gorcum, The Netherlands, on February 7, 1895, and was a student in schools there until 1913. His family moved to Canada when he was nineteen, and from 1914 to 1916 he attended Victoria College in Toronto. After that he served with the Canadian forces in France until the end of the first World War. Returning to Canada, he was a reporter for the Toronto *Globe* for two years, and from 1921 to 1924 for the Atlanta *Constitution* of Atlanta, Georgia.

From 1924 to the outbreak of World War II Mr. van Paassen was a columnist and roving foreign correspondent for the New York *Evening World* and, when that paper ceased to exist, for the North American Newspaper Alliance, the Toronto *Star* and a number of other American and Canadian newspapers. He is one of the most traveled of present-day writers, having visited and revisited Palestine, Spain, Russia, Ethiopia, Germany and Italy. During this time he studied intermittently at the *Ecole Pratique des Hautes Etudes* in Paris, and in 1934 he received the degree of Bachelor of Theology from the *Faculté Libre Protestante*. Every few years he interrupted his European sojourn for lecture tours in the United States.

Mr. van Paassen is married to the former Cornelia Sizoo, and is the father of two children. He lives in Bronxville, New York.

*Days of Our Years (autobiography), Dial Press, 1939

That Day Alone (current history), Dial Press, 1941

The Time Is Now! (essay), Dial Press, 1941

E. B. WHITE was born in Mount Vernon, New York, on July 11, 1899. He received his A.B. from Cornell in 1921. He served as a private in the United States Army during the First World War. His first job was that of newspaper reporter; later he became a free lance writer and a contributing editor of *The New Yorker*, and more recently has been associated with *Harper's Magazine*.

Mr. White's volumes of poetry, stories, and sketches are outstanding satirizations of contemporary culture. He has recently collected the best of his essays in a volume called *One Man's Meat*, chronicling his life on a Maine farm. He is the husband of Katharine Sergeant White, whom he married in 1929.

The Lady Is Cold (poetry), Harpers, 1929

Is Sex Necessary? (with JAMES THURBER), Harpers, 1929

Every Day Is Saturday, Harpers, 1934

The Fox of Peapack, and Other Poems, Harpers, 1938

*Quo Vadimus?, Harpers, 1939

A Subtreasury of American Humor (anthology; with KATHARINE S. WHITE), Coward-McCann, 1941

One Man's Meat, Harpers, 1942

Mr. White's works, unless otherwise indicated, are humorous essays.

WILLIAM ALLEN WHITE has made famous the town of Emporia, Kansas, and has exercised from there an influence which has been felt throughout the nation. He was born there on February 10, 1868, the son of a doctor, and was educated at the University of Kansas.

Since 1895 he has been the proprietor and editor of the *Emporia Gazette*, and his editorials have been one of the shaping forces in American political and social thought ever since his "What's the Matter with Kansas?" aided the election of McKinley in 1896.

Mr. White married Sallie Lindsay in 1893; they have one son. In 1917 he was sent to France as an observer for the American Red Cross, and in 1937-1938 he was president of the American Society of Newspaper Editors. He is a member of the Pulitzer Prize Committee, and since 1926 has been a judge for the Book-of-the-Month Club. In 1940 he founded and was chairman of the Committee to Defend America by Aiding the Allies.

The Real Issue, and Other Stories, Macmillan, 1896
The Court of Boyville (short stories), Macmillan, 1899
Stratagems and Spoils (short stories), Macmillan, 1901
In Our Town (short stories), Macmillan, 1906
A Certain Rich Man (novel), Macmillan, 1909
The Old Order Changeth (political essays), Macmillan, 1910
God's Puppets (short stories), Macmillan, 1916
In the Heart of a Fool (novel), Macmillan, 1918
The Martial Adventures of Henry and Me (war travel novel), Macmillan, 1918
*The Editor and His People (collected editorials), Macmillan, 1924
The Life of Woodrow Wilson (biography), Houghton Mifflin, Boston, 1924
The Life of Calvin Coolidge (biography), Houghton Mifflin, Boston, 1925
Masks in a Pageant (political essays), Macmillan, 1928
What It's All About (reporting), Macmillan, 1936
Forty Years on Main Street (collected editorials), Farrar & Rinehart, 1937
A Puritan in Babylon: The Story of Calvin Coolidge (biography), Macmillan, 1938
The Changing West (essays), Macmillan, 1939

THORNTON WILDER, twice winner of the Pulitzer Prize—once for a novel and once for a play—has said that all his works deal "with the mystery of death and judgment, the tragedy of beauty, and pity of ending of life's comedy." He was born in Madison, Wisconsin, on April 17, 1897, the son of a newspaper editor. When he was nine years old, his father went to China as American consul-gen-

eral at Hong Kong and Shanghai; Thornton Wilder attended school at Chefoo, and continued his education in this country after his return, graduating from Yale in 1920.

After one year of graduate study at the American Academy in Rome, Mr. Wilder was house master and teacher of French at Lawrenceville School in New Jersey until 1928. Meanwhile in 1927 he achieved a wide popularity with *The Bridge of San Luis Rey*, which was awarded the Pulitzer Prize. The following year he spent in Europe, working on his third novel, returning in 1929 to make a lecture tour of this country, and from 1930 to 1936 he was on the faculty of the University of Chicago.

Recently Mr. Wilder's interest has lain primarily in the theatre. After having published several collections of one-act plays, he attained another outstanding success with *Our Town*, which received the 1939 Pulitzer Prize.

Mr. Wilder is unmarried, and lives in New Haven, Connecticut.

The Cabala (novel), Boni, 1926
The Bridge of San Luis Rey (novel), Boni, 1927
The Angel That Troubled the Waters (one-act plays), Coward-McCann, 1928
The Woman of Andros (novel), Boni, 1930
*The Long Christmas Dinner and other Plays, Coward-McCann, 1931
Heaven's My Destination (novel), Harpers, 1935
Lucrece (play, translated from ANDRÉ OBEY'S *Le Viol de Lucrèce*), Houghton Mifflin, Boston, 1933
Our Town (play), Coward-McCann, 1938
The Merchant of Yonkers (play), Harpers, 1939

WILLIAM CARLOS WILLIAMS, physician and writer, was born in Rutherford, New Jersey, September 17, 1883, of an English father and a French (Martinique), Spanish-Jewish mother. Of his childhood he has said, "My mother and father talked nothing but Spanish so that I could not or should not understand what they were saying. Thus I got to understand Spanish perfectly and received no bad habits of English speech." He attended school at Chateau de Lancy near Geneva, continued in New York City, entered the University of Pennsylvania, and received there his M.D. in 1906. He has practiced Medicine in Rutherford since 1910.

Dr. Williams has written many volumes of poetry, short stories, and novels, and has always been an experimenter in form. In 1926 he was awarded the *Dial* Prize in recognition of his services to letters.

He was married in 1912 to Florence Herman, and has two sons.

Poems, privately printed, Rutherford, N. J., 1909

The Tempers (poetry), Matthews, London, 1913

Al Que Quiere! (poetry), Four Seas, Boston, 1917

Kora in Hell (poetry), Four Seas, Boston, 1920

Sour Grapes (poetry), Four Seas, Boston, 1921

Spring and All (poetry), Contact, Paris, 1922

The Great American Novel (essays), Three Mountains Press, Paris, 1923

In the American Grain (essays), Boni, 1925

A Voyage to Pagany (novel), Macaulay, 1928

The Last Nights of Paris (translation from the French of PHILIPPE SOUPAULT), Macaulay, 1929

The Cod Head (pamphlet), Abernethy, Chapel Hill, N. C., 1932

The Knife of the Times, and Other Stories, Dragon Press, Ithaca, N. Y., 1932

Novelette, and Other Prose, Humphries, Boston, 1932

Collected Poems, 1921-1931, Objectivist Press, 1934

An Early Martyr, and Other Poems, Alcestis Press, 1935

Adam and Eve and the City (poetry), Alcestis Press, 1936

White Mule (novel), New Directions, Norfolk, Conn., 1937

Complete Collected Poems, 1906-1938, New Directions, Norfolk, Conn., 1938

Life Along the Passaic River (short stories), New Directions, Norfolk, Conn., 1938

In the Money (novel), New Directions, Norfolk, Conn., 1940

The Broken Span (poetry), New Directions, Norfolk, Conn., 1941

EDMUND WILSON is known primarily as a critic, but he also has plays, poetry, and a novel to his credit. He was born in Red Bank, New Jersey, on May 8, 1895, received his preparatory schooling at the Hill School in Pottstown, Pennsylvania, and his A.B. from Princeton in 1916. After a year as a reporter on the New York *Evening Sun,* he served in the army for almost two years during the First World War, and on his return to this country was for two years managing editor of *Vanity Fair.* From 1926 to 1931 he was associate editor of *The New Republic.*

Mr. Wilson's third wife is Mary McCarthy,

the writer, whom he married in 1938. They have one son, Reuel, and live in Wellfleet, Massachusetts.

The Undertaker's Garland (verse and prose sketches; with JOHN PEALE BISHOP), Knopf, 1922

Discordant Encounters (dialogues and plays), Boni, 1926

I Thought of Daisy (novel), Scribners, 1929

Poets, Farewell! (poems), Scribners, 1929

Axel's Castle (literary criticism), Scribners, 1931

The American Jitters—A Year of the Slump (social reporting), Scribners, 1932

Travels in Two Democracies (social studies on Russia and the United States), Harcourt, Brace, 1936

This Room and This Gin and These Sandwiches (plays), New Republic, 1937

The Triple Thinkers (essays on literature), Harcourt, Brace, 1938

To the Finland Station (historical study of communism), Harcourt, Brace, 1940

The Boys in the Back Room (notes on California novelists), Colt Press, San Francisco, 1941

The Wound and the Bows (essays), Houghton Mifflin, Boston, 1941

Note-Books of Night (poems), Colt Press, San Francisco, 1942

RICHARD WRIGHT, of whose *Native Son* Dorothy Canfield Fisher has said that it "plumbs blacker depths of human experience than American literature has yet had, comparable only to Dostoievski's revelation of human misery in wrong-doing," was born near Natchez, Mississippi, on September 4, 1908, and attended school there. He began working at the age of fifteen in Memphis, Tennessee, and later did odd jobs in Chicago.

Mr. Wright was on the Federal Writers Project in Chicago in 1935 and in New York in 1938. It was at this time that he began writing for magazines and contributing to *The New Masses* and the New York *Daily Worker.* His *Uncle Tom's Children,* a collection of four stories, received in 1938 the *Story Magazine* prize of $500 for the best book submitted by anyone associated with the Federal Writers' Project; and in 1939 he won a Guggenheim Fellowship, and in 1941 the Spingarn Medal.

Native Son, a Book-of-the-Month Club choice, was dramatized by Mr. Wright and Paul Green in 1941. Mr. Wright lives now in Brooklyn, New York.

Uncle Tom's Children (four novellas), Harpers, 1938

Native Son (novel), Harpers, 1940

*How "Bigger" Was Born (pamphlet), Harpers, 1940

Native Son (play from the novel; with PAUL GREEN), Harpers, 1941

Bright and Morning Star (short story), International Publishers, 1941

12 Million Black Voices (Negro folk history), Viking Press, 1941

STARK YOUNG has divided his life pretty evenly between teaching and journalism and writing. He was born in Como, Mississippi, on October 11, 1881, was graduated from the University of Mississippi in 1901 and received his M.A. from Columbia in 1902. He then entered on a teaching career as instructor of English at the University of Mississippi from 1904 to 1907, instructor and professor at the University of Texas until 1915, and as professor of English literature at Amherst from 1915 to 1921.

Mr. Young then turned to journalism. From 1921 to 1924 he was a member of the editorial staff of *The New Republic*, and from 1921 to 1940 associate editor of *Theatre Arts Monthly*. In 1924 and 1925 he was dramatic critic for the New York *Times*, and is now again on the staff of *The New Republic*.

His published works include novels, poetry, plays, essays on the theatre, translations of Chekhov, Molière, Regnard, and an anthology. He is unmarried, and lives in Austin, Texas.

The Blind Man at the Window (poetry), Grafton Press, Boston, 1906

Guenevere (verse play), Grafton Press, Boston, 1906

One-Act Plays, Stewart, Kidd, Cincinnati, 1911

Three Plays, Stewart, Kidd, Cincinnati, 1919

The Flower in Drama (essays on the theatre), Scribners, 1923

The Three Fountains (studies on Italy), Scribners, 1924

The Saint (play), Boni & Liveright, 1925

Sweet Times, and the Blue Policeman (plays for children), Holt, 1926

The Colonnade (play), Theatre Arts, 1926

Glamour (essays on the theatre), Scribners, 1926

Heaven Trees (novel), Scribners, 1926

The Theatre (essays), Scribners, 1927

The Torches Flare (novel), Scribners, 1927

River House (novel), Scribners, 1929

The Street of the Islands (short stories), Scribners, 1930

So Red the Rose (novel), Scribners, 1934

Feliciana (short stories), Scribners, 1935

A Southern Treasury of Life and Literature (anthology), Scribners, 1937

The Sea Gull (translation from CHEKHOV), Scribners, 1939

The Three Sisters (translation from CHEKHOV), French, 1941

Acknowledgments

FOR the assistance of all those who ballotted on the authors to be included, the editor extends his warmest thanks. He is grateful to the critics, to many librarians and the owners of book stores for their advice, and to several of his colleagues at Columbia University, notably Dr. Vernon Loggins, Dr. Donald Clark, Dr. Ernest Brennecke and Dr. Angus Burrell; to Dr. Thomas K. Brown III for his untiring efforts in shaping the biographies and preparing the exhaustive bibliographies for the volume, and to Captain Louis Henry Cohn, of the House of Books, for much invaluable aid in bibliographical data not otherwise available; to Alfred Knopf for his generous aid with many authors on his list; to Pascal Covici, Bennett Cerf, Saxe Commins, and the others in the great publishing houses who have been unfailingly helpful in connection with the authors they publish; to the members of the Drama Critics' Circle for their frank and generous evaluation of American playwrights; to George Jean Nathan, the critic, for much kind personal assistance; to I.M.P., for valuable acidic commentaries at an early stage of the process; to Gene Saxton of Harpers, and to William Rose Benét for his fine help in the case of a fellow poet; to Bernice Baumgarten of Brandt & Brandt for much copyright assistance; to Maurice Speiser, the lawyer and connoisseur, for much invaluable help; to Lewis Gannett, the critic; Mr. John Hall Wheelright, the poet and editor, for assistance in the absence of Mr. Santayana, and to Frederick Lewis Allen and Joseph Wood Krutch for their suggestions, and to Edith Keane for the onerous burden of proof-reading. Also to the following for editorial assistance: Thomas Brown, Sylvia Fireman, Melvin A. Friedman, George W. Joel, Ann Lipton, Harold Matson, Sidney G. Phillips, A. B. Algase, Ethel Pushkoff, and C. H. Wilhelm.

The editor and publishers also wish to express their gratitude for permission to reprint selections from the works of those authors and publishers listed below.

Adamic, Louis: *My America.* Harper & Brothers.
Adams, James Truslow: *The Epic of America.* By permission of Little, Brown & Company and the Atlantic Monthly Press.

1171

Ade, George: *Single Blessedness and Other Observations*. 1922. Doubleday, Doran & Company, Inc.

Aiken, Conrad: *Bring! Bring!* The author.

Anderson, Maxwell: *Winterset*. Anderson House.

Bemelmans, Ludwig: *Small Beer*. Cop. 1935, 1936, 1937, 1939 by Ludwig Bemelmans. By permission of The Viking Press, Inc., New York.

Benchley, Robert: *The Treasurer's Report and Other Aspects of Community Singing*. Harper & Brothers.

Benét, Stephen Vincent: "The Devil and Daniel Webster" from *Thirteen O'Clock*. Farrar & Rinehart, Inc., Cop. 1936 by Stephen Vincent Benét.

Benét, William Rose: *The Dust Which Is God*. Cop. 1941 by Dodd, Mead & Company, Inc.

Boyle, Kay: *They Weren't Going to Die*. Ann Watkins, Inc.

Bromfield, Louis: *The Rains Came*. The author.

Brooks, Van Wyck: "Emily Dickinson" from *New England Indian Summer*. "Hawthorne in Salem" from *Flowering of New England*. E. P. Dutton & Co., Inc.

Buck, Pearl: *Today and Forever*. David Lloyd, agent.

Cabell, Branch: Excerpts from *Hamlet Had An Uncle, First Gentleman of America, The King Was in the Counting House*. Farrar & Rinehart, Inc.

Caldwell, Erskine: *Jackpot*. Duell, Sloan & Pearce, Inc.

Callaghan, Morley: *Now That April's Here*. Random House.

Canby, Henry Seidel: *The Age of Confidence*. Farrar & Rinehart, Inc.

Canfield, Dorothy: *Seasoned Timber*. Cop. 1939. Harcourt, Brace and Company, Inc.

Cather, Willa: *Obscure Destinies*. Alfred A. Knopf, Inc.

Chase, Mary Ellen: *A Goodly Heritage*. Henry Holt and Company.

Chase, Stuart: *The Economy of Abundance*. The Macmillan Company.

Cobb, Irvin S.: *Speaking of Operations*. Cop. 1915. Doubleday, Doran & Company, Inc.

Coffin, Robert P. Tristram: "Isaiah Winter's Lion," "Kennebec Weather," "Cap'n Bibber's Coot" from *The Kennebec*. Farrar & Rinehart, Inc. "The Train" from *Lost Paradise*. "Late Christmas" from *There Will Be Bread and Love*. All others from *Collected Poems*. The Macmillan Company.

Cummings, E. E.: *Speech From a Play*. The author.

DeKruif, Paul: *Why Keep Them Alive?* Cop. 1936, by Harcourt, Brace and Company, Inc.

De Voto, Bernard: *Mark Twain's America*. Little, Brown & Co.

Dewey, John: *Freedom and Culture*. G. P. Putnam Sons.

Doolittle, Hilda: *The Collected Poems of H.D.* Liveright Publishing Corp.

Dos Passos, John: *Adventures of a Young Man*. Houghton Mifflin Company.

Dreiser, Theodore: *Chains*. G. P. Putnam Sons.
Edman, Irwin: *Philosopher's Holiday*. Cop. 1938 by Irwin Edman. The Viking Press, Inc., New York.
Farrell, James: *Guillotine Party*. Vanguard Press, Inc.
Faulkner, William: *That Evening Sun*. Random House.
Ferber, Edna. *No Room at the Inn*. The author.
Frost, Robert: "Come In," "Wilful Homing," "The Gift Outright" from *Witness Tree*. All others from *Collected Poems of Robert Frost*. Henry Holt and Company.
Gibbs, Woollcott: *The Customer Is Always Wrong*. The New Yorker.
Glasgow, Ellen: *The Sheltered Life*. Cop. 1932. Reprinted by permission from Doubleday, Doran & Company, Inc.
Gunther, John: *Inside Europe*. Cop. 1933, 1934, 1935, 1936, 1937, 1938, 1940 by John Gunther. Harper & Brothers.
Hellman, Lillian: *A Bleached Lady*. New Masses and New Republic.
Hemingway, Ernest: *The Fifth Column and the First Forty-Nine Other Stories*. Charles Scribner's Sons.
Hergesheimer, Joseph: *An Old House*. Alfred A. Knopf, Inc.
Hughes, Langston: *The Dream Keeper*.
Jeffers, Robinson: *Roan Stallion and Other Poems*. Random House.
Krutch, Joseph Wood: *Five Masters*. Random House.
Leacock, Stephen: *My Remarkable Uncle*. Dodd, Mead and Company, Inc.
Lewis, Sinclair: *Babbitt*. Cop. 1922. Harcourt, Brace and Company, Inc.
MacLeish, Archibald: *America Was Promises*. Duell, Sloan & Pearce, Inc.
Marquand, John P.: *The Late George Apley*. Reprinted by permission of Little, Brown & Company.
Masters, Edgar Lee: *Selected Poems*. The Macmillan Company.
Mencken, Henry L.: *Newspaper Days*. Alfred A. Knopf, Inc.
Millay, Edna: "I Shall Forget" from *A Few Figs From Thistles*. Cop. 1918, 1919, 1922, by Edna St. Vincent Millay. "Cherish You Then" from *Second April*, Cop. 1921, by Edna St. Vincent Millay. "Pity Me Not," "What Lips My Lips," "Euclid Alone" from *The Harp Weaver and Other Poems*. Cop. 1920, 1921, 1922, 1923 by Edna St. Vincent Millay. "Not That It Matters," "On Hearing a Symphony" from *The Buck In the Snow*. Cop. 1928, by Edna St. Vincent Millay. "Where Can the Heart," "Only the Diamond" from *Wine From These Grapes*. Cop. 1934, by Edna St. Vincent Millay. All others from *Fatal Interview*. Cop. 1931, by Edna St. Vincent Millay. Published by Harper & Brothers, N. Y.
Moore, Marianne: *What Are Years?* The Macmillan Company.
Morley, Christopher: "Dogwood Tree" from *John Mistletoe*. "A Song for Eros" from *Trojan Horse*. J. B. Lippincott Co.
Nash, Ogden: *The Face Is Familiar*. Little, Brown & Company.
Nathan, George Jean: *The Critic and the Drama*. Alfred A. Knopf, Inc.

Nathan, Robert: Chapter 2 from *One More Spring.*

Nevins, Allan: "In Defense of History" from *Gateway to History.*
D. Appleton-Century Co., Inc. Pages 131 to 136 from *Hamilton Fish,*
Dodd, Mead & Company, Inc.

Odets, Clifford: *Rocket to the Moon.* Random House.

O'Neill, Eugene: *The Great God Brown.* Random House.

Parker, Dorothy: *The Standard of Living.* The New Yorker.

Peattie, Donald Culross: *A Book of Hours.* The Author.

Perelman, S. J.: *Look Who's Talking.* Random House.

Porter, Katherine Anne: *Flowering Judas and Other Stories.* Cop. 1935 by
Katherine Anne Porter. By permission of Harcourt, Brace and Company, Inc.

Rawlings, Marjorie Kinnan: *Cross Creek.* Charles Scribner's Sons.

Repplier, Agnes: *Eight Decades.* Houghton Mifflin Company.

Rice, Elmer: *The Adding Machine.* Samuel French.

Richter, Conrad: *Sea of Grass.* Alfred A. Knopf, Inc.

Rukeyser, Muriel: "Mediterranean" from *U. S. 1.* Cop. 1938 by Muriel
Rukeyser.

Sandburg, Carl: *The People, Yes.* Cop. 1942. Harcourt, Brace and Company, Inc.

Saroyan, William: *Razzle-Dazzle.* Cop. 1942. Harcourt, Brace and Company, Inc.

Sheean, Vincent: *Not Peace But a Sword.* Cop. 1939. Reprinted by permission from Doubleday, Doran & Co., Inc.

Sherwood, Robert Emmet: *Abe Lincoln In Illinois.* Charles Scribner's Sons.

Shirer, William: *Berlin Diary.* Alfred A. Knopf, Inc.

Sinclair, Upton: *The Jungle.* The author.

Skinner, Cornelia Otis: *Soap Behind the Ears.* Dodd, Mead & Co., Inc.

Steinbeck, John: *The Long Valley.* Cop. 1938 by John Steinbeck. By permission of The Viking Press, Inc., New York.

Stevens, Wallace: *Harmonium.* Alfred A. Knopf, Inc.

Stuart, Jesse: *Second April.* Harper's Magazine.

Sullivan, Frank: *The Jukes Family.* The New Yorker.

Tarkington, Booth: *Mr. White, The Red Barn, Hell And Bridewater.*
Cop. 1935 by Booth Tarkington. Doubleday, Doran & Company.

Thurber, James: *My Life and Hard Times.* The author.

Untermeyer, Louis: *Selected Poems and Parodies of Louis Untermeyer.* By
permission of Harcourt, Brace and Company, Inc.

Van Doren, Carl: *Swift.* Cop. 1930 by Carl Van Doren. By permission of
The Viking Press, Inc., New York.

Van Doren, Mark: *Collected Poems.* Henry Holt and Company.

Van Loon, Hendrik: *The Arts.* Simon & Schuster, Inc.

Van Paassen, Pierre: *Days of Our Years.* Dial Press, Inc.

White, E. B.: *Quo Vadimus?* Harper & Brothers and the author.

White, William Allen: *Emporia Gazette.* The author.

Wilder, Thornton: *The Long Christmas Dinner and Other Plays in One Act.* Coward-McCann, Inc.

Williams, William Carlos: *Collected Poems of William Carlos Williams.* Published by New Directions.

Wilson, Edmund: *Travels in Two Democracies.* Cop. 1936, by Harcourt, Brace and Company, Inc.

Wright, Richard: *Native Son.* Harper & Brothers.

Young, Stark: *Mei Lan-Fang.* New Republic.

Index by Authors

Index by Titles